The University of Chicago School Mathematics Project

Advanced Algebra

Second Edition

Teacher's Edition

Part 1, Chapters 1-6

About the Cover Ellipses and other conic sections are important topics in this book. *UCSMP Advanced Algebra* emphasizes facility with algebraic expressions and forms, powers and roots, and functions based on these concepts. Logarithmic, trigonometric, polynomial, and other special functions are studied both for their abstract properties and as tools for modeling real-world situations.

Authors

Sharon L. Senk   Denisse R. Thompson   Steven S. Viktora
Zalman Usiskin   Nils P. Ahbel   Suzanne Levin
Marcia L. Weinhold   Rheta N. Rubenstein   Judith Halvorson Jaskowiak
James Flanders   Natalie Jakucyn   Gerald Pillsbury

ScottForesman

Editorial Offices: Glenview, Illinois
Regional Offices: Sunnyvale, California • Tucker, Georgia
Glenview, Illinois • Oakland, New Jersey • Dallas, Texas

ACKNOWLEDGMENTS

Authors

Sharon L. Senk
Associate Professor of Mathematics, Michigan State University, East Lansing, MI

Denisse R. Thompson
Assistant Professor of Mathematics Education, University of South Florida, Tampa, FL

Steven S. Viktora
Chairman, Mathematics Department, New Trier High School, Winnetka, IL

Zalman Usiskin
Professor of Education, The University of Chicago

Nils P. Ahbel
Mathematics Teacher, Kent School, Kent, CT (Second Edition only)

Suzanne Levin
UCSMP (Second Edition only)

Marcia L. Weinhold
Mathematics Teacher, Kalamazoo Area Mathematics and Science Center, Kalamazoo, MI (Second Edition only)

Rheta N. Rubenstein
Mathematics Department Head, Renaissance H.S., Detroit, MI (First Edition only)

Judith Halvorson Jaskowiak
Mathematics Teacher, John F. Kennedy H.S., Bloomington, MN (First Edition only)

James Flanders
UCSMP (First Edition only)

Natalie Jakucyn
UCSMP (First Edition only)

Gerald Pillsbury
UCSMP (First Edition only)

UCSMP Production and Evaluation

Series Editors: Zalman Usiskin, Sharon L. Senk
Director of Second Edition Studies:
  Gurcharn Kaeley
Director of First Edition Studies: Sandra Mathison
  (State University of New York, Albany), Assistant
  to the Director: Catherine Sarther
Technical Coordinator: Susan Chang
Second Edition Teacher's Edition Editor:
  David Witonsky

We wish also to acknowledge the generous support of the **Amoco Foundation** and the **Carnegie Corporation of New York** for the development, testing, and distribution of the First Edition of these materials, and the continuing support of the **Amoco Foundation** for the Second Edition.

We wish to thank the many editors, production personnel, and design personnel at ScottForesman for their magnificent assistance.

Design Development

Curtis Design

Multicultural Reviewers for ScottForesman

Winifred Deavens
St. Louis Public Schools, St. Louis, MO

Seree Weroha
Kansas City Public Schools, Kansas City, KS

Efraín Meléndez
Los Angeles Unified School District, CA

Linda Skinner
Edmond Public Schools, Edmond, OK

ISBN: 0-673-45805-9

1.800.554.4411

http://www.scottforesman.com

2 3 4 5 6 7 8 9—DR—0 1 0 0 9 9 9 8 9 7 9 6

Contents
of Teacher's Edition

The complete Table of Contents for the Student Edition begins on page *vi*.

Your UCSMP Professional Sourcebook is found at the back of this book, starting on page T20.

UCSMP Advanced Algebra

SECOND EDITION

*"This program is the closest to what NCTM is saying should be taught.
Students at many levels of mathematics ability feel success in using the program.
This cannot be said for other textbook programs."*

Jack Deal
Bethel Park, Pennsylvania

The University of Chicago School Mathematics Project

It works

Carefully developed by a prestigious team of authors in full accordance with the goals of the NCTM Standards, UCSMP has been refined through field testing and feedback from users. Millions of successful students and an ever-growing network of enthusiastic teachers have proven that UCSMP is a program that works.

Why it works as today's curriculum

UCSMP's flexible six-year curriculum emphasizes connections within mathematics and to other disciplines, develops concepts through real-world applications, implements the latest technology, and encourages independent learning.

How it works for today's students

Clear and inviting, *UCSMP Advanced Algebra* offers continual opportunities for problem solving, practice and review, and end-of-chapter mastery. Attention to individual needs and a broad approach to assessment help you offer success to all students.

The following section provides an overview of *UCSMP Advanced Algebra*. For more detailed information, see the Professional Sourcebook at the back of this book (page T20).

The following section provides an overview of *UCSMP Advanced Algebra*. For more detailed information, see the Professional Sourcebook at the back of this book (page T20).

WHAT'S NEW in the Second Edition

In the Student Edition:
- Appealing, student-friendly layout
- Reading Organizers to outline each lesson
- In-class and In-lesson Activities
- Student Projects in every chapter
- Widespread use of graphics calculators
- Early introduction of functions

In the Teacher's Edition:
- Warm-up ideas for introducing each lesson
- Enhanced integration and connections
- Optional activities to reinforce and extend topics
- Frequent suggestions for adapting to individual needs
- Ideas for Setting Up the next lesson

PLUS—

In the support package:
- Two forms of Lesson Masters for extra practice
- An enhanced Assessment Sourcebook
- Activity Kit
- Study Skills Handbook
- Multimedia applications in *Wide World of Mathematics* (Videotape, Videodisc, and CD-ROM)

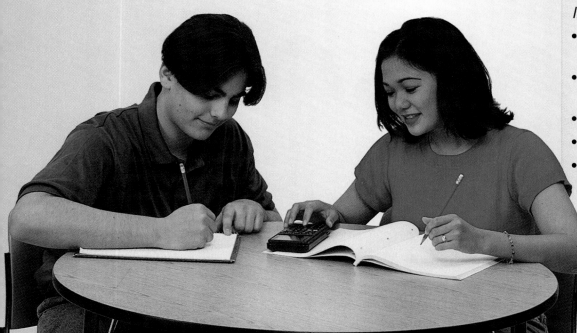

UCSMP — It works

Program development

The UCSMP Secondary Component Materials have been developed with extensive input from classroom teachers and a special advisory board. The project has been funded by several major corporations which recognize the need for exciting new materials for mathematics education.

An innovative approach

UCSMP is the first full mathematics curriculum to implement the NCTM Standards by teaching concepts *through* their applications, emphasizing the reading and writing of mathematics, providing a wide variety of meaningful problem-solving opportunities, and incorporating the latest technology.

"With UCSMP, our students have grown in personal maturity and have learned more mathematics. UCSMP is beautifully organized, constantly reviewing for depth and integrating for breadth. It is student centered, and our students using UCSMP are demonstrating a high degree of confidence and competence."

Barry Walker
Birmingham, Alabama

Proven success

The UCSMP materials have been carefully refined through years of field testing and feedback from users of the First Edition. Teachers throughout the country have discovered that UCSMP is the way to offer success to the greatest number of students.

The **best** book to help students learn advanced algebra has gotten even better!

Results of the Second Edition Evaluation					
		Mean Scores of Students in Matched Pairs (Standard Deviations are in Parentheses.)			
Group	**N**	**Pretest Part 1**	**Pretest Part 2**	**Posttest** *Advanced Algebra*	**Posttest** *PS&U*
UCSMP 2nd Edition	177	14.90 (4.35)	6.33 (2.22)	**20.19** (5.55)	**10.38** (5.44)
non-UCSMP	180	14.44 (4.48)	6.44 (2.37)	15.49 (4.71)	6.39 (3.54)

For more details, see the Professional Sourcebook at the back of Part 1 of the Teacher's Edition.
Mean scores in boldface for "UCSMP 2nd Edition" are significantly higher than the corresponding scores for non-UCSMP students.

These results confirm conclusions from the first edition studies, namely that *Advanced Algebra* students maintain their hold on traditional advanced algebra skills while enriching their advanced algebra background in the application of algebra and in problem solving and understanding of mathematics.

"Students taking the ACT averaged 12 to 14 out of a perfect score of 36. After 3 years of UCSMP, our average for the same assessment rose to over 21!"

Brenda Hull
Cathedral City, California

Why it works as today's curriculum

Grades	Top 10% of 5th graders	50th-90th percentile of 6th graders	30th-70th percentile of 7th graders	15th-50th percentile of 8th graders
6	Transition Mathematics			
7	Algebra	Transition Mathematics		
8	Geometry	Algebra	Transition Mathematics	
9	Advanced Algebra	Geometry	Algebra	Transition Mathematics
10	Functions, Statistics, and Trigonometry	Advanced Algebra	Geometry	Algebra
11	Precalculus and Discrete Mathematics	Functions, Statistics, and Trigonometry	Advanced Algebra	Geometry
12	Calculus (Not part of UCSMP)	Precalculus and Discrete Mathematics	Functions, Statistics, and Trigonometry	Advanced Algebra

A flexible curriculum

UCSMP provides a complete program for students in middle school and high school. It spreads the usual secondary mathematics content over six years, allowing students to both broaden and deepen their understanding of each topic.

"I do not get the question, 'Why are we doing this topic?' anymore. The real-life applications are excellent. I enjoy teaching out of the UCSMP books so much more than the various series that I used during the past 21 years."

Conrad Wayne
Richton Park, Illinois

Real-world applications

By constantly answering the question "When are we ever going to have to use this?" *UCSMP Advanced Algebra* develops lessons more meaningfully and motivates students to learn. *See pages 19, 110, 120, 202–203, and 568 for further examples.*

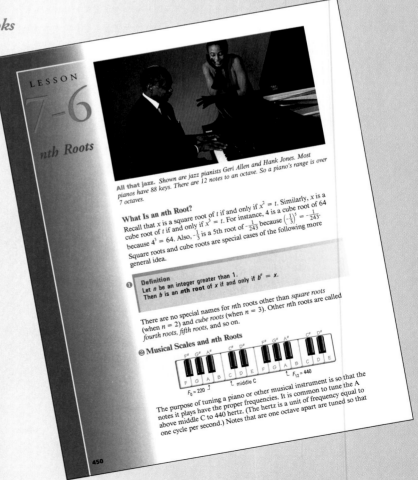

Integration and connections

UCSMP Advanced Algebra thoroughly integrates and makes connections to other areas of mathematics, to other disciplines, and to the real world. Students see how each mathematical idea fits into a larger context. *See pages 169, 284, 325, 419, and 532 for further examples.*

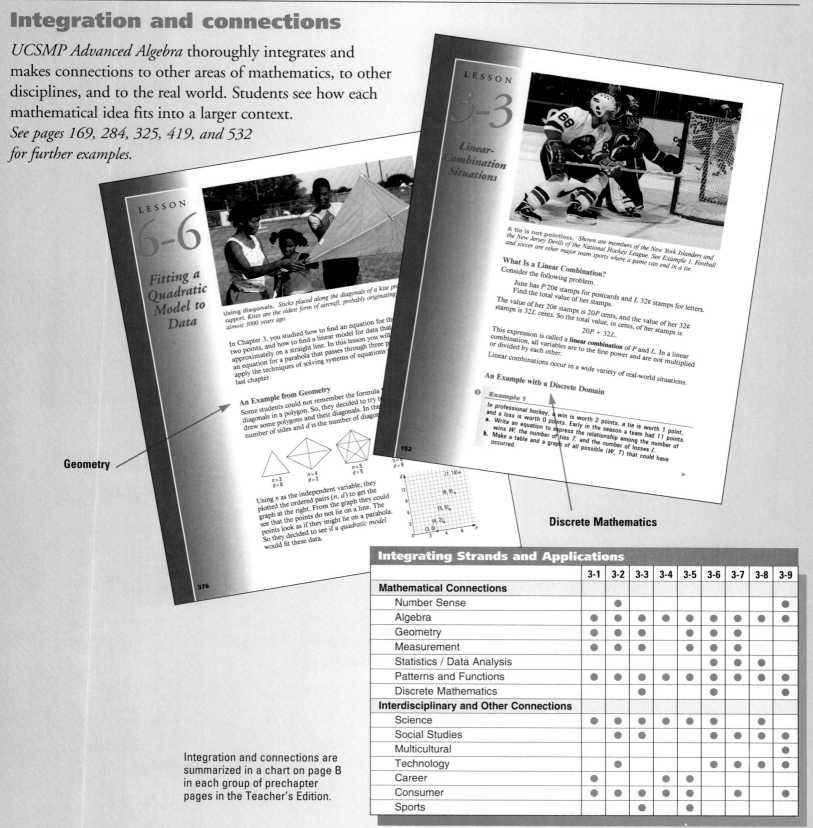

LESSON

6-6

Fitting a Quadratic Model to Data

Using diagonals. *Sticks placed along the diagonals of a kite provide support. Kites are the oldest form of aircraft. probably originating almost 3000 years ago.*

In Chapter 3, you studied how to find an equation for the line through two points, and how to find a linear model for data that lie approximately on a straight line. In this lesson you will find an equation for a parabola that passes through three points. You will apply the techniques of solving systems of equations from the last chapter.

An Example from Geometry

Some students could not remember the formula for the number of diagonals in a polygon. So, they decided to try to find a pattern. They drew some polygons and their diagonals. In these polygons, n is the number of sides and d is the number of diagonals.

$n = 3$
$d = 0$

$n = 4$
$d = 2$

$n = 5$
$d = 5$

$n = 6$
$d = 9$

Using n as the independent variable, they plotted the ordered pairs (n, d) to get the graph at the right. From the graph they could see that the points do not lie on a line. The points look as if they might lie on a parabola. So they decided to see if a *quadratic model* would fit these data.

(7, 14)

(6, 9)

(5, 5)

(4, 2)

(3, 0)

376

Geometry

LESSON

3-3

Linear-Combination Situations

A tie is not pointless. *Shown are members of the New York Islanders and the New Jersey Devils of the National Hockey League. See Example 1. Football and soccer are other major team sports where a game can end in a tie.*

What Is a Linear Combination?
Consider the following problem.

June has P 20¢ stamps for postcards and L 32¢ stamps for letters. Find the total value of her stamps.

The value of her 20¢ stamps is 20P cents, and the value of her 32¢ stamps is 32L cents. So the total value, in cents, of her stamps is

$$20P + 32L.$$

This expression is called a **linear combination** of P and L. In a linear combination, all variables are to the first power and are not multiplied or divided by each other.

Linear combinations occur in a wide variety of real-world situations.

An Example with a Discrete Domain

Example 1

In professional hockey, a win is worth 2 points, a tie is worth 1 point, and a loss is worth 0 points. Early in the season a team had 11 points.
a. Write an equation to express the relationship among the number of wins W, the number of ties T, and the number of losses L.
b. Make a table and a graph of all possible (W, T) that could have occurred.

152

Discrete Mathematics

Integration and connections are summarized in a chart on page B in each group of prechapter pages in the Teacher's Edition.

Integrating Strands and Applications

	3-1	3-2	3-3	3-4	3-5	3-6	3-7	3-8	3-9
Mathematical Connections									
Number Sense		●							●
Algebra	●	●	●	●	●	●	●	●	●
Geometry	●	●	●			●	●	●	
Measurement	●	●	●			●	●	●	
Statistics / Data Analysis						●	●	●	
Patterns and Functions	●	●	●	●	●	●	●	●	●
Discrete Mathematics		●				●			●
Interdisciplinary and Other Connections									
Science	●	●	●	●	●			●	
Social Studies		●	●			●	●	●	●
Multicultural									●
Technology		●				●	●	●	
Career	●			●	●				
Consumer	●	●	●	●	●		●		●
Sports			●		●				

Sample from Chapter 3

Why it works

Technology

State-of-the-art technology enhances mathematical understanding and strengthens problem-solving skills. Applications using calculators, graphics calculators, and computers are incorporated throughout the text. New multimedia applications in *Wide World of Mathematics* (Videotape, Videodisc, and CD-ROM) make learning more interactive and engaging. *See pages 94, 98, 177, 217, and 632 for further examples.*

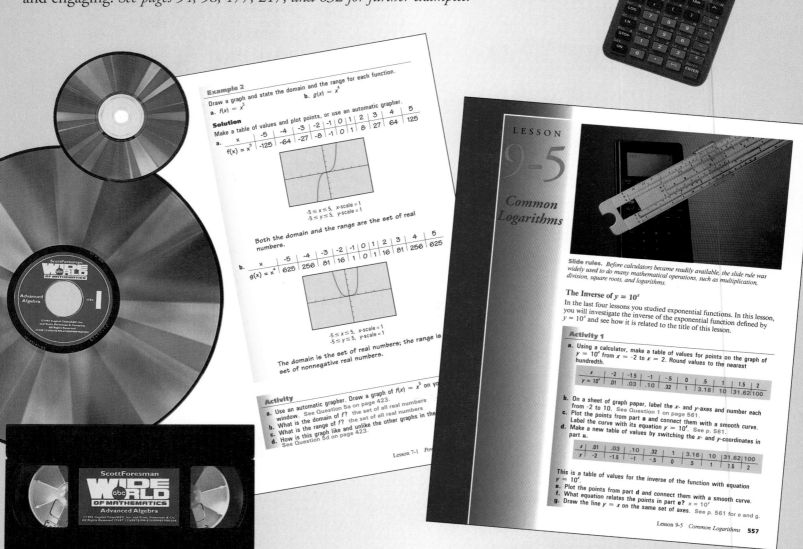

"UCSMP allows students to get hands-on technology experience from graphics calculators, scientific calculators, and computers integrated into class instruction and student work."

Queen E. Henderson
Dallas, Texas

Activities and Projects

Activities and Projects in each chapter provide engaging ways for students to work individually or in groups to explore and extend their knowledge. Your Teacher's Edition also includes additional Optional Activities.

See pages 50, 107, 168, 239, and 546 for further examples of Activities. See pages 5 (Teacher's Edition), 61–62, and 128–129 for further examples of Projects.

IN-CLASS ACTIVITY

Introducing Lesson 10-4

Rotations, Sines, and Cosines

Materials: Each pair should have a good quality compass, a protractor, graph paper, and a calculator. Work on this Activity with a partner.

1 Draw a set of coordinate axes on the graph paper. Let each side of a square on your coordinate grid represent 0.1 unit. With the origin as the center, use a compass to draw a circle with radius 1. Label the positive x-intercept of the circle as A_0. Your circle should look like the one at the right. See margin.

2 a. With a protractor, locate the image of $A_0 = (1, 0)$ under R_{20}. Label this point A_{20}. See margin. b) See margin.
b. Use the grid to estimate the x-coordinate and y-coordinate of A_{20}.
c. Use a calculator to find cos 20° and sin 20°. See margin.
cos 20° ≈ .9397; sin 20° ≈ .3420

3 a. With a protractor, locate $R_{40}(1, 0)$. Label it A_{40}.
b. Use the grid to estimate the x- and y-coordinates of A_{40}. See margin.
c. Use a calculator to find cos 40° and sin 40°. See margin.
cos 40° ≈ .7660; sin 40° ≈ .6428

4 a. Locate $R_{55}(1, 0)$. Label it A_{55}. a, b) See margin.
b. Estimate the x- and y-coordinates of this point.
c. Use a calculator to evaluate cos 55° and sin 55°.
cos 55° ≈ .5736; sin 55° ≈ .8192

5 Look back at your work for Questions 2 to 4. What relation do you see between the x- and y-coordinates of $R_\theta(1, 0)$, cos θ, and sin θ? See below.
b. Use the relation to estimate the values of cos 73° and sin 73° from your figure without a calculator. See margin.
c. How close are your predictions to the actual values? cos 73° ≈ .2924; sin 73° ≈ .9563

a) $R_\theta(1, 0) = (\cos θ, \sin θ)$

622

A project presents an opportunity for you to extend your knowledge of a topic related to the material of this chapter. You should allow more time for a project than you do for typical homework questions.

PROJECTS 6 CHAPTER SIX

1 Projectile Motion
Paths of objects other than batted baseballs are almost parabolic. Find out about other objects that travel in parabolic paths. Make a poster or write a brief report illustrating and describing these paths. Find equations for some of the paths.

2 Sum and Product of Roots
Checking solutions to quadratic equations can be tedious, but there is an easier way to check than by substitution. The method checks the sum and the product of the roots. Look back over some quadratic equations you have solved. Let ... be the roots of the equation ... $bx + c = 0$. For each equation calculate ... and $r_1 \cdot r_2$. What patterns do you notice? ... you prove your generalizations hold for ... quadratics? Use your results to check some ... the solutions to quadratic equations in ... his chapter.

3 The Graph-Translation Theorem and Other Functions
The Graph-Translation Theorem applies to graphs of all functions, not just the quadratic and absolute value functions used in this chapter. Consider the family of inverse variation functions.
a. Graph the "parent" function $y = \frac{1}{x}$.
b. Graph 3 or 4 "offspring" whose equations have the form $y = \frac{1}{x - h}$.
c. Graph 3 or 4 "offspring" whose equations have the form $y = \frac{1}{x} + k$.
d. Graph 3 or 4 "offspring" whose equations have the form $y = \frac{1}{x - h} + k$.
e. Write a brief report summarizing the patterns you observe.

$y = \frac{1}{x}$

408

---

4 Quadratic Models
Look through an almanac or the *Statistical Abstract of the United States.* Find some current data for which x and y appear to be related by a quadratic model. Find an equation for a quadratic ...

6 Predicting the Areas of States or Countries
In a square with area A and side s, $s^2 = A$ exactly. The length of a side of shapes that are close to Squares can be a good predictor of area, even if the prediction is not exact. Use an atlas to find the lengths of sides ...

... se to ... ngth ... with a ... ap to ... miles ... te or ... k up its ... opedia. ... and ... rt ... ph, ... of ... d, and

409

How it works for today's students

Inviting design

The text's appealing and functional format and unique lesson development make concepts easy to follow and comprehend. Colorful pages and a wealth of contemporary visuals—including greatly enhanced graphs—help stimulate students' interest throughout the course.

"It has been exciting for me to see students actively involved in the learning of mathematics. Students are talking and doing mathematics and finding success with UCSMP. The notes to the teachers are right on target. The research behind this project is evident."

Kathleen A. Connelly
Florissant, Missouri

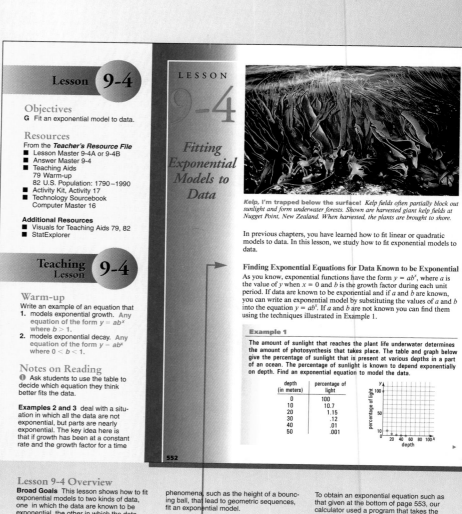

Lesson 9-4

Objectives
G Fit an exponential model to data.

Resources
From the *Teacher's Resource File*
■ Lesson Master 9-4A or 9-4B
■ Answer Master 9-4
■ Teaching Aids
  79 Warm-up
  82 U.S. Population: 1790–1990
■ Activity Kit, Activity 17
■ Technology Sourcebook
  Computer Master 16

Additional Resources
■ Visuals for Teaching Aids 79, 82
■ StatExplorer

Teaching Lesson 9-4

Warm-up
Write an example of an equation that
1. models exponential growth. Any equation of the form $y = ab^x$ where $b > 1$.
2. models exponential decay. Any equation of the form $y = ab^x$ where $0 < b < 1$.

Notes on Reading
① Ask students to use the table to decide which equation they think better fits the data.

Examples 2 and 3 deal with a situation in which all the data are not exponential, but parts are nearly exponential. The key idea here is that if growth has been at a constant rate and the growth factor for a time

---

LESSON 9-4

Fitting Exponential Models to Data

Kelp, I'm trapped below the surface! *Kelp fields often partially block out sunlight and form underwater forests. Shown are harvested giant kelp fields at Nugget Point, New Zealand. When harvested, the plants are brought to shore.*

In previous chapters, you have learned how to fit linear or quadratic models to data. In this lesson, we study how to fit exponential models to data.

Finding Exponential Equations for Data Known to be Exponential
As you know, exponential functions have the form $y = ab^x$, where a is the value of y when $x = 0$ and b is the growth factor during each unit period. If data are known to be exponential and if a and b are known, you can write an exponential model by substituting the values of a and b into the equation $y = ab^x$. If a and b are not known you can find them using the techniques illustrated in Example 1.

Example 1
The amount of sunlight that reaches the plant life underwater determines the amount of photosynthesis that takes place. The table and graph below give the percentage of sunlight that is present at various depths in a part of an ocean. The percentage of sunlight is known to depend exponentially on depth. Find an exponential equation to model the data.

depth (in meters)	percentage of light
0	100
10	10.7
20	1.15
30	.12
40	.01
50	.001

552

Lesson 9-4 Overview

Broad Goals This lesson shows how to fit exponential models to two kinds of data, one in which the data are known to be exponential, the other in which the data might be exponential.

Perspective As we do with all the fitting of data to equations, we begin with a situation that fits the model. Students have learned that compound interest situations, certain growth and decay situations, and other

552

phenomena, such as the height of a bouncing ball, that lead to geometric sequences, fit an exponential model.

If the initial value is known, then we have the y-intercept of $y = ab^x$, which is the value of a. The value of b can be found by substituting any other known pair (x, y) in the model. This is the process used in Solution 1 of **Example 1**. Solution 2 of **Example 1** proceeds using two other points.

To obtain an exponential equation such as that given at the bottom of page 553, our calculator used a program that takes the logarithms of the given y-values, finds the line of best fit to the logarithms of the values, and then translates that line back into an exponential equation. That is, it used the points (0, log 100 = 2), (10, log 10.7 = 1.0293838), (20, .0606978), (30, –.9208188), (40,–2), and (50,–3). It found that line to be $y \approx -.1002x + 2.033$,

These pages represent a typical lesson.

Reading Organizers

Communication

Instead of spending valuable time explaining the textbook, you can devote more time each day to exploring additional examples and applications. Students learn to read and understand mathematics on their own, and to express this understanding both orally and in writing. Reading Organizers in each lesson help direct students' attention to key ideas in the reading.

Solution 1

We need to find a and b in the equation $y = ab^x$. Using the point (0, 100), $100 = ab^0$. Thus $a = 100$ and the equation is of the form $y = 100b^x$. Now we choose another point and substitute. We choose (20, 1.15).

$1.15 = 100b^{20}$ Substitute.
$0.0115 = b^{20}$ Divide each side by 100.
  Take the 20th root of each side
$0.8 \approx b$ (or raise to the $\frac{1}{20}$ power).

So an equation for the data is $y \approx 100 \cdot (.8)^x$.

Solution 2

The point (0, 100), which tells us the y-intercept, was very convenient to use in Solution 1 because $b^0 = 1$, and the value of a could be easily found. If you do not know the y-intercept, the following method can be used to find a and b in $y = ab^x$. Choose two data points and substitute into $y = ab^x$. The result is a system of two equations in a and b.

Substitute (10, 10.7) into $y = ab^x$. $10.7 = ab^{10}$ (1)
Substitute (40, .010) into $y = ab^x$. $.010 = ab^{40}$ (2)
Divide (2) by (1). $\frac{.010}{10.7} = \frac{ab^{40}}{ab^{10}}$
Simplify. $9.3458 \cdot 10^{-4} = b^{30}$
Take the 30th root of each side. $.7925 \approx b$
Substitute $b \approx .7925$ into one of the $10.7 = a(.7925)^{10}$
first two equations. We use equation (1).
Solve for a. $109.5 \approx a$
An equation for the data is $y = 109.5(.7925)^x$.

Notice that the equations in Solutions 1 and 2 are not identical. This indicates that all the data points do not fit exactly on the same exponential curve. Let $y_1 = 100(.8)^x$ and $y_2 = 109.5(.7925)^x$. To decide which is better, you could make a table of values comparing the values predicted by these models to the actual percentage y_A of sunlight.

Each equation predicts values close to the actual value, y_A. Alternately, you could graph each equation and see how close the actual y-values are to the curves.

x	y_A	y_1	y_2
0	100	100	109.5
10	10.7	10.74	10.70
20	1.15	1.153	1.046
30	.12	.124	.1022
40	.01	.013	.01
50	.001	.0014	.00098

Many automatic graphers have the ability to find an exponential equation that models a set of data. You should check to see if your grapher has such a feature, and if so, learn how to use it. Our grapher gives

$$y = 107.9(.794)^x$$

as the best exponential model for the data in Example 1.

Lesson 9-4 *Fitting Exponential Models to Data* **553**

period of length t is x, then the growth factor for an interval within it of length $\frac{t}{n}$ is $\sqrt[n]{x}$.

The calculation of the annual growth factor in **Example 2** is one which can be important to know. For example, you might have values that give some idea of the amount of inflation, such as a purchase price and a selling price for the same house in two different years. From that information, you can determine the annual percent increase in the investment and you can thus determine whether the selling price is higher or lower than one would expect.

The yearly growth rate 1.03 used in **Example 3** was found by dividing the 1860 population by the 1790 population and then taking the 70th root.

Additional Examples

1. Use the data from **Example 1**.
   a. Use the two points (0, 100) and (50, .001) to obtain an equation for the data.
   $y \approx 100(.7943)^x$
   b. Use the two points (20, 1.15) and (30, .12) to obtain an equation for the data.
   $y \approx 105.7(.7977)^x$
2. The U.S. Bureau of the Census has estimated that the population of Cuba will be 11,613,000 in the year 2000, and 12,795,000 in the year 2020. What annual growth rate is assumed between 2000 and 2020? 0.49%

which it translated back into the exponential equation $y \approx 107.9(.794)^x$. The correlation between x and y in the line is .9889 . . ., very close to perfect, indicating that the data are almost perfectly exponential.

Optional Activities

Activity 1 Social Studies Connection
After discussing **Question 7,** you might refer students to the December 1988 issue of *National Geographic* (Vol. 174, No. 6, pages 916–917), which contains a bar graph showing the growth of the world population for 1450–2020. Have students find an exponential model for the world population between different time periods. [Answers will vary.]

553

How it works

Problem solving

Students learn to use mathematics effectively through problem-solving experiences that include use of higher-order thinking skills in daily assignments, a wide variety of problem types in the questions, and open-ended problems. *See pages 41, 57, 112–113, 191, 437, and 536 for further examples.*

---

3. The population of Cincinnati, Ohio, was approximately 503,000 in 1960 and 364,000 in 1990. Find an exponential model for the population of Cincinnati between 1960 and 1990.
$y = 364,000(.9893)^x$, where x is the number of years from 1990.

Notes on Questions

Questions 1–2 Error Alert The equations are close but not identical. Emphasize that students should choose the points carefully.

Questions 4–5 You may wish to use **Teaching Aid 82** with these questions.

Question 6 Multicultural Connection In 1990, about 7.9% of the population of the U.S. was born in a foreign country and about 14% of the population spoke a language other than English. Spanish was the most commonly spoken non-English language in 39 states. The most commonly spoken non-English language in Louisiana, Maine, New Hampshire, and Vermont was French; in Montana, Minnesota, North Dakota, and South Dakota, German; in Alaska, Yupik; in Rhode Island, Portuguese; and in Hawaii, Japanese.

(Notes on Questions continue on page 556.)

---

a)

x	y_3
0	107.9
10	10.75
20	1.07
30	0.107
40	0.0106
50	0.00106

Activity

a. Let $y_3 = 107.9(.794)^x$. Evaluate y_3 for the values of x in the table on the previous page. **See left.**
b. Which model, y_1, y_2, or y_3 is more accurate at a depth of 50 meters? y_3

Deciding Whether an Exponential Model Is Appropriate

Sometimes you may not be sure that an exponential model is appropriate. If that is the case, consider the growth factor between various data points. If it is constant, an exponential model is appropriate; if not, another model must be found. Consider again the population of the United States from 1790 to 1990 given on page 531. Below we give data from only the first eight and last three censuses.

Year	Population	Decade Growth Factor
1790	3,930,000	
1800	5,300,000	1.349
1810	7,240,000	1.366
1820	9,640,000	1.331
1830	12,870,000	1.335
1840	17,070,000	1.326
1850	23,190,000	1.359
1860	31,440,000	1.356
1970	203,300,000	1.134
1980	226,540,000	1.114
1990	248,710,000	1.098

The **decade growth factor** in the table is the ratio of the population in a specific year to the population 10 years earlier.

For example, the decade growth factor for 1820 is $\frac{9,640,000}{7,240,000}$ or approximately 1.331, indicating a 33.1% population increase from 1810 to 1820. The **yearly** or **annual growth factor** for a given decade is the positive number b such that b^{10} gives the decade growth factor.

Example 2

Calculate the annual growth factor between 1810 and 1820.

Solution

The decade growth factor is 1.331. Solve $b^{10} = 1.331$.
Take the 10th root of each side or raise each side to the $\frac{1}{10}$ power. Only the positive root is appropriate here. $\sqrt[10]{1.331} \approx 1.029$.
This indicates that the annual growth factor is about 2.9% from 1810 to 1820. In other words, the population in 1811 was about 1.029 times the population in 1810.

Notice that during the years 1790 to 1860 the decade growth factors are almost constant. Over that seventy-year period, the annual growth factor was about 3%. However, in recent years the decade growth factors are lower, indicating a lower annual growth rate. This means that a single exponential model does not fit the complete set of data. But different exponential models can be used for smaller time intervals.

554

Shown is an 1860 painting by Charles Hargems depicting the first Pony Express Ride.

Example 3

Find an exponential model for the U.S. population between 1790 and 186...

Solution

We know the annual growth rate from the previous discussion, so $b \approx 1.03$ in the equation $y = ab^x$. The growth factor needs to be raise... to a power that gives the number of years it has been applied. We choose 1830, a starting point close to the middle of this time period. If is the year, $x - 1830$ gives the number of years before or after 1830. The exponent is 0 where $x = 1830$, so the initial value is about 13 million. An equation for the population in millions is

$$y = 13(1.03)^{x - 1830}.$$

The equation given in the solution to Example 3 is not the only exponential equation that can be used to model the data. If you want greater accuracy you can use

$$y = 12.87(1.03)^{x - 1830}.$$

If you choose a different starting point, say 1840, you will get a different equation. You are asked to experiment with other equations in the Questions. But as was the case in the two Solutions to Example 1, each will be a reasonably good model for the data set.

QUESTIONS

Covering the Reading

In 1–3, refer to Example 1.
1. **a.** Use the point (30, .12) and the method of Solution 1 to find an equation to model the data. $y = 100 \cdot (0.799)^x$
   b. Use this equation to predict y when $x = 30$. $\approx .119$

2. **a.** Use the points (20, 1.15) and (50, .001) and the method of Solution 2 to find an equation to model the data. $y = 125(0.791)^x$
   b. Use this equation to predict y when $x = 30$. .110

3. Write your answers to the Activity in the Lesson. **See page 554.**

In 4 and 5, refer to the U.S. population data given in the lesson.
4. Find the annual growth factor from 1830 to 1840. $\approx 2.9\%$

5b) ≈ 30.83 million
c) ≈ 31.55 million
d) the equation in Example 3

5. **a.** Find a model for the population between 1790 and 1860 for whic... the starting point is 1840. $y = 17.07(1.03)^{x - 1840}$
   b. Use the equation in part **a** to predict the U.S. population in 1860...
   c. Use the equation in Example 3 to predict the population in 1860.
   d. Which equation gives a better prediction for the population in 1860? **See left for b–d.**

6b) Because in recent years the decade growth factor has dropped substantially.

6. **a.** Use the equation in Example 3 to estimate the U.S. population in the year 1990. $\approx 1,472,000,000$
   b. Why is the answer to part **a** such a bad estimate? **See left.**

Lesson 9-4 *Fitting Exponential Models to Data* 55...

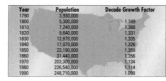

(LESSON MASTER 9-4 B — Questions on SPUR Objectives)

Vocabulary
1. Suppose the decade growth factor for a population is D and the annual growth factor is A. Write an equation that relates D and A. $D = A^{10}$

Uses Objective G: Fit an exponential model to data.

2. Multiple choice: For which set of data below is an exponential model most appropriate? Explain why. **B**

3. An experiment began with 200 of a certain type of bacteria. The bacteria grew exponentially, and 4 hours later there were 18,000.
   a. Fit an exponential model to these data. $y = 200 (3.08)^x$
   b. After 12 hours, how many bacteria will be present? $\approx 145,760,100$ bac.

4. In a horticultural experiment, the monthly growth of a plant was monitored. The results of the experiment are in the table below.

Sample: The growth factor between subsequent pairs of data points is the constant B.

554

Optional Activities

Activity 2 You can use *Activity Kit, Activity 17* either before or after this lesson. In the activity, students conduct an experiment involving the cooling of a hot glass of water. The situation models exponential decay.

Activity 3 You may wish to assign *Technology Sourcebook, Computer Master 16*. Students use *StatExplorer* or similar software to fit an exponential model to data on the temperature of cooling water.

Adapting to Individual Needs

Extra Help Some students may be surprised that the equation for the data that is found in Solution 1 of **Example 1** is not the same as the equation found in Solution 2 of the same example. Refer these students to the graph of the data given on page 552 and stress that all the data points do not fit *exactly* on the same exponential curve. Point out that they are finding an equation that fits the data, but that there is not an equation that *exactly* fits the data.

English Language Development Because this lesson contains many applications throughout the reading and the questions, encourage students to use their bilingual dictionaries.

> *"UCSMP improves problem-solving abilities by increased exposure to real-world applications."*

Jane Shirley
Colorado Springs, Colorado

Practice and review

Continual opportunities for practice and review throughout *UCSMP Advanced Algebra* help students strengthen conceptual understanding and ensure optimum performance.
See pages 74–75, 93, 160, 219, and 266–269 for further examples.

Follow-up 9-4
for Lesson

Practice
For more questions on SPUR Objectives, use **Lesson Master 9-4A** (shown on page 553) or **Lesson Master 9-4B** (shown on pages 554–555).

Assessment
Written Communication Have students refer to **Example 1** and write a paragraph explaining the method for determining an equation for data that are known to be exponential. [Students demonstrate an understanding of how to fit an exponential model to data.]

Extension
As an extension of **Question 8**, have students find the life expectancy as a function of age of either males or females in a country other than Finland. Then have them repeat each part of **Question 8**, using the data they found. [Answers will vary.]

Project Update Project 1, *Car Loans*, Project 2, *Modeling the Growth of HIV*, and Project 3, *Predicting Cooling Times*, on pages 593–594, relate to the content of this lesson.

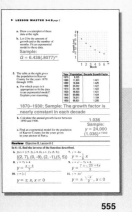

555

Notes on Questions
Question 8 There are no best answers to **parts b and c** because the data are neither linear nor exponential.

Health Connection The life expectancy of people in Finland at birth is quite close to that of people in the United States. Males in the U.S. in 1990 were expected to live 71.8 years, females 78.8 years; in Finland in 1989, males were expected to live 75.0 years, females 78.9 years. Projections suggest that life expectancy for those born in the U.S. in 2000 will reach 73 years for males and 80 years for females.

Additional Answers
7a. A year in the middle of the range, 1890, was chosen as a starting point, which led to an equation model of the form $y = ab^{x - 1890}$. Substituting (1890, 63) in the equation gives a value of 63 for a. The value for b, the annual growth factor, was calculated by taking the tenth root of the decade growth factor, which is $\frac{63}{50} = 1.26$. So $b = \sqrt[10]{1.26} = 1.02$, and thus $y = 63(1.02)^{x - 1890}$.

b. After 1910, the population increased more slowly than before 1910, so the annual growth factor of about 2% would no longer apply.

8a.

(graph: Life expectancy vs Age, y-axis 70–80, x-axis 0 10 20 30 40 50 60)

9a.

(graph showing $y = e^{3x}$, points (-1, .3678794412), (0, 1), (1, 20))

556

Different expectations.
When Daisy Fuentes (top) was born in 1966, the life expectancy was 69 yr. When Jaleel White (middle) was born in 1977, the life expectancy was 66 yr. When George Burns (bottom) was born in 1896, the life expectancy was 51 yr.

age	life expectancy
0	70.85
10	71.48
20	71.87
40	73.43
60	77.08

Applying the Mathematics

7. Refer to the graph and data on page 531. See margin.
   a. Show how the equation for 1870–1910 was obtained.
   b. Explain why this model is not a good fit for the data after 1910.

8. The table at the left gives the life expectancy for males in Finland as a function of their age.
   a. Make a scatterplot of these data. See margin.
   b. Fit an exponential model to this data. $y = 70.39(1.0014)^x$
   c. Fit a linear model to this data. $y = .0999x + 70.34$
   d. Use each of the models to predict the life expectancy of a 30-year-old Finnish male. exponential: 73.41; linear: 73.34
   e. Over this time period, compare the differences in the two models. For what ages do the two models begin to give quite different values? Answers will vary. Sample: The difference between the two models is greatest at age 60.

Review

9. a. Graph $y = e^{3x}$ for $-2 < x < 2$. Label the coordinates of three points on the graph. See margin.
   b. State the domain and range of this function. *(Lesson 9-3)* domain: set of all real numbers; range: set of all positive numbers

10. The amount A of radioactivity from a nuclear explosion is given by $A = A_0 e^{-2t}$, where t is measured in days after the explosion. What percent of the original radioactivity is present 5 days after the explosion? *(Lesson 9-3)* 4.54×10^{-5}

11. Tina invests $850 in an account with a 2.75% annual interest rate. What will be her balance if she leaves the money untouched for 4 years compounded as follows? *(Lessons 7-4, 9-3)*
    a. annually $947.43   b. daily $948.83   c. continuously $948.84

12. Consider the sequence defined by $\begin{cases} g_1 = .375 \\ g_n = .8g_{n-1} \end{cases}$ for integers $n \geq 2$. *(Lessons 3-1, 7-5, 9-1, 9-2)*
    a. List the first five terms of this sequence. 0.375, 0.3, 0.24, 0.192, 0.1536
    b. Which phrase applies to this sequence: exponential growth, exponential decay, constant increase, constant decrease? exponential decay

In 13 and 14, simplify without using a calculator. *(Lessons 7-3, 7-6, 7-7)*

13. $\left(\frac{1}{3}\right)^{-4}$ 81

14. $64^{\frac{7}{6}}$ 128

15. Simplify $(a + 2b)^2 - (2a + b)^2$. *(Lesson 6-1)* $-3a^2 + 3b^2$

16. Suppose m varies inversely with n, and $m = 18$ when $n = 18$. Find m when $n = 3$. *(Lesson 2-2)* $m = 108$

Exploration

17. Find the life expectancy for either U. S. males or U. S. females of various ages. Try to model the data with an exponential function. Answers will vary.

556

Adapting to Individual Needs
Challenge
Give students the following question.
Suppose 10 grams of highly radioactive material decay to 9 grams in 30 days. Write a function describing y, the amount of material present, as a function of x, the amount of time in days $[y = 10(.996)^x]$, and graph the function. From the graph, explain how to estimate the half-life. [Find the x-value when $y = 5$. The half-life of the material is approximately 173 years.]

Student diversity

UCSMP materials have been carefully designed to accommodate the full range of today's diverse student population. Your Teacher's Edition is full of ideas for addressing the needs of each student.
See pages 9, 28, 248, and 252 for further examples.

How it works

Progress checks for students

A Progress Self-Test at the end of each chapter helps students determine how well they've assimilated chapter concepts. Various types of problems, keyed to chapter objectives, provide ideal preparation for chapter tests and teach study skills.

PROGRESS SELF-TEST

Take this test as you would take a test in class. Use graph paper and a calculator. Then check your work with the solutions in the Selected Answers section in the back of the book.

8) $1 - 9i$

In 1–3, consider the parabola with equation $y = x^2 - 8x + 12$.   1) $y + 4 = (x - 4)^2$

1. Rewrite the equation in vertex form.

2. What is the vertex of this parabola? $(4, -4)$

3. What are the x-intercepts of this parabola? $2;\ 6$

In 4–7, perform the operations and simplify.

4. $2i \cdot i$ -2

5. $\sqrt{-8} \cdot \sqrt{-2}$ -4

6. $\frac{4 + \sqrt{-8}}{2}$ $2 + i\sqrt{2}$

7. $(3i + 2)(6i - 4)$ -26

8. If $z = 2 - 4i$ and $w = 1 + 5i$, what is $z - w$?

9. *Multiple choice.* How does the graph of $y - 2 = -(x + 1)^2$ compare with the graph of $y = -x^2$?   c
   (a) It is 1 unit to the right and 2 units below.
   (b) It is 1 unit to the right and 2 units above.
   (c) It is 1 unit to the left and 2 units above.
   (d) It is 1 unit to the left and 2 units below.

10. Graph the solution set to $y - 2 = -(x + 1)^2$.
    See margin.

In 11–13, find all solutions.

11. $3x^2 + 14x - 5 = 0$ $\frac{1}{3}$ or -5

12. $(m + 40)^2 = 2$ $-40 \pm \sqrt{2}$

13. $3x^2 + 15 = 18x - 60$ $3 \pm 4i$

14. *True or false.* $\sqrt{x^2} = |x|$ for all real values of x.   True

In 15 and 16, use the equation $y = ax^2 + bx + c$, assuming $a \neq 0$ and a, b, and c are real numbers.

15. How many x-intercepts does the graph have
    a. if its discriminant is 0?   one
    b. if its discriminant is 1?   two

16. If $y = 0$, describe the nature of the roots
    a. if its discriminant is 0.   There is one real root.
    b. if its discriminant is -5.   There are two complex conjugate roots.

17) $2a^2 + 18$ 18) $64v^2 + 16v + 1$

In 17 and 18, expand.

17. $(a - 3)^2 + (a + 3)^2$ 18. $(8v + 1)^2$

19. A ball is thrown upward from an initial height of 20 meters at an initial velocity of 10 meters per second. Write an equation for the height h of the ball t seconds after being thrown. $h = -4.9t^2 + 10t + 20$

In 20 and 21, the height in feet h of a ball at time t is given by $h = -16t^2 + 12t + 4$.

20. How high is the ball .5 second after it is thrown?   6 ft

21. When does the ball hit the ground?   after 1 sec

22. A rectangular piece of metal is 40 cm by 30 cm. A strip s cm wide is cut parallel to each side of the metal. What is the area of the remaining rectangle in terms of s?

23. *Multiple choice.* Which parabola is not congruent to the others?   a
    (a) $y = 2x^2$ (b) $y =$
    (c) $y = (x + 2)^2$ (d) $y +$

24. There is a pattern to the numb handshakes needed in a group everyone shakes hands with e exactly once. Examine the tab

Number of people n	1	2
Number of handshakes	0	1

a. Draw a scatterplot of thes
b. Fit a quadratic model to
c. How many handshakes v if 100 people shake hand other exactly once?   495

25. $y = 2x^2 - 6x + 4$ is written in standard form. Rewrite this equation in vertex form, and write a sentence detailing information about the graph you can obtain just by looking at the equation in this form. $y + \frac{1}{2} = 2\left(x - \frac{3}{2}\right)^2$

It opens upward, has the vertex $\left(\frac{3}{2}, -\frac{1}{2}\right)$ and has an axis of symmetry $x = \frac{3}{2}$.

22) $4s^2 - 140s + 1200$
24b) $H = \frac{1}{2}n^2 - \frac{n}{2}$

The chart below keys the **Progress Self-Test** questions to the objectives in the **Chapter Review** on pages 413–415 or to the **Vocabulary** (Voc.) on page 411. This will enable you to locate those **Chapter Review** questions that correspond to questions missed on the **Progress Self-Test**. The lesson where the material is covered is also indicated on the chart.

Question	1	2	3	4	5	6	7	8	9	10
Objective	B	B	C	D	D	D	D	D	I	J
Lesson	6–5	6–5	6–7	6–8	6–8	6–8	6–9	6–9	6–3	6–3

Question	11	12	13	14	15	16	17	18	19	20
Objective	C	C	C	E	K	F	A	A	G	G
Lesson	6–7	6–7	6–7	6–2	6–10	6–10	6–1	6–1	6–7	6–7

Question	21	22	23	24	25
Objective	G	G	I	H	B
Lesson	6–7	6–1	6–3	6–6	6–5

A chart for each Progress Self-Test (at the back of the Student Edition) keys test questions to chapter objectives.

"I believe that my students are questioning the legitimacy of their answers more now than before."

Laurie Paladichuk
Miles City, Montana

End-of-chapter mastery

Comprehensive chapter reviews based on SPUR objectives — Skills, Properties, Uses, and Representations — ensure a multidimensional understanding of key concepts.

Properties

Uses

Skills

Representations

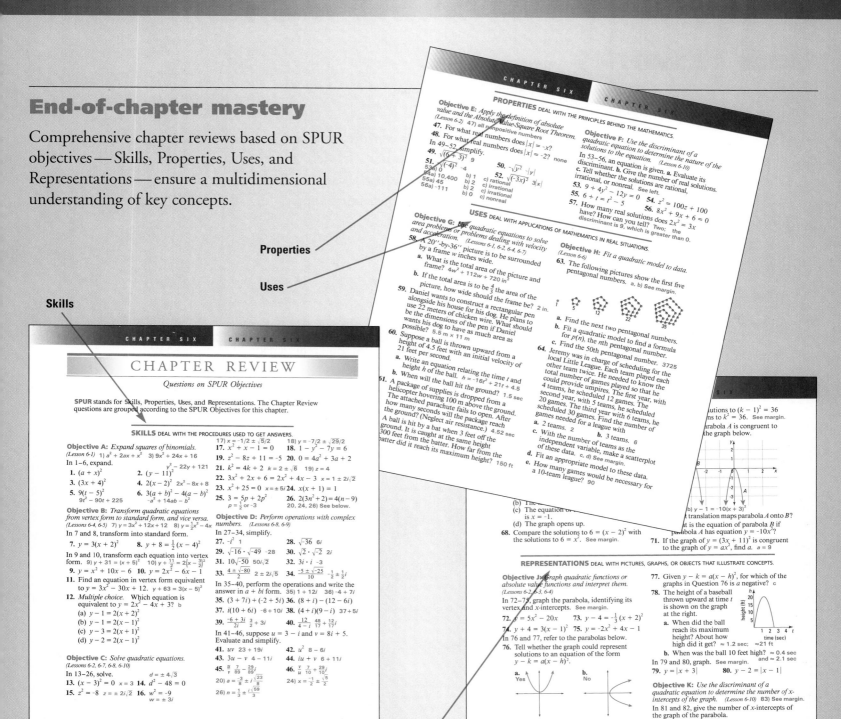

"Not only does UCSMP prepare students for the 21st century, but it's helping teachers to rethink what mathematics is important to teach and how to teach it."

Frank J. Volpe, Jr.
Mt. Olive, New Jersey

How it works

Multiple forms of assessment

Your *Assessment Sourcebook* includes quizzes, test forms A and B, performance tests C and D, and a cumulative test for each chapter, and comprehensive tests after Chapters 3, 6, 9, and 13. Plus, Quiz and Test Writer software enables you to adapt existing tests or create your own in various forms. Your *Assessment Sourcebook* also includes abundant resources for portfolio, problem-solving, cooperative-group, and self-assessment.

"Test results are getting higher as students spend more time in UCSMP courses."

Hilary Booth
St. Petersburg, Florida

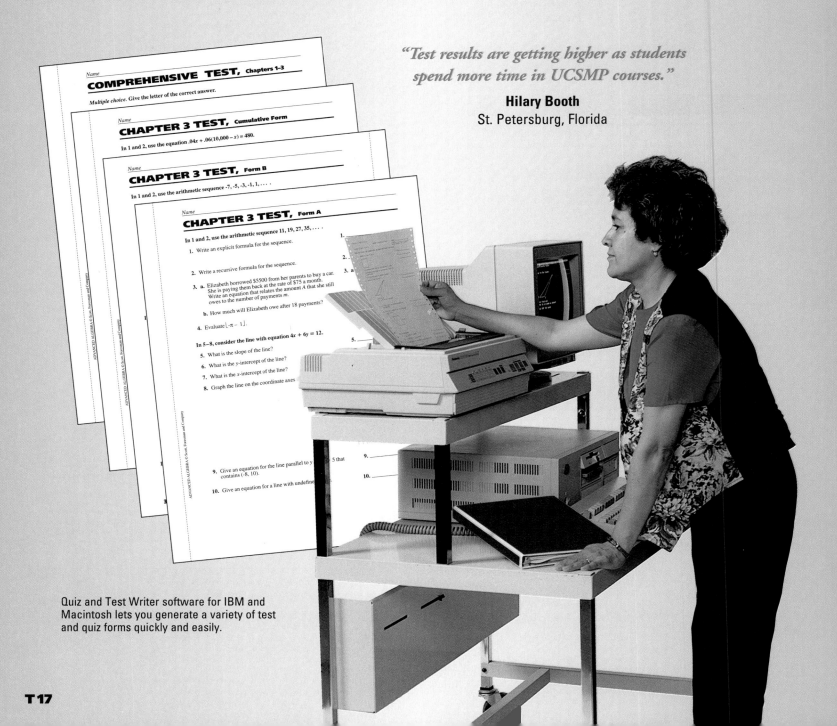

Quiz and Test Writer software for IBM and Macintosh lets you generate a variety of test and quiz forms quickly and easily.

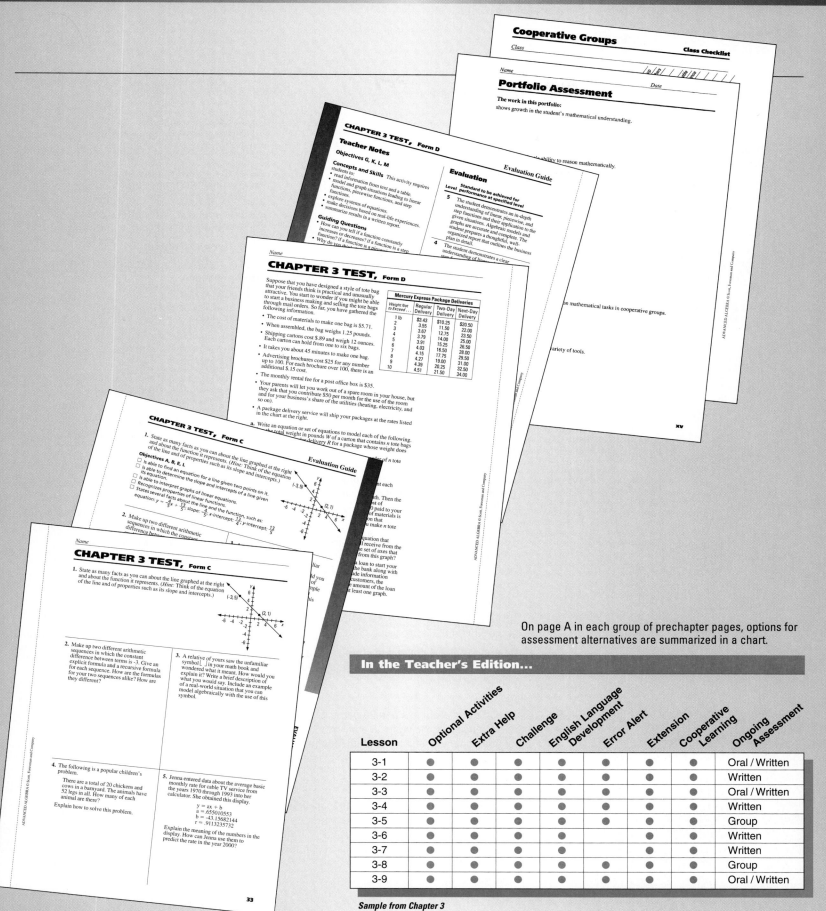

On page A in each group of prechapter pages, options for assessment alternatives are summarized in a chart.

In the Teacher's Edition...

Lesson	Optional Activities	Extra Help	Challenge	English Language Development	Error Alert	Extension	Cooperative Learning	Ongoing Assessment
3-1	●	●	●	●	●	●	●	Oral / Written
3-2	●	●	●	●	●	●	●	Written
3-3	●	●	●	●	●	●	●	Oral / Written
3-4	●	●	●	●	●	●	●	Written
3-5	●	●	●	●	●	●	●	Group
3-6	●	●	●	●	●	●	●	Written
3-7	●	●	●	●	●	●	●	Written
3-8	●	●	●	●	●	●	●	Group
3-9	●	●	●	●	●	●	●	Oral / Written

Sample from Chapter 3

The works

Components of *UCSMP Advanced Algebra, Second Edition*

Student Edition
0-673-45804-0.

Teacher's Edition (in two parts).
0-673-45807-5.

Teacher's Resource File
Contains hundreds of blackline masters and a Solution Manual correlated to the Student Edition. Booklets are also available separately. 0-673-45855-5.

☐ **Lesson Masters A.** Single-page blackline masters correlated to each lesson in the Student Edition—ideal for extra practice. 0-673-45809-1.

☐ **Lesson Masters B.** Two pages of practice for each lesson, for students who need extra help. 0-673-45808-3.

☐ **Teaching Aid Masters.** All Warm-ups and many Additional Examples from the Teacher's Edition margin notes, tables, graphs, drawings, visual organizers, and more. 0-673-45810-5.

☐ **Assessment Sourcebook.** Quizzes, standard tests, performance assessment, and cumulative tests for each chapter, plus comprehensive tests and guidelines for portfolio, problem-solving, cooperative-group, and self-assessment. 0-673-45811-3.

☐ **Technology Sourcebook.** Blackline-master activities for use with both calculators and computers. Helps students explore and extend concepts through the latest technologies. 0-673-45813-X.

☐ **Answer Masters.** Answers for all questions in the Student Edition. 0-673-45812-1.

☐ **Solution Manual.** Complete step-by-step solutions to all questions in the Student Edition. 0-673-45814-8.

Visual Aids
Overhead transparencies of all Answer Masters and Teaching Aids, including Warm-ups and many Additional Examples from the Teacher's Edition margin notes, to enhance your classroom presentations. 0-673-45817-2.

Activity Kit
Includes an Activity Sourcebook with blackline-master activities that enhance interest and understanding, encourage curiosity, and strengthen mathematical thinking. Also includes manipulatives for the overhead projector. 0-673-45822-9.

Study Skills Handbook
A UCSMP exclusive containing tips and models to help students develop study skills. 0-673-45823-7.

Geometry Template (package of 25)
Unique to UCSMP, this sturdy plastic tool is a combination compass and protractor and includes rulers, a grid, various geometric figures, and a center finder. 0-673-45825-3.

Explorer Series Software
Includes a Reference Guide and blackline-master activities.

☐ **GraphExplorer**
IBM: 0-673-44304-3; Macintosh: 0-673-44305-1.

☐ **GeoExplorer**
IBM: 0-673-45332-4; Macintosh: 0-673-44272-1; Apple: 0-673-45331-6.

☐ **StatExplorer**
IBM: 0-673-44302-7; Macintosh: 0-673-44303-5.

☐ **UCSMP Explorer Series Combo Package**
Includes GraphExplorer, GeoExplorer, and StatExplorer.
IBM/Tandy/Comp.: 0-673-45850-4
Macintosh: 0-673-45851-2.

Quiz and Test Writer software (IBM and Macintosh)
Create a wealth of custom quizzes and tests quickly and easily, with a minimum of computer expertise. Includes extra challenge problems.
IBM: 0-673-45881-4; Macintosh: 0-673-45882-2.

Wide World of Mathematics Videotape, Videodisc, CD-ROM (Windows, Macintosh)
Interactive activities in a motivating newscast format demonstrate how math concepts are used in the real world. Activities introduce lessons in the Student Edition and can be used for demonstrations or in a laboratory setting.
Advanced Algebra Videotape Package: 0-673-45874-1.
Advanced Algebra Videodisc Package: 0-673-45873-3.
CD-ROM Macintosh/Windows: 0-673-45875-X.

TO ORDER, JUST CALL
1-800-554-4411

UC**S**MP
SCOTT FORESMAN

The University of Chicago School Mathematics Project

Advanced Algebra

Second Edition

About the Cover Ellipses and other conic sections are important topics in this book. *UCSMP Advanced Algebra* emphasizes facility with algebraic expressions and forms, powers and roots, and functions based on these concepts. Logarithmic, trigonometric, polynomial, and other special functions are studied both for their abstract properties and as tools for modeling real-world situations.

Authors

Sharon L. Senk   Denisse R. Thompson   Steven S. Viktora
Zalman Usiskin   Nils P. Ahbel   Suzanne Levin
Marcia L. Weinhold   Rheta N. Rubenstein   Judith Halvorson Jaskowiak
James Flanders   Natalie Jakucyn   Gerald Pillsbury

ScottForesman

Editorial Offices: Glenview, Illinois
Regional Offices: Sunnyvale, California • Tucker, Georgia
Glenview, Illinois • Oakland, New Jersey • Dallas, Texas

i

ACKNOWLEDGMENTS

Authors

Sharon L. Senk
Associate Professor of Mathematics, Michigan State University, East Lansing, MI

Denisse R. Thompson
Assistant Professor of Mathematics Education, University of South Florida, Tampa, FL

Steven S. Viktora
Chairman, Mathematics Department, New Trier High School, Winnetka, IL

Zalman Usiskin
Professor of Education, The University of Chicago

Nils P. Ahbel
Mathematics Teacher, Kent School, Kent, CT (Second Edition only)

Suzanne Levin
UCSMP (Second Edition only)

Marcia L. Weinhold
Mathematics Teacher, Kalamazoo Area Mathematics and Science Center, Kalamazoo, MI (Second Edition only)

Rheta N. Rubenstein
Mathematics Department Head, Renaissance H.S., Detroit, MI (First Edition only)

Judith Halvorson Jaskowiak
Mathematics Teacher, John F. Kennedy H.S., Bloomington, MN (First Edition only)

James Flanders
UCSMP (First Edition only)

Natalie Jakucyn
UCSMP (First Edition only)

Gerald Pillsbury
UCSMP (First Edition only)

UCSMP Production and Evaluation

Series Editors: Zalman Usiskin, Sharon L. Senk
Director of Second Edition Studies:
  Gurcharn Kaeley
Director of First Edition Studies: Sandra Mathison (State University of New York, Albany), Assistant to the Director: Catherine Sarther
Technical Coordinator: Susan Chang
Second Edition Teacher's Edition Editor:
  David Witonsky

We wish also to acknowledge the generous support of the **Amoco Foundation** and the **Carnegie Corporation of New York** for the development, testing, and distribution of the First Edition of these materials, and the continuing support of the **Amoco Foundation** for the Second Edition.

We wish to thank the many editors, production personnel, and design personnel at ScottForesman for their magnificent assistance.

Design Development

Curtis Design

Multicultural Reviewers for ScottForesman

Winifred Deavens
St. Louis Public Schools, St. Louis, MO

Seree Weroha
Kansas City Public Schools, Kansas City, KS

Efraín Meléndez
Los Angeles Unified School District, CA

Linda Skinner
Edmond Public Schools, Edmond, OK

It is impossible for UCSMP to thank all the people who have helped create and test these books. We wish particularly to thank Carol Siegel, who coordinated the use of the test materials in schools; Lianghuo Fan, Alev Yalman, Scott Anderson, Jason Goeppinger, Eric Landahl, Jim Guszcza, and Colleen Webb of our editorial staff; Eric Chen, Timothy Day, Thao Do, Tony Ham, Zenobia K. Mehta, Jeong Moon, Adil Moiduddin, Antoun Nabhan, Young Nam, and Wei Tang of our technical staff; and Kwai Ming Wa, Sungeum Choi, Merilee Maeir, Catherine Moushon, Raymound Moushon, Noah Berlatsky, and Claudia Ceccarelli of our evaluation staff.

A first draft of *Advanced Algebra* was written and piloted during the 1985–1986 school year, revised and tested during the 1986–1987 school year, and again revised and tested during the 1987–1988 school year. We appreciate the assistance of the following teachers who taught these preliminary versions, participated in the research, and contributed ideas to help improve the text:

Rita Belluomini
Rich South High School
Richton Park, Illinois

Timothy Craine
Renaissance High School
Detroit, Michigan

Mary Crisanti
Lake Park West High School
Roselle, Illinois

Joe DeBlois
West Genessee High School
Camillus, New York

Cynthia Harris
Taft High School
Chicago Public Schools

Marilyn Hourston
Whitney Young High School
Chicago Public Schools

Marvin Koffman
Kenwood Academy
Chicago Public Schools

Sharon Llewellyn
Renaissance High School
Detroit, Michigan

Kenneth Lucas
Glenbrook South High School
Glenview, IL

Donald Thompson
Hernando High School
Brooksville, Florida

Jill Weitz
Brentwood School
Los Angeles, California

Since the ScottForesman publication of the First Edition of *Advanced Algebra* in 1990, thousands of teachers and schools have used the materials and have made additional suggestions for improvements. The materials were again revised, and the following teachers and schools participated in field studies in 1993–1994:

Leah Regulinski
Boulder High School
Boulder, Colorado

Sally Richardson
Mt. Zion High School
Mt. Zion, Illinois

Bryan Friddle
Pontotoc High School
Pontotoc, Mississippi

Maria Saucedo
Hanks High School
El Paso, Texas

Ray Thompson
Thornton Fractional South
High School, Lansing, IL

Lynne G. Rees
Lassiter High School
Marietta, Georgia

Debra L. Schmeltzer
Argo Community High School
Summit, Illinois

Karen Kuchenbrod Umbaugh
Sentinel High School
Missoula, Montana

Marcia M. Booth
Framingham High School
Framingham, Massachusetts

Al Schectman
Steinmetz Academic Center
Chicago Public Schools

Julie Knittle
Shawnee Mission NW High
School, Shawnee, Kansas

Carla Randall
Lake Oswego High School
Lake Oswego, Oregon

Robert Young
Springfield High School
Springfield, Pennsylvania

We wish also to acknowledge the contribution of the text *Advanced Algebra with Transformations and Applications,* by Zalman Usiskin (Laidlaw, 1975), to some of the conceptualizations and problems used in this book.

THE UNIVERSITY OF CHICAGO SCHOOL MATHEMATICS PROJECT

The University of Chicago School Mathematics Project (UCSMP) is a long-term project designed to improve school mathematics in grades K–12. UCSMP began in 1983 with a 6-year grant from the Amoco Foundation. Additional funding has come from the National Science Foundation, the Ford Motor Company, the Carnegie Corporation of New York, the General Electric Foundation, GTE, Citicorp/Citibank, and the Exxon Education Foundation.

UCSMP is centered in the Departments of Education and Mathematics of the University of Chicago. The project has translated dozens of mathematics textbooks from other countries, held three international conferences, developed curricular materials for elementary and secondary schools, formulated models for teacher training and retraining, conducted a large number of large and small conferences, engaged in evaluations of many of its activities, and through its royalties has supported a wide variety of research projects in mathematics education at the University. UCSMP currently has the following components and directors:

Resources	Izaak Wirszup, Professor Emeritus of Mathematics
Elementary Materials	Max Bell, Professor of Education
Elementary Teacher Development	Sheila Sconiers, Research Associate in Education
Secondary	Sharon L. Senk, Associate Professor of Mathematics, Michigan State University Zalman Usiskin, Professor of Education
Evaluation Consultant	Larry Hedges, Professor of Education

From 1983 to 1987, the director of UCSMP was Paul Sally, Professor of Mathematics. Since 1987, the director has been Zalman Usiskin.

Advanced Algebra

The text *Advanced Algebra* has been developed by the Secondary Component of the project, and constitutes the core of the fourth year in a six-year mathematics curriculum devised by that component. The names of the six texts around which these years are built are:

Transition Mathematics
Algebra
Geometry
Advanced Algebra
Functions, Statistics, and Trigonometry
Precalculus and Discrete Mathematics

The content and questions of this book integrate geometry, discrete mathematics, and statistics together with algebra. Pure and applied mathematics are also integrated throughout. It is for these reasons that the book is deemed to be part of an integrated series. However, algebra is the trunk from which the various branches of mathematics studied in this book emanate, and prior exposure to a year of algebra and a year of geometry or their equivalent is assumed. It is for this reason that we call this book simply *Advanced Algebra*.

The First Edition of *Advanced Algebra* introduced many features that have been retained in this edition. There is **wider scope,** including significant amounts of geometry and statistics. These topics are not isolated as separate units of study or enrichment. They are employed to motivate, justify, extend, and otherwise enhance important concepts of algebra. The geometry is particularly important because many students have in the past finished geometry and never seen that important content again. A **real-world orientation** has guided both the selection of content and the approaches allowed the student in working out exercises and problems, because being able to do mathematics is of little use to an individual unless he or she can apply that content. We require **reading mathematics,** because students must read to understand mathematics in later courses and must learn to read technical matter in the world at large. The use of **up-to-date technology** is integrated throughout, with *automatic graphers* assumed.

Four dimensions of understanding are emphasized: skill in carrying out various algorithms; developing and using mathematics properties and relationships; applying mathematics in realistic situations; and representing or picturing mathematical concepts. We call this the SPUR approach: **S**kills, **P**roperties, **U**ses, **R**epresentations.

The **book organization** is designed to maximize the acquisition of both skills and concepts. Ideas introduced in a lesson are reinforced through Review questions in the immediately succeeding lessons. This daily review feature allows students several nights to learn and practice important concepts and skills. Then, at the end of each chapter, a carefully focused Progress Self-Test and a Chapter Review, each keyed to objectives in all the dimensions of understanding, are used to solidify performance of skills and concepts from the chapter so that they may be applied later with confidence. Finally, to increase retention, important ideas are reviewed in later chapters.

Since the ScottForesman publication of the First Edition of *Advanced Algebra* in 1990, the entire UCSMP secondary series has been completed and published. Thousands of teachers and schools have used the first edition and some have made

suggestions for improvements. There have been advances in technology and in thinking about how students learn. As such, many revisions have been made to improve the materials. We have moved many lessons and reorganized others. We have added many new applications, updated others, and introduced lessons on linear, quadratic, and exponential modeling. We deleted the chapter dealing with higher dimensions because so few teachers reached this material and we felt stronger attention needed to be given to the earlier chapters.

Those familiar with the First Edition will note a rather significant reorganization of the treatment of functions. The material in Chapter 7 of the First Edition has been dispersed. The study of functions begins in Chapter 1 in the Second Edition, and function language and notation appear throughout the course. We were encouraged to do this by the widespread availability of graphing technology which makes it much easier to approach functions. Consequently we introduce **automatic graphers,** as we did in the First Edition, but in this edition they are *required* because they are used throughout as a pattern-finding, concept-developing, and problem-solving tool.

There are also a number of features new to this edition, including the following: **Activities** have been incorporated into many lessons to help students develop concepts before or as they read. There are **projects** at the end of each chapter because in the real world much of the mathematics done requires a longer period of time than is customarily available to students in daily assignments. There are many more questions requiring **writing,** because writing helps students clarify their own thinking, and writing is an important aspect of communicating mathematical ideas to others.

Comments about these materials are welcomed. Please address comments to:
UCSMP, The University of Chicago,
5835 S. Kimbark, Chicago, IL 60637.

CONTENTS

CHAPTER 1 4

FUNCTIONS

CHAPTER 2 70

VARIATION AND GRAPHS

LINEAR FUNCTIONS

MATRICES

vii

GETTING STARTED

Welcome to UCSMP Advanced Algebra.
We hope you enjoy this book—it was written for you.

What Is Advanced Algebra?

Advanced Algebra might be best described as "what every high school graduate should know about mathematics that has not been learned in previous courses." It contains the mathematics that educated people around the world use in conversation, and that most colleges want or expect you to have studied. But it is not a hodge-podge of topics. Familiar ideas such as properties of numbers, graphs, expressions, equations, and inequalities appear throughout the book. In addition, you will study many new topics, including matrices, logarithms, trigonometry, and conic sections.

Throughout the course we will use the concept of function to help organize ideas.

The name *Advanced Algebra* may sound as if this class will be like algebra—but more difficult. That is half true. The content of this book is related to what you learned in first-year algebra. However, this book is not necessarily more difficult. Some questions are harder, but you know a lot more than you did then. In particular, you know much more geometry, and you have had a year of practice with algebra.

Studying Mathematics

An important goal of this book is to help you learn mathematics on your own, so that you will be able to deal with the mathematics you see in newspapers, magazines, on television, on any job, and in school. The authors, who are all experienced teachers, offer the following advice:

1 You can watch basketball hundreds of times on television. Still, to learn how to play basketball, you must have a ball in your hand and actually dribble, shoot, and pass it. Mathematics is no different. You cannot learn much algebra just by watching other people do it. You must participate. You must think through and work problems. Some teachers have this slogan:

Mathematics is not a spectator sport.

Notes on Reading
The reading abilities of students who use UCSMP *Advanced Algebra* will differ. One way to approach a lesson is to have students read the pages on their own and then ask questions about what they have read.

Cooperative Learning Emphasize the cooperative nature of learning. Encourage students to discuss questions with each other in school or call each other at home if they have difficulty with a problem or idea. You might want to make sure that each student in your class has the phone numbers of at least two other students. However, be sure to distinguish the difference between *cooperation* and *copying*.

If you plan to use cooperative groups often during the year, you might divide the class into small groups. After students have read a section, each group should go through the questions; instruct one student from each group to write the answers on a sheet of paper. You might want to walk around the room to monitor the groups and to keep them on task.

Reading Mathematics Reading a mathematics textbook may be a new experience for those students who are not familiar with UCSMP texts. To read well, students must read carefully and watch for important terms and symbols. Encourage students to use the headline phrases that identify some of the key ideas taught in the lessons. Point out that these headlines can help students organize their thoughts, preview the reading, and locate answers to questions about the lesson.

Overview
These pages contain three important types of information about this book:
1. a list of the materials that are needed for the book;
2. a description of the expectations related to the active-learning approach of the book, including participation, reading, writing, and problem solving;
3. a set of questions designed to familiarize students with the locations of various features in the book.

Before beginning this chapter, make sure that students have read the section entitled *To The Student* so they know what materials they are expected to have in class and at home.

It is assumed throughout this book that students have access to both an *automatic grapher* (either a graphics calculator or a computer with function-graphing software) and a calculator with the features of a standard scientific calculator. Most graphics calculators satisfy both requirements. Students will need scientific calculator capabilities for the In-class Activity preceding Lesson 1-3, and they will need a calculator with an (ANS) key, or its equivalent, for Lesson 1-8. Automatic graphers are used for the first time with the In-class Activity that precedes Lesson 2-5. If you expect your students to purchase their own

For more information on reading skills, see *General Teaching Suggestions: Reading* in the *Professional Sourcebook*, which begins on page T20 in Part 1 of the Teacher's Edition.

Also point out that as students read, they should stop to examine any graphs or charts and to study all computations that might be in the examples. Looking at pictures and photographs and reading captions are also considered part of the lesson. Point out that important terms are printed in boldface type throughout this book.

✎ **Writing** Writing is an important aspect of this course. When students are expected to give a response by writing a sentence or paragraph, the pencil logo (shown at the beginning of this paragraph) will appear in the Teacher's Edition notes.

Notes on Questions

If students are not in groups, we suggest that you have the class as a whole answer the *Questions Covering the Reading* (**Questions 1–5**), and then have students work on **Questions 6–13** on their own or with a partner.

Questions 1–5 Point out that students should try to put their answers in their own words, even though answers to *Questions Covering the Reading* may be found word for word in the lesson.

Question 2 This question provides an opportunity to discuss the types of calculators that students should have and those (if any) that will be available in class for student use. Students will need scientific calculators for the In-class Activity preceding Lesson 1-3.

2 You are expected to read each lesson. Sometimes you may do this as a class or in a small group; other times you will do the reading on your own. No matter how you do the reading, it is vital for you to understand what you have read. Here are some ways to improve your reading comprehension:

Read slowly and thoughtfully, paying attention to each word, graph, and symbol.

Look up the meaning of any word you do not understand.

Work examples yourself as you follow the steps in the text.

Draw graphs by hand or on your automatic grapher when following a complicated example.

Reread sections that are unclear to you.

Discuss difficult ideas with a fellow student or your teacher.

3 Writing can help you understand mathematics, too. You will often be asked to justify your solution to a problem, to write a formal argument, or to make up your own example to illustrate an idea. Writing good explanations takes practice. You should use solutions to the examples in each lesson to guide your writing.

Equipment Needed for this Course

To be a successful student in any high school mathematics course, you need notebook paper, graph paper, sharpened pencils, good erasers, and a ruler. It is best if the ruler is made of transparent plastic, and marked in both centimeters and inches.

For this book, you need to have technology (a graphics calculator or a computer with suitable software) throughout the year while reading the lessons, doing homework, participating in class, and taking tests and quizzes. With technology, you will be able to solve realistic problems without having to do tedious calculations, and you will be able to learn more mathematics than would otherwise be possible. You will also find such technology useful in

other courses. If you do not have technology available for your use at all times, you will not be able to do some of the questions, and others will be very time consuming.

Your technology must be able to:

1. deal with arithmetic operations ($+$, $-$, $\times$, $\div$), the numbers pi (π) and e, square roots ($\sqrt{\ }$), reciprocals (x^{-1} or $\frac{1}{x}$), powers (x^y or $x^\wedge y$), trigonometric functions (*sin, cos,* and *tan*), and logarithm functions (*log* and *ln*);

2. graph functions of one variable involving the above expressions;

3. find lines of best fit and other regression equations;

4. accommodate the writing, editing, storing, and running of programs.

Your school may give you technology to use or advise you on which technology to purchase. If you buy a graphics calculator, we recommend that you get one that is also capable of generating tables, operating on lists, and performing matrix operations.

graphics calculators, show them one that is similar to the kind you expect them to purchase.

Please stress that students will not be told when to use a calculator. However, they should be instructed to use calculators *when appropriate*. We expect that students will use calculators in class, for homework, with projects, and on tests. We have deliberately not included "use an automatic

grapher" even when such graphers might be needed because we want students to consider these tools as naturally as they view paper and pencils.

Students are expected to read this book; those students who have used previous books in this series will be accustomed to reading mathematics. Specific suggestions are given throughout this chapter to assist you in teaching students to read mathematics.

Setting Up Lesson 1-1

Homework If you have a short class period (15–25 minutes) the next day, or if your students have not studied from a UCSMP text before, assign the reading and **Questions 1–17** in Lesson 1-1. Otherwise, assign the reading and all the Questions in Lesson 1-1.

For more information on homework, see *General Teaching Suggestions: Homework* in the *Professional Sourcebook*, which

Getting Off to a Good Start

It is always helpful to spend some time getting acquainted with your textbook. The questions that follow are designed to help you become familiar with *UCSMP Advanced Algebra*.

We hope you join the thousands of students who have enjoyed this book. We wish you much success.

QUESTIONS

Covering the Reading

1. Name four topics that Advanced Algebra includes. **See margin.**

2. What tools other than paper and pencil are needed for this course? **See margin.**

3. How can the statement "Mathematics is not a spectator sport" be applied to the study of Advanced Algebra? **See margin.**

4. Identify two strategies that you might use to improve your reading comprehension. **See margin.**

5. What kinds of writing will you be asked to do in Advanced Algebra? **See margin.**

Knowing Your Textbook

In 6–13, answer the questions by looking at the Table of Contents, the lessons and chapters of the textbook, or material at the end of the book.

6. Refer to the Table of Contents. What lesson would you read to learn about step functions? **Lesson 3-9**

7. What are the four categories of questions in each lesson? **Covering the Reading, Applying the Mathematics, Review, and Exploration**

8. Suppose you just finished the questions in Lesson 2-8.
   a. On what page can you find answers to check your work? **page 900**
   b. Which answers are given? **See margin.**

9. At the end of Question 25 in Lesson 1-4, you see *(Lesson 1-3)*. What does this mean? **See margin.**

10. Refer to the Chapter Review at the end of a chapter. What does SPUR mean? **See margin.**

11. This book has some Appendices. How many are there and what do they cover? **See margin.**

12. Use the Index in the back of your book to find *decibel*. **Lesson 9-6**
    a. In what lesson is this discussed?
    b. What is the approximate relative intensity in decibels of a very loud rock concert? **120 dB to 125 dB**

13. Each chapter is introduced with an application of a major idea from the chapter. Read page 5. The relation between time and value given in the table and graph is an example of a __?__. **function**

begins on page T20 in Part 1 of the Teacher's Edition.

Materials If you decide to do the *Challenge* on page 10 in the Teacher's Edition, you will need to refer to a variety of textbooks—biology, chemistry, physics, social studies, and so on.

Error Alert Some students may think that they can skip the Chapter 1 Opener on

pages 4–5. Tell them that they should read the chapter opener because there may be questions in Lesson 1-1 that refer to it.

Adapting to Individual Needs

The student text is written for the vast majority of students. The chart at the right suggests two pacing plans to accommodate the needs of your students. Students in the Full Course should complete the entire text by the end of the year. Students in the Minimal Course will spend more time when there are quizzes and more time on the Chapter Review. Therefore, these students may not complete all of the chapters in the text.

Options are also presented to meet the needs of a variety of teaching and learning styles. For each lesson, the Teacher's Edition provides sections entitled: *Video* which describes video segments and related questions that can be used for motivation or extension; *Optional Activities* which suggests activities that employ materials, physical models, technology, and cooperative learning; and *Adapting to Individual Needs* which regularly includes **Challenge** problems, **English Language Development** suggestions, and suggestions for providing **Extra Help.** The Teacher's Edition also frequently includes an **Error Alert,** an **Extension,** and an **Assessment** alternative. The options available in Chapter 1 are summarized in the chart below.

Chapter 1 Pacing Chart

Day	Full Course	Minimal Course
1	1-1	1-1
2	1-2	1-2
3	1-3	1-3
4	Quiz; 1-4	Quiz*; begin 1-4.
5	1-5	Finish 1-4.
6	1-6	1-5
7	Quiz; 1-7	1-6
8	1-8	Quiz*; begin 1-7.
9	1-9	Finish 1-7.
10	Self-Test	1-8
11	Review	1-9
12	Test*	Self-Test
13		Review
14		Review
15		Test*

*in the Teacher's Resource File

In the Teacher's Edition...

Lesson	Optional Activities	Extra Help	Challenge	English Language Development	Error Alert	Extension	Cooperative Learning	Ongoing Assessment
1-1	●	●	●	●	●	●	●	Written
1-2	●	●	●	●		●	●	Written
1-3	●	●	●	●	●		●	Oral/Written
1-4	●	●	●	●	●	●	●	Written
1-5	●	●	●	●	●	●	●	Written
1-6	●	●	●	●	●	●	●	Group
1-7	●	●	●	●		●	●	Written
1-8	●	●	●	●		●	●	Group
1-9	●	●	●	●		●	●	Written

In the Additional Resources...

Lesson	In the Teacher's Resource File								Video Segments
	Lesson Masters, A and B	Teaching Aids*	Activity Kit*	Answer Masters	Technology Sourcebook	Assessment Sourcebook	Visual Aids**	Technology	
Opener		4					4		
1-1	1-1	1, 5		1-1			1, 5, AM		1-1
1-2	1-2	1, 6, 7		1-2	Calc 1		1, 6, 7, AM		
In-class Activity				1-3			AM		
1-3	1-3	1		1-3		Quiz	1, AM		
1-4	1-4	2, 8, 9		1-4			2, 8, 9, AM		
1-5	1-5	2		1-5			2, AM		
1-6	1-6	2		1-6		Quiz	2, AM		
In-class Activity				1-7			AM		
1-7	1-7	3, 8, 10, 11	1	1-7	Comp 1		3, 8, 10, 11, AM	Spreadsheet	
1-8	1-8	3, 12		1-8			3, 12, AM		
1-9	1-9	3	2	1-9			3, AM		
End of chapter						Tests			

*Teaching Aids are pictured on pages 4C and 4D. The activities in the Activity Kit are pictured on page 4C.

**Visual Aids provide transparencies for all Teaching Aids and all Answer Masters.

Also available is the Study Skills Handbook which includes study-skill tips related to reading, note-taking, and comprehension.

Integrating Strands and Applications

	1-1	1-2	1-3	1-4	1-5	1-6	1-7	1-8	1-9
Mathematical Connections									
Number Sense		●							
Algebra	●	●	●	●	●	●	●	●	●
Geometry	●	●	●	●	●	●	●	●	
Measurement	●	●	●		●	●	●	●	
Logic and Reasoning				●	●				
Statistics/Data Analysis		●	●						
Patterns and Functions	●	●	●	●	●	●	●	●	●
Interdisciplinary and Other Connections									
Literature	●								
Science	●	●	●	●		●	●	●	●
Social Studies	●	●	●	●	●	●	●	●	●
Multicultural	●				●		●		
Technology		●				●		●	●
Career					●	●			●
Consumer	●	●	●	●	●	●	●	●	●
Sports		●			●				

Teaching and Assessing the Chapter Objectives

Chapter 1 Objectives (Organized into the SPUR categories—Skills, Properties, Uses, and Representations)	Lessons	Progress Self-Test Questions	Chapter Review Questions	Chapter Test, Forms A and B	Chapter Test, Forms C	Chapter Test, Forms D
				In the Teacher's Resource File		
Skills						
A: Evaluate expressions and formulas, including correct units in answers.	1-1, 1-2	12	1–4	9	1,3	
B: Use function notation.	1-3	5, 6	5–10	5, 6	3	✓
C: Solve and check linear equations.	1-5	9, 10, 11, 20a	11–18	14, 15	3	
D: Rewrite formulas.	1-6	7, 14	19–24	7, 11	2	
E: Evaluate sequences.	1-7, 1-8, 1-9	1, 2a, 3, 4	25–28	1, 2, 3, 17	4	
F: Write a recursive definition for a sequence.	1-8, 1-9	2b	29–32	4, 17	4	
Properties						
G: Determine whether a relation defined by a table, a list of ordered pairs, or a simple equation is a function.	1-2	17, 18	33–37	13		✓
H: Determine the domain and range of a function defined by a table, a list of ordered pairs, or a simple equation.	1-2	15	38–42	10, 12		✓
Uses						
I: Use addition, subtraction, multiplication, and division to write expressions which model real-world situations.	1-1	8	43–48	8	1	✓
J: Use functions to solve real-world problems	1-2, 1-3, 1-4, 1-7, 1-8, 1-9	13, 19, 21	49–56	16		
K: Use linear equations to solve real-world problems.	1-5, 1-6	20b, 22	57–60	18		
Representations						
L: Determine the domain, range, and values of a function from its graph.	1-4	23, 24, 25	61–64	19, 20	5	
M: Apply the Vertical-Line Test for a function.	1-4	16	65–68	21	5	

Assessment Sourcebook
Quiz for Lessons 1-1 through 1-3   Chapter 1 Test, Forms A–D
Quiz for Lessons 1-4 through 1-6

Quiz and Test Writer

Activity Kit

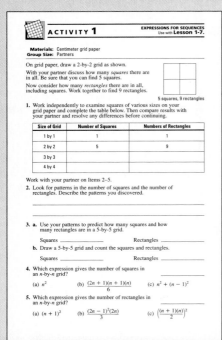

ACTIVITY 1

EXPRESSIONS FOR SEQUENCES
Use with **Lesson 1-7.**

Materials: Centimeter grid paper
Group Size: Partners

On grid paper, draw a 2-by-2 grid as shown.
With your partner discuss how many *squares* there are in all. Be sure that you can find 5 squares.
Now consider how many *rectangles* there are in all, including squares. Work together to find 9 rectangles.

5 squares, 9 rectangles

1. Work independently to examine squares of various sizes on your grid paper and complete the table below. Then compare results with your partner and resolve any differences before continuing.

Size of Grid	Number of Squares	Numbers of Rectangles
1 by 1	1	1
2 by 2	5	9
3 by 3		
4 by 4		

Work with your partner on Items 2–5.

2. Look for patterns in the number of squares and the number of rectangles. Describe the patterns you discovered.

_____

3. **a.** Use your patterns to predict how many squares and how many rectangles are in a 5-by-5 grid.

   Squares _____   Rectangles _____

   b. Draw a 5-by-5 grid and count the squares and rectangles.

   Squares _____   Rectangles _____

4. Which expression gives the number of squares in an *n*-by-*n* grid?

   (a) n^2 (b) $\frac{(2n+1)(n+1)(n)}{6}$ (c) $n^2 + (n-1)^2$

5. Which expression gives the number of rectangles in an *n*-by-*n* grid?

   (a) $(n+1)^2$ (b) $\frac{(2n-1)^2(2n)}{3}$ (c) $\left(\frac{(n+1)(n)}{2}\right)^2$

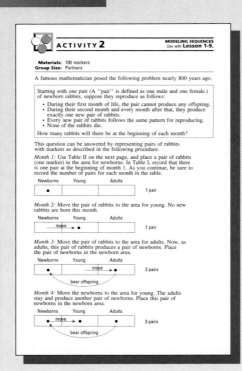

ACTIVITY 2

MODELING SEQUENCES
Use with **Lesson 1-9.**

Materials: 100 markers
Group Size: Partners

A famous mathematician posed the following problem nearly 800 years ago.

Starting with one pair (A "pair" is defined as one male and one female.) of newborn rabbits, suppose they reproduce as follows:

- During their first month of life, the pair cannot produce any offspring.
- During their second month and every month after that, they produce exactly one new pair of rabbits.
- Every new pair of rabbits follows the same pattern for reproducing.
- None of the rabbits die.

How many rabbits will there be at the beginning of each month?

This question can be answered by representing pairs of rabbits with markers as described in the following procedure.

Month 1: Use Table II on the next page, and place a pair of rabbits (one marker) in the area for newborns. In Table I, record that there is one pair at the beginning of month 1. As you continue, be sure to record the number of pairs for each month in the table.

Newborns   Young   Adults

●   1 pair

Month 2: Move the pair of rabbits to the area for young. No new rabbits are born this month.

Newborns   Young   Adults

move → ●   1 pair

Month 3: Move the pair of rabbits to the area for adults. Now, as adults, this pair of rabbits produces a pair of newborns. Place the pair of newborns in the newborn area.

Newborns   Young   Adults

●   move → ●   2 pairs
    bear offspring

Month 4: Move the newborns to the area for young. The adults stay and produce another pair of newborns. Place this pair of newborns in the newborn area.

Newborns   Young   Adults

●   move → ●   ●   3 pairs
    bear offspring

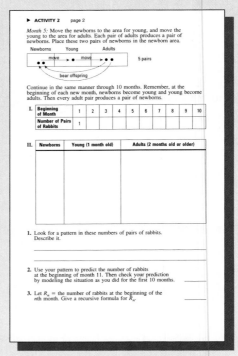

▶ **ACTIVITY 2**   page 2

Month 5: Move the newborns to the area for young, and move the young to the area for adults. Each pair of adults produces a pair of newborns. Place these two pairs of newborns in the newborn area.

Newborns   Young   Adults

●● move → ● move → ●●   5 pairs
        bear offspring

Continue in the same manner through 10 months. Remember, at the beginning of each new month, newborns become young and young become adults. Then every adult pair produces a pair of newborns.

I.

Beginning of Month	1	2	3	4	5	6	7	8	9	10
Number of Pairs of Rabbits	1									

II.

Newborns	Young (1 month old)	Adults (2 months old or older)

1. Look for a pattern in these numbers of pairs of rabbits. Describe it.

_____

2. Use your pattern to predict the number of rabbits at the beginning of month 11. Then check your prediction by modeling the situation as you did for the first 10 months.

3. Let R_n = the number of rabbits at the beginning of the *n*th month. Give a recursive formula for R_n.

Teaching Aids

Warm-up   Lesson 1-1

Write each phrase or sentence using symbols.

1. Twice a number.

2. Two less than a number.

3. Two is less than a number.

4. Two is greater than or equal to a number.

5. A number is approximately equal to 2.

Warm-up   Lesson 1-2

1. To determine the retail price *r* of all merchandise, a store owner multiplies the wholesale price *w* by 1.5. Write an equation relating *r* and *w*.

2. Make a table showing at least five values for *r* and *w*.

Warm-up   Lesson 1-3

1. If $y = 4x - 1$, find *y* when $x = 0$.

2. If $y = 2x + \frac{x^2}{10}$, find *y* when $x = 5$.

3. If $y = \frac{6-x}{x^2}$, find *y* when $x = 2$.

4. If $y = 2^x$, find *y* when $x = 10$.

Warm-up   Lesson 1-4

Give the domain and range of each function.

1. $\{(1, 10), (2, 12), (3, 17), (4, 25)\}$

2. $y = 6$ 3. $y = |x|$ 4. $y = \frac{2x}{x+1}$

Warm-up   Lesson 1-5

Marshall won the cash prize in the benefit raffle. He put one third of the money into his bank account, used one half of the money to make his monthly car payment, and used the rest of the cash to buy some new clothes. If Marshall spent $75 on new clothes, how much money did he win?

Warm-up   Lesson 1-6

Which formula would you use to solve the problem? Explain your answer.

1. What is the width *w* of a rectangular room that has a length ℓ of 28 feet and an area *A* of 84 square feet?
   a. $A = \ell w$ **b.** $\ell = \frac{A}{w}$ **c.** $w = \frac{A}{\ell}$

2. A triangular sail has an area *A* of 60 ft². The base *b* of the sail is 12 feet wide. What is the height *h* of the sail?
   a. $b = \frac{2A}{h}$ **b.** $h = \frac{2A}{b}$ **c.** $A = \frac{bh}{2}$

Warm-up   Lesson 1-7

Use the sequence *t* of positive even integers for these questions: 2, 4, 6, 8, 10, . . .

1. What does t_4 equal?

2. Write a symbolic translation of "the fifth term of the sequence is 10."

3. Write what you would say if you were asked to read "$t_8 = 16$" aloud.

4. Suppose t_n represents the general, or *n*th, term of the sequence. Give a formula for t_n.

Warm-up   Lesson 1-8

1. To repay a $200 loan, Jessie makes a payment of $20 a month. At the end of each month she receives a statement telling how much money she still owes. Make a list of her outstanding debts for the first six months.

2. The first term of a sequence is $100. Each term after that is found by multiplying the preceding term by 1.06 and rounding to the nearest cent. Find the first six terms of the sequence.

Warm-up   Lesson 1-9

Find the first four terms of the sequence defined by:
$$\begin{cases} t_1 = 50 \\ t_n = 1.05t_{n-1}, \text{ for integers } n \geq 2. \end{cases}$$

The Death of Superman

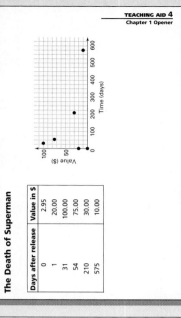

Days after release	Value in $
0	2.95
1	20.00
31	100.00
54	75.00
210	30.00
575	10.00

Graph Paper

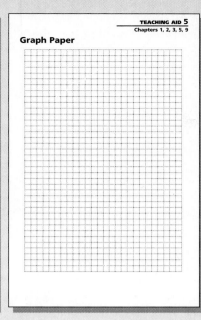

Visual Organizer: Origins of Functions

Origin	Domain	Range
Formula	• independent variable	• dependent variable
Table	• first row • left column	• second row • right column
Calculator key	• input	• output

Additional Examples

1. The table below shows the average temperature *T* in degrees Fahrenheit for each month *M* in Honolulu, Hawaii.

M	T		M	T
Jan.	73		July	80
Feb.	73		Aug.	81
Mar.	74		Sept.	81
Apr.	76		Oct.	80
May	78		Nov.	77
June	79		Dec.	74

a. Is *T* a function of *M*? Justify your answer.

b. Is *M* a function of *T*? Justify your answer.

2. Give the domain and the range of the function in *Additional Example 1a*.

3. The total cost *c* of *v* cans of vegetable soup at 59¢ per can is given by the formula $c = 59v$.

a. Is *c* a function of *v*? Why or why not?

b. What are the domain and the range of this function?

Four-Quadrant Graph Paper

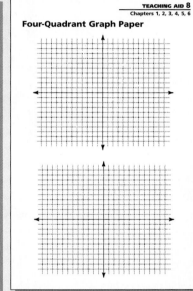

Additional Examples

1. The graph below gives the distances a person traveled away from home during a 7-hour trip.

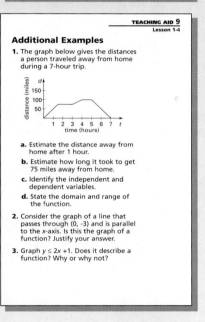

a. Estimate the distance away from home after 1 hour.

b. Estimate how long it took to get 75 miles away from home.

c. Identify the independent and dependent variables.

d. State the domain and range of the function.

2. Consider the graph of a line that passes through (0, -3) and is parallel to the *x*-axis. Is this the graph of a function? Justify your answer.

3. Graph $y \leq 2x + 1$. Does it describe a function? Why or why not?

Question 16

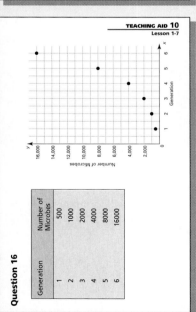

Generation	Number of Microbes
1	500
2	1000
3	2000
4	4000
5	8000
6	16000

Pascal's Triangle

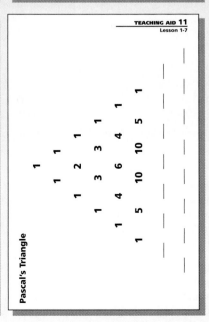

Extension

In 1-3, each figure is formed by a series of regular polygons. Have students assume that the length of each side of each polygon is 1 and write both explicit and recursive formulas for the sequence of perimeters of the figures. Then have them write a formula for a similar series of hexagons.

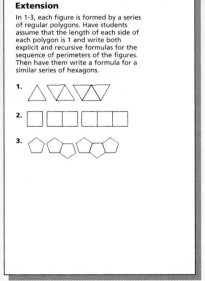

1.

2.

3.

Chapter Opener

Pacing

All of the lessons in this chapter are designed to be covered in one day. At the end of the chapter, you should plan to spend 1 day to review the Progress Self-Test, 1–2 days for the Chapter Review, and 1 day for a test. You may want to spend a day on projects, and a day may be needed for quizzes. Therefore, this chapter should take 13–14 days.

Using pages 4–5

The Chapter 1 Opener gives an example of a function that is described in three ways: in prose (in the second paragraph of the page), with a table, and with a graph.

The graph showing the values of *The Death of Superman* is on **Teaching Aid 4**.

You might mention that another common way to describe a function is with an equation or formula. However, the function described here is not particularly predictable; therefore, it is not described with an equation. Students will see functions described with equations beginning in Lesson 1-2.

Point out the list of lesson titles so that students will have an idea of what they will be studying in Chapter 1. Explain that there are three themes in these lessons: a review of solving equations, functions, and sequences.

Photo Connections

The photo collage makes real-world connections to the content of the chapter: functions.

Functions?

4

Chapter 1 Overview

This chapter is designed to review concepts of elementary algebra within the context of new material on functions. Language and important notation are introduced and reviewed using formulas and sequences.

The formal study of sequences in Chapter 1 is probably new to most students. These general ideas are applied to arithmetic sequences in Chapter 3 and to geometric sequences in Chapter 8.

Functions are a fundamental concept used to describe relationships among variables. Students will use functions throughout this book and in virtually every mathematics course they take after *Advanced Algebra*.

Lesson 1-1 reviews the language of expressions and sentences in algebra. Lessons 1-2 and 1-3 introduce the terminology and notation that are associated with all functions. Lesson 1-4 relates this language

to graphs of functions. Lessons 1-5 and 1-6 deal with the solving of equations. Lesson 1-7 introduces a special type of function—the sequence with explicit formulas for the *n*th term. Lesson 1-8 sets up Lesson 1-9 to describe sequences with recursive formulas.

The strong geometric flavor in Chapter 1 with graphs and visual patterns, continues throughout the book and serves three

FUNCTIONS

Many people are avid collectors. People all over the world collect things ranging from antique jewelry to comic books to stamps. Some people are collectors because they use the items or find them interesting. Other people collect things as investments, hoping they will increase in value over time. For instance, a *Superman* comic which sold in 1970 for 25¢ now sells for a price between $12.00 and $30.00, depending on the condition and content of the comic book.

Of course, not all items continue to increase in value over time. The collector's edition of *The Death of Superman* originally sold for $2.95 on November 17, 1992, the day it was released. The next day, after all issues had been sold, the comic book was worth $20.00. By December 18, the price had skyrocketed to $100.00. But then the price began to drop. On January 10, 1993, the collectors edition was worth only $75.00 and by June 15, 1993, the comic book's value had decreased to $30.00, and had been stable for some time. By June 15, 1994, the price for a copy of *The Death of Superman* in mint condition was $10.00.

The six pairs of dates and values given above can be represented in a table or in a graph.

Days after release	Value in $
0	2.95
1	20.00
31	100.00
54	75.00
210	30.00
575	10.00

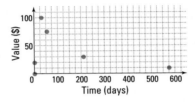

It is difficult to predict the future value of the comic book from these points. However, when a graph or table has a regular pattern, you can often estimate values in the future with some confidence.

The relation between time and value is an example of a *function*. In this course you will study many kinds of functions, their properties, and their uses. In this chapter you will learn how to describe functions with words, tables, graphs, and symbols. Because an understanding of functions depends on your ability to use algebraic expressions and sentences correctly, you will also review these important ideas in this chapter.

5

Stamps Algebraic expressions can be used to describe the value of x stamps at y cents per stamp.

Comic Art Approximately 150 million comic books are sold annually in the United States and Canada. The amount of profit from the sale of a comic book is a function of the number of copies sold.

Airplanes The distance d an airplane travels, its rate of speed r, and the length of time t it travels are variables in the distance formula $d = rt$. In Lesson 1-6, this formula is rewritten to solve for t. The situation determines the most useful form of a formula.

Cells The number of cells produced each time cells split forms a sequence of numbers. Any term in the sequence can be calculated directly by using an explicit formula.

Bees A male bee has one parent, two grandparents, and three great-grandparents. A recursive formula can be used to find the number of ancestors of a male bee in each generation.

Chapter 1 Projects

At the end of each chapter, you will find projects related to the chapter. At this time, you might want to have students look over the projects on pages 61–62. Have each student tentatively select a project on which to work. As students read and progress into the chapter, they can finalize their project choices.

Sometimes students might work on a project alone; at other times, they might collaborate with classmates for a presentation and discussion. We recommend that you allow for diversity, and encourage students to use their imaginations when presenting their projects.

Some teachers wait until Chapter 2 or 3 to have students do projects and give their students options from all the chapters. For more information on projects, see *General Teaching Suggestions: Projects* in the *Professional Sourcebook*, which begins on page T20 in Part 1 of the Teacher's Edition.

purposes. First, many students profit greatly from a visual representation of the concepts they are learning. Second, blending geometry with algebra shows the interrelationships between these two branches of mathematics. Last, students' knowledge of geometry is reviewed and enhanced. The end-of-chapter material, optional in many books, is an integral part of this chapter and should not be omitted.

If students are required to have their own graphics calculators, be sure they know what kinds are acceptable. See *To the Student: Getting Started* on page 1 of both the Student Edition and the Teacher's Edition. If you have not used computers in your classroom, you may want to read *General Teaching Suggestions: Technology* in the *Professional Sourcebook*, which begins on page T20 in Part 1 of the Teacher's Edition.

Objectives

A Evaluate expressions and formulas, including correct units in answers.

I Use addition, subtraction, multiplication, and division to write expressions which model real-world situations.

Resources

From the *Teacher's Resource File*
- Lesson Master 1-1A or 1-1B
- Answer Master 1-1
- Teaching Aids
  1   Warm-up
  5   Graph Paper

Additional Resources
- Visuals for Teaching Aids 1, 5

Teaching
Lesson **1-1**

Warm-up

You can use the *Warm-up*, or the *Additional Examples* on page 8, as questions for students to work on as you begin class.

As students arrive for class, write the following questions on the board or use **Teaching Aid 1.**

Write each phrase or sentence using symbols. **Samples are given.**
1. Twice a number $2n$
2. Two less than a number $n - 2$
3. Two is less than a number. $2 < n$
4. Two is greater than or equal to a number. $2 \geq n$
5. A number is approximately equal to 2. $n \approx 2$

LESSON

1-1

The Language of Algebra

"That's some of my earlier work."

The language of algebra uses numbers and variables. A **variable** is a symbol that can be replaced by any member of a set of numbers or other objects. When numbers and variables are combined using the operations of arithmetic, the result is called an **algebraic expression,** or simply an **expression.**

The expression πr^2 uses the variable r and the numbers π and 2. An algebraic expression with two variables is $a + b$.

❶ An **algebraic sentence** consists of expressions related with a verb. The most common verbs in algebra are = (is equal to), < (is less than), > (is greater than), ≤ (is less than or equal to), ≥ (is greater than or equal to), ≠ (is not equal to), and ≈ (is approximately equal to). Some algebraic sentences are $A = \pi r^2$, $a + b = b + a$, and $3x + 9 < 22$.

Algebra is the study of expressions, sentences, and other relations involving variables. Because many expressions and sentences are based on patterns in arithmetic, algebra sometimes is called generalized arithmetic.

Writing Expressions and Sentences

From your earlier study of algebra, you should know how to write expressions and sentences describing real situations, and how to evaluate expressions or sentences.

Lesson 1-1 Overview

Broad Goals The broad goal of this lesson is to immediately get students thinking about and doing algebra through the translation and evaluation of algebraic expressions.

Perspective There are three basic ways to translate a statement from English into algebra: word-for-word direct translating, patterning, and using models. We assume students are familiar with word-for-word

translating from previous courses. **Example 1** illustrates patterning and using models; **Example 2** illustrates patterning.

The evaluation of expressions and formulas is considered to be review at this point, but the inclusion of unit analysis (as seen in **Example 3**) will probably be new for students.

Optional Activities

Activity 1
Materials: Graph paper or **Teaching Aid 5**

After discussing the opener, have students **work in groups** and estimate what they think the value of *The Death of Superman* is today. Have them give reasons for their estimates. Then have students graph all of the estimates and find the mean, median, and mode of the numbers.

Example 1

Express the cost of y cans of orange juice at x cents per can.

Solution 1

Use a special case. 5 cans at 60¢ per can would cost
$5 \cdot 60¢ = 300¢ = \$3.00$. That suggests multiplication.
So *y cans at x cents per can will cost xy cents.*

Solution 2

Recognize a general model for multiplication. The unit "cents per can," which can be written as $\frac{cents}{can}$, signals a *rate.* Multiply y cans by the rate factor $x \frac{cents}{can}$, to obtain the total cost. The unit of xy is the "product" of the units.

$$x \frac{cents}{can} \cdot y \; cans = xy \; cents$$

You may have noticed that part of the solution in Example 1 is written **using this typestyle.** This style is used to indicate what you might write on your homework paper as the solution to the problem.

Example 2

Kim collects stamps. She now has 9000 stamps. If Kim buys 40 stamps each month, how many stamps will she have after m months?

Solution

Make a table. Notice in this table that the arithmetic is not carried out. This makes the pattern easier to see.

Months from now	Number of stamps
1	$9000 + 1 \cdot 40$
2	$9000 + 2 \cdot 40$
3	$9000 + 3 \cdot 40$
4	$9000 + 4 \cdot 40$

The number in the left column, which gives the number of months, is always in a particular place in the expressions at the right. That shows a pattern.

| m | $9000 + m \cdot 40$ |

Kim will have 9000 + 40m stamps after m months.

Check

To check the expression $9000 + 40m$, pick a value for m not in the table. We pick $m = 5$, indicating 5 months from now. Then substitute this value into the expression $9000 + 40m = 9000 + 40 \cdot 5 = 9200$. Now extend the table to $m = 5$, by adding 40 as you go from one row to the next. As you can see, it checks.

Months from now	Number of stamps
1	9040
2	9080
3	9120
4	9160
5	9200

Lesson 1-1 *The Language of Algebra* **7**

Notes on Reading

You might want to use Activity 1 in *Optional Activities* on page 6 to introduce this lesson. Graph paper or **Teaching Aid 5** is needed for this activity.

Reading Mathematics This lesson has been designed to get students off to a successful start in reading mathematics. To read well, students must read carefully and watch for important terms and symbols. We strongly recommend discussing this lesson after students have read it and answered the questions on their own. If possible, give students time to read in class.

For more information on reading skills, see *General Teaching Suggestions: Reading* in the *Professional Sourcebook*, which begins on page T20 in Part 1 of the Teacher's Edition.

❶ Emphasize that algebraic sentences include both inequalities and equations.

❷ The script font that is introduced in Solution 1 of **Example 1** is used to indicate what students might write.

❸ Students who have studied from previous UCSMP texts will have seen the patterning found in **Example 2** many times. Still, you might want to point out that the approaches found here (making a table, looking for patterns, and drawing a conclusion) are excellent problem-solving techniques that often work when other methods fail.

Optional Activities

Activity 2
After doing **Question 36**, you might have students use three 3s to write expressions for each of the numbers 1 through 10.
[Sample:

$1 = \frac{\sqrt{3} \cdot \sqrt{3}}{3}$, $2 = 3 - (3 \div 3)$, $3 = 3 - 3 + 3$,

$4 = 3 \div 3 + 3$, $5 = 3! - \frac{3}{3}$, $6 = 3 \times 3 - 3$,

$7 = 3! + \frac{3}{3}$, $8 = 3! + \frac{3!}{3}$, $9 = \sqrt{3} \cdot \sqrt{3} + 3!$;

$10 = 3 \times 3 + \lceil .\overline{3} \rceil$]

Video

Wide World of Mathematics
The segment, *Death of Superman*, features the publication of the last issue of the Superman comic book series. This segment may be used to introduce a discussion of the use of algebraic expressions. Related questions and an investigation are provided in videodisc stills and in the Video Guide. A related CD-ROM activity is also available.

Videodisc Bar Codes

Search Chapter 4

Play

Additional Examples

These additional examples correspond to the examples in the Pupil Edition. You might want to use them when discussing the lesson.

1. Express the cost of w pencils at b cents per pencil. **bw cents**
2. Allen has $75 in the bank. If he saves $25 each month, how much money, excluding interest, will he have in the bank after m months? **$75 + m \cdot 25$ dollars**
3. Use the formula $V = \frac{4}{3}\pi r^3$ to find the volume of a ball that is 10 centimeters in diameter. **≈ 524 cubic centimeters**

Notes on Questions

Cooperative Learning It is always appropriate to go over questions in class. However, remind students that selected answers to odd-numbered questions are provided at the back of the book. Encourage students to check their answers to odd-numbered questions and to try to resolve any difficulties before coming to class.

✏️ **Question 8 Writing** This is the first of many questions in which students write their own examples. This task helps students focus on what is given and what is to be found; it also makes them sensitive to the sorts of information that are required to solve a problem. **Questions 9 and 24–27** are also of this type.

(Notes on Questions continue on page 10.)

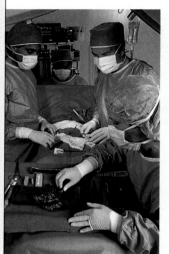

Doctor's orders. *The order in which operations are carried out is important in medicine— as well as in most everyday procedures that are done.*

You could also describe the situation in Example 2 with a sentence. Suppose S = the number of stamps Kim has after m months. Then you could write $S = 9000 + 40m$.

As Examples 1 and 2 show, there is often more than one way to translate situations into algebra. You should try to learn a variety of ways. The expression you get a second way can be used to check the expression you got the first way.

Evaluating Expressions and Formulas

Substituting for the variables in an expression and calculating a result is called **evaluating the expression.** In order to evaluate expressions, you must use the rules for grammar and punctuation of the language of algebra. The following rules for *order of operations* are used to evaluate expressions worldwide.

> **Rules for Order of Operations**
> 1. Perform operations within parentheses ( ), brackets [ ], or other grouping symbols, like square root symbols or fraction bars, from the inner set of symbols to the outer set. Inside grouping symbols, use the order given in Rules 2, 3, and 4.
> 2. Take powers.
> 3. Multiply and divide in order from left to right.
> 4. Add and subtract in order from left to right.

An **equation** is a sentence stating that two expressions are equal. A **formula** is an equation stating that a single variable is equal to an expression with one or more different variables on the other side. Below are some examples.

$A = \pi r^2$	both an equation and a formula
$S = 2w\ell + 2wh + 2\ell h$	both an equation and a formula
$a + b = b + a$	an equation that is not a formula

Formulas are useful because they express important ideas with very few symbols and because they can be applied easily to many situations. Here is an example of evaluating an expression in a science formula with more than one variable in the expression. It also illustrates how we work with units in formulas.

Example 3

The formula $d = \frac{1}{2}gt^2$ tells how to find d, the distance an object has fallen during time t, when it is dropped in free fall near the Earth's surface. The variable g represents the acceleration due to gravity. Near the Earth's surface, $g = 9.8 \frac{m}{sec^2}$. About how far will a rock fall in 5 seconds if it is dropped near the Earth's surface?

▶

8

Adapting to Individual Needs

Extra Help
When applying the rules for order of operations, students sometimes forget that fraction bars and square-root symbols function as grouping symbols. Give students the exercises shown at the right, and have them tell which part of the expression is evaluated first. Then have them evaluate the expression.

1. $8 + \frac{3}{5-3}$ $[5 - 3; 9\frac{1}{2}]$

2. $16 - 7\sqrt{25 - 9}$ $[25 - 9; -12]$

3. $5 - \frac{3+5}{8}$ $[3 + 5; 4]$

4. $\frac{0}{7} + \sqrt{4}$ $[\frac{0}{7}; 2]$

Solution

Substitute $g = 9.8 \frac{m}{sec^2}$ and $t = 5$ sec into the formula.

$$d = \frac{1}{2}gt^2$$
$$= \frac{1}{2}\left(9.8 \frac{m}{sec^2}\right)(5 \text{ sec})^2$$
$$= \frac{1}{2} \cdot 9.8 \frac{m}{sec^2} \cdot 25 \text{ sec}^2$$
$$= 4.9 \cdot 25 \text{ m}$$
$$d = 122.5 \text{ m}$$

In 5 seconds, a rock dropped near the Earth's surface will fall about 122.5 meters.

Check

The time units cancel out and you are left with meters. This is an appropriate measure for distance, so the unit checks. Does the distance seem reasonable to you?

QUESTIONS

Covering the Reading

These questions check your understanding of the reading. If you cannot answer a question, you should go back and reread the lesson to help you find an answer.

In 1 and 2, refer to the information about the value of *The Death of Superman*.

1. How much did the comic book increase in value between November 17 and December 18, 1992? **$97.05**

2. a. How many variables are described in the table and graph? **two**
  b. Name them. **time in days, value in dollars**

3. Name all the variables in $2\pi r$. **r**

4. Tell whether $2\pi r$ is an example of each of the following.
  a. an equation **No**   **b.** an expression **Yes**
  c. a formula **No**   **d.** a sentence **No**

Super hero. *Superman first appeared in the comics in 1938. Although he "died" in the November 17, 1992 issue, he was "brought back" in the April 15, 1993 issue.*

In 5–7, translate into words.

5. $\leq$ **is less than or equal to**   **6.** $\neq$ **is not equal to**   **7.** $\approx$ **is approximately equal to**

8. Give an example of an algebraic expression not found in the reading. **Sample: ℓw**

9. Give an example of an algebraic sentence. **Sample: $C = 2\pi r$**

10. a. What is the cost of 10 cans of tomato juice costing c cents per can?
  b. What is the cost of m cans of tomato juice costing c cents each?
  a) 10c cents   b) mc cents

11. A person now owns 25 stamps and is buying 3 stamps a week. How many stamps will there be after w weeks? **25 + 3w**

Lesson 1-1 *The Language of Algebra* **9**

Adapting to Individual Needs

English Language Development

To help students distinguish between expressions and sentences, write the following on the board:

Expression	Sentence
The sea water	The sea water *is* salty.
x plus 7	x plus 7 *equals* 15.
$x + 7$	$x + 7 = 15$
$x - 3$	$x - 3 > 0$

Note that sentences contain verbs; expressions do not. Point out that $=, \leq, \geq$ represent some of the verbs used in mathematical sentences.

Suggest that students with limited English proficiency write each unfamiliar term or phrase they encounter on a different index card. Tell them to include a definition in their own words and an illustration, if appropriate.

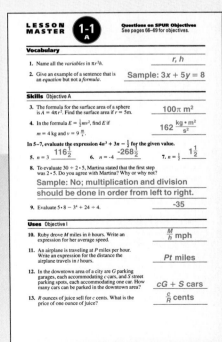

Questions 18–23 Error Alert
Encourage students who are having difficulty with these questions to substitute numerical values for the variables.

Additional Answers

36. The numbers 14, 17, 22, 23, and 25 cannot be written with three 9s. Samples:

$1 = (\sqrt{9} \times \sqrt{9}) \div 9$
$2 = \sqrt{9} - 9 \div 9$
$3 = \sqrt{9} + 9 - 9$
$4 = \sqrt{9} + 9 \div 9$
$5 = (\sqrt{9})! - 9 \div 9$
$6 = 9 - 9 \div \sqrt{9}$
$7 = 9 \div .9 - \sqrt{9}$
$8 = 9 - 9 \div 9$
$9 = 9 + 9 - 9$
$10 = 9 + 9 \div 9$
$11 = (9 + .9) \div .9$
$12 = 9 + 9 \div \sqrt{9}$
$13 = 9 \div .9 + \sqrt{9}$
$15 = 9 + 9 - \sqrt{9}$
$16 = 9 \div .9 + (\sqrt{9})!$
$18 = 9 \times \sqrt{9} - 9$
$19 = 9 \div .9 + 9$
$20 = (9 + 9) \div .9$
$21 = 9 + 9 + \sqrt{9}$
$24 = 9 \times \sqrt{9} - \sqrt{9}$

24) Sample: A can of soda costs x cents. The price increases y cents. What is the new soda price?

25) Sample: Mark is building a deck requiring x feet of lumber. He already has y feet of lumber. How much more lumber should he buy, or how much lumber will he have left?

Children of the Hopi tribe learn to identify kachinas—powerful spirits of the earth, sky, and water—by playing with kachina dolls.

26) Sample: Your gas tank holds x gallons. If gas costs y cents per gallon, how much does a tank of gas cost?

27) Sample: A meteor falls x meters in y seconds. At what rate is it approaching the Earth?

10

12. To evaluate $3 \cdot 5^{(4-2)}$, you must do these steps. Put them in order.
   (1) Multiply.   (2) Take the power.   (3) Do the subtraction.
   (3), (2), (1)

In 13–15, a sentence is given. **a.** Is the sentence an equation? **b.** Is the sentence a formula?

   15a) Yes b) No

13. $A = \pi r^2$ a) Yes
    b) Yes
14. $6s^2 > 0$ a) No
    b) No
15. $2(L + W) = 2L + 2W$

In 16 and 17, refer to Example 3. How far will a rock fall in four seconds if it is dropped from the given spot?

16. near the Earth's surface 78.4 m

17. near the surface of the moon, where $g = 1.6 \frac{m}{\sec^2}$ 12.8 m

Applying the Mathematics

These questions extend the concepts of the lesson. You should take your time, study the examples and explanations, and try a variety of methods. Check your answers to odd-numbered questions with the ones in the back of the book.

18. Suppose a collector now owns K kachina dolls and is buying 6 dolls per year. How many dolls will the collector have after y years?
    $K + 6y$ dolls

In 19–23, tell which expression, (a) $x + y$, (b) $x - y$, (c) $y - x$, (d) xy, (e) $\frac{x}{y}$, or (f) $\frac{y}{x}$, will lead to a correct answer.

19. You give a friend y dollars. You had x dollars. What do you have left?
    b

20. Mrs. Bell is y years old. A friend is x years older. How old is the friend? a

21. You drove x miles in y hours. What was your rate? e

22. You buy x granola bars at y cents per bar. What is the total cost? d

23. A picture of a building is x times actual size. The height of the building is y. What is the height of the building in the picture? d

In 24–27, make up one example of a situation different from those in this lesson that can lead to the expression. See left.

24. $x + y$ 25. $x - y$ 26. xy 27. $\frac{x}{y}$

In 28–30, evaluate each expression when $x = 15$, $y = -3$, and $z = 2$.

28. $\frac{x}{y} - z^3$ -13   29. $\frac{x}{(y - z)^3}$ -0.12   30. $\frac{x}{y - z^3}$ $-1.\overline{36}$

31. Young's formula, $C = \left(\frac{g}{g + 12}\right)A$, has been used to determine how much medicine C to give to a child under age 13 when the adult dosage A is known. Here g is the child's age measured in years. Suppose an adult dosage for a medicine is 600 milligrams. What is the dosage for a 3-year-old according to this formula? (Caution! Do not apply this formula yourself. Medicines should only be taken under the supervision of a physician or pharmacist.) 120 mg

Adapting to Individual Needs

✏️ **Challenge Writing**
Materials: Other textbooks

After completing the lesson, you might have students look through other textbooks—biology, chemistry, physics, social studies, and so on—to find formulas. Then have them explain in writing what each formula means, what each of the variables represents, and when or how the formula is used.

32. Dennis plans to use 1150 ft of fence to enclose the rectangular pasture shown below. One side borders a river where there is already a thick hedge. It needs no fencing.

a. Let x be the width of the pasture as labeled. Write an expression for the length in terms of x. **1150 − 2x**
b. Write an expression for the area of the pasture in terms of x.
c. Suppose the pasture must enclose at least 60,000 square feet. Write a sentence relating the area expression in part **b** to the area the pasture must enclose. **(1150 − 2x)x ≥ 60,000**
b) **(1150 − 2x)x**

Review

Every lesson contains review questions to practice on ideas you have studied earlier. If the idea is from an earlier course, the question is designated as being from a previous course.

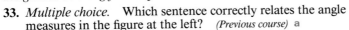

33. *Multiple choice.* Which sentence correctly relates the angle measures in the figure at the left? *(Previous course)* **a**
(a) $x + y + z = 180$ (b) $x + y = 180 + z$
(c) $y + z = x + y$ (d) none of these

34. What is a polygon with six sides called? *(Previous course)* **hexagon**

35. a. Solve $3x = 5x + 18$ for x. **x = −9**
  b. Check your work. *(Previous course)*
    Does 3 · (−9) = 5 · (−9) + 18? Does −27 = −45 + 18?
    −27 = −27. Yes, it checks.

Exploration

These questions extend the concepts of the lesson. Often they have many possible answers. Sometimes they require you to use dictionaries, encyclopedias, or other sources.

36. Many integers can be written with three 9s. For instance,

$$4480 = 9! \div (9 \times 9) \text{ and}$$
$$720 = 9^{\sqrt{9}} - 9.$$

What integers from 1 to 25 can be written with three 9s? Allow yourself the operations of $+, -, \times, \div, \sqrt{}, !$, decimal points, powers, 99, and parentheses. **See margin.**

Lesson 1-1   *The Language of Algebra*   **11**

Question 18 Multicultural Connection In the Pueblo Indian culture, a *kachina* is any one of hundreds of ancestral spirits. Kachinas allow themselves to be seen when men of the tribe wear kachina masks and perform traditional rituals.

Questions 33–35 Point out that *Review Questions* appear in every lesson. These questions review work from earlier lessons or from a previous course. We cannot stress enough how vital the review questions are to this course. A large part of the practice that students will have on any given topic is distributed throughout *Reviews*; some practice is in the current chapter, and some appears later in the book. Encourage students to use the section references at the end of each question to locate additional material if they need help. We not only want to teach students how to read a textbook; we also want them to learn how to use it as a resource.

In this review, **Questions 33–34** deal with topics from geometry. At appropriate times, geometric concepts, examples, and applications are used throughout the text. Those students who have not completed a geometry course will need additional help with the geometric content of this book.

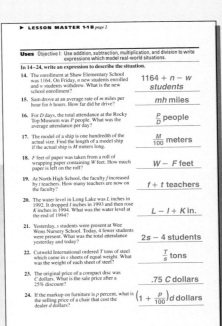

► **LESSON MASTER 1-1B** *page 2*

Uses Objective I: Use addition, subtraction, multiplication, and division to write expressions which model real-world situations.

In 14–24, write an expression to describe the situation.

14. The enrollment at Shaw Elementary School was 1164. On Friday, *n* new students enrolled and *w* students withdrew. What is the new school enrollment?   **1164 + n − w students**

15. Sam drove at an average rate of *m* miles per hour for *h* hours. How far did he drive?   **mh miles**

16. For *D* days, the total attendance at the Rocky Top Museum was *P* people. What was the average attendance per day?   **$\frac{P}{D}$ people**

17. The model of a ship is one hundredth of the actual size. Find the length of a model ship if the actual ship is *M* meters long.   **$\frac{M}{100}$ meters**

18. *F* feet of paper was taken from a roll of wrapping paper containing *W* feet. How much paper is left on the roll?   **W − F feet**

19. At North High School, the faculty *f* increased by *t* teachers. How many teachers are now on the faculty?   **f + t teachers**

20. The water level in Long Lake was *L* inches in 1992. It dropped *I* inches in 1993 and then rose *K* inches in 1994. What was the water level at the end of 1994?   **L − I + K in.**

21. Yesterday, *s* students were present at Wee Wons Nursery School. Today, 4 fewer students were present. What was the total attendance yesterday and today?   **2s − 4 students**

22. Cutweld International ordered *T* tons of steel which came in *s* sheets of equal weight. What was the weight of each sheet of steel?   **$\frac{T}{s}$ tons**

23. The original price of a compact disc was *C* dollars. What is the sale price after a 25% discount?   **.75 C dollars**

24. If the markup on furniture is *p* percent, what is the selling price of a chair that cost the dealer *d* dollars?   **$\left(1 + \frac{P}{100}\right)d$ dollars**

Setting Up Lesson 1-2

Homework Have students read Lesson 1-2 on their own and do the questions. Point out that **Activity 1** and **Activity 2** on pages 13–14 are to be done as they read.

For more information on homework, see *General Teaching Suggestions: Homework* in the *Professional Sourcebook,* which begins on page T20 in Part 1 of the Teacher's Edition.

Materials Students will need newspapers and magazines or other textbooks for **Question 32** on page 17. They will also need newspapers for Activity 1 in *Optional Activities* on page 13.

Objectives

A Evaluate expressions and formulas, including correct units in answers.
G Determine whether a relation defined by a table or a simple equation is a function.
H Determine the domain and range of a function defined by a table, a list of ordered pairs, or a simple equation.
J Use functions to solve real-world problems.

Resources

From the *Teacher's Resource File*
■ Lesson Master 1-2A or 1-2B
■ Answer Master 1-2
■ Teaching Aids
   1 Warm-up
   6 Origins of Functions
   7 Additional Examples
■ Technology Sourcebook
   Calculator Master 1

Additional Resources
■ Visuals for Teaching Aids 1, 6, 7
■ Newspapers and magazines

Teaching Lesson **1-2**

Warm-up

You can use the *Warm-up*, or the *Additional Examples* on page 15, as questions for students to work on as you begin class.

1. To determine the retail price *r* of all merchandise, a store owner multiplies the wholesale price *w* by 1.5. Write an equation relating *r* and *w*. $r = 1.5w$

What Is a Function?

Net pay. *The person shown at the lower right is a tennis instructor at a summer camp in California. An instructor's total pay is often a function of the number of hours worked.*

The Definition of Function

Bjorn has a summer job from which he earns $5.00 per hour. His weekly pay in dollars is given by the formula

$$P = 5H,$$

where *H* is the number of hours worked.

Below is a table of possible values for *H* and *P*.

H	1	2	3	6.5	10	20
P	5.00	10.00	15.00	32.50	50.00	100.00

In the equation $P = 5H$, *P* is called the **dependent variable** because its value (Bjorn's pay) *depends* on the number of hours worked. The variable *H* is called the **independent variable.**

> **Definition**
> A **function** is a correspondence or pairing between two variables such that each value of the first (independent) variable corresponds to exactly one value of the second (dependent) variable.

In the formula $P = 5H$, each value that is substituted for *H* results in just one value of *P*. Hence, the relationship described by this equation is a function.

When the relationship between two variables is a function, we say that the dependent variable **is a function of** the independent variable. In the formula above we say that *P* is a function of *H*.

Lesson 1-2 Overview

Broad Goals This lesson introduces and applies the basic vocabulary associated with functions: function, independent variable, dependent variable, domain, and range.

Perspective Three origins of functions are given in this lesson. The first origin is from a formula—specifically from $P = 5H$. The second origin is from a table, as in **Example 1**. The third origin is from

calculator keys, as shown below **Example 3** on page 14.

There is quite a lot of terminology in this lesson, but do not be concerned about immediate mastery; the ideas are reviewed throughout the rest of the chapter.

Example 1

The table below shows a relation between the year Y and the percent P of public high schools in the United States with desktop computers available for student use.

Y	1981	1982	1983	1984	1985	1986	1987	1988	1989	1990	1991
P	42.7	57.8	86.1	94.6	97.4	98.7	99.0	99.1	99.1	98.8	99.4

a. Is P a function of Y?
b. Is Y a function of P?
Justify your answers.

Solution

a. Think: Is any value of Y paired with more than one value of P? No. Each value of Y is paired with only one value of P; so P is a function of Y.
b. Y is not a function of P, because $P = 99.1$ is paired with two different years, $Y = 1988$ and $Y = 1989$.

In Example 1, because P is a function of Y, Y is the independent variable and P is the dependent variable in the function.

As indicated above, functions can be described with formulas or with tables. In Lesson 1-4, you will see how functions can also be described with graphs.

❶ Domain and Range of a Function

The **domain of a function** is the set of values which are allowable substitutions for the independent variable. The **range of a function** is the set of values of the dependent variable that can result from the substitutions for the independent variable. The substitutions for the independent variable are often called **input**, and the resulting values of the dependent variable are often called **output.**

Example 2

Refer to Example 1, where P is a function of Y. Give the domain and range of the function.

Solution

The domain is the set of all values of the independent variable Y. So The domain is {1981, 1982, 1983, 1984, 1985, 1986, 1987, 1988, 1989, 1990, 1991}. The range is {42.7, 57.8, 86.1, 94.6, 97.4, 98.7, 99.0, 99.1, 98.8, 99.4}.

Notice in the range of Example 2, the element 99.1 is listed once. Recall that when listing elements of a set, each element needs to be listed only once, and you may list the elements in any order.

Lesson 1-2 *What Is a Function?* **13**

---

2. Make a table showing at least five values for r and w.
Sample table:

w ($)	1.00	2.00	3.00	4.00	10.00
r ($)	1.50	3.00	4.50	6.00	15.00

Notes on Reading

❶ As you present the terminology associated with origins of functions, you might want to use the *Visual Organizer* shown below and on **Teaching Aid 6.**

Stress that variables stand for numbers. In the opening paragraph, H does not stand for *hours*; it stands for *number* of hours. "Hours" is the unit rather than the variable. In **Example 1**, P is not "public high schools" but the "*number* of public high schools with microcomputers."

Students should be familiar with the names for the domains shown on the top of page 14. Some books define the natural numbers to include zero; the choice is really arbitrary. Zero might even be called a counting number, since it is the count of a set with no elements (for example, the number of living dinosaurs). The idea of the domain of a variable may be new to students; this concept, however, is quite important and will arise repeatedly during problem-solving activities. A common domain not listed in the text is the set of positive real numbers.

Some sets of numbers are used frequently as domains.

❷ The set of **natural numbers** or **counting numbers** is $\{1, 2, 3, 4, 5, \ldots\}$.

The set of **whole numbers** is $\{0, 1, 2, 3, 4, 5, \ldots\}$.

The set of **integers** is $\{\ldots, -3, -2, -1, 0, 1, 2, 3, \ldots\}$.

The set of **rational numbers** is the set of numbers that can be represented as ratios of the form $\frac{a}{b}$, where a and b are integers and $b \neq 0$.

Samples: $0, 1, -7, \frac{2}{3}, 1\frac{9}{11}, -\frac{34}{10}, 0.0004, 9.6\overline{18}, \sqrt{16}$

The set of **real numbers** is the set of numbers that can be represented by decimals.

Samples: $0, 1, -7, 35$ million, $2.34, \pi, \sqrt{5}$

Example 3

The area A of a circle with radius r is given by $A = \pi r^2$.
a. Is A a function of r? Why or why not?
b. Identify the domain and range of the function.

Solution

a. Each value of r substituted into the equation gives just one value of A. So, A is a function of r.
b. The domain of this function is the set of possible values of r. The range is the set of possible values of A. Radii and areas of circles must be positive numbers. So Both the domain and range of this function are the set of positive real numbers.

Notice that if we think of r and A as measures of length and area as in Example 3, we could also say that r is a function of A. For every area A there is a unique radius r. However, if we think of the formula $A = \pi r^2$ simply as an equation, and allow r to be negative as well, then r is not a function of A. For instance, the value $A = 25\pi$ corresponds to two different values of r: $r = 5$ and $r = -5$.

$$25\pi = \pi(5)^2 \text{ and } 25\pi = \pi(-5)^2$$

❸ **Functions on a Calculator**

Many of the rules programmed into a calculator are designed to give you a single answer (the output) when you enter a value (the input) in the domain of the function. Here are some calculator keys, the related functions, their domains, and the values which produce error messages.

Key	Function	Domain	Inputs Giving Errors
x^2 , the squaring key	$y = x^2$	set of all real numbers	none
$\sqrt{\ }$, the square root key	$y = \sqrt{x}$	the set of nonnegative real numbers	$x < 0$
$1/x$, or x^{-1} , the reciprocal key	$y = \frac{1}{x}$	the set of nonzero real numbers	$x = 0$

14

On some calculators, to evaluate expressions using squaring, square roots, or reciprocals, you press the function key followed by the value. Graphics calculators often work this way. So to evaluate $\sqrt{50}$ you might press the following:

$$\boxed{\sqrt{}}\ 50\ \boxed{\text{EXE}}.$$

On other scientific calculators, to evaluate expressions using function keys you press the number followed by the function key. On such calculators to evaluate $\sqrt{50}$ you might enter

$$50\ \boxed{\sqrt{}}.$$

Activity 1

Use the function keys on your calculator to evaluate these expressions. Record the key sequence you use, as well as your answer.

a. $\sqrt{65}$ **b.** $(-1.4142)^2$ **c.** $\frac{1}{2000}$

See left.

Recall that calculators often display very large and very small numbers using scientific notation. For instance, some calculators display the result of $(1,500,000)^2 = 2,250,000,000,000$ as $\boxed{2.25E\ 12}$.

The E in such a display does not mean error. Rather, the display means $2.25 \cdot 10^{12}$.

Activity 2

Evaluate the expressions using a calculator. For each, copy the display and rewrite it in scientific notation.

a. $(260,000)^2$ **b.** $\frac{.0005}{(2500)^2}$ **c.** $\frac{\sqrt{5}}{\sqrt{80,000,000}}$

See left.

QUESTIONS

Covering the Reading

1. Define *function*. See left.

2. Consider the table below. See left.

x	0	1	2	3	4	5
y	5	7	4	4	-6	7

a. Is y a function of x? Explain your answer.
b. Is x a function of y? Explain your answer.

3. The volume of a cube with each edge of length e is given by $V = e^3$. Is V a function of e? Justify your answer. Yes; each value of e substituted into the equation gives one value of V.

In 4 and 5, define each term. See left.

4. domain of a function **5.** range of a function

Lesson 1-2 *What Is a Function?* **15**

Activity 1 answers: Samples are given.
a) $\boxed{\sqrt{x}}$ 65 $\boxed{\text{ENTER}}$; 8.062257748
b) $\boxed{(}\ \boxed{(-)}\ 1.4142\ \boxed{)}\ \boxed{x^2}$ $\boxed{\text{ENTER}}$; 1.99996164
c) 1 $\boxed{\div}$ 2000 $\boxed{\text{ENTER}}$; 5E -4

Activity 2 answers: Samples are given.
a) $\boxed{6.76E\ 10}$; 6.76×10^{10}
b) $\boxed{8E\ -11}$; 8×10^{-11}
c) $\boxed{2.5E\ -4}$; 2.5×10^{-4}

1) A function is a correspondence or pairing between two variables such that each value of the first variable corresponds to exactly one value of the second variable.

2a) Yes; each value of x is paired with just one value of y.
b) No; $y = 4$ is paired with both $x = 2$ and $x = 3$.

4) The domain of a function is the set of values which are allowable substitutions for the independent variable.

5) The range of a function is the set of values that can result from the substitutions for the independent variable.

Additional Examples

These examples are shown on **Teaching Aid 7**.

1. The table below shows the average temperature T in degrees Fahrenheit for each month M in Honolulu, Hawaii.

M	T	M	T
Jan.	73	July	80
Feb.	73	Aug.	81
Mar.	74	Sept.	81
Apr.	76	Oct.	80
May	78	Nov.	77
June	79	Dec.	74

a. Is T a function of M? Justify your answer. **Yes; each M is paired with only one value of T.**

b. Is M a function of T? Justify your answer. **No; several values of T are paired with more than one value of M.**

2. Give the domain and the range of the function in *Additional Example 1a*. **Domain = the set of months of the year; Range = {73, 74, 76, 77, 78, 79, 80, 81}**

3. The total cost c of v cans of vegetable soup at 59¢ per can is given by the formula $c = 59v$.
a. Is c a function of v? Why or why not? **Yes; each value of v gives just one value of c.**
b. What are the domain and the range of this function? **The domain is the set of whole numbers; the range is the set of multiples of 59.**

▶ **LESSON MASTER 1-2 A** *page 2*

8. The table at the right gives the high school enrollment, in millions, in the United States from 1985 to 1991. Is the female enrollment a function of the year? Explain your answer.

Year	Male	Female
1985	7.2	6.9
1986	7.2	7.0
1987	7.0	6.8
1988	6.7	6.4
1989	6.6	6.3
1990	6.5	6.4
1991	6.8	6.4

Sample: yes; each year is paired with exactly one female enrollment figure.

Properties Objective H

9. If y is a function of x, what real numbers are *not* in the domain of $y = \frac{1}{x^2 - 64}$? **8, -8**

In 10 and 11, identify the domain and the range for the function.
10. $\{(2, 4), (7, 11), (9, 13), (8, -4)\}$
Domain **{2, 7, 8, 9}** Range **{-4, 4, 11, 13}**
11. $y = x^4 - 3$
Domain **all real numbers** Range **{y: y ≥ -3}**

Uses Objective J

12. The volume of a sphere is given by $V = \frac{4}{3}\pi r^3$. How much air does it take to blow up a beach ball to a radius of 8 inches? **≈ 2145 in³**
13. Near the surface of Jupiter, the distance d that an object falls in t seconds is given by $d = \frac{1}{2}gt^2$, where $g = 84.48\ \frac{ft}{sec^2}$. Find the distance an object falls in 3 seconds. **380.16 ft**
14. Sara recently bought a house. She made a down payment of $10,600 and will make payments of $369.35 each month.
a. Write a formula that gives the total amount p she has paid as a function of the number of months n she has been making her payments. **$p = 10,600 + 369.35n$**
b. Find the total amount she will pay if she pays the house off in 15 years. **$77,083**

Adapting to Individual Needs

Activity 3 Technology Connection In *Technology Sourcebook, Calculator Master 1*, students use a program to convert from Fahrenheit temperatures to Celsius.

Extra Help
When determining if one variable is a function of another, encourage students to remember that if y is a function of x, each value of x *is* paired with only one value of y. Students should ask themselves the question, "Is any value of x paired with more than one value of y?" If the answer is no, y is a function of x. If the answer is yes, y is not a function of x.

15

Notes on Questions

Questions 18–19 The purpose of these questions is to discourage students from reading the lesson without doing the activities. Advise students to do the activities while they are reading.

Question 23 Social Studies Connection Many people are postponing marriage until they are older. For example, in the U.S. in 1960, almost 40% of all 19-year-old women were married; by 1990, only about 11% of all 19-year-old women were married.

✎ **Question 24 Writing** This is the first of many questions in the book that asks students to compare and contrast different situations. Encourage students to write full sentences and to give answers in their own words.

Question 32 Students will need newspapers and magazines for this question.

Follow-up for Lesson 1-2

Practice

For more questions on SPUR Objectives, use **Lesson Master 1-2A** (shown on pages 14–15) or **Lesson Master 1-2B** (shown on pages 16–17).

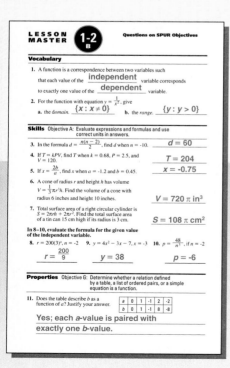

18a) 8.062257748
   Sample: √ 65
   ENTER
b) 1.99996164
   Sample: (-1.4142)
   x^2 ENTER
c) 5E – 4
   Sample: 1 ÷ 2000
   ENTER

22c)

Sample: The sum of the interior angles of hexagon *ABCDEF* equals the total sum of the interior angles in triangles *AEF, ABE, BCE* and *CDE*. By the Triangle Sum Theorem, the sum of the interior angles of a triangle is 180°. So, 4 · 180° = 720°.

---

6. *True or false.* Every function has both a domain and range. **True**

In 7 and 8, use the table below, and consider T = the average length of a school term (in days) as a function of a year Y.

Y	1910	1920	1930	1940	1950	1960	1970	1980	1990
T	157.5	161.9	172.7	175.0	177.9	178.0	178.9	178.5	179.8

7. Which is the independent variable? **Y**

8. What is the range of the function?
   {157.5, 161.9, 172.7, 175.0, 177.9, 178.0, 178.9, 178.5, 179.8}

9. List the set of positive integers less than 7. **{1, 2, 3, 4, 5, 6}**

In 10–12, identify each number as an integer, a rational number, or a real number. A number may belong to more than one set.

10. 1437 *real; rational; integer*
11. $\frac{15}{19}$ *real; rational*
12. $-\sqrt{11}$ *real*

13. Name a real number that is not an integer. *Sample: $\sqrt{7}$*

14. Name a rational number that is
   a. a whole number. *Sample: 1*
   b. not a whole number. *Sample: 1/2*

In 15–17, consider the x^2, √, and 1/x keys on your calculator. Which, if any, produce an error message when the given value is input?

15. -25 √
16. 0 1/x
17. 6.5 *none*

18. What answers did you get for Activity 1? *See left.*

19. What answers did you get for Activity 2? *Sample: a) 6.76 E 10; 6.76 × 10^10   b) 8E −11;   8.0 × 10^−11   c) 2.5E −4;   2.5 × 10^−4*

Applying the Mathematics

20. Consider the function $y = x^2$.
   a. What is its domain? *the set of all real numbers*
   b. What is its range? (Hint: Think about the kind of number that results when you square either a positive or negative number.) *The set of all nonnegative real numbers.*

21. The area A of an equilateral triangle with sides of length s is given by the formula $A = \frac{s^2}{4}\sqrt{3}$.
   a. State the domain for s. *the set of positive real numbers*
   b. Find the area of an equilateral triangle with sides of 10 cm. Round your answer to the nearest tenth. *43.3 cm²*

22. The formula $T = 180(n - 2)$ describes T as a function of n. Here T is the total number of degrees in the interior angles of a polygon with n sides. (Formulas from geometry are summarized in Appendix A.)
   a. What is the domain of the function? *the set of all natural numbers > 2*
   b. Find the total number of degrees in the interior angles of a hexagon. *720°*
   c. Draw a hexagon. Check that your answer to part **b** is correct either by using a protractor, or by giving a logical argument based on the Triangle Sum Theorem. *See left.*

16

Adapting to Individual Needs

English Language Development
Ask students if they know the meaning of the word *function* in ordinary English. If not, give some examples: The *function* (purpose) of the stomach is to digest food. A car *functions* (works) on gasoline. Explain that the word *function* implies a relationship between two items and that this definition extends to mathematics. However, in mathematics a function is a special relationship as defined on page 12.

There are several new terms in this lesson that students should add to index cards. Point out the vocabulary list for Lesson 1-2 on page 63. You might want to have English-speaking students help classmates with limited English proficiency define and/or illustrate the new terminology.

MEDIAN AGE AT FIRST MARRIAGE		
Year	Males	Females
1900	25.9	21.9
1910	25.1	21.6
1920	24.6	21.2
1930	24.3	21.3
1940	24.3	21.5
1950	22.8	20.3
1960	22.8	20.3
1970	23.2	20.8
1980	24.7	22.0
1989	26.2	23.8
1990	26.1	23.9
1991	26.3	24.1
1992	26.5	24.4

23. Refer to the table at the left. Let
Y = the year, M = median age at
first marriage for males, and
F = median age at first marriage
for females.
 a. Is M a function of Y? Explain
 your answer. **See left.**
 b. Is F a function of M? Why or
 why not? **See left.**

24. The word "function" was most likely a part of your vocabulary
before you read the definition given in this section. Describe how the
word "function" is used in normal conversation. Compare your use
to the one given here. What commonalities exist? What differences?
See left.

In 25 and 26, evaluate each function for the given value of the
independent variable.

25. $p = 300(2)^n$, $n = 5$ **9600**   **26.** $w = 4t^2 + 7t - 2$, $t = 3$ **55**

23a) Yes; each year
corresponds to
exactly one value.
b) No; $M = 24.3$
corresponds to
both $F = 21.3$ and
$F = 21.5$.

24) Sample: the word
"function" usually
describes the use,
purpose, or role of
something. This
definition agrees
with the
mathematical
meaning because
the "use" of an
independent
variable is to give
values for the
dependent variable.
The definition
differs in that the
everyday use of
"function" does not
necessarily refer to
a correspondence
between two sets.

Review

*A lesson reference following a review question indicates a place where the
idea of the question is discussed.*

In 27–30, tell whether the answer is $a + b$, $a - b$, $b - a$, ab, $\frac{a}{b}$, or $\frac{b}{a}$.
(Lesson 1-1)

27. A football player gains a yards on one play and gains b yards on the
next. What is the total gain? $a + b$

28. A football player gains a yards on one play and loses b yards on the
next. What is the total gain? $a - b$

29. How many different outfits can be made from b skirts and a shirts?
ab

30. Suppose you spend b dollars to buy a grams of perfume. What is the
cost per gram? $\frac{b}{a}$

31. *Multiple choice.* Which property is illustrated by the statement
$(4 \cdot x) \cdot y = 4 \cdot (x \cdot y)$? *(Previous course)* b
 (a) Commutative Property of Multiplication
 (b) Associative Property of Multiplication
 (c) Distributive Property
 (d) Inverse Property

Exploration

32. Look through a newspaper, magazine or one of your other texts for a
table of pairs of numbers or objects. Does the table describe a
function? Why or why not? **Answers may vary.**

Lesson 1-2 *What Is a Function?* **17**

17

Grouping Symbols and Calculators

IN-CLASS
ACTIVITY

Work in small groups. Each person should have a calculator. Do each question individually; then share your solution with others in your group.

In 1 and 2, recall that when using a calculator to evaluate expressions with square roots, you may need parentheses where none are written.

1 **a.** Evaluate $\sqrt{9 + 4^2}$ in your head. **5**
  b. Evaluate $\sqrt{9 + 4^2}$ on your calculator. Write the key strokes which give you the correct answer. **See margin.**

2 The formula $d = \sqrt{12{,}800h + h^2}$ gives the distance (in km) to the horizon from a point h km above the surface of the Earth. When $h = 4300$, $d \approx 8600$. Find the distance to the horizon from a point that is 1300 km above the surface of the Earth. **≈ 4300 km**

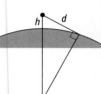

In 3 and 4, recall that the fraction bar also acts as a grouping symbol.

3 **a.** Evaluate $y = x + \frac{x^2}{20}$ when $x = 75$. **y = 356.25**
  b. Evaluate $y = \frac{x + x^2}{20}$ when $x = 75$. **y = 285**
(The answers to parts **a** and **b** are not equal.)

4 **a.** Evaluate $y = \frac{1}{x^2 - 3}$ when $x = 0.7$. **y ≈ -0.398**
  b. Evaluate $y = \frac{1}{x^2} - 3$ when $x = 0.7$. **y ≈ -0.959**
(Again the answers to parts **a** and **b** are not equal.)

5 Graphics calculators sometimes give different answers than other calculators to expressions involving constants that are juxtaposed (written next to each other). For instance, to find the volume of a beach ball with a radius of 5 inches, you could evaluate $V = \frac{4}{3}\pi r^3$ when $r = 5$. Input each expression below into your calculator as written. (y^x or $\wedge$ is the powering key.)

a. 4 ÷ 3 × π × 5 y^x 3
b. 4 ÷ 3π × 5 y^x 3
c. 4 × π × 5 y^x 3 ÷ 3
d. (4 ÷ 3) × π × 5 y^x 3
e. (4 ÷ 3π) × 5 y^x 3

Which give(s) the correct results on your calculator? Explain why the other answers are wrong or why you get an error message. **See margin.**

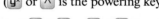

Drive right? *Shown are several of London's famous cabs. Because cars in Great Britain travel on the left side of the road, they are manufactured with the controls on the right side.*

The table of values below was distributed several years ago by the Highway Code of Great Britain. It gives information about three distances (thinking, braking, and stopping distances), each of which is a function of a car's speed.

Speed of car	mph	10	20	30	40	50	60
Thinking distance	ft	10	20	30	40	50	60
Braking distance	ft	5	20	45	80	125	180
Stopping distance	ft	15	40	75	120	175	240

The *thinking distance* is the distance a car travels after a driver decides to stop but before he or she applies the brakes. The *braking distance* is the distance the car needs in order to come to a complete stop after the driver applies the brakes. The *stopping distance* is the sum of the thinking and braking distances.

The data in the table above can be described with variables.

Suppose the car's speed (in mph) $= x$.

Then the thinking distance (in feet) $= x$,

and the braking distance (in feet) $= \frac{x^2}{20}$.

So the stopping distance (in feet) $= x + \frac{x^2}{20}$.

Lesson 1-3 *Function Notations* **19**

Lesson 1-3

Objectives
B Use function notation.
J Use functions to solve real-world problems.

Resources
From the **Teacher's Resource File**
■ Lesson Master 1-3A or 1-3B
■ Answer Master 1-3
■ Assessment Sourcebook: Quiz for Lessons 1-1 through 1-3
■ Teaching Aid 1: Warm-up

Additional Resources
■ Visual for Teaching Aid 1

Teaching Lesson 1-3

Warm-up
You can use the *Warm-up*, or the *Additional Examples* on page 21, as questions for students to work on as you begin class.

1. If $y = 4x - 1$, find y when $x = 0$.
   $y = -1$
2. If $y = 2x + \frac{x^2}{10}$, find y when $x = 5$. $y = 12.5$
3. If $y = \frac{6-x}{x^2}$, find y when $x = 2$. $y = 1$
4. If $y = 2^x$, find y when $x = 10$. $y = 1024$

Notes on Reading
Reading Mathematics Students should practice reading and evaluating functions using both types of function notation. Use **Example 3** to emphasize that there are two

Lesson 1-3 Overview

Broad Goals This lesson introduces the two main notations for a function f: Euler's notation $y = f(x)$ and the arrow or mapping notation $f: x \rightarrow y$.

Perspective In some books, the expression $f(x)$ refers to a function. Today, however, more and more people consider this poor mathematical grammar. In this book, we may *describe* a function with the equation $f(x) = x + 2$, but we name the

function by the single letter f. We reserve $f(x)$ to stand for the y-values of the function. It is also consistent with the geometry applications of transformations in which r_m stands for a reflection over line m, and $r_m(P)$ stands for the image of point P under the reflection.

Mapping notation makes the distinction between a function and its values quite clear. Mapping notation is used to stress

the fact that a domain value determines a range value. The $f(x)$ notation is used where there are sentences to solve. We sometimes call $f(x)$ notation "Euler's $f(x)$ notation" to emphasize that symbols are invented by people.

Lesson 1-4

Objectives
J Use functions to solve real-world problems.
L Determine the domain, range, and values of a function from its graph.
M Apply the Vertical-Line Test for a function.

Resources
From the **Teacher's Resource File**
■ Lesson Master 1-4A or 1-4B
■ Answer Master 1-4
■ Teaching Aids
  2 Warm-up
  8 Four-Quadrant Graph Paper
  9 Additional Examples

Additional Resources
■ Visuals for Teaching Aids 2, 8–9
■ Newspapers and magazines

Teaching Lesson 1-4

Warm-up
You can use the *Warm-up*, or the *Additional Examples* on pages 26–27, as questions for students to work on as you begin class.

Give the domain and range of each function.
1. {(1, 10), (2, 12), (3, 17), (4, 25)} {1, 2, 3, 4}; {10, 12, 17, 25}
2. $y = 6$ **all reals; 6**
3. $y = |x|$ **all reals; all reals ≥ 0**
4. $y = \dfrac{2x}{x+1}$ **all reals; all reals except –1**

LESSON 1-4

Graphs of Functions

Because a function is a set of ordered pairs, when both coordinates are real numbers, we can associate each ordered pair with a point in the plane. That is, we can make a graph of the function.

Recall that each point in the coordinate plane has (x, y) coordinates. If $y = f(x)$, then you can also say that each point on the graph has coordinates of the form $(x, f(x))$. Below is the part of the table used in Lesson 1-3 for a stopping-distance function.

Speed of car (mph) = x	10	20	30	40	50	60
Stopping distance (ft) = S(x)	15	40	75	120	175	240

The graph on the left below is a graph of the stopping-distance function S for values of x from 0 to 60. All the points on it are of the form $(x, S(x))$. To find the value of $S(40)$ from the graph, start at 40 on the x-axis. Read up to the curve of the function S and then across to find the value on the y-axis. So $S(40) = 120$. Notice that this agrees with the values in the table above.

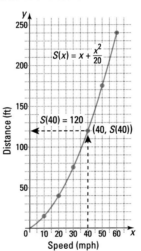

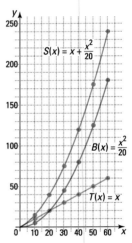

In the graph on the right above, we have plotted points to represent the three functions T, B, and S studied in the previous lesson. Notice how Euler's notation helps to distinguish the y-coordinates of the graphs. Euler's $f(x)$ notation is very handy when more than one function is being studied.

24

Lesson 1-4 Overview

Broad Goals This lesson builds on students' strengths in making and reading graphs. It gives the graphical interpretation of the concepts of domain and range of a function and of function notation, and it provides a visual test (the Vertical-Line Test) for deciding whether or not a relation is a function.

Perspective There are two common essentially equivalent definitions for

function. One is the notion that a function is a special kind of correspondence. This is the *mapping definition* given in Lesson 1-2. The other is the notion that a function is a special kind of relation. This is the *ordered-pair definition* given in this lesson. For evaluating functions, the mapping definition, which emphasizes input and output, gives a better conception. But for graphing functions, the ordered pair definition with its Vertical-Line Test is obviously more appropriate.

Optional Activities

Materials: Graph paper or **Teaching Aid 8**

After answering **Questions 17 and 18**, have each student **work with a partner**. Give students the equations $y = x^3$, $y = 2x + 6$, and $y = x^2 - 1$. Have them graph each equation and tell if it is a function. Then have them rewrite the equation interchanging the x and y, graph the new equation, and tell if it is also a function.

❶ Finding Domain and Range from a Graph

Recall that the domain of a function is the set of allowable values for the independent variable. For the functions *T, B,* and *S,* the situation and the table determine the domain. The allowable speeds are from 0 to 60 mph. So the domain of each function is $\{x: 0 \le x \le 60\}$. This is read "the set of all *x* from 0 to 60."

The range of a function is the set of values of the dependent variable that result from all possible substitutions for the independent variable. The range of the function *B* can be found by examining the graph at the bottom of page 24. When *x* has values from 0 to 60, the values of $B(x)$ range from 0 to 180. So the range of *B* is $\{y: 0 \le y \le 180\}$.

If a graph is plotted in the (x, y) coordinate plane, then *x* is considered the independent variable, and *y* is the dependent variable. If other coordinates are used, the independent variable is the first coordinate and is plotted along the horizontal axis. The dependent variable is the second coordinate and is plotted along the vertical axis.

❷ Example 1

Refer to the graph below. The oven temperature *T* varies with the length of time *t* the oven has been on. The oven, whose initial temperature was 80°, was set for 350°. The actual temperature was measured and then graphed over a 30-minute interval.

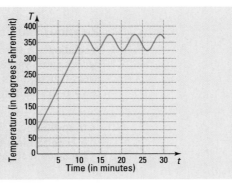

Cooking up a storm.
Pictured is a commercial oven. Widespread use of gas ranges began in the early 1900s. Electric ranges became popular after 1930.

a. Estimate the oven temperature when the oven had been on for 20 minutes.
b. Estimate how much time it took the oven to first reach 350°.
c. Identify the independent and dependent variables.
d. State the domain and range of the function.

Solution

a. Use the graph and read the value of *T* when *t* is 20. The temperature is about 325°F.
b. Read up to 350° on the vertical axis. Read across until you first reach the graph. Now read down from this point. It took about 10 minutes for the oven to first reach 350°. ▶

Lesson 1-4 *Graphs of Functions* **25**

Notes on Reading

Emphasize that when the graph of a function is given, the domain can be determined by scanning along the horizontal axis, and the range can be determined by scanning along the vertical axis. Scanning along one dimension is also useful for deciding whether a relation is a function and for later work with inverses.

❶ You might want to introduce the vocabulary *real function* for a function whose domain and range contain only real numbers. Real functions can be graphed in the coordinate plane; other functions cannot.

Point out that the domain and the range of a function may be restricted to a subset of the real numbers, either by the mathematical expressions in the function or by the context in which the function is being applied.

❷ Students may not realize why the graph in **Example 1** is wavy. Explain that an oven contains a thermostat that automatically turns it off when the temperature gets somewhat higher than the setting and turns it on when the temperature gets somewhat lower than the setting.

The Vertical-Line Test, described at the top of page 27, may be easier for some students to understand if it is rewritten using if-then language: *If* a vertical line intersects the graph of a relation in more than one point, *then* the relation is not a function.

Another approach to explaining the Vertical-Line Test is to tell students to imagine a vertical line moving across the graph from left to right and to observe the points of intersection with the graph as the line moves. If the line intersects the graph in more than one point at a time, the graph does not represent a function.

$[y = x^3$

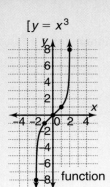

function

$x = y^3$

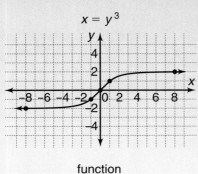

function

$y = 2x + 6$

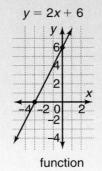

function

$x = 2y + 6$

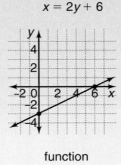

function

$y = x^2 - 1$

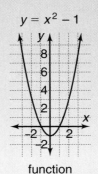

function

$x = y^2 - 1$

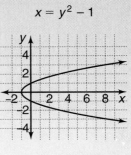

not a function]

Additional Examples

These examples are shown on **Teaching Aid 9**.

1. The graph below gives the distances a person traveled away from home during a 7-hour trip.

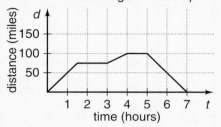

a. Estimate the distance away from home after 1 hour.
   50 miles
b. Estimate how long it took to get 75 miles away from home.
   1.5 hours
c. Identify the independent and dependent variables.
   ***t* is the independent variable; *d* is the dependent variable.**
d. State the domain and range of the function.
   Domain: $\{t: 0 \leq t \leq 7\}$
   Range: $\{d: 0 \leq d \leq 100\}$

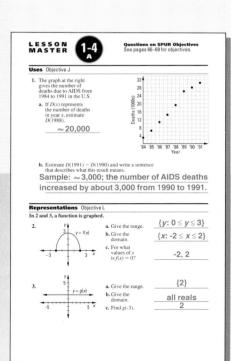

c. The independent variable is graphed on the horizontal axis and the dependent variable is graphed on the vertical axis. Hence, **Time is the independent variable, and oven temperature is the dependent variable.**
d. The domain is the set of possible values of *t,* the time (in minutes) when the temperature was monitored. The temperature was monitored during 30 minutes. So **The domain is $\{t: 0 \leq t \leq 30\}$.** The range is the set of all values of *T,* the temperature in degrees Fahrenheit. On the graph notice that the values of *T* vary from 80° to 375°.

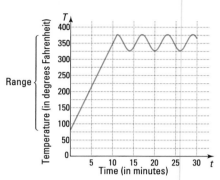

Thus, **The range of the function is $\{T: 80 \leq T \leq 375\}$.**

Relations and Functions

A **relation** is any set of ordered pairs. Any correspondence or pairing between two variables can be written as a set of ordered pairs. Thus every function is a relation. Using the language of relations, we can reword the definition of function given in Lesson 1-2.

> **Definition**
> A **function** is a relation in which no two different ordered pairs have the same first coordinate.

As shown in Example 2 not all relations are functions. Not all graphs represent functions.

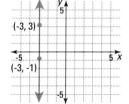

Example 2

Consider the vertical line graphed at the left. Is the line the graph of a function? Justify your answer.

Solution

Two different points on the graph have the same first coordinate, for instance (-3, -1) and (-3, 3). By definition, in a function there cannot be two ordered pairs with the same first coordinate unless the second coordinates are also the same. Therefore, this line is not the graph of a function.

26

Adapting to Individual Needs

Extra Help
When students use a graph to determine if a relation is a function, they might overlook all the possible points. For example, refer students to **Exercise 18** on page 28. If the points (9, -3), (16, -4), and (25, -5) are graphed they might assume that *y* is a function of *x*, which is not true. Remind students that when the points (9, 3), (16, 4), and (25, 5) are graphed, it is clear that *y* is not a function of *x*.

English Language Development
Explain that in English, a *relation* implies a connection between items—the amount of money earned is *related* to the number of hours worked, there is a *relationship* between temperature and the clothes a person wears, articles in newspapers discuss international *relations*. Then you might want to clarify the mathematical difference between a *relation* and a *function*. Point out that both relations and functions are sets of

When different points have the same first coordinate, they lie on the same vertical line. This simple idea shows that you can tell whether a relation is a function from its graph.

Theorem (Vertical-Line Test for Functions)
No vertical line intersects the graph of a function in more than one point.

A function *can* have two ordered pairs with the same second coordinate. For instance, the oven-temperature function graphed in Example 1 contains several points with $T = 325°$. This means that a horizontal line can intersect the graph of a function more than once.

QUESTIONS

Covering the Reading

In 1–3, refer to the graphs of functions T, B, and S in this lesson.

1. Give their common domain. {x: 0 ≤ x ≤ 60}

2. Give the range of S. {y: 0 ≤ y ≤ 240}

3. a. Explain how to estimate $B(45)$ from the graph. See left.
b. Evaluate $B(45)$ using an equation. B(45) = 101.25

3a) To find the value of B(45) from the graph, start at 45 on the x-axis. Read up to the curve of the function B, then across to the left to find the value on the y-axis.

In 4–6, refer to Example 1. Call this function f.

4. What was the temperature of the oven when it was turned off?
≈370°F

5. Estimate $f(5)$ and explain what it means. f(5) = 210. The temperature of the oven was 210°F when the oven had been on for 5 minutes.

6. What is the maximum value of f? 375°F

In 7 and 8, the graph of a function is given. State **a.** its domain, and **b.** its range.

7.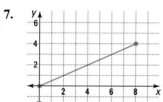

8.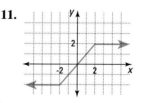

a) {x: 0 ≤ x ≤ 8}   b) {y: 0 ≤ y ≤ 4}   a) {x: -5 ≤ x ≤ 5}   b) {y: 0 ≤ y ≤ 5}

In 9–11, a relation is graphed. Is the relation a function? How can you tell? See left.

9) Yes; every x-value corresponds with exactly one y-value.

10) No; there are two y-values for some x-values.

11) Yes; every x-value corresponds with exactly one y-value.

9. 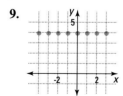   **10.** 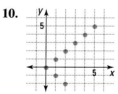   **11.**

Lesson 1-4   *Graphs of Functions*   **27**

ordered pairs, but a relation is any set of ordered pairs while a function is a special set in which no two different ordered pairs have the same first coordinate. This idea can be emphasized by using a Venn diagram like the one shown at the right. The diagram shows that all functions are relations but that not all relations are functions.

Relation Any set of ordered pairs of numbers.

Function A set of ordered pairs no two of which have the same first coordinates.

---

2. Consider the graph of a line that passes through (0, –3) and is parallel to the x-axis. Is this the graph of a function? Justify your answer. **Yes; no two points on the graph have the same first coordinate.**

3. Graph $y \le 2x + 1$. Does it describe a function? Why or why not? **No, each value for x corresponds to an infinite number of y values. For instance, let x = 0. Then y could be any number less than or equal to one. Specifically (0, –4) and (0, –5) are two ordered pairs that satisfy $y \le 2x + 1$. The graph does not pass the Vertical-Line Test.**

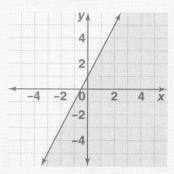

Notes on Questions

✎ **Questions 14, 20, and 24**
Writing These questions should be answered with complete sentences.

Questions 17–18 Students will need four-quadrant graph paper or **Teaching Aid 8** for these questions.

Questions 19–20 History Connection In 1885, Carl Friedrich Benz designed a three-wheeled vehicle that was the world's first practical automobile powered by an internal-combustion engine. Later Benz's company merged with Daimler-Motoren-Gesellshaft to form Daimler-Benz, the company that today makes Mercedes-Benz automobiles.

Question 26 Error Alert Multiple letters are often used to name functions in computer programs. Caution students *not* to think of CTOF as the product of four variables.

Follow-up 1-4 for Lesson

Practice

For more questions on SPUR Objectives, use **Lesson Master 1-4A** (shown on pages 26–27) or **Lesson Master 1-4B** (shown on pages 28–29).

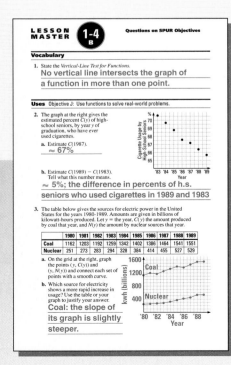

LESSON MASTER 1-4 B Questions on SPUR Objectives

Vocabulary
1. State the *Vertical-Line Test for Functions*.
   No vertical line intersects the graph of a function in more than one point.

Uses Objective J: Use functions to solve real-world problems.

2. The graph at the right gives the estimated percent C(y) of high-school seniors, by year y of graduation, who have ever used cigarettes.
   a. Estimate C(1987).
   ≈ 67%
   b. Estimate C(1989) − C(1983). Tell what this number means.
   ≈ 5%; the difference in percents of h.s. seniors who used cigarettes in 1989 and 1983

3. The table below gives the sources for electric power in the United States for the years 1980-1989. Amounts are given in billions of kilowatt-hours produced. Let y = the year, C(y) the amount produced by coal that year, and N(y) the amount by nuclear sources that year.

	1980	1981	1982	1983	1984	1985	1986	1987	1988	1989
Coal	1162	1203	1192	1259	1342	1402	1386	1464	1541	1551
Nuclear	251	273	283	294	328	384	414	455	527	529

   a. On the grid at the right, graph the points (y, C(y)) and (y, N(y)) and connect each set of points with a smooth curve.
   b. Which source for electricity shows a more rapid increase in usage? Use the table or your graph to justify your answer.
   Coal: the slope of its graph is slightly steeper.

28

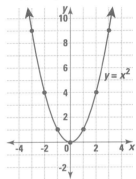

Applying the Mathematics

In 12–16, refer to the graph below. Let $A(t)$ be Alice's weight at age t and $B(t)$ be Bill's weight at age t. The domain of both these functions is $\{t: 0 \le t \le 20\}$.

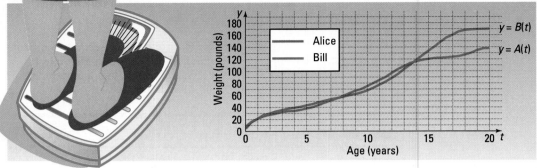

12. What is the range of A? {y: 8 ≤ y ≤ 138}

13. Estimate $B(5)$ from the graph. B(5) ≈ 42

14. Approximate $B(10) - A(10)$ from the graph, and explain what your answer means. ≈5; at age 10, Alice was 5 pounds heavier than Bill.

15. For what three values of t is $A(t) = B(t)$? t = 1, 8, 14

16. During what age intervals did Bill weigh more than Alice?
    1 ≤ t ≤ 8; 14 ≤ t ≤ 20

In 17 and 18, two pairs of numbers satisfying the equation are given.
a. Find three more pairs of numbers that satisfy the sentence.
b. Plot these points and connect them to draw the graph.
c. Is y a function of x?

17a) Sample: (0, 0); (1, 1); (2, 4)
b) Sample:

[graph of $y = x^2$]

17. $y = x^2$

x	y
−1	1
−2	4

a–b) See left.
c) Yes

18a) Sample: (0, 0); (1, 1); (4, 2)
b) Sample:

[graph of $x = y^2$]

18. $x = y^2$

x	y
1	−1
4	−2

a–b) See left.
c) No

In 19 and 20, refer to the table below, which gives the values (in dollars) of the Corvette Coupe Hatchback V-8 and the Mercedes Benz Sedan 300E in 1986, their year of manufacture, and every year thereafter. (Data are from the NADA Official Used Car Guide.)

Year	1986	1987	1988	1989	1990	1991	1992	1993
Corvette	27,027	22,775	20,600	18,750	16,950	14,025	13,050	12,200
Mercedes	34,700	31,675	29,650	26,350	24,100	19,400	16,775	15,450

Let x = the year, $C(x)$ = the value of the Corvette in that year, and $M(x)$ = the value of the Mercedes in that year.

19. Graph the points $(x, C(x))$, and connect them with a smooth curve. Graph the points $(x, M(x))$ on the same set of axes and connect them using a smooth curve. Label each graph. See margin.

20. Which car do you think has held its value better? Use the table or your graph to justify your answer. See left.

20) Sample: Corvette. The change of $C(x)$ looks less steep than the change of $M(x)$, implying the rate of depreciation is less for the Corvette.

28

Adapting to Individual Needs

Challenge
Pose this problem: As each person leaves a room, he or she shakes the hand of each person remaining. How many handshakes are there for 1 to 7 people? Have students make a table to show the results. Then have them find a formula for the function h in which the domain is the set of the possible number of people n in the room and the range is the set of the possible total number of handshakes $h(n)$.

[Sample table:

n	1	2	3	4	5	6	7
h(n)	0	1	3	6	10	15	21

$h(n) = \dfrac{n^2 - n}{2}, n \ge 1$]

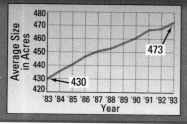
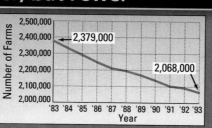

In 21–24, refer to the graphs below. The two graphs give information about the number of farms and the average size (in acres) of these farms across the United States from 1983 to 1993.

Farms: Larger, but Fewer

Average Size in Acres (vertical axis: 420–480)
473
430
Year: '83 '84 '85 '86 '87 '88 '89 '90 '91 '92 '93

Number of Farms (vertical axis: 2,000,000–2,500,000)
2,379,000
2,068,000
Year: '83 '84 '85 '86 '87 '88 '89 '90 '91 '92 '93

21. Estimate the average size of a farm in 1990. **≈ 460 acres**

22. If the average-size function is called A, then A: $1985 \rightarrow$ __?__. **≈ 440**

23. If the number-of-farms function is called N, find $N(1991)$.
    ≈ 2,105,000

24. **a.** Calculate $A(1993) \cdot N(1993) - A(1983) \cdot N(1983)$. **-44,806,000**
    b. Explain in words what the computation in part **a** represents.
    The decrease in the total amount of farmland from 1983 to 1993 is 44,806,000 acres.

Review

25. Let $f(x) = 1 + 3x^3$. Evaluate each expression. *(Lesson 1-3)*
    a. $f(2)$ **25**   **b.** $f(-2)$ **-23**   **c.** $f\left(\frac{n}{2}\right)$ **$1 + \frac{3n^3}{8}$**

26. The function *CTOF* converts degrees Celsius to degrees Fahrenheit. If *CTOF*: $x \rightarrow 1.8x + 32$, then *CTOF*$(100) =$ __?__. *(Lesson 1-3)* **212**

27. Let $n =$ the number of sides of a polygon and $f(n) =$ the number of diagonals. The figures at the left show that $f(4) = 2$ and $f(5) = 5$. *(Lessons 1-2, 1-3)*
    a. Find $f(3)$ and $f(6)$.   **b.** What is the domain of f?
    $f(3) = 0$; $f(6) = 9$ **$\{3, 4, 5, 6, \ldots\}$**

28. Carla and Darla own a total of 150 books. If Carla owns b books, how many does Darla own? *(Lesson 1-1)* **$150 - b$**

In 29 and 30, solve and check. *(Previous course)*

29. $\frac{1}{2}n - 72 = 50$ **$n = 244$**
    $\frac{1}{2}(244) - 72 = 50$? $122 - 72 = 50$? Yes.

30. $x = \frac{2}{3}x + 8$ **$x = 24$**
    $24 = \frac{2}{3}(24) + 8$?
    $24 = 16 + 8$? Yes.

Exploration

31. Find a coordinate graph in a newspaper or magazine. Does it represent a function? Why or why not? If it is a function, identify its domain and range. **Answers may vary.**

Lesson 1-4 *Graphs of Functions* **29**

Setting Up Lesson 1-5

Questions 29 and 30 on page 29 lead into the discussion of equation solving in Lesson 1-5.

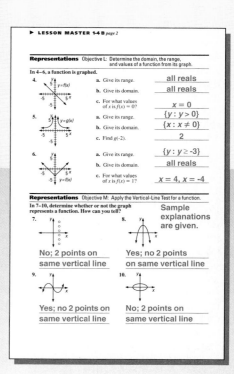

Objectives

C Solve and check linear equations.
K Use linear equations to solve real-world problems.

Resources

From the *Teacher's Resource File*
- Lesson Master 1-5A or 1-5B
- Answer Master 1-5
- Teaching Aid 2: Warm-up

Additional Resources
- Visual for Teaching Aid 2

Teaching Lesson 1-5

Warm-up

You can use the *Warm-up,* or the *Additional Examples* on page 32, as questions for students to work on as you begin class.

Marshall won the cash prize in the benefit raffle. He put one third of the money into his bank account, used one half of the money to make his monthly car payment, and used the rest of the cash to buy some new clothes. If Marshall spent $75 on new clothes, how much money did he win? **$450**

Notes on Reading

❶ If students do not understand the construction of the equation in **Example 2,** note that total interest is an application of the Putting-Together Model for Addition; the equation reads *interest at 6% plus interest at 4% equals total interest.*

Solving Equations

A bird in the hand. *This parrot, in São Paulo, Brazil, will choose the ticket for a player in a lottery game. See Example 2.*

Suppose you know that y is a function of x. Two key questions often arise.

1. Given the value of x, what is the value of y?
2. Given the value of y, what is the value of x?

If the function is described with an equation, then answering the first question usually involves evaluating an expression. Answering the second question usually involves solving an equation. Example 1 illustrates these two situations.

Example 1

Lionel just bought a used car with 33,000 miles on it. He expects to drive it about 800 miles/month. If m = the number of months Lionel has had the car, then $f(m) = 33,000 + 800m$ is the expected total number of miles the car will have been driven after m months.
a. How many miles will be on the car after Lionel has had it for a year?
b. After how many months will the car be due for its 50,000-mile check-up?

Solution

a. One year equals 12 months. You are asked to find $f(m)$ when $m = 12$. Evaluate $f(12)$.
$$f(m) = 33,000 + 800m$$
$$f(12) = 33,000 + 800(12)$$
$$= 33,000 + 9600$$
$$= 42,600$$
The car will have about 42,600 miles on it after one year.
b. You must find m when $f(m) = 50,000$. Solve the equation $33,000 + 800m = 50,000$.
$$800m = 17,000 \quad \text{Subtract 33,000 from each side.}$$
$$m = 21.25 \quad \text{Divide each side by 800.}$$
After about 21 months the car will be due for its 50,000-mile check-up.

Lesson 1-5 Overview

Broad Goals This lesson reviews the Distributive Property and the solving of linear equations in the context of functions. In particular, the examples and exercises show that these properties work as well with fractions and decimals (numbers that often appear in applications) as they do with integers.

Perspective Earlier texts of the UCSMP series stress the solving of linear equations,

and mastery is expected at that time. However, some students still need more practice. We try to distribute the practice in order to provide a continual review and to introduce other important concepts.

Using the Distributive Property

Recall that when you subtract (or add the opposite of) a number from each side of an equation, you are applying the Addition Property of Equality to find an *equivalent* but simpler equation. This is one of the properties of real numbers used in algebra that are listed in Appendix A. You should skim this Appendix now, and refer to it whenever you need to check the meaning or name of a particular property. In the next Example, another property, the Distributive Property, is applied to solve an equation containing parentheses.

> **Distributive Property**
> For all real numbers a, b, and c, $\quad c(a + b) = ca + cb$.

❶ Example 2

Suppose you win a lottery and suddenly have $50,000 to invest. You decide to put part of the money in a CD (certificate of deposit) which pays 6% annual interest, and put the rest in a savings account which pays 4%. If d dollars are invested at 6%, then

$$E(d) = .06d + .04(50,000 - d)$$

gives the interest earned in one year. How much should you put in each place to earn $2400 per year?

❷ Solution 1

You are given that $E(d) = 2400$, and asked to find d. Solve an equation.

$.06d + .04(50,000 - d) = 2400$

$.06d + 2000 - .04d = 2400$	Distribute the .04.
$2000 + .02d = 2400$	Add like terms.
$.02d = 400$	Subtract 2000 from each side.
$d = 20,000$	Divide each side by .02.
$50,000 - d = 30,000$	

You should put $20,000 in the CD at 6%, and $30,000 in the savings account at 4%.

Solution 2

You can avoid working with decimals by multiplying each side by 100. This clears the decimals.

$100[.06d + .04(50,000 - d)] = 100 \cdot 2400$	Multiplication Property of Equality
$6d + 4(50,000 - d) = 240,000$	Distribute the 100.
$6d + 200,000 - 4d = 240,000$	Distribute the 4.
$2d + 200,000 = 240,000$	Add like terms.
$2d = 40,000$	Subtract 200,000 from each side.
$d = 20,000$	Multiply each side by $\frac{1}{2}$.
$50,000 - d = 30,000$	

You should put $20,000 in the CD at 6% and $30,000 in the savings account at 4%.

Lesson 1-5 *Solving Equations* **31**

Error Alert Students have to be very careful when using the Distributive Property in Solution 2 of **Example 2.** When multiplying $.04(50000 - d)$ by 100, some students want to multiply .04 by 100 and $(50000 - d)$ by 100. Students must distinguish between $100[.04(50000 - d)]$ and $100[0.04 + (50000 - d)]$. The former uses the Associative Property while the latter uses the Distributive Property.

❷ When justifications are given for the steps in solving an equation, students must read both across and down—across to see the justification and down to see how each step follows from the previous one. In solving equations, it is important to not be distracted by all of the steps and to examine only how each step follows from the previous one.

There are two ways to write justifications. One way is to name the property, such as the "Multiplication Property of Equality" as shown in the first step of Solution 2 of **Example 2.** The other way is to indicate what was done, such as "Multiply each side by $\frac{1}{2}$" as shown in the last justification. Students should be able to give either type of justification.

Error Alert Students frequently have problems when "clearing fractions" from an equation that contains fractions on only one side; they err by using multiplication only on that side of the equation. Use **Example 3** on page 32 to illustrate that each side of an equation can be thought of as having implicit parentheses. Thus, the equation to be solved is $(\frac{1}{4}E + \frac{1}{5}E + \frac{1}{6}E + 46) = (E)$. The Multiplication Property of Equality is applied to both sides of the equation; in this case both sides are multiplied by 60.

Optional Activities

As you discuss **Example 3,** you might have students **work in groups** and use prime factorization to find the least common denominator of the fractions. Then have them explain what they did. [Sample explanation: Write the prime factorization of each denominator. The LCD is the product of the prime factors, each taken the greatest number of times they appear in any one denominator. When each original fraction is written with the LCD, the numerator is multiplied by the prime factors that are not part of the original denominator. For denominators of 4, 5, and 6: $4 = 2^2$, $5 = 5$, and $6 = 2 \cdot 3$; LCD $= 2^2 \cdot 3 \cdot 5 = 60$.]

31

1. Refer to **Example 1** on page 30.
   a. How many miles will be on the car after a year and a half? **47,400 miles**
   b. Estimate when the car will have been driven 100,000 miles. **After Lionel has had it for about 7 years**

2. An individual put $500 into two accounts. One paid 5.5% annual interest, and the other paid 4% annual interest. How much was invested in each account if the total yearly interest was $21.88? **Let x = amount invested at 5.5%: $.055x + .04(500 - x) = 21.88$; $125 was invested at 5.5% and $375 was invested at 4%.**

3. A concert group plans to visit 3 cities on a tour. One third of the total distance to be traveled by the group is from its home city to the first city. One fifth of the total distance is from the first city to the second city. It is 273 miles from the second city to the third city. Find the total number of miles traveled. **Let d = number of total miles traveled: $\frac{1}{3}d + \frac{1}{5}d + 273 = d$; $d = 585$ miles**

4. Suppose $f(w) = 3w - (4 - 6w)$. For what value of w is $f(w) = 113$? **$w = 13$**

(Notes on Questions start on page 34.)

Follow-up for Lesson 1-5

Practice

For more questions on SPUR Objectives, use **Lesson Master 1-5A** (shown on page 33) or **Lesson Master 1-5B** (shown on pages 34–35).

Check
First, check the equation.
Does $.06 \cdot 20{,}000 + .04(50{,}000 - 20{,}000) = 2400$? Yes.
Now, check the situation.
If $20,000 is invested at 6%, the interest is $1200. If $30,000 is invested at 4%, the interest is $1200. The total interest earned is $2400.

In Example 2, it might seem silly to invest some funds at a lower rate. But money from a CD cannot be withdrawn early without paying a penalty. Also, a higher interest rate often means a higher risk. So it is wise not to put all your money in one place.

R and R. *During a recent year, people under the age of 25 spent an average of $233 on entertainment fees and admissions. Some of that money was spent on concerts given by entertainers such as Gloria Estefan.*

Clearing Fractions in Equations

If you want to eliminate or "clear" an equation of fractions, multiply each side of the equation by a common multiple of the denominators. If there is more than one term on either side of the equation, you will then need to apply the Distributive Property. Example 3 illustrates this procedure.

Example 3

Stuart Dent works part-time to earn spending money and to save for college. Each month he plans to save $\frac{1}{4}$ of his earnings, to spend $\frac{1}{5}$ of his earnings on clothes, and to spend $\frac{1}{6}$ of his earnings on transportation. The remainder will be used for entertainment. Last month Stuart had $46 to spend on entertainment. How much did he earn last month?

Solution

Write a sentence to describe the situation. Let E equal Stuart's monthly earnings. The total of Stuart's savings and his expenses equals this monthly earnings. So,

$$\overset{\text{savings}}{\frac{1}{4}E} + \overset{\text{expenses}}{\frac{1}{5}E + \frac{1}{6}E} + \overset{\text{earnings}}{46} = E$$

Solve the equation. To "clear" the fractions, multiply each side of the equation by 60, the least common denominator of $\frac{1}{4}$, $\frac{1}{5}$, and $\frac{1}{6}$.

$$60\left(\frac{1}{4}E + \frac{1}{5}E + \frac{1}{6}E + 46\right) = 60E$$

$15E + 12E + 10E + 2760 = 60E$	Distribute the 60.
$37E + 2760 = 60E$	Add like terms.
$2760 = 23E$	Subtract $37E$ from each side.
$120 = E$	Multiply by $\frac{1}{23}$.

Stuart earned $120 last month.

Check
Does $\frac{1}{4}(120) + \frac{1}{5}(120) + \frac{1}{6}(120) + 46 = 120$?
$30 + 24 + 20 + 46 = 120$. It checks.

Adapting to Individual Needs

Extra Help
You may need to remind students that solving an equation involves writing a series of equivalent equations. Suggest that students cover the right columns, or reasons, in Solutions 1 and 2 of **Example 2**. Then have students explain how one equivalent equation is obtained from another.

English Language Development
You might want to discuss the phrase "*equivalent* but simpler equation," given in the paragraph at the top of page 31. Explain that equivalent equations are equations with the same solutions. Then direct attention to the equations in **Example 2**, Solution 1. Each equation has the same solution, 20,000, but the equation $d = 20{,}000$ is simpler than $.06d + .04(50{,}000 - d) = 2400$.

Opposite of a Sum Theorem

The Opposite of a Sum Theorem is derived from the Distributive Property.

> **Opposite of a Sum Theorem**
> For all real numbers a and b, $-(a + b) = -a + -b$.

In Example 4, this theorem is applied to solve an equation.

Example 4

Suppose $f(m) = 6m - (5 - 9m)$. For what value of m is $f(m) = 13$?

Solution

Solve $6m - (5 - 9m) = 13$.

$$6m - 5 + 9m = 13 \qquad \text{Opposite of a Sum Theorem}$$
$$15m - 5 = 13 \qquad \text{Add like terms.}$$
$$15m = 18 \qquad \text{Add 5 to each side.}$$
$$m = \frac{18}{15} = \frac{6}{5} \qquad \text{Multiply each side by } \tfrac{1}{15}.$$

Check

Substitute $\frac{6}{5}$ for m and follow the order of operations.

Does $6\left(\frac{6}{5}\right) - \left(5 - 9 \cdot \frac{6}{5}\right) = 13$?

Does $\frac{36}{5} - \left(5 - \frac{54}{5}\right) = 13$?

Does $\frac{36}{5} - 5 + \frac{54}{5} = 13$?

Does $\frac{90}{5} - 5 = 13$? Yes.

QUESTIONS

Covering the Reading

In 1 and 2, Lucinda bought a used car with 14,000 miles on it. She expects to drive it about 600 miles/month. So $f(m) = 14{,}000 + 600m$ gives the number of miles she can expect to see on the odometer at the end of m months.

1. How many miles should Lucinda expect to have on her car after 2 years?
   28,400 miles

2. After how many months will the car be due for a 40,000-mile check-up?
   about 43 months

In 3 and 4, refer to Example 2.

3. a. Evaluate $E(5000)$. $E(5000) = 2{,}100$
   b. Explain the meaning of your answer to part **a** in terms of investments. Sample: $5000 was invested at 6% and $45,000 was invested at 4%. Annual interest from these investments was $2,100.

4. a. Solve $E(d) = 3000$. $d = \$50{,}000$
   b. Explain the meaning of your answer to part **a** in terms of investments. Sample: $50,000 was invested at 6% and produced an annual interest of $3000.

Lesson 1-5 *Solving Equations* **33**

Adapting to Individual Needs

Challenge
Water that passes through a purification system can reach a storage tank through Pipe *A* or Pipe *B*. Pipe *A* can fill the storage tank in 20 minutes. It takes 30 minutes for Pipe *B* to fill the same tank. How long will it take to fill the storage tank if both pipes are used at the same time? [12 minutes]

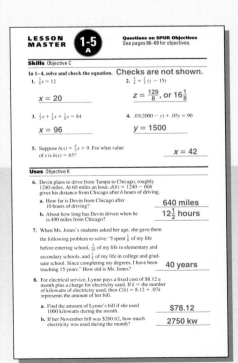

33

Notes on Questions

Questions 7–8 Point out that you can clear fractions by multiplying by any common multiple of the denominators. The fractions would be cleared, but the products would be greater.

Questions 12–14 This formula may be familiar to students who have studied UCSMP *Algebra*.

Multicultural Connection Evidence of games similar to bowling has been found in both ancient Egypt and ancient Polynesia. In the Middle Ages, Germans rolled stones at nine wooden clubs called *kegles*. In the Netherlands, a similar game was called *Dutch pins*. The Dutch brought their game to New York in the 1600s. However, gambling on the sport became so widespread that in 1841 the Connecticut legislature outlawed "bowling at nine pins." To evade the ban, bowlers added another pin; hence today's game of bowling involves ten pins.

Question 16 One reason for including this question is to have students write z's differently from 2s. Many mathematicians put lines through z's to make this distinction. In Europe, it is customary to put horizontal lines through 7s to distinguish them from 1s.

5a) $.07(75,000) + .05(100,000 - 75,000) = 6500$?
$5250 + 1250 = 6500$? Yes, it checks.

b) **Sample:** Suppose you invest $100,000 in two accounts. You invest part in an account paying 7% interest and the rest in an account paying 5% interest. How much should you invest in each account to earn $6,500?

Time to spare. *Bowling can be traced to the Middle Ages in Germany, England, and the Netherlands. Native Americans were also known to have various forms of bowling. The American Bowling Congress was organized in 1895.*

6a) $\frac{1}{2}(210) + \frac{1}{5}(210) + 63 = 210$?
$105 + 42 + 63 = 210$? Yes, it checks.

b) If you spend $\frac{1}{2}$ of your money on clothes and $\frac{1}{5}$ of your money on groceries and have $63 left, how much did you initially have?

In 5 and 6, an equation is given. **See left for check and part b.**
a. Solve the equation and check your solution.
b. Make up a question that could be answered by solving the equation.

5. $.07x + .05(100,000 - x) = 6500$ **6.** $\frac{1}{2}x + \frac{1}{5}x + 63 = x$ **x = 210**
  $x = 75,000$

In 7 and 8, **a.** identify the least common multiple of the denominators.
b. Solve the equation.

7. $\frac{m}{3} + \frac{m}{7} = 1$ a) 21 b) $m = \frac{21}{10}$ **8.** $\frac{1}{6}x + \frac{2}{3}x = 30$ a) 6 b) x = 36

9. a. According to the Opposite of a Sum Theorem, $-(-2x + 9) = $ _____.
  b. Solve the equation $12x - (-2x + 9) = 26$. $x = \frac{5}{2} = 2.5$
  a) $2x - 9$

In 10 and 11, **a.** solve each equation, and **b.** check your work.

10. $4x - (x - 1) = 7$ **x = 2** **11.** $3n - (9 + 5n) = 18$ **n = -13.5**
$4(2) - (2 - 1) = 7$? $8 - 1 = 7$? Yes. $3(-13.5) - (9 + 5(-13.5)) = 18$?
  $-40.5 - 9 + 67.5 = 18$? Yes.

Applying the Mathematics

In 12–14, a bowler's *handicap* is a bonus given to some bowlers in a league. The handicap H is a function of A, the bowler's average score, and is sometimes determined by the formula $H = .8(200 - A)$, when $0 < A < 200$.

12. What is the handicap for a bowler whose average is 120? **64**

13. If a bowler has a handicap of 30, what is the bowler's average?
  162.5

14. What is the domain of the function? **the set of integers greater than 0 and less than 200**

In 15–19, solve.

15. $3y + 60 = 5y + 42$ **16.** $2z + 2 = 2 - 2z$ **17.** $\frac{12}{y} = 5$
  y = 9 **z = 0** $y = \frac{12}{5} = 2.4$

18. $\frac{2}{3}x + 80 = x + 25$ **19.** $0.05x + 0.1(2x) + 0.25(100 - 3x) = 20$
  x = 165 **x = 10**

20. A farmer grows three crops: wheat, corn, and alfalfa. He farms all the land he owns. On his farm, $\frac{1}{3}$ of the land is planted with wheat, $\frac{2}{5}$ is planted with corn, and 60 acres are planted with alfalfa.
  a. How many acres of crops are on this farm? **225 acres**
  b. How many acres of wheat are there? **75 acres**
  c. How many acres of corn are there? **90 acres**

21. Suppose $f(n) = \frac{1}{n + 2}$. a) $f(18) = \frac{1}{20}$
  a. What is $f(18)$? **b.** If $f(n) = \frac{1}{99}$, find n. **n = 97**

22. Tell whether the sentence is equivalent to $20(x + 5) = 55$.
  a. $4(x + 5) = 11$ **b.** $x + 5 = \frac{11}{4}$ **c.** $4(x + 1) = 11$
    Yes   Yes   No

34

Review

In 23–26, refer to the graph below. In the graph, x = the year, $I(x)$ = the value in billions of dollars of imports into the United States, and $E(x)$ = the value of exports from the United States, also in billions of dollars.
(Lessons 1-3, 1-4)

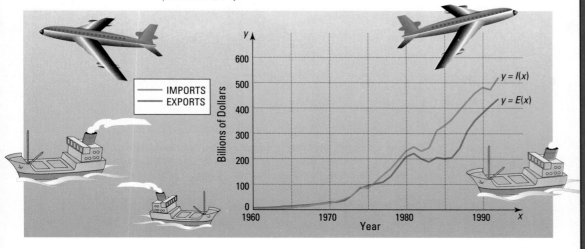

23. Estimate $I(1975)$. **$I(1975) \approx \$100$ billion**

24. In what unit is the dependent variable of the function E measured?
billions of dollars

25. In what year(s) was $E(x) > \$100$ billion? **approximately 1976 to 1992**

26. A negative *balance of trade* exists when a country's imports are greater than its exports. Write a few sentences about the balance of trade in the U.S. from 1960 to 1992. **See left.**

26) Sample: A positive balance of trade existed until approximately 1976. The leveling off of exports around 1980 caused a negative balance of trade to come about.

27. A cylindrical column of a building has a lateral area of 320 ft^2. If its radius is 5 ft, what is its height? (Refer to the Appendix of Geometry Formulas if necessary.) *(Previous course)* **≈ 10.19 ft**

Exploration

28. The Greek mathematician Diophantus, who lived in the second century A.D., was the first person to replace unknowns by single letters. There is a famous problem by which you can calculate how long he lived. The *Greek Authority* states: "Diophantus passed one sixth of his life in childhood, one twelfth in youth, and one seventh more as a bachelor. Five years after his marriage was born a son who died four years before his father, at half his father's final age." How long did Diophantus live? **84 years**

Question 21 After substitution, the equation for part **b** is $\frac{1}{99} = \frac{1}{n+2}$. Students may want to solve this equation by using the Means–Extremes property of proportions or by multiplying both sides by $99(n + 2)$. However, it is more efficient to recognize that these two numbers have the same reciprocals— $99 = n + 2$, so $n = 97$.

Question 22 Each part of this question should be done without solving the sentences.

Questions 23–26 Consumer Connection Many people are surprised at the size of the trade deficit. You might ask students to investigate the current deficit and compare it to the deficits of previous years.

Question 27 Error Alert Some students, even after completing a full year of geometry, have difficulty answering questions about surface area and volume. Yet in the real world, objects are 3-dimensional. The ideas of volume and surface area are also important in calculus. You may want to show students some 3-dimensional objects to help them better understand these concepts.

Question 28 An equation that can be used to solve this problem is
$L = \frac{1}{6}L + \frac{1}{12}L + \frac{1}{7}L + 5 + 4 + \frac{1}{2}L$,
where L represents the father's final age.

Setting Up Lesson 1-6

Materials Students using Activity 2 in *Optional Activities* on page 37 will need a symbol manipulator.

If you have not used computers in your classroom, you may want to read *General Teaching Suggestions: Technology* in the *Professional Sourcebook*, which begins on page T20 in Part 1 of the Teacher's Edition.

▶ **LESSON MASTER 1-5 B** *page 2*

16. How many bows each using two thirds of a yard of ribbon can be made from 20 yards of ribbon? **30 bows**

17. Nancy has 120 cm of wood molding to make a picture frame. If she wants the frame to be twice as long as it is wide, what should be the outside dimensions of the frame? **40 cm by 20 cm**

18. The total bill for a restaurant meal, including 8% tax and 15% tip (both on only the cost of the meal), was $9.84. What was the cost of the meal? **$8**

19. When Pedro called Gary, the call cost $1.58. If the rate for the call was 53¢ for the first three minutes and 15¢ for each additional minute or fraction thereof, how long did Pedro and Gary talk? **10 minutes**

20. Yuko needs materials for a felt banner. She needs a half yard each of green and blue felt and 1 yard of white felt. She also needs two wooden dowels at $1.25 each and cord costing $4. If she has only $12 to spend, how much can she afford to spend per yard for the felt? **$2.75**

21. Maria wishes to invest in bonds which pay 6% annual dividends. How much must she invest in order to realize $2,120 at the end of the first year? **$2,000**

22. After consecutive discounts of 10% and 20%, a winter coat was sale-priced at $144. What was the original price of the coat? **$200**

Objectives
D Rewrite formulas.
K Use linear equations to solve real-world problems.

Resources
From the *Teacher's Resource File*
- Lesson Master 1-6A or 1-6B
- Answer Master 1-6
- Assessment Sourcebook: Quiz for Lessons 1-4 through 1-6
- Teaching Aid 2: Warm-up

Additional Resources
- Visual for Teaching Aid 2

Teaching Lesson 1-6

Warm-up
Diagnostic Which formula would you use to solve the problem? Explain your answer. **All formulas are correct. Answers will vary.**

1. What is the width w of a rectangular room that has a length ℓ of 28 feet and an area A of 84 square feet?
   a. $A = \ell w$ **b.** $\ell = \frac{A}{w}$
   c. $w = \frac{A}{\ell}$

2. A triangular sail has an area A of 60 ft². The base b of the sail is 12 feet wide. What is the height h of the sail?
   a. $b = \frac{2A}{h}$ **b.** $h = \frac{2A}{b}$
   c. $A = \frac{bh}{2}$

Rewriting Formulas

Formula driven. *Pictured is a* Seahawk I *jet of* Alaska Airlines. *Most commercial airplanes have on-board computers that continually calculate the estimated flight time based on distance and rate (including wind speed).*

Consider the formula

$$d = rt,$$

where d is the distance an object travels, r is the rate at which it travels, and t is the time the object travels. If you want to calculate the distance traveled on an airplane going at a rate of 650 $\frac{\text{miles}}{\text{hour}}$ for 2.5 hours, you can use this formula. It gives d *in terms of r and t,* the variables for which you have values.

$$d = (650 \text{ miles/hour}) \cdot (2.5 \text{ hours}) = 1625 \text{ miles}$$

But suppose you want to know how much time you would need to travel 380 miles if you drive a car at an average rate of 60 $\frac{\text{miles}}{\text{hour}}$. It might be helpful to have a formula that gives t *in terms of d and r,* that is, a formula that is solved for t. Using properties in Appendix B, you can write:

$$d = rt$$
$$\frac{d}{r} = \frac{rt}{r} \qquad \text{Divide both sides by } r.$$
$$\frac{d}{r} = t \qquad \text{Simplify.}$$

To find t, substitute the values for d and r.

$$t = \frac{d}{r} = \frac{380 \text{ mi}}{60\frac{\text{miles}}{\text{hour}}} \approx 6.3 \text{ hours}$$

You would need about 6.3 hours to travel 380 miles.

The formulas $d = rt$ and $t = \frac{d}{r}$ are equivalent as long as $r \neq 0$. The first is solved for d; the second is solved for t. Notice that when a formula is **solved for a variable,** that variable has a coefficient and an exponent equal to one. That variable is said to be written **in terms of** the others.

Lesson 1-6 Overview
Broad Goals This lesson emphasizes the importance of solving a formula for some variable other than the original isolated variable. The lesson also provides another day to work on solving open sentences.

Perspective The discussion on this page provides the impetus for rewriting formulas. Students have to understand that such manipulations make subsequent evaluations of the formula much easier. It is not uncommon for trade manuals to give three formulas where one would suffice; a manual might give $d = rt$, $r = \frac{d}{t}$, and $t = \frac{d}{r}$.

Example 1 is an often-used conversion that may be quite familiar to students. Some of them may have seen this formula with $\frac{9}{5}$ used in place of 1.8. **Example 2** gives practice solving a linear equation that, due to the fraction and the three variables, does not look like a linear equation. This type of problem is difficult for many students. **Example 3** shows that a formula can sometimes be rewritten without necessarily solving for a particular variable. This is a concept that will probably be new to most students and may require a discussion in class.

The most useful version of a formula depends upon the situation.

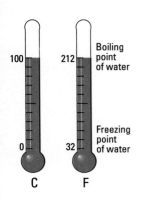

100 — C
0

212 — F
Boiling point of water
32
Freezing point of water

Example 1

Pierre lives in New Orleans, where he measures temperature using the Fahrenheit scale. When he visited his cousin Rae in Montreal, Canada, he found that temperature was reported in degrees Celsius. Because Celsius temperature readings didn't mean much to him, Pierre converted temperatures in Celsius C to Fahrenheit F using this formula:

$$F = 32 + 1.8C.$$

Rae visited Pierre the following summer. Rewrite the formula so she can use it to convert degrees Fahrenheit to Celsius.

Solution

$$\begin{aligned} F &= 32 + 1.8C & &\text{Given} \\ F - 32 &= 1.8C & &\text{Subtract 32 from both sides.} \\ \frac{F - 32}{1.8} &= C & &\text{Divide both sides by 1.8.} \end{aligned}$$

So $C = \frac{F - 32}{1.8}$ is an equivalent formula that is suitable for Rae.

Check

Evaluate the formula for a pair of temperatures you know are equivalent. The boiling point of water is 212°F or 100°C.

Does $100 = \frac{212 - 32}{1.8}$? Yes.

Notice that when using the formula $F = 32 + 1.8C$, Pierre thinks of F as a function of C. When using the formula $C = \frac{F - 32}{1.8}$, Rae thinks of C as a function of F.

Example 2

Scuba divers sometimes use the formula $t = \frac{33v}{x + 33}$ to determine the time t (in minutes) they can dive with a given volume v of air compressed into tanks (in cubic feet) to a depth of x feet below sea level. Rewrite the formula for v in terms of x and t.

Solution

$$\begin{aligned} t &= \frac{33v}{x + 33} \\ t(x + 33) &= 33v & &\text{Multiply each side by } x + 33. \\ \frac{t(x + 33)}{33} &= v & &\text{Divide each side by 33.} \end{aligned}$$

The formula is solved for v. If you wish to simplify it to contain fewer constants, you can rewrite it as follows.

$$\begin{aligned} \frac{tx + 33t}{33} &= v & &\text{Use the Distributive Property.} \\ \frac{tx}{33} + \frac{33t}{33} &= v & &\text{Addition of Fractions Theorem} \\ \frac{tx}{33} + t &= v & &\text{Simplify the fraction.} \end{aligned}$$

Optional Activities

Activity 1
After discussing **Example 3**, you might ask students if the area of a rectangle is twice the product of its diagonals. Tell them to show why or why not. [Sample: The area of a rectangle with sides a and b is ab. By the Pythagorean theorem, the length of each diagonal is $\sqrt{a^2 + b^2}$, and their product is $a^2 + b^2$; $a^2 + b^2 = 2ab$ only when $a = b$, that is, only when the rectangle is a square.

Activity 2 Technology Connection
Materials: Symbol manipulator

Symbol manipulators will solve a formula for a given variable. If you have access to a symbol manipulator, you might have students learn to use it and then use it to solve several of the homework questions.

Notes on Questions

Question 9 Any of the three equations may be used to find N when given L and h; choice (a), however, is the easiest.

Question 13 History Connection
Most houses built by Northwest Coast American Indians were rectangular and had plank walls and roofs. Many of these houses were large—40 feet wide and 100 feet long—and designed for multiple-family use. Sometimes the planks were attached to a permanent framework so the houses could be taken down and transported from one location to another.

(Notes on Questions continue on page 40.)

Follow-up for Lesson 1-6

Practice

For more questions on SPUR Objectives, use **Lesson Master 1-6A** (shown on page 37) or **Lesson Master 1-6B** (shown on pages 38–39).

Sometimes you may want to rewrite a formula without solving for a particular variable. Consider the next example.

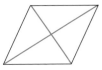

Example 3

When a quadrilateral has perpendicular diagonals with lengths d_1 and d_2, then its area A satisfies $A = \frac{1}{2}d_1d_2$. What is always true about the product of the lengths of the diagonals?

Solution
The product of the diagonal lengths is d_1d_2. Multiplying both sides of $A = \frac{1}{2}d_1d_2$ by 2 solves the equation for this expression. So
$$2A = d_1d_2.$$

Thus, **In a quadrilateral with perpendicular diagonals, the product of the lengths of its diagonals is twice its area.**

Three kinds of quadrilaterals with perpendicular diagonals are kites, rhombuses, and squares, so the theorem in Example 3 has many applications.

QUESTIONS

Covering the Reading

In 1–3, refer to the formula $d = rt$ at the beginning of the lesson.

1. How far can a race car traveling 190 mph go in 1.4 hr?
   266 miles

2. The formula $t = \frac{d}{r}$ is solved for __?__. **t**

3. Find an equivalent formula that is solved for r. **$r = \frac{d}{t}$**

In 4 and 5, complete the sentence "___ is written in terms of ___" for the given formula.

4. $V = s^3$ **V; s**   5. $A = \frac{1}{2}bh$ **A; b and h**

6. Refer to Example 1. Find the Celsius temperature equivalent to 98.6°F.
   37°C

7. Refer to Example 2. Solve the formula for x. **$x = \frac{33V}{t} - 33$**

8. Refer to Example 3. If the area of a rhombus is 24 cm², find the product of its diagonals. **48 cm²**

Applying the Mathematics

9. *Multiple choice.* Which formula is easiest to use if you are given L and h and want to find N? **a**
   (a) $N = 7Lh$ (b) $L = \frac{N}{7h}$ (c) $h = \frac{N}{7L}$

Adapting to Individual Needs

Extra Help
Some students may have difficulty identifying what each variable in a formula represents. When you discuss a formula like $d = rt$, you might write "distance equals rate times time" on the board, defining each word as you write it. For a formula like $A = \frac{1}{2}bh$, write b and h in different colors. Then draw a triangle on the board and identify the base and height with these same colors.

Challenge
Pick's Theorem states that if all the vertices of a polygon P are lattice points of a rectangular lattice, and if I = the number of lattice points contained completely in the interior of P, and B = the number of lattice points on the boundary of P, then the area $A(P)$ of P is found by the function $A(P) = I + \frac{1}{2}B - 1$.

Show students an example of Pick's Theorem. Then have them use the theorem

10. *Multiple choice.* Which equation is easiest to use if you are given L and want to find T? **b**
  (a) $L = 100 + .0004T$ (b) $T = 2500(L - 100)$
  (c) $.0004T = L - 100$

11. The formula $C = \pi D$ gives the circumference of a circle in terms of its diameter D.
  a. Solve this formula for π. $\pi = \frac{C}{D}$
  b. Use your result in part **a** to write a sentence that gives the definition of π. Sample: π is the ratio of the circumference of a circle to its diameter.

12. The formula $C = 2\pi r$ gives the circumference of a circle in terms of its radius r. Find the *ratio* of C to r. $\frac{C}{r} = 2\pi$

In 13–15, the *pitch P* of a gabled roof is a measure of the steepness of the slant of the roof. **Pitch** is the ratio of the vertical rise R to half the span S of the roof. That is, $P = \frac{R}{.5S}$.

rise
span

13. The picture below shows the framing of a plankhouse built by Native Americans on the Pacific coast of North America. Measure the rise and span of the building and estimate its pitch.
  Sample: $P = \frac{.8 \text{ cm}}{.5 \cdot 4.2 \text{ cm}} \approx 0.38$

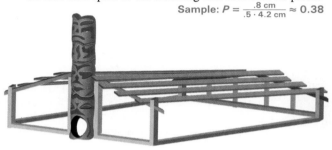

14. a. Solve the pitch formula for R. $R = .5PS$
  b. A family is planning to build an A-frame beach house like one of those shown below. The builder proposes a span of 10 meters and a pitch of 0.9. What is the rise of the roof? 4.5 m

Shown are A-frame vacation homes in Michigan.

15. a. Solve the pitch formula for S. $S = \frac{2R}{P}$
  b. If a builder wants a roof to have a pitch of $\frac{4}{12}$ and a rise of 10 feet, what must be the span of the building? 60 ft

▶ LESSON MASTER 1-6 B *page 2*

Uses Objective K: Use linear equations to solve real-word problems.

13. The volume of the Great Pyramid of Cheops in Giza, Egypt, was about 2,559,900 m³. Use the formula $V = \frac{1}{3}Bh$ to determine the original height of the pyramid if the area of its base B was about 52,600 m². ≈ 146 m

In 14 and 15, use the formulas from Items 6 and 7.
14. Cindy and Tony invested $5,000 at an annual rate of 3.5%. Determine
  a. the amount of interest at the end of the first year. $175
  b. the total value at the end of the first year. $5,175

15. The annual rate of Cathy and Mike's investment was 4%. If the total value of their investment at the end of one year was $2,600, how much had they invested? $2,500

16. The temperature given on a bank thermometer was 25°C.
  a. Was this temperature above or below freezing? above
  b. Give the temperature in degrees Fahrenheit. Refer to the formula in Item 9. 77°F
  c. Try to write a simple "rule of thumb" for estimating a Fahrenheit temperature when given a Celsius reading. Sample: Double the Celsius reading and add 32.

17. Young's formula, $C = \left(\frac{g}{g + 12}\right)A$, tells how much medicine C to give a child of age g under age 13 when the adult dosage A is known. If the dosage for a 12-year-old child is 600 mg, what is the dosage for someone 18 years old? 1,200 mg

18. A pine-tree nursery plants each seedling in the center of a square 4 m on each side. How many seedlings can be planted in a rectangular field 200 m by 300 m? 3,750 seedings

19. A 4-cubic-foot bag of peat moss is in the shape of a rectangular solid 32 in. long and 18 in. wide. How high is a stack of 4 bags if they are stacked on their largest sides? The formula for volume is $V = \ell wh$. 48 in.

20. The building code for a ramp states that the ratio of the horizontal distance d to the height h of the ramp must be at least 12 to 1. How much horizontal distance must be allowed for a ramp that accompanies six 8-inch-high stairs? 576 in.

to find the area of the polygons in Figures 1 and 2 at the right. Finally have them solve Pick's Theorem for I and for B.

Example:

$I = 0, B = 4$
$A(P) = 0 + \frac{1}{2}(4) - 1$
$A(P) = 1$

Figure 1

$[A(P) = \frac{1}{2}]$

$[I = -(\frac{1}{2}B - 1) + A(P), \text{ or } I = A(P) - \frac{1}{2}B + 1;$
$B = 2(A(P) - I + 1), \text{ or } B = 2A(P) - 2I + 2]$

Figure 2

$[A(P) = 6]$

39

Question 16 Error Alert Students may have some difficulty solving for m_1. Remind them to clear fractions as a first step and to think of m_1 as a single variable.

Question 18 The term *Skill Sequence* indicates that the parts of the question are related. Later parts of such questions often apply the skills needed to work earlier parts of the questions.

Question 24 A critical idea in this question is the property that the diagonals of a rhombus are perpendicular to each other. When rhombuses are defined as special parallelograms, this property is not so obvious. But in UCSMP *Geometry*, rhombuses are defined as special kinds of kites, and this property arises from the symmetry of a kite.

More generally, the formula can be deduced for any quadrilateral with perpendicular diagonals by noting that if $\overline{OR}$ and $\overline{MH}$ are perpendicular diagonals of a quadrilateral *RHOM*, then a rectangle drawn like the one in the diagram will always have area twice that of *RHOM*.

Swing time. *Because changes in temperature expand or contract a pendulum's rod, some grandfather clocks come with mechanisms to keep the total length of the pendulum constant.*

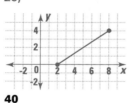

16a) $m_1 = \dfrac{Fd^2}{Gm_2}$

20)

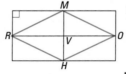

40

16. In the late 1660s, Isaac Newton discovered the Law of Universal Gravitation described by the formula
$$F = \frac{Gm_1 m_2}{d^2}$$
where F is the force between two bodies with masses m_1 and m_2, G is the gravitational constant, and d is the distance between the bodies.
a. Solve for m_1. **See left.**
b. Solve the formula for the product of the masses. $m_1 m_2 = \frac{Fd^2}{G}$

17. Solve the formula $t = a + (n - 1)d$ for n. $n = \frac{t-a}{d} + 1$

Review

18. *Skill sequence.* Solve each equation. *(Lesson 1-5)*
   a. $\frac{1}{3}n = 60$ b. $\frac{1}{3}n + 15 = 60$ c. $\frac{1}{3}n + \frac{1}{2}n + 15 = 60$
   $n = 180$ $n = 135$ $n = 54$
19. Solve $5 - 2(x - 7) - (3 - x) = 4$. *(Lesson 1-5)* $x = 12$

20. Draw a graph of a function that has domain equal to $\{x: 2 \le x \le 8\}$ and range equal to $\{y: 0 \le y \le 4\}$. *(Lesson 1-4)* **See left for sample.**

In 21 and 22, use the formula
$$T = 2\pi \sqrt{\frac{L}{g}}$$
which gives the time T (in seconds) for one complete swing of a pendulum that is L meters long near the surface of the Earth. (g is the acceleration due to gravity, 9.8 m/sec².) *(Lessons 1-1, 1-2)*

21. Find the time for a pendulum 50 cm long to complete one swing.
   1.42 sec
22. a. *True or false.* T is a function of L. **True**
   b. If the statement in part **a** is true, identify the domain of the function. **the set of all positive real numbers**

23. *Multiple choice.* Which of the following does not equal the complex fraction $\dfrac{\frac{a}{b}}{\frac{c}{d}}$? *(Previous course)* c

   (a) $\frac{ad}{bc}$ (b) $\frac{a}{b} \div \frac{c}{d}$ (c) $\frac{ac}{bd}$ (d) $\frac{a}{b} \cdot \frac{d}{c}$

24. Let d_1 and d_2 be the lengths of the diagonals of rhombus *RHOM*. Use the diagram at the left and write a few sentences to explain why the area A of the rhombus equals $\frac{1}{2}d_1 d_2$. *(Previous course)* **See below.**

Exploration

25. Look in a science book to find a formula with three variables not mentioned in this lesson. Explain what the variables represent. Solve the formula for each variable. **Answers will vary.**

24) Sample: Each triangle with vertex V has area $\dfrac{\frac{1}{2}d_1 \cdot \frac{1}{2}d_2}{2}$, so the total area of the four triangles is $4\left(\dfrac{\frac{1}{2}d_1 \cdot \frac{1}{2}d_2}{2}\right) = \frac{1}{2}d_1 \cdot d_2$. The four triangles make up rhombus *RHOM*.

English Language Development
Most likely, your non-English-speaking students have grown up in a country that uses the Celsius scale, which they are likely to call the Centigrade scale, and now have to convert Fahrenheit temperatures to Celsius mentally. You might have these students explain to the class how they make this conversion—some students might have a shortcut method that they use.

Setting Up Lesson 1-7
The In-class Activity on page 41 should be completed before Lesson 1-7 is assigned.

Patterns and Sequences

IN-CLASS
A C T I V I T Y

Work on this activity in small groups. Each group will need paper and a calculator.

Informally, a *sequence* is an ordered list. Here is a sequence of rectangular figures made from dots ●.

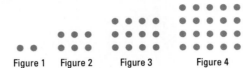

Figure 1   Figure 2   Figure 3   Figure 4

The number of dots in each of the figures produces a sequence of numbers:

$$2, 6, 12, 20, \ldots$$

1 **a.** Draw the 5th figure. See margin.
   b. How many dots are needed to make the 5th figure? 30

2 **a.** Complete a table of values with the following entries.

n	number of dots in Figure n
1	2
2	6
3	12
4	20
5	30
6	42

   b. Is the set of ordered pairs of the form (n, number of dots in nth figure) a function? Why or why not? See below.
   c. If so, what is the domain of this function? See below.

3 How many dots are needed to make the 10th figure? Explain how you got your answer. 110 dots;
11 dots in 10 rows produces 110 dots.

4 How many dots are needed to make the 55th figure? 3080
(Hint: Look for patterns.) Explain how you got your answer. 55 rows with 56 dots in each row produces 3080 dots.

5 How many dots are needed to make the nth figure? Justify your answer. $n(n + 1)$; n rows with ($n + 1$) dots in each row produces $n(n + 1)$ dots.

2b) Yes; each figure (n) corresponds to a single number of dots.
c) set of natural numbers;

41

1-7

Objectives
E Evaluate sequences.
J Use functions to solve real-world problems.

Resources

From the Teacher's Resource File
- Lesson Master 1-7A or 1-7B
- Answer Master 1-7
- Teaching Aids
  3 Warm-up
  8 Four-Quadrant Graph Paper
  10 Question 16
  11 Pascal's Triangle
- Activity Kit, Activity 1
- Technology Sourcebook
  Computer Master 1

Additional Resources
- Visuals for Teaching Aids 3, 8, 10, 11
- Spreadsheet

Teaching Lesson 1-7

Warm-up

Diagnostic Use the sequence t of positive even integers for these questions: 2, 4, 6, 8, 10, . . .
1. What does t_4 equal? **8**
2. Write a symbolic translation of "the fifth term of the sequence is 10." $t_5 = 10$
3. Write what you would say if you were asked to read "$t_8 = 16$" aloud. **Sample: t sub 8 equals 16, or the value of the eighth term of the sequence is 16.**
4. Suppose t_n represents the general, or nth, term of the sequence. Give a formula for t_n. $t_n = 2n$

1-7

Explicit Formulas for Sequences

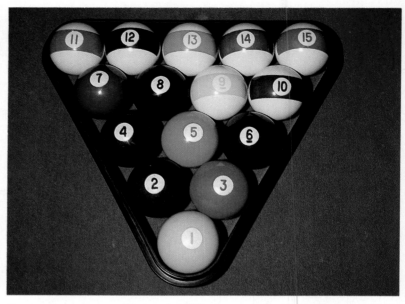

Sequences on cue. *Most pocket billiard games start with 15 balls racked in a triangular array. The array is a representation of the fifth triangular number. In some games, the numbered balls must be pocketed in sequence.*

What Is an Explicit Formula for a Sequence?

Here is another sequence of dots.

The number of dots in each of the figures above produces a sequence of numbers:

$$1, 3, 6, 10, 15.$$

These numbers are often called the *triangular numbers* because of the way they can be represented by the triangular figures of dots.

Each number in the sequence is called a **term.** Thus,

the 1st term (of the sequence) is 1;
the 2nd term is 3;
the 3rd term is 6;
the 4th term is 10;
the 5th term is 15.

Activity

a. Draw a picture to represent the 6th triangular number.
b. What is the 6th term of the sequence of triangular numbers? 21

Lesson 1-7 Overview

Broad Goals This lesson introduces the subscript notation for sequences and for the evaluation of sequences.

Perspective Sequences appear early in this book because (1) they provide a good vehicle for reviewing subscripts; (2) they involve formulas; (3) they are examples of functions; (4) they are important in developing and identifying patterns, which is an

effective problem-solving strategy; (5) they are interesting to students.

An algebraic description of sequences will be new to most students. However, given a sequence, students should be able to determine the next term in the pattern. Students have seen subscripted variables such as x_1, y_1, x_2, y_2 as coordinates of points or in the formula for the slope of a line. However, they may not be familiar with the concept

of a subscript as a counter or as a means of identifying a particular item.

Here is one way to find a formula for *generating* all terms of the sequence of triangular numbers. Notice that if you take a duplicate of each triangular figure and place it as shown below, a rectangular array is formed.

These are the same rectangular figures you used in the In-class Activity on page 41. Thus, each triangular number can be represented by half a rectangular array. For instance, the number of dots representing the 4th triangular number is half the number of dots in a 4 by 5 rectangular array.

$$\frac{1}{2} \cdot 4 \cdot 5 = 10$$

This idea can be used to develop a general formula for any triangular number.

Number of Term	Term (Number of Dots)
1	$\frac{1}{2} \cdot 1 \cdot 2 = 1$
2	$\frac{1}{2} \cdot 2 \cdot 3 = 3$
3	$\frac{1}{2} \cdot 3 \cdot 4 = 6$
4	$\frac{1}{2} \cdot 4 \cdot 5 = 10$
5	$\frac{1}{2} \cdot 5 \cdot 6 = 15$
6	$\frac{1}{2} \cdot 6 \cdot 7 = 21$
⋮	⋮
n	$\frac{1}{2} \cdot n \cdot (n + 1)$

Thus, the number of dots in the nth triangular figure is

$$\frac{1}{2} \cdot n \cdot (n + 1) = \frac{n(n + 1)}{2}.$$

If we let $t(n) =$ the nth triangular number, then

$$t(n) = \frac{n(n + 1)}{2}.$$

The domain of this function is the set of natural numbers $\{1, 2, 3, \ldots\}$; the range is the set of terms $\{1, 3, 6, 10, 15, 21, \ldots\}$.

The sentence $t(n) = \frac{n(n + 1)}{2}$ is called an **explicit formula for the nth term** of the sequence 1, 3, 6, 10, 15, 21, . . . because we use it to calculate the nth term explicitly, or directly, by substituting a value for n. In the next lesson, you will learn about another type of formula for generating terms of a sequence. Explicit formulas are important because they can be used to calculate any term in the sequence by substituting a particular value for n.

Lesson 1-7 *Explicit Formulas for Sequences* **43**

Optional Activities

Activity 1
As you discuss **Questions 17–19**, you might use the pattern shown at the right to derive the explicit formula. Yoshi's total salary for each year after the first year is his old salary plus a 5% raise or 105% of his previous salary. (Students of UCSMP *Algebra* will have seen this kind of example.)

This is a geometric sequence of the type that students will study in detail in Chapter 7.

Year	Salary
1	18,000
2	18,000(1.05)
3	$18,000(1.05)^2$
4	$18,000(1.05)^3$
•	•
•	•
•	•
n	$18,000(1.05)^{n-1}$

Activity 2
After discussing triangular numbers, you might tell students that every whole number greater than 0 can be written as the sum of, at most, three triangular numbers. Have students give some examples. [Samples: $1 = 1$, $2 = 1 + 1$, $23 = 21 + 1 + 1$, $40 = 15 + 15 + 10$]

❶ Reading Mathematics Notation usually presents the greatest difficulty that students encounter with sequences. Often they cannot read the notation—they are in the same position you might be in if you had to read a letter written in an unfamiliar language. You may want to pick phrases and sentences from this lesson and ask students to read them.

For example, $t_n = \frac{n(n+1)}{2}$ is read: "t sub n equals n times the quantity n plus one, all divided by 2."

In **Example 2**, $t_n = 3n$ is read: "t sub n equals 3 times n." Contrast $t_n = 3n$ with $t_n = n^3$, which is read "t sub n equals n cubed" or "t sub n equals n to the third power."

In **Example 3**, $P_n = 500(2)^{n-1}$ is read: "P sub n equals 500 times the quantity 2 to the n minus one power."

Students also have to see that n serves two purposes in this notation. In $t_n = 3n$, the expression $3n$ describes a pattern that is used to generate the terms. Here, n is the independent variable. In t_n, n also indicates that the dependent variable t depends on n. You might point out the following analogies:

Name of Function	Independent Variable	Value of Function
f	x	$f(x)$
t	n	t_n

Pacing Be careful that you do not get bogged down at this time. There will be ample opportunity for work with subscripted variables throughout the remainder of the chapter. Students are typically quite comfortable with subscript notation by the end of the chapter.

Example 1

What is the 20th triangular number?

Solution

To find the 20th term in the sequence, evaluate $t(20)$.

$$t(20) = \frac{20(20+1)}{2} = \frac{20 \cdot 21}{2}$$

The 20th triangular number is 210.

❶ Notation for Sequences

In general, a **sequence** is a function whose domain is the set of natural numbers or the natural numbers from 1 to n. A special notation is often used with sequences. Instead of writing $t(10) = 55$ to indicate that the 10th term is 55, we can also write

$$t_{10} = 55.$$

This is read "t sub 10 equals 55." The number 10 is called a *subscript* or *index*. It is called a **subscript** because it is written below and to the right of a variable. t_1 is read "t sub 1" and t_n is read "t sub n." Both t_1 and t_n are called **subscripted variables.** The subscript of t_1 is 1; the subscript of t_n is n.

The subscript is often called an **index** because it *indicates* the position of the term in the sequence. For example, if t_n represents the nth term of the triangular-number sequence, then

$$t_1 = 1, \quad t_2 = 3, \quad t_3 = 6, \quad t_4 = 10, \quad t_5 = 15, \text{ and } t_n = \frac{n(n+1)}{2}.$$

Using Explicit Formulas to Generate Terms of a Sequence

Example 2

Consider the formula $t_n = 3n$, for integers $n \geq 1$.
a. What are the first four terms of the sequence it defines?
b. Evaluate t_{20}, and explain what it represents.

Solution

a. Substitute $n = 1, 2, 3,$ and 4 one at a time into the formula for t_n.
$t_1 = 3 \cdot 1 = 3$
$t_2 = 3 \cdot 2 = 6$
$t_3 = 3 \cdot 3 = 9$
$t_4 = 3 \cdot 4 = 12$
b. Substitute $n = 20$ into the formula.
$t_{20} = 3 \cdot 20 = 60$
This means that the 20th term of the sequence 3, 6, 9, 12, . . . is 60.

Sequences arise naturally in many situations in science, business, finance, and other areas. The next example looks at a sequence in biology.

Optional Activities

Activity 3
Tell students to find the sum of the numbers in each of the six rows of Pascal's Triangle shown in **Question 29**. Then have them look for a pattern and write an expression for the sum of the numbers in the nth row. The top row is called the 0th row.
[row 0: $1 = 2^0$ row 3: $8 = 2^3$
row 1: $2 = 2^1$ row 4: $16 = 2^4$
row 2: $4 = 2^2$ row 5: $32 = 2^5$
The sum of the numbers in row n: $S_n = 2^n$]

Activity 4
You might want to use *Activity Kit, Activity 1* as either a lead-in or a follow-up to the lesson. In this activity, students use a geometric investigation to generate two sequences.

Activity 5 Technology Connection
You might consider using *Technology Sourcebook, Computer Master 1,* with Lessons 1-7 and 1-8. Students generate tables from explicit formulas by using parametric equations.

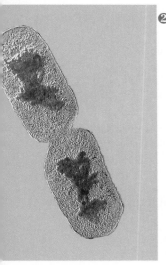

Time to split. *Shown is the bacterium* Escherichia coli *splitting into two cells called daughter cells. E. coli bacteria have played a major role in genetic engineering.*

A microbe reproduces by splitting to make 2 cells. Each of these cells then splits in half to make a total of 4 cells. Each of these splits to make a total of 8, and so on. Each splitting is called a *generation*. If a colony begins with 500 microbes, the following equation gives the number of microbes in the *n*th generation (assuming no microbes die).

$$P_n = 500(2)^{n-1}$$

a. Write the first term of the sequence of populations of microbes.
b. Write the fifth term of the sequence.

Solution

Notice that the variable is in the exponent.
a. For the population in the first generation, substitute 1 for *n* in the formula.
$P_1 = 500(2)^{1-1} = 500(2)^0 = 500(1) = 500$
This checks with the given information. **There are 500 microbes in the first generation.**
b. For the population in the fifth generation, use $n = 5$ in the formula.
$P_5 = 500(2)^{5-1} = 500(2)^4 = 500(16) = 8000$
There are 8000 microbes in the fifth generation.

QUESTIONS

Covering the Reading

1. An ordered list of items is called a __?__. **sequence**

2. What is each item in a sequence called? **a term**

3. Explain why the numbers 1, 3, 6, 10, and 15 are called triangular numbers. **because they can be represented by triangular figures of dots**

4. **a.** What answers did you get for the Activity in the lesson? **See left.**
   b. Show how to use the formula $t_n = \dfrac{n(n+1)}{2}$ to check these answers.
   $t_6 = \dfrac{6(6+1)}{2} = \dfrac{42}{2} = 21$? **Yes, it checks.**

5. Find the 25th triangular number. **325**

6. **a.** Draw the next term in the sequence.

   b. Give a formula for S_n, the number of dots in the *n*th term.
   $S_n = n^2$

In 7–9, consider the sequence *c* whose first five terms are 1, 8, 27, 64, 125.

7. What number is the 4th term? **64**

8. How is the sentence "$c_3 = 27$" read? **c sub 3 equals 27.**

9. $c_5 = \underline{\ ?\ }$ **125**

4a)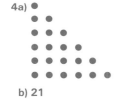

b) 21

Lesson 1-7 *Explicit Formulas for Sequences* **45**

---

② **Science Connection** You might want to explain that microbes are a diverse group of simple life forms that include protozoans, algae, molds, bacteria, and viruses. Research is developing ways to channel and exploit the activities of microbes for the benefit of medicine, industry, and agriculture.

Additional Examples

1. Use $n(n + 1)$ to give the 15th rectangular number. **240**
2. Consider the formula
   $t_n = 15 + 2(n-1)$
   for integers $n \geq 1$.
   a. What are the first four terms of the sequence generated by the formula? **15, 17, 19, 21**
   b. Find t_8. **29**
3. Suppose you drop a ball from the top of a 50-foot wall, and, on each bounce, the ball rises to 75% of its previous height. The heights of the ball after each bounce form a sequence.
   a. Write the first three terms of the sequence.
   37.5, 28.125, 21.09375
   b. After how many bounces will the ball rise less than 10 feet?
   6 bounces
4. Consider the sequence *t* of squares of consecutive positive integers.
   a. What is the value of t_4? **16**
   b. Give an explicit formula for t_n.
   $t_n = n^2$
   c. What is the value of t_{250}?
   62,500

Adapting to Individual Needs

Extra Help

Some students might be confused by the difference between a subscript and an exponent (a superscript). Point out that t^2 and t_2 have two very different meanings. In this lesson, subscripts are used to designate the position of terms in a sequence. Remind students that exponents can be used with either a variable, as in x^3, or a numerical base, as in 2^4. Subscripts, however, are used only with variables.

English Language Development

Explain that the prefix *sub-* means under or below. You might use a drawing to show that, for instance, a *sub*marine is a boat that operates underwater, or that a *sub*way is an underground railroad. Similarly, a *sub*script is a number or letter written *below* and to the right of a term to indicate the position of the term. In t_{12}, 12 is the subscript indicating that t_{12} is the twelfth term.

45

Notes on Questions

Question 16 The table and graph are given on **Teaching Aid 10**.

Questions 17–19 Activity 1 in *Optional Activities* on page 43 relates to this situation.

Questions 26, 28 Students may use four-quadrant graph paper or **Teaching Aid 8** for these questions.

Question 29 Pascal's Triangle is given on **Teaching Aid 11**. The Challenge in Lesson 1-8 refers to answers to this question. Pascal's Triangle is a *two-dimensional* sequence, which some students might see more clearly if the numbers are written like this:

```
1   1   1   1   1   1
1   2   3   4   5   . . .
1   3   6   10  . . .
1   4   . . .
1
.       . . .
.       . . .
.       . . .
```

Follow-up for Lesson 1-7

Practice

For more questions on SPUR Objectives, use **Lesson Master 1-7A** (shown on page 45) or **Lesson Master 1-7B** (shown on pages 46–47).

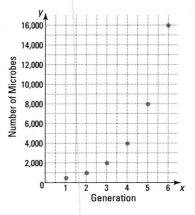

In 10–12, consider the sentence $a_4 = 15$.

10. Which number is the subscript? **4**

11. The number 15 is the __?__ term of a sequence. **4th**

12. Rewrite the sentence using Euler's notation. $a(4) = 15$

13. Use sequence notation to rewrite the sentence "The 6th term of sequence t is 23." $t_6 = 23$

In 14 and 15, an explicit formula for a sequence is given for integers $n \geq 1$. Write the first four terms of the sequence.

14. $a_n = 5n - 3$ **2, 7, 12, 17**   15. $S_n = \dfrac{n(3n - 1)}{2}$ **1, 5, 12, 22**

16. Refer to Example 3.
   a. Copy the table below and use the explicit formula to fill in the missing numbers.

Generation	Number of Microbes
1	500
2	1000
3	2000
4	4000
5	8000
6	16000

   b. Graph the values from the table.
   c. Should the points on the graph be connected? Why or why not? Relate your answer to the domain of the function.
   No;   the domain of the function represents generation numbers, so it is the set of all positive integers.

Applying the Mathematics

In 17–19, Yoshi started with a company at an annual salary of $18,000. He expects an increase of 5% at the end of each year. Then the formula $s_n = 18,000(1.05)^{n-1}$ gives Yoshi's salary in his nth year.

17. Calculate the first three terms of the sequence. 18,000; 18,900; 19,845

18. At this growth rate, what would Yoshi's salary be in his 30th year with this company? **$74,090.44**

19. Given the function with equation $s_n = 18,000(1.05)^{n-1}$, identify:
   a. the independent variable; b. the dependent variable; and
   c. the domain of the function. a) n b) s c) Sample: the set of positive integers less than 40

Adapting to Individual Needs

Challenge

Have students find the next term in each sequence and explain how they determined this term.

1. 1, 2, 9, 28, 65, . . . [126; one more than the cube of the whole numbers: $0^3 + 1 = 1$, $1^3 + 1 = 2$, $2^3 + 1 = 9$, $3^3 + 1 = 28$, and so on]

2. 2, 4, 7, 12, 19, 30, . . . [43; the differences between terms are the consecutive primes: $4 - 2 = 2$, $7 - 4 = 3$, $12 - 7 = 5$, and so on.]

3. 1, 2, 2, 4, 8, 32, . . . [256; each term after the second is the product of the two previous terms.]

You might have students make up their own sequences and have classmates identify the pattern.

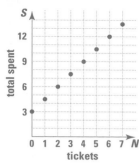

23) $n = \frac{S}{180} + 2$ or $\frac{S + 360}{180}$

26c)

20. Let t be the sequence whose first seven terms are 93, 86, 79, 72, 65, 58, and 51. What do you think t_8 should equal? Why?
44; the difference between consecutive terms is 7.

In 21 and 22, *multiple choice.* Which is a formula for the nth term of the sequence?

21. 2, 4, 8, 16, 32, . . . c
  (a) $t_n = 2n$ (b) $t_n = n^2$ (c) $t_n = 2^n$

22. 2, 9, 28, 65, 126, . . . c
  (a) $t_n = 7n - 5$ (b) $t_n = 7n^2 - 2$ (c) $t_n = n^3 + 1$

Review

23. A formula for the sum S of the angle measures in an n-gon is $S = 180(n - 2)$. Solve this formula for n. *(Lesson 1-6)* See left.

24. When the Mustafas bought their new home, they were not told the capacity of the heating oil tank. When the tank was $\frac{1}{10}$ full, they had 280 gallons of oil delivered. Then the tank was $\frac{8}{10}$ full.
  a. Let $x =$ the capacity of the oil tank. Write an equation that can be used to find the capacity of the tank. $\frac{1}{10}x + 280 = \frac{8}{10}x$
  b. Solve and check the equation in part **a.** *(Lesson 1-5)*
$x = 400$ gallons; 1/10 (400) + 280 = 8/10 (400)? 40 + 280 = 320? Yes, it checks.

25. Let $P(x)$ be the perimeter of the triangle at the left. *(Lessons 1-1, 1-5)*
  a. Write a formula for $P(x)$ in terms of x. $P(x) = 3x + 4$
  b. Evaluate $P(40)$. $P(40) = 124$
  c. Solve $P(x) = 40$. $x = 12$

26. A carnival charges a $3.00 admission fee and $1.50 for each ride ticket. If S is the total spent at the carnival for admission and rides, then S is a function of the number N of tickets bought, and can be written as $S = 1.5N + 3$. *(Lessons 1-2, 1-4)*
  a. Specify the domain of this function. the set of whole numbers
  b. Write the four smallest numbers in the range of this function.
  c. Graph this function. See left. b) 3, 4.5, 6, 7.5

27. What percent of 80 is 56? *(Previous course)* 70%

28. Draw $\triangle ABC$ as shown at the left on graph paper. Draw its image under a size change of magnitude 3. *(Previous course)* See margin.

Exploration

29. The array at the left is part of an infinite pattern called *Pascal's triangle.* The first and last terms of each row are 1. Each other term, from the third row on, is the sum of the two numbers diagonally above it.
  a. Write the next four rows in the array. See margin.
  b. Where can you find the number sequence that comes from the dot pattern at the start of this lesson? the third diagonal
  c. Describe at least one other interesting sequence in this array.
  Sample: the second diagonal is the sequence of natural numbers.

```
        1
      1   1
    1   2   1
  1   3   3   1
1   4   6   4   1
1  5  10  10  5  1
```

Lesson 1-7 *Explicit Formulas for Sequences*   **47**

Additional Answers
28.

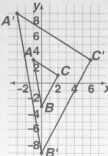

29a.

```
          1    6   15   20   15    6    1
        1    7   21   35   35   21    7    1
      1    8   28   56   70   56   28    8    1
    1    9   36   84  126  126   84   36    9    1
```

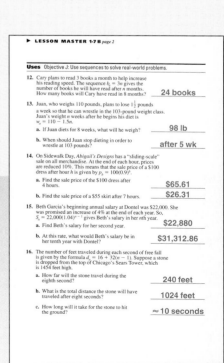

47

Objectives
E Evaluate sequences.
F Write a recursive definition for a sequence.
J Use functions to solve real-world problems.

Resources

From the Teacher's Resource File
- Lesson Master 1-8A or 1-8B
- Answer Master 1-8
- Teaching Aid
  3 Warm-up
  12 Extension
- Technology Sourcebook
  Computer Master 1

Additional Resources
- Visuals for Teaching Aids 3, 12

Teaching Lesson 1-8

Warm-up

1. To repay a $200 loan, Jessie makes a payment of $20 a month. At the end of each month she receives a statement telling how much money she still owes. Make a list of her outstanding debts for the first six months.
    $180, $160, $140, $120, $100, $80

2. The first term of a sequence is $100. Each term after that is found by multiplying the preceding term by 1.06 and rounding to the nearest cent. Find the first six terms of the sequence.
    $100, $106, $112.36, $119.10, $126.25, $133.82

LESSON

1-8

Recursive Formulas for Sequences

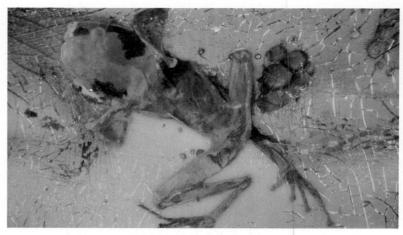

Guess my age. *The age of this frog in amber can be found by carbon dating. After each 5700-year period, half of the ^{14}C carbon atoms decay. The sequence a_n of fractions of ^{14}C left after n 5700-year periods is $\frac{1}{2}, \frac{1}{4}, \frac{1}{8}, \ldots$*

As you saw in the last lesson, if you know an explicit formula for a sequence, then you can write the terms of a sequence rather quickly. For instance, the formula $a_n = -3 + 5n$ generates the following terms.

$$a_1 = -3 + 5 \cdot 1 = 2$$
$$a_2 = -3 + 5 \cdot 2 = 7$$
$$a_3 = -3 + 5 \cdot 3 = 12$$
$$a_4 = -3 + 5 \cdot 4 = 17$$

We say that the formula $a_n = -3 + 5n$ *generates the sequence*

$$2, 7, 12, 17, 22, \ldots.$$

Generating Sequences Using a Calculator

You can also use a calculator to generate this sequence. Notice that the sequence begins with 2 and that each term after that is obtained by adding 5 to the previous term. Try the following key strokes on your calculator and check that your display matches the one below.

❶ Key strokes: 2 [+] 5 [ENTER] [+] 5 [ENTER] [+] 5 [ENTER] [+] 5 [ENTER]
Display: [2] [7] [12] [17] [22]

If your calculator does not have an [ENTER] key, you should be able to use the same key strokes if you replace [ENTER] by [EXE] or [=].

Activity 1

Use your calculator to generate the sequence
   40, 20, 10, 5, 2.5, ...
What key strokes did you use?
40 [ENTER] [÷] 2 [ENTER] [÷] 2 [ENTER] [÷] 2 [ENTER] . . .

Lesson 1-8 Overview

Broad Goals This lesson and the next one have the same goals: to get students to see how sequences can be formed recursively and to be able to use standard notation for recursive sequences. This lesson concentrates on the first goal.

Perspective It is natural to think recursively. For instance, in defining the sequence 1990, 1991, 1992, 1993, 1994, few people think of the explicit definition $Y_n = 1989 + n$.

Most people think of this as a sequence, with first term 1990, in which each term after the first one is found by increasing the previous term by 1. The latter definition is a recursive definition for the sequence given in words.

This lesson presents three different ways of using calculators to generate sequences recursively. The first way, described on this page, is by repeatedly pressing some sort

of operation key. On some four-function calculators, this can be done with the use of a constant [K] key. The second way is perhaps the most obvious: use the calculator for calculation when the numbers get large. The calculations of **Example 1** or Solution 2 of **Example 2** could be done this way. The third, and most sophisticated, way is shown in Activity 2; it is found in the most recent generation of graphics calculators. These

What Is a Recursive Formula?

Notice that no explicit formula was used to generate the sequence in Activity 1. Instead, each term of the sequence was derived from the preceding one. For instance, to find the 6th term of the sequence

$$40, 20, 10, 5, 2.5, \ldots,$$

you could divide the preceding term (the 5th term) by 2 or multiply the preceding term by 0.5. Each of these ideas involves thinking *recursively*.

❷ A **recursive formula** or **recursive definition** for a sequence is a set of statements that
a. indicates the first term (or first few terms), and
b. tells how the *n*th term is related to one or more of the previous terms.

So the sequence 40, 20, 10, 5, 2.5, . . . could be described recursively as

$$\begin{cases} \text{first term} = 40 \\ \text{new term} = \text{previous term divided by 2} \\ \qquad\qquad\quad \text{for all terms after the first} \end{cases}$$

The brace { indicates that both lines are needed for the recursive definition.

❸ | **Example 1**

Consider the sequence defined as follows.

$$\begin{cases} t_1 = 1 \\ t_n = (\text{previous term})^2 + 3, \text{ for integers } n \geq 2 \end{cases}$$

Write the first four terms of the sequence.

Solution
The first term is given.
   $t_1 = 1$
According to the second line of the definition,
   $t_2 = (\text{previous term})^2 + 3.$
But the previous term is 1. So
   $t_2 = 1^2 + 3 = 4.$
To find t_3, use the second line of the definition again.
   $t_3 = (\text{previous term})^2 + 3$
Now the previous term, t_2, is equal to 4. So
   $t_3 = 4^2 + 3 = 19.$
Finally, $t_4 = (\text{previous term})^2 + 3.$ So
   $t_4 = 19^2 + 3 = 364.$
The first four terms are 1, 4, 19, 364.

Notes on Reading
Although the vocabulary and the symbolism for recursion will be new to most students, the concept itself is not new. Students naturally describe sequences recursively, saying, for example, that "the sequence grows by adding 5."

❶ Point out that in key sequences, buttons are represented by names inside rectangles unless they are numerical; in that case, we simply write the number. Displays are shown in ovals.

❷ Emphasize that recursive formulas have two parts: a starting point and a rule for finding the *n*th term from one or more previous terms.

Note the use of the one-sided brace. Students who have studied from UCSMP *Algebra* have seen this brace used to identify a system of equations. In that usage, the brace has the same meaning it has here, namely, that statements in the brace are connected by the word "and."

❸ In **Example 1,** we use the phrase "previous term" rather than a variable. In **Example 2,** this phrase is replaced by (ANS). Each of these replacements provides a smooth transition to the variable a_{n-1}, which is introduced in the next lesson.

calculators essentially allow the user to program the recursion automatically; they then generate one term after another with the pressing of a single key.

The entire lesson can be done without having a sophisticated calculator—even without a calculator at all—but there is no doubt that the student who has such a calculator in hand while reading will find it easier to understand the ideas.

In 1 and 2, consider the sequence defined by the recursive formula and write the first six terms of the sequence.

1. $\begin{cases} S_1 = 1, \\ S_n = 3 \cdot \text{previous term} - 1 \\ \qquad \text{for integers } n \geq 2 \end{cases}$

   1, 2, 5, 14, 41, 122

2. $\begin{cases} T_1 = 10 \\ T_n = \boxed{\text{ANS}} + 6 \\ \qquad \text{for integers } n \geq 2 \end{cases}$

   10, 16, 22, 28, 34, 40

3. Louis is trying to learn a very long and difficult piano piece that has 400 measures. After learning the first page, which has 24 measures, he decided that he would learn 4 measures a day. The sequence 28, 32, 36, 40, . . . gives the number of measures he will have learned after n days.
   a. In words, describe this sequence recursively.
      The first term is 28; each term after the first term is 4 greater than the previous term.
   b. Write a recursive formula for this sequence using the $\boxed{\text{ANS}}$ key.

   $\begin{cases} M_1 = 28 \\ M_n = \boxed{\text{ANS}} + 4 \\ \qquad \text{for integers } n \geq 2 \end{cases}$

4. Write the calculator key sequence that generates the sequence 1, 4, 7, 10, 13, ...
   Samples:

   1 $\boxed{+}$ 3 $\boxed{\text{ENTER}}$ $\boxed{+}$

   3 $\boxed{\text{ENTER}}$ $\boxed{+}$ 3 $\boxed{\text{ENTER}}$

   $\boxed{+}$ 3 $\boxed{\text{ENTER}}$ . . . ; or

   1 $\boxed{\text{ENTER}}$ $\boxed{+}$ 3

   $\boxed{\text{ENTER}}$ $\boxed{\text{ENTER}}$ . . .

Recursive Formulas on Calculators

On many graphics calculators, the $\boxed{\text{ANS}}$ key is used to refer to the result of the previous calculation. So the $\boxed{\text{ANS}}$ key can be used in the recursive definition to refer to the previous term. Using this key, you could write the sequence 40, 20, 10, 5, 2.5, . . . in Activity 1 as follows.

$$\begin{cases} a_1 = 40 \\ a_n = \dfrac{\boxed{\text{ANS}}}{2}, \text{ for integers } n \geq 2 \end{cases}$$

Activity 2

a. Clear the screen on a graphics calculator. Press 40 and then $\boxed{\text{ENTER}}$ or $\boxed{\text{EXE}}$. This stores the first term or *initializes* the value of a_1.

b. The second line tells you how to find a_2 and all subsequent terms. After initializing a_1 on the calculator display, press $\boxed{\text{ANS}} \div 2$, followed by $\boxed{\text{ENTER}}$ or $\boxed{\text{EXE}}$. What is displayed? 20

c. Press $\boxed{\text{ENTER}}$ again. The calculator will use the second term as the value for $\boxed{\text{ANS}}$ and divide this value by 2 to generate the third term.

d. Keep pressing the $\boxed{\text{ENTER}}$ or $\boxed{\text{EXE}}$ key. How many terms of the sequence

$$\begin{cases} a_1 = 40 \\ a_n = \dfrac{\boxed{\text{ANS}}}{2}, \text{ for integers } n \geq 2 \end{cases}$$

are greater than 0.1? 9

As shown in Example 2, the $\boxed{\text{ANS}}$ key may be combined with several other operations.

Example 2

Consider the sequence defined by the recursive formula below.

$$\begin{cases} t_1 = 6 \\ t_n = 3 \cdot \boxed{\text{ANS}} - 5, \text{ for integers } n \geq 2 \end{cases}$$

Find the first five terms of this sequence.

Solution 1

Initialize the first term on a graphics calculator by pressing 6 and then $\boxed{\text{ENTER}}$ or $\boxed{\text{EXE}}$. Now enter the formula to find the other terms:

3 $\boxed{\times}$ $\boxed{\text{ANS}}$ $\boxed{-}$ 5.

As you press $\boxed{\text{ENTER}}$ or $\boxed{\text{EXE}}$, you will generate the terms

$$6, 13, 34, 97, 286.$$

▶

50

► **Solution 2**

Evaluate the formula by hand.

$t_1 = 6$ is given.

$\boxed{\text{ANS}}$ refers to the previous term t_1 of the sequence.

So, $t_2 = 3 \cdot t_1 - 5$

$ = 3 \cdot 6 - 5$

$ = 13.$

To evaluate t_3, think of $t_2 = 13$ as the previous term.

Thus, $t_3 = 3 \cdot t_2 - 5$

$ = 3 \cdot 13 - 5$

$ = 34.$

Now use $t_3 = 34$ as the value of $\boxed{\text{ANS}}$.

$t_4 = 3 \cdot t_3 - 5$

$ = 3 \cdot 34 - 5$

$ = 97$

Finally, $t_5 = 3 \cdot t_4 - 5$

$ = 3 \cdot 97 - 5$

$ = 286.$

Notice that the first term of the sequence in Example 2 is 6, the term given to you in the definition. Although 13 is the first term given by the rule for t_n, it is the second term of the sequence. Remember, t_n represents the nth term.

Activity 3

Find the first five terms of the sequence defined by

1, -2, -8, -20, -44
$$\begin{cases} t_1 = 1 \\ t_n = 2 \cdot \boxed{\text{ANS}} - 4, \text{ for integers } n \geq 2. \end{cases}$$

Writing Recursive Formulas

If you can describe a sequence in words, then you can use that description to write a formula for the sequence.

Example 3

When Jennifer started her new job, she enrolled in a payroll deduction plan to save for a car. The first month she had $25 deducted. Thereafter, she decided to deduct $50 each month. The sequence

$$25, 75, 125, 175, 225, \ldots$$

gives the amount deducted after n months.
a. Use words to write a recursive definition of the sequence.
b. Write a recursive formula for this sequence using the $\boxed{\text{ANS}}$ key.

Adapting to Individual Needs

Extra Help

Some students who were able to work with recursive formulas in the last lesson may have trouble when they are confronted with the recursive formulas in this lesson. Stress that the exercises in the lesson are basically the same as those in the last lesson. The only difference is the notation used in the formulas. If students are confused by the symbol t_{n-1}, point out that they can replace t_{n-1} with $\boxed{\text{ANS}}$. For instance, in **Example 1** on page 49, the second part of the formula could be written as $t_n = \boxed{\text{ANS}} \boxed{x^2} \boxed{+} 3$ for integers $n \geq 2$.

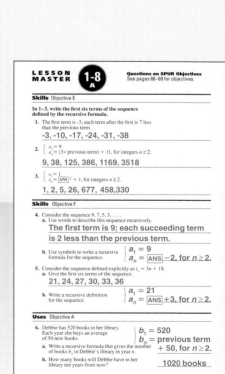

Question 11c Accept all sorts of answers in words, including the phrase "previous term" and the use of $\boxed{\text{ANS}}$.

Question 12 This looks as if it might be the increasing sequence of positive odd numbers starting with 1, but it could be the sequence of units' digits of that sequence, which would repeat 1, 3, 5, 7, 9, 1, 3, 5, 7, 9, ...

Question 16 This is the sequence of triangular numbers.

Solution

a. Identify the first term, and how each term after the first is related to previous terms. **The first term is 25. Each term after the first is found by adding 50 to the previous term.**

b. Translate the words in part **a** into symbols.

$$\begin{cases} t_1 = 25 \\ t_n = \boxed{\text{ANS}} + 50, \text{ for integers } n \geq 2 \end{cases}$$

QUESTIONS

Covering the Reading

In 1 and 2, write the first four terms of the sequence generated by the calculator instructions.

1. Begin with 24; repeatedly press $\boxed{\times}$ 1.5 $\boxed{\text{ENTER}}$ (or $\boxed{\text{EXE}}$).
   24, 36, 54, 81

2. Begin with 4; repeatedly press $\boxed{-}$ 9 $\boxed{\text{ENTER}}$ (or $\boxed{\text{EXE}}$).
   4, -5, -14, -23

In 3 and 4, refer to Activity 1 and the sequence 40, 20, 10, 5, ...

3. Write calculator instructions as in Questions 1 and 2 using multiplication to generate the first four terms.
   Sample: Begin with 40; repeatedly press $\boxed{\times}$ .5 $\boxed{=}$

4. The 10th term of this sequence is .078125. What is the 11th term?
   .0390625

In 5–7, write the first five terms of the sequence defined by the recursive formula.

5. The first term is 7; each term after the first is 10 more than the previous term. **7, 17, 27, 37, 47**

6. $\begin{cases} t_1 = -20 \quad \text{-20, -5, -1.25, -.3125, -.078125} \\ t_n = \frac{1}{4} \cdot \text{ previous term, for integers } n \geq 2 \end{cases}$

7. $\begin{cases} t_1 = 25 \\ t_n = 5 \cdot \boxed{\text{ANS}} + 6, \text{ for integers } n \geq 2 \quad \text{25, 131, 661, 3311, 16,561} \end{cases}$

8. *Multiple choice.* Which rule states that the nth term is seven less than the previous term? **d**
   (a) $t_n = 7 \cdot \boxed{\text{ANS}}$ (b) $t_n = 7 - \boxed{\text{ANS}}$
   (c) $t_n = \boxed{\text{ANS}} + 7$ (d) $t_n = \boxed{\text{ANS}} - 7$

9. Refer to Activity 2. How many terms of the sequence

$$\begin{cases} a_1 = 40 \\ a_n = \dfrac{\boxed{\text{ANS}}}{2}, \text{ for integers } n \geq 2 \end{cases}$$

are greater than 0.1? **9**

10. What is the answer to Activity 3? **1, -2, -8, -20, -44**

LESSON MASTER 1-8 B   Questions on SPUR Objectives

Skills Objective E: Evaluate sequences.

1. The first two terms of a sequence are 2 and 2. Each term after the second is the sum of the previous two terms. Write the next 6 terms. **4, 6, 10, 16, 26, 42**

In 2 and 3, give the first five terms of the sequence defined by the recursive formula.

2. The first term is 100. Each term after the first is one half of the previous term. **100, 50, 25, $\frac{25}{2}$, $\frac{25}{4}$**

3. The first term is -1. Each term after the first is 1 more than the cube of the previous term. **-1, 0, 1, 2, 9**

In 4–7, give the first six terms of the sequence defined by the recursive formula. The formula is given for integers $n \geq 2$.

4. $\begin{cases} s_1 = 5 \\ s_n = \boxed{\text{ANS}} + 6 \end{cases}$ 5. $\begin{cases} a_1 = -8 \\ a_n = \boxed{\text{ANS}} + 2 \end{cases}$
   5, 11, 17, 23, 29, 35   **-8, -6, -4, -2, 0, 2**

6. $\begin{cases} a_1 = 6 \\ a_n = 2 \cdot \boxed{\text{ANS}} \end{cases}$ 7. $\begin{cases} t_1 = 1 \\ t_n = (-1)^n \cdot \boxed{\text{ANS}} \end{cases}$
   6, 12, 24, 48, 96, 192   **1, 1, -1, -1, 1, 1**

In 8 and 9, *multiple choice.*

8. The explicit formula $x_n = 3(4)^{n-1}$ gives the same sequence as which recursive formula for integers $n \geq 2$? **b**
   (a) $\begin{cases} x_1 = 6 \\ x_n = 3 + 3 \cdot \boxed{\text{ANS}} \end{cases}$ (b) $\begin{cases} x_1 = 3 \\ x_n = 4 \cdot \boxed{\text{ANS}} \end{cases}$ (c) $\begin{cases} x_1 = 3 \\ x_n = 3 + 4 \cdot \boxed{\text{ANS}} \end{cases}$

9. Which is a recursive definition for the sequence of squares of integers 1, 4, 9, 16, 25, 36, . . . ? **c**
   (a) $\begin{cases} s_1 = 1 \\ s_n = \boxed{\text{ANS}}^2, \\ \text{for integers } n \geq 2. \end{cases}$ (b) $\begin{cases} s_1 = 1 \\ s_n = \boxed{\text{ANS}} + 3, \\ \text{for integers } n \geq 2. \end{cases}$ (c) $\begin{cases} s_1 = 1 \\ s_n = \boxed{\text{ANS}} + 2n - 1, \\ \text{for integers } n \geq 2. \end{cases}$

Adapting to Individual Needs

English Language Development

You might want to spend some time talking about the words *explicit* and *recursive*. *Explicit* means clear or direct; for example, "To get from school to your house, I need *explicit* directions." In mathematics, an explicit formula is one that gives the term directly. For instance, the formula $t_n = n^2$ gives the nth term in the sequence of square numbers directly once a value for n is substituted.

In English, *recur* means to happen again—a *recurring* letter in the word Mississippi is "s." In mathematics, a recursive formula is one in which each term is derived by applying a condition over and over again. For example, the sequence defined as: "Begin with five and find each term after the first by multiplying the preceding term by 2," applies the condition "multiply by 2" over and over again and generates the sequence 5, 10, 20, 40, ...

11c) Sample:
$$\begin{cases} t_1 = 100 \\ t_n = \text{previous term} - 6, \\ \quad \text{for integers} \\ \quad n \geq 2 \end{cases}$$

13a)
$$\begin{cases} S_1 = 15 \\ S_n = \text{previous term} + 2, \\ \quad \text{for integers} \\ \quad n \geq 2 \end{cases}$$

11. Consider the sequence that begins 100, 94, 88, 82, 76, ...
  a. What is the first term? 100; b) 6 less than
  b. From the second term on, each term is __?__ the previous term.
  c. Write a recursive formula for the sequence. See left.

12. Consider the sequence of odd numbers beginning with 1, 3, 5, 7, 9, ... Write a recursive definition for the sequence in words. The first term is 1. Each new term is the previous term plus 2 for all terms after the first.

Applying the Mathematics

In 13 and 14, suppose that in a movie theater, the first row has 15 seats. Each succeeding row has 2 more seats than the row in front of it.

13. a. Write a recursive formula for a sequence that gives the number of seats S_n in row n. See left.
  b. Find the number of seats in the tenth row. $S_{10} = 33$

14. a. Is the set of ordered pairs of the form (n, S_n) a function? Why or why not? Yes; each value of n corresponds to exactly one value of S.
  b. If this set is a function, what is its domain? the set of natural numbers

15. a. Write the first four terms of the sequence defined by $x_n = 3(4)^{n-1}$.
  b. Write the first four terms of the sequence defined by
$$\begin{cases} y_1 = 3 \\ y_n = 4 \cdot \boxed{\text{ANS}}, \text{ for integers } n \geq 2. \end{cases}$$
  c. *True or false.* The sequences defined in parts **a** and **b** have the same terms. True
  a) 3, 12, 48, 192   b) 3, 12, 48, 192

16. a. Write the first six terms of the sequence defined recursively as
1, 3, 6, 10, 15, 21
$$\begin{cases} t_1 = 1 \\ t_n = \boxed{\text{ANS}} + n, \text{ for integers } n \geq 2. \end{cases}$$
  b. Write the first six terms of the sequence defined explicitly as
1, 3, 6, 10, 15, 21
$$t_n = \frac{n(n+1)}{2}.$$
  c. What do you conclude from your answers to part **a** and part **b**?
  Parts a and b generate the same sequence.

17. Explain in your own words why a recursive formula must have two parts. Sample: A recursive sequence is dependent on previous terms. Therefore, an initial value is needed in order to use the formula.

18. The table at the left gives the postage rate for letters up to 11 ounces in 1995.
  a. Describe in words the sequence that gives the postage for an integer weight of n ounces.
  b. Write a recursive formula for the sequence that gives the postage rate for a letter weighing n ounces.

Sample: $\begin{cases} P_1 = .32 \\ P_n = \text{previous term} + .23, \text{ for integers } n \geq 2 \end{cases}$

a) The rate for 1 ounce of mail is 32¢. Each ounce after that has a rate of 23¢ more than the previous weight.

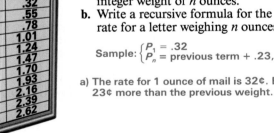

Weight Not Over (oz)	Rate ($/letter)
1	.32
2	.55
3	.78
4	1.01
5	1.24
6	1.47
7	1.70
8	1.93
9	2.16
10	2.39
11	2.62

Lesson 1-8 *Recursive Formulas for Sequences* **53**

Adapting to Individual Needs

Challenge
Have students refer to their answers to **part c** of **Question 29** on page 47; tell them to try to write a recursive formula for the sequences they wrote. [Sample:
1. The numbers on the second diagonal of Pascal's triangle form the sequence 1, 2, 3, 4, 5, ... A formula is:
$$\begin{cases} t_1 = 1 \\ t_n = t_{n-1} + 1, \text{ for integers } n \geq 2. \end{cases}$$

2. The numbers on the third diagonal are 1, 3, 6, 10, 15, ... A formula is:
$$\begin{cases} t_1 = 1 \\ t_n = t_{n-1} + n, \text{ for integers } n \geq 2. \end{cases}$$

3. The numbers on the fourth diagonal are 1, 4, 10, 20, 35, ... A formula is:
$$\begin{cases} t_1 = 1 \\ t_2 = 4 \\ t_n = 2t_{n-1} - t_{n-2} + n, \\ \quad \text{for integers } n \geq 3. \end{cases}$$

Follow-up 1-8 for Lesson

Practice
For more questions on SPUR Objectives, use **Lesson Master 1-8A** (shown on page 51) or **Lesson Master 1-8B** (shown on pages 52–53).

Assessment
Group Assessment Have students **work in small groups** to generate recursive formulas. One student should name the first term of the sequence. The second student should give the second part of a recursive formula that shows how the nth term is generated from the previous term. Then have students take turns generating terms of the sequence after the first term. [Students demonstrate an understanding of recursive formulas by making up formulas and correctly generating terms of a sequence.]

(Follow-up continues on page 54.)

▶ **LESSON MASTER 1-8 B** *page 2*

Skills Objective F: Write a recursive definition for a sequence.
In 10–12, a sequence is given. Write a recursive definition a. in words and b. in symbols.

10. 891, 297, 99, 33, 11, ...
  a. _____ b. _____

11. 1, -5, -11, -17, -23, ...
  a. _____ b. _____

12. 5, 10, 20, 40, 80, ...
  a. _____ b. _____

Uses Objective J: Use sequences to solve real-world problems.

13. Becky invested $5000 in a savings account that pays 4% compounded annually. She plans to withdraw $100 at the end of each year. The recursive formula at the right gives her account balance at the end of the nth year.
$\begin{cases} B_0 = 5000 \\ B_n = 1.04 \cdot \boxed{\text{ANS}} - 100, \\ \quad \text{for integers } n \geq 1 \end{cases}$
  a. Give the account balance at the end of year 1. _____
  b. Give the account balance at the end of year 3. _____
  c. By how much will Becky's investment have increased after 5 years? _____

14. Tim received $20 from his parents on his first birthday, $25 on his second birthday, $30 on his third birthday, and so on.
  a. Write a recursive formula for this situation.
  b. How much did Tim receive on his tenth birthday?
  c. Find the total amount of money Tim's parents had given him for his ten birthdays.

53

Extension

Give each student a copy of **Teaching Aid 12**. In 1–3, each figure is formed by a series of regular polygons. Have students assume that the length of each side of each polygon is 1 and write both explicit and recursive formulas for the sequence of perimeters of the figures. Then have them write a formula for a similar series of hexagons.

1.  [3, 4, 5, . . .]

2. ☐ ☐☐ ☐☐☐ [4, 6, 8, . . .]

3.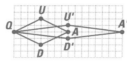

[5, 8, 11, . . .]

[Explicit formulas: triangles: $t_n = n + 2$; squares: $t_n = 2n + 2$; pentagons: $t_n = 3n + 2$; hexagons: $t_n = 4n + 2$.

Recursive formulas:

Triangles: $\begin{cases} t_1 = 3 \\ t_n = \boxed{\text{ANS}} + 1 \\ \quad \text{for integers } n \geq 2 \end{cases}$

Squares: $\begin{cases} t_1 = 4 \\ t_n = \boxed{\text{ANS}} + 2 \\ \quad \text{for integers } n \geq 2 \end{cases}$

Pentagons: $\begin{cases} t_1 = 5 \\ t_n = \boxed{\text{ANS}} + 3 \\ \quad \text{for integers } n \geq 2 \end{cases}$

Hexagons: $\begin{cases} t_1 = 6 \\ t_n = \boxed{\text{ANS}} + 4 \\ \quad \text{for integers } n \geq 2 \end{cases}$]

Notes on Questions

Question 21 Multicultural Connection The largest ethnic group in Peru, the Quechua Indians, accounts for almost half of the population. Other large ethnic groups include the mestizos and the whites; smaller ethnic groups include blacks and Asians.

Shown are students from Santa Ana High School in Cuzco, Peru at the school's 100th anniversary. Cuzco was the capital of the Inca Empire.

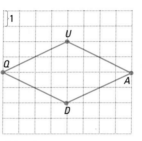

23c) Sample:

Review

19. In the first year of its existence, a company had a gross income of $100,000. Each year, the company hopes to increase its gross income by 50%. The sequence $c_n = 100,000\,(1.5)^{n-1}$ gives the yearly gross income hoped for in year n. *(Lesson 1-7)*
  a. Find c_3. $c_3 = 225{,}000$
  b. What gross income does the company hope to have in the 10th year of its existence?   **$3,844,335.94**

20. The force F required to accelerate a mass of m kilograms a meters per second squared is given by $F = ma$. Here, force is measured in newtons. *(Lessons 1-5, 1-6)*
  a. Solve this formula for a. $a = \dfrac{F}{m}$
  b. If a force of 225 newtons is applied to an object with mass 25 kilograms, what is the acceleration of the object?   **9 m/sec²**

21. The formula $P = 21{,}782 + 450x$ gives an estimate of the population of Peru (in thousands) from 1990 to the year 2025, where x is the number of years after 1990.
  a. Estimate the population of Peru in 2010.   **30,782,000 people**
  b. In what year will the estimated population exceed 29,000,000? *(Lesson 1-2, Previous course)*   **2006**

22. a. Make up a set of five ordered pairs that represents a function.
  b. Make up a set of five ordered pairs that does not represent a function. *(Lesson 1-2)*   Sample: {(2, −2), (1, −1), (0, 0), (1, 1), (2, 2)}
  a) Sample: {(1, 1), (2, 2), (3, 3), (4, 4), (5, 5)}

23. Refer to the quadrilateral at the left. *(Previous course)*
  a. Find its area.   **16 square units**
  b. Find its perimeter. $8\sqrt{5} \approx 17.9$ units
  c. Copy the figure, and on a coordinate grid, draw a quadrilateral that has the same area, but a larger perimeter.   **See left.**

24. Suppose n is an integer.
  a. What is the next larger integer? $n + 1$
  b. What is the next smaller integer? *(Previous course)* $n - 1$

Exploration

25. Consider the sequence defined recursively by

$$\begin{cases} t_1 = 1000 \\ t_n = .5\left(\boxed{\text{ANS}} + \dfrac{a}{\boxed{\text{ANS}}} \right), \text{ for integers } n \geq 2. \end{cases}$$

  a. Suppose $a = 25$. Evaluate the terms of this sequence until all the terms appear to be the same value or close to the same value. This value is called the *limit* of the sequence.   limit = 5
  b. Repeat part **a** with $a = 49$.   limit = 7
  c. Repeat part **a** with $a = 2$.   limit = $\sqrt{2} \approx 1.4$
  d. Use your results from parts **a** through **c** to make a conjecture about what this sequence does.
    Sample: The sequence has a limit of $\sqrt{a}$.

54

The sequence 17, 12, 7, 2, -3, . . . can be defined recursively with words. In words you can write:

> The first term is 17.
> Each term after the first is found by
> subtracting 5 from the previous term.

The equations below generate this sequence on a graphics calculator.

$$\begin{cases} t_1 = 17 \\ t_n = \boxed{\text{ANS}} - 5, \text{ for integers } n \geq 2 \end{cases}$$

❶ You know that the symbol t_n denotes the nth term. The term that precedes the nth term is the $(n-1)$st term. (Think: one less than n is $n-1$.) Thus t_{n-1} denotes the $(n-1)$st term. So the symbol t_{n-1} can be used in place of $\boxed{\text{ANS}}$ to denote the previous term. Thus, the sequence above can also be defined as follows.

$$\begin{cases} t_1 = 17 \\ t_n = t_{n-1} - 5, \text{ for integers } n \geq 2 \end{cases}$$

The next two examples show how to use t_{n-1} in descriptions of sequences.

Example 1

Consider the sequence defined as follows.

$$\begin{cases} t_1 = 60 \\ t_n = 2 \cdot t_{n-1}, \text{ for integers } n \geq 2 \end{cases}$$

a. Describe the sequence in words.
b. Find the first four terms of the sequence.

Solution

a. You need to identify the first term, and the rule for generating all following terms. The statement $t_n = 2 \cdot t_{n-1}$ means that to get t_n, the previous term t_{n-1} must be multiplied by 2. **The first term is 60. Each term after the first is found by multiplying the previous term by 2.**

b. The first term is $t_1 = 60$. To find the next three terms, substitute $n = 2$, 3, and 4 in the rule for t_n.
The second term is t_2. $t_2 = 2 \cdot t_{2-1} = 2t_1 = 2 \cdot 60 = 120$
The third term is t_3. $t_3 = 2 \cdot t_{3-1} = 2t_2 = 2 \cdot 120 = 240$
The fourth term is t_4. $t_4 = 2 \cdot t_{4-1} = 2t_3 = 2 \cdot 240 = 480$
The first four terms of the sequence are 60, 120, 240, 480.

Objectives
E Evaluate sequences.
F Write a recursive definition for a sequence.
J Use functions to solve real-world problems.

Resources
From the *Teacher's Resource File*
■ Lesson Master 1-9A or 1-9B
■ Answer Master 1-9
■ Teaching Aid 3: Warm-up
■ Activity Kit, Activity 2

Additional Resources
■ Visual for Teaching Aid 3

Teaching **1-9**
Lesson

Warm-up
Diagnostic Find the first four terms of the sequence defined by:

$$\begin{cases} t_1 = 50 \\ t_n = 1.05t_{n-1}, \text{ for integers } n \geq 2. \end{cases}$$

50, 52.5, 55.125, 57.88125

Notes on Reading
Example 1 illustrates the use of a sequence whose nth term is completely determined by knowing the previous term. **Example 2** requires not only knowing the previous term but also knowing the place of the term in the sequence. **Example 3** requires knowing the two previous terms.

❶ You might want to discuss the notation in this lesson with the class.

Lesson 1-9 Overview
Broad Goals This lesson introduces the description of recursive formulas using variables in subscripts to represent the previous term or terms.

Perspective Some sequences, such as the sequence of squares 1, 4, 9, 16, 25, . . ., are more easily described with explicit formulas for the nth term—in this case, $s_n = n^2$. Others, such as the Fibonacci sequence noted in this lesson, are more easily

described using recursive formulas. When an early term in a sequence is desired, it is usually easier to use a recursive formula. When looking for a later term in a sequence, using the explicit formula is usually quicker. Computers generally use recursive formulas when they generate sequences.

In Lesson 1-8, the phrase "previous term" and the symbol $\boxed{\text{ANS}}$ represented the term

immediately preceding the nth term in a sequence. One could continue to use this language, but sometimes it is useful to identify the second or third previous term, as in the Fibonacci sequence of **Example 3**. If the sequence is t, then the subscripted variables $t_{n-1}, t_{n-2}, \ldots$ for the "first term preceding n," "the second term preceding n," and so on, are clearer and more succinct.

To show why t_{n-1} stands for the term before t_n, begin by asking the following questions. Suppose t_{17} is a term of a sequence t. What term is this? [The 17th term] What is the term before this one? [t_{16}] What is the term after t_{17}? [t_{18}] Now ask corresponding questions beginning with t_{871}. Write the first two rows in the chart below on the board. Then generalize the pattern—begin by calling the middle term t_n, and ask students to name the term preceding t_{n-1} and the term following t_{n+1}. [t_{n-2} and t_{n+2}]

Previous term	Term	Next term
t_{16}	t_{17}	t_{18}
t_{870}	t_{871}	t_{872}
•	•	•
•	•	•
•	•	•
t_{n-1}	t_n	t_{n+1}

It is difficult for some students to realize that n is a variable which takes on its integer values one at a time and in order. You may have to go through each example of this lesson. Note that t_{n-1} is playing the same role that (previous term) and (ANS) played in Lesson 1-8.

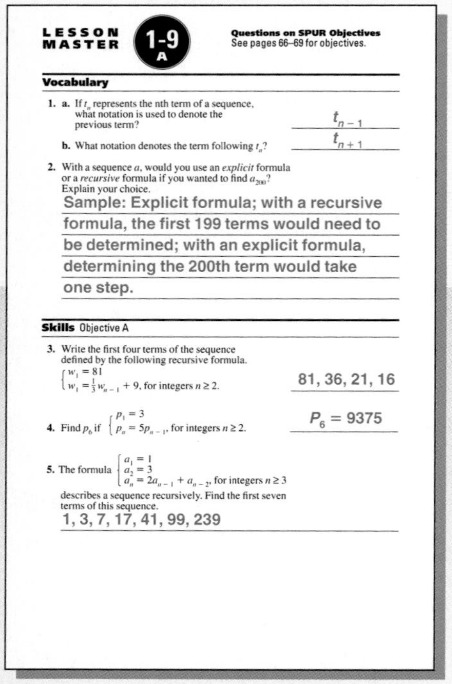

Example 2

Consider the sequence defined recursively as

$$\begin{cases} T_1 = 1 \\ T_n = T_{n-1} + n, \text{ for integers } n \geq 2. \end{cases}$$

Find T_2, T_3, and T_4.

Solution

The first term is $T_1 = 1$. To find T_2, substitute 2 for n in the rule for T_n.
When $n = 2$, $T_2 = T_{2-1} + 2$
$\quad\quad\quad\quad = T_1 + 2$
$\quad\quad\quad\quad = 1 + 2$
$\quad\quad\quad\quad = 3$.

To find T_3, substitute 3 for n in the rule for T_n.
When $n = 3$, $T_3 = T_{3-1} + 3$
$\quad\quad\quad\quad = T_2 + 3$
$\quad\quad\quad\quad = 3 + 3$
$\quad\quad\quad\quad = 6$.

To find T_4, substitute 4 for n in the rule for T_n.
When $n = 4$, $T_4 = T_{4-1} + 4$
$\quad\quad\quad\quad = T_3 + 4$
$\quad\quad\quad\quad = 6 + 4$
$\quad\quad\quad\quad = 10$.

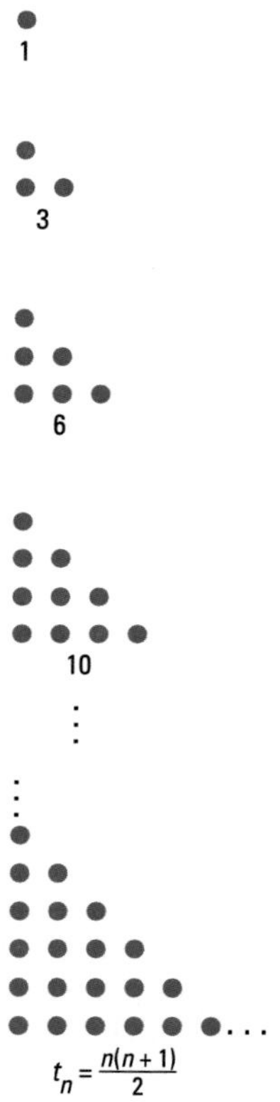

1

3

6

10

$\vdots$

$\vdots$

...

$t_n = \dfrac{n(n+1)}{2}$

Recursive and Explicit Formulas

The recursive formula in Example 2 above generates the terms

$$1, 3, 6, 10, 15, 21, \ldots.$$

These are the triangular numbers, which you studied in Lesson 1-7. There, we found that an explicit formula for this sequence is

$$t_n = \frac{n(n+1)}{2}, \text{ for integers } n \geq 1.$$

Thus, the triangular numbers can be generated both explicitly and recursively.

Recursive and explicit formulas are useful at different times. An explicit formula lets you calculate a specific term without having to calculate all the previous terms. For instance, you can find the 100th triangular number by evaluating

$$t_{100} = \frac{100(100 + 1)}{2} = 5050.$$

You do not need to know any other term of the sequence.

A recursive formula is useful when an explicit formula is not known or when an explicit formula is difficult to determine. The sequence in Example 3 illustrates such a situation. It also shows you how the nth term of a sequence may be described using more than just the previous term.

A male bee develops from an unfertilized egg. That is, a male bee has a mother, but no father. A female bee develops from a fertilized egg. That is, a female bee has both a mother and a father.

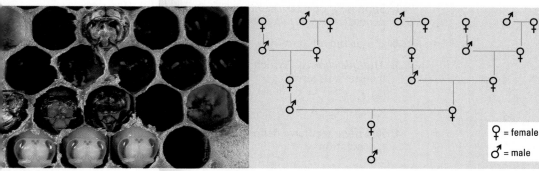

$♀$ = female
$♂$ = male

Honey, I'm home.
Pictured in this honeycomb are honeybee pupae at various stages of development.

The figure above shows the ancestors of a male bee. Counting symbols in each row of the figure from the bottom up, notice that the number of bees in each of the first six generations is 1, 1, 2, 3, 5, 8.

The first two terms are equal to 1. Beginning with the third term, each term is found by adding the previous two terms.
a. Find the 7th term of the sequence.
b. Using a_n to represent the nth term, write a recursive formula for the sequence.

Solution

a. The 7th term is the sum of the two previous terms. So the 7th term is 5 + 8, or 13.

b. If a_n is the nth term, then a_{n-1} is the $(n - 1)$st term, that is, the term before the nth term. The notation a_{n-2} denotes the $(n - 2)$nd term, that is, two terms before the nth term. So a recursive formula is
$$\begin{cases} a_1 = 1 \\ a_2 = 1 \\ a_n = a_{n-1} + a_{n-2}, \text{ for } n \geq 3. \end{cases}$$

Check

Use the formula to generate the first few terms of the sequence.
$a_1 = 1$
$a_2 = 1$
$a_3 = a_{3-1} + a_{3-2} = a_2 + a_1 = 1 + 1 = 2$
$a_4 = a_{4-1} + a_{4-2} = a_3 + a_2 = 2 + 1 = 3$
$a_5 = a_{5-1} + a_{5-2} = a_4 + a_3 = 3 + 2 = 5$
$a_6 = a_{6-1} + a_{6-2} = a_5 + a_4 = 5 + 3 = 8$
The first six terms of the sequence are 1, 1, 2, 3, 5, 8. It checks.

The sequence in Example 3 is called the Fibonacci (pronounced "Fee-boh-NOTCH-ee") sequence. It is named after Leonardo of Pisa who wrote under the name Fibonacci in the 12th century.

Lesson 1-9   *Notation for Recursive Formulas*   **57**

---

② **Science Connection** So-called killer bees were developed in Brazil in the 1950s in an effort to find a hybrid that produced large amounts of honey. In 1957, some of the bees escaped and began moving northward. The bees are not expected to survive much beyond the 34° north latitude.

Additional Examples

1. Consider the sequence defined by the recursive formula:
$$\begin{cases} t_1 = 3 \\ t_n = 2t_{n-1} + 1, \\ \quad \text{for integers } n \geq 2. \end{cases}$$

   a. Describe the sequence in words. **The first term is 3. Each term after the first is found by multiplying the previous term by 2 and adding 1.**

   b. Find the first four terms of the sequence. **3, 7, 15, 31**

2. Find v_1, v_2, v_3, v_4, and v_5 when
$$\begin{cases} v_1 = 15 \\ v_n = v_{n-1} - 4n + 2, \\ \quad \text{for integers } n \geq 2. \end{cases}$$
   15, 9, –1, –15, –33

3. Write the first eight terms of the sequence that is generated by the following formula:
$$\begin{cases} a_1 = 4 \\ a_2 = 7 \\ a_n = 2a_{n-2} - a_{n-1}, \\ \quad \text{for integers } n \geq 3 \end{cases}$$
   4, 7, 1, 13, –11, 37, –59, 133

(Notes on Questions begin on page 60.)

Optional Activities

Activity 1 Technology Connection
After discussing the lesson, you may want to introduce computer programs using explicit and recursive formulas. (Students will see this distinction in Chapter 3 in the context of arithmetic sequences.) Programs that describe the sequence 15, 17, 19, 21, 23 use the two ways shown at the right.

Explicit:
```
10 FOR N = 1 TO 5
20 T = 15 + 2*(N – 1)
30 PRINT T
40 NEXT N
50 END
```

Recursive:
```
10 LET T = 15
20 FOR N =
   1 TO 5
30 PRINT T
40 LET T =
   T + 2
50 NEXT N
60 END
```

Practice

For more questions on SPUR Objectives, use **Lesson Master 1-9A** (shown on pages 56–57) or **Lesson Master 1-9B** (shown on pages 58–59).

Assessment

Written Communication Have students **work in pairs**. Ask each student to make up a first term and a recursive formula for a sequence that uses t_n to represent the nth term and t_{n-1} to represent the term preceding the nth term. Then have students exchange formulas and write the first five terms of his or her partner's sequence. [Students provide meaningful recursive formulas and use the formulas to generate terms of a sequence.]

4) $\begin{cases} t_1 = 15 \\ t_n = 5t_{n-1} + 7, \text{ for} \\ \quad \text{integers } n \geq 2 \end{cases}$

7a) The first term of the sequence is -3. Each term after the first is found by subtracting 4 from the previous term.

Covering the Reading

1. Suppose t_n denotes the nth term of a sequence. What does t_{n-1} denote? **the $(n-1)$st term**

2. If a_n is the nth term of a sequence, what is the previous term? **a_{n-1}**

3. *Multiple choice.* Which rule states that the nth term is five times the previous term? **d**
   (a) $t_n = t_{n-1} - 5$ (b) $t_n = \frac{t_{n-1}}{5}$
   (c) $t_n = t_{n-1} + 5$ (d) $t_n = 5 \cdot t_{n-1}$

4. Rewrite a recursive definition for the sequence below using the t_{n-1} notation. **See left.**
   $\begin{cases} t_1 = 15 \\ t_n = 5 \cdot \boxed{\text{ANS}} + 7, \text{ for integers } n \geq 2 \end{cases}$

5. The first term of a sequence is 5. Each term after the first is found by multiplying the previous term by -3.
   a. Write the first four terms of the sequence. **5, -15, 45, -135**
   b. Let T_n be the nth term of the sequence. Write a recursive definition for this sequence. $\begin{cases} T_1 = 5 \\ T_n = -3T_{n-1}, \text{ for integers } n \geq 2 \end{cases}$

6. Refer to Example 1. Find the fifth and sixth terms of the sequence. $t_5 = 960; \quad t_6 = 1920$

7. Consider the sequence defined recursively by
   $\begin{cases} s_1 = -3 \\ s_n = s_{n-1} - 4, \text{ for integers } n \geq 2. \end{cases}$
   a. Describe the sequence in words. **See left.**
   b. Write the first five terms of the sequence. **-3, -7, -11, -15, -19**

8. a. Refer to Example 2. Use the recursive formula to find T_5. $T_5 = 15$
   b. What explicit formula could you evaluate to find the same term? $T_n = \frac{n(n+1)}{2}$

9. Write the first ten terms of the Fibonacci sequence. **1, 1, 2, 3, 5, 8, 13, 21, 34, 55**

10. Describe a situation that generates the Fibonacci sequence. **Sample: a family tree of bees**

"This must be Fibonacci's."

58

Optional Activities

Activity 2
You may want to use *Activity Kit, Activity 2* as either a lead-in or a follow-up to the lesson. In this activity, students use markers to model a classic problem that generates the Fibonacci Sequence.

In 11 and 12, write the first five terms of the sequence.

11. $\begin{cases} t_1 = 3 \\ t_n = 7 \cdot t_{n-1} + 4, \text{ for integers } n \geq 2 \end{cases}$ 3, 25, 179, 1257, 8803

12. $\begin{cases} s_1 = 5 \\ s_n = s_{n-1} + s_{n-1}, \text{ for integers } n \geq 2 \end{cases}$ 5, 10, 20, 40, 80

Applying the Mathematics

13. Consider the sequence 3, 14, 25, 36, 47, ...
    a. Describe the sequence in words. **See left.**
    b. Write a recursive definition for this sequence. $\begin{cases} t_1 = 3 \\ t_n = t_{n-1} + 11, \text{ for all} \\ \qquad n \geq 2 \end{cases}$

14. Consider the sequence defined recursively as
    $\begin{cases} a_1 = 1 \\ a_2 = 3 \\ a_n = a_{n-1} + 2a_{n-2}, \text{ for integers } n \geq 3. \end{cases}$
    a. Describe the sequence in words. **See left.**
    b. Write the first five terms of the sequence.
       1, 3, 5, 11, 21

15. Consider the sequence defined as follows.
    $\begin{cases} t_1 = 100 \\ t_n = t_{n-1} + n, \text{ for integers } n \geq 2. \end{cases}$
    a. Write the first five terms of the sequence. 100, 102, 105, 109, 114
    b. How is this sequence related to the sequence of triangular numbers? **See left.**

16. A dairy farmer wants to build a herd of dairy cows. The first year the farmer has 100 cows. Each year the farmer wants to increase the herd by 10%.
    a. Write a recursive definition that describes the sequence giving the number of cows c_n in year n. **See left.**
    b. In how many years will the farmer have more than 400 cows?
       in 15 years

17. The Lucas sequence begins with 1 and 3. After that, each term is the sum of the two preceding terms. The first six Lucas numbers are 1, 3, 4, 7, 11, 18.
    a. Write the next four Lucas numbers 29, 47, 76, 123
    b. Let L_n be the nth Lucas number. Write a recursive formula for the Lucas numbers. $\begin{cases} L_1 = 1 \\ L_2 = 3 \\ L_n = L_{n-2} + L_{n-1}, \text{ for integers } n \geq 3 \end{cases}$

Review

18. A sequence to be evaluated by a graphics calculator is defined as
    $\begin{cases} t_1 = 2 \\ t_n = 5 \cdot \boxed{\text{ANS}}, \text{ for integers } n \geq 2. \end{cases}$
    a. Write the first five terms of the sequence. 2, 10, 50, 250, 1250
    b. What is the first term that is greater than 10^5? *(Lesson 1-8)*
       8th term

13a) The first term is 3. Each term after the first is found by adding 11 to the previous term.

14a) The first term is 1 and the second term is 3. Each term after the second is found by adding the previous term to two times the term before the previous one.

15b) Sample: If 99 is subtracted from each term, the result is the triangular number sequence.

16a) $\begin{cases} c_1 = 100 \\ c_n = 1.1(c_{n-1}), \text{ for} \\ \qquad \text{integers } n \geq 2 \end{cases}$

Extension

In this lesson, we define the nth term by using previous terms. However, it is also very common in mathematics to define the $(n + 1)$st term using previous terms. For instance, the Fibonacci sequence can be defined as $a_1 = 1$, $a_2 = 1$, and $a_{n+1} = a_n + a_{n-1}$ for $n \geq 2$. If your students are comfortable with subscript notation, have them examine and redefine the other sequences of the lesson in this way.

Project Update Project 4, *Sums and Squares of Fibonacci Numbers*, and Project 5, *Applications of Fibonacci Numbers*, on page 62, relate to the content of this lesson.

Adapting to Individual Needs

Extra Help
To help students understand the subscript notation used in this lesson, you might identify each term in the sequence in the opening paragraph as follows:

17, 12, 7, 2, –3, . . .
$t_1, \ t_2, \ t_3, \ t_4, \ t_5, \ . . . , \ t_n$

Ask what t_n refers to when $n = 5$. [–3] Ask what t_{n-1} and t_{n-2} refer to. [2, 7] Ask what t_1 refers to. [17]

English Language Development
Suggest that students check the vocabulary list on page 63 and write all of the new terms introduced in this chapter on index cards. Then you might pair students with limited English proficiency with English-speaking classmates and suggest that they review the vocabulary together.

59

Notes on Questions

Question 26 This question reviews the distance and midpoint formulas that students should have studied in a previous course. Since these formulas are used frequently in later lessons, it is worthwhile to spend some time using them now. Point out that the midpoint formula does nothing more than average the coordinates of the endpoints of a segment. It is often easier for students to recall the concept of averaging to find the coordinates of a midpoint than to remember a formula. In a similar fashion, it is helpful to stress the Pythagorean nature of the distance formula. This can be done by deriving the distance formula with the use of the Pythagorean Theorem. These two formulas can be found in Appendix B at the back of the book.

19a) $a_4 = 40$; This means after 4 weeks, Antonio has $40.00 in his account.

19. Antonio opens a savings account. He puts in $10 per week. So, the formula $a_n = 10n$ gives the amount in his account after n weeks.
  a. Evaluate a_4, and explain what it means. See left.
  b. Which term of the sequence is 500? *(Lessons 1-5, 1-7)* 50th term

20. A formula for the area of a triangle is $A = \frac{1}{2}bh$. *(Lesson 1-6)*
  a. Solve for b. $b = \frac{2A}{h}$
  b. Suppose the area of a triangle is 147 square centimeters. Determine the length of the base if the height measures seven centimeters. 42 cm

21. The formula $P = \frac{nRT}{V}$ is used in chemistry. Solve this formula
  a. for V. $V = \frac{nRT}{P}$
  b. for T. *(Lesson 1-6)* $T = \frac{PV}{nR}$

22. Solve and check. $4c - (5c - 1) = 7$ *(Lesson 1-5)*
  $c = -6$; $4(-6) - (5(-6) - 1) = 7$? $-24 + 31 = 7$? Yes, it checks.

23. Refer to the graph at the left. State **a.** the domain, and **b.** the range of this relation. *(Lesson 1-4)* a) {x: 0 ≤ x ≤ 50} b) {y: 10 ≤ y ≤ 80}

In 24 and 25, let $m: x \to 2|x| + 3$. *(Lessons 1-2, 1-3)*

24. **a.** $m: 3 \to$ _?_ 9
  b. $m: -2 \to$ _?_ 7
  c. $m: 0 \to$ _?_ 3

25. State the domain of m. the set of all real numbers

26. Recall that the distance between two points with coordinates (x_1, y_1) and (x_2, y_2) is $\sqrt{(x_2 - x_1)^2 + (y_2 - y_1)^2}$, and the midpoint of the line segment joining them has coordinates $\left(\frac{x_1 + x_2}{2}, \frac{y_1 + y_2}{2}\right)$.
  a. Find the distance between (-4, -7) and (8, -2). 13
  b. Find the coordinates of the midpoint of the line segment with endpoints (-4, -7) and (8, -2). *(Previous course)* $\left(2, -\frac{9}{2}\right)$

Exploration

27. The formula
$$t_n = \frac{\left(\frac{1 + \sqrt{5}}{2}\right)^n - \left(\frac{1 - \sqrt{5}}{2}\right)^n}{\sqrt{5}}$$
is an explicit formula for the Fibonacci sequence.
  a. Use a calculator to give the value of t_n when $n = 1, 2, 3, 4,$ and 5.
  b. Does this formula generate the same terms as the recursive definition given in Example 3? Yes
  c. Which formula for the sequence do you prefer? Why do you prefer it? Answers may vary. Sample: The recursive definition is easier to enter into a calculator.

  a) $t_1 = 1$; $t_2 = 1$; $t_3 = 2$; $t_4 = 3$; $t_5 = 5$

Adapting to Individual Needs

Challenge
Ask students to write explicit and recursive formulas for $n!$ using the multiplication symbol but not the factorial symbol.
[Explicit: $a_n = n \cdot (n - 1) \cdot (n - 2) \ldots 3 \cdot 2 \cdot 1$

Recursive: $\begin{cases} a_1 = 1 \\ a_n = n \cdot a_{n-1} \\ \quad \text{for integers } n \geq 2 \end{cases}$]

PROJECTS
CHAPTER ONE

A project presents an opportunity for you to extend your knowledge of a topic related to the material of this chapter. You should allow more time for a project than you do for typical homework questions.

1 Values over Time
Recall that the chapter opener describes the values of *The Death of Superman* comic over time. Find another object whose value fluctuates up and down, for instance, a classic car or a share of stock. Track the value of that object over a reasonable domain. Record the values in a table and a graph. Write a paragraph explaining what might cause the value to fluctuate.

1957 Bel-Air

2 Functions and Graphs in the Newspaper
Use a newspaper that is published daily. Read it for several days.
a. Find 6 to 8 graphs you think are interesting. Look for a variety of subjects and shapes of graphs.
b. Tell whether each graph represents a function. Identify its domain and range. Make up at least one question that can be answered by the graph.

3 Temperature Formulas
In Lesson 1-6, a formula is given relating temperatures measured in the Celsius and Fahrenheit scales. In *War and Peace*, Leo Tolstoy describes a calm frost measured in "degrees Réaumur."
a. Find out when and where the Réaumur scale was used.
b. Find formulas relating degrees Réaumur to each of degrees Fahrenheit and degrees Celsius.
c. Explain how to use the formulas to compare the freezing and boiling points of water on each of these three scales.

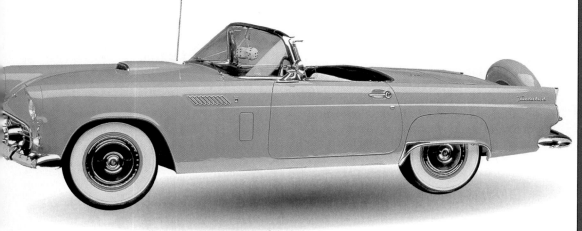

1956 Thunderbird

Chapter 1 *Projects* **61**

Chapter 1 Projects
Discuss Chapter 1 projects and what you expect students to do with them. For more information about how projects can be incorporated into the mathematics program, see *General Teaching Suggestions: Projects* in the *Professional Sourcebook* which begins on page T20 in Part 1 of the Teacher's Edition.

Chapter 1 projects relate to the content of the lessons as shown below. they can, however, be used at any time after the lessons have been taught. Suggestions for using a project are given in the lesson notes under *Project Update*.

Project	Lesson(s)
1	1-1, 1-2, 1-4
2	1-4
3	1-6
4	1-9
5	1-7
6	1-7

1 Values over Time
Students should be sure that the objects they select are ones for which information will be easy to obtain. The price of a share of stock is easy to track since the data appears in many daily newspapers. Prices of used computers are tracked but only change once a month.

2 Functions and Graphs in the Newspaper
Encourage students to identify the types of graphs they find (vertical bar graphs, horizontal bar graphs, line graphs, broken line graphs, and so on). They should cut out the graphs they select so that the comments and questions they write will be meaningful to the people reading them.

3 Temperature Formulas
Students may find information about the Réaumur thermometer and its inventor in encyclopedias, in books about scientific instruments, or in history of science books. Formulas relating the Réaumur scale to the Fahrenheit and Celsius scales may be hard to find, but students should be able to develop them for themselves.

Possible Responses
1. Responses will vary and will depend on the object whose value students track. Check to see that students gathered data for regular time intervals. If they use a broken-scale graph, the graph should clearly show that this is the case. A sample graph that tracks closing stock quotations for McDonald's Corporation for one month is shown on page 62. Since there is no trading on Saturdays and Sundays, the Friday's quote is carried over to Monday. Reasons for fluctuations will vary; for instance, the market may react favorably or unfavorably to an announcement that McDonald's is expanding into a foreign market.

(Responses continue on page 62.)

4 Sums of Squares of Fibonacci Numbers Some students may miss the pattern by trying to fill in columns. Suggest that they look at the table one row at a time. Students can check their conjectures by using the explicit formula for the Fibonacci sequence given in Exercise 27 of Lesson 1-9.

5 Applications of Fibonacci Numbers Students may need some direction in locating references for this topic. They can always use encyclopedias. Your school library's mathematics collection may contain *A Source Book of Mathematical Discovery* by Lorraine Mottershead, Dale Seymour Publications, Palo Alto, CA. Other books include *Fascinating Fibonaccis* by Trudi Hammel Garland, Dale Seymour Publications, 1981, *Fibonacci and Lucas Numbers,* by Verner E. Hoggatt, Jr., Houghton Mifflin, 1969, *Fibonacci Numbers,* by N. N. Vorob'ev, Blaisdell Press, 1961, and *An Introduction to Fibonacci Discovery,* by Brother U. Alfred, The Fibonacci Association, San Jose State University, 1965.

6 Pascal's Triangle Revisited Students can use graph paper and make staggered squares, as shown in the text and then write the numbers in these squares. The task of generating numbers in Pascal's triangle can become tedious as more and more rows are added. You may want to let students calculate the numbers by running the following program. (This program is for the TI-82 graphics calculator.) When students run the program they will be asked to enter a row number; after they enter that number, they should press [ENTER] until they have all of the numbers.

```
PASTRI
: O → B
: Disp "ROW NUMBER"
: Input A
: L6/1
: If B ≤ A
: Then
: Disp AₙCᵣB
: Pause
: B + 1 → B
: Go to 1
```

(continued)

4 Sums of Squares of Fibonacci Numbers
The Fibonacci sequence, 1, 1, 2, 3, 5, 8, 13, 21, . . . , defined in Lesson 1-9, has many interesting properties. One involves the sums of the squares of the Fibonacci numbers.
a. Copy and finish the table below:

$$
\begin{aligned}
F_1^2 &= & 1^2 &= 1 = 1 \times 1 \\
F_1^2 + F_2^2 &= & 1 + 1^2 &= 2 = 1 \times 2 \\
F_1^2 + F_2^2 + F_3^2 &= & 2 + 2^2 &= 6 = 2 \times 3 \\
F_1^2 + F_2^2 + F_3^2 + F_4^2 &= & 6 + 3^2 &= 15 = 3 \times \underline{\ \ } \\
F_1^2 + F_2^2 + F_3^2 + F_4^2 + F_5^2 &= & 15 + 5^2 &= \underline{\ \ } = \underline{\ \ } \times \underline{\ \ } \\
F_1^2 + F_2^2 + F_3^2 + F_4^2 + F_5^2 + F_6^2 &= & \underline{\ \ } + \underline{\ \ } &= \underline{\ \ } = \underline{\ \ } \times \underline{\ \ }
\end{aligned}
$$

b. Look at the pattern in the two columns containing factors of the sum. What sequence do you see in the columns?
c. Make a conjecture in words about the sum of the squares of the first *n* Fibonacci numbers:

$$F_1^2 + F_2^2 + F_3^2 + \ldots + (F_{n-1})^2 + (F_n)^2 = \underline{\ \ } \times \underline{\ \ }.$$

d. Write the conjecture in symbols, so each product on the right side is in terms of Fibonacci numbers.
e. Examine the sum of the squares of any two consecutive Fibonacci numbers $(F_{n-1})^2 + (F_n)^2$. Make a table, look for a pattern, and make a conjecture about this sum.

5 Applications of Fibonacci Numbers
The Fibonacci numbers 1, 1, 2, 3, 5, 8, 13, 21, . . . occur naturally in many contexts. One, the family tree of a male bee, is described in Lesson 1-9. Look in reference books to find some other places where Fibonacci numbers occur, and prepare a report on what you find.

6 Pascal's Triangle Revisited
In the Exploration of Lesson 1-7, diagonals of Pascal's triangle were investigated. Here we look at the pattern that even and odd numbers form in the triangle.
a. Copy the first six rows of Pascal's triangle, identifying each even number as shown below.

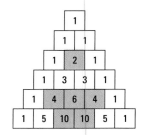

b. Continue writing rows of the triangle until you have completed a minimum of 15 rows.
c. Shade in all squares with even numbers. What patterns do you see?
d. One pattern of even numbers is associated with a Polish mathematician named Sierpinski. Find out when this mathematician lived, and what some of his mathematical work involved.

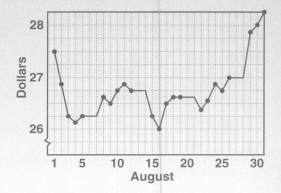

Additional Responses, page 61.
Graph tracking McDonald's Corporation stocks.

SUMMARY

The language of algebra uses numbers and variables. These are combined in expressions. Two expressions connected with a verb make up a sentence.

Formulas are equations stating that a single variable is equal to an expression with one or more variables on the other side. Formulas are evaluated or rewritten using the rules for order of operations.

A function is a correspondence between two variables in which each value of the independent variable corresponds to exactly one value of the dependent variable. If a function is defined as a set of ordered pairs, each first coordinate is paired with exactly one second coordinate. The domain of a function is the set of possible values for the independent variable,

while the range is the set of values obtained for the dependent variable.

Functions are often named by a single letter. The mapping notation $f: x \rightarrow x + 20$, Euler's notation $f(x) = x + 20$, and the formula $y = x + 20$ all describe the same function. When a function is graphed, no vertical line will intersect the graph in more than one point.

A sequence is a function whose domain is the set of natural numbers. Sequences may be defined explicitly or recursively. With an explicit formula, the nth term can be calculated directly from n. With a recursive formula, the nth term is calculated from one or more previous terms. Recursive formulas can be evaluated easily on a graphics calculator by using the $\boxed{\text{ANS}}$ key.

VOCABULARY

Below are the most important terms and phrases for this chapter.
You should be able to give a general description and a specific example of each and a precise definition for those marked with an asterisk (*).

Lesson 1-1
*variable
algebraic expression
expression
algebraic sentence
evaluating an expression
order of operations
*formula, equation

Lesson 1-2
*function
*independent variable
*dependent variable
is a function of
*domain of a function
*range of a function
input, output
*natural numbers
*counting numbers
*whole numbers
*integers
rational numbers
real numbers

Lesson 1-3
*$f(x)$ notation
argument of a function
values of a function
arrow, or mapping, notation

Lesson 1-4
relation
Vertical-Line Test

Lesson 1-5
Distributive Property
"clearing" fractions
Opposite of a Sum Theorem

Lesson 1-6
solved for a variable
in terms of
pitch

Lesson 1-7
*sequence
term of a sequence
triangular numbers
*explicit formula
subscript
subscripted variable
index
generate the terms of a
    sequence

Lesson 1-8
*recursive formula
recursive definition
$\boxed{\text{ANS}}$ key

Lesson 1-9
Fibonacci sequence

Chapter 1 *Summary and Vocabulary* **63**

Summary
The Summary gives an overview of the entire chapter and provides an opportunity for students to consider the material as a whole. Thus, the Summary can be used to help students relate and unify the concepts presented in the chapter.

Vocabulary
Terms, symbols, and properties are listed by lesson to provide a checklist of concepts a student must know. Emphasize to students that they should read the vocabulary list carefully before starting the Progress Self-Test. If students do not understand the meaning of a term, they should refer back to the indicated lesson.

---

2. Graphs, classifications, and questions will vary. Make sure students correctly identify the type of graph and that the questions they ask are relevant to the situation described.

3a. The Réaumur scale was devised by French physicist, René Antoine Ferchault de Réaumur (1683–1757). His spirit (instead of mercury) thermometer was used in Europe and Russia. On the Réaumur scale 0° and 80° correspond to the freezing and boiling points of water respectively.

b. The freezing and boiling points of water are 0°C and 100°C, so the formula $R = 0.8C$ can be used to convert degrees Celsius to degrees Réaumur. From $R = 0.8C$, students can find $C = 1.25R$. Then, using $C = 1.25R$ and $F = 1.8C + 32$ (or $F = \frac{9}{5}C + 32$), students can find that $F = \frac{9}{4}R + 32$ and $R = \frac{4}{9}(F - 32)$.

(Responses continue on page 64.)

Progress Self-Test

For the development of mathematical competence, feedback and correction, along with the opportunity to practice, are necessary. The Progress Self-Test provides the opportunity for feedback and correction; the Chapter Review provides additional opportunities and practice. We cannot overemphasize the importance of these end-of-chapter materials. It is at this point that the material "gels" for many students, allowing them to solidify skills and understanding. In general, student performance should be markedly improved after these pages.

Assign the Progress Self-Test as a one-night assignment. Worked-out *solutions* for all questions are in the Selected Answers section of the student book. Encourage students to take the Progress Self-Test honestly, grade it themselves, and then be prepared to discuss the test in class.

Advise students to pay special attention to those Chapter Review questions (pages 66–69) that correspond to questions missed on the Progress Self-Test.

Additional Answers

17. Yes, it is a function because each x-value corresponds to only one y-value.

18. No, since $x = 1$ corresponds to $y = 1$ and $y = -1$, it is not a function.

19. $\begin{cases} a_1 = 20 \\ a_n = a_{n-1} + 10, \\ \qquad \text{for integers } n \geq 2 \end{cases}$

PROGRESS SELF-TEST

Take this test as you would take a test in class. Then check your work with the solutions in the Selected Answers section in the back of the book. **1) 12, 19, 26, 33   2a) 5, 12, 19, 26**

In 1–4, use the two sequences defined here.

Sequence A Sequence B

$t_n = 5 + 7n$ $\begin{cases} S_1 = 5 \\ S_n = S_{n-1} + 7, \\ \qquad \text{for integers } n \geq 2 \end{cases}$

1. Write the first four terms of sequence A.
2. **a.** Write the first four terms of sequence B.
   b. Give a recursive definition of sequence B in words. **See below.**
3. Find t_8. **61**
4. Calculate S_8. **54**
5. If $f(x) = 9x^2 - 11x$, find $f(3)$. **48**
6. Suppose $T: n \rightarrow \dfrac{n(n+1)}{2}$. Then $T(12) = \underline{\ ?\ }$. **78**
7. *Multiple choice.* Which equation below is solved for d? **b**
   (a) $2A = d_1 d_2$ (b) $d = rt$
   (c) $d^2 = (x_1 - x_2)^2 + (y_1 - y_2)^2$
8. Suppose you travel 12 miles in t hours. Write a formula that gives your speed s in miles per hour. $s = \frac{12}{t}$ **miles per hour**

In 9–11, solve.

9. $4(3x - 8) = 11$ $x = \frac{43}{12}$
10. $1.7y = 0.9 + 0.5y$ $y = .75$
11. $.12p + .08(15,000 - p) = 1480$ $p = 7000$
13) **The set of positive real numbers**

In 12–14, use the formula $V = \frac{1}{3}\pi r^2 h$ for the volume of a cone.

12. Find the volume of the cone at the right to the nearest cubic centimeter. **101 cm³**

13. What is a reasonable domain for r? **See above.**

14. Rewrite this equation for h in terms of V and r. $h = \frac{3V}{\pi r^2}$

2b) **The first term is 5. Each term after the first is found by adding 7 to the previous term.**

64

---

15. A function f contains only the points $(1, 2)$, $(3, 4)$, and $(5, 6)$. Find its domain and range. **domain: {1, 3, 5};   range: {2, 4, 6}**

16. Refer to the graphs below. Which are graphs of functions? **b; c; d**

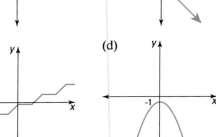

(a)   (b)

(c)   (d)

In 17 and 18, determine whether the relation is a function. Justify your answer. **See margin.**

17. $\{(95, -5), (4, 4), (5, 5)\}$

18.

x	0	1	1	2	2
y	0	1	-1	1.4	-1.4

(Consider x to be the independent variable.)

19. Cherlyn's grandparents gave her $20 on her first birthday, $30 on her second, $40 on her third, and so on, increasing by $10 each year. Let a_n = the amount received on her nth birthday. Write a recursive formula to describe this situation. **See margin.**

20. Consider the equation $\frac{1}{2}z + \frac{1}{5}z + 90 = z$.
    a. Solve for z. $z = 300$
    b. Make up a question about a real situation that could be answered by solving this equation. **Sample: Mary spent $\frac{1}{2}$ of her money on clothes, $\frac{1}{5}$ of it on groceries, and had $90 left. How much did she originally have?**

Additional responses, pages 61–62

c. Using the Celsius freezing and boiling points, 0°C and 100°C, in $R = 0.8C$ and $F = 1.8C + 32$ gives the freezing and boiling points on the Réaumur and Fahrenheit scales: 0°R and 80°R and 32°F and 212°F.

4a. The numbers that complete lines 4–6 of the table are:
Line 4: $6 + 3^2 =$ $15 = 3 \times$ 3
Line 5: $15 + 5^2 =$ $40 = 5 \times$ 8
Line 6: $40 + 8^2 = 104 = 8 \times 13$
b. Reading down the first column of factors gives the full Fibonacci sequence. Reading down the second column of factors gives the Fibonacci sequence starting with the second term.

c. The sum of the squares of the first n Fibonacci numbers is the product of the numbers n and $n + 1$ in the sequence.
d. $F_1^2 + F_2^2 + \ldots + F_n^2 = F_n \times F_{n+1}$.
e. The first five rows of the table are shown at the right.

PROGRESS SELF-TEST

21. The function $P(L) = 2\pi \sqrt{\frac{L}{g}}$, with $g =$ 9.8 m/sec² gives the period of a pendulum as a function of its length L. Find the period of a pendulum with length 1 meter to the nearest second. ≈ **2 seconds**

22. A reading program at an elementary school encourages children to read books. When a class reads 250 books, the entire class gets a pizza party. Suppose a class reads an average of 45 books a week. Then the equation $45w = B$ gives the number B of books read after w weeks. If this reading trend continues, after how many weeks will the class deserve a pizza party?
after about 6 weeks

In 23–25, refer to the graph below which shows the enrollment in public and private high schools (grades 9–12) and colleges in the U.S. from 1970 to 1990 and projected through the year 2000. Let $H(x) =$ the high school enrollment and $C(x) =$ the college enrollment during the years 1970 to 2000.

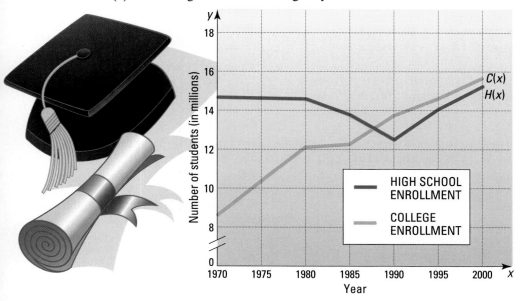

23. Estimate $C(1975)$ and describe what this value represents. ≈ **10.3 million**
24. Estimate the solution to $H(x) = C(x)$, and explain what the solution means.
25. What is the domain of the function H? {x: 1970 ≤ x ≤ 2000, where x is an integer}
23) Approximately 10.3 million students were enrolled in college in 1975.
24) 1988;   In 1988, the number of students enrolled in college was equal to the number of students enrolled in high school.

Row 1: $F_1{}^2 + F_2{}^2 = 1 + 1 = 2$
Row 2: $F_2{}^2 + F_3{}^2 = 1 + 4 = 5$
Row 3: $F_3{}^2 + F_4{}^2 = 4 + 9 = 13$
Row 4: $F_4{}^2 + F_5{}^2 = 9 + 25 = 34$
Row 5: $F_5{}^2 + F_6{}^2 = 25 + 64 = 89$
Conjecture:
$(F_n)^2 + (F_{n+1})^2 = F_{2n+1}$
5. Responses may vary. Samples are: Fibonacci sequences occur often in nature. For example, the small

flowers emanating from the center of a daisy form two sets of spirals, one set spiraling in a clockwise direction and the other in a counter-clockwise direction. In a daisy, the number of spirals in each set are in the fixed ratio 21:34, which are two adjacent Fibonacci numbers. Sets of spirals in opposing directions also occur in the scales of a pineapple and in the scales of a pine cone.

Again, the numbers are adjacent Fibonacci numbers. The shell of the nautilus mollusk is made up of a spiral of chambers. Beginning from the center, the mollusk builds larger and larger chambers as it grows, and a spiral curve whose sides have lengths equivalent to the Fibonacci sequence can be drawn.

(Responses continue on page 68.)

Chapter 1 Review

Resources

From the Teacher's Resource File
- Answer Master for Chapter 1 Review
- Assessment Sourcebook: Chapter 1 Test, Forms A–D

Additional Resources
- Quiz and Test Writer

The main objectives for the chapter are organized in the Chapter Review under the four types of understanding this book promotes–Skills, Properties, Uses, and Representations.

Skills include simple and complicated procedures for getting answers as well as the study of algorithms.

Properties cover the mathematical justifications for procedures and other theories as well as the writing of proofs.

Uses include real-world applications of the mathematics along with the modeling of real situations.

Representations include graphs and diagrams along with the invention of other metaphors to describe the mathematics.

To the *lay person* basic understanding of mathematics is usually found in Skills. The *mathematician* prefers to think of understanding in terms of Properties. The *engineer* often tests understanding by the ability to Use mathematics. The *psychologist* often views "true" understanding as being achieved through Representations or metaphors. The SPUR framework conveys the authors' views that all of these views have validity, and that together they contribute to the deep understanding of mathematics which we want students to have.

CHAPTER REVIEW

Questions on SPUR Objectives

SPUR stands for **S**kills, **P**roperties, **U**ses, and **R**epresentations. The Chapter Review questions are grouped according to the SPUR Objectives for this chapter.

SKILLS DEAL WITH THE PROCEDURES USED TO GET ANSWERS.

Objective A: *Evaluate expressions and formulas, including correct units in answers.* (Lessons 1-1, 1-2)

1. In the formula $d = \frac{n(n-3)}{2}$, find d when $n = 17$. **119**

2. If $d = \frac{1}{2}gt^2$, find d when $g = 32$ ft/sec^2 and $t = 2.5$ sec. **100 ft**

3. Evaluate $20{,}000(.9)^n$ to the nearest hundredth when $n = 10$. **6973.57**

4. Evaluate $2^{n-1} + (n-1)^2$ when $n = 4$. **17**

Objective B: *Use function notation.* (Lesson 1-3)

5. If $f(x) = 2x - 3$, what is $f(4)$? **5** 6) **-11**

6. Suppose $t: n \rightarrow 5 - 4n^2$. Then $t: -2 \rightarrow$ __?__.

7. Let $h: a \rightarrow a^5$. Then $h: -3 \rightarrow$ __?__. **-243**

8. If $M(x) = 3x^2 + 4$, then $M(2k) =$ __?__. **$12k^2 + 4$**

9. If the following table defines the function g, find $g(5)$ and $g(6)$. **$g(5) = 11$; $g(6) = 13$**

x	1	2	3	4	5	6
$g(x)$	3	5	7	9	11	13

10. This table defines the function p. Find $p(-1)$.

a	-2	-1	0	1	2
$p(a)$	7	16	4	-6	-1

$p(-1) = 16$

Objective C: *Solve and check linear equations.* (Lesson 1-5)

In 11–18, solve and check. **See margin for checks.**

11. $\frac{3}{2}x = 9$ **6**

12. $\frac{3}{10}(t - 20) = \frac{6}{5}$ **24**

13. $\frac{6}{U} = 8$ **$\frac{3}{4}$**

14. $4 = 6a - (2 - 2a)$ **$\frac{3}{4}$**

15. $3 - (m + 2) = 4m$ **$\frac{1}{5}$**

16. $.05(4500 - x) + .08x = 1200$ **32,500**

17. $\frac{x}{2} + \frac{x}{3} + 10 = x$ **60**

18. $3y - 2(y + 5) = 10y$ **$\frac{-10}{9}$**

66

---

19) $n = \frac{t-4}{-5}$

Objective D: *Rewrite formulas.* (Lesson 1-6)

19. Solve for n in the formula $t = 4 - 5n$.

20. The measure θ of an exterior angle of a regular polygon is given by $\theta = \frac{360}{n}$ where n is the number of sides. Solve for n in terms of θ. **$n = \frac{360}{\theta}$**

21. Recall the formula $d = \frac{1}{2}gt^2$. What is the ratio of d to t^2? **$\frac{g}{2}$**

22. If $x = 3y$, then $\frac{x}{y} =$ __?__. **$\frac{3}{1}$**

23. Which equation(s) is (are) solved for t?
   (a) $t = \frac{D}{R}$ (b) $10t - 5t^2 = h$ **a;**
   (c) $A = \frac{1}{2}ht$ (d) $180(n - 2) = t$ **d**

24. The area A of a trapezoid is given by $A = \frac{1}{2}h(b_1 + b_2)$. Solve this equation for h. **$h = \frac{2A}{b_1 + b_2}$**

Objective E: *Evaluate sequences.* (Lessons 1-7, 1-8, 1-9)

In 25–28, write the first five terms of the sequence.

25. $t_n = 20 + 3n$, for integers $n \geq 1$ **23, 26, 29, 32, 35**

26. $s_n = n^2 - 1$ **0, 3, 8, 15, 24**

27. $\begin{cases} t_1 = 10 \\ t_n = t_{n-1} - 7, \text{ for integers } n \geq 2 \end{cases}$ **10, 3, -4, -11, -18**

28. $\begin{cases} a_1 = 2 \\ a_n = -2 + 3a_{n-1}, \text{ for integers } n \geq 2 \end{cases}$ **2, 4, 10, 28, 82**

Additional Answers

11. 6; $\frac{3}{2}(6) = 9$? **Yes, it checks.**

12. 24; $\frac{3}{10}(24 - 20) = \frac{3}{10} \cdot 4 = \frac{6}{5}$; **It checks.**

13. $\frac{3}{4}$; $\frac{6}{\frac{3}{4}} = 8$? $6 \cdot \frac{4}{3} = 8$? **Yes, it checks.**

14. $\frac{3}{4}$; $4 = 6(\frac{3}{4}) - (2 - 2(\frac{3}{4}))$? $4 = \frac{9}{2} - (2 - \frac{3}{2})$? $4 = \frac{9}{2} - \frac{1}{2} = 4$? **Yes, it checks.**

15. $\frac{1}{5}$; $3 - (\frac{1}{5} + 2) = 4(\frac{1}{5})$? $3 - \frac{11}{5} = \frac{4}{5}$? **Yes, it checks.**

16. 32500; $0.05(4500 - 32500) + 0.08(32500) = 1200$? $-1400 + 2600 = 1200$? **Yes, it checks.**

17. 60; $\frac{60}{2} + \frac{60}{3} + 10 = 60$? $30 + 20 + 10 = 60$? **Yes, it checks.**

18. $-\frac{10}{9}$; $3 \cdot (-\frac{10}{9}) - 2(-\frac{10}{9} + 5) = 10 \cdot (-\frac{10}{9})$? $-\frac{30}{9} + \frac{20}{9} - 10 = -\frac{100}{9}$? **Yes, it checks.**

29b. $\begin{cases} t_1 = 16 \\ t_n = t_{n-1} - 5, \text{ for integers } n \geq 2 \end{cases}$

30b. $\begin{cases} a_1 = -1 \\ a_n = (a_{n-1})^2 - 1, \text{ for integers } n \geq 2 \end{cases}$

Objective F: *Write a recursive definition for a sequence.* (Lessons 1-8, 1-9) See margin for 29b, 30b.

In 29 and 30, a sequence is defined recursively to be evaluated on a graphics calculator.
a. Write the first five terms of the sequence.
b. Rewrite the definition using sequence notation.

29. $\begin{cases} t_1 = 16 & 16, 11, 6, 1, -4 \\ t_n = (\boxed{\text{ANS}}) - 5, \text{ for integers } n \geq 2 \end{cases}$

30. $\begin{cases} a_1 = -1 & -1, 0, -1, 0, -1 \\ a_n = (\boxed{\text{ANS}})^2 - 1, \text{ for integers } n \geq 2 \end{cases}$

In 31 and 32, a sequence is given. **a.** Describe the sequence in words. **b.** Write a recursive definition for the sequence. (Hint: Only one operation is needed.)

31. 6, 12, 18, 24, . . .

32. -2, -2.75, -3.5, -4.25, . . .

31a) The first term is 6. All other terms are obtained by adding 6 to the previous term.
b) $\begin{cases} t_1 = 6 \\ t_n = t_{n-1} + 6, \text{ for integers } n \geq 2 \end{cases}$

32a) The first term is -2. All other terms are obtained by subtracting .75 from the previous term.
b) $\begin{cases} t_1 = -2 \\ t_n = t_{n-1} - 0.75, \text{ for integers } n \geq 2 \end{cases}$

PROPERTIES DEAL WITH THE PRINCIPLES BEHIND THE MATHEMATICS.

Objective G: *Determine whether a relation defined by a table, a list of ordered pairs, or a simple equation is a function.* (Lesson 1-2)

33. Does the table below describe y as a function of x? Justify your answer. No; $x = -1$ corresponds to $y = 1$ and $y = -1$

x	-1	-1	-4	0	-16
y	1	-1	2	0	-4

34. Does the set below describe a function? Why or why not? {(1, 2), (2, 3), (3, 4), (4, 1)}

In 35–37, an equation is given. **a.** Make a table of four pairs of numbers that satisfy the equation. **b.** Does the equation describe a function? See margin.

35. $x = y^2$ **36.** $xy = 15$ **37.** $x = -5$

Objective H: *Determine the domain and range of a function defined by a table, a list of ordered pairs, or a simple equation.* (Lesson 1-2)

38. What real number is not in the domain of f, where $f(x) = \frac{1}{x^2}$? 0

34) Yes, each value of x corresponds to exactly one value of y.

In 39 and 40, give **a.** the domain, and **b.** the range of the function described. See margin.

39. $\{(2, -2), (3, -3), (-9, 9), \left(-\frac{1}{2}, \frac{1}{2}\right)\}$

40.

a	-2	-1	0	1	2
$m(a)$	1	-1	1	-1	1

41. Consider $y = x^4$. See margin.
a. What is the domain of the function?
b. Are there any values of x for which x^4 is negative?
c. What is the range of $y = x^4$?

42. Let $f(x) = -\sqrt{x}$.
a. What is the domain of f?
b. Are there any values of x for which $-\sqrt{x}$ is positive? Explain your answer.
a) the set of nonnegative real numbers
b) No. When $x \geq 0$, $\sqrt{x} \geq 0$. So, $-\sqrt{x}$ is either a negative number or zero.

USES DEAL WITH APPLICATIONS OF MATHEMATICS IN REAL SITUATIONS.

Objective I: *Use addition, subtraction, multiplication, and division to write expressions which model real-world situations.* (Lesson 1-1)

43. The dimensions of a building are 100 times as large as the dimensions of its model. If a floor on the model is x cm long, how long is the floor on the building? 100x cm

44. There are s students per bus and b buses. How many students are there in all? sb students

45. Carol takes M minutes to walk B blocks. What is her walking speed? $\frac{B}{M}$ blocks per minute

46. Jamal can do six problems in 5 minutes. How long will it take him to do P problems?

47. Luis has 20 sticks of gum. He gives one to each of c friends. How many sticks of gum does he have left? 20 − c sticks

46) $\frac{5}{6} \cdot P$ minutes

Chapter 1   *Chapter Review*   **67**

35a. Sample

x	0	1	1	4
y	0	1	-1	2

b. No

36a. Sample

x	1	3	5	15
y	15	5	3	1

b. Yes

37a. Sample

x	-5	-5	-5	-5
y	0	1	2	3

b. No

39a. $\{-9, -\frac{1}{2}, 2, 3\}$
b. $\{-3, -2, \frac{1}{2}, 9\}$

40a. $\{-2, -1, 0, 1, 2\}$
b. $\{-1, 1\}$

41a. the set of real numbers
b. No
c. the set of nonnegative real numbers

Whereas end-of-chapter material may be considered optional in some texts, in *UCSMP Advanced Algebra* we have selected these objectives and questions with the expectation that they will be covered. Students should be able to answer these questions with about 85% accuracy after studying the chapter.

You may assign these questions over a single night to help students prepare for a test the next day, or you may assign the questions over a two-day period. If you work the questions over two days, then we recommend assigning the *evens* for homework the first night so that students get feedback in class the next day, then assigning the *odds* the night before the test, because answers are provided to the odd-numbered questions.

It is effective to ask students which questions they still do not understand and use the day or days as a total class discussion of the material that the class finds most difficult.

Assessment

Evaluation The *Assessment Sourcebook* provides four forms of the Chapter 1 Test. Forms A and B present parallel versions in a short-answer format. Forms C and D offer performance assessment.

For information on grading, see *General Teaching Suggestions; Grading* in the *Professional Sourcebook*, which begins on page T20 in Part 1 of the Teacher's Edition.

Feedback After students have taken the test for Chapter 1 and you have scored the results, return the tests to students for discussion. Class discussion on the questions that caused trouble for most students can be very effective in identifying and clarifying misunderstandings. You might want to have them write down the items they missed and work either in groups or at home to correct them. It is important for students to receive feedback on every chapter test, and we recommend that students see and correct their mistakes before proceeding too far into the next chapter.

Additional Answers
49a. $26,000, $27,560, $29,213.60, $30,966.42, $32,824.40
  b. $78,665.59
55b. Sample: In Baltimore, the population dropped by 51,000 people from 1980 to 1990.

---

48. Juana can mow the lawn around the family business in c hours with the riding mower. Her sister Rosa can mow the lawn in d hours with the walking mower.
    a. What fraction of the lawn can Juana mow in one hour? $\frac{1}{c}$
    b. What fraction of the lawn can Rosa mow in one hour? $\frac{1}{d}$
    c. If they work together, what fraction of the lawn can they mow in one hour? $\frac{1}{c} + \frac{1}{d}$

Objective J: *Use functions to solve real-world problems.* (Lessons 1-2, 1-3, 1-4, 1-7, 1-8, 1-9)

49. Sandra's annual salary is $26,000. She gets an increase of 6% at the end of each year. The sentence $a_n = 26{,}000(1.06)^{n-1}$ gives Sandra's salary at the end of n years.
    a. Write Sandra's salary for the first five years. **See margin for 49a and b.**
    b. At this growth rate, what would Sandra's salary be after 20 years with this company?

50. The famous scientist Galileo found a relationship between the distance $d(t)$ a dropped object falls (in feet) in time t (in seconds). (Of course he used different units.) The function is defined by the rule $d(t) = 16t^2$. What is the approximate distance fallen when $t = 1.5$ sec? **36 feet**

51. The function S defined by $S(x) = x + \frac{x^2}{20}$ relates the stopping distance in feet to the car's speed x in miles per hour. How many feet does it take for a car traveling at 70 mph to stop? **315 feet**

52. Todd works out at a gym 3 times a week. Every Saturday his trainer measures the circumference of his biceps to show Todd his progress. At the beginning, the measurement was 12″, but he put on $\frac{1}{4}$″ every month.
    a. Write an equation that gives the circumference of his biceps after m months. $C = 12 + \frac{1}{4}m$
    b. What would the measurement be at the end of 2 years if this trend continued? **18″**
    c. Do you think this equation would continue to describe what's happening after 5 years of working out? Explain your answer. **Sample: No; there is a limit to the size a person's biceps can grow.**

68

In 53–55, let $P(x)$ and $B(x)$ be the populations of Philadelphia and Baltimore, respectively, in year x.

	Philadelphia	Baltimore
1900	1,290,000	509,000
1950	2,070,000	950,000
1980	1,688,000	787,000
1990	1,586,000	736,000

53. What does $B(1950)$ represent? **See below.**
54. a. Calculate $P(1980) - B(1980)$. **901,000**
    b. What does part **a** represent? **See below.**
55. a. Calculate $B(1990) - B(1980)$. **-51,000**
    b. Write in words what the calculation in part **a** represents. **See margin.**
56. Devin opened a savings account with $50. Each month he adds $15 to his account.
    a. Write the amounts in this account for the first six months. **See below.**
    b. Write a recursive formula that generates the sequence giving his savings account balance at the end of each month.
    $$\begin{cases} t_1 = 50 \\ t_n = t_{n-1} + 15, \text{ for integers } n \geq 2 \end{cases}$$

Objective K: *Use linear equations to solve real-world problems.* (Lessons 1-5, 1-6)

57. Suppose a baby blue whale weighs 4000 lb at birth and gains 200 lb a day while nursing. A formula that gives its weight W after d days of nursing is $W = 4000 + 200d$.
    a. Write an equation that can be used to find the number of days a young blue whale has been nursing if it weighs 14,000 lb. (Baby blue whales nurse for 5 to 7 months.) **See below.**
    b. Solve this equation. $d = 50$ **days**

58. At Central High School all students are in grade 10, 11, or 12. This year $\frac{2}{5}$ of the students are in grade 10, $\frac{1}{3}$ are in grade 11, and 320 are in grade 12. How many students are at Central High this year? **1200 students**

53) The population of Baltimore in 1950
54b) In 1980, 901,000 more people lived in Philadelphia than Baltimore.
56a) $50, $65, $80, $95, $110, $125
57a) $14{,}000 = 4000 + 200d$

Additional Responses, page 62.
6a–c. Rows 0–14 are shown at the right. Sample pattern: There is a small triangle in rows 4–6 and two small triangles in rows 12–14. There is a larger triangle in rows 8–14.

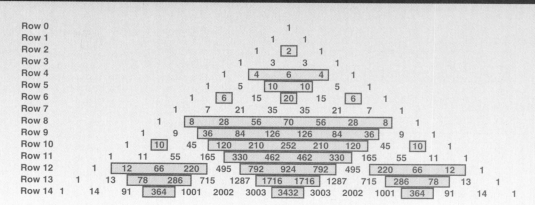

Row 0									1									
Row 1								1		1								
Row 2							1		2		1							
Row 3						1		3		3		1						
Row 4					1		4		6		4		1					
Row 5				1		5		10		10		5		1				
Row 6			1		6		15		20		15		6		1			
Row 7		1		7		21		35		35		21		7		1		
Row 8	1		8		28		56		70		56		28		8		1	
Row 9	1	9		36		84		126		126		84		36		9	1	
Row 10	1	10	45		120		210		252		210		120		45	10	1	
Row 11	1	11	55	165		330		462		462		330		165	55	11	1	
Row 12	1	12	66	220	495		792		924		792		495	220	66	12	1	
Row 13	1	13	78	286	715	1287		1716		1716		1287	715	286	78	13	1	
Row 14	1	14	91	364	1001	2002	3003		3432		3003	2002	1001	364	91	14	1	

59. When Melissa came home after a week's vacation, the temperature in her apartment had gone up to 85°. Half an hour after she turned on the air conditioner, the temperature was 82°. Suppose the equation $T = 85 - .1m$ gives the temperature, in degrees, after the air conditioner has been on m minutes. How long will it take the temperature to fall to 68°?
170 minutes or about 3 hours

60. David has a savings account with which to buy a car. After the down payment his account balance is $2400. His monthly car payment is $215 per month. Thus after x payments his account balance will be $2400 - 215x$. After how many months will David run out of money? **12 months**

REPRESENTATIONS DEAL WITH PICTURES, GRAPHS, OR OBJECTS THAT ILLUSTRATE CONCEPTS.

Objective L: *Determine the domain, range, and values of a function from its graph.* *(Lesson 1-4)*

In 61 and 62, find the domain and range of the function whose graph is shown.

61.

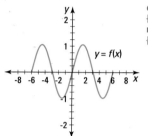

domain:
{$x: -6 \leq x \leq 6$}
range:
{$y: -1 \leq y \leq 1$}

62.

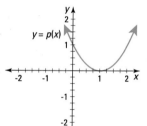

domain: the set of real numbers
range: the set of nonnegative real numbers

63. From the graph in Question 61, find the approximate value of $f(3)$. **0**

64. For what x value is $p(x) = 0$ in Question 62 above? **1**

Objective M: *Apply the Vertical-Line Test for a function.* *(Lesson 1-4)*

In 65–68, determine whether the given graph represents the graph of a function. Justify your answer. **Samples given.**

65.

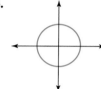

No; a vertical line intersects the graph twice.

66.

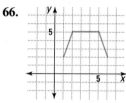

Yes; no vertical line intersects the graph in more than one point.

67.

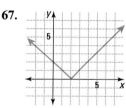

Yes; no vertical line intersects the graph in more than one point.

68.

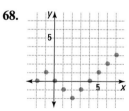

Yes; no vertical line intersects the graph in more than one point.

Chapter 1   *Chapter Review*   **69**

d. Sample response: Waclav Sierpinski was born in Poland in 1862 and died in 1969. Much of his work involved problems in number theory, and he is the author of a book containing 250 number theory problems. The growth of the field of fractals has brought the "Sierpinski" triangles to the forefront.

Homework We recommend that you assign both the reading and some questions in Lesson 2-1 for homework the evening of the test. This assignment gives students work after they have completed the test and keeps the class moving. If you do not do this, you may cover one less chapter over the course of the year. Remind students that this assignment includes reading the *Chapter 2 Opener*.

Adapting to Individual Needs

The student text is written for the vast majority of students. The chart at the right suggests two pacing plans to accommodate the needs of your students. Students in the Full Course should complete the entire text by the end of the year. Students in the Minimal Course will spend more time when there are quizzes and more time on the Chapter Review. Therefore, these students may not complete all of the chapters in the text.

Options are also presented to meet the needs of a variety of teaching and learning styles. For each lesson, the Teacher's Edition provides sections entitled: *Video* which describes video segments and related questions that can be used for motivation or extension; *Optional Activities* which suggests activities that employ materials, physical models, technology, and cooperative learning; and *Adapting to Individual Needs* which regularly includes **Challenge** problems, **English Language Development** suggestions, and suggestions for providing **Extra Help.** The Teacher's Edition also frequently includes an **Error Alert,** an **Extension,** and an **Assessment** alternative. The options available in Chapter 2 are summarized in the chart below.

Chapter 2 Pacing Chart

Day	Full Course	Minimal Course
1	2-1	2-1
2	2-2	2-2
3	2-3	2-3
4	Quiz; 2-4	Quiz*; begin 2-4.
5	2-5	Finish 2-4.
6	2-6	2-5
7	Quiz; 2-7	2-6
8	2-8	Quiz*; begin 2-7.
9	2-9	Finish 2-7.
10	Self-Test	2-8
11	Review	2-9
12	Test*	Self-Test
13		Review
14		Review
15		Test*

*in the Teacher's Resource File

In the Teacher's Edition...

Lesson	Optional Activities	Extra Help	Challenge	English Language Development	Error Alert	Extension	Cooperative Learning	Ongoing Assessment
2-1	●	●	●	●	●	●	●	Oral/Written
2-2	●	●		●	●	●	●	Written
2-3	●	●	●	●	●	●		Written
2-4	●	●	●		●	●	●	Written
2-5	●	●	●	●		●	●	Group
2-6	●	●			●	●	●	Written
2-7	●	●	●		●	●	●	Written
2-8	●	●	●			●	●	Oral
2-9	●	●	●			●	●	Oral

In the Additional Resources...

Lesson	In the Teacher's Resource File								
	Lesson Masters, A and B	Teaching Aids*	Activity Kit*	Answer Masters	Technology Sourcebook	Assessment Sourcebook	Visual Aids**	Technology	Video Segments
2-1	2-1	8, 13, 16		2-1			8, 13, 16, AM		
2-2	2-2	8, 13	3	2-2			8, 13, AM		
In-class Activity		17		2-3			17, AM		
2-3	2-3	8, 13		2-3		Quiz	8, 13, AM		
2-4	2-4	8, 14, 18		2-4	Comp 2		8, 14, 18, AM	GraphExplorer	
In-class Activity		19		2-5			19, AM		
2-5	2-5	5, 14, 18, 19		2-5	Comp 2		5, 14, 18, 19, AM	GraphExplorer	
In-class Activity		19		2-6			19, AM		
2-6	2-6	5, 14,19, 20		2-6	Comp 2	Quiz	5, 14, 19, 20, AM	GraphExplorer	
2-7	2-7	5, 15, 21	4	2-7			5, 15, 21, AM		2-7
2-8	2-8	5, 15, 22		2-8			5, 15, 22, AM		
2-9	2-9	15		2-9	Calc 2		15, AM		
End of chapter						Tests			

*Teaching Aids are pictured on pages 70C and 70D. The activities in the Activity Kit are pictured on page 70C.

**Visual Aids provide transparencies for all Teaching Aids and all Answer Masters.

Also available is the Study Skills Handbook which includes study-skill tips related to reading, note-taking, and comprehension.

Integrating Strands and Applications

	2-1	2-2	2-3	2-4	2-5	2-6	2-7	2-8	2-9
Mathematical Connections									
Algebra	●	●	●	●	●	●	●	●	●
Geometry	●	●	●	●	●	●		●	●
Measurement	●	●	●	●				●	●
Patterns and Functions	●	●	●	●	●	●	●	●	●
Discrete Mathematics						●			
Interdisciplinary and Other Connections									
Music	●								
Literature			●						
Science	●	●	●	●	●	●	●	●	●
Social Studies	●	●		●			●		
Multicultural	●								●
Technology				●	●	●			●
Career				●				●	
Consumer	●	●	●	●			●		
Sports		●							●

Teaching and Assessing the Chapter Objectives

Chapter 2 Objectives (Organized into the SPUR categories—Skills, Properties, Uses, and Representations)	Lessons	Progress Self-Test Questions	Chapter Review Questions	Chapter Test, Forms A and B	Chapter Test, Forms C	Chapter Test, Forms D
Skills						
A: Translate variation language into formulas and formulas into variation language.	2-1, 2-2, 2-9	1, 2, 3	1–8	1, 5		
B: Solve variation problems.	2-1, 2-2, 2-9	4	9–12	2, 3, 4, 14	1	
C: Find slopes (rates of change).	2-4, 2-5, 2-6	7, 12	13–18	11, 12, 13, 18	3	
Properties						
D: Use the Fundamental Theorem of Variation.	2-3	5, 6	19–25	7, 8	1	✓
E: Identify the properties of variation functions.	2-4, 2-5, 2-6	8, 9, 10, 13	26–34	18, 19	4	✓
Uses						
F: Recognize variation situations.	2-1, 2-2	11, 16	35–42	9, 10	2	✓
G: Solve real-world variation problems.	2-1, 2-2, 2-9	15, 17, 20	43–48	6	2	✓
H: Fit an appropriate model to data.	2-7, 2-8	15, 19	49–52	20, 21		
Representations						
I: Graph variation equations.	2-4, 2-5, 2-6	12, 13	53–58	16, 17	4	✓
J: Identify variation equations from graphs.	2-4, 2-5, 2-6	14	59–64	15, 22		
K: Recognize the effects of a change in scale or viewing window on a graph of a variation equation.	2-5	18	65–67	19	5	

In the Teacher's Resource File

Assessment Sourcebook
Quiz for Lessons 2-1 through 2-3
Quiz for Lessons 2-4 through 2-6
Chapter 2 Test, Forms A–D
Chapter 2 Test, Cumulative Form

Quiz and Test Writer

Activity Kit

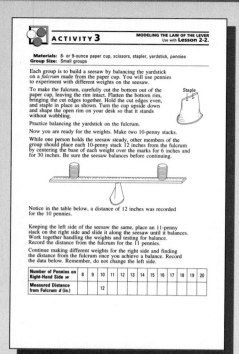

ACTIVITY 3 MODELING THE LAW OF THE LEVER
Use with **Lesson 2-2.**

Materials: 8- or 9-ounce paper cup, scissors, stapler, yardstick, pennies
Group Size: Small groups

Each group is to build a seesaw by balancing the yardstick on a *fulcrum* made from the paper cup. You will use pennies to experiment with different weights on the seesaw.

To make the fulcrum, carefully cut the bottom out of the paper cup, leaving the rim intact. Flatten the bottom rim, bringing the cut edges together. Hold the cut edges even, and staple it in place as shown. Turn the cup upside down and shape the open rim on your desk so that it stands without wobbling.

Practice balancing the yardstick on the fulcrum.

Now you are ready for the weights. Make two 10-penny stacks.

While one person holds the seesaw steady, other members of the group should place each 10-penny stack 12 inches from the fulcrum by centering the base of each weight over the marks for 6 inches and for 30 inches. Be sure the seesaw balances before continuing.

Notice in the table below, a distance of 12 inches was recorded for the 10 pennies.

Keeping the left side of the seesaw the same, place an 11-penny stack on the right side and slide it along the seesaw until it balances. Work together handling the weights and testing for balance. Record the distance from the fulcrum for the 11 pennies.

Continue making different weights for the right side and finding the distance from the fulcrum once you achieve a balance. Record the data below. Remember, do not change the left side.

Number of Pennies on Right-Hand Side w	8	9	10	11	12	13	14	15	16	17	18	19	20
Measured Distance from Fulcrum d (in.)			12										

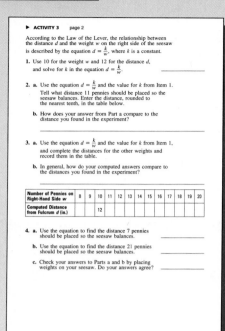

▶ **ACTIVITY 3**   page 2

According to the Law of the Lever, the relationship between the distance d and the weight w on the right side of the seesaw is described by the equation $d = \frac{k}{w}$, where k is a constant.

1. Use 10 for the weight w and 12 for the distance d, and solve for k in the equation $d = \frac{k}{w}$.

2. a. Use the equation $d = \frac{k}{w}$ and the value for k from Item 1. Tell what distance 11 pennies should be placed so the seesaw balances. Enter the distance, rounded to the nearest tenth, in the table below.

   b. How does your answer from Part a compare to the distance you found in the experiment?

3. a. Use the equation $d = \frac{k}{w}$ and the value for k from Item 1, and complete the distances for the other weights and record them in the table.

   b. In general, how do your computed answers compare to the distances you found in the experiment?

Number of Pennies on Right-Hand Side w	8	9	10	11	12	13	14	15	16	17	18	19	20
Computed Distance from Fulcrum d (in.)			12										

4. a. Use the equation to find the distance 7 pennies should be placed so the seesaw balances.

   b. Use the equation to find the distance 21 pennies should be placed so the seesaw balances.

   c. Check your answers to Parts a and b by placing weights on your seesaw. Do your answers agree?

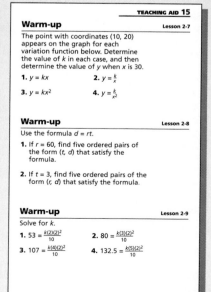

ACTIVITY 4 FITTING A MODEL TO DATA
Use with **Lesson 2-7.**

Materials: $\frac{1}{4}$-grid paper; optional materials: Strobe equipment or video camera, video cassette recorder with slow motion, and television; meter stick, ball, stopwatch
Group Size: Partners

Strobe pictures are pictures of the same object taken at equal time intervals. When the object is moving, the strobe pictures capture the path of the object.

The diagram at the right shows 10 strobe pictures taken every $\frac{1}{20}$ of a second during an experiment in which a ball was dropped from a height of about 1 meter. The dots represent the ball at each instant a picture was taken.

If your science department has the equipment to make strobe pictures, duplicate the experiment described above. Alternately, if you have access to good video equipment, tape the experiment. Play the tape back on slow motion, and make a second tape of the playback. When you play this second tape on slow motion, it should show the ball moving slowly enough to record times and distances. (You will need to time and tape a longer activity and time it after the two slow motions to determine the real time during the experiment.)

1. Estimate the total distance the ball has fallen after each time period. If you use the diagram at the right, complete the table below. If you conduct your own experiment, make a similar table showing the approximate time intervals.

Time t (sec)	0	$\frac{1}{20}$	$\frac{2}{20}$	$\frac{3}{20}$	$\frac{4}{20}$	$\frac{5}{20}$	$\frac{6}{20}$	$\frac{7}{20}$	$\frac{8}{20}$	$\frac{9}{20}$	$\frac{10}{20}$
Distance d (m)	0	.01		.2							

2. Graph the points (t, d).

3. Which of the following equations is a good model for your graph?
   (a) $d = kt$ (b) $d = kt^2$ (c) $d = \frac{k}{t}$ (d) $d = \frac{k}{t^2}$

4. Find the constant k for your model.

5. Use your model to estimate the distance the ball would have traveled in 1 second if it had been dropped from a greater height.

Teaching Aids

Teaching Aid 5, Graph Paper, (shown on page 4D) can be used with **Lessons 2-5 through 2-8.** Teaching Aid 8, Four-quadrant Graph Paper, (shown on page 4D) can be used with **Lessons 2-1 through 2-4.**

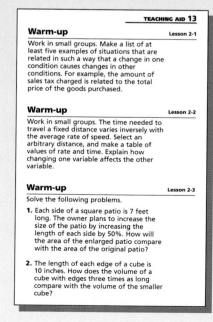

TEACHING AID 13

Warm-up Lesson 2-1

Work in small groups. Make a list of at least five examples of situations that are related in such a way that a change in one condition causes changes in other conditions. For example, the amount of sales tax charged is related to the total price of the goods purchased.

Warm-up Lesson 2-2

Work in small groups. The time needed to travel a fixed distance varies inversely with the average rate of speed. Select an arbitrary distance, and make a table of values of rate and time. Explain how changing one variable affects the other variable.

Warm-up Lesson 2-3

Solve the following problems.

1. Each side of a square patio is 7 feet long. The owner plans to increase the size of the patio by increasing the length of each side by 50%. How will the area of the enlarged patio compare with the area of the original patio?

2. The length of each edge of a cube is 10 inches. How does the volume of a cube with edges three times as long compare with the volume of the smaller cube?

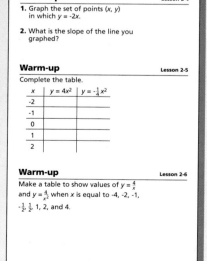

TEACHING AID 14

Warm-up Lesson 2-4

1. Graph the set of points (x, y) in which $y = -2x$.

2. What is the slope of the line you graphed?

Warm-up Lesson 2-5

Complete the table.

x	$y = 4x^2$	$y = -\frac{1}{4}x^2$
-2		
-1		
0		
1		
2		

Warm-up Lesson 2-6

Make a table to show values of $y = \frac{4}{x}$ and $y = \frac{4}{x^2}$ when x is equal to -4, -2, -1, $-\frac{1}{2}$, $\frac{1}{2}$, 1, 2, and 4.

TEACHING AID 15

Warm-up Lesson 2-7

The point with coordinates (10, 20) appears on the graph for each variation function below. Determine the value of k in each case, and then determine the value of y when x is 30.

1. $y = kx$
2. $y = \frac{k}{x}$
3. $y = kx^2$
4. $y = \frac{k}{x^2}$

Warm-up Lesson 2-8

Use the formula $d = rt$.

1. If $r = 60$, find five ordered pairs of the form (t, d) that satisfy the formula.

2. If $t = 3$, find five ordered pairs of the form (r, d) that satisfy the formula.

Warm-up Lesson 2-9

Solve for k.

1. $53 = \frac{k(2)(2)^2}{10}$
2. $80 = \frac{k(3)(2)^2}{10}$
3. $107 = \frac{k(4)(2)^2}{10}$
4. $132.5 = \frac{k(5)(2)^2}{10}$

Four-Step Algorithm

1. Write an equation that describes the variation.
2. Find the constant of variation.
3. Rewrite the variation function using the constant of variation.
4. Evaluate the function for the desired value of the independent variable.

Tables

x	$y = \frac{1}{x^3}$
original value	
doubled	
tripled	
quadrupled	

x	$y = \frac{1}{x^3}$
original value	
doubled	
tripled	
quadrupled	

Graphs of Direct-variation formulas

$y = kx$
y varies directly as x.

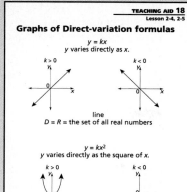

$k > 0$ $k < 0$

line
$D = R$ = the set of all real numbers

$y = kx^2$
y varies directly as the square of x.

$k > 0$ $k < 0$

parabola

D = the set of all real numbers
$R = \{y: y \geq 0\}$

D = the set of all real numbers
$R = \{y: y \leq 0\}$

Automatic Grapher Grid

$y =$ ___

___ $\leq x \leq$ ___ x-scale

___ $\leq y \leq$ ___ y-scale

$y =$ ___

___ $\leq x \leq$ ___ x-scale

___ $\leq y \leq$ ___ y-scale

$y =$ ___

___ $\leq x \leq$ ___ x-scale

___ $\leq y \leq$ ___ y-scale

$y =$ ___

___ $\leq x \leq$ ___ x-scale

___ $\leq y \leq$ ___ y-scale

Graphs of Inverse-variation formulas

$y = \frac{k}{x}$
y varies inversely as x.

$k > 0$ $k < 0$

hyperbola
$D = R$ = the set of all nonzero real numbers

$y = \frac{k}{x^2}$
y varies inversely as the square of x.

$k > 0$ $k < 0$

inverse-square curve

D = the set of all nonzero real numbers
$R = \{y: y > 0\}$

D = the set of all nonzero real numbers
$R = \{y: y < 0\}$

Additional Examples

1. Susan measured how far a marble rolled down a ramp over a period of time. She obtained the following data, where t refers to the time in seconds and D refers to the distance in inches.

t	1	2	3	4	5
D	.6	2.4	5.2	9.8	15.2

Find an equation that relates time t and distance D.

2. Rhoda and Ron measured the intensity of light at various distances from a lamp and obtained the following data where d = distance in meters and I = intensity in watts per square meter.

d	2	2.5	3	3.5	4
I	560	360	250	185	140

Find an equation that relates distance d to intensity I.

Additional Examples

X. Perri Menter performed an experiment to determine how the pressure of a liquid on an object is related to the depth of the object and the density of the liquid. She placed an object at a depth of 25 inches into various solutions that had different densities. She measured the pressure on the object and obtained the data in Table 1.

Table 1

Density D (pounds per in³)	Pressure P (pounds per in²)
0	5
0.5	15.6
1.2	37.5
1.5	46.9
2.7	84.4
3.8	118.8

Then she measured the pressure on the object at various depths in a liquid with density 1.5 lb/in³ and found the data in Table 2.

Table 2

depth d (inches)	Pressure P (pounds per in²)
0	5
25	46.9
50	93.4
75	140.6
100	187.5
125	234.4

1. Graph the data in Table 1.

2. Graph the data in Table 2.

3. Determine the relationships among the variables D, P, and d.

Chapter Opener

Pacing

All of the lessons in this chapter are designed to be covered in one day. At the end of the chapter, you should plan to spend 1 day to review the Progress Self-Test, 1–2 days for the Chapter Review, and 1 day for a test. You may want to spend a day on projects and a day with automatic graphers; a day may be needed for quizzes as well. Therefore, this chapter should take 12–16 days.

Using pages 70–71

Discuss the situation involving the construction worker. Ask students to explain why using wider or thicker boards makes the scaffold stronger and why increasing the distance between supports weakens the scaffold. Emphasize that the strength of the scaffold is dependent upon other factors as well—most significantly, the material of which the scaffold is made and the strength of the supports. Tell students that this chapter presents information on the relationships between these variables and the strength of the scaffold.

Chapter 2 Overview

Chapter 2 has three interrelated ideas. The first is the notion of functions of variation. The second is the graphical representation of these functions. The third is the modeling of data by using functions of variation.

Lessons 2-1 through 2-3 and 2-9 cover the basic language of variation. Lessons 2-1 and 2-2 present the two basic types of variation, and Lesson 2-3 concentrates on the important notion of how a change in the independent variable in a function of variation affects the dependent variable. Lesson 2-9 presents the topics of combined and joint variation.

Combined variation is the name given to situations in which direct and inverse variations occur together. In joint variation, one quantity varies directly as the product of two or more independent variables but not inversely as any variables.

Lessons 2-4 through 2-6 concentrate on graphing functions of variation. Some of this material, namely the graph of $y = kx$ and possibly the graph of $y = kx^2$, will be review for your students. We emphasize that slope is a measure of the rate of change as determined by points on a graph, and we extend this idea of slope as rate of change to nonlinear graphs.

VARIATION AND GRAPHS

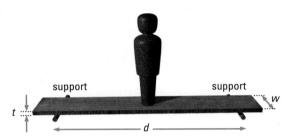

A construction worker walking on a board of a scaffold knows that too much weight will break the board. The largest weight that can be safely supported by a board depends on its width w, its thickness t, and the distance d between the board's supports.

Wider or thicker boards make the scaffold stronger. Increasing the distance between the supports weakens the scaffold. Thus, the strength varies as the dimensions of the board change or as the distance between supports changes. But how does it vary? In this chapter, you will study variation, that is, how one quantity changes as others are changed.

The chapter begins with a simple relationship called *direct variation*.

Photo Connections
The photo collage makes real-world connections to the content of the chapter: variation and graphs.

Astronaut The weight of an astronaut decreases as his or her distance from the center of the earth increases. This is an example of an inverse-variation relationship.

Windmill Windmills are used to generate electrical power. The direct-variation relationship between the amount of power a windmill generates and a cube of the wind speed is one application explored in Lesson 2-1.

Wood Wood is an abundant renewable resource. Different kinds of wood vary in strength, flexibility, stiffness, and relative lightness in weight. The Exploration in Lesson 2-8 invites students to investigate the relationship between the constant of variation k and the strength of the wood.

Scuba Diver The amount of pressure exerted on a diver at various depths is measured in units of pounds per square inch. Mathematical models can be used to describe the relationship between pressure and depth.

Scaffold In Lessons 2-8 and 2-9 a combined-variation formula is used to find the maximum weight a board on a scaffold can support.

Chapter 2 Projects
At this time you might want to have students look over the projects on pages 128–129.

Lessons 2-7 and 2-8 introduce the idea of fitting a mathematical model to data. Theoretical models can be compared with the data either by looking at their graphs or by examining tables of corresponding values. In these lessons, the emphasis is on situations that can be modeled with functions of variation. The lessons strengthen the earlier work on graphing, and they introduce modeling as a major theme of this book.

In-class Activities are included in this chapter to introduce students to automatic graphers.

Setting Up Lesson 2-1
Students will need driver's education books for **Question 29** on page 77. They will need almanacs for the *Extension*.

Objectives

A Translate direct-variation language into formulas and formulas into direct-variation language.
B Solve direct-variation problems.
F Recognize direct-variation situations.
G Solve real-world problems involving direct variation.

Resources

From the *Teacher's Resource File*
- Lesson Master 2-1A or 2-1B
- Answer Master 2-1
- Teaching Aids
  8 Four-Quadrant Graph Paper
  13 Warm-up
  16 Four-step Algorithm

Additional Resources
- Visuals for Teaching Aids 8, 13, 16
- Driver's Education books
- Almanacs

Teaching **2-1**
Lesson

Warm-up

Cooperative Learning Work in **small groups**. Make a list of at least five examples of situations that are related in such a way that a change in one condition causes changes in other conditions. For example, the amount of sales tax charged is related to the total price of the goods purchased. **Answers will vary.**

Direct Variation

You can save. *More than half the beverage cans used in the U.S. are recycled. One recycled aluminum can saves enough energy to keep a 100-watt light bulb burning for about 3.5 hours.*

❶ In many places, you can get refunds for returning aluminum cans. For example, since 1987 in New York, you can get a 5¢ refund for each can returned. Thus, if r is the total refund in cents and c is the number of cans you return, then

$$r = 5c.$$

Doubling the number of cans returned doubles your refund. Tripling the number of cans triples your refund. We say that r **varies directly as** c.

In Michigan, you can get 10¢ per can returned, so $r = 10c$. Again, r varies directly as c.

Recall the formula $A = \pi r^2$ for the area of a circle. In this formula, as the radius r increases, the area A also increases. In this case, A varies directly as r^2. Often this wording is used: The area A varies directly as the *square* of r.

$A = \pi r^2$

Direct-Variation Functions

The formulas $r = 5c$, $r = 10c$, and $A = \pi r^2$ are all of the form $y = kx^n$, where k is a nonzero constant, called the **constant of variation,** and n is a positive number. These formulas all describe *direct-variation functions.*

> **Definition**
> A **direct-variation function** is a function with a formula of the form $y = kx^n$, with $k \neq 0$ and $n > 0$.

When y varies directly as x^n we also say that y is **directly proportional to** x^n. For instance, the formula $A = \pi r^2$ can be read "the area of a circle is directly proportional to the square of its radius." Here $n = 2$ and $k = \pi$, so π is the constant of variation. In the formulas $r = 5c$ and $r = 10c$, $n = 1$. The constants of variation are 5 for New York and 10 for Michigan.

Lesson 2-1 Overview

Broad Goals This lesson introduces the language of direct variation and illustrates solving a basic direct-variation problem: If y varies directly as x, and you know the particular value of y for a particular value of x, find the value of y for another value of x.

Perspective When students are given a formula, they usually understand that the variables are related; therefore, as one variable changes, so do the others.

However, in Lesson 2-1, we are looking for a particular way in which the dependent variable changes.

The first three lessons of this chapter culminate in the Fundamental Theorem of Variation: if $y = kx^n$, and x is multiplied by c, then y is multiplied by c^n. Although it is not stated in Lesson 2-1, if n is positive, then $y = kx^n$ is an equation for a function of direct variation; if n is negative, then

$y = kx^n$ is an equation for a function of inverse variation.

Full-grown giraffes range from 4.3 to 5.9 meters in height. Taller giraffes weigh more than shorter ones, following the ideas in Example 1.

Example 1

The weight w of an adult animal of a given species is known to vary directly with the cube of its height h.
a. Write an equation relating w and h.
b. Identify the dependent and independent variables.

Solution

a. An equation for the direct variation is $w = kh^3$.
b. Because w is given in terms of h, The dependent variable is w and the independent variable is h.

Solving Direct-Variation Problems

Direct-variation functions arise in many real-world situations. For instance, after applying brakes, the braking distance d a car travels before coming to a stop is directly proportional to the square of its speed s.

$$d = ks^2$$

The value of k depends upon the type of car, the condition of its brakes, and the condition of the road. In Example 2, we illustrate how to find the value of k from known information and how to use that value to make a prediction.

Example 2

A certain car needs 25 ft to come to a stop after the brakes are applied at 20 mph. Braking distance d (in ft) is directly proportional to the square of the speed s (in mph). What distance is needed to stop this car after the brakes are applied at 60 mph?

Solution

1. Find an equation relating d and s. From the given information, $d = ks^2$.
2. Determine the constant of variation. You are given that $d = 25$ ft when $s = 20$ mph. To find k, substitute these values into $d = ks^2$.

$$25 \text{ ft} = k \cdot (20 \text{ mph})^2$$
$$25 \text{ ft} = (400 \text{ mph}^2) \cdot k$$

So
$$k = \frac{1}{16} \frac{\text{ft}}{(\text{mph})^2}$$

3. Substituting $k = \frac{1}{16}$ into $d = ks^2$ gives

$$d = \frac{1}{16} s^2$$

as a formula relating speed and braking distance for this situation.
4. Evaluate the formula when $s = 60$ mph.

$$d = \left(\frac{1}{16} \frac{\text{ft}}{(\text{mph})^2}\right) \cdot (60 \text{ mph})^2$$
$$d = \frac{1}{16} \frac{\text{ft}}{(\text{mph})^2} \cdot 3600 \text{ mph}^2$$
$$d = 225 \text{ ft}$$

The car will need 225 ft to come to a stop after the brakes are applied at 60 mph.

Lesson 2-1 *Direct Variation* **73**

Notes on Reading

Keep the list of examples students wrote for the *Warm-up* to use with Activity 1 in *Optional Activities* for Lesson 2-2.

❶ **Reading Mathematics** You may want to have students read this lesson aloud in class. Point out that the phrases *varies directly as* and *varies directly with* are both acceptable expressions.

You can facilitate the learning of direct variation, including the definitions and uses of the terms, by discussing familiar examples, such as those suggested below.
1. The cost of gas for a car varies directly as the amount of gas purchased.
2. The price of breakfast cereal varies directly as the number of boxes of cereal purchased.
3. The volume of a sphere varies directly as the cube of its radius.

❷ Stress the unit analysis that is given with the solution. This analysis emphasizes the fact that the variables (and sometimes the constants) have units associated with them. Keeping track of the units can help students with their solutions.

Safety Connection You might discuss factors other than speed that can affect braking distance. [Samples: worn tires, shock absorbers, or brakes; roadway surface conditions; pulling a heavy load; and driver reaction time]

❸ This four-step algorithm is also given on **Teaching Aid 16.** Students should recognize that they have often used four steps like these when solving problems.

A more general algorithm applies to the use of any formula. It is: (1) write the formula; (2) use a set of given values to determine any constants in the formula that are not given; (3) rewrite the formula with the values for the constants in it; (4) evaluate the formula for given values of the variables. Students will use this more general algorithm in Chapter 3; at that time they will find an equation of a line that meets certain conditions.

Additional Examples

1. The weight of an object on another planet (P) varies directly with its weight on Earth (E).
   a. Write an equation relating P and E. $P = kE$
   b. Identify the dependent and independent variables.
      Dependent variable: P;
      Independent variable: E
2. The quantity of ingredients for the crust and toppings of a pizza, and therefore the price, is proportional to its area, not its linear dimensions. So, the quantity of ingredients is proportional to the square of its radius. Suppose that a pizza 12 inches in diameter costs $7.00. If the price of pizza varies directly as the square of its radius, what would a pizza 15 inches in diameter cost?
   Let P be the price of a pizza and r be its radius. Then
   $P = kr^2$, and $k = \frac{7}{36}$. A 15-inch pizza would cost about $10.94.
3. Find the constant of variation if y varies directly as x, and $y = 32$ when $x = 0.2$. Find y when $x = 5$. $k = 160$; when $x = 5$, $y = 800$.

❸ Notice that to use variation functions to predict values, you carry out four steps.
1. Write an equation that describes the variation.
2. Find the constant of variation.
3. Rewrite the variation function using the constant of variation.
4. Evaluate the function for the desired value of the independent variable.

This four-step algorithm is used again in Example 3.

Example 3

Suppose z varies directly as the fourth power of w. If $z = 80$ when $w = 2$, find z when $w = 3$.

Solution
1. Write an equation that describes the variation.
$$z = kw^4$$
2. Find the constant of variation. You are given that $z = 80$ when $w = 2$. Substitute these values into the variation formula to find k.
$$80 = k \cdot 2^4$$
$$80 = k \cdot 16$$
$$5 = k$$
3. Rewrite the variation formula using the constant of variation.
$$z = 5w^4$$
4. Evaluate the formula for the desired value of the independent variable.
$$z = 5 \cdot 3^4$$
$$= 5 \cdot 81$$
$$z = 405$$
When $w = 3$, $z = 405$.

QUESTIONS

Covering the Reading

1. Name three variables that affect the weight a board on a scaffold can support. Sample: width, thickness, distance

2. Give an example of a direct-variation function from geometry.
   Sample: $A = \pi r^2$
3. In the function $y = 3x^5$, _?_ varies directly as _?_ and _?_ is the constant of variation. y; x^5; 3

In 4 and 5, suppose $y = -4.3x$.

4. Find y when $x = 3.1$ $y = -13.33$

5. Is this an example of a direct-variation function? How can you tell?
   Yes, it has the form $y = kx^n$, with $k = -4.3$ and $n = 1$.

Optional Activities

Activity 1 Since Additional Example 2 supposes that the cost of the pizza varies directly as the *square of the radius*, students probably used $P = \frac{7}{36}r^2$ to find that the 15-inch pizza cost $10.94. Ask students to see what happens if they use the fact that the cost varies directly as the square of the diameter. [Sample: $P = kd^2$, $k = \frac{7}{144}$, and the final answer is the same, $10.94.] Then ask them to explain why the

answer is the same. [Sample: Replace d in $P = \frac{7}{144}d^2$ with $2r$: $P = \frac{7}{144}(2r)^2 = \frac{7}{144}(4r^2) = \frac{7}{36}r^2$]

In 6 and 7, assume that y is directly proportional to the square of x.

6. *Multiple choice.* Which equation represents this situation? **b**
   (a) $y = 2x$
   (b) $y = kx^2$
   (c) $x = ky^2$
   (d) $y = 2x^k$

7. Which is the dependent variable? **y**

In 8 and 9, refer to Example 2.

8. Find the distance the car travels before coming to a stop if its brakes are applied at 40 mph. **100 ft**

9. Suppose that some other car needs 30 ft to stop if its brakes are applied at 20 mph.
   a. Find k. $\frac{3}{40} \frac{\text{ft}}{\text{mph}^2}$
   b. Write the variation function relating s and d. $d = \frac{3}{40} s^2$
   c. How far would the car travel before coming to a stop if its brakes were applied at 60 mph? **270 ft**

10. Suppose W varies directly as the fifth power of z, and $W = 96$ when $z = 2$.
    a. Find the constant of variation. **3**
    b. Find W when $z = 10$. **W = 300,000**

11. Suppose y varies directly as the cube of x, and $y = 1000$ when $x = 5$. Find y when $x = 9$. **5832**

12. Suppose $f(x) = \frac{x^2}{9}$. Is this a direct-variation function? Write a sentence or two justifying your conclusion.
    Yes, it has the form $f(x) = kx^n$ with $k = \frac{1}{9}$ and $n = 2$.

Applying the Mathematics

13. The power P generated by a windmill is directly proportional to the cube of the wind speed w.
    a. Write an equation relating P and w. Identify the dependent and the independent variables. $P = kw^3$; **P, dependent; w, independent**
    b. If a 10 mph wind generates 150 watts of power, how many watts will a 6 mph wind generate? **32.4 watts**

14. When lightning strikes in the distance, you do not see the flash and hear the thunder at the same time. You first see the lightning; then you hear the thunder. **a) $d = kt$**
    a. Write an equation to express this situation: "The distance d from the observer to the flash varies directly as the time t between the observer's seeing the lightning and hearing the thunder."
    b. Suppose that lightning strikes a known point 4 miles away, and that you hear the thunder 20 seconds later. Then, how far away has lightning struck if 30 seconds pass between the time you see the flash and hear its thunder? **6 miles**

Wind power. *Shown is a windmill "farm" in Kern County, California. The more than 16,000 windmills in the U.S. in 1990 generated about 2.5 million kilowatt-hours of electricity—enough to meet the needs of a city the size of San Francisco for a year.*

Lesson 2-1 *Direct Variation* **75**

Notes on Questions

Notes on Questions
Question 2 Use this question to review formulas for area and volume. In general, if all the figures covered by a formula are similar (in the geometric sense of the word), such as squares or spheres, then there exists a direct-variation formula for their perimeter, area, or volume. Spheres have a surface area formula of the form $y = kx^2$ and a volume formula of the form $y = kx^3$. In the surface-area formula, $k = 4\pi$. In the volume formula, $k = \frac{4\pi}{3}$. Since rectangular solids are not all similar, their surface area and volume formulas are not examples of simple direct variations.

Questions 9–11 Emphasize the algorithm for solving variation problems used in **Examples 2 and 3.** Students will use this algorithm frequently in Lessons 2-2, 2-3, and 2-9.

Question 14 Multicultural Connection For thousands of years, people did not understand lightning and they feared it. The ancient Greeks considered the ground struck by lightning as sacred and often built temples on these sites. African stories tell that lightning and thunder were created by a giant bird that dove from the clouds to the earth. Ringing bells to drive away storms was common in medieval Europe and in colonial America. Some bell ringers lost their lives when lightning struck the bell and traveled down the rope to the bell ringer on the ground.

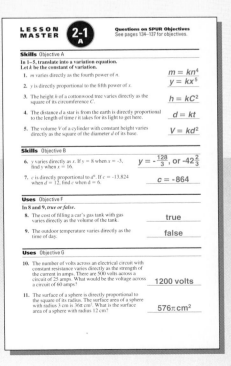

Adapting to Individual Needs

Extra Help
Some students might be confused by the term *constant of variation*. At first glance, it might seem that the term is contradictory since *constant* implies "unchanging," while *variation* implies "changing." Point out that the variables in a direct-variation function do vary, but the relation between the independent variable and the dependent variable remains the same. To illustrate this, point out that the formula $A = 6s^2$ can be used to find the surface area of a cube that has an edge of length s. Have students substitute several values for s and then write ordered pairs of the form (s^2, A). [Samples: (1, 6), (4, 24), (9, 54)] Then point out that while s and A vary, A is always 6 times s^2. Thus, 6 is called the constant of variation.

Questions 19–21 These questions review properties of powers. Students have to know these properties in order to understand the Fundamental Theorem of Variation in Lesson 2-3.

Students will need graph paper or **Teaching Aid 8** for **Questions 26–27.**

Question 28b Error Alert Some students may multiply 0.206 mile per second by 4 miles. Point out to these students that the question asks for an answer in units of time. You may wish to ask students, "How many *seconds* will it take sound to travel 4 miles?" to help them understand that 4 miles must be divided by 0.206 miles per second to get an answer in terms of seconds.

Question 29 Students will need driver's education books. It is important to note that not all braking-distance formulas are direct variations; some consider the reaction time of the driver when computing braking distance. One such formula, $d = 1.1s + 0.05s^2$, gives stopping distance d in feet for a car traveling s miles per hour. $1.1s$ represents the distance that is traveled during the driver's reaction time, and $0.05s^2$ represents the distance traveled while braking.

15. Refer to the formula $A = \pi r^2$ for the area of a circle with radius r.
   a. Complete the table below, leaving all answers in terms of π.

r	1	2	3	4	5	6	7	8	9	10
A	π	4π	9π	16π	25π	36π	49π	64π	81π	100π

   b. The area when $r = 4$ is how many times as large as the area when $r = 2$? **4 times as large**
   c. The area when $r = 6$ is how many times as large as the area when $r = 3$? **4 times as large**
   d. The area when $r = 10$ is how many times as large as the area when $r = 5$? **4 times as large**
   e. Make a conjecture. When the radius doubles, the area __?__.
   f. Follow a similar procedure to complete the following conjecture. When the radius triples, the area __?__. **is multiplied by 9**

   e) **quadruples**

Review

In 16–18, find the absolute value. *(Previous course)*

16. $|7.4|$ **7.4**   17. $|-3.9|$ **3.9**   18. $|6 - 10|$ **4**

In 19–21, write as a power of 3. *(Previous course)*

19. $3^2 \cdot 3^4$ **3^6**   20. $(3 \cdot 3)^5$ **3^{10}**   21. $(3^3)^5$ **3^{15}**

22. Rewrite 395,000,000,000 in scientific notation. *(Previous course)*
   3.95×10^{11}

In 23–25, refer to the graph below. It shows a firm's profits for the years 1990 to 1995. *(Previous course)*

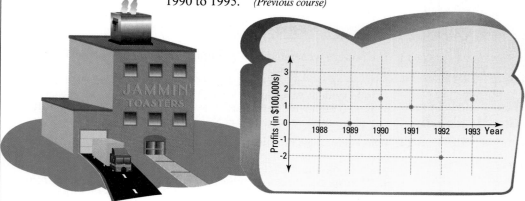

23. About how much profit did the company make in 1990? **$150,000**

24. In what year(s) did the company lose money? **1992**

25. During which intervals did the profits decline?
   1988–1989; 1990–1991; 1991–1992

76

Adapting to Individual Needs

English Language Development
Music Connection A constant is a thing, a value, or a quantity that is always the same; it does not change. To help students with limited English proficiency understand the idea of a *constant*, you might use a drum, guitar, or other musical instrument to show a constant beat; then contrast this with a variable beat.

Explain that in mathematics, a constant is a quantity that stays the same throughout a discussion. In the definition of direct variation, k is the constant—it remains the same throughout a direct variation situation.

There are several phrases related to direct variation that students might add to their index cards: *varies directly as*, *constant of variation*, *direct variation*, and *directly proportional to*.

In 26 and 27, copy the triangle below. Graph the image of the triangle under the given transformation. *(Previous course)*

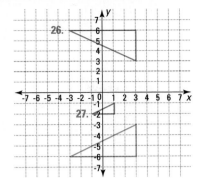

Music to your ears. *A carillon, like this one atop Lupton Hall at Oglethorpe University in Atlanta, is a set of 23 or more bells, usually having diameters that range from 3.5 in. to 10.25 ft. Carillons are popular on college campuses because the sounds produced can be heard over a wide area.*

26. reflection over the x-axis

27. size change of magnitude $\frac{1}{3}$

Exploration

28. The speed of sound in air is about 1088 feet per second.
   a. Convert the speed of sound to miles per second. $\approx 0.206 \frac{mi}{sec}$
   b. Use your answer from part **a** to find the time it takes sound to travel four miles. Compare this answer to the values in Question 14.
   c. What environmental conditions affect the speed of sound?
   b, c) See below.

29. Find a manual for learning how to drive. Often these manuals contain stopping and braking distances. Do the braking distances given in the manual vary directly as the square of the speed?

Answers will vary. A sample table of stopping distances is given below:

mph	10	20	30	40	50	60	70
stopping distance	19	42	73	116	173	248	343

28b) ≈19.42 sec;   the answers are very close
   c) Sample: temperature, pressure, elevation, or humidity

Practice
For more questions on SPUR Objectives, use **Lesson Master 2-1A** (shown on page 75) or **Lesson Master 2-1B** (shown on pages 76–77).

Assessment
Oral/Written Communication
Have students **work in pairs** to (1) make up a direct-variation function, (2) write an equation describing the variation, (3) assign values to the two variables and find the constant of variation, (4) assign a new value to the independent variable and find the corresponding value for the dependent variable. [Students demonstrate an understanding of evaluating a direct-variation function.]

Extension
Have students use an almanac and the formula in Additional Example 1 to determine how much a 100-pound person would weigh on other planets. [Samples: Mercury ≈ 37 lb; Venus ≈ 88 lb; Mars ≈ 38 lb; Jupiter ≈ 264 lb; Saturn and Uranus ≈ 115 lb; Neptune ≈ 112 lb; Pluto ≈ 4 lb.]

Project Update Project 1, *Pizza Prices*, on page 128, relates to the content of this lesson.

▶ **LESSON MASTER 2-1B** *page 2*

Uses Objective F: Recognize direct-variation situations.
In 14–16, translate into a variation situation.

14. The price p of a pizza varies directly as the square of its diameter d. — $p = kd^2$

15. The rebate r is directly proportional to the number n of coupons submitted. — $r = kn$

16. The volume V of a spherical helium balloon is directly proportional to the cube of its radius r. — $V = kr^3$

Uses Objective G: Solve real-world problems involving direct variation.

17. When lightning strikes 8 miles away, the sound of the thunder is heard about 40 seconds later. The time it takes for the sound to travel is directly proportional to the distance. How long does it take the sound to travel if lightning strikes 6 miles away? — 30 sec

18. The distance a car travels before stopping after the driver brakes varies directly as the square of the speed of the car. If a car travels 30 feet after the driver brakes when the car's speed is 20 mph, how far will the car travel after the driver brakes if the car's speed is 60 mph? — 270 ft

19. The designers of the Parthenon, a Greek temple completed in 432 B.C., utilized the golden ratio. The outline of its face fits into a golden rectangle, in which the length varies directly as its height in the ratio 1.618 to 1. The length of the temple was about 31 m. What was the original height of the Parthenon? — ≈ 19.2 m

22. The rear wheel of a 5-speed bicycle turns 770 times in a mile. The table below lists the number of pedal turns for rear-wheel turns in each gear. The number of rear-wheel turns in each gear is directly proportional to the number of pedal turns.

Gear	First	Second	Third	Fourth	Fifth
Pedal turns	9	4	1	3	5
Rear-wheel turns	14	7	2	7	14

How many times must a person pedal in a mile in each gear?

a. First __495__   **b.** Second __440__   **c.** Third __385__
d. Fourth __330__   **e.** Fifth __275__

Objectives

A Translate inverse-variation language into formulas and formulas into inverse-variation language.
B Solve inverse-variation problems.
F Recognize inverse-variation situations.
G Solve real-world problems involving inverse variation.

Resources

From the **Teacher's Resource File**
■ Lesson Master 2-2A or 2-2B
■ Answer Master 2-2
■ Teaching Aids
  8 Four-Quadrant Graph Paper
  13 Warm-up
■ Activity Kit, Activity 3

Additional Resources
■ Visuals for Teaching Aids 8, 13

Teaching Lesson **2-2**

Warm-up

Diagnostic Work in small groups.
The time needed to travel a fixed distance varies inversely with the average speed. Select an arbitrary distance and make a table of values of speed and time. Explain how changing one variable affects the other variable.

Sample for 100 miles:

r(mph)	10	15	20	40	100
t(hr)	10	6.6	5	2.5	1

As the average rate of speed increases the time decreases, and vice versa.

Inverse Variation

Division of labor. *The amount of time each student must work tends to vary inversely as the number of students.*

Metro Car Sales hires students to wash cars in the company's display lots. The manager knows from experience that one student can wash all the cars in 36 working hours. When more students work, each student needs to work fewer hours. If s equals the number of students who work and t equals the time (in hours) each student needs to work, then the product st is the total number of hours worked, and

$$st = 36, \text{ or } t = \frac{36}{s}.$$

Some combinations of s and t that might be used to finish the job are given below.

s	4	8	9	12	16
t	9	$4\frac{1}{2}$	4	3	$2\frac{1}{4}$

❶ Definition of Inverse Variation

The formula $t = \frac{36}{s}$ which determines the values in the table has the form $y = \frac{k}{x^n}$ where $n = 1$. This is an instance of *inverse variation*. We say t **varies inversely as** s. In this example, the constant of variation k is 36.

> **Definition**
> An **inverse-variation function** is a function with a formula of the form $y = \frac{k}{x^n}$, with $k \neq 0$ and $n > 0$.

When y varies inversely as x^n, we also say that y **is inversely proportional to** x^n. As with direct variation, inverse variation occurs in many kinds of situations.

Lesson 2-2 Overview

Broad Goals This lesson, a companion to Lesson 2-1, introduces the language and concept of inverse variation.

Perspective If $y = \frac{k}{x}$, then y varies inversely as x. If $y = \frac{k}{x^2}$, then y varies inversely as x^2. Regardless of the exponent of x, we call the relationship between x and y an inverse variation. Whenever there is a direct-variation formula (where the product

of two quantities is the third), such as $A = LW$, you can solve for one of the quantities and show that an inverse variation relationship exists. ($L = \frac{A}{W}$ and $W = \frac{A}{L}$.) For instance, if the area of a rectangle is fixed, the length of the rectangle is inversely proportional to the width.

Of all the variation relationships in the physical world, the inverse-square laws are

among the most important, since they occur so frequently. It is primarily because of the inverse-square laws that inverse variation is taught. The reason that inverse-square relationships are associated with light and sound intensity comes from the fact that the set of points at a given distance from a given point is a sphere. If a sound S leaves a source at a given time, that sound will be dispersed on the surface of a sphere. Thus, the given amount of sound S is dispersed

Example 1

The number n of oranges you can pack in a box is approximately inversely proportional to the cube of the average diameter d of the oranges. Write an equation to express this relation.

Solution

The cube of the diameter is d^3. So, $n \approx \frac{k}{d^3}$.

Solving Inverse-Variation Problems

Many scientific principles involve inverse-variation functions. For instance, the *Law of the Lever* states that to balance a given person seated on a seesaw, the distance d the other person is from the pivot (or fulcrum) is inversely proportional to that person's weight w. That is, $d = \frac{k}{w}$.

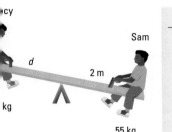

Example 2

Nancy and Sam are trying to balance on a seesaw. Sam, who weighs 55 kilograms, is sitting 2 meters from the fulcrum. Nancy weighs 50 kilograms. How far away from the fulcrum must she sit to balance Sam?

Solution

We use the same four steps as for direct-variation problems.
Let d = a person's distance in meters from the fulcrum.
Let w = a person's weight in kilograms.

1. Write an equation relating d and w. From the Law of the Lever,
$$d = \frac{k}{w}.$$

2. To find k, substitute Sam's weight and distance into $d = \frac{k}{w}$.
$$2 = \frac{k}{55}$$
$$110 = k$$

3. The work in step 2 tells you that the variation formula for this situation is
$$d = \frac{110}{w}.$$

4. Evaluate this formula when $w = 50$ kg.
$$d = \frac{110}{50}$$
$$d = 2.2$$
Nancy must sit 2.2 meters away from the fulcrum.

Check

Does 2 meters · 55 kilograms = 2.2 meters · 50 kilograms? Yes, the numbers and the units agree.

Caution: If a different person is seated on the same seesaw, the value of k in the Law of the Lever may change.

Lesson 2-2   Inverse Variation   79

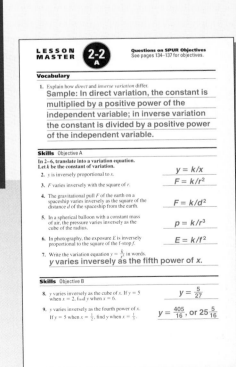

---

over an area ($4\pi r^2$) proportional to the square of the radius. Therefore, at a given point on the sphere, the original amount of sound is divided by the square of the radius, which is why the intensity is proportional to the inverse square.

Optional Activities

Activity 1 Cooperative Learning
You can use this activity after students have finished the lesson. Direct attention to the examples students found in the *Warm-up* in Lesson 2-1. Have students identify those situations which exemplify direct or inverse variation and have them translate those examples into variation equations.

Additional Examples

1. In a given room, the floor space *F* per person varies inversely as the square of the number of people in the room. Write an equation to express this relation.

   $F = \dfrac{k}{n^2}$

2. The time *T* required to do a job varies inversely as the number of workers *W*. It takes 5 hours for 8 cement finishers to do a certain job. Find *k*, the constant of variation. How long would it take 12 workers to do the same job?
   k = 40; 3 hours 20 minutes

3. The intensity of light that reaches you from a light bulb varies inversely as the square of your distance *d* from the bulb. When you are standing 10 feet away from a certain light bulb, its intensity is 130 units. What is the intensity of the bulb when you are standing 4 feet away?
   812.5 units

(Notes on Questions begin on page 82.)

But can he keep the weight off? *On June 3, 1965, Astronaut Edward H. White II became the first American to walk in space. White was the pilot of the* Gemini IV *space mission.*

The weight *W* of a body above the surface of the Earth varies inversely as the square of its distance *d* from the center of the Earth. That is, $W = \dfrac{k}{d^2}$. This instance of an *inverse-square variation* explains why astronauts are almost weightless in space.

Example 3

If an astronaut weighs 165 pounds on the surface of the Earth, what will the astronaut weigh 18,000 miles above the Earth's surface? (The radius of the Earth is approximately 4000 miles.)

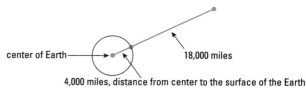

center of Earth ⟶   18,000 miles

4,000 miles, distance from center to the surface of the Earth

Solution

1. Write an equation that describes the variation. **Let W = the weight of the astronaut in pounds and d = the distance from the center of the Earth to the astronaut. Because W varies inversely as the square of the distance,**

   $$W = \dfrac{k}{d^2}.$$

   An astronaut 18,000 miles above the Earth's surface is 22,000 miles from the center of the Earth. We need to find *W* when *d* = 22,000.

2. Find *k*, the constant of variation, by substituting the values *W* = 165 lb and *d* = 4000 mi. This indicates that on the surface of the Earth, the astronaut weighs 165 lb.

   $$165 = \dfrac{k}{(4000)^2}$$
   $$165 \cdot 16,000,000 = k$$
   $$2.64 \cdot 10^9 = k$$

3. Rewrite the variation function using the constant of variation.

   $$W = \dfrac{2.64 \cdot 10^9}{d^2}$$

4. Substitute *d* = 22,000 into the inverse-square function.

   $$W = \dfrac{2.64 \cdot 10^9}{(22,000)^2}$$
   $$\approx 5.5 \text{ lb}$$

   At 18,000 miles above the Earth's surface, the astronaut weighs only about 5.5 pounds.

Optional Activities

Activity 2 Science Connection
After discussing **Example 2**, you might have students **work in pairs** and investigate how a seesaw works. [Sample: the center of gravity of a seesaw is the center of the board when no one sits on it. If different weights are placed on opposite ends of the board, the center of gravity will shift to a point between the center and the heavier end. When the heavier weight is moved toward the center of the board, the center of gravity also moves back toward the center of the board and the board will again balance.]

Activity 3 You can use *Activity Kit, Activity 3*, as either an introduction or a follow-up to the lesson. In this activity, students investigate the inverse relationship between weight and distance on a seesaw.

Covering the Reading

In 1 and 2, refer to the Metro Car Sales problem on page 78.

1. The time to finish the job varies inversely as the __?__.
   number of students

2. Only 12 students are found to work. How long will it take them to complete the job? **3 hours**

3. The equation $y = \frac{k}{x^3}$ means y varies inversely as __?__. **x^3**

4. Suppose x varies inversely as the 4th power of t. Write an equation to describe the variation. **$x = \frac{k}{t^4}$**

5. *Multiple choice.* Assume k is a nonzero constant. Which equation does not represent an inverse variation? **a**
   (a) $y = kx$ (b) $y = \frac{k}{x}$ (c) $xy = k$ (d) $y = \frac{k}{x^2}$

6. Refer to Example 2. If Sam sits 2.5 yards from the fulcrum, how far away from the fulcrum must Nancy sit to balance him? **2.75 yd**

7. Find the distance needed to balance on the seesaw shown below.
   ≈ 2.14 yd

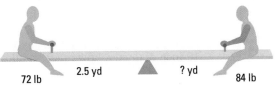

   72 lb   2.5 yd   ? yd   84 lb

8. Refer to Example 3. Find the weight of an astronaut in a space lab 300 miles above the Earth if the astronaut weighs 150 lb on Earth.
   ≈ 129.8 lb

Applying the Mathematics

9. Translate this statement into a variation equation. The time t an appliance can be run on 1 kilowatt-hour of electricity is inversely proportional to the wattage rating w of the appliance. **$t = \frac{k}{w}$**

10. If y varies inversely as x^3, and $y = 10$ when $x = 4$, find the value of y when $x = 2$. **$y = 80$**

11. The intensity I of light varies inversely as the square of the observer's distance D from the light source.
    a. Translate this statement into a variation equation. **$I = \frac{k}{D^2}$**
    b. Suppose that the light intensity is 30 lumens when the observer is 6.7 meters from the light. Find the constant of variation.
    c. Find the light intensity when the distance between the observer and the light is 20 meters. **≈ 3.37 lumens**
    b) **$k = 1346.7$ lumens · m²**

Lights, camera, . . . *Most professional photographers use hand-held light meters to measure light intensity, thereby enabling them to determine the correct exposure.*

Lesson 2-2 *Inverse Variation* **81**

Follow-up 2-2 for Lesson

Practice

For more questions on SPUR Objectives, use **Lesson Master 2-2A** (shown on pages 79–80) or **Lesson Master 2-2B** (shown on pages 81–82).

Assessment

Written Communication Have students **work in small groups.** Have each group select an inverse-variation problem from the lesson and explain how the four steps given on page 74 are carried out to solve the problem. [Students demonstrate an understanding of the four steps of evaluating an inverse variation for a value of the independent variable.]

(Follow-up continues on page 82.)

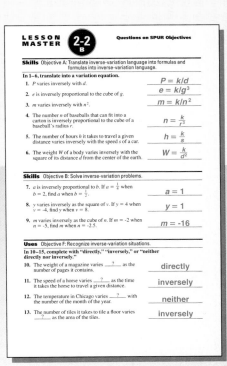

LESSON MASTER 2-2 B   Questions on SPUR Objectives

Skills Objective A: Translate inverse-variation language into formulas and formulas into inverse-variation language.

In 1–6, translate into a variation equation.
1. P varies inversely with d. $P = k/d$
2. e is inversely proportional to the cube of g. $e = k/g^3$
3. m varies inversely with n^2. $m = k/n^2$
4. The number n of baseballs that can fit into a carton is inversely proportional to the cube of a baseball's radius r. $n = \frac{k}{r^3}$
5. The number of hours h it takes to travel a given distance varies inversely with the speed s of a car. $h = \frac{k}{s}$
6. The weight W of a body varies inversely with the square of its distance d from the center of the earth. $W = \frac{k}{d^2}$

Skills Objective B: Solve inverse-variation problems.
7. a is inversely proportional to b. If $a = \frac{1}{4}$ when $b = 2$, find a when $b = \frac{1}{2}$. $a = 1$
8. y varies inversely as the square of v. If $y = 4$ when $v = -4$, find y when $v = 8$. $y = 1$
9. m varies inversely as the cube of n. If $m = -2$ when $n = -5$, find m when $n = -2.5$. $m = -16$

Uses Objective F: Recognize inverse-variation situations.
In 10–15, complete with "directly," "inversely," or "neither directly nor inversely."
10. The weight of a magazine varies __?__ as the number of pages it contains.   directly
11. The speed of a horse varies __?__ as the time it takes the horse to travel a given distance.   inversely
12. The temperature in Chicago varies __?__ with the number of the month of the year.   neither
13. The number of tiles it takes to tile a floor varies __?__ as the area of the tiles.   inversely

---

Adapting to Individual Needs

Extra Help
Some students will confuse direct variation with inverse variation. Stress that both variables in a direct variation function increase or decrease. In an inverse-variation function, one variable increases while the other variable decreases.

English Language Development
To help students understand *inverse*, explain that inverse means *opposite*. Ask students to name some words that are opposites. Then use the table for the inverse-variation equation $st = 36$, featured in the opening paragraphs of the lesson, to point out that as the values of s get larger, the values of t get smaller.

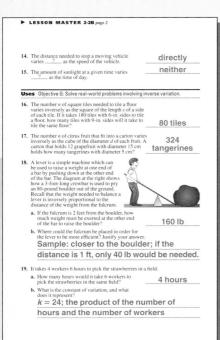

82

---

12) Sample: Volume is measured in cubic units. As the volume of oranges increases, the number that are able to fit in a box decreases. So, the number of oranges varies inversely as the cube of the average diameter.

7′6″er. Shawn Bradley, shown with the ball, was the number two pick in the 1993 NBA draft. He was signed by the Philadelphia 76ers.

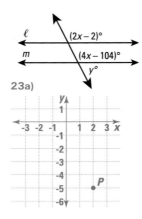

23a)

82

---

12. Refer to Example 1. Why do you think a correct variation equation is $n \approx \frac{k}{d^3}$ and not some other equation such as $n \approx kd^3$ or $n \approx \frac{k}{d^2}$? See left.

In 13 and 14, complete the sentence with the word "directly" or "inversely."

13. The volume of a sphere varies __?__ as the cube of its radius. **directly**

14. The number of tiles needed to tile a floor varies __?__ as the square of the length of a side of the tile. **inversely**

15. Consider again the Metro Car Sales problem on page 78.
a. Complete the table below.

s	1	2	3	4	5	6	7	8	9	10	11	12
t	36	18	12	9	$7\frac{1}{5}$	6	$5\frac{1}{7}$	$4\frac{1}{2}$	4	$3\frac{3}{5}$	$3\frac{3}{11}$	3

b. Compare the values of *t* when *s* = 2 and when *s* = 4, when *s* = 4 and when *s* = 8, and when *s* = 6 and when *s* = 12. Make a conjecture. When the number of people working doubles, the time __?__. **is halved**

c. Follow a similar procedure to complete the following conjecture. When the number of people working triples, the time __?__. **is multiplied by $\frac{1}{3}$**

Review

16. At some restaurants, the price of a pizza varies directly with the square of its diameter. If you pay $5.95 for a cheese pizza with a 10-inch diameter, how much should a 14-inch-diameter cheese pizza cost? *(Lesson 2-1)* **$11.66**

17. If two people have the same shape, then their weight varies directly as the cube of their height. In 1994, the basketball player Shawn Bradley was 7′6″ tall, and he weighed about 250 pounds. How much would you expect a person 5′10″ tall with Shawn's shape to weigh? *(Lesson 2-1)* **≈117.63 pounds**

18. If $f(p) = 5p^2$, find $f(3x)$. *(Lesson 1-3)* **$45x^2$**

19. Line ℓ is parallel to line *m* in the figure at the left. The expressions represent angle measures. Find *y*. *(Previous course)* **y = 80**

In 20–22, simplify. *(Previous course)*

20. $x^{10} \cdot x^3$ **x^{13}**   21. $\frac{x^{12}}{x^4}$ **x^8**   22. $(2x)^3$ **$8x^3$**

23. a. Plot the point $P = (2, -5)$. **See left.**
b. Write an equation for the horizontal line through *P*. **y = -5**
c. Write an equation for the vertical line through *P*. *(Previous course)* **x = 2**

Exploration

24. Consult a science or economics text to find some other examples of inverse variation. **Samples: The frequency of a wave traveling in a medium varies inversely as the wavelength. The price of a certain item varies inversely as the quantity of that item on the market.**

Functions of Variation

IN-CLASS
ACTIVITY

In Lesson 2-1, Question 15, you explored the effects of doubling or tripling the radius r on the area A of a circle. In Lesson 2-2, Question 15, you explored the effects of doubling or tripling the values of s on the value of t in the equation $t = \frac{36}{s}$.

In this Activity, you will explore how changes in the independent variable of two other variation functions result in changes in the dependent variable. Work on this Activity in small groups.

1 Consider the direct-variation formula $y = x^3$. a) Answers will vary.
a. Each person in your group should choose a different value for the independent variable. Double, triple, and quadruple the original value and record the values in a chart like the one shown here. Then find the corresponding values of y for each x and record them in a table.

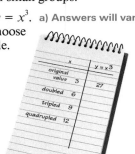

b. Draw Conclusions. Discuss your results with other members of your group and answer these questions. What happens to y when x is doubled? What happens to y when x is tripled? What happens to y when x is multiplied by four? If y is directly proportional to x^3, when x is multiplied by c, what happens to y? y is multiplied by 2^3, or 8; y is multiplied by 3^3, or 27; y is multiplied by 4^3, or 64; y is multiplied by c^3.

2 Consider the inverse-variation formula $y = \frac{1}{x^3}$.
a. Each person in your group should choose a different value for the independent variable. Double, triple, and quadruple that original value and make a chart as in part **1**. Find the corresponding values of y for each x and record them in a table. Answers will vary.
b. Draw Conclusions. Discuss your results with other members of your group and answer these questions. What happens to y when x is doubled? What happens to y when x is tripled? What happens to y when x is multiplied by four? If y is inversely proportional to x^3, when x is multiplied by c, what happens to y?
y is divided by 2^3, or 8; y is divided by 3^3, or 27;
y is divided by 4^3, or 64; y is divided by c^3.

83

In-class Activity
Resources
From the **Teacher's Resource File**
■ Answer Master 2-3
■ Teaching Aid 17: Tables

Additional Resources
■ Visual for Teaching Aid 17

This activity is intended for use in class before Lesson 2-3 is discussed. The activity should be done at the expense of discussing some of the questions in Lesson 2-2. However, be sure to discuss **Question 15** on page 82 before doing the activity.

When doing this activity, you may want to use **Teaching Aid 17,** which contains tables to record values.

Even students who successfully answered **Question 15** in Lesson 2-2 and **Question 15** in Lesson 2-1 may have trouble generalizing the result that we call the Fundamental Theorem of Variation. In this activity, students investigate two examples of the Fundamental Theorem of Variation. The first example, with $y = x^3$, leads to the conclusion that if x is multiplied by c, then y is multiplied by c^3. The second example, with $y = \frac{1}{x^3}$, leads to the conclusion that if x is multiplied by c, then y is divided by c^3. By considering these special cases, students will have a better understanding of the meaning of the general theorem.

Objectives
D Use the Fundamental Theorem of Variation.

Resources

From the Teacher's Resource File
- Lesson Master 2-3A or 2-3B
- Answer Master 2-3
- Assessment Sourcebook: Quiz for Lessons 2-1 through 2-3
- Teaching Aids
  8 Four-Quadrant Graph Paper
  13 Warm-up

Additional Resources
- Visuals for Teaching Aids 8, 13

Teaching Lesson 2-3

Warm-up
Solve the following problems.
1. Each side of a square patio is 7 feet long. The owner plans to increase the size of the patio by increasing the length of each side by 50%. How will the area of the enlarged patio compare with the area of the original patio? **The area is multiplied by 2.25, from 49 ft² to 110.25 ft².**

2. The length of each edge of a cube is 10 inches. How does the volume of a cube with edges three times as long compare with the volume of the smaller cube? **The volume becomes 27 times as large, increasing from 1000 in³ to 27,000 in³.**

The Fundamental Theorem of Variation

Modern cat. *White Bengal tigers may attain a shoulder height of 1 meter and weigh as much as 225 kg. Tigers such as this one may have descended from the extinct Saber-toothed cat. See Example 2.*

Recall that the area A of a circle varies directly with the square of its radius r. $A = \pi r^2$. Some values of r and A are given in the following table.

r	1	2	3	4	5	6	8
A	π	4π	9π	16π	25π	36π	64π

What happens to the area of a circle when the radius is tripled? One way to answer this question is to compare values from the table when the radius is tripled. For example,

$$\text{if } r = 1, \text{ then } A = \pi, \text{ and}$$
$$\text{if } r = 3, \text{ then } A = 9\pi.$$

Notice that when the radius is tripled, the area is multiplied by nine. This pattern also holds if you compare the ordered pairs $(2, 4\pi)$ and $(6, 36\pi)$. Based on the two instances above, it seems reasonable to conjecture that if you triple a circle's radius, the area is multiplied by nine. In geometry, we proved this using properties of similarity. The following example shows how to prove this using properties of algebra.

Lesson 2-3 Overview

Broad Goals This lesson discusses the Fundamental Theorem of Variation, namely, if $y = kx^n$, and x is multiplied (divided) by some number, then y is multiplied (divided) by that number to the nth power.

Perspective Students may have some knowledge of the ideas of this lesson, particularly in the case of linear direct variation. For instance, they know that if they buy three times the number of posters that

they originally planned to buy, then the cost will be three times the amount they planned to spend.

Students typically have more difficulty with nonlinear variation situations. However, you should be able to utilize what students have learned in geometry about areas and volumes of similar figures. Point out that **Example 1** is a special case of a more general theorem: If a size change of

magnitude k is applied to a figure, then the area of the figure is multiplied by k^2. If the figure is 3-dimensional, then its volume is multiplied by k^3. In UCSMP *Geometry*, this theorem is called the Fundamental Theorem of Similarity.

Example 1

Given the direct-variation formula $A = \pi r^2$, prove that if r is tripled, A is multiplied by nine.

Solution

Let A_1 be the original area (before tripling the radius). Let A_2 be the area after tripling the radius. To find A_2, r must be tripled. So replace r by $3r$. Here is a proof given in two-column form.

1. $A_1 = \pi r^2$ given
2. $A_2 = \pi(3r)^2$ substitution
3. $\quad = \pi \cdot 9r^2$ Power of a Product Property
4. $\quad = 9\pi r^2$ Associative and Commutative Properties of Multiplication
5. $\quad = 9A_1$ substitution (step 1 into step 4)

What Is the Fundamental Theorem of Variation?

In the In-class Activity on page 83, you studied the variation equations $y = x^3$ and $y = \frac{1}{x^3}$. You should have found that in $y = x^3$, when x is tripled y is multiplied by 27; and in $y = \frac{1}{x^3}$, when x is tripled, y is divided by 27.

Example 1 and the problems in the Activity are instances of the Fundamental Theorem of Variation. We state the theorem and give the proof of part **a**. You are asked to prove part **b** in the Questions.

The Fundamental Theorem of Variation
a. If y varies directly as x^n (That is, $y = kx^n$.), and x is multiplied by c, then y is multiplied by c^n.
b. If y varies inversely as x^n (That is, $y = \frac{k}{x^n}$.), and x is multiplied by a nonzero constant c, then y is divided by c^n.

Proof of Part a:
Let $y_1 = $ original value before multiplying x by c.
Let $y_2 = $ value when x is multiplied by c.
To find y_2, x must be multiplied by c.

$y_1 = kx^n$ definition of direct variation
$y_2 = k(cx)^n$ definition of y_2
$y_2 = k(c^n x^n)$ Power of a Product Property
$y_2 = c^n(kx^n)$ Associative and Commutative Properties of Multiplication
$y_2 = c^n y_1$ substitution

Notes on Reading

You can use Activity 1 in *Optional Activities* to introduce this lesson.

The proof of part a of the Fundamental Theorem of Variation is difficult for many students to follow because six variables have to be considered (c, k, n, y, y_1, and y_2). You might want to rewrite the first part of the proof as shown below—a form that resembles what students have seen in geometry.
Given: y varies directly as x^n.
            x is multiplied by c.
To Prove: y is multiplied by c^n.

Additional Examples

1. Given the direct-variation formula $d = \frac{s^2}{10}$, prove that if s is quadrupled, d is multiplied by 16.

   Let $d_1 = $ distance before quadrupling, and let $d_2 = $ distance after quadrupling.

   $d_1 = \frac{1}{10}s^2$ Given
   $d_2 = \frac{1}{10}(4s)^2$ Definition of d_2
   $\quad = \frac{1}{10} \cdot 16s^2$ Power of a Product Property
   $\quad = 16 \cdot \frac{1}{10}s^2$ Associative and Commutative Properties of Multiplication
   $\quad = 16d_1$ Substitution

(Additional Examples continue on page 86.)

LESSON MASTER 2-3 A

Questions on SPUR Objectives
See pages 134–137 for objectives.

Properties Objective D

In 1–4, suppose that in a variation problem the value of x is tripled. How is the value of y changed if

1. y varies directly as x? y is tripled.
2. y varies inversely as x? y is divided by 3.
3. y varies directly as x^2? y is multiplied by 9.
4. y varies inversely as x^3? y is divided by 27.

In 5–8, suppose that m varies directly as the fourth power of q. How does the value of m change if

5. q is doubled? m is multiplied by 16.
6. q is quadrupled? m is multiplied by 256.
7. q is multiplied by 6? m is multiplied by 1296.
8. q is multiplied by $\frac{1}{3}$? m is multiplied by $\frac{1}{81}$.

In 9–12, suppose that p varies inversely as the fifth power of n. How does the value of p change if

9. n is doubled? p is divided by 32.
10. n is quadrupled? p is divided by 1024.
11. n is multiplied by 6? p is divided by 7776.
12. n is multiplied by $\frac{1}{3}$? p is divided by $\frac{1}{243}$.

13. If $w = kz^n$ and z is multiplied by a constant c, what happens to w? w is multiplied by c^n.
14. If $w = \frac{k}{z^n}$ and z is multiplied by a constant c, what happens to w? w is divided by c^n.

Optional Activities

Activity 1
Before discussing the lesson, you might want to have students review some things they have learned about area and volume. For instance, consider a rectangular solid F with dimensions 3, 4, and 7. It has a surface area of 122 square units and its volume is 84 cubic units. Now, suppose F is similar to a rectangular solid F'. Tell students that the ratio of similitude is 5, and ask them to find the dimensions of F'. [15, 20, and 35] Then have them verify that the surface area of F' is 25 times the surface area of F and that the volume of F' is 125 times the volume of F. [The surface area of F' is 3050, which is $25 \cdot 122$; the volume of F' is 10,500, which is $125 \cdot 84$.] In general, ratios of areas vary as the square of ratios of linear dimensions; ratios of volumes vary as the cube of ratios of linear dimensions.

2. **Literature Connection** The Brobdingnagians in Jonathan Swift's *Gulliver's Travels* are similar to us, but they are 12 times as tall. Answer **parts a and b** using the fact that volumes in similar figures vary directly as the cube of height and surface areas vary directly as the square of height.
   a. Compare the relationship between their volume and surface area and ours. **Their volume is 1728 times our volume; their surface area is 144 times our surface area.**
   b. Answer **part a** assuming the Brobdingnagians were only twice as tall as we are. **Their volume is 8 times ours; their surface area is 4 times ours.**

3. The formula $I = \frac{k}{D^2}$ tells that the intensity of light varies inversely as the square of the distance from the light source. What effect does doubling the distance have on the intensity of the light? Justify your answer. **Sample: Replace D in the formula with $2D$ to get $(2D)^2 = 4D^2$. When D is multiplied by 2, I is divided by 4. The intensity of the light is $\frac{1}{4}$ the original intensity.**

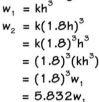

Ancient cat. *Pictured is a skeleton of the extinct Saber-toothed cat. Saber-toothed cats are named for the pair of elongated, blade-like canine teeth— up to 20 cm long—they had in their upper jaw.*

Applications of the Fundamental Theorem of Variation

The Fundamental Theorem of Variation can be applied in many situations.

Example 2

If we assume that animals of a given species are similar, then we can apply a theorem from geometry which says that the weight w of an animal of the species varies directly with the cube of its height h. If an ancient cat was 1.8 times as tall as a modern one, how many times as great was the weight of the ancient cat than the weight of the modern cat?

Solution 1

Set the problem up as in Example 1.
An equation for the variation function is $w = kh^3$.
Let w_1 = the weight of the modern cat, and
w_2 = the weight of the cat with height 1.8h.

$$w_1 = kh^3$$
$$w_2 = k(1.8h)^3$$
$$= k(1.8)^3 h^3$$
$$= (1.8)^3 (kh^3)$$
$$= (1.8)^3 w_1$$
$$= 5.832 w_1$$

So $w_2 \approx 5.8 w_1$. An ancient cat weighed about 5.8 times as much as a modern cat.

Solution 2

Because weight varies directly as the cube of the height, An equation for the variation function is $w = kh^3$. Now apply the Fundamental Theorem of Variation. This is a direct-variation function with $n = 3$. So, When h is multiplied by 1.8, w is multiplied by $(1.8)^3 = 5.832$. Thus, an ancient cat weighed about 5.8 times as much as a modern cat.

Example 3

Recall that $d = \frac{k}{w}$ is the Law of the Lever. Nathan weighs twice as much as his daughter Stephie. Compare their distances from the fulcrum when they are balanced on a seesaw. Justify your answer.

Solution

Apply the Fundamental Theorem of Variation. Because Nathan weighs twice as much as Stephie, we must find the effect of replacing w with 2w in the formula $d = \frac{k}{w}$. This is an inverse-variation function with n = 1. So when w is multiplied by 2, d is divided by 2. Thus Nathan's distance from the fulcrum is half of Stephie's distance.

86

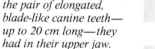
Optional Activities

Activity 2
You might want to ask students to give an algebraic solution to **Question 13.**
[Radius of smaller logo: r
Circumference of smaller logo: $2\pi r$
Radius of larger logo: $2r$
Circumference of larger logo: $2\pi(2r) = 4\pi r$
Ratio of larger to smaller circumference: $\frac{4\pi r}{2\pi r} = \frac{2}{1}$]

Adapting to Individual Needs

Extra Help
Students may have trouble understanding the Fundamental Theorem of Variation and its proof because so many different variables are used. Have these students recopy the theorem and substitute specific values for *k*, *n*, and *c*. Then have them copy the proof of the theorem using these specific values. Point out that while using specific values does not constitute a general proof, it can sometimes clarify the steps in a proof.

QUESTIONS

Covering the Reading

In 1 and 2, consider the formula $A = \pi r^2$ for the area of a circle as a function of its radius.

1. The pairs $(3, 9\pi)$ and $(6, 36\pi)$ illustrate the pattern that if the circle's radius is doubled, the area is multiplied by __?__.   4

2. a. Find two pairs of numbers that illustrate this result: if the radius is multiplied by five, then the circle's area is multiplied by 25.
   b. Follow the solution to Example 1 and prove the result in part **a**. See left.

3. If $y = kx^n$ and x is multiplied by c, then y is __?__.   multiplied by c^n

4. If $y = \frac{k}{x^n}$ and x is multiplied by c ($c \neq 0$), then y is __?__.   divided by c^n

5. Refer to Example 2. Suppose an ancient cat was 0.9 times as tall as a modern one. Compare the weight of the ancient cat to the weight of a modern cat.   An ancient cat would have weighed 0.729 times as much as a modern cat.

6. Refer to Example 3. Suppose Nathan weighs three times as much as his niece Oprah.
   a. Compare Nathan's and Oprah's distances from the fulcrum when they are balanced.   Nathan's distance is $\frac{1}{3}$ that of Oprah's.
   b. Justify your answer.   By the Fundamental Theorem of Variation, if weight is multiplied by 3, then distance is divided by 3.

Applying the Mathematics

In 7 and 8, suppose $y = 5x^4$.

7. Describe the change in y when x is tripled. Explain your reasoning. See left.

8. What happens to y when x is divided by three? Find a set of ordered pairs to illustrate your answer.
y is multiplied by $(1/3)^4$, or 1/81. Sample: (3, 405);   (1, 5)

In 9–11, state the effect that halving the x-values $\left(\text{multiplying them by } \frac{1}{2}\right)$ has on the y-values.   See left.

9. $y = 10x$ **10.** $y = 10x^2$ **11.** $y = \frac{10}{x}$

12. For a pizza party, Becki planned to order five 7-inch-diameter pizzas. At the last minute, extra guests were invited and she needed to increase the order.   a) $\approx$192.4 in^2 b) $\approx$384.8 in^2
   a. Find the number of square inches of pizza in the original order.
   b. Suppose Becki doubles the order, that is, she orders ten pizzas instead of five. How many square inches of pizza will she have?
   c. Suppose Becki doubles the size of the pizza to be ordered. That is, she orders five 14-inch-diameter pizzas. How many square inches of pizza will she have? $\approx$769.7 in^2
   d. Explain the difference in parts **b** and **c** in relation to the Fundamental Theorem of Variation.   See margin.

Adapting to Individual Needs

English Language Development
When discussing the Fundamental Theorem of Variation, you might point out that the word *fundamental* means forming a foundation or a base. The properties of direct and inverse variation given in the Fundamental Theorem of Variation form the foundation for mathematical variation.

Notes on Questions
Questions 7–15 Error Alert These questions may be difficult for some students. Suggest that they substitute numbers for the variables so they can examine specific examples before they arrive at answers to the questions. *Examining specific cases before forming a general conclusion* is a good problem-solving strategy that students should know.

Question 11 You can help students develop intuition by using algebra to arrive at the answers. This more general approach may be discussed after students have worked through specific examples with numbers. Here is an algebraic solution:
Replace x in $y = \frac{10}{x}$ with $\frac{1}{2}x$ to get:
$y = \frac{10}{\frac{1}{2}x} = \frac{10}{\frac{x}{2}} = 2 \cdot \frac{10}{x}$. This shows that y is doubled when x is halved.

Additional Answers
12d. The variation function is $A = kr^2$ where $k = \pi$. In part b, twice as many pizzas were ordered, which multiplies both k and A by 2. In part c, the radius is multiplied by 2, and the area is multiplied by 2^2 or 4.

▶ **LESSON MASTER 2-3B** *page 2*

Review Previous course
In 16–21, graph the equation.

16. $4x + 3y = 24$ 17. $y = \frac{1}{2}x + 6$

18. $xy = 12$ 19. $y = x^2$

20. $y = 2^x$ 21. $y = \frac{1}{x}$

Notes on Questions

Question 13 Activity 2 in *Optional Activities* on page 86 gives an algebraic approach to this question.

Question 17 Science Connection Chimpanzees are tailless primates that vary considerably in size, appearance, and temperament. Studies of their intelligence in natural habitats and in laboratories show that they are capable of a degree of insight and that they have the ability to manipulate tools.

Question 19 This situation is the only example of a real-world variation of the 7th power that is known to the authors. Please inform us of any other examples you might find.

Question 23 Students will need graph paper or **Teaching Aid 8**.

Follow-up for Lesson **2-3**

Practice
For more questions on SPUR Objectives, use **Lesson Master 2-3A** (shown on page 85) or **Lesson Master 2-3B** (shown on pages 86–87).

Assessment
Quiz A quiz covering Lessons 2-1 through 2-3 is provided in the *Assessment Sourcebook*.

Written Communication Have each student write two specific examples, one to illustrate Part a of the Fundamental Theorem of Variation and another to illustrate Part b. [Examples illustrate that students understand both parts of the theorem and can apply them to specific examples.]

Extension
If students have studied negative exponents in a previous course, ask them how the two parts of the Fundamental Theorem of Variation can be considered as special cases of one general statement. [The general statement is like the first part, with $n \neq 0$ and $c \neq 0$.]

In 13 and 14, refer to the logos at the left. The radius of the larger logo is twice the radius of the smaller one.

13. What is the ratio of the larger circumference to the smaller? **2:1**

14. What is the ratio of the larger area to the smaller? **4:1**

15. How is the volume of a sphere affected if its radius is doubled? Explain how you got your answer. **multiplied by 8;** $V = \frac{4}{3}\pi r^3$ **for a sphere, so if the radius is doubled, the volume is multiplied by** 2^3 **or 8.**

16. Complete the proof of part **b** of the Fundamental Theorem of Variation. **See left.**

Review

16) Let y_1 = original value before multiplying x by c.
Let y_2 = value when x is multiplied by c.
To find y_2, x must be multiplied by c.

$y_1 = \frac{k}{x^n}$	given
$y_2 = \frac{k}{(cx)^n}$	substitution
$y_2 = \frac{k}{c^n x^n}$	Power of a Product Property
$y_2 = \frac{1}{c^n} \cdot \frac{k}{x^n}$	Associative Property of Multiplication
$y_2 = \frac{1}{c^n} \cdot y_1$	substitution

23ab)
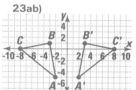

17. Use the equation $W = \frac{k}{d^2}$, where W = weight of a body and d = its distance from the center of the Earth. Suppose a chimpanzee weighs 50 lb on the surface of the Earth. How much will it weigh when orbiting in the space shuttle *Discovery* 200 miles above the Earth's surface? (Remember, the radius of the Earth is about 4000 miles) *(Lesson 2-2)* ≈**45.4 lb**

18. Suppose r varies directly as the third power of s. If $r = 24$ when $s = 8$, find r when $s = 5$. *(Lesson 2-1)* $r = 5.859375$

19. *Multiple choice.* Most of the power of a boat's motor goes into generating the wake (the track left in the water). The engine power P used to generate the wake is directly proportional to the seventh power of the boat's speed s. How can you express this relationship? *(Lesson 2-1)* **c**

(a) $P = 7s$ (b) $s = kP^7$
(c) $P = ks^7$ (d) $P = k^7 s$

20. Solve $5(3m + 5) = 4m - 8$. *(Lesson 1-5)* $m = -3$

21. Write an algebraic expression which describes each situation. *(Lesson 1-1)*
  a. One pencil costs c cents. How much do p pencils cost? cp **cents**
  b. Two pencils cost d cents. How much do r pencils cost? $\frac{rd}{2}$ **cents**

22. *Skill sequence.* Solve. Remember to find two values for x. *(Previous course)*
  a. $x^2 = 49$ **b.** $36x^2 = 49$ **c.** $2x = \frac{49}{2x}$ $x = \frac{7}{2}$ **or** $\frac{-7}{2}$
  $x = 7$ **or** -7 $x = 7/6$ **or** $-7/6$
23. a. Draw $\triangle ABC$ where $A = (-2, -5)$, $B = (-3, 1)$, and $C = (-8, 0)$.
  b. Draw the image of $\triangle ABC$ after reflection over the y-axis.
  (Previous course) **See left.**

Exploration

x	y_1	y_2	y_3	y_4
1	1	1	1	1
2	4	8	16	32
3	9	27	81	243
4	16	64	256	1024
5	25	125	625	3125
6	36	216	1296	7776

24. Complete the table of values at the left for the four functions $y_1 = x^2$, $y_2 = x^3$, $y_3 = x^4$, and $y_4 = x^5$.
  a. Describe some patterns that can be explained by the Fundamental Theorem of Variation. **See margin.**
  b. Describe some other patterns in the table.
  Answers will vary.

Adapting to Individual Needs

Challenge
Ask students to consider a square with sides s, perimeter P, and area A, and a cube with edges s, surface area SA, and volume V. Then have them show perimeter, area, surface area, and volume relationships between these figures and figures in which each dimension has been multiplied by c. [$P = 4cs$, $A = c^2s^2$, $SA = 6c^2s^2$, and $V = c^3s^3$]

Additional Answers
24a. Sample: By the Fundamental Theorem of Variation, when x is multiplied by 2, y is multiplied by 2^2 or 4; y_2 is multiplied by 2^3 or 8; y_3 is multiplied by 2^4 or 16; y_4 is multiplied by 2^5 or 32.

2-4

The Graph of y = kx

This time-lapse photo shows lightning above Tucson, Arizona

Recall from Question 14 in Lesson 2-1 that the distance you are from a lightning strike varies directly with the time elapsed between your seeing the lightning and hearing the thunder. The formula $d = \frac{1}{5}t$ describes this situation. This direct-variation function can also be represented graphically. A table and a graph for the equation $d = \frac{1}{5}t$ are given below.

t = time (in seconds)	5	10	15	20	25	30
d = distance (in miles)	1	2	3	4	5	6

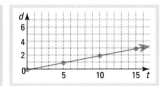

Note that neither distance nor time can be negative in this situation. Thus, the domain of this function is the set of nonnegative real numbers, and the range is also the set of nonnegative real numbers. So, when *all* real-world solutions to the equation $d = \frac{1}{5}t$ are plotted in the coordinate plane, the graph is a ray starting at the origin and passing through the first quadrant. There are no points on the graph in any other quadrants.

Slope of a Line

Recall that the steepness of a line is measured by a number called the *slope*. The slope of a line is the *rate of change* of y with respect to x determined by two points on the line. Let (x_1, y_1) and (x_2, y_2) be the two points. Then, as pictured below, the expression $y_2 - y_1$ is the vertical change (the change in the dependent variable) and $x_2 - x_1$ is the horizontal change (the change in the independent variable). The slope, or rate of change, is the quotient of these changes.

$$\text{slope} = \frac{\text{change in vertical distance}}{\text{change in horizontal distance}}$$

$$= \frac{\text{change in dependent variable}}{\text{change in independent variable}}$$

$$= \frac{\text{rise}}{\text{run}}$$

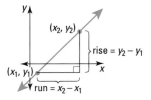

Lesson 2-4 *The Graph of y = kx* **89**

Lesson 2-4

Objectives
C Find slopes.
E Identify properties of variation functions.
I Graph variation equations.
J Identify variation equations from graphs.

Resources
From the ***Teacher's Resource File***
■ Lesson Master 2-4A or 2-4B
■ Answer Master 2-4
■ Teaching Aids
   8 Four-Quadrant Graph Paper
   14 Warm-up
   18 Graphs of Direct-Variation Formulas
■ Technology Sourcebook
   Computer Master 2

Additional Resources
■ Visuals for Teaching Aids 8, 14, 18
■ GraphExplorer

Teaching Lesson 2-4

Warm-up

1. Graph the set of points (x, y) in which $y = -2x$.

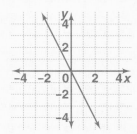

2. What is the slope of the line you graphed? –2

Lesson 2-4 Overview

Broad Goals This lesson reviews the graphs of lines through the origin and the idea of slope.

Perspective Most of this lesson should be review for students. Those who have had previous UCSMP courses will have encountered graphs and slopes of these lines in both *Algebra* and *Geometry*. There are two important ideas that should be stressed.

The first is the idea of slope as a rate of change. This idea is extended to nonlinear curves in the next lesson. The second is the idea that there are common features in the graphs of all equations of the form $y = kx$. We expect that students will quickly recognize what the graphs of important functions should look like. We also expect the converse—students should be able to look at a graph and determine if a simple equation

could produce that graph. This latter idea is emphasized in Lessons 2-7 and 2-8.

Notes on Reading

Students' performances on the *Warm-up* will give you an indication of how much you need to discuss this lesson. In some classes, you may be able to proceed directly to the questions and the In-class Activity on page 94.

❶ If students have not had much experience with slope, give some numerical examples and include the units. For instance, you can calculate the slope as $\frac{5\,mi - 2\,mi}{25\,sec - 10\,sec} = \frac{1}{5}$ mile per second. Explain that the slope has *meaning*—it is a rate. The slope is the speed at which thunder travels, namely the speed of sound in air, because light travels so fast that it can be considered instantaneous in this situation.

Students who have studied from *Transition Mathematics* or UCSMP *Algebra* will have seen the Comparison Model for Subtraction (*a − b* is the amount by which *a* exceeds *b*) and the Rate Model for Division (*a/b* is the rate of *a*'s per *b*'s). A special case of comparison is *change*; that is, *a − b* is the change from *b* to *a*. Thus, the slope formula is literally a rate that is formed from two changes. This is why there are both subtraction and division in the slope formula.

Stress that the slope of a line *does not* depend upon the points chosen for calculating it.

❷ The graph of $y = kx$ is also given on **Teaching Aid 18**.

Error Alert A common error when calculating slope is inverting the ratio. The phrase "rise over run," which comes from $\frac{rise}{run}$, or better yet $\frac{"ryse"}{run}$, can help students remember that the change in vertical distance (*y*) is the first member of the ratio.

Awesome grade. *This road is in Quebec. A grade of 18% warns the driver that for every horizontal change of 100 meters there will be a vertical change of 18 meters.*

> **Definition**
> The **slope** of the line through two points (x_1, y_1) and (x_2, y_2) equals
> $$\frac{y_2 - y_1}{x_2 - x_1}.$$

❶ Example

Find the slope of the line with equation $d = \frac{1}{5}t$, where *t* is the independent variable (time in seconds) and *d* is the dependent variable (distance in miles).

Solution

Use the definition of slope. Because *d* is on the vertical axis and *t* is on the horizontal axis, the ordered pairs are of the form (*t, d*).

Find two points on the line; either point can be considered (t_2, d_2). Here we use $(t_1, d_1) = (10, 2)$ and $(t_2, d_2) = (15, 3)$.

$$slope = \frac{d_2 - d_1}{t_2 - t_1} = \frac{3 - 2}{15 - 10}\,\frac{mi}{sec} = \frac{1}{5}\,\frac{mi}{sec}$$

Refer back to the graph at the beginning of this lesson. Notice that for every change of 5 units to the right there is a change of 1 unit up. This is equivalent to saying that for every change of 1 horizontal unit, there is a change of $\frac{1}{5}$ of a vertical unit.

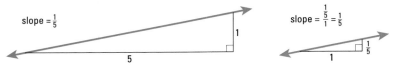

Notice also that the slope $\frac{1}{5}$ of the line $d = \frac{1}{5}t$ is the constant of variation of this direct-variation equation.

❷ Properties of the Function with Equation $y = kx$

In general, the domain of the function with equation $y = kx$ is the set of real numbers. When $k \neq 0$ the range is the set of real numbers. Below are graphs of $y = kx$ for four values of *k*: 2, $\frac{3}{4}$, $-\frac{3}{4}$, and -2.

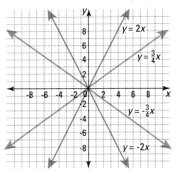

Optional Activities

Activity 1
Materials: Graph paper or **Teaching Aid 8**

After discussing the definition of slope on page 90, you might want to talk about the slope of a line as the distance that the line moves up (or down) as one moves one unit to the right on the line. Some of your students may be very comfortable with this conception of slope; it is accurate and

useful and found in UCSMP *Algebra* and *Geometry*. Consider, for instance, the graph of $y = 2.5x$. Have students start at any point on the line and move one unit to the right. Ask them the distance the line moves up or down [up 2.5 units]. Explain that this is the slope. Have students repeat the procedure for the graph of $y = -2.5x$. [For a move of one unit to the right, the line moves down 2.5 units; the slope is -2.5.]

Activity 2 Career Connection You can extend **Question 25** on page 93 by having students determine how the terms are used in various professions. Suggest that they talk to (a) an accountant or an investment banker; (b) a roofer or an architect; (c) a road construction worker, or a commercial or amateur pilot.

Observe that in each case the graph is a line through the origin with slope k. For example, the slope of $y = 2x$ is 2, and the slope of $y = -\frac{3}{4}x$ is $-\frac{3}{4}$. This is true for all values of k. When $k > 0$, the graph slants up as you read from left to right. When $k < 0$, the graph slants down as you read from left to right.

> **Theorem**
>
> The graph of the direct-variation function $y = kx$ has constant slope k.

Proof:
Let (x_1, y_1) and (x_2, y_2) be two distinct points on $y = kx$, with $k \neq 0$. Then, substitute these values into the variation function.

$$y_1 = kx_1$$
$$y_2 = kx_2$$

Subtract the equations. $\quad y_2 - y_1 = kx_2 - kx_1$

Use the Distributive Property. $\quad y_2 - y_1 = k(x_2 - x_1)$

Solve for k. $\quad \frac{y_2 - y_1}{x_2 - x_1} = k$

So k is the slope.

6b)

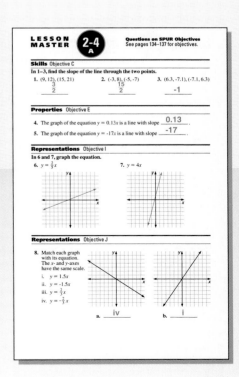

x	$y = 3x$	$y = \frac{1}{2}x$
4	12	2
3	9	$\frac{3}{2}$
2	6	1
1	3	$\frac{1}{2}$
0	0	0
-1	-3	$-\frac{1}{2}$
-2	-6	-1
-3	-9	$-\frac{3}{2}$
-4	-12	-2

QUESTIONS

Covering the Reading

1. The slope of a line is found by dividing the change in __?__ distance by the change in __?__ distance between two points on the line.
   vertical; horizontal
2. Write a definition of slope in terms of independent and dependent variables. **Slope is the change in the dependent variable divided by the change in the independent variable.**
3. By definition, $\frac{y_2 - y_1}{x_2 - x_1}$ is the slope of the line through which points? **(x_1, y_1), (x_2, y_2)**
4. What is the slope of the line $d = \frac{1}{5}t$? **$\frac{1}{5}$**
5. A slope of $-\frac{3}{4}$ means that for every change of 4 units to the right there is a change of __?__ units __?__; it also means that for every change of 1 horizontal unit there is a vertical change of __?__ of a unit.
   3; down; -3/4
6. Use the functions $y = 3x$ and $y = \frac{1}{2}x$.
   a. Complete the table at the left.
   b. On a single set of axes, graph both lines using the values from the table. **See left.**
   c. What is the slope of the line with equation $y = 3x$? **3**
   d. What is the slope of the line with equation $y = \frac{1}{2}x$? **$\frac{1}{2}$**

Adapting to Individual Needs

Activity 3 Technology Connection
You may want to consider using *Technology Sourcebook, Computer Master 2,* with Lessons 2-4, 2-5, and 2-6. Students draw graphs of formulas that represent direct and inverse variation, and they make and test conjectures.

Extra Help
Materials: Graph paper or **Teaching Aid 8**

To convince students that it does not matter which two points are used to find the slope of a line, draw any line (except a horizontal line) through the origin on a coordinate grid. Then find the slope using several pairs of points, noting that the slopes are the same no matter which pairs of points are used.

Notes on Questions

Questions 9–12 The numbers in these situations were purposely chosen to prevent students from calculating the slope solely by counting squares on a grid.

Question 13 Students are required to draw a graph for **part d.** Stress that *c* and *g* both represent quantities greater than or equal to 0; thus, the graph lies entirely in the first quadrant. Remind students that the horizontal and vertical axes need not be drawn to the same scale and, for this reason, the scales used for graphing should be clearly indicated.

Follow-up for Lesson 2-4

Practice

For more questions on SPUR Objectives, use **Lesson Master 2-4A** (shown on page 91) or **Lesson Master 2-4B** (shown on pages 92–93).

Quick dive. *Pictured is the submarine Santa Fe. A submarine dives by flooding its ballast tanks with water. The added weight causes the ship to lose its positive buoyancy. A submarine can dive to a depth of over 100 feet in less than a minute.*

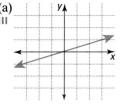

13b) domain: nonnegative real numbers
 range: nonnegative real numbers
c) Sample: (4, 5), (7, 8.75), (14, 17.5)
d)

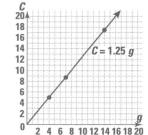

$C = 1.25g$

---

7. The graph of every direct-variation function $y = kx$ is a __?__, with slope __?__, and passing through the point __?__. **line; k; (0, 0)**

8. Graphs that slant up as you read from left to right have __?__ slope; graphs that slant down as you read from left to right have __?__ slope. **positive; negative**

Applying the Mathematics

In 9–12, find the slope of

9. a mountain road which goes up 60 meters for each 1000 meters traveled horizontally. $\frac{3}{50}$

10. a submarine dive if the submarine drops 2000 feet while moving forward 8000 feet. $-\frac{1}{4}$

11. the line through the points (6, 42) and (0, 0). **7**

12. the line through the points (-2, 8) and (5, -40). $-\frac{48}{7}$

13. The cost *c* of gasoline varies directly with the number of gallons *g* bought. **b, c, d) See left.**
 a. If 15 gallons cost $18.75, determine an equation for the variation function. $c = 1.25g$
 b. Give the domain and range of this variation function.
 c. Find three ordered pairs of the function in part **a.**
 d. Graph these pairs. They should lie on the same ray.
 e. What is the slope of the ray in part **d?** **1.25 dollars/gal**
 f. What does the slope represent in this situation?
  For every gallon increase, the cost increases by $1.25.

14. Match each graph with its equation. On each graph, the *x*-axis and the *y*-axis have the same scale.
 I: $y = 3x$ **II:** $y = -3x$ **III:** $y = \frac{1}{3}x$ **IV:** $y = -\frac{1}{3}x$

(a) III
(b) II

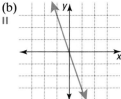

(c) IV
(d) I

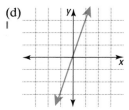
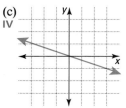

Adapting to Individual Needs

English Language Development
To help students understand the definition of slope given on page 90, make sure that they understand the terms *horizontal* and *vertical*. You might want to show them physical examples of the terms by holding a pencil vertically and holding a ruler horizontally. You can also use the image of the horizon line to help students remember *horizontal*.

Challenge Consumer Connection
Explain that the interest which people earn on savings is subject to income tax. The "effective yield" is the interest rate after taxes are considered. The interest a person receives may be reduced by 15%, 28%, 31%, or 36%, depending on the person's federal tax bracket.

For each tax bracket, have students suppose they are earning 5% interest before

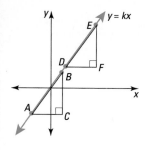

$y = kx$

15) $\triangle ABC \sim \triangle DEF$ by Angle Angle Similarity. Because they are similar, their corresponding sides are proportional. So, the ratios between the vertical and horizontal legs, or slopes, are equal.

22a) The first term is six. Each term after the first is three times the previous term plus one.

15. At the left is a graph of $y = kx$. Explain how similar triangles can be used to show that the slope of the line is the same no matter which points are chosen to find the slope. **See left.**

Review

16. In the variation function $W = \frac{k}{d^2}$, what is the effect on W if
 a. d is tripled? W **is divided by** 3^2 **or 9.**
 b. d is halved? *(Lesson 2-3)* W **is multiplied by** 2^2 **or 4.**

17. Assume that the cost of a spherical ball bearing varies directly as the cube of its diameter. What is the ratio of the cost of a ball bearing 6 mm in diameter to the cost of a ball bearing 3 mm in diameter? *(Lesson 2-3)* **8:1**

In 18–21, state whether the equation is a function of direct variation, a function of inverse variation, or neither. *(Lessons 2-1, 2-2)*

18. $y = -\frac{8}{x}$ **inverse variation**

19. $y = -\frac{x}{8}$ **direct variation**

20. $y = x - 11$ **neither**

21. the Law of the Lever
inverse variation

22. Consider the sequence defined recursively as follows. *(Lessons 1-8, 1-9)*
$$\begin{cases} t_1 = 6 \\ t_n = 3t_{n-1} + 1, \text{ for integers } n \geq 2 \end{cases}$$
 a. Describe the sequence in words. **See left.**
 b. Find the first four terms of the sequence. **6, 19, 58, 175**

23. Ohm's Law, $I = \frac{V}{Z}$, relates current I (in amperes) to voltage V (in volts) and impedance Z (in ohms). *(Lesson 1-6)*
 a. Solve this formula for Z. $Z = \frac{V}{I}$
 b. Solve this formula for V. $V = ZI$

24. *Skill sequence.* Solve for x. *(Lessons 1-5, 1-6)*
 a. $3x = 2$ $x = \frac{2}{3}$
 b. $3x = 2y$ $x = \frac{2y}{3}$
 c. $3x = 2y + 6$ $x = \frac{2y + 6}{3}$ or $\frac{2}{3}y + 2$
 d. $3(x + 5) = 2y + 6$
   $x = \frac{2y + 6}{3} - 5$ or $\frac{2}{3}y - 3$

Exploration

25. Each of the following terms is a synonym for "slope." Find out who might use each term. **Samples are given.**
 a. marginal cost
   an economist
 b. pitch
   a carpenter
 c. grade
   an engineer

Lesson 2-4 *The Graph of $y = kx$* **93**

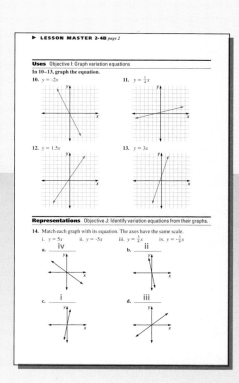

▶ **LESSON MASTER 2-4B** *page 2*

Uses Objective I: Graph variation equations
In 10–13, graph the equation.
10. $y = -2x$ **11.** $y = \frac{1}{4}x$
12. $y = 1.5x$ **13.** $y = 3x$

Representations Objective J: Identify variation equations from their graphs.
14. Match each graph with its equation. The axes have the same scale.
 i. $y = 5x$ ii. $y = -5x$ iii. $y = \frac{3}{4}x$ iv. $y = -\frac{3}{4}x$
 a. iv   **b.** ii
 c. i   **d.** iii

93

Resources

From the *Teacher's Resource File*
- Answer Master 2-5
- Teaching Aid 19: Automatic Grapher Grids

Additional Resources
- Visual For Teaching Aid 19

You may wish to use **Teaching Aid 19** with this activity.

This activity is designed to be done in class before Lesson 2-5 is discussed. It gives you an opportunity to determine what technology skills your students have and what they know about automatic graphers. It also provides an opportunity to discuss the features of the graphers. The activity should be done even at the expense of discussing some of the questions in Lesson 2-4.

Students' automatic graphers should have the capability to draw the graph of an equation $y = kx$. The activity has students examine the graph of $y = kx$ for various values of k to see how each value affects the graph. Work toward the following generalization: the graphs of $y = kx$ and $y = -kx$ are reflection images of each other over the line $y = x$.

Additional Answers

1a.

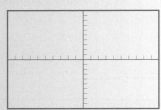

$-10 \leq x \leq 10$, x-scale $= 1$
$-10 \leq y \leq 10$, y-scale $= 1$

2ai.

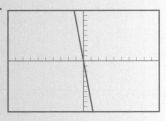

$-10 \leq x \leq 10$, x-scale $= 1$
$-10 \leq y \leq 10$, y-scale $= 1$

Introduction to Automatic Graphers

IN-CLASS
ACTIVITY

Work with a partner or in small groups. Each student needs an automatic grapher.

An **automatic grapher** is either a graphics calculator or function graphing software for use on a computer. Of course, no grapher is completely automatic. Here we discuss what you need to know in order to use any automatic grapher. Consult your calculator owner's manual or your function grapher's documentation for specific information about your grapher.

The part of the coordinate plane that shows on your grapher's screen is called a **window**. Every automatic grapher has a **default window,** that is, a window that is set by the manufacturer. The default window that is used on one automatic grapher is shown below.

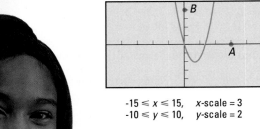

$-15 \leq x \leq 15$, x-scale $= 3$
$-10 \leq y \leq 10$, y-scale $= 2$

A description of the window is given below the display. Here, x goes from -15 to 15, and y goes from -10 to 10.

x-scale $= 3$ means that the tick marks along the x-axis are 3 units apart. Point A is $(9, 0)$.

y-scale $= 2$ means that the tick marks along the y-axis are 2 units apart. Point B is $(0, 8)$.

You should include a description like this whenever you sketch the output from your grapher.

1 a. Sketch the default window for your grapher. See margin.
   b. Describe one way to change the window on your grapher.
   Enter different values for the minimum value of x, the maximum value of x, the minimum value of y, or the maximum value of y.

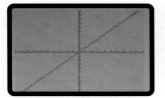 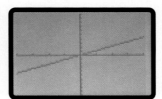

2 Find out how to enter equations on your grapher. **a) See margin.**
   a. Draw a graph of $y = -8x$ using each of the following windows.
   i. your default window
   ii. $-15 \le x \le 15$, x-scale = 3; $-10 \le y \le 10$, y-scale = 2
   iii. $-3 \le x \le 3$, x-scale = .5; $-30 \le y \le 30$, y-scale = 5
   iv. $-1.5 \le x \le 3.5$, x-scale = .25; $-5 \le y \le .5$, y-scale = 1
   b. What is the slope of each line in part **a**? -8
   c. Discuss the graphs with other members of your group. How do the
   dimensions of the viewing window affect your visual impression of
   the graph? Write a few sentences that describe your conclusion.
   Include sketches of the graphs you just made. **See below.**
   d. Find out how to trace along the graph. Use the *trace* feature to
   determine the following values.
   i. Find y when $x = 1.7$. -13.6
   ii. Find x when $y = -12$. 1.5
   How close are your grapher's answers to those you get by calculating
   with paper and pencil? **very close**

3 Clear your screen. Use any convenient window. Graph $y = x$,
   $y = 3x$, and $y = 9x$ on one set of axes. Copy these onto another
   sheet of paper. **See margin.**   **4) Answers will vary.**

4 Clear your screen. Set it to the default window. Then do the
   following: enter an equation of the form $y = kx$, where $k \ne 0$,
   without letting the others in your group see the equation. Show your
   screen to the others, and have them identify what equation you used.

5 Is your automatic grapher capable of printing a *hard copy,* that is,
   a paper copy of your screen? If so, find out how to do this. Print a
   hard copy of one of the graphs in Questions 2–4. **Answers will vary.**

**2c) Sample: Changing the window makes the angle at which the graph is
drawn change.**

Questions 2a–c Stress that the
slope of a line does not change
when you view the line on different
windows even though the tilt of the
visual image of the line that is shown
may change. **Question 2d** may
surprise many students because
the grapher may not always give the
correct answer. You may want to
have students explore how changing
the window affects the numerical
accuracy of their answers.

Additional Answers
2aii.

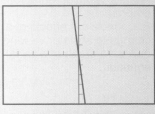

$-15 \le x \le 15$, x-scale = 3
$-10 \le y \le 10$, y-scale = 2

2aiii.

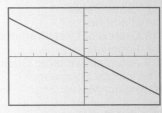

$-3 \le x \le 3$, x-scale = .5
$-30 \le y \le 30$, y-scale = 5

2aiv.

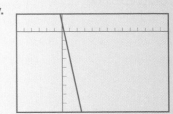

$-1.5 \le x \le 3.5$, x-scale = .25
$-5 \le y \le .5$, y-scale = 1

3.

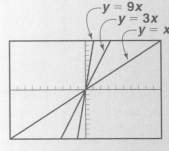

$y = 9x$
$y = 3x$
$y = x$

$-10 \le x \le 10$, x-scale = 1
$-10 \le y \le 10$, y-scale = 1

Objectives

C Find rates of change.
E Identify the properties of graphs of functions with equations of the form $y = kx^2$.
I Graph equations of the form $y = kx^2$.
J Identify variation equations from graphs.
K Recognize the effects of a change in scale or viewing window on a graph of a variation equation.

Resources

From the Teacher's Resource File

■ Lesson Master 2-5A or 2-5B
■ Answer Master 2-5
■ Teaching Aids
   5 Graph Paper
   14 Warm-up
   18 Graphs of Direct-Variation Formulas
   19 Automatic Grapher Grids
■ Technology Sourcebook
   Computer Master 2

Additional Resources

■ Visuals for Teaching Aids 5, 14, 18, 19
■ GraphExplorer

The Graph of $y = kx^2$

Seeing red. *If the red car is traveling at a speed of 35 mph, has the driver put on the brakes soon enough to stop before the red light? One of the first things a student driver learns is how to use the brakes to stop a car safely and smoothly.*

Rate of Change

In Lesson 2-1, you learned that the distance it takes a car to stop after the brakes are applied varies directly with the square of the car's speed. The formula $d = \frac{1}{16}s^2$ describes this relation for a certain car. A table and a graph are given below.

❶

s	d
0	0
10	6.25
20	25
30	56.25
40	100
50	156.25
60	225
70	306.25

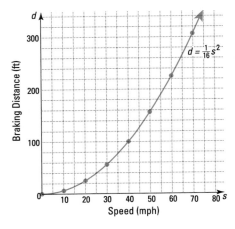

Notice that the points do not all lie on a straight line. You can verify this by calculating the rate of change between different points on the graph.

Lesson 2-5 Overview

Broad Goals This lesson extends the idea of slope (rate of change) to nonlinear graphs and introduces some of the properties of parabolas. Additional properties of quadratics are introduced in Chapter 6.

Perspective An important idea to emphasize is that constant slope is a characteristic of linear relations and that nonconstant slope is a characteristic of nonlinear relations.

Another key concept deals with the effect of the sign and value of k on the graph of $y = kx^2$. Students should be able to use this information to sketch the graph quickly. The capability of an automatic grapher to generate examples quickly has greatly facilitated the learning of this material, which formerly was quite tedious.

Parabolas will be covered again in this book, so all of the important properties of parabolas are not introduced in this lesson. Students should be able to graph $y = kx^2$ quickly, know if the graph opens up (or down), and understand how the value of k affects how fast the graph goes up (or down).

Example 1

Find the following rates of change, and explain what each means.
a. r_1, the rate of change from (20, 25) to (40, 100)
b. r_2, the rate of change from (40, 100) to (60, 225)

Solution

a. Use the definition of slope.

$$r_1 = \frac{100 \text{ ft} - 25 \text{ ft}}{40 \text{ mph} - 20 \text{ mph}} = \frac{75 \text{ ft}}{20 \text{ mph}} = \frac{3.75 \text{ ft}}{\text{mph}}$$

This means that on the average, when driving between 20 mph and 40 mph, for every increase of 1 mph in speed, you need 3.75 more feet to stop your car.

b. Similarly, $r_2 = \frac{225 \text{ ft} - 100 \text{ ft}}{60 \text{ mph} - 40 \text{ mph}} = \frac{125 \text{ ft}}{20 \text{ mph}} = 6.25 \frac{\text{ft}}{\text{mph}}$.

So on the average, between $s = 40$ and $s = 60$, for every change of 1 mph (the horizontal unit), there is a change of 6.25 feet of braking distance (the vertical unit).

Check

Look at the points on the graph. Let $A = (20, 25)$, $B = (40, 100)$, and $C = (60, 225)$. Is $\overline{BC}$ steeper than $\overline{AB}$? Yes, it is.

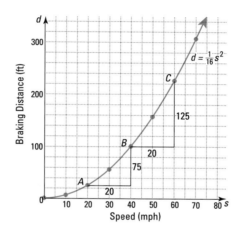

Because the rate of change determined by different pairs of points on the graph of $d = \frac{1}{16}s^2$ is not constant, two conclusions can be drawn:

1. The graph of $d = \frac{1}{16}s^2$ is not a line.

2. The steepness of the graph cannot be described by a single number.

Notice that the slope is larger where the graph is steeper; this means that the function is increasing faster.

The equation $d = \frac{1}{16}s^2$ is a direct-variation function of the form $y = kx^2$. All graphs of equations of this form share some properties.

Warm-up

Complete the table.

x	$y = 4x^2$	$y = -\frac{1}{4}x^2$
-2	16	-1
-1	4	$-\frac{1}{4}$
0	0	0
1	4	$-\frac{1}{4}$
2	16	-1

Notes on Reading

❶ **Reading Mathematics** Point out that the scale on each axis is different, which makes it difficult to estimate the slopes by looking at the picture. Stress the importance of considering the scales on the axes *before* making assumptions about slope. Remind students that they should consider the scales when reading *any* graph.

Be sure students understand that the rate of change determined by points on a parabola depends on the points chosen for calculating the rate of change, whereas with a line the rate of change can be determined by any two points.

Students may use graph paper or **Teaching Aid 5** in *Optional Activities.*

Optional Activities

Using Physical Models
Materials: Flashlight, graph paper or
          Teaching Aid 5

Have students work in **small groups.** Each group will need graph paper and a flashlight. Have them draw a set of axes on the graph paper, hold a lighted flashlight at the origin so the light is centered on an axis, and trace the shape of the lighted area. Ask them what shape they have traced.
[A parabola]

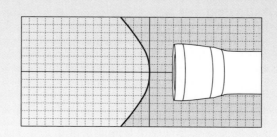

97

❷ The graph of $y = kx^2$ is also given on **Teaching Aid 18.**

❸ Students who have taken previous UCSMP courses have studied reflections; they should recall that reflection symmetry is a property of many figures, including rectangles, isosceles triangles, circles, and regular polygons. For students who are encountering reflections for the first time, connect reflections with folding over the line of symmetry. Reflection symmetry is an idea that is easy for students to understand.

Additional Examples

1. Use the graph from **Example 1** on page 97. Find the rate of change.
   a. r_3, from (10, 6.25) to (30, 56.25). **2.5 ft/mph**
   b. r_4, from (30, 56.25) to (50, 156.25). **5 ft/mph**
2. Graph (a) $y = x^2$, (b) $y = 3x^2$, and (c) $y = \frac{1}{3}x^2$ on the same axes.

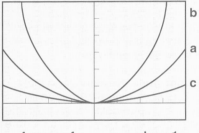

$$-4 \le x \le 4, \qquad x\text{-scale} = 1$$
$$-5 \le y \le 30, \qquad y\text{-scale} = 5$$

Example 2

Graph solutions to $y = 2x^2$, $y = x^2$, and $y = \frac{1}{4}x^2$.

Solution 1

Use an automatic grapher with any window that allows you to see each graph clearly. Shown below is a good display and the window used to create it.

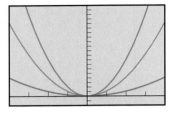

$$-4 \le x \le 4, \qquad x\text{-scale} = 1$$
$$-2 \le x \le 20, \qquad y\text{-scale} = 1$$

When you use an automatic grapher to draw a graph, you should also either print a hard copy or copy the graph by hand. In either case you should always label the axes, include a scale, and plot a few points. When you make two or more graphs on the same axes, be sure to label the graphs with the equations you used. Your paper should look something like either graph below.

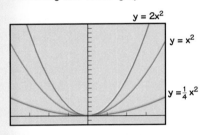
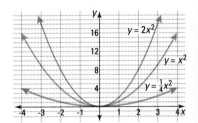

$$-4 \le x \le 4, \qquad x\text{-scale} = 1$$
$$-2 \le x \le 20, \qquad y\text{-scale} = 1$$

Solution 2

Make a table of values. To save space, the value of the independent variable is written only once.

x	0	1	2	3	-1	-2	-3
$y = x^2$	0	1	4	9	1	4	9
$y = 2x^2$	0	2	8	18	2	8	18
$y = \frac{1}{4}x^2$	0	$\frac{1}{4}$	1	$\frac{9}{4}$	$\frac{1}{4}$	1	$\frac{9}{4}$

Then plot the points. The graph should look something like the one drawn by hand in Solution 1.

Adapting to Individual Needs

Extra Help
Refer students to the graph on page 97. Point out that $\overline{AB}$ and $\overline{BC}$ are line segments. Therefore, we can use the slope formula to find their slopes. However, the graph of $d = \frac{1}{16}s^2$ is a curve, but the section of the graph between (20, 25) and (40, 100) is closely approximated by $\overline{AB}$. Likewise, the section of the graph from (40, 100) to (60, 225) is closely approximated by $\overline{BC}$.

Consequently, the rates of change we calculate in **parts a and b** of **Example 1** are *averages*.

❸ The graphs of $y = x^2$, $y = 2x^2$, and $y = \frac{1}{4}x^2$ in Example 2 are curves called *parabolas*. Each parabola passes through the point (0, 0). Further, each parabola coincides with its reflection image over a line, specifically, the *y*-axis. So, each parabola is **reflection-symmetric,** and the *y*-axis is called the **line of symmetry.**

The Graph of $y = kx^2$ when $k < 0$

Example 3 shows graphs of $y = kx^2$ for three negative values of *k*.

Example 3

Graph $y = -2x^2$, $y = -x^2$, and $y = -\frac{1}{4}x^2$ on the same axes.

Solution

We use an automatic grapher with the window $-4 \leq x \leq 4$ and $-20 \leq y \leq 2$. On the left below is the grapher's display. On the right below is a graph drawn from the display.

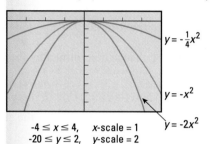

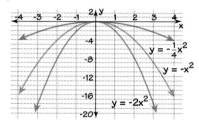

$-4 \leq x \leq 4$,   *x*-scale = 1
$-20 \leq y \leq 2$,   *y*-scale = 2

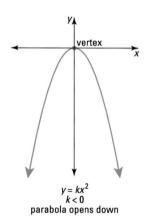

$y = kx^2$
$k > 0$
parabola opens up

$y = kx^2$
$k < 0$
parabola opens down

When you are asked to *copy* a graph from your automatic grapher, you must label the axes, include a scale, and label the equations used. However, you don't need to identify a large number of points. Usually it is enough to name those points that highlight key features of the graph. You can find those points by substitution or by using the TRACE feature of your grapher.

Domain and Range

In general, the domain of the function with equation $y = kx^2$ is the set of all real numbers. When $k > 0$, the range is the set of nonnegative real numbers, and the parabola *opens up*. That is, the vertex of the parabola is its *minimum* point. When $k < 0$, the range is the set of nonpositive real numbers and the parabola *opens down*. That is, the vertex of the parabola is its *maximum* point.

Lesson 2-5   *The Graph of* $y = kx^2$ **99**

3. Graph (a) $y = -x^2$, (b) $y = -3x^2$, and (c) $y = -\frac{1}{3}x^2$ on the same axes.

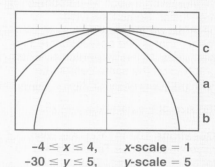

$-4 \leq x \leq 4$,   *x*-scale = 1
$-30 \leq y \leq 5$,   *y*-scale = 5

4. By looking at an equation of the form $y = kx^2$, what can you tell about the graph? **Sample: It is the graph of a parabola symmetric to the *y*-axis with its vertex at the origin. When $k > 0$, the parabola opens up and the vertex is its minimum point. When $k < 0$, the parabola opens down and the vertex is its maximum point.**

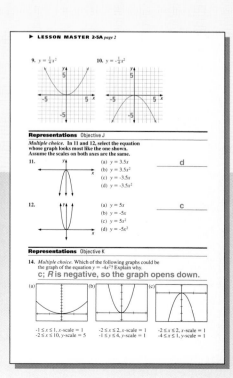

Adapting to Individual Needs

English Language Development
Materials: Mirror

To demonstrate the meaning of *symmetry,* fold a piece of paper in half and cut out a shape. Show students that the shape is identical on each side of the fold; explain that we say the shape is *symmetric* and that the fold is the *line of symmetry.* Use a mirror to show that each point on one side of the line of symmetry has a reflection image on the other side.

Question 4 It is common to say that graphs of parabolas get wider or thinner, even though all parabolas are similar. Some look wider because we are viewing less of them—that is, the parabolas are *bigger* (closer to us). In particular, when graphed on the same coordinate grid, the parabola $y = \frac{1}{a}x^2$ is a times the size of the parabola $y = x^2$.

Questions 10–11 You may wish to have students use **Teaching Aid 19** for these questions. There may be discrepancies among students' answers to **Question 11**. When that is the case, discuss the consequences of estimation. If the number of houses that can be served by the water main is an overestimate, the owners will have water-supply problems. If the number of houses is an underestimate, it will not affect the owners' water supply.

(Notes on Questions continue on page 102.)

Additional Answers

11c.

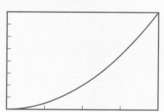

$0 \le x \le 40,\quad x\text{-scale} = 10$
$0 \le y \le 800,\quad y\text{-scale} = 100$

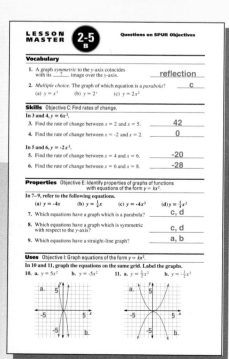

Example 4

How are the graphs in Example 3 like and unlike those in Example 2?

Solution

The graphs in Example 3 $\left(y = -2x^2,\ y = -x^2,\ \text{and}\ y = -\frac{1}{4}x^2\right)$ are shaped like those in Example 2 $\left(y = 2x^2,\ y = x^2,\ \text{and}\ y = \frac{1}{4}x^2\right)$. Each curve passes through the origin and is symmetric to the y-axis. In each case, the graph of $y = ax^2$ appears to be congruent to the graph of $y = -ax^2$. However, the curves in Example 3 open down, while those in Example 2 open up.

QUESTIONS

Covering the Reading

4a)

x	$y = x^2$	$y = 3x^2$	$y = -3x^2$
-2	4	12	-12
-1	1	3	-3
0	0	0	0
1	1	3	-3
2	4	12	-12

b)

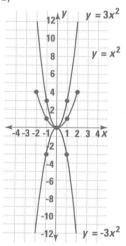

c) The graph of $y = -3x^2$ is the reflection image of the graph of $y = 3x^2$. The graph of $y = x^2$ is wider than the other two graphs. All three graphs are parabolas and pass through point (0, 0).

In 1 and 2, refer to the formula $d = \frac{1}{16}s^2$ relating speed and braking distance.

1. Find the rate of change determined by the pair of points and explain what it means. **See explanations below.**
   a. (10, 6.25) and (20, 25) **1.875 ft/mph**
   b. (50, 156.25) and (60, 225) **6.875 ft/mph**

2. *True or false.* The rate of change on the graph is constant, regardless of the points used. **False**

3. The graph of $y = kx^2$ ($k \ne 0$) is what type of curve? **parabola**

4. Consider the equations $y = x^2$, $y = 3x^2$, and $y = -3x^2$. **See left.**
   a. Make a table of values for $x = -2, -1, 0, 1$, and 2.
   b. Graph the solutions on one set of axes. Use as the domain the set of real numbers between -2 and 2 inclusive. Do not use an automatic grapher.
   c. Compare and contrast the three graphs.

5. Explain what it means to say that the graph of $y = kx^2$ is symmetric to the y-axis. **The graph coincides with its reflection image over the y-axis.**

6. Suppose $k < 0$. State the domain and range of the function $f(x) = kx^2$. **domain: the set of real numbers; range: the set of nonpositive numbers**

7. In general, for what values of k does the graph of $y = kx^2$
   a. open up? **$k > 0$**
   b. open down? **$k < 0$**

1a) On the average, when driving between 10 mph and 20 mph, for every increase of 1 mph in speed, you need 1.875 more feet of braking distance.
b) On the average, when driving between 50 mph and 60 mph, for every change of 1 mph in speed, there is a change of 6.875 feet of braking distance.

Adapting to Individual Needs

Challenge

Explain that when using an automatic grapher, it may be difficult to see the graph when k is either very large or very small. Have students show $y = x^2$ on their default window. Then have them find windows that will change the shape of $y = .01x^2$ and $y = 10,000x^2$ so that they appear to be the same as $y = x^2$. [Graphs are shown at the right.]

Graph of $y = x^2$ on default window

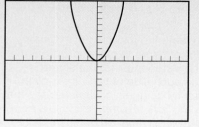

$-10 \le x \le 10,\quad x\text{-scale} = 1$
$-10 \le y \le 10,\quad y\text{-scale} = 1$

-10 ≤ x ≤ 10, x-scale = 1
-10 ≤ y ≤ 10, y-scale = 1

11a)

d	N
0	0
10	50
20	200
30	450
40	800

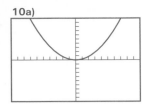

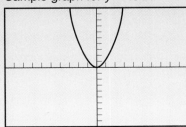

Applying the Mathematics

8. Match each graph with its equation. Each graph has the same scale.

$y = \frac{1}{2}x^2$ $y = -2x$ $y = -x^2$ $y = 1.3x^2$

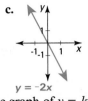 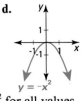

a.   **b.**   **c.**   **d.**

$y = 1.3x^2$ $y = \frac{1}{2}x^2$ $y = -2x$ $y = -x^2$

9. Explain why the point $(0, 0)$ is on the graph of $y = kx^2$ for all values of k. When x = 0, y = k(0)² = 0. Therefore, when x = 0, y = 0.

10. a. Use an automatic grapher to graph $y = \frac{1}{5}x^2$ on the window $-10 \le x \le 10$ and $-10 \le y \le 10$. See left.
  b. Use the trace feature of your grapher to estimate the value of the function when $x = 3$. Sample: y = 1.86
  c. Compare the value obtained in part **b** with the value obtained by substituting $x = 3$ into $y = \frac{1}{5}x^2$. y = 1.8; they are very close.
  d. Use the trace feature to find the value(s) of x when $y = 10$.
  Sample: x = 7.05 or x = -7.05

11. Let N represent the number of houses that can be served by a water main of diameter d centimeters. Since the amount of water that can flow through a pipe is directly proportional to the area of a cross section of pipe, it is reasonable to assume $N = kd^2$. Suppose

$$N = \tfrac{1}{2}d^2.$$

  a. Make a table of solutions to this equation. For values of d use 0, 10, 20, 30, and 40. See left.
  b. From your table, estimate the number of houses that can be served by a water main of diameter 35 cm. Sample: 610 houses
  c. Graph $N = \frac{1}{2}d^2$. See margin.
  d. From your graph, estimate the number of homes that can be served by a water main of diameter 35 cm. ≈625 houses
  e. How well do your estimates from parts **b** and **d** agree? They are close.
  f. From the variation equation, determine the actual number of homes that can be served by a water main of diameter 35 cm.
  612 homes

12. Refer to the table and graph of $y = x^2$ in Example 2.
  a. Find the rate of change:
      i. from $(0, 0)$ to $(1, 1)$. 1   **ii.** from $(1, 1)$ to $(2, 4)$. 3
      iii. from $(2, 4)$ to $(3, 9)$. 5   **iv.** from $(3, 9)$ to $(4, 16)$. 7
  b. Use your results from **i–iv** in part **a** to make a conjecture about the rate of change between the points (n, n^2) and $(n + 1, (n + 1)^2)$.
  c. Prove your conjecture by calculating the rate of change for the points in part **b.** $\frac{(n + 1)^2 - n^2}{n + 1 - n} = \frac{n^2 + 2n + 1 - n^2}{1} = 2n + 1$
  b) The rate of change is 2n + 1.

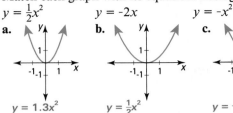

The pressure's on. *Most cities pump water into elevated storage tanks, such as this one in Stanton, Iowa, to help keep the water pressure high. When water is released from the tank, gravity pulls the water downward, giving it the pressure to rush through the water mains.*

Sample graph for $y = .01x^2$

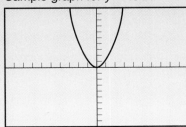

−100 ≤ x ≤ 100,   x-scale = 10
−10 ≤ y ≤ 10,   y-scale = 1

Sample graph for $y = 10,000x^2$

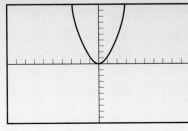

−.1 ≤ x ≤ .1,   x-scale = .01
−10 ≤ y ≤ 10,   y-scale = 1

Follow-up for Lesson 2-5

Practice
For more questions on SPUR Objectives, use **Lesson Master 2-5A** (shown on pages 98−99) or **Lesson Master 2-5B** (shown on pages 100−101).

Assessment
Group Assessment Have students **work in groups of three.** Tell one student in each group to name a direct-variation function of the form $y = kx^2$. Have a second student sketch the graph. Then have the third student graph $y = -kx^2$. Continue the assessment by having students rotate roles. [Students demonstrate an understanding of how to graph direct-variation functions.]

Extension
Students know that the graph of $y = kx^2$ opens up for $k > 0$ and opens down for $k < 0$. Have students graph equations of the form $y = kx + b$ for $b > 0$ and $b < 0$. Then ask them to describe how the value of b affects the graph. [b gives the y-intercept of the vertex.]

Project Update Project 3, *Sums or Differences of Variation Functions*, on page 128, relates to the content of this lesson.

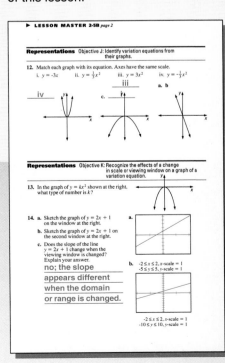

101

Notes on Questions

Question 16 Science Connection
The development of the Kelvin scale is due to the Irish scientist William Thompson (1824–1907), known as Lord Kelvin. Kelvin was knighted by Queen Victoria and given the title Baron Kelvin of Largs in 1866 in recognition of his work in engineering and physics.

Question 19 This question should not be skipped. Many students welcome an opportunity to review something that they already know from geometry.

Additional Answers
13a.

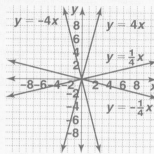

Sound architecture. The Sydney Opera House, internationally famous for its innovative design, contains a 1700-seat main hall, a 1550-seat auditorium, and a small theater.

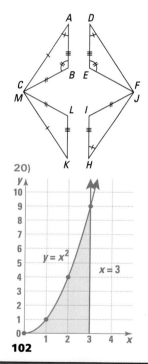

20)

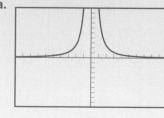

102

13. **a.** Graph the following four equations on one set of axes.
   (Previous course, Lesson 2-4) **See margin.**
   $$y = 4x \qquad y = \tfrac{1}{4}x \qquad y = -\tfrac{1}{4}x \qquad y = -4x$$
   b. Find the slope of each graph. **4; $\tfrac{1}{4}$; $-\tfrac{1}{4}$; -4**
   c. Give the equations of two lines that appear to be perpendicular.
   $y = 4x$ and $y = (-1/4)x$; or $y = -4x$ and $y = (1/4)x$

14. What is another name for slope? *(Lesson 2-4)* **rate of change**

15. Architects designing auditoriums use the fact that sound intensity I is inversely proportional to the square of the distance d from the sound source. *(Lessons 2-2, 2-3)*
   a. Write the variation equation that represents this situation. **$I = \tfrac{k}{d^2}$**
   b. A person moves to a seat 4 times as far from the source. How will the intensity of sound be affected? **The intensity of sound will be divided by 16.**

16. The Fahrenheit and Celsius scales indicate temperature. Temperature can also be measured on the Kelvin scale, in kelvins. At a fixed pressure, the volume V of a fixed amount of air varies directly with its Kelvin temperature t. The lowest possible temperature occurs when t is zero, about -273°C. Suppose that a balloon contains 7.5 liters of air at 300 kelvins (about room temperature). *(Lesson 2-1)*
   a. Write a variation formula for V in terms of t. **$V = 0.025t$**
   b. Use this formula to predict the volume of air in the balloon at temperatures of 400, 500, 600, and 1000 kelvins. **10 L; 12.5 L; 15 L; 25 L**

17. Consider a sequence defined explicitly as
   $$t_n = 4n^2 + 3n - 2.$$
   a. What is the domain of the sequence? **The set of natural numbers.**
   b. Find the first five terms of the sequence. *(Lessons 1-2, 1-7)* **5, 20, 43, 74, 113**

18. Solve for x: $y = -\tfrac{1}{4}x$. *(Lesson 1-6)* **$x = -4y$**

19. **a.** Which of the triangles pictured at the left can be proved congruent to $\triangle ABC$? Name them, with vertices in correct order. **$\triangle DEF$, $\triangle KLM$**
   b. Give the justification for each triangle congruence you find.
   (Previous course) **$\triangle DEF \cong \triangle ABC$ by ASA Congruence Theorem; $\triangle KLM \cong \triangle ABC$ by SSS Congruence Theorem**

Exploration

20. Accurately graph the curve $y = x^2$ from $x = 0$ to $x = 3$. Estimate the area bounded by the curve, the x-axis, and the line $x = 3$. The area between the curve and the x-axis is an integer number of square units. What is this number? **See left for graph. 9 square units**

Additional Answers, page 103

1a.

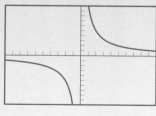

$-10 \le x \le 10$, x-scale = 1
$-10 \le y \le 10$, y-scale = 1

2a.

$-10 \le x \le 10$, x-scale = 1
$-10 \le y \le 10$, y-scale = 1

d. No; $\tfrac{10}{x^2} \ne 0$ for value of x

e. No; $\tfrac{10}{x^2} \ne 0$ for any value of x

3a. Sample: They will be reflected over the x-axis.

Automatic Graphers and Inverse Variation

IN·CLASS
ACTIVITY

In-class Activity

Resources

From the *Teacher's Resource File*
- Answer Master 2-6
- Teaching Aid 19: Automatic Grapher Grids

Additional Resources
- Visual for Teaching Aid 19

Work on this Activity with a partner. Each pair needs at least one automatic grapher.

1 Clear the screen and set the grapher to its default settings.

a. Graph the function with equation $y = \frac{10}{x}$. You should see points in two quadrants. Sketch the graph. **See margin.**

b. Set the cursor on the graph at some positive value of x by using the trace key. Trace along the curve to the right. Describe what happens to y as x gets larger and larger. What is the value of y when $x = 200$? **y gets smaller; at x = 200, y = .05**

c. Set the cursor on the graph at some negative value of x. Trace along the curve to the left. Describe what happens to y as x gets smaller and smaller. What is the value of y when $x = -200$? **See below.**

d. Does the graph of $y = \frac{10}{x}$ ever intersect the x-axis? If yes, give the coordinates of the point(s) of intersection. If no, explain why not. **No; $\frac{10}{x} \neq 0$ for any value of x.** **e) No; x cannot be zero.**

e. Does the graph of $y = \frac{10}{x}$ ever intersect the y-axis? If yes, give the coordinates of the point(s) of intersection. If no, explain why not.
c) y gets larger; at x = -200, y = -.05

2 Clear the screen. **See margin for a, d, e.**

a. Graph the function with equation $y = \frac{10}{x^2}$. Sketch the graph.

b. Place the cursor on the graph at some positive value of x. Trace along the curve to the right. Describe what happens to y as x gets larger and larger. **y gets smaller.**

c. Set the cursor on the graph at some negative value of x. Trace along the curve to the left. Describe what happens to y as x gets smaller and smaller. **y gets smaller.**

d. Does the graph of $y = \frac{10}{x^2}$ ever intersect the x-axis? If yes, give the coordinates of the point(s) of intersection. If no, explain why not.

e. Does the graph of $y = \frac{10}{x^2}$ ever intersect the y-axis? If yes, give the coordinates of the point(s) of intersection. If no, explain why not.

3 In Questions 1 and 2 you investigated graphs of functions with equations of the forms $y = \frac{k}{x}$ and $y = \frac{k}{x^2}$. In those questions you set $k = 10$. Suppose $k = -10$. **See margin.**

a. Make a conjecture about what you think the graphs will look like.

b. Test your conjecture by graphing $y = -\frac{10}{x}$ and $y = -\frac{10}{x^2}$. Sketch the graphs, and write a sentence about some properties of each function.

In this activity, students explore graphs of two variation functions that have asymptotes. The activity should be done even at the expense of discussing some of the questions in Lesson 2-5.

You may wish to use **Teaching Aid 19** with this activity.

Cooperative Learning Some students may not be comfortable using automatic graphers. You might have students **work in pairs;** this will allow them to help one another with both the mathematics and the technical features of the automatic graphers.

Some automatic graphers connect every pixel. Hence, they often display an asymptote as if it were part of the function. However, students will not have problems with the graphs in this Activity because the asymptotes in these cases are the x- and y-axes.

In **Questions 1b and 2b,** students explore without any formal vocabulary or notation the meaning of the limit of $\frac{10}{x}$ as x approaches infinity. In **Questions 1c and 2c,** they explore what, in more advanced courses, is the limit of $\frac{10}{x}$ as x approaches negative infinity. *We do not recommend the introduction of limit notation here.*

103

Additional Answers

3b. Graph of $y = -\frac{10}{x}$:

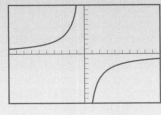

$-10 \leq x \leq 10$, x-scale = 1
$-10 \leq y \leq 10$, y-scale = 1

Graph of $y = -\frac{10}{x^2}$:

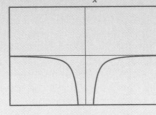

$-10 \leq x \leq 10$, x-scale = 1
$-10 \leq y \leq 10$, y-scale = 1

Sample: $y = -\frac{10}{x}$ and $y = \frac{10}{x}$ are reflection images over the x-axis. $y = -\frac{10}{x^2}$ and $y = \frac{10}{x^2}$ are reflection images over the x-axis. The graphs of neither $y = -\frac{10}{x}$ nor $y = -\frac{10}{x^2}$ will ever intersect the x-axis or the y-axis.

Objectives

C Find rates of change.
E Identify properties of variation functions.
I Graph inverse-linear variation and inverse-square variation equations.
J Identify equations of inverse-linear and inverse-square functions from graphs.

Resources

From the Teacher's Resource File
- Lesson Master 2-6A or 2-6B
- Answer Master 2-6
- Assessment Sourcebook: Quiz for Lessons 2-4 through 2-6
- Teaching Aids
  5 Graph Paper
  14 Warm-up
  19 Automatic Grapher Grids
  20 Graphs of Inverse-Variation Formulas
- Technology Sourcebook
  Computer Master 2

Additional Resources
- Visuals for Teaching Aids 5, 14, 19, 20
- GraphExplorer

Teaching Lesson 2-6

Warm-up

Make a table to show values of $y = \frac{4}{x}$ and $y = \frac{4}{x^2}$ when x is equal to $-4, -2, -1, -\frac{1}{2}, \frac{1}{2}, 1, 2,$ and 4.

LESSON 2-6

The Graphs of $y = \frac{k}{x}$ and $y = \frac{k}{x^2}$

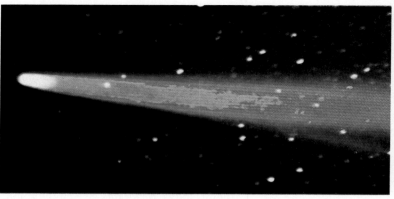

Energy deficit. *Periodic comets, like* Comet P/Halley *shown above, have negative total energy and so travel along an ellipse. Comets with positive total energy travel along a hyperbola and are seen only once, never to return.*

The Graph of $y = \frac{k}{x}$

The graph of every function with an equation of the form $y = \frac{k}{x}$, where $k \neq 0$, is a *hyperbola*. In the preceding In-class Activity you graphed the hyperbolas with equations $y = \frac{10}{x}$ and $y = -\frac{10}{x}$.

Example 1

a. Draw the graphs of $f(x) = \frac{16}{x}$ and $g(x) = -\frac{16}{x}$.
b. Identify the domain and range of the function f.

Solution

a. Use an automatic grapher.

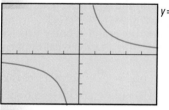 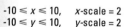 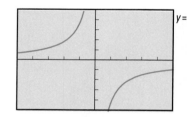

$-10 \leq x \leq 10,$ x-scale = 2
$-10 \leq y \leq 10,$ y-scale = 2

$-10 \leq x \leq 10,$ x-scale = 2
$-10 \leq y \leq 10,$ y-scale = 2

b. To find the domain, think: what numbers can x be? In the equation $f(x) = \frac{16}{x}$, any real number except 0 can be substituted for x. So, **For the function f, the domain = $\{x: x \neq 0\}$.** To find the range, think: what values can y have? From the graph, notice that y can be either positive or negative, large or small. But if $y = 0$, you would have $0 = \frac{16}{x}$ or $0 \cdot x = 16$ which is impossible. So, **For the function f, the range = $\{y: y \neq 0\}$.**

104

Lesson 2-6 Overview

Broad Goals This lesson is a counterpart to Lessons 2-4 and 2-5, as the graphs of functions of inverse-linear and inverse-square variation are discussed.

Perspective The hyperbola is introduced in this lesson as the graph of the equation $y = \frac{k}{x}$, rather than as the more common equation $xy = k$. The form $y = \frac{k}{x}$ is used

because it more clearly expresses the concept of inverse-linear variation and because it emphasizes that y is a function of x. This form also facilitates introducing the important concept of the graph of the inverse-square variation function later in this lesson.

The notion of slope as rate of change is used again; this time it explores the idea that negative slope implies that the curve is falling. Students who take calculus will see this idea developed more thoroughly.

Students often find it difficult to graph accurately enough to see the differences between the graphs of $y = \frac{k}{x}$ and $y = \frac{k}{x^2}$. In this case, an automatic grapher is particularly useful for demonstrating that the inverse-square curve hugs the axes more than the hyperbola does. The difference between the graphs are important because, starting in Lesson 2-7, students will be shown graphs like these and asked to give the equations.

Notice that each hyperbola consists of two separate parts, called **branches.** When $k > 0$, the branches of $y = \frac{k}{x}$ lie in the first and third quadrants; if $k < 0$, the branches lie in the second and fourth quadrants. In each case the domain and the range are the set of all nonzero real numbers.

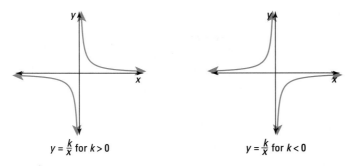

$y = \frac{k}{x}$ for $k > 0$ $y = \frac{k}{x}$ for $k < 0$

In some situations, only one branch of a hyperbola is relevant. For instance, recall the Metro Car Sales example of Lesson 2-2. The number of students s hired to wash cars and the number of hours t each will need to work are related by the equation $t = \frac{36}{s}$. A table of values for this equation and a graph are shown below.

s	1	2	3	4	5	6	7	8	9	10	12	18	24	30	36
t	36	18	12	9	$7\frac{1}{5}$	6	$5\frac{1}{7}$	$4\frac{1}{2}$	4	$3\frac{3}{5}$	3	2	$1\frac{1}{2}$	$1\frac{1}{5}$	1

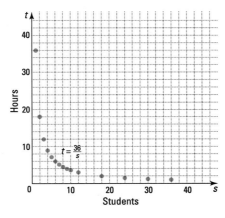

The domain is the set of natural numbers. Notice that it does not make sense to connect the points of this graph. Thus, the graph consists of a set of **discrete** (distinct or not connected) points on one branch of the hyperbola $y = \frac{36}{x}$.

Sample table:

x	$y = \frac{4}{x}$	$y = \frac{4}{x^2}$
-4	-1	$\frac{1}{4}$
-2	-2	1
-1	-4	4
$-\frac{1}{2}$	-8	16
$\frac{1}{2}$	8	16
1	4	4
2	2	1
4	1	$\frac{1}{4}$

Notes on Reading

The graphs of $y = \frac{k}{x}$ and $y = \frac{k}{x^2}$ are also given on **Teaching Aid 20.**

This lesson is shorter and easier than it may appear to students— much of its length is due to the number of graphs. To give students concrete experiences showing differences among the various graphs in this lesson, you might begin the discussion by having them graph $y = \frac{16}{x}$ and $y = \frac{16}{x^2}$ on the same window.

Additional Examples

Students may use graph paper, **Teaching Aid 5, or Teaching Aid 19** to record their answers.

1a. Graph $f(x) = \frac{3}{x}$ and $g(x) = \frac{-3}{x}$.

Graph of $f(x) = \frac{3}{x}$:

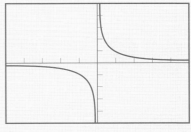

$-10 \le x \le 10,$ x-scale $= 2$
$-10 \le y \le 10,$ y-scale $= 2$

Graph of $g(x) = \frac{-3}{x}$:

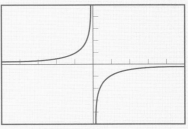

$-10 \le x \le 10,$ x-scale $= 2$
$-10 \le y \le 10,$ y-scale $= 2$

Optional Activities

Science Connection You might use this activity after students have completed the lesson. Explain that horsepower is the power needed to lift 550 pounds one foot in one second. Students can use the formula $H = \frac{wd}{550t}$, where $H =$ horsepower, $w =$ weight, $d =$ vertical distance traveled in feet, and $t =$ time in seconds, to compute the horsepower needed for a 125-pound person to climb a staircase with a vertical distance of 10 feet. Have them rewrite the formula with $w = 125$ and $d = 10$, and graph it. They should note that the graph is that of a hyperbola and that only the first-quadrant portion of the graph applies to this situation. Ask students how much horsepower would be needed to climb the stairs in 1 second; 2 seconds; 5 seconds. [2.27 seconds; 1.14 seconds; 0.45 seconds] Ask what happens to the horsepower as the number of seconds increases. [It decreases.]

b. Identify the domain and range of the function f. **Both are the set of nonzero reals.**

2a. Graph $y = \frac{36}{x^2}$ and $y = \frac{-36}{x^2}$.

Graph of $y = \frac{36}{x^2}$:

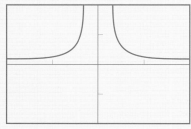

$-10 \le x \le 10, \quad x\text{-scale} = 5$
$-10 \le y \le 10, \quad y\text{-scale} = 5$

Graph of $y = \frac{-36}{x^2}$:

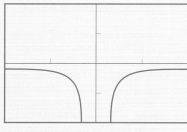

$-10 \le x \le 10, \quad x\text{-scale} = 5$
$-10 \le y \le 10, \quad y\text{-scale} = 5$

b. Describe the symmetry in the graphs. **They are symmetric to the y-axis.**

c. Identify the asymptotes of the graphs. **x-axis and y-axis**

(Notes on Questions begin on page 109.)

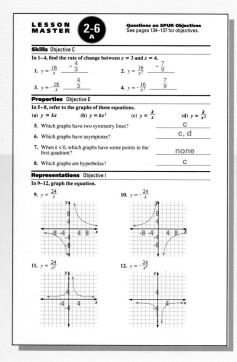
The Graph of $y = \frac{k}{x^2}$

You have also studied inverse-square variation. The graph of an inverse-square variation function does not have a special name, so we just call it an **inverse-square curve**.

Example 2

a. Graph $y = \frac{16}{x^2}$ and $y = -\frac{16}{x^2}$.

b. Describe the symmetry in each graph.

Solution

a. Use an automatic grapher.

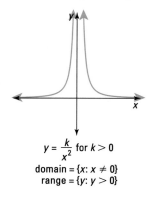 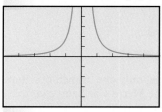

$-10 \le x \le 10, \quad x\text{-scale} = 2$
$-10 \le y \le 10, \quad y\text{-scale} = 2$

$-10 \le x \le 10, \quad x\text{-scale} = 2$
$-10 \le y \le 10, \quad y\text{-scale} = 2$

b. Each graph is symmetric to the y-axis.

Notice that the inverse-square curve, like a hyperbola, has two distinct branches. These two branches, however, do not form a hyperbola because the shape and relative positions of the branches differ from those of the branches of a hyperbola. The domain of every inverse-square function is $\{x: x \ne 0\}$. The range depends on the value of k.

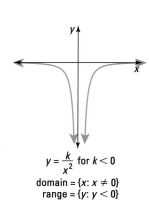

$y = \frac{k}{x^2}$ for $k > 0$

domain $= \{x: x \ne 0\}$
range $= \{y: y > 0\}$

$y = \frac{k}{x^2}$ for $k < 0$

domain $= \{x: x \ne 0\}$
range $= \{y: y < 0\}$

Adapting to Individual Needs

Extra Help
When equations are of the form of $xy = k$ or $x^2y = k$, students may not recognize that the first equation yields an inverse-square curve. Point out that although $xy = k$ is similar to $y = kx$, the graphs are different. Likewise, $x^2y = k$ is similar to $y = kx^2$, but again, the graphs are different. The difficulty identifying the graphs can be avoided if the equations express y in terms of x.

Challenge
Materials: Graph paper or **Teaching Aid 5**

Have students graph all pairs of numbers with a product of 20. [Sample graph shown on page 107.] Ask if both branches of the graph apply to this situation and, if so, why. [Yes, because the product of two positive numbers as well as the product of two negative numbers is positive.] Then have them write a variation equation for the graph.

Asymptotes

In general, when $x = 0$, $y = \frac{k}{x}$ and $y = \frac{k}{x^2}$ are undefined. So neither curve crosses the y-axis. However, when x is near 0, the functions are defined.

Activity

Graph $y = \frac{16}{x}$ on the window $-1 \le x \le 1$, $-100 \le y \le 100$. You should see something like the curve below. **Sample answers are given.**

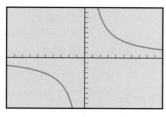

-1 $\le$ x $\le$ 1,   x-scale = .1
-100 $\le$ y $\le$ 100,   y-scale = 10

a. Set the cursor on the branch of the hyperbola in the first quadrant near $x = 1$. Trace to the left. Thus, the cursor will approach the line $x = 0$ from the right. Record the coordinates of three points on the hyperbola. (.8723, 18.3414); (.7234, 22.1176); (.5106, 31.333)

b. Set the cursor on the other branch of the hyperbola near the line $x = -1$. Trace so that the cursor approaches 0 from the left. Record the coordinates of three points on the curve.
(-.85106, -18.8); (-.8085, -19.7894); (-.17021, -94)

You should have found in the Activity that, as the cursor gets closer and closer to $x = 0$ from the right, the y-value gets larger and larger without bound. Similarly, as the cursor gets closer and closer to $x = 0$ from the left, the y-value gets smaller and smaller without bound. If as the values of x get closer and closer to a vertical line, the values of the function get larger and larger without bound (or smaller and smaller without bound), that line is called a **vertical asymptote** of the function. The y-axis is a vertical asymptote to the graphs of $y = \frac{k}{x}$ and $y = \frac{k}{x^2}$, provided $k \ne 0$.

Similarly, the x-axis is a **horizontal asymptote** to the graph of $y = \frac{k}{x}$ and $y = \frac{k}{x^2}$. As x gets very very large (or very very small), the value of y gets closer and closer to the x-axis.

In general, asymptotes may be vertical, horizontal, or oblique. But not all graphs have asymptotes. For instance, the parabola $y = kx^2$ does not have any asymptotes. When a graph has an asymptote, that asymptote is *not* part of the graph.

$[y = \frac{20}{x}]$ Ask if this is a discrete function.
[Students may have chosen discrete points, but the function is continuous except at $x = 0$.]

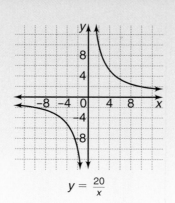

$$y = \frac{20}{x}$$

Follow-up **2-6**
for Lesson

Practice

For more questions on SPUR Objectives, use **Lesson Master 2-6A** (shown on pages 106–107) or **Lesson Master 2-6B** (shown on pages 108–109).

Assessment

Quiz A quiz covering Lessons 2-4 through 2-6 is provided in the *Assessment Sourcebook.*

Written Communication Have students **work in pairs.** Each student should write one equation of the form $y = \frac{k}{x}$ and another of the form $y = \frac{k}{x^2}$ on a piece of paper. Then have partners exchange papers and, for each equation, sketch a graph, list at least six ordered pairs, and give the domain and range. [Students demonstrate an understanding of graphing inverse-linear equations and inverse-square variation equations.]

(The Follow-up continues on page 108.)

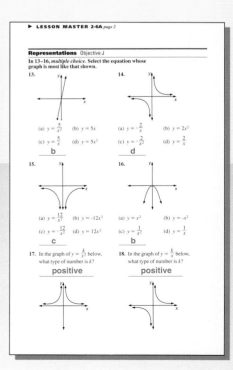

107

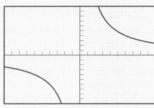
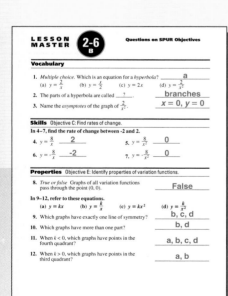
2a)
x	y
-3	-4
-2	-6
-1	-12
1	12
2	6
3	4
4	3
6	2
12	1

b)

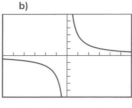

$-12 \le x \le 12, \quad x\text{-scale} = 2$
$-12 \le y \le 12, \quad y\text{-scale} = 2$

6a) s represents the number of students, so s can only be a natural number.

b) Since $s > 0$, then $\frac{36}{s} > 0$ and $t > 0$. Points with positive coordinates can only be in the first quadrant.

11a) $k = 200$ ft-lb; $d = \frac{200}{w}$

b) Sample:
w	d
10	20
20	10
30	$6\frac{2}{3}$
40	5
50	4
60	$3\frac{1}{3}$
70	$2\frac{6}{7}$
80	$2\frac{1}{2}$
90	$2\frac{2}{9}$
100	2

c)

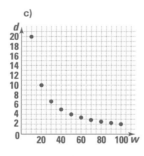

108

QUESTIONS

Covering the Reading

1. Suppose $k \ne 0$. What is the graph of $y = \frac{k}{x}$ called?   a hyperbola

In 2 and 3, consider the function f with equation $f(x) = \frac{12}{x}$.

2. **a.** Make a table of values. Include at least six ordered pairs in the first quadrant.   See left for a and b.
   b. Draw a graph of this function for $-12 \le x \le 12$ and $-12 \le y \le 12$.

3. State the domain and range of f.   domain: $\{x: x \ne 0\}$;   range: $\{y: y \ne 0\}$

In 4 and 5, refer to Example 1.

4. In which quadrants are the branches of the graph of $g(x) = -\frac{16}{x}$?   II and IV

5. State the domain and range of g.   domain: $\{x: x \ne 0\}$;   range: $\{y: y \ne 0\}$

6. Refer to the graph of $t = \frac{36}{s}$ in this lesson.   See left.
   a. Why doesn't it make sense to connect the points on this graph?
   b. Why are there no points in the 2nd or 3rd quadrants?

7. Suppose $k \ne 0$. Tell whether the equation has a graph that is symmetric to the y-axis.
   (a) $y = \frac{k}{x}$ No   (b) $y = \frac{k}{x^2}$ Yes   (c) $y = kx$ No   (d) $y = kx^2$ Yes

8. In which quadrants are the branches of $y = \frac{k}{x^2}$
   a. if k is positive?   I and II   **b.** if k is negative?   III and IV

9. **a.** Explain what happens to the y-coordinate of the graph of $y = \frac{16}{x}$ when x is negative and is getting closer and closer to 0. Use your work from the lesson's Activity.   y gets smaller.
   b. Identify two asymptotes of the graph of $y = \frac{16}{x}$.   the x-axis and the y-axis

10. Does the graph of $y = \frac{16}{x^2}$ have any asymptotes? If so, give an equation for each.   Yes; $x = 0$; $y = 0$

Applying the Mathematics

11. Ian is on a seesaw. He weighs 40 pounds and is sitting 5 feet from the fulcrum. $\left(\text{Remember, the Law of the Lever is } d = \frac{k}{w}.\right)$ See left for a–c.
    a. Find k and write a variation equation for this situation.
    b. Make a table of weights and distances from the pivot that would balance Ian.
    c. Plot your values from part **b.**
    d. Should you connect your points with a smooth curve? Explain why or why not.   Yes, w can be any positive real number.

14c.

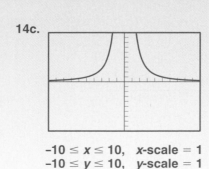

$-10 \le x \le 10, \quad x\text{-scale} = 1$
$-10 \le y \le 10, \quad y\text{-scale} = 1$

16a.

12. Examine the graph of $y = \frac{16}{x}$ from Example 1.
   a. How many symmetry lines does the graph have? **2**
   b. Write an equation for each symmetry line. **$y = x$; $y = -x$**
   c. Does the graph of $y = -\frac{16}{x}$ have the same symmetry lines? If not, what are the equations for its symmetry line(s)? **Yes**

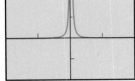

-10 ≤ x ≤ 10, x-scale = 5
-10 ≤ y ≤ 10, y-scale = 5

13. At the left is the graph of $f(x) = \frac{1}{x^2}$ on the window $-10 \le x \le 10$ and $-10 \le y \le 10$ as drawn by an automatic grapher. Is there a value of x with $f(x) = 0$? Justify your answer. **No. If $f(x) = 0$, then $\frac{1}{x^2} = 0$ or $x^2 \cdot 0 = 1$ which is impossible. Therefore, $f(x) \ne 0$ for all values of x.**

14. a. Use an automatic grapher to draw a graph of $y = \frac{24}{x}$.
   b. Find the rate of change from $x = 2$ to $x = 6$ for $y = \frac{24}{x}$. **-2**
   c. Use an automatic grapher to draw a graph of $y = \frac{24}{x^2}$.
   d. Find the rate of change from $x = 2$ to $x = 6$ for $y = \frac{24}{x^2}$. **$-1\frac{1}{3}$**
   e. Which of the two graphs is falling faster from $x = 2$ to $x = 6$?
   $y = \frac{24}{x}$ a, c) See margin.

Review

15. In the figure at the left, parabolas P_1 and P_2 are congruent. If parabola P_1 has equation $y = 6x^2$, what is an equation for parabola P_2? *(Lesson 2-5)* **$y = -6x^2$**

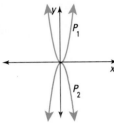

16. a. Draw a line that passes through the origin and has slope $\frac{5}{3}$. **See margin.**
   b. Write an equation for the line in part **a**. *(Lesson 2-4)* **$y = \frac{5}{3}x$**

17. Is line m graphed at the left an example of a direct variation? Justify your answer. *(Lesson 2-4)*
   No;   a direct variation graph must go through the origin.

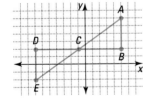

18. A small spherical balloon has a diameter of 6 inches when blown up. A larger spherical balloon has a diameter of 10 inches.
   a. How many more cubic inches of air are needed to blow up the large balloon than is needed for the small one? **$\frac{392}{3}\pi \approx 410.5$ in³**
   b. How many times the amount of air is in the larger balloon than is in the smaller balloon? *(Lesson 2-3)* **The larger balloon has $\frac{125}{27}$ times the amount of air in the smaller balloon.**

19a) Mikki cleared the fractions by multiplying both sides of the equation by 6, the least common denominator.

19. When she tried to solve the equation $\frac{1}{2}x + \frac{1}{3}x + 5 = 10$, Mikki's first step was $3x + 2x + 30 = 60$. **See left.**
   a. Explain what Mikki did.
   b. Finish the solution to the equation. *(Lesson 1-5)* **$x = 6$**

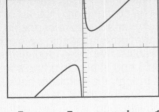

20. In the graph at the left, the grid lines are 1 unit apart. Each labeled point is at the intersection of grid lines. Are triangles ABC and EDC congruent? Explain your answer. *(Previous course)*
   Yes. Sample explanation: SAS Congruence Theorem

Exploration

21. a. Use an automatic grapher to draw the graph of $y = 3x + \frac{1}{x}$. **See margin.**
   b. Identify the asymptote(s) of the graph in part **a**.
   $x = 0$; $y = 3x$

Lesson 2-6   *The Graphs of $y = \frac{k}{x}$ and $y = \frac{k}{x^2}$*   **109**

21a.

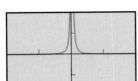

-5 ≤ x ≤ 5, x-scale = 1
-10 ≤ y ≤ 10, y-scale = 1

Notes on Questions
Question 11 The domain for *d* is $0 < d < \frac{\ell}{2}$ where ℓ is the length of the seesaw. A typical seesaw board is between 8 and 16 ft long.

Question 14 This question helps students connect the graphical description of a function (**parts a and c**) with the numerical description (**parts b and d**). No window is given, so students must think about which window to use. If the default window (or another window the student chooses) does not clearly show the differences between the graphs, suggest using the window $0 \le x \le 10$, $0 \le y \le 25$. You may want to poll your class to find out how many students relied on the graph and how many relied on the numerical values to answer **part e.**

Question 21 Students may be surprised by the appearance of an oblique asymptote. Notice that as $|x|$ gets larger, the function values get closer and closer to $3x$, which accounts for the existence of this asymptote.

Setting Up Lesson 2-7
Materials Students will need science books for **Question 20** on page 115. If you do the *Extension* on page 115, students will need newspapers and magazines showing graphs of economic data. If you do Activity 2 in *Optional Activities*, students will need equipment to make strobe pictures.

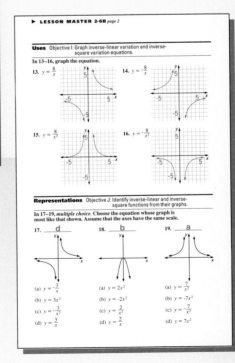

Lesson 2-7

Objectives

H Fit an appropriate model to data.

Resources

From the Teacher's Resource File
- Lesson Master 2-7A or 2-7B
- Answer Master 2-7
- Teaching Aids
   5 Graph Paper
   15 Warm-up
   21 Additional Examples
- Activity Kit, Activity 4

Additional Resources
- Visuals for Teaching Aids 5, 15, 21
- Science book
- Newspapers and magazines

Teaching **2-7**
Lesson

Warm-up

The point with coordinates (10, 20) appears on the graph for each variation function below. Determine the value of *k* in each case, and then determine the value of *y* when *x* is 30.

1. $y = kx$ $k = 2; y = 60$

2. $y = \dfrac{k}{x}$ $k = 200; y = 6\frac{2}{3}$

3. $y = kx^2$ $k = \frac{1}{5}; y = 180$

4. $y = \dfrac{k}{x^2}$ $k = 2000; y = 2\frac{2}{9}$

2-7

Fitting a Model to Data I

Under pressure. *Scuba divers, like this one at Poor Knights Island, New Zealand, can safely dive about 18 meters (59 feet).*

The following table and graph give the water pressure (in pounds per square inch, or psi) exerted on a diver at various depths (in feet).

depth of diver (ft)	0	10	25	40	55	75
pressure on diver (psi)	0	4.3	10.8	17.2	23.7	32.3

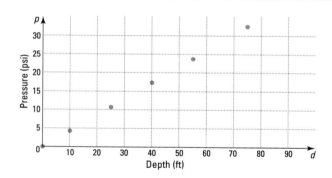

Lesson 2-7 Overview

Broad Goals This is an exceedingly important lesson. Its major non-tested goal is to have students realize that many of the formulas they have been using in their study of mathematics originate from induction of actual data. In this lesson, students see data that look as if they come from variables which are related by direct or inverse variation, and they find an equation that describes the data.

Perspective Each time students translate a real situation into an algebraic equation or numerical calculation, they are using a mathematical model.

Students who have studied UCSMP *Algebra* or other texts have had experience trying to find a line of good fit through a scatterplot. In doing so, students were describing a set of data with a linear mathematical model.

The mathematical models presented in this lesson are of a similar kind. Instead of looking specifically for a linear relationship, we look for a variation relationship between two or more variables. We try to identify the kind of relationship and, if possible, the specific equation. Although the numbers have been simplified, this technique is used by scientists, economists, engineers, and others to find formulas that describe the relationships they are studying.

① Because the pressure on the diver depends on his or her depth, pressure is the dependent variable and is placed on the vertical axis. Notice that the water pressure on a deep-sea diver increases as the diver goes deeper. How is the pressure related to the depth of water? The points seem to lie on a line through the origin. Therefore, it seems appropriate to describe the relation between these variables by saying the pressure varies directly as the depth. It makes sense that the origin is on this line because on the surface—that is, 0 feet under the water—the water pressure is 0 pounds per square inch (psi).

If p represents the pressure and d represents the depth, the formula for this variation is $p = kd$. The constant k can be determined from one of the data points. For instance, substitute $p = 4.3$ and $d = 10$ into the equation.

$$4.3 = k \cdot 10$$
$$k = 0.43 \left(\text{The unit is } \tfrac{\text{psi}}{\text{ft}} \cdot \right)$$

So, the relation between p and d can be expressed as

$$p = 0.43d.$$

It is important to check that this formula holds for all the data in the table. One way to do this is to make a table for the function $p = 0.43d$. For instance, if $d = 25$, then $p = 0.43(25) = 10.75$.

Shown below is a table for $p = 0.43d$ using the values of d given in the table on page 110.

d	0	10	25	40	55	75
p	0	4.3	10.75	17.2	23.65	32.25

Notice that the ordered pairs in this table are very close to the experimental data given in the table on page 110. This suggests that this function describes or *models* the situation well.

The equation $p = 0.43d$ is a *mathematical model* of the real-world relation between pressure and depth. A **mathematical model** for a real situation is a description of that situation using the language and concepts of mathematics. A good model holds true for all the given information. The formula $p = 0.43d$ gives very close approximations for all the values in the table so it is a good model for this diving situation.

The model $p = 0.43d$ makes it possible to predict the pressure on a diver at depths other than those given in the table. At a depth of 125 ft, for instance, the model predicts that the pressure on a diver would be

$$p = (0.43)(125) = 53.75.$$

That is, the pressure would be about 54 psi.

Notes on Reading
You might want to begin the class by showing graphs of variation functions, such as those below, and asking students for possible equations for the graphs and possible values for *x*, *y*, and *k*.

a. $[y = kx^2, x > 0, y > 0, k > 0]$

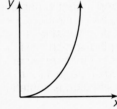

b. $[y = \tfrac{k}{x} \text{ or } y = \tfrac{k}{x^2}, x > 0, y > 0, k > 0]$

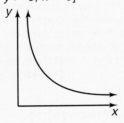

c. $[y = kx; x > 0, y > 0, k > 0]$

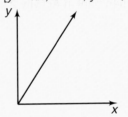

① At times, students may have trouble identifying variables as either independent or dependent. In many cases, it is quite evident which is the independent variable and which is the dependent variable. For example, we think of the length of time it takes to drive a certain distance without stopping as being dependent on the speed of the car. Accordingly, we identify speed as the independent variable and time as the dependent variable.

Optional Activities

Activity 1 Science Connection
You might want to use *Activity Kit, Activity 4* after discussing **Question 11**. In this activity, students find a model to describe the relationship between time and distance when a ball is dropped.

Activity 2 Art Connection
Materials: Equipment to make strobe pictures, graph paper, or **Teaching Aid 5**

If your science department has equipment to make strobe pictures, you might want to conduct an experiment similar to the one in Activity 1. Then have groups of students write a description of what happened, make

a table, graph the data, and describe the results.

Objectives

A Translate joint- and combined-variation language into formulas and formulas into joint- and combined-variation language.
B Solve problems involving joint or combined variation.
G Solve real-world problems involving joint or combined variation.

Resources

From the *Teacher's Resource File*
■ Lesson Master 2-9A or 2-9B
■ Answer Master 2-9
■ Teaching Aid 15: Warm-up
■ Technology Sourcebook Calculator Master 2

Additional Resources
■ Visuals for Teaching Aid 15

Teaching **2-9**
Lesson

Warm-up

Solve for *k*.

1. $53 = \frac{k(2)(2)^2}{10}$ $k = 66.25$

2. $80 = \frac{k(3)(2)^2}{10}$ $k \approx 66.67$

3. $107 = \frac{k(4)(2)^2}{10}$ $k = 66.875$

4. $132.5 = \frac{k(5)(2)^2}{10}$ $k = 66.25$

Combined and Joint Variation

This photo is from the Chinese New Year parade in Chinatown in Los Angeles.

Combined Variation

When direct and inverse variations occur together, the situation is called **combined variation.** Perhaps the simplest equation of combined variation is

$$y = \frac{kx}{z}$$

where *k* is the constant of variation. The equation can be translated as "*y* varies directly as *x* and inversely as *z*."

A combined-variation equation can have more than two variables, and the independent variables can have any positive exponent. You saw an instance of this in Lesson 2-8 with the formula:

$$M = \frac{kwt^2}{d}.$$

This formula gives the maximum weight *M* in pounds that can be supported by a board of width *w* in., thickness *t* in., and distance *d* ft between supports.

You should be able to write a combined-variation situation expressed in words as an equation.

Example 1

The time *T* that it takes a parade to pass a reviewing stand varies directly as the length *L* of the parade and inversely as the speed *s* of the parade. Write a general equation to model this situation.

Solution

Because *T* is described in terms of *L* and *s*, *T* is the dependent variable. Because *T* varies directly as *L*, *L* will be in the numerator. Because *T* varies inversely as *s*, *s* will be in the denominator. The equation is

$$T = \frac{kL}{s}.$$

122

Lesson 2-9 Overview

Broad Goals This lesson builds on the ideas and examples of Lesson 2-8, but students now learn how to find the constant of variation. The context of combined and joint variation provides an opportunity to review the method of solving variation problems that was presented earlier in the chapter.

Perceptive The formula derived from the **Examples** in Lesson 2-8 is used throughout this lesson. First it is presented as an

example of combined variation; it then appears after **Example 1** to obtain the constant of variation. If the constant of variation is known, the question in **Example 2** can be answered.

Joint variation is then discussed using the formula for the volume of a cone as an example. Finally, **Example 3** provides another example of joint variation.

Finding the Constant of Variation in a Combined-Variation Model

To find k, the constant of variation in a combined-variation model, use the same idea you used to find the constant for direct and inverse variation. Find one instance that relates all the variables simultaneously, and substitute all values into the general variation equation. For instance, to find k in the equation $M = \frac{kwt^2}{d}$, refer to any one of the tables in Lesson 2-8. For example, the first table relating M and w gives six possible pairs of numbers for w and M. For each of these pairs, $t = 2$ in. and $d = 10$ ft.

w (in.)	1	2	3	4	5	6
M (lb)	27	53	80	107	133	160

Now choose a pair of values for w and M. If you use $M = 27$ lb and $w = 1$ in., and substitute into the formula, you get

$$27 = \frac{k(1)(2)^2}{10}.$$

Unit analysis

$$lb = \frac{k \cdot in. \cdot in^2}{ft}$$

$$k = \frac{ft\text{-}lb}{in^3}$$

The unit analysis shows the unit for k. So, the constant of variation is

$$k = 67.5 \, \frac{ft\text{-}lb}{in^3}.$$

This value for k should be checked by using other data points. You will do this in the Questions at the end of the lesson. Thus, the formula becomes

$$M = \frac{67.5 \, wt^2}{d}$$
$$= 67.5 \, \frac{wt^2}{d}.$$

Now it is possible to use this model.

❶ Example 2

Find the maximum weight that can be supported by a board 3.75 in. wide and 1.75 in. thick with supports 8 ft apart.

Solution

Use the preceding formula with $d = 8$ ft, $w = 3.75$ in. and $t = 1.75$ in.

$$M = \frac{67.5 \, wt^2}{d}$$
$$= \frac{(67.5)(3.75)(1.75)^2}{8}$$
$$\approx 96.9$$

Unit analysis

$$\text{unit of } M = \frac{\frac{ft\text{-}lb}{in^3} \cdot in. \cdot in^2}{ft}$$
$$= \frac{ft\text{-}lb}{ft}$$
$$\text{unit of } M = lb$$

The board can support about 97 lb.

Optional Activities

Activity 1 Science Connection
Additional Example 3 deals with electrical power. You might have students select an appliance, estimate the amount of electricity needed to run it for a specified period of time, and determine its operating cost based on electricity rates in your area. [Sample: A 100-watt light bulb that burns 8 hours every day for 30 days uses 24,000 watts, or 24 kilowatt-hours, of electricity. In Chicago, this electricity would cost about $2.60.]

Activity 2 Technology Connection
In *Technology Sourcebook, Calculator Master 2,* a program is provided to help students explore combined and joint variation.

Notes on Questions

Students will need graph paper or **Teaching Aid 5** for **Questions 14, 16, and 19.**

Question 16 Students can use this graph to check the answer to **Question 15.**

Question 24 Almost any physics book is a good reference for this question.

Follow-up for Lesson 2-9

Practice

For more questions on SPUR Objectives, use **Lesson Master 2-9A** (shown on page 125) or **Lesson Master 2-9B** (shown on pages 126–127).

Additional Answers

14a.

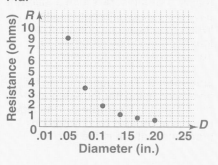

Energy efficient. This is a double-pane thermal window. In cold weather the window restricts heat from getting out of the house, and in warm weather it restricts heat from getting into the house.

16)

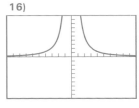

$-10 \leq x \leq 10$, x-scale = 1
$-10 \leq y \leq 10$, y-scale = 1

126

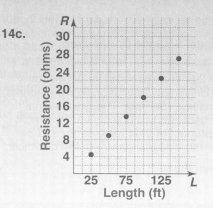

12) y does not change. When x is doubled, y is doubled, but when z is doubled, y is halved.

11. Consider the formula $V = \ell wh$ for the volume V of a rectangular solid with length ℓ, width w, and height h.
   a. Rewrite the formula as an English sentence using the language of variation. See below.
   b. What is the constant of variation? 1

12. Suppose y varies directly as x and inversely as z. Describe how y changes when x and z are both doubled. Explain how you arrived at your conclusion. See left.

13. The amount of heat H lost through a single pane of glass varies jointly as the area A of the pane and the difference $T_I - T_O$ in temperatures on either side of the window. a) $H = kA(T_I - T_O)$
   a. Translate this statement into an equation of variation.
   b. Suppose when the indoor temperature is 70°F (T_I) and the outdoor temperature is 0°F (T_O), the heat lost through a 12-ft^2 window is 950 Btu (British thermal units). Find the constant of variation. $k = 1.13$ Btu/(ft^2·°F)
   c. Rewrite the equation of variation using the constant found in part **b.** $H \approx 1.13\, A(T_I - T_O)$
   d. Find the amount of heat lost through a 16-ft^2 window if the indoor temperature is 75°F and the outdoor temperature is -5°F.
   1446.4 Btu

11a) The volume of a rectangular solid varies jointly as its length, width, and height.

Review

14. The resistance R in an electrical circuit is related to the diameter D of the wire and the length L of the wire. In an experiment, Dahlia obtained the following data using 50-ft lengths of wire. *(Lessons 2-7, 2-8)*

D (in.)	.05	.08	.11	.14	.17	.20
R (ohms)	9.0	3.5	1.9	1.1	0.8	0.6

   a. Graph these data points. See margin.
   b. How does R vary with D? R varies inversely as the square of D.
   c. With wire of diameter .05 in., she obtained the following data.

L (ft)	25	50	75	100	125	150
R (ohms)	4.5	9	13.5	18	22.5	27

   Graph these data points. See margin.
   d. How does R vary with L? R varies directly as L.
   e. Write an equation that relates R, D, and L. You do not need to find the constant of variation. $R = \frac{kL}{D^2}$

In 15–18, use the function with equation $f(x) = \frac{20}{x^2}$. *(Lessons 1-2, 1-3, 2-6)*

15. Which is greater: $f(3)$ or $f(5)$? f(3)

16. Sketch a graph of this equation on the window $-10 \leq x \leq 10$, $-10 \leq y \leq 10$. See left.

17. *True or false.* The graph of $y = \frac{20}{x^2}$ is a hyperbola. False

18. State the domain and range of f.
   domain: $\{x: x \neq 0\}$;   range: $\{y: y > 0\}$

14c.

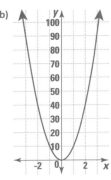

19a)

x	y
-3	90
-2	40
-1	10
0	0
1	10
2	40
3	90

b)

19. Use the equation $y = 10x^2$.   *(Lesson 2-5)*
  a. Make a table of values for $-3 \leq x \leq 3$. See left.
  b. Use the values in your table to graph the equation. See left.
  c. What is the name of this curve? parabola
  d. Find the rate of change from $x = 1$ to $x = 2$. 30
  e. Would the answer to part **d** be the same for any two points on the graph? Explain your answer.
  No; a parabola does not have a constant rate of change.

20. One general equation for a combined variation is $y = k\frac{xz}{w}$. Solve for k in terms of the other variables.   *(Lesson 1-6)* $k = \frac{wy}{xz}$

21. Given a function f defined by $f: x \rightarrow 4x^2 + 2$, find $f(\pi)$.   *(Lesson 1-3)*
  $f(\pi) = 4\pi^2 + 2 \approx 41.48$

In 22 and 23, an instance of a general property is given. Name the property.   *(Appendix A)*

22. $(4 + a) + z = (a + 4) + z$ **23.** $\frac{2}{3} + \frac{x}{3} = \frac{2 + x}{3}$
   Commutative Property of Addition   Adding Fractions Property

---

Exploration

24. Question 13 referred to heat loss through a window
  a. Find out what unit is used for heat in the metric system. joules; calories
  b. How is this unit related to the Btu?
   Btu $\approx$ 1,055 joules $\approx$ 252 calories
   3.968 Btu = 1000 calories (15° calories)

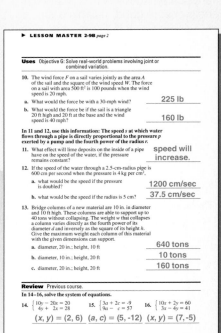

Chapter 2 Projects

Chapter 2 projects relate to the content of the lessons as shown below.

Project	Lesson(s)
1	2-1
2	2-7, 2-8, 2-9
3	2-4, 2-5, 2-6
4	2-6, 2-7, 2-8
5	2-2

1 Pizza Prices The information for this project is easy to obtain by telephone. However, to avoid the prospect that favorite restaurants will be inundated by students' calls, you might want to identify students to call certain restaurants. Students should request information for the same type of pizza from each store they call. Also, prices should not include tax or delivery charges. It may be wise to ask if the charge for extra ingredients is a flat charge or one that varies with the diameter of the pizza.

2 The Maximum Load of a Balsa Board You may want to suggest that students work in small groups on the project. Suggest that they write a careful description of how they conducted trials to collect data. They should also list decisions they were confronted with as they designed their setup. How, for example, did they decide on appropriate weight increments? Urge students to apply knowledge from areas such as physics or industrial arts that might help ensure good, reliable data.

A project presents an opportunity for you to extend your knowledge of a topic related to the material of this chapter. You should allow more time for a project than you do for typical homework questions.

PROJECTS 2 CHAPTER TWO

1 Pizza Prices

Consult several neighborhood restaurants that serve pizza in round pans. Choose a particular type of pizza, for instance, thin crust with mushrooms and onions. Find out the cost of this pizza, and the diameter of the pan.

a. For each restaurant, make a table of values, showing cost as a function of diameter for that type of pizza. Include diameters and prices for a small, medium, and large pizza.

b. Considering only area, price should vary with the square of the diameter. Do any of the restaurants you contacted follow this model? If yes, what equation describes their prices? If no, what other model seems to fit your data?

c. If the price structures are consistent, what should each of your restaurants charge for a giant pizza with a 30″ diameter?

2 The Maximum Load of a Balsa Board

Collect pieces of balsa wood of various lengths, widths, and thicknesses. Reconstruct X. Perri Menter's experiments regarding the maximum load M a board can hold described in Lessons 2-7, 2-8, and 2-9. Find an equation relating d, w, t, and M for balsa wood.

3 Sums or Differences of Variation Functions

Use an automatic grapher to explore graphs of sums of functions of variation equations.

a. For each function sketch a graph, state its domain and range, and identify any asymptotes of the graph.

(i) $y = x + \frac{1}{x}$

(ii) $y = x^2 + \frac{1}{x}$

(iii) $y = x^2 + \frac{1}{x^2}$

(iv) $y = x^2 + x$

b. Make up at least four other functions that can be expressed as sums or differences of variation functions. Sketch graphs of these functions.

c. Describe some patterns in the graphs.

Possible responses.

1a. Sample diameters and prices at Restaurants A, B, C, and D.

	Small	Medium	Large
A	10 in. $7.00	13 in. $10.00	15 in. $13.00
B	12 in. $7.50	14 in. $9.70	16 in. $11.90
C	10 in. $6.20	12 in. $8.62	14 in. $11.31
D	10 in. $6.65	13 in. $9.70	15 in. $13.95

b. None of these restaurants have prices that vary exactly as the square of the diameter. The following equations are possible linear or quadratic models; x represents diameter and y represents cost.

A: Linear: $y = 1.2x - 5$
   Quadratic: $y = 0.1x^2 - 1.3x + 10$
B: Linear: $y = 1.1x - 5.7$
   Quadratic: None

C: Linear: $y = 1.2775x - 6.62$
   Quadratic: $y = 0.34x^2 + 0.47x - 1.85$
D: Linear: $y = 1.43x - 8$
   Quadratic: $y = 0.222x^2 - 4.08x + 23.5$
Pricing at B comes closest to fitting direct variation with the square of the diameter.

4 Variation and Light

Use a small, bright, pocket-sized flashlight and a sheet of typing paper. Put the paper on a desk in a dimly lit room, and shine the light on the paper from various distances, for example, 1 in., 2 in., 4 in., 9 in., . . . , until the image becomes too dim to see.

a. At each step, measure the diameter of the circular image produced by the light beam. Create a table with the distance d of the flashlight from the paper in the first column, and the diameter D of the circular image in the second.

b. Graph the data in part a.

c. Write a formula showing how the diameter of the image depends on the distance. Does the diameter vary directly or inversely as d?

light

d. Borrow a light meter from a photographer or a science teacher. Repeat the above process, but rather than measure the diameters of the image, measure the *intensity*, or brightness, of the image at each step.

e. Theoretically the intensity I varies inversely as the square of d. How closely do your data fit this model?

5 The Law of the Lever

Does the Law of the Lever actually work? Get at least six people together of different weights and weigh each one of them. Choose one person to sit and remain on a see-saw a fixed distance from the fulcrum (This person determines the constant of variation in the law of the lever.) Have each of the remaining persons in turn sit on the see-saw and balance with the first person. Measure the distance from the fulcrum for each person.

3 Sums or Differences of Variation Functions

A little trial and error will be needed to obtain satisfactory viewing windows. To recognize asymptotes, viewing areas larger than those shown in the sample answers will be needed. The broad idea to be emphasized is that when one fraction is the sum of two others, one of the others will dominate when its values are large and the other's values are small. Students will probably need to trace to approximate certain maximum and minimum values for determining ranges of some functions.

4 Variation and Light

Physics teachers often have light meters that can be used for this experiment. Without special light sources and careful measurement, it will be a little difficult to come very close to theoretical expectations. However, students should be able to come close enough to get some feel for how the intensity of light varies with distance from the source. You might want to ask students about this activity's implications for amateur photography. People who take flash photos at night in dark, outdoor areas are not likely to get good results unless they are close to the subject they are photographing. The film cannot get enough reflected light to produce a good photo if the camera is too far from the subject.

5 The Law of the Lever

Before students gather data they should check the seesaw to be sure it is well-balanced when no one is on it. They should also check that it moves well when in use. (A little oil or other lubricant may be needed.) Since several students are needed for data, you may want to suggest this project as a group activity.

---

c. The equations from part b give these prices for 30-inch diameter pizza. The prices for the linear model are first.
A: $31.00; $61.00
B: $27.30
C: $31.71; $318.25
D: $34.90; $102.70

2. Data will vary. You should review each case on its own merits, taking into consideration both the amount of data collected and the care with which it was obtained. Review with students how closely their results agree with the model $M = \frac{kwt^2}{d}$. If their data were not in reasonable agreement with this model, discuss why this may be the case.

(Responses continue on page 130.)

Summary

The Summary gives an overview of the entire chapter and provides an opportunity for students to consider the material as a whole. Thus, the Summary can be used to help students relate and unify the concepts presented in the chapter.

The graphs of direct-variation formulas are also given on **Teaching Aid 18,** and the graphs of inverse-variation formulas are also given on **Teaching Aid 20.**

Vocabulary

Terms, symbols, and properties are listed by lesson to provide a checklist of concepts a student must know. Emphasize that students should read the vocabulary list carefully before starting the Progress Self-Test. If students do not understand the meaning of a term, they should refer back to the indicated lesson.

SUMMARY

Two types of functions studied in this chapter are direct variation and inverse variation. When $k \neq 0$ and $n > 0$, formulas of the form $y = kx^n$ represent direct-variation functions, and those of the form $y = \frac{k}{x^n}$ represent inverse-variation functions. Four special cases of direct and inverse variation occur frequently in real-world situations. The graph, domain D, and range R of each case is indicated below.

Direct-variation formulas

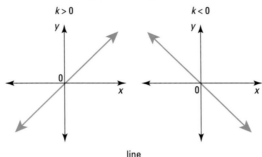

$y = kx$
y varies directly as x.

$k > 0$ $k < 0$

line
$D = R$ = the set of all real numbers

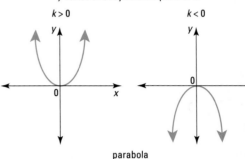

$y = kx^2$
y varies directly as the square of x.

$k > 0$ $k < 0$

parabola
D = the set of all real numbers D = the set of all real numbers
$R = \{y: y \geq 0\}$ $R = \{y: y \leq 0\}$

Inverse-variation formulas

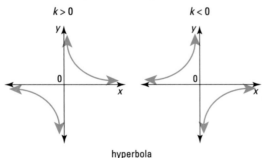

$y = \frac{k}{x}$
y varies inversely as x.

$k > 0$ $k < 0$

hyperbola
$D = R$ = the set of all nonzero real numbers

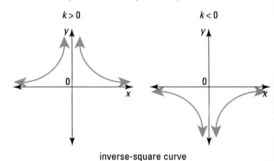

$y = \frac{k}{x^2}$
y varies inversely as the square of x.

$k > 0$ $k < 0$

inverse-square curve
D = the set of all nonzero real numbers D = the set of all nonzero real numbers
$R = \{y: y > 0\}$ $R = \{y: y < 0\}$

130

Additional responses, page 128
3a. Sample graphs are shown.
   (i) Domain: $\{x: x \neq 0\}$
     Range: $\{y: y \leq -2 \text{ or } y \geq 2\}$
     Asymptotes: $x = 0, y = x$

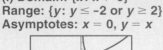

   $-5 \leq x \leq 5,$ x-scale = 1
   $-5 \leq y \leq 5,$ y-scale = 1

(ii) Domain: $\{x: x \neq 0\}$
Range: set of all real numbers
Asymptotes: $x = 0$

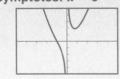

$-5 \leq x \leq 5,$ x-scale = 1
$-5 \leq y \leq 5,$ y-scale = 1

(iii) Domain: $\{x: x \neq 0\}$
Range: $\{y: y > 2\}$
Asymptotes: $x = 0$

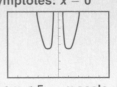

$-5 \leq x \leq 5,$ x-scale = 1
$0 \leq y \leq 8,$ y-scale = 1

In a formula where y is given in terms of x, it is natural to ask how changing x (the independent variable) affects the value of y (the dependent variable). In direct or inverse variation, when x is multiplied by a constant, the changes in y are predicted by the Fundamental Theorem of Variation. If y varies directly as x^n, then when x is multiplied by c, y is multiplied by c^n. If y varies inversely as x^n, then when x is multiplied by c, y is divided by c^n.

The rate of change from (x_1, y_1) to (x_2, y_2) is $\frac{y_2 - y_1}{x_2 - x_1}$, the slope of the line connecting them. For graphs of the form $y = kx$, the rate of change is the constant k. For other curves, the rate of change is not constant but varies depending on which points are used to calculate the rate of change.

Variation formulas may involve three or more variables. If all the independent variables are multiplied, then joint variation occurs. If they are not all multiplied, the situation is one of combined variation. Variation formulas can be derived from real data by examining two variables at a time and comparing their graphs with those given on page 130. We call this idea modeling, or forming a mathematical model of the data. Automatic graphers are useful tools to help in graphing or comparing functions.

The applications of slope, variation, and modeling are numerous. They include many perimeter, area, and volume formulas, the inverse-square laws of sound and gravity, and a variety of relationships among physical quantities such as distance, time, force, and pressure.

VOCABULARY

Below are the most important terms and phrases for this chapter.
You should be able to state each in words and give a specific example.
For the starred (*) terms, you should be able to supply a good definition.

Lesson 2-1
varies directly as
constant of variation
*direct variation
directly proportional to

Lesson 2-2
varies inversely as
*inverse variation
inversely proportional to
fulcrum
Law of the Lever
inverse-square variation
conjecture, prove

Lesson 2-3
Fundamental Theorem of Variation

Lesson 2-4
*slope
*rate of change

Lesson 2-5
automatic grapher
window
default window
parabola
reflection-symmetric
line of symmetry
copy
trace
opens up
opens down

Lesson 2-6
hyperbola
branches of a hyperbola
discrete
inverse-square curve
vertical asymptote
horizontal asymptote

Lesson 2-7
*mathematical model

Lesson 2-8
Converse of the Fundamental
Theorem of Variation

Lesson 2-9
combined variation
joint variation

(iv) Domain: set of all real numbers;
Range: {$y: y \geq -.25$}
Asymptotes: none

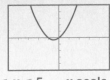

$-5 \leq x \leq 5$, x-scale $= 1$
$-5 \leq y \leq 5$, y-scale $= 1$

3b. In each of the four sample graphs that follow, the scale is:
   $-5 \leq x \leq 5$ x-scale $= 1$
   $-5 \leq y \leq 5$ y-scale $= 1$

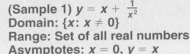

(Sample 1) $y = x + \frac{1}{x^2}$
Domain: {$x: x \neq 0$}
Range: Set of all real numbers
Asymptotes: $x = 0$, $y = x$

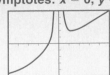

(Responses continue on page 132.)

Progress Self-Test

For the development of mathematical competence, feedback and correction, along with the opportunity to practice, are necessary. The Progress Self-Test provides the opportunity for feedback and correction; the Chapter Review provides additional opportunities for practice. We cannot overemphasize the importance of these end-of-chapter materials. It is at this point that the material "gels" for many students, allowing them to solidify skills and understanding. In general, student performance should be markedly improved after these pages.

Assign the Progress Self-Test as a one-night assignment. Worked-out *solutions* for all questions are in the Selected Answers section of the student book. Encourage students to take the Progress Self-Test honestly, grade themselves, and then be prepared to discuss the test in class.

Advise students to pay special attention to those Chapter Review questions (pages 134–137) that correspond to questions missed on the Progress Self-Test.

Additional Answers
3. *y* varies directly as the fifth power of *x*.
5. The *y*-value is quadrupled; Sample: (1, 3); (2, 12)
10. $\{x: x \neq 0\}$
11c. The surface area of a sphere varies directly with the square of its radius.

PROGRESS SELF-TEST

Take this test as you would take a test in class. Use graph paper and a ruler. Then check your work with the solutions in the Selected Answers section in the back of the book.
See margin for 3, 5, 10, 11c, 12a,b, 13a, 15a,b, 16
In 1 and 2, translate into a variation formula.

1. The number of trees *n* that can be planted per acre varies inversely as the square of the trees' distance *d* apart. $n = \frac{k}{d^2}$

2. The weight *w* that a bridge column can support varies directly as the fourth power of its diameter *d* and inversely as the square of its length *L*. $w = \frac{kd^4}{L^2}$

3. Write the variation formula $y = kx^5$ in words.

4. If *S* varies directly as the square of *p* and $S = 10$ when $p = 3$, find *S* when $p = 8$. $S = \frac{640}{9} \approx 71.1$

5. For the variation equation $y = 3x^2$, what is the change in the *y*-value when an *x*-value is doubled? Give two specific pairs of (x, y) values that support your conclusion.

6. For the variation $y = \frac{6}{x}$, what is the change in the *y*-value when an *x*-value is multiplied by c $(c \neq 0)$? *y* is divided by *c*.

7. Find the rate of change of $y = x^2$ between $x = 3$ and $x = 4$. 7

8. *True or false.* All graphs of variation equations pass through the origin. **False**

9. The graph of $y = kx^2$ is called a __?__ and opens up if __?__. parabola; $k > 0$

10. Suppose $f(x) = \frac{17}{x^2}$. What is the domain of *f*?

11. Fill in the blank with "inversely," "directly," or "neither inversely nor directly."

   a. The surface area of a sphere varies __?__ as the cube of its radius. **neither**

   b. The number of different shares you can buy varies __?__ as the cost of each share, if you invest exactly $10,000. **inversely**

   c. Explain your reasoning in part **a.**

12. a. Make a table of values for $y = -5x$. Include at least five pairs.

   b. Make a graph of the equation in part **a.**

   c. Find the slope of the graph in part **b.** -5

132

13. a. Use an automatic grapher to sketch a graph of $y = \frac{5}{x}$.

   b. Identify any asymptotes to the graph in part **a.** the x-axis and y-axis

14. *Multiple choice.* Find the equation whose graph looks the most like the graph shown below. **c**

   (a) $y = -3x$ (b) $y = -\frac{3}{x}$

   (c) $y = -\frac{3}{x^2}$ (d) $y = -\frac{x}{3}$

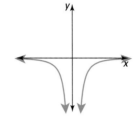

15. A student removing the bolts from the back of a large cabinet in a science lab knew that it was easier to turn a bolt with a long wrench than with a short one. The student decided to investigate the force required with various wrenches, and obtained the following data.

Length of wrench (in.) *L*	3	5	6	8	9
Force (lb) *F*	120	72	60	45	40

   a. Graph these data points.

   b. Which variation equation is a better model for this situation, $F = \frac{k}{L}$ or $F = \frac{k}{L^2}$? Justify your answer. $F = k/L$

   c. How much force would be required to turn one of the bolts with a 12-in. wrench? **30 lb**

16. Give a real-world example of a direct-variation situation, other than one that is in this test.

17. Suppose the price of a single scoop of ice cream varies directly with the cube of the diameter of the scoop. If a scoop 2 inches in diameter costs 79¢, how much should a 3-inch-diameter scoop cost? **$2.67**

Additional responses, page 128

(Sample 2) $y = x^3 + \frac{1}{x}$
Domain: $\{x: x \neq 0\}$
Range $\approx \{y: y \leq -1.755\}$ or $y \geq 1.755$
Asymptotes: $x = 0$, $y = x$

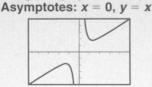

(Sample 3) $y = x + \frac{1}{x^3}$
Domain: $\{x: x \neq 0\}$
Range $\approx \{y: y \leq -1.755)$ or $y \geq 1.755$
Asymptotes: $x = 0$, $y = x$

(Sample 4) $y = x^2 - \frac{1}{x^3}$
Domain: $\{x: x \neq 0]$
Range: set of all real numbers.
Asymptotes: $x = 0$

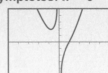

PROGRESS SELF-TEST

18. Here is a graph of $y = x^2$ on the window $-4 \le x \le 4$, $0 \le y \le 10$.

-4 ≤ x ≤ 4, x-scale = 1
0 ≤ y ≤ 10, y-scale = 1

Which of the graphs below cannot be a graph of this equation on some other window? **d**

(a)

-2 ≤ x ≤ 2, x-scale = 1
0 ≤ y ≤ 5, y-scale = 1

(b)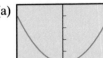

-2 ≤ x ≤ 2, x-scale = 1
0 ≤ y ≤ 12, y-scale = 1

(c)

-1 ≤ x ≤ 4, x-scale = 1
0 ≤ y ≤ 12, y-scale = 1

(d)

-4 ≤ x ≤ 4, x-scale = 1
0 ≤ y ≤ 12, y-scale = 1

19. Suppose that variables V, h, and g are related as illustrated in the graphs below. The points on the first graph lie on or near a parabola. The points on the second graph lie on a line through the origin.

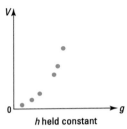

h held constant

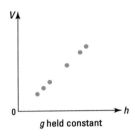

g held constant

Write a general equation approximating the relationship among V, h, and g. **$V = khg^2$**

20. Poiseuille's Law states that the speed S at which blood flows through arteries and veins varies directly with the blood pressure P and the fourth power of the radius r of the blood vessel. Suppose that blood flows at a rate of 0.09604 cm³/sec through an artery of radius 0.065 cm when the blood pressure is 100 mmHg. What would be the blood pressure if plaque reduced the artery to 0.05 cm radius, and the speed stayed the same? **285.6 mmHg**

Additional Answers, continued

12a.

x	y
-2	10
-1	5
0	0
1	-5
2	-10

b.

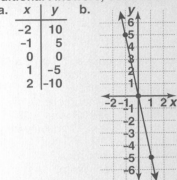

$y = -5x$

13a.

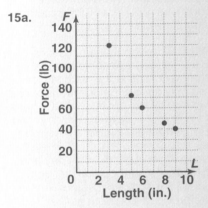

-10 ≤ x ≤ 10, x-scale = 1
-10 ≤ y ≤ 10, y-scale = 1

15a.

b. $F = \frac{k}{L}$; If $F = \frac{k}{L}$, when $L = 3$ and $F = 120$, $k = 360$ in. · lb and $F = \frac{360}{L}$. This formula is valid for the rest of the data.

16. Sample: The number of CDs a student could buy with a week's paycheck varies directly as the number of hours worked.

Additional responses, page 129

4a. Responses will depend on light sources and accuracy of measurements. A sample table is shown.

d (in.)	1	2	3	3.5	4
D (in.)	3	6.25	10	11	12

b. The graph shown at the right is based on data in sample table.

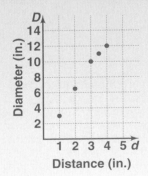

Distance (in.)

c. The direct variation equation $D = 3k$ comes reasonably close to describing how d and D are related.

d. Responses will vary. Readings may depend on where the meter is placed. The light may be most intense at the center of this area and less intense on the fringes.

(Responses continue on page 134.)

Chapter 2 Review

Resources

From the **Teacher's Resource File**
- Answer Master for Chapter 2 Review
- Assessment Sourcebook: Chapter 2 Test, Forms A–D Chapter 2 Test, Cumulative Form

Additional Resources
- Quiz and Test Writer

The main objectives for the chapter are organized in the Chapter Review under the four types of understanding this book promotes–Skills, Properties, Uses, and Representations.

Whereas end-of-chapter material may be considered optional in some texts, in *UCSMP Advanced Algebra* we have selected these objectives and questions with the expectation that they will be covered. Students should be able to answer these questions with about 85% accuracy after studying the chapter.

You may assign these questions over a single night to help students prepare for a test the next day, or you may assign the questions over a two-day period. If you work the questions over two days, we recommend assigning the *evens* for homework the first night so that students get feedback in class the next day and then assigning the *odds* the night before the test because answers are provided to questions they still do not understand. Use the day or days as a total class discussion of the material that the class finds most difficult.

CHAPTER REVIEW

Questions on SPUR Objectives

SPUR stands for **S**kills, **P**roperties, **U**ses, and **R**epresentations. The Chapter Review questions are grouped according to the SPUR Objectives for this chapter.

SKILLS DEAL WITH THE PROCEDURES USED TO GET ANSWERS.

Objective A: *Translate variation language into formulas and formulas into variation language.*
(Lessons 2-1, 2-2, 2-9) See margin for 6–8.

In 1–3, translate into a variation equation.
1. y varies directly as the square of x. $y = kx^2$
2. s varies inversely with p. $s = \frac{k}{p}$
3. z varies jointly as x and t. $z = kxt$
4. In the formula, $r = kstu$, r varies __?__ with __?__. jointly; s, t, u
5. If $V = k\pi r^2$, then V varies __?__ as __?__.

In 6–8, write each variation equation in words.
6. $w = kh^4$ 7. $y = \frac{k}{x^2}$ 8. $t = \frac{kz^3}{w^2}$

5) directly; the square of r

Objective B: *Solve variation problems.*
(Lessons 2-1, 2-2, 2-9)
9. y varies directly as x. If $x = 4$, then $y = -12$. Find y when $x = -7$. 21
10. y varies directly as the square of x. When $x = -5$, $y = 75$. Find y when $x = 8$. 192

11. y varies inversely as the cube of x. If $x = 4$, $y = -\frac{1}{16}$. Find y when $x = \frac{1}{2}$. -32
12. z varies directly as the square of x and inversely as y. When $x = 3$ and $y = 5$, $z = 4.5$. Find z when $x = -2$ and $y = -1.5$. $\frac{-20}{3} = -6.\overline{6}$

Objective C: *Find slopes (rates of change).*
(Lessons 2-4, 2-5, 2-6) 13) $\frac{9}{5} = 1.8$ 14) $-\frac{1}{3}$
13. Find the slope of the line through the points (15, 27) and (20, 36).
14. What is the slope of the line at the right?

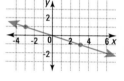

In 15 and 16, $y = 5x^2$.
15. Find the rate of change from $x = -2$ to $x = -1$. -15
16. Find the rate of change from $x = -3$ to $x = -2$.

In 17 and 18, find the rate of change from $x = 3$ to $x = 4$.
17. $y = \frac{9}{x}$ $\frac{-3}{4} = -.75$ 18. $y = \frac{9}{x^2}$ $\frac{-7}{16} = -.4375$

16) -25

PROPERTIES DEAL WITH THE PRINCIPLES BEHIND THE MATHEMATICS.

Objective D: *Use the Fundamental Theorem of Variation.* (Lesson 2-3)

In 19 and 20, suppose that the value of x is tripled. Tell how the value of y changes.
19. y varies directly as x. y is tripled.
20. y varies directly as x^3. y is multiplied by 27

In 21 and 22, suppose that p varies inversely as the square of q. How does the value of p change if q is
21. doubled?   22. multiplied by ten?
    p is divided by $2^2 = 4$. p is divided by $10^2 = 100$.

23. If $y = \frac{k}{x^n}$ and x is multiplied by any nonzero constant c, then y is __?__. divided by c^n
24. If $y = kx^n$ and x is divided by any nonzero constant c, then y is __?__. divided by c^n
25. Suppose $y = \frac{kx^n}{z^n}$ and both x and z are multiplied by any nonzero constant c. What is the effect on y? not affected

134

Additional responses, page 129
4e. **Responses will depend on the data obtained in part d. If results are too different from theoretical expectations, you might review the students' procedures and suggest ways to obtain better data.**
5. **A sample is given. The person who stayed in a fixed position weighed 60.0 kg and was 2 m from the fulcrum. The table shows weights (kg) and distances (m) for the other five people.**

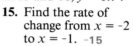

kg	56.8	66.8	68.6	59.1	54.1
m	2.10	1.83	1.70	2.00	2.20

A scatterplot using these data did not make it clear whether the relationship was linear or involved inverse variation. When the people weighing 56.8 kg and 66.8 kg sat one right behind the other, they balanced the person in the fixed position by being 1.1 m from the fulcrum.

When the point (123.6, 1.1) was added to the scatterplot, it came much closer to the graph of $d = \frac{120}{w}$ than to the fixed line. The issue was decided in favor of the inverse-variation function predicted by the Law of the Lever.

Objective E: *Identify the properties of variation functions.* *(Lessons 2-4, 2-5, 2-6)*

26. The graph of the equation $y = kx$ is a __?__ having slope __?__. **line;   k**

27. Graphs of all direct-variation formulas go through the point __?__. **(0, 0)**

In 28–30, refer to these four equations:
(a) $y = kx$ (b) $y = kx^2$
(c) $y = \frac{k}{x}$ (d) $y = \frac{k}{x^2}$.

28. Which equations have graphs that are symmetric to the y-axis? **b;   d**

29. The graph of which equation is a parabola? **b**

30. *True or false.* When $k > 0$, all of the equations have points in quadrant I. **True**

31. Identify the domain and range of $f(x) = kx^2$ for $k > 0$. **See below.**

32. Identify the asymptotes to an equation of an inverse-square variation. **The x- and y-axes**

33. For what values of x is the inverse variation $y = \frac{k}{x}$ undefined? **x = 0**

34. Write a short paragraph explaining how the graphs of $y = -2x^2$ and $y = \frac{-2}{x^2}$ are alike and how they are different. **See margin.**

31) domain: the set of real numbers;   range: the set of nonnegative real numbers

---

USES DEAL WITH APPLICATIONS OF MATHEMATICS IN REAL SITUATIONS.

Objective F: *Recognize variation situations.* *(Lessons 2-1, 2-2)*

In 35–38, translate into a variation equation.

35. The number n of congruent marbles that fit into a box is inversely proportional to the cube of the radius r of each marble. $n = \frac{k}{r^3}$

36. The area A of an image on a movie screen is directly proportional to the square of the distance d from the projector to the screen. $A = kd^2$

37. The gravitational pull p of a star on a planet with mass m varies directly as the mass and inversely as the square of the distance d of the planet from the star. $p = \frac{km}{d^2}$

38. At a given speed, the distance a plane travels is directly proportional to the time traveled.

In 39–42, complete with "directly," "inversely," or "neither directly nor inversely."

39. The number of people invited to dinner varies __?__ as the amount of space each guest has at the table. **inversely**

40. The temperature in a house varies __?__ as the number of hours the air conditioner has been on. **neither inversely or directly**

41. The volume of a cylinder of height 10 cm varies __?__ as the square of its radius. **directly**

42. Your distance above the ground while on a Ferris wheel varies __?__ as the number of minutes you have been riding on it. **neither inversely or directly**

38) $d = kt$

Objective G: *Solve real-world variation problems.* *(Lessons 2-1, 2-2, 2-9)*

43. Suppose the price of a pizza varies directly with the square of its diameter. At Vic Yee's pizza parlor an 8-inch pizza costs $6.00. How much would a 12-inch pizza cost? **$13.50**

44. The refund r you get varies directly with n the number of cans you recycle. If you get a $7.50 refund for 150 cans, how much should you get for 400 cans? **$20.00**

45. One of Murphy's Laws is that the time t a committee spends debating a budget item is inversely proportional to d, the number of dollars involved. If a committee spends 10 minutes debating a $300 item, how much time is spent debating a $1000 item? **3 min**

46. Recall that the weight of a body varies inversely with the square of its distance from the center of the Earth. If Daniel weighs 75 lb on the surface of the Earth, how much would he weigh in space 50,000 miles from the Earth's surface? (The radius of the Earth is approximately 4000 miles.) **.41 lb**

47. The force needed to keep a car from skidding on a curve varies directly as the weight of the car and the square of the speed and inversely as the radius of the curve. It requires 266 lb of force to keep a 2200-lb car, traveling at 30 mph, from skidding on a curve of radius 500 ft. How much force is required to keep a 3000-lb car, traveling at 45 mph, from skidding on a curve of radius 400 ft? **≈ 1020.2 lb of force**

Chapter 2   *Chapter Review*   **135**

Assessment

Evaluation The *Assessment Sourcebook* provides five forms of the Chapter 2 Test. Forms A and B present parallel versions in a short-answer format. Forms C and D offer performance assessment. The fifth test is Chapter 2 Test, Cumulative Form. About 75% of this test covers Chapter 2 and 25% of it covers Chapter 1.

For information on grading, see *General Teaching Suggestions; Grading* in the *Professional Source-book*, which begins on page T20 in the Teacher's Edition.

Feedback After students have taken the test for Chapter 2 and you have scored the results, return the tests to students for discussion. Class discussion of the questions that caused trouble for the most students can be very effective in identifying and clarifying misunderstandings. You might want to have them write down the items they missed and work, either in groups or at home, to correct them. It is important for students to receive feedback on every chapter test, and we recommend that students see and correct their mistakes before proceeding too far into the next chapter.

Additional Answers
6. *w* varies directly as the fourth power of *h*.
7. *y* varies inversely as the square of *x*.
8. *t* varies directly as the third power of *z* and inversely as the square of *w*.
34. Sample: Both equations have graphs which lie entirely in quadrants III and IV and are symmetric to the *y*-axis. The graph of $y = -2x^2$ is a continuous curve and approaches the *x*-axis as *x* goes to zero, and goes further from the *x*-axis as *x* gets more positive or more negative. It has no asymptotes. The graph of $y = \frac{-2}{x^2}$ has two branches and approaches the *x*-axis as *x* gets more positive or more negative, and goes further from the *x*-axis as *x* goes to zero. It has two asymptotes, $x = 0$ and $y = 0$.

135

Additional Answers

49a.

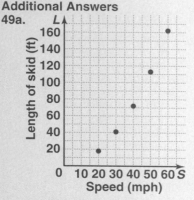

Length of skid (ft) vs Speed (mph)

b. $L = kS^2$

c. Sample: $k \approx .045 \frac{ft}{(mph)^2}$;
$L = .045S^2$

d. 220.5 ft

50a.

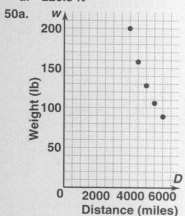

Weight (lb) vs Distance (miles)

b. $w = \frac{k}{D^2}$

c. $k = 3.2 \times 10^9 \frac{miles^2}{lb}$;
$w = \frac{3.2 \times 10^9}{D^2}$

d. about 199.5 lb

51ai.

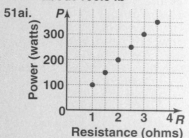

Power (watts) vs Resistance (ohms)

51aii. *P* varies directly as *R*.
Sample: The slope between any two points is constant.

51bi.

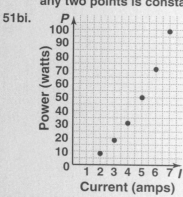

Power (watts) vs Current (amps)

---

48. An object is tied to a string and then twirled in a circular motion. The tension in the string varies directly as the square of the speed and inversely as the radius of the circle. When the radius is 5 ft and the speed is 4 ft/sec, then the tension in the string is 90 lb. If the radius is 3.5 ft and the speed is 4.4 ft/sec, find the tension in the string. ≈ 155.6 lb

Objective H: *Fit an appropriate model to data.*
(Lessons 2-7, 2-8) **49-51)** See margin.

In 49–50, a situation and question are given.

a. Draw a graph to represent the situation.

b. Find a general variation equation to represent the situation.

c. Find the value of the constant of variation and rewrite the variation equation.

d. Answer the question asked in the problem.

49. Officer Friendly measured the length *L* of car skid marks when the brakes were applied at different speeds *S*. He obtained the following data.

S (mph)	20	30	40	50	60
L (ft)	18	41	72	113	162

How far would a car skid if the brakes are applied at 70 mph?

50. A man weighs 200 lb at sea level. The following table gives his weight *W* at various distances *D* from the center of the Earth.

D (miles)	4000	4500	5000	5500	6000
W (lb)	200	158	128	106	89

How much would the man weigh on the top of Mt. Everest, which is about 4005.5 miles from the Earth's center? about 199.5 lb

51. Cyrus N. Tist tried to discover how the power in an electric circuit is related to the strength of the current and the resistance of the wire.

a. When he held the current *I* constant at 10 amps, he obtained the following data relating power *P* and resistance *R*.

R (ohms)	1	1.5	2	2.5	3	3.5
P (watts)	100	150	200	250	300	350

136

---

i. Graph these data points.

ii. How does *P* vary with *R*? Justify your answers.

b. Then Cy held the resistance constant at 2 ohms. He obtained the data relating power *P* and current *I* shown below.

I (amps)	2	3	4	5	6	7
P (watts)	8	18	32	50	72	98

i. Graph these data points.

ii. How does *P* vary with *I*?

c. Write a general equation of variation relating *P*, *R*, and *I*.

d. Find the constant of variation, and write a variation equation relating *P*, *R*, and *I*.

e. Predict the value of *P* when *I* = 20 amps and *R* = 4 ohms.

52. Erika performed an experiment to determine how the pressure *P* of a liquid on an object is related to the depth *d* of the object and the density *D* of the liquid. She obtained the graph on the left by keeping the depth constant and measuring the pressure on an object in solutions with different densities. She obtained the graph on the right by keeping the density constant and measuring the pressure on an object in a solution at various depths.

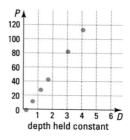

depth held constant

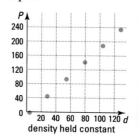

density held constant

Write a general equation relating *P*, *d*, and *D*. (Do not find the constant of variation.) Explain your reasoning.
$P = kDd$; Sample: The first graph shows that the pressure *P* varies directly as the density *D*. The second graph shows that the pressure *P* varies directly as the depth *d*.

51bii. *P* varies directly as I^2.

c. $P = kRI^2$

d. $k = 1$; $P = RI^2$

e. $P = 1600$ watts

53a.
Sample:

x	y
−2	−1
−1	−0.5
0	0
1	0.5
2	1

b.

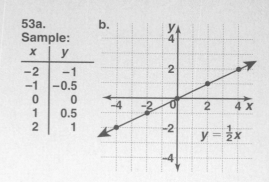

$y = \frac{1}{2}x$

REPRESENTATIONS DEAL WITH PICTURES, GRAPHS, OR OBJECTS THAT ILLUSTRATE CONCEPTS.

Objective I: *Graph variation equations.*
(Lessons 2-4, 2-5, 2-6) **See margin.**

In 53–56, an equation is given. **a.** Make a table of values. **b.** Graph the equation.

53. $y = \frac{1}{2}x$　　　　**54.** $y = -2x$

55. $y = -2x^2$　　　**56.** $y = \frac{1}{2}x^2$

In 57 and 58, use an automatic grapher to sketch the graph of each equation.

57. $y = \frac{36}{x}$　　　　**58.** $y = \frac{36}{x^2}$

Objective J: *Identify variation equations from graphs.* *(Lessons 2-4, 2-5, 2-6)*

Multiple choice. In 59–62, select the equation whose graph is most like the one shown. Assume the scales on the axes are equal.

59. (a) $y = 4x$
　c　(b) $y = -4x^2$
　　　(c) $y = -\frac{1}{4}x$
　　　(d) $y = -\frac{1}{4}$

60. (a) $y = 10x^2$
　b　(b) $y = -x^2$
　　　(c) $y = -10x$
　　　(d) $y = -\frac{10}{x^2}$

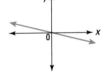

61. (a) $y = \frac{x^2}{6}$
　b　(b) $y = \frac{6}{x}$
　　　(c) $y = \frac{-6}{x}$
　　　(d) $y = \frac{-6}{x^2}$

62. (a) $y = \frac{x^2}{6}$
　d　(b) $y = \frac{6}{x}$
　　　(c) $y = \frac{-6}{x}$
　　　(d) $y = \frac{-6}{x^2}$

63. In the graph of $y = kx^2$ shown at the right, what type of number must k be?
positive real

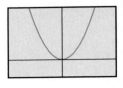

64. In the graph of $y = \frac{k}{x^2}$ shown at the right, what type of number is k? **negative real**

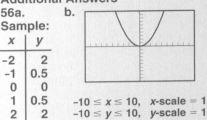

Objective K: *Recognize the effects of a change in scale or viewing window on a graph of a variation equation.* *(Lesson 2-5)*

In 65 and 66, a graph of $y = 4x$ is drawn below using the window $-5 \le x \le 5$, $-25 \le y \le 25$.

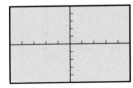

$-5 \le x \le 5$,　x-scale = 1
$-25 \le y \le 25$,　y-scale = 5

65. Sketch a graph of $y = 4x$ on the window shown at the right.
See margin.

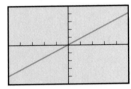

$-5 \le x \le 5$,　x-scale = 1
$-5 \le y \le 5$,　y-scale = 1

66. Does the slope of the line $y = 4x$ change when the viewing window is changed? Explain your answer. **See margin.**

67. Consider the function $f(x) = \frac{18}{x^2}$.
　a. Give the dimensions of a window that shows both branches of the graph.
　b. Give the dimensions of a window that shows only one branch of the graph. **See margin.**

Chapter 2　*Chapter Review*　**137**

Homework We recommend that you assign both the reading and some questions in Lesson 3-1 for homework the evening of the test. This assignment gives students work to do after they have completed the test and keeps the class moving. If you do not do this, you may cover one less chapter over the course of the year. Remind students that this assignment includes reading the *Chapter 3 Opener*.

Additional Answers

56a.
Sample:

x	y
-2	2
-1	0.5
0	0
1	0.5
2	2

b.

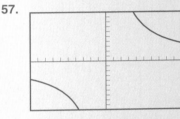

$-10 \le x \le 10$,　x-scale = 1
$-10 \le y \le 10$,　y-scale = 1

57.

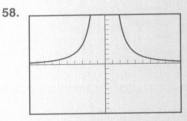

$-10 \le x \le 10$,　x-scale = 1
$-10 \le y \le 10$,　y-scale = 1

58.

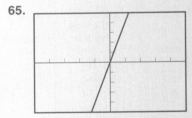

$-10 \le x \le 10$,　x-scale = 1
$-10 \le y \le 10$,　y-scale = 1

65.

$-5 \le x \le 5$,　x-scale = 1
$-5 \le y \le 5$,　y-scale = 1

66. No. The slope appears to become greater, but it is 4 in both cases.

67a. Sample: $-10 \le x \le 10$; $-5 \le y \le 10$
　b. $-20 \le x \le 0$; $-5 \le y \le 10$

54a.
Sample:

x	y
-2	4
-1	2
0	0
1	-2
2	-4

b.

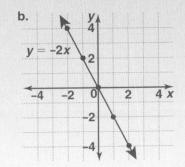

$y = -2x$

55a.
Sample:

x	y
-2	-8
-1	-2
0	0
1	-2
2	-8

b.

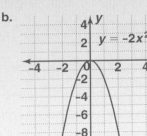

$y = -2x^2$

Adapting to Individual Needs

The student text is written for the vast majority of students. The chart at the right suggests two pacing plans to accommodate the needs of your students. Students in the Full Course should complete the entire text by the end of the year. Students in the Minimal Course will spend more time when there are quizzes and more time on the Chapter Review. Therefore, these students may not complete all of the chapters in the text.

Options are also presented to meet the needs of a variety of teaching and learning styles. For each lesson, the Teacher's Edition provides sections entitled: *Video* which describes video segments and related questions that can be used for motivation or extension; *Optional Activities* which suggests activities that employ materials, physical models, technology, and cooperative learning; and *Adapting to Individual Needs* which regularly includes **Challenge** problems, **English Language Development** suggestions, and suggestions for providing **Extra Help.** The Teacher's Edition also frequently includes an **Error Alert,** an **Extension,** and an **Assessment** alternative. The options available in Chapter 3 are summarized in the chart below.

Chapter 3 Pacing Chart

Day	Full Course	Minimal Course
1	3-1	3-1
2	3-2	3-2
3	3-3	3-3
4	Quiz; 3-4	Quiz*; begin 3-4.
5	3-5	Finish 3-4.
6	3-6	3-5
7	Quiz; 3-7	3-6
8	3-8	Quiz*; begin 3-7.
9	3-9	Finish 3-7.
10	Self-Test	3-8
11	Review	3-9
12	Test*	Self-Test
13		Review
14		Review
15		Test*

*in the Teacher's Resource File

In the Teacher's Edition...

Lesson	Optional Activities	Extra Help	Challenge	English Language Development	Error Alert	Extension	Cooperative Learning	Ongoing Assessment
3-1	●	●	●	●	●	●	●	Oral/Written
3-2	●	●	●	●	●	●	●	Written
3-3	●	●	●	●	●	●	●	Oral/Written
3-4	●	●	●	●	●	●	●	Written
3-5	●	●	●	●	●	●	●	Written
3-6	●	●	●	●			●	Written
3-7	●	●	●	●			●	Oral
3-8	●	●	●		●		●	Group
3-9	●	●	●	●	●	●	●	Oral/Written

In the Additional Resources...

Lesson	In the Teacher's Resource File							Technology	Video Segments
	Lesson Masters, A and B	Teaching Aids*	Activity Kit*	Answer Masters	Technology Sourcebook	Assessment Sourcebook	Visual Aids**		
3-1	3-1	8, 23, 26	5	3-1			8, 23, 26, AM		
3-2	3-2	8, 23, 27		3-2			8, 23, 27, AM		
3-3	3-3	8, 23		3-3		Quiz	8, 23, AM		
3-4	3-4	8, 24		3-4			8, 24, AM		
3-5	3-5	8, 24		3-5			8, 24, AM		
In-class Activity				3-6			AM		
3-6	3-6	24, 28, 29		3-6	Comp 3	Quiz	24, 28, 29, AM	GraphExplorer	3-6
3-7	3-7	25	6	3-7			25, AM		
3-8	3-8	25		3-8			25, AM		
3-9	3-9	8, 25, 30		3-9			8, 25, 30, AM		
End of chapter						Tests			

*Teaching Aids are pictured on pages 138C and 138D. The activities in the Activity Kit are pictured on page 138C.

**Visual Aids provide transparencies for all Teaching Aids and all Answer Masters.

Also available is the Study Skills Handbook which includes study-skill tips related to reading, note-taking, and comprehension.

Integrating Strands and Applications

	3-1	3-2	3-3	3-4	3-5	3-6	3-7	3-8	3-9
Mathematical Connections									
Number Sense		●							●
Algebra	●	●	●	●	●	●	●	●	●
Geometry	●	●	●			●	●		
Measurement	●	●	●		●	●	●		
Statistics/ Data Analysis						●	●	●	
Patterns and Functions	●	●	●	●	●	●	●	●	●
Discrete Mathematics			●			●			●
Interdisciplinary and Other Connections									
Science	●	●	●	●	●	●		●	
Social Studies						●	●	●	●
Multicultural									●
Technology		●				●	●	●	●
Career	●			●	●		●		
Consumer	●	●	●	●	●		●		●
Sports			●		●				

Teaching and Assessing the Chapter Objectives

Chapter 3 Objectives (Organized into the SPUR categories—Skills, Properties, Uses, and Representations)	Lessons	Progress Self-Test Questions	Chapter Review Questions	Chapter Test, Forms A and B	In the Teacher's Resource File	
					Chapter Test, Forms	
					C	D
Skills						
A: Determine the slope and intercepts of a line given its equation.	3-1, 3-2, 3-4	3	1–6	5, 6, 7	1	
B: Find an equation for a line given two points on it or given a point on it and its slope.	3-2, 3-5	5, 6	7–12	9	1	
C: Evaluate expressions based on step functions.	3-9	13	13–16	4	3	
D: Evaluate or find explicit and recursive formulas for arithmetic sequences.	3-7, 3-8	10, 15, 16	17–23	1, 2	2	
Properties						
E: Recognize properties of linear functions.	3-1, 3-2, 3-4, 3-5	2, 4, 7	24–35	10, 15, 16, 17	1	
F: Recognize properties of arithmetic sequences.	3-7, 3-8	10, 12	36–44	12	2	
Uses						
G: Model constant-increase or constant-decrease situations or situations involving arithmetic sequences.	3-1, 3-7, 3-8	9	45–48	3		✓
H: Model situations leading to linear combinations.	3-3	8	49–50	11	4	
I: In a real-world context, find an equation for a line containing two points.	3-5	14	51–52	18		
J: Fit lines to data.	3-6	18	53–56	20	5	
K: Model situations leading to piecewise-linear functions or step functions.	3-1, 3-5, 3-9	19	57–62	14	3	✓
Representations						
L: Graph or interpret graphs of linear equations.	3-2, 3-4	1	63–70	8, 13	1	✓
M: Graph or interpret graphs of piecewise-linear functions or step functions.	3-1, 3-9	11, 17	71–75	19		✓

Assessment Sourcebook
Quiz for Lessons 3-1 through 3-3
Quiz for Lessons 3-4 through 3-6

Chapter 3 Test, Forms A–D
Chapter 3 Test, Cumulative Form

Comprehensive Test, Chapters 1–3

Quiz and Test Writer

Activity Kit

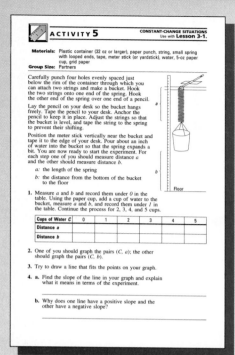

Materials: Plastic container (32 oz or larger), paper punch, string, small spring with looped ends, tape, meter stick (or yardstick), water, 5-oz paper cup, grid paper
Group Size: Partners

Carefully punch four holes evenly spaced just below the rim of the container through which you can attach two strings and make a bucket. Hook the two strings onto one end of the spring. Hook the other end of the spring over one end of a pencil.

Lay the pencil on your desk so the bucket hangs freely. Tape the pencil to your desk. Anchor the pencil to keep it in place. Adjust the strings so that the bucket is level, and tape the string to the spring to prevent their shifting.

Position the meter stick vertically near the bucket and tape it to the edge of your desk. Pour about an inch of water into the bucket so that the spring expands a bit. You are now ready to start the experiment. For each step one of you should measure distance *a* and the other should measure distance *b*.

a: the length of the spring

b: the distance from the bottom of the bucket to the floor

1. Measure *a* and *b* and record them under 0 in the table. Using the paper cup, add a cup of water to the bucket, measure *a* and *b*, and record them under 1 in the table. Continue the process for 2, 3, 4, and 5 cups.

Cups of Water C	0	1	2	3	4	5
Distance *a*						
Distance *b*						

2. One of you should graph the pairs (*C*, *a*); the other should graph the pairs (*C*, *b*).

3. Try to draw a line that fits the points on your graph.

4. a. Find the slope of the line in your graph and explain what it means in terms of the experiment.

b. Why does one line have a positive slope and the other have a negative slope?

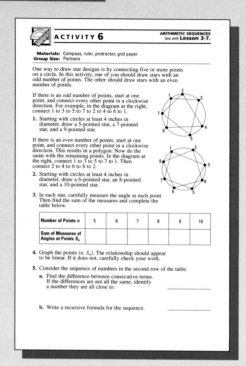

Materials: Compass, ruler, protractor, grid paper
Group Size: Partners

One way to draw star designs is by connecting five or more points on a circle. In this activity, one of you should draw stars with an odd number of points. The other should draw stars with an even number of points.

If there is an *odd* number of points, start at one point, and connect every other point in a clockwise direction. For example, in the diagram at the right, connect 1 to 3 to 5 to 7 to 2 to 4 to 6 to 1.

1. Starting with circles at least 4 inches in diameter, draw a 5-pointed star, a 7-pointed star, and a 9-pointed star.

If there is an *even* number of points, start at one point, and connect every other point in a clockwise direction. This results in a polygon. Now do the same with the remaining points. In the diagram at the right, connect 1 to 3 to 5 to 7 to 1. Then connect 2 to 4 to 6 to 8 to 2.

2. Starting with circles at least 4 inches in diameter, draw a 6-pointed star, an 8-pointed star, and a 10-pointed star.

3. In each star, carefully measure the angle at each point. Then find the sum of the measures and complete the table below.

Number of Points *n*	5	6	7	8	9	10
Sum of Measures of Angles at Points S_n						

4. Graph the points (*n*, S_n). The relationship should appear to be linear. If it does not, carefully check your work.

5. Consider the sequence of numbers in the second row of the table.

a. Find the difference between consecutive terms. If the differences are not all the same, identify a number they are all close to. _____

b. Write a recursive formula for the sequence. _____

Teaching Aids

Teaching Aid 8, Four-quadrant Graph Paper, (shown on page 4D) can be used with **Lessons 3-1 through 3-5 and 3-9.**

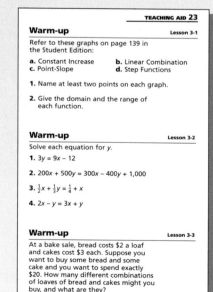

Warm-up   Lesson 3-1

Refer to these graphs on page 139 in the Student Edition:

a. Constant Increase   **b.** Linear Combination
c. Point-Slope   **d.** Step Functions

1. Name at least two points on each graph.

2. Give the domain and the range of each function.

Warm-up   Lesson 3-2

Solve each equation for *y*.

1. $3y = 9x - 12$

2. $200x + 500y = 300x - 400y + 1,000$

3. $\frac{1}{2}x + \frac{1}{3}y = \frac{1}{4} + x$

4. $2x - y = 3x + y$

Warm-up   Lesson 3-3

At a bake sale, bread costs $2 a loaf and cakes cost $3 each. Suppose you want to buy some bread and some cake and you want to spend exactly $20. How many different combinations of loaves of bread and cakes might you buy, and what are they?

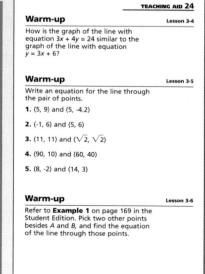

Warm-up   Lesson 3-4

How is the graph of the line with equation $3x + 4y = 24$ similar to the graph of the line with equation $y = 3x + 6$?

Warm-up   Lesson 3-5

Write an equation for the line through the pair of points.

1. (5, 9) and (5, -4.2)

2. (-1, 6) and (5, 6)

3. (11, 11) and ($\sqrt{2}$, $\sqrt{2}$)

4. (90, 10) and (60, 40)

5. (8, -2) and (14, 3)

Warm-up   Lesson 3-6

Refer to **Example 1** on page 169 in the Student Edition. Pick two other points besides *A* and *B*, and find the equation of the line through those points.

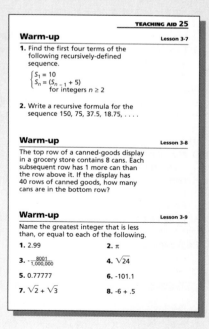

Warm-up   Lesson 3-7

1. Find the first four terms of the following recursively-defined sequence.

$$\begin{cases} S_1 = 10 \\ S_n = (S_{n-1} + 5) \\ \quad \text{for integers } n \geq 2 \end{cases}$$

2. Write a recursive formula for the sequence 150, 75, 37.5, 18.75, ...

Warm-up   Lesson 3-8

The top row of a canned-goods display in a grocery store contains 8 cans. Each subsequent row has 1 more can than the row above it. If the display has 40 rows of canned goods, how many cans are in the bottom row?

Warm-up   Lesson 3-9

Name the greatest integer that is less than, or equal to each of the following.

1. 2.99   **2.** π

3. $-\frac{8001}{1,000,000}$ **4.** $\sqrt{24}$

5. 0.77777   **6.** -101.1

7. $\sqrt{2} + \sqrt{3}$ **8.** -6 + .5

Additional Examples

1. Claire sells sports cars. She gets a base salary of $30,000 a year plus 2% of her sales. If Claire's sales for the year total D dollars, what will her salary be for the year?

2. Rick gets an allowance of $15 per week. Whenever his parents pick up a dirty dish he has left behind, Rick loses $0.30.
   a. Write an equation modeling this situation.
   b. Graph the equation from **part a.**
   c. If Rick received no allowance last week, how many dirty dishes did his parents pick up?

3. The graph below describes Leah's weight over the first 16 weeks of her life. Write a story explaining the meaning of each segment of the piecewise-linear graph.

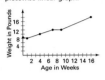

Two Lines with the Same Slope are Parallel

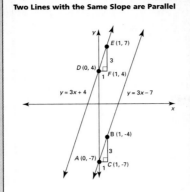

Additional Examples

1. Use the line through the points $A = (1900, 1500)$ and $B = (2000, 2500)$ to fit a line to the data points for the population of Kansas (in thousands) for each decade year from the 1900 census through the 1990 census.

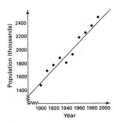

2. Predict the population of Kansas in the year 2025 using
   a. the equation in Question 1.
   b. the equation for the regression line.

3. Use linear regression to find an equation of the line through the points (0, 32) and (100, 212).

Questions 16-19

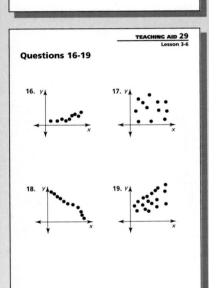

The Greatest Integer Function

$$f(x) = \lfloor x \rfloor$$

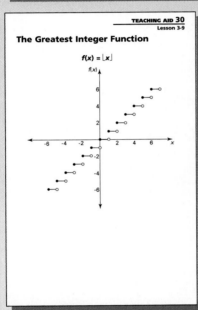

138D

Chapter Opener

Pacing

All of the lessons in this chapter are designed to be covered in one day. At the end of the chapter, you should plan to spend 1 day to review the Progress Self-Test, 1–2 days for the Chapter Review, and 1 day for a test. You may want to spend a day on projects, and a day may be needed for quizzes. Therefore, this chapter should take 12–15 days.

Using pages 138–139

Students who have studied UCSMP *Algebra* should have encountered the first three types of linear functions shown on page 139 along with their names. You might ask students which names they recognize.

These four examples relate to the lessons in the chapter as follows:

Constant Increase	3-1 and 3-2
Linear Combination	3-3 and 3-4
Point-Slope	3-5
Step Functions	3-9

Chapter 3 Overview

Chapter 3 introduces situations that lead to the various forms of linear relations and then connects these relations to Chapter 2 as generalizations of $y = kx$. Most students will remember some of these concepts from their earlier studies of algebra and geometry, but there is enough new material to make this review interesting and worthwhile. In later chapters, students will be expected to extend their work in Chapter 3 to graph-

ing nonlinear functions and to finding equations for curves.

The lessons in this chapter flow easily from one to the next. Lessons 3-1 and 3-2 explain how constant-increase and -decrease situations lead to the slope-intercept form of a line and its graph. Lessons 3-3 and 3-4 explain how linear-combination situations lead to equations in standard form and to the graphs of these equations.

Equations for horizontal and vertical lines are reviewed in Lessons 3-2 and 3-4 respectively. Lesson 3-5 explains how to go from a graph or from two points to an equation of a line; it also presents the Point-Slope Theorem. Lesson 3-6 fits a line to more than two points and introduces the idea of linear correlation. Lessons 3-7 and 3-8 build on the ideas of sequences that were presented in Chapter 1. These two lessons describe arithmetic sequences as

LINEAR FUNCTIONS

In Chapter 2 you studied direct-variation situations modeled by functions with equations of the form $y = kx$, or $f(x) = kx$. The graph of $f(x) = kx$ is a line, so f is called a *linear function*. Many other situations can be modeled by linear functions. Here are examples similar to the ones you will study in this chapter.

Constant Increase
A crate weighs 3 kilograms when empty. It is filled with oranges weighing 0.2 kilogram each. Then $W = 3 + .2n$ gives the weight W in kilograms of a crate containing n oranges.

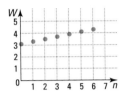

Linear Combination
A group bought A adult tickets at \$7 each and S student tickets at \$3 each. The group spent \$42. The equation $7A + 3S = 42$ relates A, S, and the total amount spent.

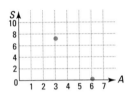

Point - Slope
Stuart Dent is conducting an experiment with a spring and a weight. The spring is 15 centimeters long with a 10-gram weight attached, and its length increases 0.8 centimeters for each additional gram weight. Then $L - 15 = .8(W - 10)$ relates spring length L and weight W.

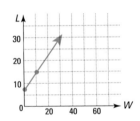

Step Functions
In 1995, first-class postage in the United States was 32¢ for the first ounce, and 23¢ for each additional ounce. The graph at the right pictures the relation between weight w in ounces and cost C in dollars.

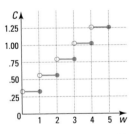

139

Photo Connections
The photo collage makes real-world connections to the contents of the chapter: linear functions.

Telephone: A linear function can be used to describe the relationship between the length and the cost of a long-distance phone call.

Cyclist: Piecewise-linear graphs are discussed in Lesson 3-1. This type of graph can be used to chart a cyclist's distance from the starting point throughout the duration of a bicycle trip.

Beakers: Chemists may use a linear combination to represent a situation in which two different quantities of chemicals are combined to produce a specific mixture.

Roof: The steepness of a roof and the value of m in the linear equation $y = mx + b$ refer to the same concept—slope. The slope of a roof is an important consideration during the construction of a building.

Geese: The normal flight speed for geese is 45 to 50 miles per hour, but some geese fly as fast as 75 miles per hour when frightened. Students can use this information to write a problem that can be solved by using a linear equation.

Chapter 3 Projects
At this time you might want to have students look over the projects on pages 192–193.

special types of linear functions. In Lesson 3-8, students are shown how to move back and forth between recursive formulas and explicit formulas. In Lesson 3-9, we introduce the special piecewise-linear functions known as step functions and their graphs.

Objectives

A Determine the slope and y-intercept of a line given its equation.

E Recognize properties of linear functions.

G Model constant-increase or constant-decrease situations.

K Model situations leading to piecewise-linear functions.

M Graph or interpret graphs of piecewise-linear functions.

Resources

From the Teacher's Resource File
- Lesson Master 3-1A or 3-1B
- Answer Master 3-1
- Teaching Aids
  - 8 Four-Quadrant Graph Paper
  - 23 Warm-up
  - 26 Additional Examples
- Activity Kit, Activity 5

Additional Resources
- Visuals for Teaching Aids 8, 23, 26

Teaching Lesson **3-1**

Warm-up

Refer to these graphs on page 139:
a. Constant Increase
b. Linear Combination
c. Point-Slope
d. Step Functions
1. Name at least two points on each graph. **Samples:**
   a. (0, 3), (6, 4.2)
   b. (6, 0), (3, 7)
   c. (0, 7), (10, 15)
   d. (1, .32), (2, .55)

3-1

Constant-Increase or Constant-Decrease Situations

Temperature hike. *These hikers are prepared for changes in weather. As they climb higher the temperature tends to decrease; when they climb lower the temperature tends to increase.*

Constant-Increase Situations

In many situations there is an initial condition and a constant change applied to that condition. This kind of situation can always be modeled by a linear equation.

❶ **Example 1**

The current temperature is 5°C and has been increasing 2°C an hour. If this trend continues, what will the temperature be *x* hours from now?

Solution

Write the temperature for several hours to find a general pattern. Let y = the temperature (in °C), x hours from now.

x	y
0	$5 + 0 \cdot 2 = 5$
1	$5 + 1 \cdot 2 = 7$
2	$5 + 2 \cdot 2 = 9$
3	$5 + 3 \cdot 2 = 11$
4	$5 + 4 \cdot 2 = 13$
5	$5 + 5 \cdot 2 = 15$

An equation relating temperature and hours is
$$5 + x \cdot 2 = y$$
or
$$y = 2x + 5.$$
The temperature x hours from now will be 2x + 5.

In $y = 2x + 5$, each value of *x* results in just one value for *y*. Thus, *y* is a function of *x; y* is the dependent variable and *x* is the independent variable. Solutions to the equation $y = 2x + 5$ are all the ordered pairs (x, y) whose values satisfy the equation.

Lesson 3-1 Overview

Broad Goals The goal of this lesson is to show how the slope-intercept form of linear functions arises naturally from situations of constant increase or constant decrease.

Perspective Two types of situations that lead to linear equations are constant increase or constant decrease, which are presented in this lesson, and linear combination, which is presented in Lesson 3-3. Classifying situations in this way is far more

powerful than classifying them by context, such as age, distance-rate-time, work, digit, and so on, because context does not tell why a particular piece of mathematics is appropriate for the situation. The models for *operations* found in *Transition Mathematics* and UCSMP *Algebra* are analogous to the models for *expressions* here—specifically to the models for linear expressions.

Constant-increase and constant-decrease situations lead to equations of the form $y = mx + b$. In these equations, *m* and *b* have simple interpretations: *m* is the amount of increase or decrease per unit change of *x*, and *b* is the initial value.

In Chapter 9, students will encounter situations of exponential growth or decay; the difference between those situations and the ones in this chapter is that there the initial

Positive values of x represent times in the future, and negative values of x represent "hours ago," or times in the past. The graph of $y = 2x + 5$ is a *line* including points to the left of the vertical axis and below the horizontal axis, as shown at the right. The domain and range of the function are each the set of real numbers.

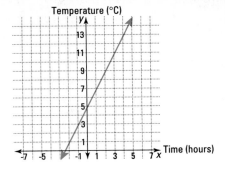

The graph of $y = 2x + 5$ crosses the y-axis at $(0, 5)$. We say that the *y-intercept* is 5. The y-intercept is the **initial condition** or the starting point in the situation, in this case, 5°. The slope of this line is the rate of change in the situation, 2°C per hour. To confirm this, we find the slope determined by the two points $(0, 5)$ and $(3, 11)$.

$$\frac{y_2 - y_1}{x_2 - x_1} = \frac{(11 - 5)°}{(3 - 0)\text{ hours}} = \frac{6°}{3\text{ hours}} = 2\frac{\text{degrees}}{\text{hour}}$$

❷ The form $y = mx + b$, or $f(x) = mx + b$, is called the **slope-intercept form** of an equation for a line. Any function whose graph is a line is called a *linear function*. In general, a **linear function** is a function with an equation of the form $y = mx + b$.

Constant-Decrease Situations

Example 1 involves a *constant-increase situation*. Example 2 involves a *constant-decrease situation*. Every constant-increase or constant-decrease situation can be described by a linear function.

❸ **Example 2**

At the beginning of the month, Katie bought a 50-pound sack of wild-bird feed. She puts $\frac{2}{3}$ of a pound of feed in the bird feeder each morning.
a. Let y be the number of pounds left in the sack after x days. Write an equation in slope-intercept form relating y and x.
b. Graph the equation from part **a.**
c. How long will it take for the bird feed to run out?

Solution
a. This is an instance of constant decrease. So an equation is
$$y = mx + b,$$
where m and b need to be found. The rate of change m is $\frac{2}{3}$ of a pound per day. Because the amount of feed in the sack is decreasing, $m = -\frac{2}{3}$. The initial amount of food is 50 pounds, so 50 is the value of y when $x = 0$. Thus, the y-intercept is 50, and the equation is
$$y = -\frac{2}{3}x + 50.$$

▶

Feed the birds. *The house finch is a nonmigratory bird often seen at winter bird feeders, like the one shown here.*

Lesson 3-1 *Constant-Increase or Constant-Decrease Situations* **141**

value is continually multiplied by, rather than increased or decreased by, the same number.

This lesson is built around three carefully planned examples. **Example 1** shows how to obtain a linear equation from a constant-increase situation. This naturally leads to the ideas of slope and intercept, which should be review for all students. **Example 2** is analogous to **Example 1** for a constant-

decrease situation. An extension of these concepts occurs in a *piecewise*-linear function; **Example 3** involves a situation that is partly constant increase, partly constant decrease, and partly no change. Piecewise-linear functions will probably be new to students.

2. Give the domain and the range of each function.
   a. D = set of whole numbers
      R = {3, 3.2, 3.4, 3.6, . . .}
   b. D = {0, 3, 6}; R = {0, 7, 14}
   c. D = set of nonnegative reals
      R = set of reals greater than or equal to 7
   d. D = set of nonnegative reals
      R = {32, 55, 78, . . . }

Notes on Reading

❶ **Cooperative Learning** After discussing **Examples 1 and 2**, have students **work in groups** to suggest other real-world examples of constant increase and constant decrease.

❷ Point out that the graph of $y = mx + b$ is the image of the graph of the direct-variation function $y = mx$ under the translation b units up. This idea will be applied in later chapters to raise or lower any graph; at that time we will think of the equation as $y - b = mx$.

❸ Note that virtually all models are accurate only over a limited domain. You might ask students to explain why substitutions for x that are greater than 75 are not reasonable in **Example 2**. [The supply of bird feed lasts only 75 days.] Ask why the initial value of the constant increase or constant decrease is important. [It is the point from which the particular increase or decrease is computed.] Explain that this value is the y-intercept when the equation of the linear increase or decrease is graphed. Also point out that the constant rate of change is the slope of the line.

You might also mention that 75 is the *x-intercept*—the *x*-value where the line intersects the *x*-axis. We delay mention of the term until Lesson 3-4 because both intercepts are more naturally discussed together when graphing equations of the form $Ax + By = C$.

Although **Example 2** may seem long, note that it has three parts; discuss each part separately. Point out the power of the equation in part **a**—it gives a great deal of information about the bird feed. **Part b** graphs this information to give a different look at the situation. **Part c** could be answered either with a large graph or by solving an equation; we chose to do the latter.

141

Example 3 may require some interpretation for students. At first, students may think that the graph represents either the shape of the path of Horace's trip or the speed at which he is traveling. Although the graph does not represent Horace's speed, his speed can be calculated as a rate of change, provided he is traveling in a direction that is directly to or from his house. The rate of change is the slope of the line which contains that part of the graph. **Questions 14–17** are important because they help students interpret this graph.

Students will need graph paper or **Teaching Aid 8** for this lesson.

Additional Examples

These examples are also given on **Teaching Aid 26.**

1. Claire sells sports cars. She gets a base salary of $30,000 a year plus 2% of her sales. If Claire's sales for the year total D dollars, what will her salary be for the year? $S = 30,000 + .02D$

2. Rick gets an allowance of $15 per week. Whenever his parents pick up a dirty dish he has left behind, Rick loses $0.30.
   a. Write an equation modeling this situation. $A = 15 - 0.3d$
   b. Graph the equation from **part a.**

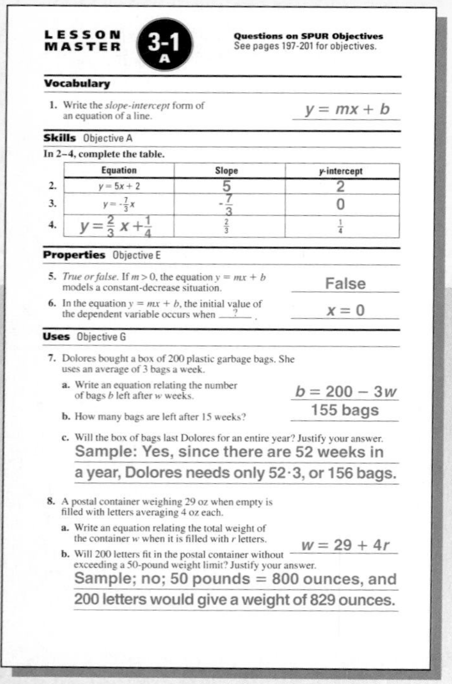

---

b. Make a table of values for the equation $y = -\frac{2}{3}x + 50$ from part **a.** Observe that we chose x-values that are multiples of 3 to make the computations easier. Part of the graph is shown below. Because the number of days is always an integer, the points are not connected.

x	0	3	6	9	12
y	50	48	46	44	42

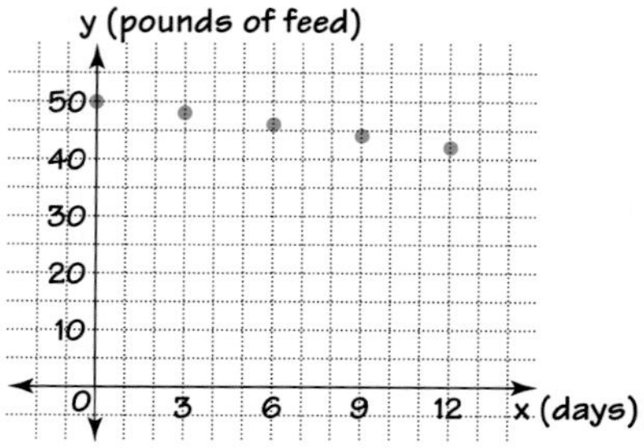

y (pounds of feed) graph

c. The supply runs out when $y = 0$. Substitute 0 for y in $y = -\frac{2}{3}x + 50$ and solve for x.

$$0 = -\tfrac{2}{3}x + 50 \qquad \text{substitution}$$
$$0 = -2x + 150 \qquad \text{Multiply by 3 to clear fractions.}$$
$$2x = 150 \qquad \text{Add } 2x \text{ to each side.}$$
$$x = 75 \qquad \text{Multiply each side by } \tfrac{1}{2}.$$

The supply will run out in **75 days.**

In general, any constant-increase or constant-decrease situation can be modeled by an equation of the form $y = mx + b$. The graph of this equation is a line with slope m and y-intercept b. The slope m corresponds to the rate of change in the situation. The **y-intercept** b, which is the value of y when x is 0, corresponds to the initial value of the dependent variable.

In cases of constant increase, as in Example 1, the graph of the line slants up from left to right, indicating a *positive* slope. In cases of constant decrease, as in Example 2, the graph slants down from left to right, indicating a *negative* slope. In cases where the rate of change is 0, the graph of the line is horizontal.

Piecewise-Linear Functions

In some situations, the rate of change is constant for a while, but then changes to another constant rate. In such situations, the graph consists of two or more segments or rays. Such a graph is called **piecewise linear.** It is a union of segments or pieces of two or more linear functions.

142

LESSON MASTER 3-1 A

Questions on SPUR Objectives
See pages 197–201 for objectives.

Vocabulary

1. Write the *slope-intercept* form of an equation of a line. $y = mx + b$

Skills Objective A
In 2–4, complete the table.

	Equation	Slope	y-intercept
2.	$y = 5x + 2$	5	2
3.	$y = -\frac{7}{3}x$	$-\frac{7}{3}$	0
4.	$y = \frac{2}{3}x + \frac{1}{4}$	$\frac{2}{3}$	$\frac{1}{4}$

Properties Objective E

5. *True or false.* If $m > 0$, the equation $y = mx + b$ models a constant-decrease situation. **False**

6. In the equation $y = mx + b$, the initial value of the dependent variable occurs when ___?___. $x = 0$

Uses Objective G

7. Dolores bought a box of 200 plastic garbage bags. She uses an average of 3 bags a week.
   a. Write an equation relating the number of bags b left after w weeks. $b = 200 - 3w$
   b. How many bags are left after 15 weeks? **155 bags**
   c. Will the box of bags last Dolores an entire year? Justify your answer. **Sample: Yes, since there are 52 weeks in a year, Dolores needs only 52·3, or 156 bags.**

8. A postal container weighing 29 oz when empty is filled with letters averaging 4 oz each.
   a. Write an equation relating the total weight of the container w when it is filled with r letters. $w = 29 + 4r$
   b. Will 200 letters fit in the postal container without exceeding a 50-pound weight limit? Justify your answer. **Sample: no; 50 pounds = 800 ounces, and 200 letters would give a weight of 829 ounces.**

Optional Activities

Activity 1
You might want to use *Activity Kit, Activity 5,* as either an introduction or follow-up to the lesson. In this activity, students use springs to investigate constant increase and decrease situations.

Activity 2 Using Physical Models
Materials: Small objects like chalk or paper clips, graph paper or **Teaching Aid 8**

One way to show the ideas of constant increase and decrease is to use physical objects, such as paper clips or chalk. Place a few objects on a desk top to illustrate an initial condition. Have each student add two more objects to the initial group. Then draw a graph to show how the number of objects on the desk increases with the number of students who participate. A constant decrease can be illustrated by having each student remove two objects from an initial

❹ **Example 3**

Horace made the graph below to describe his bicycle trip to a state park, 48 km from his home. It gives his distance D, in kilometers from home, as a function of t, the time in hours after leaving home. Write a story explaining the meaning of each segment of the piecewise linear graph.

Horace's Bicycle Trip

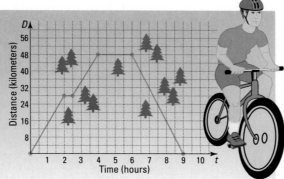

Shown are bikers at the edge of a canyon near Moab, Utah.

Solution

The graph shows that Horace started from home and bicycled at a constant rate for 2 hours, ending up 28 kilometers from home. So he traveled at a rate of 14 km/hr. After a half-hour stop, he traveled at a constant rate for another hour and a half, until he reached the state park 48 kilometers from home. During this part of the trip he traveled 20 km in 1.5 hr, so his rate was about 13.3 km/hr. He stayed at the park for two hours. Finally, he returned home traveling at a constant rate and reached home 9 hours after starting out.

QUESTIONS

Covering the Reading

1) Samples: temperature increasing at a constant rate over a period of time; supply of bird feed decreasing at a constant rate over a period of time; distance traveled over a continuous period of time where rate is constant for awhile, then changes to a different rate for a period of time.

1. Give three examples of situations which can be modeled by linear functions or piecewise-linear functions. **See left.**

In 2–5, refer to Example 1.

2. **a.** Name the independent variable. **x**
   b. Name the dependent variable. **y**

3. What was the temperature after $3\frac{1}{2}$ hours? **12°C**

4. In the equation $y = 2x + 5$, 5 represents the __?__ on the graph and the __?__ in the problem. **y-intercept; initial temperature**

5. *True or false.* The 2°C increase per hour is the slope of the line. **True**

Lesson 3-1   Constant-Increase or Constant-Decrease Situations **143**

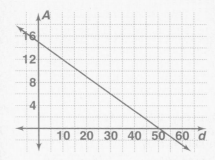

c. If Rick received no allowance last week, how many dirty dishes did his parents pick up? **50**

3. The graph below describes Leah's weight over the first 16 weeks of her life. Write a story explaining the meaning of each segment of the piecewise-linear graph.

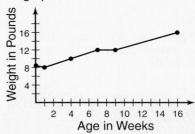

Sample: Leah weighed 8.5 lb at birth. During week 1, she lost about 0.5 lb. During weeks 2–4 she gained 2 lb. During weeks 5–7 Leah gained 2 lb. During weeks 8–9, she lost about 0.5 lb. During weeks 10–16, Leah gained 4.5 lb. After 16 weeks, Leah weighed 16 lb.

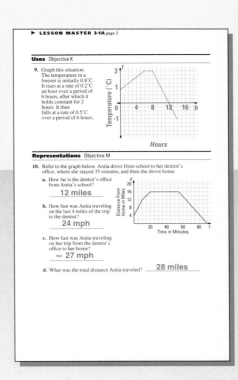

---

group of objects. Again, draw a graph to show how the number of objects decreases with the number of students who participate.

Activity 3
After discussing piecewise-linear functions, you might suggest that students make a similar graph about something such as their growth rate as an infant or a trip they have taken.

Adapting to Individual Needs
Extra Help
If the graph in **Example 3** confuses students, point out that D, the dependent variable, refers to Horace's distance from home, not the distance he traveled. During the first part of the trip, D increases as Horace travels farther from home or stays the same when he stops. During the last 3 hours, D decreases because he is traveling toward home. Therefore, D decreases until it equals 0—the time at which he returns home.

Notes on Questions

Question 19 Error Alert Common errors include writing $C = 100 - 3h$ or $C = 100 - 4h$. Remind students to check their equations against the data points in the table.

Question 20 This question illustrates the idea that direct linear variations may also be thought of as constant-increase or constant-decrease situations that have initial values of zero.

Question 21 Note that the slope of each part of the graph tells the rate at which Carmen is going away from home (if the slope is positive) or toward home (if the slope is negative). She is either at rest or traveling in a circle with home at the center if the slope is zero.

Questions 23–26 These questions are a review to prepare for the next two lessons.

Follow-up for Lesson 3-1

Practice

For more questions on SPUR Objectives, use **Lesson Master 3-1A** (shown on pages 142–143) or **Lesson Master 3-1B** (shown on pages 144–145).

In 6 and 7, refer to the equation $y = mx + b$.

6. The coefficient of x tells you the __?__ of the line. slope

7. In cases of constant increase or constant decrease, the y-intercept b corresponds to __?__. the initial condition

8. What is a linear function?
A function with an equation of the form $y = mx + b$ whose graph is a line.

In 9 and 10, refer to Example 2.

9. How many pounds of bird feed are left after 21 days? 36 lb

10. In how many days will there be 16 pounds of bird feed? 51 days

11. The graph at the left can represent a situation of constant __?__.
increase

In 12 and 13, an equation for a line is given. **a.** Give its slope. **b.** Give its y-intercept.

12. $y = x + 3$ a) 1 b) 3   13. $y = kx$ a) k b) 0

In 14–17, refer to the bicycle trip in Example 3.

14. What does the slope of the segment from $(0, 0)$ to $(2, 28)$ represent?
Horace's speed in the first 2 hours was 14 km/hr.

15. *True or false.* On the trip from home to the state park, Horace traveled at a constant rate. False

16. How fast (in kilometers per hour) was Horace going during the last three hours of his trip? 16 km/hr

17. What is the total amount of time that Horace stopped during his trip? $2\frac{1}{2}$ hours

Applying the Mathematics

18. The line $y = \frac{3}{4}x + 7$ is graphed at the left. See left for b, d.
    a. From the equation, what is its slope? $\frac{3}{4}$
    b. Use the points $(0, 7)$ and $(8, 13)$ to verify your answer to part **a**.
    c. What is the y-intercept? 7
    d. Does this equation describe a function? Explain your answer.

19. An auto dealer is having a Fourth-of-July extravaganza. The dealership plans to be open for 72 hours straight. Suppose the dealer has 100 new cars on the lot and is able to sell 4 cars every 3 hours.
    a. Let h be the number of hours the dealer has been open and let C be the number of cars remaining on the lot. Find three other pairs of values that satisfy this relation. Sample answers are given.

h	0	3	6	9	12
C	100	96	92	88	84

    b. Write an equation that gives C as a function of h. $C = 100 - \frac{4}{3}h$
    c. After how many hours will there be only 60 cars left? 30 hours
    d. If the dealership is able to maintain the pace of selling 4 cars every 3 hours, will the dealer sell all the cars on the lot during the sale? How can you tell?
    No, it would take 75 hours to sell all the cars.

18b) $\frac{13 - 7}{8 - 0} = \frac{6}{8} = \frac{3}{4}$

d) Yes. Sample: Its graph passes the vertical line test.

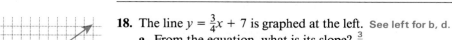

Adapting to Individual Needs

English Language Development
You might use real-world examples to illustrate constant-increase or constant-decrease situations. Suppose a student has $25 and is saving $5 every week for a CD player. Explain that since the amount of money is increasing by the same amount each week, it is increasing at a *constant* rate. Use a similar type of example to illustrate a constant rate of decrease.

Challenge
Have students write an equation to model this situation: When Jane baby-sits, she is paid $1 per child and $3.75 per hour. [$P = 3.75h + n$ where $P =$ pay, $h =$ hours, and $n =$ number of children.] If Jane earned $25.50 and baby-sat for a whole number of hours, for how many children did she baby-sit and for how long? [3 children, 6 hours]

LESSON MASTER 3-1 B   Questions on SPUR Objectives

Vocabulary

1. A function with an equation of the form $y = mx + b$ is a __?__ function.   **linear**

2. Give an example of a *constant-decrease* situation.
Sample: Lanie bought a 32-oz jar of plant fertilizer. She uses $\frac{1}{2}$ oz every month.

Skills Objective A: Determine the slope and y-intercept of a line given its equation.

In 3–9, complete the table.

	Equation	Slope	y-intercept
3.	$y = -3x + 8$	-3	8
4.	$y = \frac{4}{5}x - 1$	$\frac{4}{5}$	-1
5.	$y = 6x$	6	0
6.	$y = x + 2$	1	2
7.	$y = \frac{8}{3}x + \frac{2}{3}$	$\frac{8}{3}$	$\frac{2}{3}$
8.	$y = ax + k$	a	k
9.	$y = dx$	d	0

Properties Objective E: Recognize properties of linear functions.

In 10–12, x is the independent variable, y is the dependent variable, and $y = mx + b$.

10. In a constant increase situation, is m positive, negative, or equal to zero?   **positive**

11. In a constant decrease situation, is m positive, negative, or equal to zero?   **negative**

12. The initial value of the independent variable occurs when $x =$ __?__ and $y =$ __?__   **0   b**

20b)

x	y
-2	-7
-1	$-\frac{7}{2}$
0	0
1	$\frac{7}{2}$
2	7

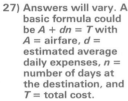

$y = \frac{7}{2}x$

27) **Answers will vary. A basic formula could be $A + dn = T$ with A = airfare, d = estimated average daily expenses, n = number of days at the destination, and T = total cost.**

Dream vacation.
Shown is Waikiki Beach in Honolulu, Hawaii. Honolulu is a popular vacation spot.

20. Suppose y varies directly as x, and that y is 7 when x is 2.
  a. Find the constant of variation and write an equation describing the variation. $\frac{7}{2}$; $y = \frac{7}{2}x$
  b. Make a table of values and graph the equation. **See left.**
  c. Verify that this direct-variation equation fits the $y = mx + b$ model by identifying the slope and y-intercept.
  d. Which situation does this variation represent: constant increase or constant decrease? **constant increase**
  c) slope = 7/2; y-intercept = 0

21. On the graph below, M = the number of miles Carmen is from home at time T. Carmen walks to school, then to her job after school, and then home.

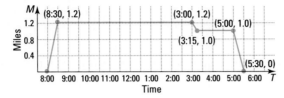

  a. How far is the school from Carmen's home? **1.2 miles**
  b. How long does it take Carmen to walk to school? **30 min or .5 hr**
  c. Find the slope of the segment from (3:00, 1.2) to (3:15, 1.0) using hours as the unit for time. **-0.8 mi/hr**
  d. Write a question which can be answered by using the graph. Answer your question.
  Sample: How long does Carmen work after school? Answer: $1\frac{3}{4}$ hr

---

Review

22. a. Find the area of a circle inscribed in a square whose sides are 6 cm long. **9π cm^2**
  b. Find the area of a circle inscribed in a square whose sides are x cm long. *(Previous course)* **$1/4\pi x^2$ cm^2**

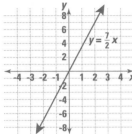

23. a. Draw the line with slope $\frac{1}{4}$ that contains the point $(0, 0)$. **See margin.**
  b. Write an equation for this line. *(Lesson 2-4)* $y = \frac{1}{4}x$

24. Solve for y: $x + 2y = 5$. *(Lesson 1-6)* $y = -\frac{1}{2}x + \frac{5}{2}$

25. Solve for x: $1.5 + 0.5x = 0.45(x + 5)$. *(Lesson 1-5)* $x = 15$

26. Suppose B ounces of blended fruit juice contain 10% apple juice. How many ounces of juices other than apple juice are in the blend? *(Previous course)* **0.9 B ounce**

Exploration

27. What place in the world would you most like to visit? Find out how much it would cost to go there by air, and estimate how much your average daily expenses would be. Write an equation that can be used to calculate the total cost T of your visit if you stay for n days. **See above left.**

Lesson 3-1 *Constant-Increase or Constant-Decrease Situations* **145**

Additional Answers
23a.

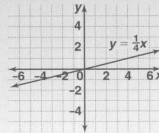

$y = \frac{1}{4}x$

Setting Up Lesson 3-2

Questions 23–25 provide a review for the next lesson and can be used as a lead-in for the lesson. **Question 26** reviews mixtures in preparation for the linear combinations in Lesson 3-3.

Assessment

Oral/Written Communication Have students **work in groups.** Each group should describe a constant-increase or a constant-decrease situation, write an equation to model the situation, and graph the equation. Have students explain how the slope of the line is related to their situation. [Students demonstrate an understanding of constant-increase or constant-decrease situations.]

Extension

Have students explain if the information in the table below describes a piecewise-linear function, a constant-increase situation, or a constant-decrease situation.

Mr. Crain, Mr. Nye, and Mr. Marino live on different floors in the same high-rise apartment building, but pay different amounts of rent each month.

Tenant	Floor	Rent
Mr. Crain	19th	$715
Mr. Nye	15th	$635
Mr. Marino	12th	$575

[Constant-increase situation; the line that passes through the three points slants up from left to right.]

Project Update Project 1, *A Graphical Investigation,* and Project 6, *Graphing Piecewise Functions,* on pages 192–193, relate to the content of the lesson.

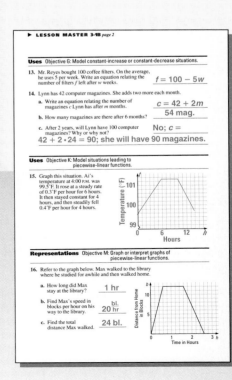

Objectives

A Determine the slope and y-intercept of a line given its equation.
B Find an equation for a line given a point on it and its slope.
E Recognize properties of linear functions.
L Graph or interpret graphs of linear equations.

Resources

From the *Teacher's Resource File*
■ Lesson Master 3-2A or 3-2B
■ Answer Master 3-2
■ Teaching Aids
   8 Four-Quadrant Graph Paper
  23 Warm-up
  27 Two Lines with the Same Slope Are Parallel

Additional Resources
■ Visuals for Teaching Aids 8, 23, 27

Teaching Lesson **3-2**

Warm-up

Solve each equation for y.
1. $3y = 9x - 12$
   $y = 3x - 4$
2. $200x + 500y = 300x - 400y + 1{,}000$
   $y = \frac{1}{9}x + \frac{10}{9}$
3. $\frac{1}{2}x + \frac{1}{3}y = \frac{1}{4} + x$
   $y = -\frac{3}{2}x + \frac{3}{4}$
4. $2x - y = 3x + y$
   $y = -\frac{1}{2}x$

The Graph of $y = mx + b$

Equation solver. *Shown are methods commonly used to find the solutions to an equation.*

As you saw in the last lesson, the solutions to an equation of the form $y = mx + b$ lie on a line with slope m and y-intercept b. To graph an equation of this form you can: (1) make a table of values and plot points; (2) use an automatic grapher; or (3) use the slope and y-intercept to draw the line. You should be able to use all three methods.

Graphing Using Slope and Intercept

❶ **Example 1**

Graph the line $y = 4x + 7$ using its slope and y-intercept.

Solution
The y-intercept is 7, so the line contains $(0, 7)$. Use the slope to locate another point. A slope of 4 means that every horizontal change of one unit to the right corresponds to a vertical change of four units up. Starting at $(0, 7)$, count 1 unit right and 4 up. This gives the new point $(0 + 1, 7 + 4) = (1, 11)$. Plot $(1, 11)$ and draw the line. Label it $y = 4x + 7$.

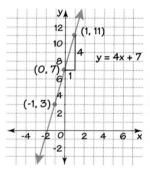

Lesson 3-2 Overview

Broad Goals In this lesson, students review the graphing of lines using their slope and y-intercept. The properties of slope are also reviewed.

Perspective Lesson 3-1 identified applications of slope and y-intercept; this lesson relates these ideas directly to graphing. It is important for students to be able to graph a linear equation quickly—the techniques discussed in this lesson will enable them to do so.

Most students encountered slope in their first study of algebra, but some students may not fully understand the idea. Students who have used the UCSMP *Algebra* and *Geometry* textbooks will have studied slope twice; UCSMP *Algebra* concentrates on applications of slope, and both books mention that parallel lines have equal slopes.

Optional Activities

Activity 1
Research allowable slopes for wheelchair ramps. [sample: According to *The American Disabilities Act,* the maximum slope for a wheelchair ramp is 0.08—for every 1 inch of change in the rise of the ramp, there has to be at least a 12-inch change in the run. There is no minimum slope.]

Check

The point (1, 11) satisfies the equation $y = 4x + 7$, because $11 = 4 \cdot 1 + 7$. The two points (0, 7) and (1, 11) determine a line, so the graph must be correct.

It is usually faster to graph a line using its slope and y-intercept than to construct a table of solutions. Often, it is even faster than using an automatic grapher. In fact, most automatic graphers require you to rewrite an equation in slope-intercept form before it can be graphed. Example 2 illustrates how this can be done.

Rewriting an Equation in Slope-Intercept Form

Example 2

Graph the line $2y = -3x + 16$.

Solution 1

To solve for y, divide each side by 2. $y = -\frac{3}{2}x + 8$

In this form, you can see that the slope is $-\frac{3}{2}$ and the y-intercept is 8.

First plot (0, 8). A slope of $-\frac{3}{2}$ means a vertical change of $-\frac{3}{2}$ units for every horizontal change of 1 unit. This is the same as 3 units down for every 2 units to the right. So, add 2 to the x-coordinate and -3 to the y-coordinate of (0, 8). $(0 + 2, 8 - 3) = (2, 5)$. Draw the line through the y-intercept and this point, and label the line $y = -\frac{3}{2}x + 8$.

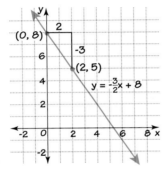

Check

Substitute the coordinates of the two points you plotted into the original equation.
Check (0, 8). Does $2(8) = -3(0) + 16$? Yes.
Check (2, 5). Does $2(5) = -3(2) + 16$? Yes.

Lesson 3-2 *The Graph of* $y = mx + b$ **147**

Notes on Reading

❶ Students should appreciate the ease of graphing when using the slope and y-intercept, as shown in **Example 1.** However, remind students that this will not eliminate the need for making tables; students will still find tables useful when graphing nonlinear equations such as parabolas and hyperbolas.

Lines with positive slope rise as they cross the coordinate plane from left to right, while lines with negative slope fall as they cross the coordinate plane from left to right. If the scales on the axes are the same, then the slope of a line can be estimated from its slant. But in applications where the scales on the axes differ, one cannot estimate the slope of a line by merely looking at its slant.

Activity 2
Materials: Automatic grapher, graph paper or **Teaching Aid 8**

Ask students to graph the following lines on the same coordinate plane. Then have them identify similarities and differences among the lines and draw a conclusion.
$y = 3x - 8$
$y = 3x + 6$
$y = 3x - 2$
$y = 3x$
$y = 3x + 5$
[Students should recognize that all the lines are parallel to each other and all have the same slope but different y-intercepts. Help students conclude that parallel lines have the same slope.]

147

❷ Horizontal lines and their equations are discussed in **Example 3**; vertical lines are not studied until Lesson 3-4. However, the proof of the second theorem on page 149 mentions the line with equation $x = 1$. Even though questions on vertical lines will not appear for several lessons, at this time you may want to remind students of the difference between equations for horizontal and vertical lines.

❸ **Reading Mathematics** This diagram is found on **Teaching Aid 27**. Proofs for the two theorems concerning parallel lines may be difficult for some students. Encourage them to read this material slowly, using the diagram to locate each line, angle, and triangle. Note that the proof that equal slopes imply parallel lines uses SAS Congruence. The proof of the converse of the statement that equal slopes imply parallel lines, namely that parallel lines imply equal slopes, uses AAS Congruence. You may find that students appreciate seeing that an idea they learned in one mathematics course is useful in another course. They may also be surprised at this.

Students will need graph paper or **Teaching Aid 8** for this lesson.

▶ **Solution 2**

Solve for y as in Solution 1.
Graph $y = -1.5x + 8$ using an automatic grapher. Copy and label what you see on the window of your grapher.

$-10 \leq x \leq 10$	x-scale = 2
$-10 \leq y \leq 10$	y-scale = 2

Check

Trace to find the coordinates of two points on the line. Our grapher shows (0, 8) and (1.06, 6.40). We checked (0, 8) in solution 1. Checking (1.06, 6.40) in the original equation, we see that $2(6.40) = 12.80$ and $-3(1.06) + 16 = 12.82$. It checks.

Horizontal Lines

Recall that lines with negative slope go down to the right. Lines with positive slope go up to the right. Lines with 0 slope are horizontal. (Vertical lines are a different matter; they are discussed in Lesson 3-4.)

❷ **Example 3**

a. Graph the line $y = 2$.
b. Identify the domain and range of the function represented by this graph.

Solution

a. The equation $y = 2$ is equivalent to $y = 0x + 2$. This shows that the y-intercept is 2. So the line contains (0, 2) and the slope is 0. A slope of 0 means that for a horizontal change of 1 unit there is a vertical change of 0 units. In other words, there is no vertical change and the graph is a horizontal line.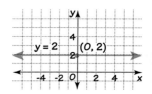

b. Because x does not appear in the equation, x can be any real number. However, y has the single value 2. Thus, The domain is the set of all real numbers and the range is {2}.

In general, a line is horizontal if and only if it has an equation of the form $y = b$. Its slope is 0 and its y-intercept is b.

148

Adapting to Individual Needs

Extra Help
When students graph a line by using the slope and y-intercept, point out that they must first determine the y-intercept and use that as the starting point. Then they can determine a second point by using the slope. Remind students that a slope such as 4 can be written as $\frac{4}{1}$. Also remind them that a slope is a ratio and can therefore be written in many different ways. For example,

a slope of $\frac{3}{2}$ can be written as $\frac{3}{2}, \frac{6}{4}, \frac{9}{6}, \frac{3/2}{1},$ and so on. We can pick any ratio that is convenient for locating the second point. But often the easiest is to go over one unit to the right and up or down the amount of the slope.

English Language Development
Students who have limited English proficiency and who are having difficulty understanding the concept of parallel lines may benefit from looking at a physical representation of parallel lines. You might hold two pencils in several different but parallel positions. Then ask students to hold the pencils so they are parallel.

❸ Parallel Lines and Slope

Consider the graphs of $y = 3x - 7$ and $y = 3x + 4$ shown at the right. Both lines have slope 3. On each line, as you move 1 unit to the right, the line rises 3 units. Right triangles ABC and DEF are congruent by SAS Congruence, so these lines form congruent corresponding angles with the y-axis at A and D. Consequently, $\overline{AB}$ and $\overline{DE}$ are parallel.

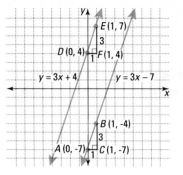

This argument can be repeated with any two lines that have the same slope. Thus, the following theorem can be proved.

> **Theorem**
> If two lines have the same slope, then they are parallel.

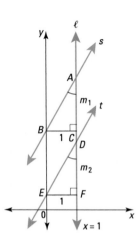

The converse of the theorem above is: If two lines are parallel, then they have the same slope. This can also be proved. Suppose lines s and t are parallel and not vertical. Let m_1 be the slope of s, and m_2 be the slope of t. We want to show $m_1 = m_2$. Draw line ℓ with equation $x = 1$. Note that ℓ is a transversal to the parallel lines. Draw horizontal segments from the y-intercepts of lines s and t to line ℓ as shown at the left. Then $m_1 = $ slope of $s = \frac{AC}{BC} = \frac{AC}{1} = AC$, and $m_2 = $ slope of $t = \frac{DF}{EF} = \frac{DF}{1} = DF$. Now recall that corresponding angles formed by parallel lines and a transversal are congruent. So $\angle BAC \cong \angle EDF$. By AAS Triangle Congruence, then, right triangles ABC and DEF are congruent, so $AC = DF$. Since $m_1 = AC$ and $DF = m_2$, the slopes are equal. We have proved the theorem below.

> **Theorem**
> If two non-vertical lines are parallel, then they have the same slope.

QUESTIONS

Covering the Reading

1. In the equation $y = mx + b$, the slope is __?__ and the y-intercept is __?__. **m; b**

2. A slope of 7 means a __?__ change of __?__ units for every horizontal change of one unit. **vertical; 7**

Lesson 3-2 The Graph of $y = mx + b$ **149**

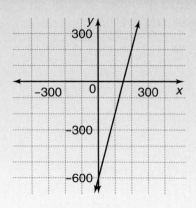

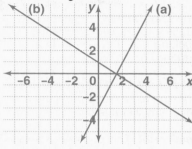
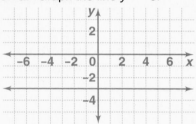
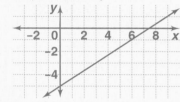
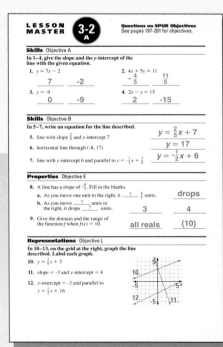
149

Additional Answers

15a.
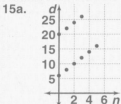

17a.
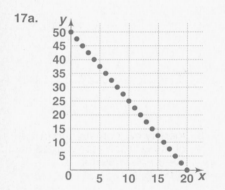

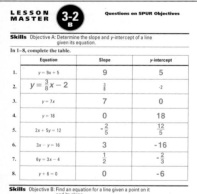

7)
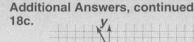

13a)

$y = \frac{2}{5}x - 6$

14a)
$y = 2x$
$y = 2$

150

3. Tell whether or not the rate of change means a slope of $-\frac{5}{6}$.
   a. a vertical change of -6 units for a horizontal change of 5 units No
   b. a vertical change of $-\frac{5}{6}$ unit for every horizontal change of 1 unit Yes
   c. a vertical change of 6 units for a horizontal change of -5 units No
   d. a vertical change of 1 unit for a horizontal change of $-\frac{5}{6}$ unit No

4. Refer to the line graphed in Example 1. Start at the point (1, 11).
   a. Going 1 unit to the right and 4 units up puts you at what point? (2, 15)
   b. Verify that your answer to part **a** lies on the line.
      Does $15 = 4 \cdot 2 + 7$? Does $15 = 8 + 7$? Yes, it checks.

5. Refer to the line graphed in Example 2. It appears that (4, 2) lies on the line. Verify that this is true using the given equation for the line.
   Does $2(2) = -3(4) + 16$? Does $4 = -12 + 16$? Yes, it checks.

6. Consider the equation $4y = -7x - 20$.
   a. Rewrite the equation in slope-intercept form. $y = \frac{-7}{4}x - 5$
   b. Identify the slope and y-intercept. slope $= \frac{-7}{4}$; y-intercept $= -5$

7. Graph the line whose equation is $y = 1$. See left.

8. The equation $y = b$ represents a __?__ line with slope __?__. horizontal; zero

9. If two lines are parallel, what can be said about their slopes? Their slopes are equal.

In 10 and 11, refer to the proofs dealing with parallel lines and slopes.

10. In the proof that lines with the same slope are parallel, name the corresponding sides and angles which were used to show $\triangle ABC$ to be congruent to $\triangle DEF$. $\overline{AC} \cong \overline{DF}$; $\angle ACB \cong \angle DFE$; $\overline{CB} \cong \overline{FE}$

11. In the proof that parallel lines have the same slope, which corresponding sides and angles were used to show $\triangle ABC \cong \triangle DEF$? $\angle BAC \cong \angle EDF$; $\angle ACB \cong \angle DFE$; $\overline{BC} \cong \overline{EF}$

12. Suppose line ℓ is parallel to $y = \frac{1}{3}x - 2$.
    a. What is the slope of ℓ? $\frac{1}{3}$
    b. What is a possible y-intercept of ℓ? any real number

Applying the Mathematics

---

13. a. Draw the line with y-intercept -6 and slope $\frac{2}{5}$. See left.
    b. Write the equation of this line in slope-intercept form. $y = \frac{2}{5}x - 6$
    c. Use the equation to find x when y is 3. Check your answer by showing that the point is on the line. $x = 22\frac{1}{2}$; Does $3 = \frac{2}{5}\left(22\frac{1}{2}\right) - 6$? Does $3 = 9 - 6$? Yes, it checks.

14. a. Graph the lines $y = 2$ and $y = 2x$ on the same set of axes. See left.
    b. Where do the lines intersect? (1, 2)

15. The Washington family has 20 newspapers in their recycling bin and is recycling 2 more newspapers each day. The Ebert family also recycles 2 newspapers a day; they now have only 6 papers. a) See margin
    a. Graph the number of newspapers n each family has after d days.
    b. Relate the graphs to the content of this lesson. The rate of change (slope) for both lines is the constant 2, so the lines are parallel.

16. A line does not cross the x-axis but goes through the point (17, -68).
    a. Give an equation for the line. $y = -68$
    b. What is the slope of the line? zero

150

150

Additional Answers, continued

18c.
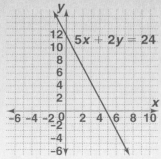
$5x + 2y = 24$

25e. Sample conjecture: The bisector of the acute angle formed by $y = \frac{1}{c}x$ and $y = cx$ is $y = x$ when c is positive, or $y = -x$ when c is negative.

Bird care. *House finch nestlings are cared for by both the male and the female. The male serenades and feeds his mate as she incubates the eggs.*

17. Recall Katie's bird feed from Lesson 3-1. **a) See margin.**
    a. Graph the amount of bird feed y that will be left in the sack after x days if Katie puts 2.5 pounds of feed into the feeder each day.
    b. Write an equation relating x and y. **$y = -2.5x + 50$**

18. Consider the equation $5x + 2y = 24$.
    a. Rewrite the equation in slope-intercept form. **$y = -\frac{5}{2}x + 12$**
    b. Identify the slope and the y-intercept. **slope $= -\frac{5}{2}$; y-intercept $= 12$**
    c. Graph the line using the slope and the y-intercept.
    See margin.

Review

In 19–21, tell whether the slope of the line is positive, negative, or zero. *(Lesson 3-1)*

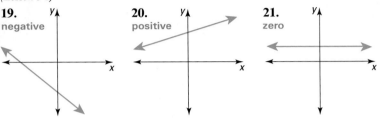

19. negative **20.** positive **21.** zero

22. A tank has a slow leak. The water level starts at 100 inches and falls $\frac{1}{2}$ inch per day. *(Lesson 3-1)*
    a. What kind of situation is this: constant increase or constant decrease? **constant decrease**   **b) $L = 100 - \frac{1}{2}d$**
    b. Write an equation relating day d and the water level L.
    c. After how many days will the tank be empty? **200 days**

23. Find S_4 if $S_1 = 2$ and $S_n = 3 \cdot S_{n-1}$. *(Lesson 1-9)* **$S_4 = 54$**

24. a. How much alcohol is in a 9-oz solution of water and alcohol that is 20% alcohol? **1.8 oz**
    b. How much alcohol is in an x-oz solution of water and alcohol that is 20% alcohol? **0.2x oz**
    c. How much water is in an x-oz solution of water and alcohol that is 20% alcohol? *(Previous course, Lesson 1-1)* **0.8x oz**

Exploration

25. Consider the lines with equations $y = \frac{1}{5}x$ and $y = 5x$.
    a. Graph both lines on the same pair of coordinate axes. **See left.**
    b. Find the slope of each line. **$\frac{1}{5}$; 5**
    c. Determine an equation for the bisector of the acute angles formed by these lines. **$y = x$ d) See left.**
    d. Repeat parts **a–c,** using lines with equations $y = \frac{1}{3}x$ and $y = 3x$.
    e. Make a conjecture generalizing this problem and its results. **See margin.**
    f. Test your conjecture with an example where the lines have negative slopes. **See margin.**

Lesson 3-2 *The Graph of $y = mx + b$* **151**

25a)

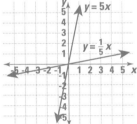

d)

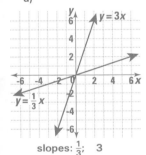

slopes: $\frac{1}{3}$; 3
$\angle$bisector: $y = x$

25f.

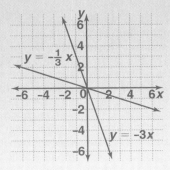

The bisector of the acute angle formed by $y = -3x$ and $y = -\frac{1}{3}x$ is $y = -x$.

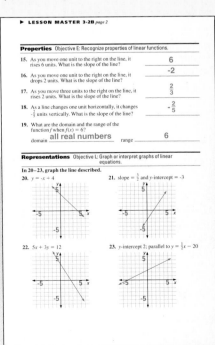

151

Lesson 3-3

Objectives
H Model situations leading to linear combinations.

Resources
From the Teacher's Resource File
- Lesson Master 3-3A or 3-3B
- Answer Master 3-3
- Assessment Sourcebook: Quiz for Lessons 3-1 through 3-3
- Teaching Aids
  8 Four-Quadrant Graph Paper
  23 Warm-up

Additional Resources
- Visuals for Teaching Aids 8, 23

Teaching Lesson 3-3

Warm-up
At a bake sale, bread costs $2 a loaf and cakes cost $3 each. Suppose you want to buy some bread and some cake and you want to spend exactly $20. How many different combinations of loaves of bread and cakes might you buy, and what are they? **3; 7 loaves and 2 cakes, 4 loaves and 4 cakes, 1 loaf and 6 cakes**

Notes on Reading
❶ **Sports Connection** Ice hockey probably developed from the hockey-type game of *shinty*—a game that was played by British soldiers stationed in Canada in the 1860s. The game spread quickly throughout Canada and soon became popular in the United States. The National Hockey League was organized in

152

LESSON 3-3
Linear-Combination Situations

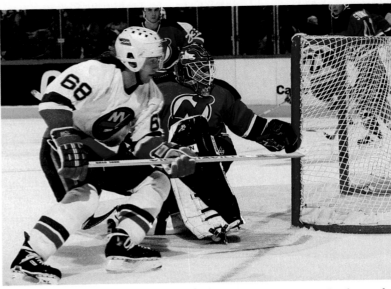

A tie is not pointless. *Shown are members of the New York Islanders and the New Jersey Devils of the National Hockey League. See Example 1. Football and soccer are other major team sports where a game can end in a tie.*

What Is a Linear Combination?
Consider the following problem.

> June has P 20¢ stamps for postcards and L 32¢ stamps for letters. Find the total value of her stamps.

The value of her 20¢ stamps is $20P$ cents, and the value of her 32¢ stamps is $32L$ cents. So the total value, in cents, of her stamps is

$$20P + 32L.$$

This expression is called a **linear combination** of P and L. In a linear combination, all variables are to the first power and are not multiplied or divided by each other.

Linear combinations occur in a wide variety of real-world situations.

An Example with a Discrete Domain

❶ **Example 1**

In professional hockey, a win is worth 2 points, a tie is worth 1 point, and a loss is worth 0 points. Early in the season a team had 11 points.
a. Write an equation to express the relationship among the number of wins W, the number of ties T, and the number of losses L.
b. Make a table and a graph of all possible (W, T) that could have occurred.

152

Lesson 3-3 Overview
Broad Goals This lesson focuses on the connection between linear-combination situations and equations of the lines. The graphs indicate why the phrase "linear combination" is suitable.

Perspective Just as constant-increase or constant-decrease situations lead into linear equations in slope-intercept form, linear combinations lead into equations in

the standard form $Ax + By = C$. This is the subject of both Lesson 3-3 and Lesson 3-4.

It is often necessary to write equations in standard form when solving linear systems. Systems of equations will be discussed in Chapter 5. Thus, the kinds of situations given in this lesson will be quite useful in that chapter.

It is possible, and quite common, to have linear combinations of more than two variables, as shown in **Example 1.** The graph of $Ax + By + Cz = D$, an equation with three variables, is a plane. Students will encounter systems of three linear equations in three variables in Chapter 5. If there are more than three variables, the graph is called a *hyperplane*. It is impossible to fully picture a hyperplane in three dimensions, but its properties can be treated algebraically.

152

Solution

a. Each win is worth 2 points, so W wins are worth $2W$ points. A tie is worth 1 point, so T ties are worth $1T$ points. Because losses are worth 0 points, L losses add $0L$ to the total. This total is 11, so

$$2W + 1T + 0L = 11$$

that is
$$2W + T = 11.$$

b. Because of the situation, W and T must be nonnegative integers. Substitution and trial and error show that the only possible solutions are those shown in the table and the graph below.

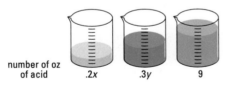

W	T
0	11
1	9
2	7
3	5
4	3
5	1

Check

Check each ordered pair. For instance, 2 wins are worth 4 points, and 7 ties are worth 7 points. Altogether, this is 11 points. So $(2, 7)$ checks.

An Example with a Continuous Domain

Linear-combination situations occur whenever quantities are mixed, as in chemicals, foods, diets, and medicines.

Example 2

A chemist mixes x ounces of a 20% acid solution with y ounces of a 30% acid solution. The final mixture contains 9 ounces of acid.
a. Write an equation relating x, y, and the total number of ounces of acid.
b. How many ounces of the 30% acid solution must be added to 2.7 ounces of the 20% acid solution to get 9 ounces of acid in the final mixture?

Solution

a. Find the amount of acid in each solution, and set the sum equal to 9. Let x = the number of ounces of 20% acid solution, and let y = the number of ounces of 30% acid solution.

| number of oz of acid | .2x | .3y | 9 |

Since 20% of the x ounces are acid, the amount of acid is 20% of x, or $0.2x$. Similarly, 30% of the y ounces are acid, so the amount of acid is $0.3y$. The total number of ounces of acid is thus $0.2x + 0.3y$. There are 9 ounces of acid, so an equation is $0.2x + 0.3y = 9$.

Lesson 3-3 *Linear-Combination Situations* **153**

1917, and ice hockey became an Olympic event at the 1920 Winter Games.

② Remind students to consider appropriate substitutions for the variables when graphing a linear combination, to determine in which quadrant a graph lies before starting to draw the graph, and to determine whether the graph is discrete or continuous.

Error Alert Students often decide too quickly that a situation can be modeled by a linear combination. Encourage students to keep track of units. For example, consider the following situation: A car gets 25 miles to a gallon for city driving and 32 miles to a gallon for highway driving. The gas tank holds 14 gallons of gasoline. If the car is driven x miles in the city and y miles on the highway and runs out of gas, write an equation relating x and y and the size of the tank. Explain that the equation $25x + 32y = 14$ does not model this situation. Students can check this fact using units: $25x$ is $(25 \frac{\text{miles}}{\text{gallon}})(x \text{ miles})$. Note that the reciprocal rates must be used to get an answer in gallons—$(\frac{1}{25} \frac{\text{gallon}}{\text{mile}})(x \text{ miles})$ gives the number of gallons used in the city. Similarly, $(\frac{1}{32} \frac{\text{gallon}}{\text{mile}})(y \text{ miles})$ gives the number of gallons used on the highway. Thus an equation is $\frac{x}{25} + \frac{y}{32} = 14$.

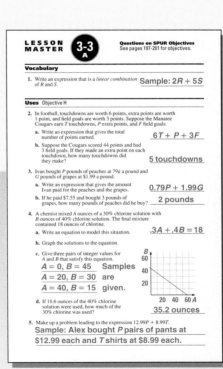

Additional Examples

1. Becky sold $36 worth of tickets for the Pep Club Picnic. Adult tickets cost $5 and student tickets cost $2. There is no charge for children under 6 years of age.
   a. Write an equation to express the relationship among the number of adult tickets A, student tickets S, and children's tickets C Becky sold.
   $5A + 2S + 0C = 36$ or
   $5A + 2S = 36$
   b. Make a table and graph all possible (S, A) that could have occurred.

S	18	13	8	3
A	0	2	4	6

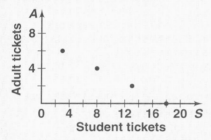

2. Mixtures A and B contain weed killer and water. Mixture A is 5% weed killer, and mixture B is 15% weed killer.
   a. Write an equation relating A, B, and T, the total amount of the weed killer.
   $0.05A + 0.15B = T$

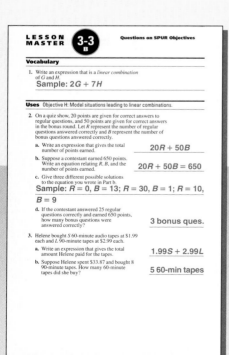

▶ b. Substitute 2.7 for x.
$$0.2(2.7) + 0.3y = 9$$
$$0.54 + 0.3y = 9$$
$$0.3y = 8.46$$
$$y = 28.2$$
So 28.2 ounces of the 30% acid solution must be added to 2.7 ounces of the 30% acid solution to get 9 ounces of acid in the final solution.

The equation $0.2x + 0.3y = 9$ from Example 2 can be graphed by solving for y and recognizing the slope-intercept form.

$$
\begin{array}{ll}
0.2x + 0.3y = 9 & \\
2x + 3y = 90 & \text{Multiply each side by 10 to clear decimals.} \\
3y = -2x + 90 & \text{Subtract } 2x \text{ from each side.} \\
y = -\tfrac{2}{3}x + 30 & \text{Divide each side by 3.}
\end{array}
$$

Thus, the slope is $-\frac{2}{3}$ and the y-intercept is 30. The graph is shown below.

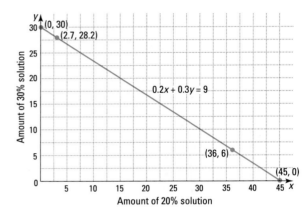

The graph lies entirely on the axes or in the first quadrant because the number of ounces of either solution must be a nonnegative real number. It is the segment connecting $(0, 30)$ and $(45, 0)$. Each point on the segment refers to a different mixture of the acid solutions. The point $(2.7, 28.2)$ stands for 2.7 oz of 20% solution and 28.2 oz of 30% solution, as was found in Example 2b. The point $(36, 6)$ means that 36 oz of the 20% solution could be mixed with 6 oz of the 30% solution to yield 9 oz of acid.

Any linear-combination situation in two variables is modeled by an equation whose graph is a line or a part of a line. This is the origin of the phrase "linear combination."

154

Adapting to Individual Needs

Extra Help

Most equations in this lesson are in standard form $Ax + By = C$. Remind students that any equation in $Ax + By = C$ form can be changed to slope-intercept form. For example, $0.2x + 0.3y = 9$ in **Example 2** is changed to slope-intercept form by first multiplying both sides by 10 to clear decimals. (It is not necessary to clear decimals first, but it makes the computation simpler.) Point out that the power of 10 by which to multiply depends on the decimals in the equation. If the equation were $0.2x + 0.03y = 9$, both sides would be multiplied by 100.

Covering the Reading

1. The expression $20P + 32L$ is called a __?__ of P and L.
   linear combination

2. Suppose you buy P pizzas at $12 each and D drinks at 75¢ each. Write an expression that tells how much you spend. **$12P + .75D$**

3. At a sale, Greta bought B blouses at $15 each, S skirts at $24 each, and H pairs of shoes at $26 a pair. Write a linear combination to find the amount she spent at the sale. **$15B + 24S + 26H$**

In 4 and 5, refer to Example 1.

4. With T as the dependent variable, (3, 5) is a solution to $2W + T = 11$. This solution means the team won __?__ games, tied __?__ games, and earned a total of __?__ points. **3; 5; 11**

5. In 1993–94 the Montreal Canadiens earned 96 points. If the Canadiens won 41 games that season, how many ties did they have? **14**

6. Suppose that x ounces of a solution that is 60% acid are combined with y ounces of a 90% acid solution.
   a. How many ounces of acid are in the 60% solution? **$.6x$**
   b. How many ounces of acid are in the 90% solution? **$.9y$**
   c. How many total ounces of acid are there in the combination? **$.6x + .9y$**
   d. If Alex wants 18 ounces of acid in the final mixture, what equation relates x, y, and the 18 total ounces of acid? **$.6x + .9y = 18$**
   e. Write the equation from part **d** in slope-intercept form. **$y = -\frac{2}{3}x + 20$**
   f. Graph the solutions to the equation. **See left.**
   g. How many ounces of the 90% solution must be added to 9 ounces of the 60% solution to get 18 ounces of acid in the final mixture? **14 oz**

6f)
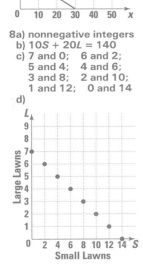
$y = -\frac{2}{3}x + 20$

8a) nonnegative integers
b) $10S + 20L = 140$
c) 7 and 0; 6 and 2;
   5 and 4; 4 and 6;
   3 and 8; 2 and 10;
   1 and 12; 0 and 14
d)

Applying the Mathematics

7. Suppose zucchini sells for 49¢ a pound and tomatoes sell for 59¢ per pound.
   a. What will be the cost of 2.5 pounds of zucchini and 3.4 pounds of tomatoes? **$3.23**
   b. What will be the cost of Z pounds of zucchini and T pounds of tomatoes? **$.49Z + .59T$**
   c. Write an equation indicating the amounts of zucchini Z and tomatoes T you can buy for $5.00. **$.49Z + .59T = 5$**

8. William spent Saturday mowing lawns. He charged $10 for small lawns and $20 for large lawns and earned $140. Let S be the number of small lawns and L be the number of large lawns. **See left.**
   a. What type of numbers makes sense for S and L in this context?
   b. Write an equation relating S, L, and the amount of money earned.
   c. Give all possible numbers of large and small lawns William could have mowed.
   d. Graph the equation of part **b**.

Lesson 3-3 *Linear-Combination Situations* **155**

---

b. How many ounces of 5% solution must be added to 50 ounces of 15% solution to get 12 ounces of weed killer in the final solution? **90 ounces**

c. Draw a graph to illustrate all possible (A, B) that give 12 ounces of weed killer in the final mixture.

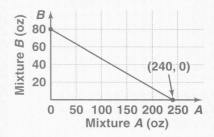

Mixture B (oz)
Mixture A (oz)
(240, 0)

Notes on Questions

Question 6 Although this question is directly patterned after **Example 2,** some students may still have difficulty. Discuss the parts one by one. Remind students to be careful when choosing scales for their graphs. Work through the solution of the equation in **part e;** many students may still have trouble with decimal coefficients.

Question 8 Error Alert Some students may forget that this graph is discrete. To help clarify the concept ask them if the situation involves cutting part of a lawn.

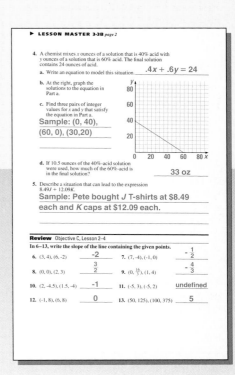

► LESSON MASTER 3-3B *page 2*

4. A chemist mixes x ounces of a solution that is 40% acid with y ounces of a solution that is 60% acid. The final solution contains 24 ounces of acid.
   a. Write an equation to model this situation. **$.4x + .6y = 24$**
   b. At the right, graph the solutions to the equation in Part a.
   c. Find three pairs of integer values for x and y that satisfy the equation in Part a. **Sample: (0, 40), (60, 0), (30,20)**
   d. If 10.5 ounces of the 40%-acid solution were used, how much of the 60%-acid is in the final solution? **33 oz**

5. Describe a situation that can lead to the expression $8.49J + 12.09K$. **Sample: Pete bought J T-shirts at $8.49 each and K caps at $12.09 each.**

Review Objective C, Lesson 2-4
In 6–13, write the slope of the line containing the given points.
6. (3, 4), (6, -2) **-2**
7. (7, -4), (-1, 0) **$-\frac{1}{2}$**
8. (0, 0), (2, 3) **$\frac{3}{2}$**
9. (0, $\frac{16}{3}$), (1, 4) **$-\frac{4}{3}$**
10. (2, -4.5), (1.5, -4) **-1**
11. (-5, 3), (-5, 2) **undefined**
12. (-1, 8), (6, 8) **0**
13. (50, 125), (100, 375) **5**

Adapting to Individual Needs

English Language Development
Students may be familiar with the word *combination* because they use combination locks on their lockers or bicycles. Explain that a series of numbers and movements must be performed to open the lock. Similarly, a *linear combination* involves putting together, or combining, two linear situations.

Notes on Questions

Question 14 This is the first question in the chapter that asks students to write the equation of a line, given only its graph.

Question 17 Cooperative Learning This is a good discussion question. You may find that some students equate positive slope with going uphill and negative slope with going downhill; they do not realize that the graph shows the *distance* from a starting point rather than the *height* of the path taken.

Question 20 You might compare the grading system mentioned in this question to the grading system used in your school.

Practice

For more questions on SPUR Objectives, use **Lesson Master 3-3A** (shown on page 153) or **Lesson Master 3-3B** (shown on pages 154–155).

Assessment

Quiz A quiz covering Lessons 3-1 through 3-3 is provided in the *Assessment Sourcebook.*

Oral/Written Communication Have students **work in pairs.** Each student should write a linear-combination equation with whole-number coefficients. Then the other student should make up a problem which has that equation as its solution. [Students demonstrate an understanding of linear-combination equations and how they apply to real-world situations.]

Extension

Students are not asked to draw a graph for **Question 7,** but you might ask them to describe the graph and to identify a point on the graph. [The graph is a line segment with the set of points (Z, T) connecting and including $(\frac{5.00}{0.49}, 0)$ and $(0, \frac{5.00}{0.59})$. The domains of Z and T might be considered the nonnegative real numbers.]

Project Update Project 5, *Linear Combinations,* on page 193, relates to the content of this lesson.

156

---

11)

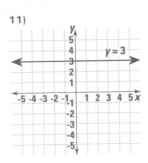

9. The Ironman triathlon is a sporting event made up of a 2.4-mile swim, a 112-mile bicycle race, and a marathon run of 26.2 miles. If a competitor goes at a rate of S minutes per mile swimming, B minutes per mile biking, and R minutes per mile running, what will be the competitor's total time for the triathlon?
$2.4S + 112B + 26.2R$ **minutes**

10. Make up a problem whose solution is $3H + 4T = 12$.
Sample: Write an equation showing how many pounds of candy hearts at $3/lb and chocolate turtles at $4/lb can be purchased for $12.

Review

In 11 and 12, graph on a coordinate plane.   *(Lesson 3-2)* **See left.**

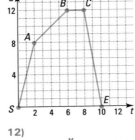

11. $y = 3$ **12.** $y = \frac{3}{4}x - 3$

13. What is the slope of a line parallel to $3y = 2x + 7$? *(Lesson 3-2)* $\frac{2}{3}$

14. For the line graphed at the left, determine each of the following.
   a. its slope $\frac{2}{3}$
   b. its y-intercept -4
   c. an equation   *(Lessons 3-1, 3-2)* $y = \frac{2}{3}x - 4$

15. The math department at a school has 100 reams of paper at the start of the school year. (A ream of paper contains 500 sheets.) Each day the department uses about $\frac{3}{4}$ of a ream.   *(Lesson 3-1)*
   a. Let d be the number of days and R be the number of reams remaining. Write a formula for R in terms of d. $R = 100 - \frac{3}{4}d$
   b. When the supply gets down to 10 reams, a new supply of paper needs to be ordered. After how many school days will paper need to be ordered? **after 120 days**

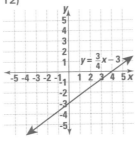

In 16 and 17, refer to the graph at the left, which shows the distance d in kilometers Terry is from a starting point S after t hours.   *(Lesson 3-1)*

16. a. Find the slope of $\overline{CE}$. -6
   b. Explain what the slope tells you about Terry's trip. **See below.**

17. *True or false.*   During some part of the journey Terry traveled uphill. How can you tell? **False;   you can't tell whether Terry went uphill or not.**

In 18 and 19, find the distance between the given points.   *(Previous course)*

18. $(1, 3)$ and $(6, 15)$ **13**   **19.** (a, b) and (c, d) $\sqrt{(a-c)^2 + (b-d)^2}$

16b) Terry travels for 2 hours at the speed of 6 km/hr back to the starting point.

12)

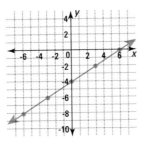

Exploration

20. In many schools, a person's grade-point average is calculated using linear combinations. Some schools give 4 points for each A, 3 points for each B, 2 points for each C, and 1 point for each D. Suppose a person gets 7 As, 3 Bs, and 2 Cs.
   a. Calculate this person's total number of points. **41**
   b. Divide your answer in part **a** by the total number of classes (12) to get the grade-point average. ≈ 3.42
   c. Calculate your own grade-point average for last year using this scheme. **Answers will vary.**

156

Adapting to Individual Needs

Challenge Science Connection
Solution A contains 20% acid and solution B contains 40% acid. How many ounces of each solution should a chemist mix together to create a 50-ounce solution that is 25% acid? [$.20A + .40B = .25 (50)$; $B = 50 - A$; $.20A + .40(50 - A) = .25(50)$; $A = 37.5$ oz, $B = 12.5$ oz]

Chemists provide solutions. *Industrial chemists perform a variety of tasks. Some, like the one shown, do quality control work testing different items. Others conduct research, developing and testing new products.*

Recall the equation $0.2x + 0.3y = 9$ which describes the following linear combination situation from Lesson 3-3.

> A chemist mixes x ounces of a 20% acid solution with y ounces of a 30% acid solution. The final mixture contains 9 ounces of acid.

Because of the situation, both x and y must be positive. The graph was a segment. However, if you allow x and y to be any real numbers, then the graph of $0.2x + 0.3y = 9$ is the line shown below.

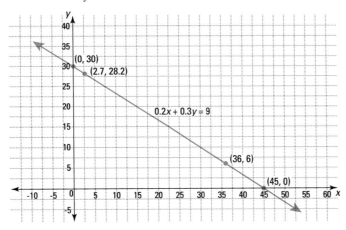

The equation $0.2x + 0.3y = 9$ is of the form $Ax + By = C$, with $A = 0.2$ and $B = 0.3$. When A and B are not both zero, the equation $Ax + By = C$ is called the **standard form of an equation for a line.**

Lesson 3-4 *The Graph of $Ax + By = C$* **157**

Lesson **3-4**

Objectives
A Determine the slope and intercepts of a line given its equation.
E Recognize properties of linear functions.
L Graph or interpret graphs of linear equations.

Resources
From the **Teacher's Resource File**
■ Lesson Master 3-4A or 3-4B
■ Answer Master 3-4
■ Teaching Aids
  8 Four-Quadrant Graph Paper
  24 Warm-up

Additional Resources
■ Visuals for Teaching Aids 8, 24

Teaching **3-4**
Lesson

Warm-up
How is the graph of the line with equation $3x + 4y = 24$ similar to the graph of the line with equation $y = 3x + 6$? **The *y*-intercept of both lines is 6.**

Lesson 3-4 Overview

Broad Goals In this lesson, students study graphs of situations in which a linear combination $Ax + By$ equals a constant C. Several important concepts are reviewed: the graph of $Ax + By = C$, the x- and y-intercepts, the graphs of $x = h$ and $y = k$, and the method of graphing that uses both intercepts.

Perspective Students should be able to graph from standard form as well as from

slope-intercept form. This is an easy lesson—review for almost all students—and it allows time to review the quiz you might have given on Lessons 3-1 to 3-3.

The lesson begins by graphing the situation of **Example 2** from Lesson 3-3. This is generalized to show that any equation of the form $Ax + By = C$ has a graph that is a line. Then the various forms of this equation are discussed or reviewed: the oblique form,

which is easily graphed using x- and y-intercepts; the form $x = h$ leading to vertical lines; the form $y = k$, which students have seen before.

❶ Error Alert Example 1 is not difficult, but students often confuse the graphs of $x = h$ and $y = k$. One way to eliminate this confusion is to have students read the equations as "x-value equals h" and "y-value equals k."

Students also confuse the slopes of $x = h$ and $y = k$. Have students think of an application, such as the steepness of a ski hill. A vertical line could be thought of as an impossible slope to ski; there is no tilt—an undefined slope. A horizontal line corresponds to flat land with no tilt at all—a 0 slope.

❷ When reviewing **Example 2,** encourage students to determine x- and y-intercepts *mentally* if possible. Explain that when an equation is in standard form $Ax + By = C$, and when either or both values A and B are factors of C, then intercepts can be found quickly. Since substituting 0 for x has the effect of eliminating the x-term, have students "cover" the x-term and mentally solve the resulting equation for y, thus obtaining the y-intercept. Likewise, have them cover the y-term and mentally solve for x, obtaining the x-intercept.

Stress that the graphing method of using two intercepts is very useful with graphs that require large scales, such as $5x + 3y = 4500$, where the x-intercept is 900 and the y-intercept is 1500. These values suggest intervals of the axes of length 100 or 300. Using the slope-intercept method is cumbersome because a slope of $-\frac{5}{3}$ is not easily located on the graph. Larger scales appear frequently in applications both in this book and elsewhere.

An Equation for Any Line

The graph of $0.2x + 0.3y = 9$ is an instance of the following theorem.

> **Theorem**
> The graph of $Ax + By = C$, where A and B are not both 0, is a line.

Proof:
There are two cases to consider, depending on whether $B \neq 0$ or $B = 0$. When $B \neq 0$, the equation $Ax + By = C$ can be rewritten in slope-intercept form.

$$Ax + By = C$$
$$By = -Ax + C \qquad \text{Add } -Ax \text{ to each side.}$$
$$y = -\frac{A}{B}x + \frac{C}{B} \qquad \text{Multiply by } \frac{1}{B} \ (B \neq 0).$$

This is an equation of a line with slope $-\frac{A}{B}$ and y-intercept $\frac{C}{B}$. If $A \neq 0$, then the slope is not 0, and the line is oblique. If $A = 0$, then the slope is 0, and the line is horizontal. Then the line has equation $y = \frac{C}{B}$.
When $B = 0$, the equation $Ax + By = C$ can be written as follows.

$$Ax = C$$
$$x = \frac{C}{A} \qquad \text{Multiply by } \frac{1}{A} \ (A \neq 0).$$

This is an equation of a vertical line.

Vertical Lines

The equation $x + 0 \cdot y = 2$ is of the form $Ax + By = C$ with $B = 0$.

❶ **Example 1**

a. Graph the line $x + 0 \cdot y = 2$.   **b.** Find the slope of the line.

Solution

a. In $x + 0 \cdot y = 2$, y can take on any value, but x is always 2. That is, $x = 2$. It is easy to make a table and plot the points.

x	y
2	-2
2	0
2	3
2	5

b. Pick two points on the line. We use the points (2, 0) and (2, 3).

$$m = \frac{3 - 0}{2 - 2} = \frac{3}{0}$$

Since division by 0 is undefined, **There is no slope.** The slope is said to be *undefined*. By the same argument, the slope of any vertical line $x = h$ is undefined.

Optional Activities

You might use this activity at the beginning of the lesson when you discuss the equation $0.2x + 0.3y = 9$. Explain that, unlike the slope-intercept form for an equation of a line, there is no unique linear-combination form for such an equation. Have students **work in groups,** and find an equation in $Ax + By = C$ form equivalent to $0.2x + 0.3y = 9$ under each of the following conditions.

1. When $A = 1$ [$x + 1.5y = 45$]
2. When $B = 1$ [$\frac{2}{3}x + y = 30$]
3. When A and B are integers with no common factors [$2x + 3y = 90$]
4. When A and B are unit fractions [$\frac{x}{45} + \frac{y}{30} = 1$]

You might tell students that the last equation is called the *intercept form* for the equation of a line.

Adapting to Individual Needs

Extra Help
Sometimes students do not see that an equation such as $x = 5$ or $y = -10$ can be written in the standard form $Ax + By = C$. Remind them that $x = x + 0 \cdot y$. So $x = 5$ is identical to $x + 0 \cdot y = 5$. Similar reasoning can be used to rewrite $y = -10$ as $0 \cdot x + y = -10$. Also point out that $A = 1$ in the first equation and $B = 1$ in the second equation, even though we do not usually write a coefficient of 1.

It's a frame-up. *Frames for most houses are made of wood, but steel frames like the one shown here are becoming more common. Can you find oblique, horizontal, and vertical lines in this picture?*

Only oblique and horizontal lines can be written in slope-intercept form. But any line in the coordinate plane has an equation that can be written in standard form.

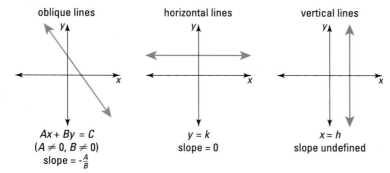

oblique lines

$Ax + By = C$
$(A \neq 0, B \neq 0)$
slope $= -\frac{A}{B}$

horizontal lines

$y = k$
slope $= 0$

vertical lines

$x = h$
slope undefined

Notice that all oblique lines and all horizontal lines can be graphs of functions. A vertical line cannot be the graph of a function.

Graphing a Line Using Intercepts

Although you could rewrite the standard form of a linear equation in slope-intercept form in order to make a graph, it is often much quicker to graph such equations by hand using the x- and y-intercepts. The **x-intercept** is the value of x at the point where a graph crosses the x-axis. This point has second coordinate 0.

Example 2

Graph the equation $6x - 3y = 12$ using its intercepts.

Solution

To find the x-intercept, substitute 0 for y, and solve for x.

$$6x - 3(0) = 12$$
$$x = 2$$

The x-intercept is 2.

To find the y-intercept, substitute 0 for x, and solve for y.

$$6(0) - 3y = 12$$
$$y = -4$$

The y-intercept is -4.

Plot (2, 0) and (0, -4). Draw the line containing them, as shown at the right.

Check

The point (1, -2) appears to be on the graph. Substitute to see if its coordinates satisfy the equation.

Does $6(1) - 3(-2) = 12$?

Does $6 + 6 = 12$? Yes, it checks.

Lesson 3-4 *The Graph of Ax + By = C* **159**

Adapting to Individual Needs

English Language Development

You might want to remind students with limited English proficiency that a horizontal line goes "straight across" and a vertical line goes "up and down." Then, to ensure that they understand these terms, have them hold their pencils in horizontal positions and in vertical positions. Now explain that an *oblique line* is neither horizontal nor vertical, and demonstrate oblique positions with a pencil.

Challenge

Ask students why the lines $5x + 3y = 7$ and $5x + 3y = -2$ are parallel. [They have the same slope, $-\frac{5}{3}$.] Then ask if $5x + 3y = 9$ is also parallel to these lines. [Yes, it too has a slope of $-\frac{5}{3}$.] Finally, ask students to find the equation of the line that is parallel to all three of these lines and passes through the point (-3, 6). [$5x + 3y = 3$]

Students will need graph paper or **Teaching Aid 8** for this lesson.

Additional Examples

1. a. Graph the line $x + 0 \cdot y = -3$.

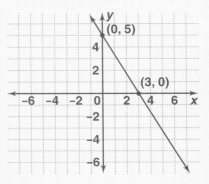

b. Find the slope of the line.
undefined

2. Graph the equation $10x + 6y = 30$ by using its intercepts.

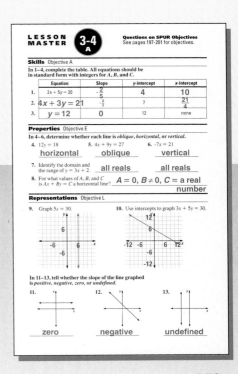

(0, 5)

(3, 0)

159

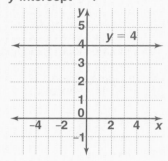
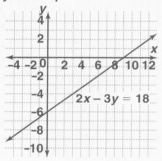

160

1a) $Ax + By = C$, where A and B are not both 0.

2b)

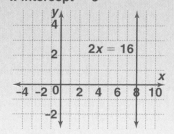

c) Pick two points such as $(-6, 0)$ and $(-6, 1)$; the slope $= \frac{1 - 0}{-6 - (-6)} = \frac{1}{0}$; division by zero is undefined; therefore, the slope is undefined.

12c)

13c)

Covering the Reading

1. **a.** What is the standard form of an equation for a line? See left.
   b. Given the equation $5x - 2y = 24$, identify A and B. $A = 5, B = -2$
2. **a.** Rewrite the equation $x = -6$ in standard form. $x + 0y = -6$
   b. Graph the equation from part **a.** See left.
   c. Use the definition of slope to explain why the slope of $x = -6$ is undefined. See left.

In 3–5, refer to the proof of the theorem in this lesson.

3. **a.** If neither A nor B is 0, the equation $Ax + By = C$ can be written in slope-intercept form as ? . $y = \frac{-A}{B}x + \frac{C}{B}$
   b. The slope of the line is ? . $\frac{-A}{B}$
   c. The y-intercept of the line is ? . $\frac{C}{B}$

4. If $A = 0$ and $B \neq 0$, then the line is ? and has ? slope. horizontal; zero

5. If $A \neq 0$ and $B = 0$, then the line is ? . vertical

6. Match the line with a description of its slope.
   a. horizontal line i   (i) zero slope
   b. vertical line iii   (ii) nonzero slope
   c. oblique line ii   (iii) slope undefined

7. The line whose equation is of the form $y = mx + b$ is oblique when m ? 0. $\neq$

8. How many intercepts does an oblique line have? two

9. The graph of $y = 7$ is a ? line with y-intercept ? . horizontal; 7

10. *True or false.* Every equation of the form $Ax + By = C$, where A and B are not both 0, represents a function. Justify your answer. False; when $B = 0$, the vertical line is not a function.

11. To find the x-intercept of a graph of points (x, y), for which variable should you substitute 0? y

In 12 and 13, an equation is given. **a.** Find its x-intercept. **b.** Find its y-intercept. **c.** Graph the line using the points from parts **a** and **b**. See left.

12. $4x - 3y = 24$
   a) 6 b) -8

13. $5x + 6y = 15$
   a) 3 b) $\frac{5}{2}$

Applying the Mathematics

In 14–16, an equation for a line is given. **a.** Tell whether the line is vertical, horizontal, or oblique and justify your answer. **b.** Give all intercepts for each line. **c.** Graph each equation. See margin.

14. $y = 4$ 15. $2x - 3y = 18$ 16. $2x = 16$

17. Give an equation in standard form for the line with y-intercept $-\frac{1}{5}$ and slope 2. $10x - 5y = 1$

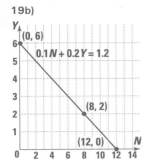

19b)

$0.1N + 0.2Y = 1.2$

Points: (0, 6), (8, 2), (12, 0)

20a) domain: the set of real numbers
b) range: the set of real numbers

21a) domain: {2}
b) range: the set of real numbers

Drug education. *Pictured is a police officer teaching young students in an anti-drug program.*

22a) domain: the set of real numbers
b) range: {3}

24a) $0.04S + 0.02R = 50$
b) Sample:

S	R
625	1250
0	2500
1250	0

18. A line has no *y*-intercept and goes through the point (15, 34). Give an equation for the line. $x = 15$

19. Meg combines *N* oz of a solution that is 10% chlorine with *Y* oz of a solution that is 20% chlorine. She ends up with a mixture that contains 1.2 oz of chlorine. **b) See left.**
   a. Write an equation relating *N*, *Y*, and the amount of chlorine in the mixture. $.10N + .20Y = 1.2$
   b. Graph the equation you obtained in part **a** by finding the *N*- and *Y*-intercepts. Consider *N* to be the independent variable.
   c. Use your graph to find out how many ounces of the 20% solution must be added to 8 oz of the 10% solution to get the final mixture. **2 oz**

In 20–22, the equation represents a relation in the (*x*, *y*) plane. **a.** Give the set of possible values of *x*. **b.** Give the set of possible values of *y*. **See left.**

20. $3x + 2y = 6$ **21.** $3x = 6$ **22.** $2y = 6$

Review

23. It costs $10.20 to run a 3-line classified advertisement in a local paper for five days, and $12.35 to run the same ad for seven days. What is the cost of *x* ads for five days and *y* ads for seven days? *(Lesson 3-3)* $10.20x + 12.35y$

24. You have some money saved from your job. You invest *S* of it in a savings account that pays 4% interest and the rest *R* in a checking account that pays 2%. You earn $50 interest in one year. **See left.**
   a. Write an equation relating *S*, *R*, and the total amount of interest.
   b. Give three possible pairs of values for *R* and *S*. *(Lesson 3-3)*

25. A city police department pays police officers $2500 per month and sergeants $3000 per month. The total payroll for the month for officers and sergeants is $310,000. *(Lesson 3-3)*
   a. Write an equation relating the number of police officers *P*, the number of sergeants *S*, and the total monthly payroll.
   b. If there are 10 sergeants, how many police officers are there? **112**
   a) $2500P + 3000S = 310,000$

26. Do the changes mean a slope of $-\frac{4}{3}$? *(Lessons 2-4, 3-2)*
   a. a vertical change of -3 units for a horizontal change of 4 units **No**
   b. a vertical change of -4 units for a horizontal change of 3 units **Yes**
   c. a vertical change of $-\frac{4}{3}$ units for a horizontal change of 1 unit **Yes**
   d. a vertical change of 1 unit for a horizontal change of $-\frac{4}{3}$ units **No**

Exploration

27. a. Find the *x*- and *y*-intercepts of $\frac{x}{2} + \frac{y}{7} = 1$. *x*-intercept = 2; *y*-intercept = 7
   b. Find the *x*- and *y*-intercepts of $\frac{x}{-5} + \frac{y}{6} = 1$. *x*-intercept = -5; *y*-intercept = 6
   c. Based on parts **a** and **b** above, make a conjecture about the *x*- and *y*-intercepts of $\frac{x}{a} + \frac{y}{b} = 1$. Either prove or give a counterexample to your conjecture. **See margin.**

Lesson 3-4 *The Graph of Ax + By = C* **161**

27c. *x*-intercept = *a*, *y*-intercept = *b*.
   Proof: To find *x*-intercept, let *y* = 0.
   This gives $\frac{x}{a} + \frac{0}{b} = 1$;
   $\frac{x}{a} = 1$; *x* = *a*.
   To find *y*-intercept, let *x* = 0.
   This gives $\frac{0}{a} + \frac{y}{b} = 1$;
   $\frac{y}{b} = 1$; *y* = *b*.

Setting Up Lesson 3-5

Materials If you do the *Optional Activities* on page 164 you will need electricity rates, telephone rates, or water rates in your area.

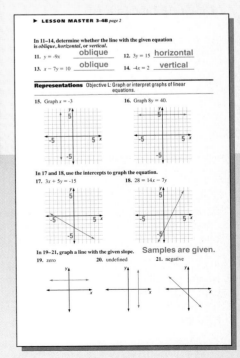
161

Objectives

B Find an equation for a line given two points on it or given a point on it and its slope.

E Recognize properties of linear functions.

I In a real-world context, find an equation for a line containing two points.

K Model situations leading to piecewise-linear functions.

Resources

From the *Teacher's Resource File*
- Lesson Master 3-5A or 3-5B
- Answer Master 3-5
- Teaching Aids
   8 Four-Quadrant Graph Paper
   24 Warm-up

Additional Resources
- Visuals for Teaching Aids 8, 24

Teaching Lesson **3-5**

Warm-up

Diagnostic Write an equation for the line through the pair of points.
1. (5, 9) and (5, -4.2) $x = 5$
2. (-1, 6) and (5, 6) $y = 6$
3. (11, 11) and $(\sqrt{2}, \sqrt{2})$ $y = x$
4. (90, 10) and (60, 40)
   $x + y = 100$
5. (8, -2) and (14, 3) $y = \frac{5}{6}x - \frac{26}{3}$
   or $y + 2 = \frac{5}{6}(x - 8)$

Two points determine a line. You use this idea every time you draw a line through two points with a ruler. It is a postulate from geometry. In algebra, this idea raises the question: What is an equation of the line through two given points? This lesson will show you how to get such an equation.

Finding a Linear Equation

Example 1

Suppose you remember that 32°F = 0°C and 212°F = 100°C, but you have forgotten the conversion formula. You know that the formula is linear. Reconstruct the formula with F as a function of C.

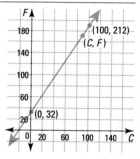

Solution 1

Because F is a function of C, the independent variable is C and the dependent variable is F. So, ordered pairs are of the form (C, F). Start with the slope-intercept form and substitute C for x and F for y.

$$F = mC + b$$

The values of m and b must be found. To find the slope m, use the given points (0, 32) and (100, 212).

$$m = \frac{212 - 32}{100 - 0} = \frac{180}{100} = 1.8$$

The F-intercept is 32, so $b = 32$. Substitute the values for the slope and the intercept into $F = mC + b$ to get

$$F = 1.8C + 32.$$

Solution 2

Using the points (0, 32) and (100, 212), find $m = 1.8$. Let (C, F) be any other point on the line. Substitute (C, F) and either (0, 32) or (100, 212) into the slope formula. We use (100, 212).

$$\frac{F - 212}{C - 100} = 1.8$$

To put this equation in slope-intercept form, multiply both sides by $C - 100$.

$$F - 212 = 1.8(C - 100)$$

Now solve for F.

$$F - 212 = 1.8C - 180$$
$$F = 1.8C + 32$$

Lesson 3-5 Overview

Broad Goals This lesson connects the slope-intercept, linear-combination, and point-slope forms of an equation of a line.

Perspective From their study of algebra or geometry, UCSMP students will be familiar with finding an equation for a line through two points. Yet, for most students this review is helpful.

In geometry, students learn that there is one line (a) through two points (usually a postulate); (b) through a point parallel to a given line (often a postulate—Playfair's Parallel Postulate); and (c) through a point perpendicular to a given line (usually a theorem). This lesson shows students how to determine the equations for (a) and (b) algebraically. There are two reasons for waiting until Chapter 4 to discuss (c)—at that time, a simple way to determine the

slopes of perpendicular lines will be given, and a second look at this idea will provide a convenient review.

In all of these cases, the problem is reduced to finding an equation for a line with a given slope through a given point. We have used (x_1, y_1) to name the given point. We could have used (h, k)—letters which we use later in the Graph-Translation Theorem—but they are not traditional in this context. However,

Each of the equations $F = 1.8C + 32$ and $F - 212 = 1.8(C - 100)$ describes the situation of Example 1. The slope-intercept form is useful for computing values of F quickly if you know the values of C. The form $F - 212 = 1.8(C - 100)$ shows the slope and a specific point on the graph, and it can be used to find the slope-intercept form.

Point-Slope Form of a Line

The method of Solution 2 of Example 1 can be generalized as follows.

❶ **Point-Slope Theorem**
If a line contains (x_1, y_1) and has slope m, then it has equation $y - y_1 = m(x - x_1)$.

> **Proof:**
> Let ℓ be the line with slope m containing (x_1, y_1). If (x, y) is any other point on ℓ, then using the definition of slope,
> $$m = \frac{y - y_1}{x - x_1}.$$
> Multiplying both sides by $x - x_1$ gives:
> $$y - y_1 = m(x - x_1).$$
> This is the desired equation of the theorem.

The equation $y - y_1 = m(x - x_1)$ is called a **point-slope equation** for a line. The most convenient form to use depends on the information given. If you know the slope and the y-intercept, use $y = mx + b$. If you know the slope and some point other than the y-intercept, use $y - y_1 = m(x - x_1)$. If you know two points, find the slope and then use either point in the point-slope form. The following examples illustrate this procedure.

Example 2

Find an equation of the line through $(3, 5)$ and $(6, -1)$.

Solution

First, find the slope.
$$m = \frac{-1 - 5}{6 - 3} = \frac{-6}{3} = -2$$
Then, use the point-slope form with either point. We use $(3, 5)$. The equation is
$$y - 5 = -2(x - 3).$$
In standard form, this equation is $2x + y = 11$.

Check 1

Is the point $(3, 5)$ on the line? Does $5 - 5 = -2(3 - 3)$? Yes.
Is the point $(6, -1)$ on the line? Does $-1 - 5 = -2(6 - 3)$? Yes.

Check 2

Use the other point in the point-slope form. The point $(6, -1)$ gives
$$y - -1 = -2(x - 6) \text{ or } y + 1 = -2(x - 6).$$
In standard form, this becomes $2x + y = 11$, the same as before.

You might ask students which of the equations in the *Warm-up* were easy to find. Students may be able to find the first four equations easily; finding the last equation requires a systematic approach.

Make sure students understand that they are finding "*an* equation" for the line through two points, not "*the* equation." A line has many equations; only if one asks for an equation of a particular form is there a single equation for the line.

❶ Point out that these subscripts do not stand for terms in a sequence as they did in Chapter 1. Here they indicate a particular known point, as opposed to the general point (x, y).

Example 4 provides another opportunity to examine piecewise-linear functions.

Additional Examples

1. Suppose you know that the formula relating blood pressure and age is linear and that normal systolic blood pressures are 110 for a 20-year-old and 130 for a 60-year-old. Construct a formula in which blood pressure B is a function of age A. $B = \frac{1}{2}A + 100$

2. Find an equation for the line L through $(-3, 6)$ and $(5, 0)$.
   $y = -\frac{3}{4}(x - 5)$

(Additional Examples continue on page 164.)

the translation idea helps explain this theorem: The line through (x_1, y_1) with slope m is the image of $y = mx$ under a translation x_1 units over and y_1 units up.

This lesson begins with a conversion example that will be familiar to students of UCSMP *Algebra* and which is generalized in the Point-Slope Theorem. The Point-Slope Theorem will also be used to derive the explicit formula for an arithmetic sequence in Lesson 3-8.

Some books discuss the two-point form for an equation of a line: if a line contains (x_1, y_1) and (x_2, y_2), then an equation for the line is $\frac{y_2 - y_1}{x_2 - x_1} = \frac{y - y_1}{x - x_1}$. We feel that it is unnecessary to study this procedure as a separate form because it is so easy to see

that the left side of the equation is equal to the slope.

3. The cost of running the Bayshore Hotel is $2250 per day when 25 rooms are occupied and $5250 when 125 rooms are occupied.
  a. If the relationship between the number of occupied rooms r and the cost c of running the hotel is linear, write an equation relating c and r. **Samples:**
$c - 2250 = 30(r - 25)$, or
$c - 30r = 1500$
  b. Use the equation in **part a** to find the cost of running the hotel when 75 rooms are occupied. **$3750**

4. According to a chart of the Blue Star Life Insurance Company, the lightest recommended weight for an adult woman with a medium frame and a height of 4 ft 10 in. is 109 lb. This weight increases 2 lb/in. to a height of 5 ft 1 in. Then it goes up 3 lb/in. to a height of 6 ft.
  a. Draw a graph showing how the weight in pounds W for an adult woman with a medium frame is related to her height in inches h.

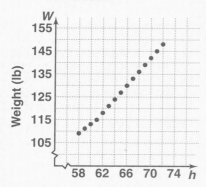

  b. Find two equations that together describe the relation between the lightest recommended weight W in pounds for a given height h in inches.
For $58 \le h \le 61$,
$W - 109 = 2(h - 58)$;
for $61 < h \le 72$,
$W - 115 = 3(h - 61)$.

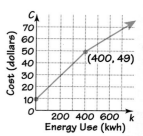

Water power. *Shown is a hydroelectric plant in Quebec, near James Bay. Quebec is a leading producer of hydroelectric power in North America. These plants supply about 95% of Quebec's electricity.*

164

Example 3

In a physics experiment, a spring is 12 centimeters long with a 15-gram weight attached. Its length increases 0.5 centimeter with each additional gram of weight.
a. Write an equation relating the spring length L and weight W.
b. Find the length of the spring with a 20-gram weight attached.

Solution

a. The slope is 0.5 cm/gram. Because the units for slope are centimeters per gram, the length is the dependent variable and the weight is the independent variable. The point (15, 12) is on the line. Substituting this point into the point-slope form gives
$$L - 12 = 0.5(W - 15).$$
b. Substitute 20 for W.
$$L - 12 = 0.5(20 - 15)$$
$$L = 14.5$$
The spring is 14.5 centimeters long with a 20-gram weight.

Finding Equations for Piecewise-Linear Graphs

It is usually not possible to find a single equation to describe a piecewise-linear graph. However, each segment or ray can be described with an equation and the domain to which it applies.

Example 4

During the winter months, an electric company calculates bills for the kilowatt-hours (kwh) its residential customers use based on the following:
    $9.00 monthly service fee;
    $ .10 per kwh energy charge for the first 400 kwh;
    $ .07 per kwh energy charge for each kwh over 400.
a. Draw a graph showing how cost C (in dollars) is related to usage k (in kwh).
b. Express the relation between C and k in symbols.

Solution

a. For the first 400 kwh the increase is constant. This piece of the graph is a segment with one endpoint (0, 9) and a slope of $.10 per kwh. The other endpoint is the point where $k = 400$. When k = 400,
$C = 9 + .10(400) = 49.$
At (400, 49) a new constant rate of increase begins. Because the slope of $.07 per kwh is less for this piece of the graph, this piece increases more slowly. This part of the graph is a ray, since the rate of $.07 per kwh applies to all values of k greater than 400. The graph is shown at right.

164

▶ **b.** The slope of the segment from the point (0, 9) to the point (400, 49) is 0.1. Thus,
$$C = .1k + 9 \text{ for } 0 \le k \le 400.$$
An equation for the ray beginning at (400, 49) with slope 0.07 is given by the point-slope form:
$$C - 49 = .07(k - 400)$$
$$C = .07(k - 400) + 49$$
$$C = .07k + 21, \text{ for } k > 400.$$
In summary, this situation can be described symbolically as follows:
$$C = \begin{cases} .1k + 9, \text{ for } 0 \le k \le 400 \\ .07k + 21, \text{ for } k > 400. \end{cases}$$

QUESTIONS

Covering the Reading

1. How many points determine a line? 2

2. A line contains the points (6, 4) and (2, 8).
   a. Find its slope. -1;
   b. Use (6, 4) and the slope from part **a** to write an equation for the line. $y - 4 = -1(x - 6)$
   c. Does (2, 8) satisfy the equation of part **b**? Justify your answer.
   Yes; does $8 - 4 = -1(2 - 6)$? $4 = -(-4)$? Yes, it checks.
3. *True or false.* A line is determined by its slope and any point on it.
   True
4. The point-slope form of the equation for a line with slope m and passing through point (x_1, y_1) is __?__. $y - y_1 = m(x - x_1)$

5. A line passes through the points (7, 12) and (5, 16).
   a. Find the slope of the line. -2
   b. Use the slope and the point (7, 12) in the point-slope form to find an equation of the line. $y - 12 = -2(x - 7)$
   c. Put your answer to part **b** in standard form. $2x + y = 26$
   d. Check that (5, 16) satisfies the equation.
   Does $2(5) + 16 = 26$? $10 + 16 = 26$? Yes, it checks.
6. Refer to Example 3. Suppose a spring is 10 cm long with a 25-gram weight attached and its length increases 0.2 cm with each additional gram weight. a) $L - 10 = 0.2(W - 25)$
   a. Write an equation relating spring length L and weight W.
   b. Find the spring length with a 20-gram weight. 9 cm

7. To find an equation for a line from the given information, which is generally easier to use, the point-slope form or the slope-intercept form?
   a. given the slope and a point other than the y-intercept point-slope
   b. given the y-intercept and the slope slope-intercept
   c. given two points point-slope

In 8 and 9, write an equation for the line with the given properties.

8. slope 6 and y-intercept -1 $y = 6x - 1$

9. slope $\frac{2}{3}$ and passing through (7, 1) $y - 1 = \frac{2}{3}(x - 7)$

Lesson 3-5 *Finding an Equation of a Line* **165**

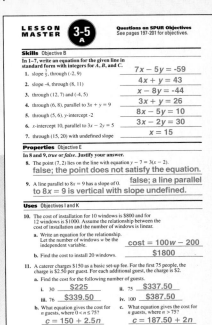

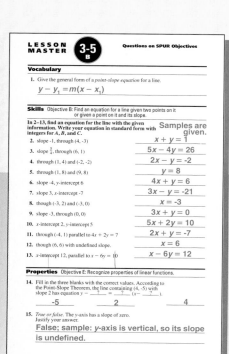

16c)

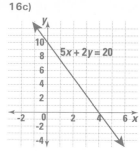

$5x + 2y = 20$

In 10 and 11, refer to Example 4.

10. Find the monthly electric cost for a family that uses 500 kwh of electricity. **$56**

11. *Multiple choice.* The formula $C = .07k + 21$ gives the cost of k kwh of electricity for which values of k? **c**
   (a) $k > 0$ (b) $0 \le k \le 400$ (c) $k > 400$

Applying the Mathematics

12. Scientists often use kelvins to measure temperature. On this scale, $32°F = 273.15$ kelvins and $212°F = 373.15$ kelvins. Let F represent the Fahrenheit temperature and K represent the Kelvin temperature. The relationship is linear. Find an equation giving temperature in kelvins as a function of temperature in degrees Fahrenheit. **Sample:** $K - 273 = \frac{5}{9}(F - 32)$

13. A printer finds that it costs $1290 to print 30 books and $1335 to print 45 books. Let c be the cost of printing b books. Assume c can be written as a linear function of b.
   a. Find an equation giving cost as a function of the number of books printed. **Sample:** $c - 1290 = 3(b - 30)$
   b. How much will it cost to print 0 books? (This is the set-up cost.)
   c. How much will it cost to print 100 books? **$1500**   b) **$1200**

14. Given the line with equation $y = \frac{4}{3}x - 7$, find an equation for the line that contains the point $(6, 4)$ and is parallel to the given line.
   $y - 4 = \frac{4}{3}(x - 6)$

15. Use the following phone rates: A customer is allowed to make a maximum of 80 local calls per month for a $13.15 fee. Each local call after the 80th is billed at a rate of $0.035 per call.
   a. Find the monthly phone bills for families making 70 local calls, 80 local calls, and 100 local calls. **$13.15; $13.15; $13.85**
   b. Draw a graph of the relation between the cost C and the number of local calls n. **See margin.**
   c. Describe this situation algebraically by finding an equation for each segment or ray. $\begin{cases} C = 13.15, n \le 80 \\ C = 13.15 + 0.035(n - 80), n > 80 \end{cases}$

Review

16. Consider the equation $5x + 2y = 20$. *(Lesson 3-4)*
   a. Find the x-intercept. **4**
   b. Find the y-intercept. **10**
   c. Graph the equation using the intercepts. **See above left.**

17. Let $P = (3, 4)$, $Q = (3, -5)$, $R = (-2, -5)$, and $S = (-2, 4)$.
   a. Graph rectangle $PQRS$. **See margin.**
   b. Give equations for the lines containing the four sides. **See above.**
   c. Find the area of $PQRS$. *(Previous course, Lessons 3-2, 3-4)* **45 units^2**

17b) $\overline{PQ}$: $x = 3$;
$\overline{QR}$: $y = -5$
$\overline{RS}$: $x = -2$;
$\overline{SP}$: $y = 4$

Suspense. At temperatures near 0 kelvins, some materials allow electricity to flow without resistance, a condition known as superconductivity. In the experiment shown here, a small electric charge was applied to a superconducting block of metal. Without resistance, the charge continues to flow, inducing a magnetic field in which the small metal cylinder is suspended.

166

Additional Answers
15b.

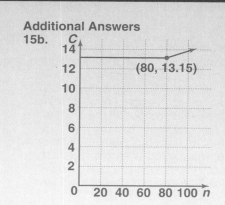

(80, 13.15)

Dance career. *Ballet dancers usually become professional by age 20 and retire by 45.*

18. As of November, 1994, the greatest combined number of points ever scored in a professional basketball game was 370 by the Denver Nuggets and the Detroit Pistons in December, 1983. A free throw is worth 1 point, a regular field goal is worth 2 points, and a three-point shot is worth 3 points. Suppose there were A free throws, B regular field goals, and C three-point shots made in that game. Write an equation which relates all these numbers. *(Lesson 3-3)*
$A + 2B + 3C = 370$

19. Recall that the weights of similarly-shaped people vary directly as the cube of their heights. Suppose a professional ballerina who is 5'8" tall weighs 120 pounds. How much would a 5'1" person with the same shape weigh? *(Lesson 2-1)* $\approx$ **87 lb**

20. Write an inequality to describe the points graphed on the number line below. *(Previous course)* $-3 < x < 5$

21. If $3x + 8 = 40$, find the value of $6x + 16$. *(Previous course)* **80**

22. Triangle MOP is shown below. Graph the reflection image of $\triangle MOP$ over the x-axis. Label the points M', O', and P', respectively, and give their coordinates. *(Previous course)*
$M' = (-90, -90);$ $O' = (-50, -90);$ $P' = (-70, 30)$

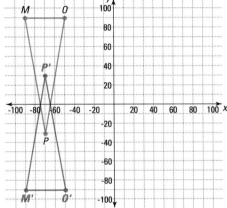

Exploration

23. In 1957, the world record in the 800-meter freestyle swimming event was about 10 min 30 sec for women and 9 min 15 sec for men. Between 1957 and 1980, these records decreased at a rate of about 4 sec/yr for women and 3 sec/yr for men.
    a. According to this information, what should the records have been in 1992? **7 min 30 sec for men; 8 min 10 sec for women**
    b. Check a book of records and see if these predictions for 1992 were true. **7 min 11.95 sec for men; 8 min 25.52 sec for women**
    c. According to this information, predict the records for the year 2000, and explain how you made your predictions. **See left.**

23c) Sample: 6 min 45 sec for men; 8 min for women. Using actual records, calculate the rate of change (-3.5 for both men and women). Use point-slope form and find an equation of a line: men: $y - 555 = -3.5 (x - 1957)$; women: $y - 630 = -3.5 (x - 1957)$. Substitute 2000 in for x and solve for y.

Lesson 3-5 *Finding an Equation of a Line* **167**

Question 21 The answer to this question can be found by *chunking*, the process of grouping small bits of information into a single piece of information. Many students will solve the equation for x and substitute that value in the expression $6x + 16$. If students recognize that $6x + 16$ is a multiple of $3x + 8$, the computation is done more quickly.
$3x + 8 = 40$
$2(3x + 8) = 2(40)$
$6x + 16 = 80$

Question 22 This question reviews reflections over a line; it will prepare students for Chapter 4.

Question 23 The time for the current women's world record in the 800-meter freestyle swimming event is far better than the time for the men's world record in the same event in the 1960s.

Additional Answers, continued
17a.
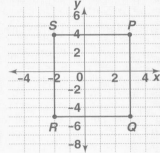

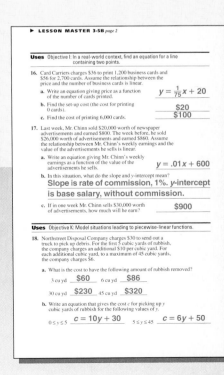

Setting Up Lesson 3-6

Have students do the In-class Activity on page 168 before they read Lesson 3-6.

Materials If you do the *Optional Activities* on page 171, students will need almanacs.

From the **Teacher's Resource File**
■ Answer Master 3-6

This activity reviews the concepts of scatterplots and "fitting a line to the data by eye," and it sets up a situation in which modeling and predicting can be used. Students who have studied UCSMP *Algebra* will have already fit a line to data.

When discussing answers to **Question 3,** students should find that the slopes of their lines are fairly close to one another (most should be between 300 and 350) and that the *y*-intercepts are between 500 and 1000.

If you have time, you may want to calculate the mean of the slopes and the mean of the *y*-intercepts from each pair of students. These means should be quite close to the values of the slope and the *y*-intercept of the regression line, which is the line of best fit. The ScottForesman software *StatExplorer* has a modeling feature that allows students to eyeball linear models by clicking on two points on the screen. Then students can ask for the line of best fit and see the differences in the sums of squares of residual values.

When you finish the activity, you may want to explain how to use linear-regression features on a calculator. Students will have to be familiar with this feature for the questions in Lesson 3-6.

Introducing Lesson 3-6

Using Linear Models to Approximate Data

IN-CLASS
ACTIVITY

Work with a partner.

Many real-world situations involve more than two pairs of measurements. These pairs can be graphed, and, although the points might not all lie on a line, it may be possible to find a line that is close to many of the points. Finding an equation for such a line is the purpose of this Activity.

The table and the graph below show the number of cars and the number of people killed in traffic accidents in ten countries in 1990.

Country	Cars (millions)	Traffic deaths
Argentina	4.3	3,054
Australia	7.7	4,210
Belgium	3.8	1,937
Bulgaria	1.3	1,409
Canada	12.6	4,210
France	23.6	10,198
Israel	0.8	439
Italy	27.3	8,717
Japan	34.9	14,398
W. Germany	30.7	7,435

Traffic Deaths and Number of Cars for Selected Nations

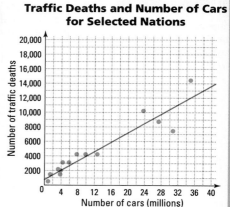

Source: U.S. Bureau of the Census,
Statistical Abstract of the United States: 1993

1 Graph the data in the table or copy the graph.

2 With your partner, draw a line on your graph that both of you agree best describes the trend in the points. This is called "fitting a line to the data by eye."
See above.

3 Estimate the coordinates of two points on your line, and use a technique discussed in Lesson 3-5 to find an equation for this line. A = (4, 2000); B = (38, 13,000); $y - 2000 = 323.5(x - 4)$ or $y = 323.5x + 706$

4 In 1990, there were about 143.5 million cars in the United States. Use the equation for the line you found in step 3 to estimate the number of traffic deaths in the United States in 1990.
Sample: ≈47,000

158

Traffic jam. *Shown is traffic that has come to a halt due to an accident on an autobahn in Germany. Autobahns, four-lane express highways in Germany, have no speed limits.*

❶ In the Activity on page 168, you were first given a **scatterplot** of discrete points. If you used the points $A = (4, 2000)$ and $B = (38, 13,000)$ to find an equation for a line close to the points in the scatterplot, then your graph would look like the one below.

Example 1

Use the line through the points $A = (4, 2000)$ and $B = (38, 13,000)$ to fit a line to the data points about number of cars and traffic deaths.

Solution

First, find its slope.

$$\text{slope} = \frac{13,000 - 2000}{38 - 4}$$

$$= \frac{11,000}{34}$$

$$\approx 323.5$$

Then, use one of the points with this slope in the point-slope form. We use $(4, 2000)$.

$$y - 2000 = 323.5(x - 4)$$

Solve for y.

$$y - 2000 = 323.5x - 1294$$
$$y = 323.5x + 706$$

An equation of the line is $y = 323.5x + 706$.

Traffic Deaths and Number of Cars for Selected Nations

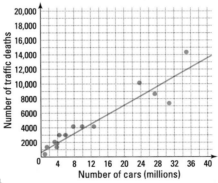

Number of traffic deaths (y-axis, 0 to 20,000)
Number of cars (millions) (x-axis, 0 to 40)

Lesson 3-6 *Fitting a Line to Data* **169**

Lesson 3-6 Overview

Broad Goals This lesson covers two methods for finding an equation for a line that roughly models a set of data. The first is to eyeball a possible line, find two points on it, and determine the equation of the line through those points. The second is to use preprogrammed software to determine the line of best fit (the least-squares line).

Perspective At least five kinds of situations lead to data that lie on or near a line. (1) The variables are precisely linearly related, as with the Fahrenheit and Celsius temperatures in Lesson 3-5. (2) The variables are *in theory* linearly related, such as the amount of weight placed on a spring and its length; in practice there will be measurement error or other factors that cause the data not to fit exactly to a line. (3) We expect the variables to be related, and we are not surprised to see a strong linear relationship, as in the situation on

page 169. (4) Two variables increase or decrease together (such as the heights of elementary school students and how much mathematics they know), but there is no particular reason for a relationship to be linear. (5) We know the variables are related non-linearly, but we are looking at such a small part of the domain that the curve appears to be straight.

(Overview continues on page 170.)

You might point out a nontrivial difference between eyeballing and finding the line of best fit. When we "eyeball," we tend to think of the distance between points and the lines using the shortest distance—the perpendicular distance between each point and the line. In contrast, the line of best fit utilizes the *vertical* distance between the point and the line, which minimizes prediction errors. Specifically, the line of best fit minimizes the sum of the squares of the vertical distances between the data points and the line. Consequently, if the variables are reversed, the eyeballed line might not change, but the line of best fit usually does change.

❸ Point out that the correlation coefficient is not the slope of the line but that its sign is the same as the sign of the slope of the line.

Additional Examples

The graph in Additional Example 1 is on **Teaching Aid 28**.

1. Use the line through the points $A = (1900, 1500)$ and $B = (2000, 2500)$ to fit a line to the data points for the population of Kansas (in thousands) for each decade year from the 1900 census through the 1990 census.
$y = 10x - 17,500$

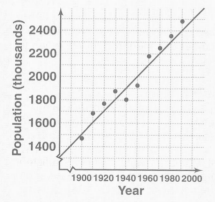

Lin Reg
$y = ax + b$
$a = 317.7984259$
$b = 929.0631395$
$r = .9351770652$

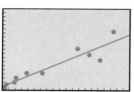

$0 \leq x \leq 40, \quad x\text{-scale} = 2$
$0 \leq y \leq 20,000, \quad y\text{-scale} = 1000$

Before. *Prior to 1986, Chicago's Lake Shore Drive (shown between the tall, white Amoco Oil Building and the black building in front) contained two right angles.*

This equation describes the relation between x and y in the data set reasonably well. The slope 323.5 tells you that for each increase of 1,000,000 in the number of cars in a country there is an increase of about 324 in the number of traffic deaths. The y-intercept 706 indicates that in a country with no cars, there would be 706 traffic deaths. Of course, this would not happen. Thus, this linear model does not apply to countries with a small number of cars.

Finding the Line of Best Fit

As you saw from the Activity, many possible equations could arise from fitting a line by eye. In fact, everybody who does the Activity could have a different, but reasonable, equation for a line through the points.

❷ Which line is the best fit for these data? Some computer software packages and most graphics calculators will find the equation of a line called the *line of best fit* or the *least squares line* or the *regression line*. Why this line is the "best" is explained in more advanced courses, but it is based on conventions that are accepted all over the world.

To find the regression line, use a calculator or computer to calculate the line of best fit. For details, check the manual or ask your teacher.

You may find that your calculator or computer displays only the slope and the y-intercept of the regression line; you must write the equation yourself. For instance, one calculator displays an equation of the regression line for the data set about traffic deaths as shown at the left. Thus, the regression equation is about $y = 317.8x + 929.1$. Notice that the slope and y-intercept of this line are close to those in Example 1.

Example 2

In 1990, there were approximately 143.5 million cars in the United States. Predict the number of traffic deaths using
a. the equation in Example 1.
b. the equation for the regression line.

Solution
a. Substitute 143.5 for x in the equation
$$y = 323.5x + 706.$$
$$y = 323.5 \cdot 143.5 + 706$$
$$y = 47,128.25$$
About 47,128 people would be predicted to die in traffic accidents if this line is accurate.
b. Substitute 143.5 for x in the equation
$$y = 317.8x + 929.1.$$
$$y = 317.8 \cdot 143.5 + 929.1$$
$$y = 46,533.4$$
About 46,533 people would have been predicted to die in traffic accidents using this model.

Lesson 3-6 Overview, continued

In this lesson, we examine an interesting data set. In **Example 1** we fit a line to the data by eyeballing and using the equation through two points. **Example 2a** uses this line to estimate one of the variables from the other, and **Example 2b** uses a regression line found by using an automatic grapher. **Example 3** shows that when a line of best fit is found with only two points, the

result is the line through the points, as one should expect.

In this course, we do not expect students to understand how the line of best fit is found. A more in-depth discussion is found in the next UCSMP book, *Functions and Statistics with Trigonometry*. Students who have studied UCSMP *Algebra* should have fit lines to

data. However, they will not be familiar with the idea of correlation coefficient and the calculation of the line of best fit.

After. *To improve traffic safety, Lake Shore Drive was curved (shown under construction on landfill in the foreground).*

The actual number of traffic deaths in the U.S. in 1990 was 46,586. The prediction using the line of best fit is very accurate in this instance.

Correlation Coefficient

Most software packages and calculators display a third number, *r*, when finding the regression line. The number *r* is called the *correlation coefficient.* The correlation coefficient is a number from -1 to 1.

③ The sign of *r* indicates the direction of the relation between the variables. If *r* is positive, the slope of the regression line is positive. If *r* is negative, the slope of the regression line is negative. For the data in Example 2, $r \approx 0.935$. Because the correlation coefficient is positive, the slope of the regression line is also positive.

The absolute value of the correlation coefficient indicates the *strength* of the linear relationship. When $|r| = 1$, there is a perfect linear relationship; the points are collinear. Such perfect correlations are rare. The closer the magnitude of *r* is to 1, the stronger the linear relationship is. A correlation coefficient of 0 or close to 0 indicates there is no linear relationship between the variables. The value of *r* for the situation in this lesson, 0.935, is close to 1. It indicates a reasonably strong linear relationship between the variables. In other words, the regression equation is a reasonably accurate model for this set of data.

The Line of Best Fit Through Two Points

Because two points determine a line, the equation of the line of best fit determined by two points will have a perfect correlation of ± 1. So, you can use a calculator or computer to find an equation for the line between two given points. Example 3 shows how this is done.

Example 3

Use linear regression to find an equation of the line through the points (-1, 5) and (2, -4).

Solution

Enter the points as data points. Then find the equation of the regression line. Our graphics calculator gives
$$y = -3x + 2$$
with $r = -1$.

Check

Substitute each ordered pair into this equation to see if the ordered pair satisfies the equation. For instance, if $x = -1$, then $y = -3 \cdot -1 + 2 = 3 + 2 = 5$, which checks. If $x = 2$, then $y = -3 \cdot 2 + 2 = -4$, which checks.

Notice that the correlation coefficient in Example 3 is -1. This was to be expected; this is a perfect linear fit, and the slope of the line is negative.

Lesson 3-6 *Fitting a Line to Data* **171**

2. Predict the population of Kansas in the year 2025 using
   a. the equation in Question 1. **2,750,000**
   b. the equation for the regression line. **$y = 10.4x - 18,274$; 2,786,000**
3. Use linear regression to find an equation of the line through the points (0, 32) and (100, 212). **$y = 1.8x + 32$ (Note a correlation of 1, which agrees with the equation found in Lesson 3-5.)**

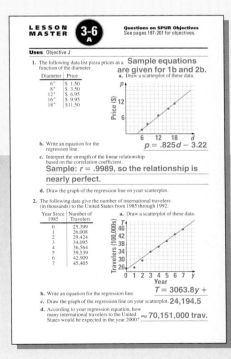

Optional Activities

Activity 1 Geography Connection
Materials: Graph paper or **Teaching Aid 8,** almanac

After discussing the lesson, you might have students **work in groups** to find population data for a period of at least 100 years for a city, state, or country of their choosing. Have them make graphs, find lines of best fit, and project future populations.

Discuss the data, noting whether the population is increasing, decreasing, or remaining relatively constant.

Activity 2 Technology Connection
In *Technology Sourcebook, Computer Master 3,* students use a statistical package to draw a scatterplot, calculate, and graph the line of best fit.

Follow-up for Lesson 3-6

Practice

For more questions on SPUR Objectives, use **Lesson Master 3-6A** (shown on page 171) or **Lesson Master 3-6B** (shown on pages 172–173).

Assessment

Quiz A quiz covering Lessons 3-4 through 3-6 is provided in the *Assessment Sourcebook*.

Written Communication Have each student write a paragraph to describe how finding the line of best fit by using an automatic grapher is different from the method in **Example 1**. [Students demonstrate that they know how to find the line of best fit by using an automatic grapher, as well as by using the Point-Slope Theorem.]

Extension

Have students write a recursive formula for finding the sum of the measures of the interior angles of a convex n-gon. [$S_3 = 180$; $S_n = S_{n-1} + 180$, for integers $n \geq 4$]

Project Update Project 4, *Time-Series Data*, on page 193, relates to the content of this lesson.

Covering the Reading

1. Refer to the scatterplot in the Activity on page 168. What does the ordered pair (34.9, 14,398) signify? **In Japan in 1990, there were 34.9 million cars and 14,398 traffic deaths.**
2. Briefly describe two ways to fit a line to data. **Find the regression line; fit a line by sight.**
3. Refer to the graph in Example 1.
   a. How many data points are above the line determined by the equation $y = 323.5x + 706$? **8**
   b. How many data points are below this line? **5**

In 4–7, use the given equation to estimate the number of traffic deaths in a country where there are 50 million cars.

4. your equation from the In-class Activity on page 168 **Answers will vary.**
5. the equation $y = 323.5x + 706$ of Example 1 **16,881**
6. the equation $y = 317.8x + 929.1$ of the regression line from the lesson **16,819**
7. *Multiple choice.* Which seems to be the most reasonable domain for x in the regression equation $y = 317.8x + 929.1$? **d**
   (a) the set of all real numbers
   (b) $\{x: 0 \leq x \leq 40\}$
   (c) $\{x: 0.5 \leq x \leq 40\}$
   (d) $\{x: x \geq 0.5\}$

8) The absolute value of the correlation coefficient indicates the strength of the linear relationship; if $|r| = 1$, there is a perfect correlation. The sign of the correlation coefficient indicates the direction of the relationship. If r is positive, then the slope is positive. If r is negative, then the slope is negative.

8. Explain what the correlation coefficient measures. **See left.**
9. *True or false.* The correlation coefficient of a set of data points is the same as the slope of the equation of the regression line. **False**
10. What does a correlation coefficient of 0 indicate? **There is no linear relationship between the variables.**

In 11 and 12, refer to the owner's manual or other documentation for your technology.

11. What is the *line of best fit* called on your calculator or computer? **Sample: Lin Reg ($ax + b$)**
12. Does your technology give an equation for the line of best fit or merely the slope and y-intercept? **Answers may vary.**
13. a. Use the regression line to find an equation of the line through the points (6, 7) and (-2, 13). **$y = -0.75x + 11.5$**
    b. Find the value of the correlation coefficient, and explain what it indicates about the equation you just formed. **-1; there is a perfect linear fit since two points determine a line.**

172

Lesson Master 3-6B

LESSON MASTER 3-6 B Questions on SPUR Objectives

Vocabulary

1. a. What is the range of r, the *correlation coefficient* for a set of data? **$-1 \leq r \leq 1$**
   b. Suppose $r = -0.9$ for a line fit to a set of data. What does this tell you about the strength of the linear relationship between the variables? **Sample: There is a strong linear relationship.**

Uses Objective J: Fit lines to data.

2. The following data give the number of city-council members in six cities with various populations. **Sample equation is given for b.**

Population	45,000	16,000	320,000	108,000	61,000	176,000
City-Council Members	8	7	24	19	12	15

a. Draw a scatterplot of the data.
b. Find an equation of the regression line. **$y = .000052x + 7.9$**
c. Graph the regression line on your scatterplot.
d. Use your equation to predict the numbers of city-council members in a city with a population of 250,000. **≈ 21 members**
e. Interpret the strength of the linear relationship based on the correlation coefficient. **Sample: It is reasonably strong, since $r \approx .89$.**

Adapting to Individual Needs

Extra Help
When students are asked to determine the line of best fit by eyeballing, stress that more than one line is possible. Generally, however, the slopes of the lines should be approximately equal, as should the y-intercepts as well. This will not be readily apparent unless the equations are written in slope-intercept form.

English Language Development
To help students remember the term *scatterplot,* arrange some pennies in a row; then scatter them. Explain that in the first case, the pennies are in a particular order. In the second case they are not in any order. Then compare this with plotting points that satisfy a linear equation to get a line and plotting the data points in the table on page 168 to get scattered points or a scatterplot.

In 14 and 15, use the figure at the right. It shows the line of best fit for survey data of the scores on a test and the number of hours spent studying for that test. An equation for the line is $y = 3.510x + 51.642$, and $r = 0.89$.

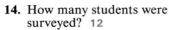

14. How many students were surveyed? **12**

15. Consider the student who studied ten hours.
  a. What did this student score on the test? **≈92**
  b. What test score was predicted by the regression equation? **≈86.7**

In 16–19, multiple choice. What is the best description of the relation between the variables in the scatterplot?
(a) strong negative correlation
(b) weak positive correlation
(c) strong positive correlation
(d) correlation approximately 0

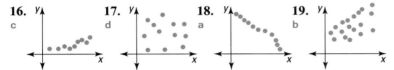

16. c **17.** d **18.** a **19.** b

20. The average weight in kilograms for girls of various ages in the United States is given below.

20a, g)

age in years	.5	1	2	3	4	6	8	10
weight in kg	7.2	9.1	11.3	13.6	15	20.4	25.4	31.3

  a. Draw a scatterplot of these data or print a hard copy from your technology. **See left.**
  b. Find an equation of the regression line. **about $y = 2.45x + 6.08$**
  c. What is the unit for the slope of the regression line? **kg/yr**
  d. Write a sentence about the meaning of the y-intercept in this situation. **the average weight of newborn girls is 6.08 kg.**
  e. Find the correlation coefficient. **≈0.998**
  f. What does the correlation coefficient suggest about the relationship between the variables? **They have an almost perfect linear relationship.**
  g. Draw the graph of the regression line on your scatterplot. **See left.**
  h. Use your equation for the regression line to predict the average weight of a seven-year-old girl. **≈23.2 kg**
  i. Over what domain do you expect the regression equation to be a good model for the relation between the age and weight of a female in the United States? Explain your reasoning. **Sample domain: {x: 0 ≤ x ≤ 20} After adolescence, most girls do not continue to grow at the same rate.**

Lesson 3-6 *Fitting a Line to Data* **173**

Notes on Questions

Questions 16–19 The graphs for these questions appear on **Teaching Aid 29**.

Question 20 Health Connection
Being overweight can be harmful to your health, but dieting can also be dangerous. To reach and maintain healthy weight levels, the Dietary Guidelines for Americans recommend a diet that is high in carbohydrates and low in fat, sugar, and sodium. The Guidelines also recommend eating foods that provide adequate levels of vitamins, minerals, and fiber. Those who love sweet, rich foods are advised to aim for moderation; while foods such as soft drinks, candies, and desserts do not have to be eliminated entirely, they should be eaten sparingly.

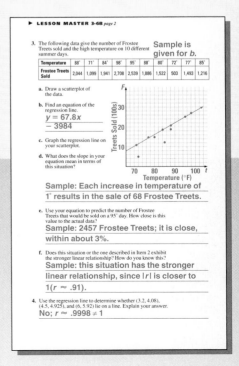

Question 21 This shows an alternate way to find the formula for the sum of the measures of the interior angles of a convex n-gon.

Question 22 Some students may do this question using point-slope; some may use the regression line. You may want to compare methods.

Question 27 This question helps set up the step functions that are presented in Lesson 3-9.

Question 28 The property in **part c** of this question is true for all data sets.

Review

21. The sum of the measures of the angles of a triangle is 180°. In a convex quadrilateral the sum is 360°. Let n be the number of sides in a convex polygon and S be the sum of its angle measures. Use these two points to find an equation relating n and S, assuming there is a linear relationship. Let S be the dependent variable. *(Lesson 3-5)* $S - 180 = 180(n - 3)$

22. Find an equation of the line whose graph is shown below. *(Lesson 3-5)* Sample: $y - 3 = \frac{-9}{20}(x - 5)$ or $y = -0.45x + 5.25$

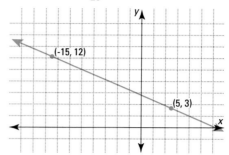

23. Graph f when $f(x) = \begin{cases} -8, & \text{for } x < 1 \\ -8x, & \text{for } x \geq 1. \end{cases}$ *(Lessons 3-2, 3-5)* See left.

24. Graph $90x - 75y = 4500$. *(Lesson 3-4)* See left.

25. Suppose x ounces of a 40% acid solution are mixed with y ounces of a 20% acid solution, and the result contains 10 ounces of acid. *(Lesson 3-3)* a) $.4x + .2y = 10$
   a. Write an equation relating x, y, and the total ounces of acid.
   b. How many ounces of the 40% acid solution must be mixed with 5.1 ounces of the 20% acid solution to get 10 ounces of acid? 22.45 oz

26. Consider the sequence defined as follows. *(Lesson 1-9)*
   $\begin{cases} t_1 = 20 \\ t_n = t_{n-1} - 3, \text{ for integers } n \geq 2 \end{cases}$
   a. Write the first four terms of the sequence. 20, 17, 14, 11
   b. If $t_{12} = -13$, what does t_{13} equal? -16

27. It costs $1.25 to park for up to an hour in a hospital parking lot plus $.75 for each additional half hour or fraction thereof. How much does it cost to park in this lot for 4 hours and 15 minutes? *(Previous course)* $6.50

Exploration

b) $\bar{y} = 5600.7$

28. Refer to the regression line given in this lesson.
   a. Find the average of the x-values of the data. Call it $\bar{x}$. $\bar{x} = 14.7$
   b. Find the average of the y-values of the same data. Call it $\bar{y}$.
   c. $(\bar{x}, \bar{y})$ is called the *center of gravity* of this data set. Verify that the center of gravity is on the regression line.
   Does 5600.7 = 317.8 (14.7) + 929.1? Yes, 5600.7 is very close to 5600.76.

23)

24)

174

Video

Wide World of Mathematics
The segment, *Iron Kids,* features triathletes aged seven to 14 years in the Iron Kids Triathlon. The segment provides motivation for an introductory lesson on linear combinations. Related questions and an investigation are provided in videodisc stills and in the Video Guide. A related CD-ROM activity is also available.

Videodisc Bar Codes

Search Chapter 14

Play

Setting Up Lesson 3-7

Question 26 will help students review recursive sequences in preparation for the next lesson.

Materials If you do Activity 1 of the *Optional Activities* on page 176, you will need a computer spreadsheet program.

Mechanically inclined. *Auto mechanics receive training from experienced mechanics, factory service instructors, or formal schools.*

What Is an Arithmetic Sequence?

If you buy a new car, you may be advised to have an oil change after driving 1000 miles and then every 3000 miles thereafter. Then the following sequence gives the mileage when oil changes are required:

$$1000, 4000, 7000, 10,000, 13,000, 16,000, \ldots$$

This is a constant-increase situation. There is a constant difference of 3000 between successive terms. A sequence with a *constant difference* between successive terms is called an **arithmetic sequence.** (Here the word *arithmetic* is used as an adjective; it is pronounced *arith<u>me</u>tic*.)

A recursive formula for the sequence above is

$$\begin{cases} a_1 = 1000 \\ a_n = a_{n-1} + 3000, \text{ for integers } n \geq 2. \end{cases}$$

The second line of this formula can be rewritten as

$$a_n - a_{n-1} = 3000.$$

This shows that the difference between the *n*th term and the $(n-1)$st term is a constant. So this recursive formula defines an arithmetic sequence.

This result can be generalized.

Theorem

The sequence defined by the recursive formula

$$\begin{cases} a_1 \\ a_n = a_{n-1} + d, \text{ for integers } n \geq 2 \end{cases}$$

is the arithmetic sequence with first term a_1 and constant difference *d*.

Proof:
When $n \geq 2$, we can rewrite the second line as $a_n - a_{n-1} = d$. This means that the difference between consecutive terms is the constant *d*. By definition, the sequence is arithmetic.

Lesson 3-7 *Recursive Formulas for Arithmetic Sequences* **175**

Lesson 3-7 Overview

Broad Goals This lesson presents a detailed explanation of a specific example of a recursive formula for sequences—namely, the recursive formula for arithmetic sequences—and connects it with the slopes and intercepts of earlier lessons in the chapter.

Perspective *Arithmetic sequence, arithmetic progression,* and *linear sequence* are synonyms. Each phrase refers to a

sequence in which consecutive terms differ by a constant *d.* The synonym *arithmetic progression*—which is no longer extensively used—suggests that each term is found from the preceding term. *Arithmetic sequence* uses the term "arithmetic" but connects the term to the more general idea of sequence. *Linear sequence* is the most descriptive of the three terms. (A corresponding triumvirate of names with the same properties appears in Chapter 8:

geometric sequence, geometric progression, and *exponential sequence.*) The formula defined by the theorem on page 175 is one of the simplest recursive formulas. In many respects, recursive formulas for arithmetic sequences are more natural than explicit ones. When given an explicit formula for an arithmetic sequence, the recursive formula can be determined, and vice versa.

(Overview continues on page 176.)

Reading Mathematics It is often helpful to have students translate a recursive formula into words. For the arithmetic sequence $a_1 = -5$, $a_n = a_{n-1} + 3$, the translation is, "The first term is –5. To get the nth term in the sequence, add 3 to the previous term." A translation of the general formula is, "The first term is a_1; all other terms of the sequence are found by adding d to the previous term."

You might note the various ways in which arithmetic sequences are presented in this lesson: in words (the example at the beginning of the lesson and **Example 2**), with a formula (**Example 1**), with a graph (as shown on the bottom of page 176), and with a computer program or a graphics-calculator program (as shown on page 177). Students understand this lesson if they can move from any one of these presentations to any other.

❶ **Social Studies Connection** In 1990, people in the United States traveled an estimated 3.7 trillion intercity miles. Of this number, certified airlines accounted for 358 billion miles or about 10%. The average airplane trip was 829 miles, and the average one-way passenger fare by plane was $107.86. Between 1980 and 1990, travel fares doubled for all modes of transportation except air travel; during that time air fares rose only 28%.

An eyeful. *The Eiffel Tower, designed by Gustave Eiffel for the 1889 World's Fair in Paris, rises 300 meters. The tower has restaurants, a weather station, and is used to transmit television programs.*

Example 1

Consider the sequence generated by
$$\begin{cases} a_1 = 2000 \\ a_n = a_{n-1} + 40, \text{ for integers } n \geq 2. \end{cases}$$
a. Describe this sequence in words.
b. Write the first five terms of the sequence.

Solution

a. **This is an arithmetic sequence with first term 2000 and constant difference 40.** A constant difference of 40 means that each term is 40 more than the previous term.
b. To generate terms after the first, add 40 to the previous term. **The first five terms are 2000, 2040, 2080, 2120, 2160.**

The constant difference of an arithmetic sequence can also be negative.

❶ ### Example 2

Briana borrowed $370 from her parents for airfare to Europe. She will pay them back at the rate of $30 per month. Let a_n be the amount she still owes after n months. Find a recursive formula for this sequence.

Solution

After 1 month she owes $340, so $a_1 = \$340$. Each month she pays back $30, so the difference between successive terms is $d = -30$. A recursive formula for this sequence is

$$\begin{cases} a_1 = 340 \\ a_n = a_{n-1} - 30, \text{ for integers } n \geq 2. \end{cases}$$

Examples 1 and 2 illustrate that, in a recursive formula for an arithmetic sequence, the initial condition is the first term; the constant increase or decrease is the constant difference.

Graphs of Arithmetic Sequences

Because an arithmetic sequence represents a constant-increase or constant-decrease situation, its graph is a set of collinear points. Here is the graph of the sequence that began this lesson.

n	a_n
1	1000
2	4000
3	7000
4	10,000
5	13,000
⋮	⋮

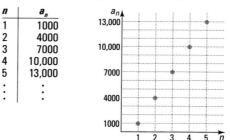

$$\begin{cases} a_1 = 1000 \\ a_n = a_{n-1} + 3000, \\ \text{for integers } n \geq 2 \end{cases}$$

For this reason, arithmetic sequences are also called **linear sequences.**

Lesson 3-7 Overview, continued

Recursive formulas for sequences are used in computer programming more often than explicit formulas are. This concept also underlies the idea of proof by mathematical induction. **Example 1** asks students to interpret an arithmetic sequence defined recursively. In **Example 2,** a situation that leads to a sequence is given, and an example is graphed. Then a description with a computer program is given side by side with a program written for a graphics calculator.

Because graphics calculators have different programming languages and features, you may have to spend some time going through this material. However, keep in mind that the focus of this lesson is on recursive formulas and not on programming.

When the recursive formula is thought of as defining a linear function, $a_n = a_{n-1} + d$, the slope of its graph is d, and the y-intercept (if the graph were continued) is $a_1 - d$.

Optional Activities

Activity 1 Technology Connection
Materials: Computer spreadsheet program

Recursive definitions are also appropriate for use with spreadsheets. For example, have students put 1 in A1 and $= A1 + 1$ in A2. Then put a value for a_1 in B1 and $= B1 + d$ in B2. Copy the A and B columns down as many times as necessary.

❷ Generating Sequences Recursively Using Programs

Calculator and computer programs can generate arithmetic sequences using recursive formulas. The following programs generate the first six terms of the sequence graphed on page 176. The program on the right below is for a graphics calculator; the one on the left is in the BASIC computer language.

```
BASIC
10 LET A = 1000
20 FOR N = 1 TO 6
30 PRINT A          } loop
40 A = A + 3000
50 NEXT N
60 END
```

```
CALCULATOR
: 1000→A
: For(N,1,6)
: Disp A        } loop
: A + 3000→A
: End
```

The first line of each program defines the first term of the sequence and stores it in a memory location called A. Each program contains a *loop*. The For line tells the calculator or computer to execute the commands six times. Disp A tells the calculator to display the current value of A on the screen. PRINT A tells the computer to print the current value of A. The line A = A + 3000 tells the computer to add 3000 to the previous term and store the result in A. Both programs produce the output below.

```
1000
4000
7000
10000
13000
16000
```

These are the same six terms generated in the opening paragraph of this lesson.

2) An arithmetic sequence represents a constant-increase or constant-decrease situation, so its graph is a set of collinear points.

3b)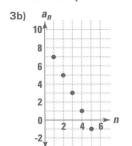

QUESTIONS

Covering the Reading

1. Give a recursive formula for the arithmetic sequence with first term a_1 and constant difference d. $\begin{cases} a_1 = a_1 \\ a_n = a_{n-1} + d \text{ for integers } n \geq 2 \end{cases}$

2. Explain why arithmetic sequences are sometimes called linear sequences. **See left.**

3. Consider the sequence $\begin{cases} a_1 = 7 \\ a_n = a_{n-1} - 2, \text{ for integers } n \geq 2. \end{cases}$
   a. Find the first five terms of the sequence. **7, 5, 3, 1, -1**
   b. Graph the sequence. **See left.**
   c. The points from your graph in part **b** should lie on a line. What is the slope of this line? **-2**

Lesson 3-7 *Recursive Formulas for Arithmetic Sequences* **177**

---

❷ The calculator program used by the Texas Instruments TI-82 is used here. Note the parallel construction of the TI-82 and BASIC programs. This is not the case with all graphics-calculator programs. For instance, some older graphics calculators do not have FOR . . . NEXT or FOR . . . END loops. If students have TI-81 or TI-82 calculators, they can also graph and generate sequences using the DOT mode.

Additional Examples

1. Consider the sequence generated by

$$\begin{cases} a_1 = 53 \\ a_n = a_{n-1} - 7 \\ \qquad \text{for integers } n \geq 2. \end{cases}$$

   a. Describe this sequence in words. **Sample: This is an arithmetic sequence with first term 53 and constant difference -7.**
   b. Write the first five terms of the sequence. **53, 46, 39, 32, 25**

(Additional Examples continue on page 178.)

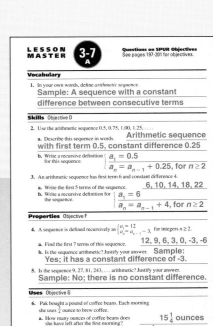

Adapting to Individual Needs

After students complete this lesson, you might have them generate each of the sequences in the lesson in a different column on a spreadsheet.

Activity 2
You might want to use *Activity Kit, Activity 6,* as a follow-up to this lesson. In this activity, students measure the angles in stars to generate an arithmetic sequence.

Extra Help
Some students are confused by the fact that the difference *d* in an arithmetic sequence is sometimes positive and sometimes negative. Point out that *d* is always determined by subtracting the $(n-1)$st term from the *n*th term. If each succeeding term in the sequence is smaller than the preceding one, then the difference *d* will be negative.

2. Due to an increasing population, the town of Valley Heights is concerned about its water supply. The town council has voted to immediately add 20,000 acre-feet of water to its reservoir capacity of 3 million acre-feet and to add an additional 20,000 acre-feet of water each year. Write a recursive formula to express the capacity of the reservoir in n years.

$$\begin{cases} a_1 = 3{,}020{,}000 \\ a_n = a_{n-1} + 20{,}000, \\ \qquad \text{for integers } n \geq 2 \end{cases}$$

Notes on Questions

Question 11 Since this question lends itself to a variety of problem-solving strategies, ask students to tell how they solved this problem.

Questions 13–14 Some students may write programs that use explicit formulas. This is acceptable, and their programs can be used to introduce the next lesson.

Question 22 If students find one other positive integer that satisfies the conditions, they should be commended. Students are usually surprised to find that all the numbers that satisfy these conditions can form an arithmetic sequence.

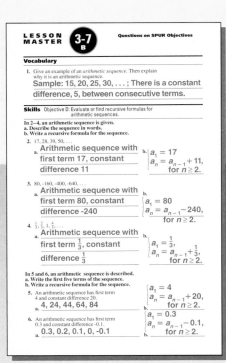

7a) Sample:
```
10 LET A = 1
20 FOR N = 1 to 25
30 PRINT A
40 A = A + 6
50 NEXT N
60 END
```

9) $\begin{cases} a_1 = 13 \\ a_n = a_{n-1} + 6, \text{ for} \\ \qquad \text{integers } n \geq 2 \end{cases}$

10a) $\begin{cases} a_1 = 400 \\ a_n = a_{n-1} + 400, \text{ for} \\ \qquad \text{integers } n \geq 2 \end{cases}$

12) 625
640
655
670
685
700
715
730
745
760
775
790
805
820
835

178

---

4. What is the relation between the slope of the graph of an arithmetic sequence and the constant difference of the sequence? They are equal.

5. Refer to Example 2. How much money will Briana owe her parents after 10 months? **$70**

In 6 and 7, refer to the sequence $\begin{cases} a_1 = 1 \\ a_n = a_{n-1} + 6, \text{ for integers } n \geq 2. \end{cases}$

6. Write the first four terms of this sequence. 1, 7, 13, 19

7. a. Write a calculator or computer program to generate the first 25 terms of this sequence. See left.
b. Run the program and identify the 25th term. 145

Applying the Mathematics

8. *Multiple choice.* Which sequence is *not* an arithmetic sequence?
(a) 5, 9, 13, 17, . . . (b) 3, 6, 12, 24, . . . b
(c) $\frac{1}{2}$, 1, $\frac{3}{2}$, 2, $\frac{5}{2}$, . . . (d) 0, -1, -2, -3, -4, . . .

9. Write a recursive formula for the arithmetic sequence 13, 19, 25, 31, ... See left.

10. Mr. Jefferson has a tax-sheltered annuity in which he is saving money for retirement. He deposits $400 a month into the account. Suppose he started with a zero balance.
a. Write a recursive formula for the total amount he has deposited after each month. See left.
b. How much has he deposited after 5 months? **$2000**

11. In a set of steps leading to a ship, the third step is 52 inches above the water and the fifth step is 63 inches above the water. Assuming all steps have equal rise, how far is the ninth step above the water? 85 in.

12. What will the following BASIC program print when run? See left.

```
10 LET A = 625
20 FOR N = 1 TO 15
30 PRINT A
40 A = A + 15
50 NEXT N
60 END
```

In 13 and 14, write a calculator or computer program to generate:
See margin.
13. the first 1000 positive odd numbers.

14. the first 500 positive multiples of 11.

Adapting to Individual Needs

English Language Development
Be sure students are aware of the two pronunciations of *arithmetic*. In the sentence "Children study arithmetic in grade school," the accent is on the second syllable. In the sentence "We are studying arithmetic sequences in this lesson," the accent is on the third syllable.

Challenge
The 11th term of an arithmetic sequence is 100 and the 15th term is 125. What is the 13th term of the sequence? [112.5]

year after 1900	reported number of child abuse cases (in millions)
76	.67
78	.80
80	1.15
82	1.22
84	1.65
86	2.05
88	2.20
90	2.55
92	2.86
93	2.99

15a, c)

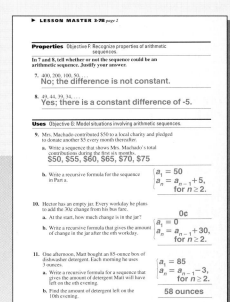

number of cases (millions)

year after 1900

f) Sample: better reporting of child-abuse cases; increased awareness of the problem of child abuse

Review

15. The table at the left shows the number of cases of child abuse from 1976 to 1993 as reported by the National Committee for the Prevention of Child Abuse.
    a. Make a scatterplot of these data. **See left.**
    b. Find an equation for the line of best fit. **about $y = .14x - 10.25$**
    c. Draw the regression line on the scatterplot. **See left.**
    d. Use the regression equation to predict the number of child abuse cases reported in the year 1990. **≈2.35 million**
    e. Use the regression equation to predict the number of child abuse cases that will be reported in the year 2002. **≈4.03 million**
    f. Describe at least two factors that might cause your estimate in part **e** to be too high. *(Lesson 3-6)* **See left.**

16. Find an equation for the line which passes through (75, 90) and is parallel to the line with equation $y = -.4x - 20$. *(Lessons 3-2, 3-5)*
    $y - 90 = -.4(x - 75)$

17. How are lines ℓ and m with the equations below related?
    ℓ: $3x + 4y = 12$
    m: $y = -\frac{3}{4}x + 3$
    Justify your answer. *(Lessons 3-2, 3-4)*
    They are identical; both lines have slope -3/4 and y-intercept 3.

18. Suppose z varies jointly as x and y. If z is 25 when x is 40 and y is 60, find z when x is 15 and y is 75. *(Lesson 2-9)* **$z = \frac{375}{32} \approx 11.72$**

19. The number n of square tiles needed to cover a floor varies inversely as the square of the length s of a side of a tile. How is the number of tiles affected if the length of a side of a tile is doubled? *(Lesson 2-3)* **The number of tiles needed is divided by 4.**

20. The function A defined by $A(e) = 6e^2$ gives the surface area of a cube with edge length e. Find $A(4.2)$. *(Lesson 1-3)* **$A(4.2) = 105.84$ units^2**

21. Match each inequality to its graph. *(Previous course)*
    a. $-2 < x < 5$ iv (i)
    b. $-2 \le x < 5$ ii (ii)
    c. $-2 < x \le 5$ iii (iii)
    d. $-2 \le x \le 5$ i (iv)

Exploration

22. Describe all the positive integers that meet all three of these conditions at the same time:
    a. They leave a remainder of 1 when divided by 2.
    b. They leave a remainder of 3 when divided by 4.
    c. They leave a remainder of 5 when divided by 6.
    (Hint: 35 is one such number.)
    $\begin{cases} a_1 = 11 \\ a_n = a_{n-1} + 12, \text{ for integers } n \ge 2 \end{cases}$

Lesson 3-7 *Recursive Formulas for Arithmetic Sequences* **179**

Follow-up for Lesson 3-7

Practice

For more questions on SPUR Objectives, use **Lesson Master 3-7A** (shown on page 177) or **Lesson Master 3-7B** (shown on pages 178–179).

Assessment

Oral Communication Ask students to explain how they would determine whether a list of numbers is an arithmetic sequence. [Students should discuss the constant difference between successive terms of an arithmetic sequence.]

Extension

History Connection Answers to questions such as those in **Question 22** involve the Chinese Remainder Theorem—an algorithm discovered in ancient China. Give students the following example of the theorem from a manuscript called *Sunzi suanjing (Master Sun's Mathematical Manual),* and have them find the answer.

We have things of which we do not know the number; if we count them by threes, the remainder is 2; if we count them by fives, the remainder is 3; if we count them by sevens, the remainder is 2. How many things are there? [23]

Additional Answers

13. 10 LET A = 1
    20 FOR N = 1 TO 1000
    30 PRINT A
    40 A = A + 2
    50 NEXT N
    60 END

14. : 11 → A
    : For (N, 1, 500)
    : DISP A
    : A + 11 → A
    : END

Objectives

D Evaluate or find explicit formulas for arithmetic sequences.
F Recognize properties of arithmetic sequences.
G Model situations involving arithmetic sequences.

Resources

From the *Teacher's Resource File*
■ Lesson Master 3-8A or 3-8B
■ Answer Master 3-8
■ Teaching Aid 25: Warm-up

Additional Resource
■ Visual for Teaching Aid 25

Teaching Lesson **3-8**

Warm-up

The top row of a canned-goods display in a grocery store contains 8 cans. Each subsequent row has 1 more can than the row above it. If the display has 40 rows of canned goods, how many cans are in the bottom row? **47 cans**

Notes on Reading

❶ Students should not assume a given sequence is arithmetic unless they are given a formula or they are told that it is. For example, the sequence 3, 5, 7, . . . is most frequently continued by students with the terms 9, 11, 13, 15, and so on. Yet 3, 5, 7, . . . could also mean the sequence of odd prime numbers, which is not an arithmetic sequence.

LESSON

3-8

Explicit Formulas for Arithmetic Sequences

Consider again the sequence from Lesson 3-7 that gives the mileage when oil changes are required:

$$1000, 4000, 7000, 10{,}000, 13{,}000, 16{,}000, \ldots$$

It has the recursive formula

$$\begin{cases} a_1 = 1000 \\ a_n = a_{n-1} + 3000, \text{ for integers } n \geq 2. \end{cases}$$

Suppose you wanted the 50th term of the sequence. To use the recursive formula, you would need to find the first 49 terms. This is rather inefficient. It would be much easier to find the 50th term if you had an *explicit* formula for the sequence. The next example shows how an explicit formula can be found.

Developing an Explicit Formula for an Arithmetic Sequence

❶ **Example 1**

a. Find an explicit formula for the arithmetic sequence of oil-change mileages 1000, 4000, 7000, 10,000, 13,000, 16,000, ...
b. Find a_{50} and tell what it represents.

Solution 1

a. To develop an explicit formula, use the constant difference of 3000 to write each term after the first. Consider the pattern in this table.

number of term	term
1	1000
2	$1000 + 1 \cdot 3000 = 4000$
3	$1000 + 2 \cdot 3000 = 7000$
4	$1000 + 3 \cdot 3000 = 10{,}000$
5	$1000 + 4 \cdot 3000 = 13{,}000$
⋮	⋮
n	$1000 + (n - 1) \cdot 3000$

So, an explicit formula for the sequence is
$$a_n = 1000 + (n - 1) \cdot 3000$$
or
$$a_n = 3000n - 2000.$$

❷ **Solution 2**

a. The sequence can be thought of as (1, 1000), (2, 4000), (3, 7000), and so on. These points lie on a line with slope 3000. Use this slope and (1, 1000) in the point-slope form.
$$y - 1000 = 3000(x - 1)$$
Substitute. $\quad a_n - 1000 = 3000(n - 1)$
Solve for a_n. $\quad a_n = 1000 + 3000(n - 1) = 3000n - 2000$

▶

Lesson 3-8 Overview

Broad Goals This lesson provides students with a method for finding an explicit formula for an arithmetic sequence defined by a recursive formula. It also emphasizes the relationship between explicit formulas for arithmetic sequences and the slope and y-intercept of linear equations.

Perspective Everything students have learned for lines is analogous for linear sequences. For instance, just as it is

possible to find the equation of a line through two points, it is also possible to find a formula for a linear sequence given any two of its terms. Similarly, just as it is possible to find the equation of a line given one point and its slope, so is it possible to find a formula for a linear sequence given one term and its constant difference. Thus, this lesson provides a chance to review Lessons 3-1 and 3-2 by applying the slope-intercept form to sequences.

Specifically, by restricting the domain to natural numbers, the equation $y = mx + b$ can generate arithmetic sequences. Because the domains have been restricted, we use n for x, a_n for y, and d for constant difference (in place of the slope m). The argument used in this lesson proves that the nth term of an arithmetic sequence satisfies $a_n = d(n - 1) + a_1$, or $a_n = dn + a_1 - d$.

b. a_{50} is the 50th term. Substitute 50 for n.
$$a_{50} = 3000\,(50) - 2000$$
$$a_{50} = 148{,}000$$
If you kept the car long enough, the car would need its 50th oil change at 148,000 miles.

Example 1 suggests the following theorem.

Theorem (nth Term of an Arithmetic Sequence)
The nth term a_n of an arithmetic sequence with first term a_1 and constant difference d is given by the explicit formula
$$a_n = a_1 + (n - 1)d.$$

Proof:
Each term of the arithmetic sequence is of the form $(x, y) = (n, a_n)$. The first term is the ordered pair $(1, a_1)$. The slope is the constant difference which we call d. Use these values in the point-slope form of a linear equation.

$$y - y_1 = m(x - x_1)$$
$$a_n - a_1 = d(n - 1)$$
Solve for a_n. $\quad a_n = a_1 + (n - 1)d$

Example 2

Find the 40th term of the arithmetic sequence 100, 97, 94, 91, ...

Solution 1

The first term $a_1 = 100$, and the constant difference $d = -3$. So $a_n = 100 + (n - 1) \cdot -3$. Because the 40th term is to be found, substitute $n = 40$ into the formula of the theorem:
$$a_{40} = 100 + (40 - 1) \cdot -3 = 100 + 39 \cdot -3 = -17.$$
The 40th term is -17.

Solution 2

The arithmetic sequence with first term equal to 100 and constant difference equal to -3 can be described recursively as follows.
$$\begin{cases} a_1 = 100 \\ a_n = a_{n-1} - 3 \end{cases}$$
Write a program to generate the first 40 terms of this sequence. When you run the program, you will see that the last term is -17.

You should be able to translate from a recursive to an explicit formula for an arithmetic sequence, and vice versa. To go from recursive to explicit form, use the method of Example 1, or substitute the known values of a and d into the result of the theorem above. To go from explicit to recursive form, you should substitute the known values of a and d into the recursive pattern for an arithmetic sequence, as in the check to Example 2.

Lesson 3-8 *Explicit Formulas for Arithmetic Sequences* **181**

---

❷ Discuss the relationship between b in the equation $y = mx + b$ and a_1 in the equation $a_n = a_1 + d(n - 1)$. Stress that the first term of an arithmetic sequence is a_1 and that b is the term which immediately precedes the first term. In the arithmetic sequence 12, 15, 18, 21, . . . , $a_1 = 12$ and $b = 9$. Since b represents the y-intercept, when x is 0, we say that b represents the *zeroth* term in a sequence.

❸ **Error Alert** Students sometimes make the mistake of forgetting to multiply through by the negative number in a formula for a sequence that is decreasing. You may want to show several examples in which $d < 0$. Also, students sometimes start with an inappropriate formula when asked to find a formula for a_n, given terms other than the first term. If the fifth term is given, they might write $a_n = a_5 + (n - 5)d$. Encourage students to check their formulas by substituting known values.

Optional Activities

This activity is similar to the *Extension* in Lesson 1-8. You can use it after students have completed the lesson. Explain that each figure at the right is formed by a series of regular polygons and that the perimeters of the figures form an arithmetic sequence. Tell students to assume that the length of each side of each polygon is 1 and have them find a_n for each sequence. Then have them find the 25th term of the sequence.

1. △ ▽ ▽△
$[a_n = 3 + (n - 1) \cdot 1 = 2 + n;\ 27]$

2. ▢ ▢▢ ▢▢▢
$[a_n = 4 + (n - 1) \cdot 2 = 2 + 2n;\ 52]$

3. ⬠ ⬠⬠ ⬠⬠⬠
$[a_n = 5 + (n - 1) \cdot 3 = 2 + 3n;\ 77]$

4. ⬡ ⬡⬡ ⬡⬡⬡
$[a_n = 6 + (n - 1) \cdot 4 = 2 + 4n;\ 102]$

Now ask students to find a formula for the nth term of a similar series of figures formed by regular k-gons.
$[a_n = k + (n - 1) \cdot (k - 2) = 2 + (k - 2)n]$

Pictured is the Rialto Square Theater in Joliet, Illinois.

④ A recursive formula for this sequence is easy to find: $a_1 = 20$; $a_n = a_{n-1} + 2$ for $n \geq 2$. But this formula does not answer the question; it illustrates the need for explicit formulas even when recursive formulas are available. It usually takes less time for a program to generate an arithmetic sequence that is defined recursively than it does to generate the same sequence when it is defined explicitly—in a recursive definition, the computer has to perform fewer operations.

Do not be surprised if students begin to write the formulas for arithmetic sequences very quickly. For many students, these problems become automatic after a while.

Additional Examples

1. **a.** Find an explicit formula for the arithmetic sequence
   12, 14.5, 17, 19.5, ...
   $a_n = 12 + 2.5(n - 1)$
   b. Find a_{25}. **72**
2. Find the 75th term of the arithmetic sequence
   27, 28.5, 30, 31.5, ... **138**
3. The first row in the auditorium has 15 seats in it. Each subsequent row has 3 more seats than the row in front of it. If the last row has 78 seats, how many rows are in the auditorium? **22**

Example 3

In a concert hall the first row has 20 seats in it, and each subsequent row has two more seats than the row in front of it. If the last row has 64 seats, how many rows are in the concert hall?

④ **Solution**

Because each succeeding row has two additional seats, the number of seats in each row generates the sequence
$$20, 22, 24, 26, \ldots, 64.$$
You know that $a_1 = 20$ and $d = 2$.
So $\qquad a_n = 20 + (n - 1)2$,
where n = the number of the row and a_n = the number of seats in the nth row. Here a_n = 64, and we wish to find n.
$$64 = 20 + (n - 1)2$$
$$44 = 2(n - 1) \qquad \text{Subtract 20 from both sides.}$$
$$22 = n - 1 \qquad \text{Divide both sides by 2.}$$
$$23 = n \qquad \text{Add 1 to both sides.}$$
There are 23 rows of seats in the concert hall.

Check

Substitute $a_1 = 20$, $d = 2$, and $n = 23$ into $a_n = a_1 + (n - 1)d$.
$$a_{23} = 20 + (23 - 1)2 = 20 + 44 = 64$$
The last row has the correct number of seats.

Programs Using Explicit Formulas

Calculators and computers can also generate arithmetic sequences using explicit formulas. The following programs will generate the first six terms of the sequence in Example 1.

```
BASIC
10 FOR N = 1 TO 6
20 LET A = 3000 * N − 2000
30 PRINT A
40 NEXT N
50 END
```

```
CALCULATOR
: For (N, 1, 6)
: 3000N − 2000→A
: Disp A
: End
```

Again the loop tells the calculator or computer to execute the instructions within the loop six times. The second line in each program defines the nth term. The third line tells the calculator or computer to display it. When the program is run the following will appear. These are the same values as those of the sequence in Example 1.

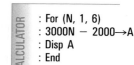

```
1000
4000
7000
10000
13000
16000
```

Adapting to Individual Needs

Extra Help
Be sure students understand the use of subscripts in a_n and a_{n-1}. Point out that the subscripts refer to the position of the terms in the sequence. The term a_n always follows a_{n-1}. The difference d is obtained by subtracting a_{n-1} from a_n. If $a_n > a_{n-1}$, then d is positive. If $a_n < a_{n-1}$, then d is negative.

QUESTIONS

Covering the Reading

1. What is the 20th term of the sequence of Example 1? **58,000**

2. What is the nth term of an arithmetic sequence with first term a_1 and constant difference d? $a_n = a_1 + (n-1)d$

3. **a.** Find an explicit formula for the nth term of the arithmetic sequence
   $$13, 15, 17, 19, 21, \ldots . \quad a_n = 13 + (n-1)2$$
   b. Calculate the 51st term of this sequence. **113**

In 4 and 5, an arithmetic sequence is given. **a.** Find an explicit formula for the nth term. **b.** Find the 100th term.

4. $6, 15, 24, 33, \ldots$ a) $a_n = 6 + (n-1)9$ b) **897**

5. $16, 14.5, 13, 11.5, \ldots$ a) $a_n = 16 + (n-1)(-1.5)$ b) **-132.5**

6. Find the 400th term in the arithmetic sequence $9, 19, 29, 39, \ldots$.
   3999

7. Refer to Example 3. Suppose that in some other concert hall the first row has 40 seats, each subsequent row has two more seats than the row in front of it, and the last row has 70 seats. How many rows of seats are there? **16 rows**

8) 10 FOR N = 1 TO 10
   20 LET A = 40 + 3 * N
   30 PRINT A
   40 NEXT N
   50 END

8. Modify one of the programs at the end of the lesson so that it shows the first ten terms of the sequence defined explicitly as $a_n = 40 + 3n$. **See left.**

Applying the Mathematics

9. Suppose $t_n = 10 + 7(n-1)$.
   a. Is this formula explicit, recursive, or neither? How can you tell?
   b. Find t_{89}. **626**   a) explicit;   you can find any specific term without relying on previous terms.

10. Write a recursive formula for the arithmetic sequence in which $a_n = 10.8 + 2.4n$. $\begin{cases} a_1 = 13.2 \\ a_n = a_{n-1} + 2.4, \text{ for integers } n \geq 2 \end{cases}$

11. Consider the sequence
    $$\begin{cases} a_1 = 8.1 \\ a_n = a_{n-1} + 1.7, \text{ for integers } n \geq 2. \end{cases}$$
    a. Write its first three terms. **8.1, 9.8, 11.5**
    b. Write an explicit formula for the sequence. $a_n = 8.1 + (n-1)1.7$

Lesson 3-8 *Explicit Formulas for Arithmetic Sequences* **183**

Follow-up
for Lesson **3-8**

Practice
For more questions on SPUR Objectives, use **Lesson Master 3-8A** (shown on page 183) or **Lesson Master 3-8B** (shown on pages 184–185).

Assessment
Group Assessment Have students **work in groups.** Have each group of students write an example of a real-world situation that represents an arithmetic sequence. Then have students find an explicit formula for the sequence and the 20th term of the sequence. [Students provide a meaningful explicit formula for an arithmetic sequence and correctly use it to generate the 20th term.]

Extension
You might ask students to prove the following linear-sequence properties. In the *Challenge* on page 184, students are asked to generalize and prove the statement in **Question 1.** Prove: In any linear sequence a, a_5 is the average of a_3 and a_7.
$$\left[\frac{a_3 + a_7}{2} = \frac{a_1 + 2d + a_1 + 6d}{2} = \frac{2a_1 + 8d}{2} = a_1 + 4d = a_5 \right]$$

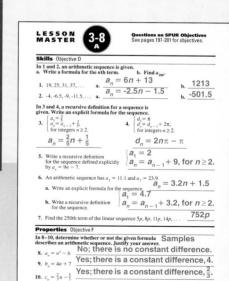

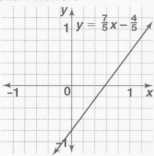
12. The BASIC program below generates several terms of a sequence using a recursive formula. **12a) 15**

```
10 LET A = 15
20 FOR N = 1 TO 10
30 PRINT A
40 A = A + 3.5
50 NEXT N
60 END
```

15
18.5
22
25.5
29
32.5
36
39.5
43
46.5

a. What sequence is printed when the program is run?
b. Modify this program for a calculator or computer so that the sequence is defined explicitly.
Change line 40 to LET A = 15 + 3.5 * (N − 1) and delete line 10

13. Stu and Penelope decided to include bicycling as part of their exercise program. They start by biking 14 miles the first week. By the twenty-fifth week they want to bike 74 miles a week. If the number of miles biked in successive weeks forms an arithmetic sequence, what should be their weekly increase? **2.5 mi/week**

In 14 and 15, a local radio station is holding a contest to give away cash. The announcer makes a telephone call, and if the person who answers guesses the correct amount of money to be given away, he or she wins the money. If the person misses, $20 is added to the money to be given away.

14. On the 12th call, a contestant won $675. How much was to be given away on the 1st call? **$455**

15. Suppose the initial amount is $140. On what call will the winner receive $1100? **49**

16. In a contest, the first-place winner gets $100,000. The tenth-place winner gets $23,500. If the winning amounts form an arithmetic sequence, find the cash difference between prizes. **$8500 decrease after the first prize**

Calling all stations.
There are about 10,500 radio stations operating in the U.S. today. Some stations use contests to lure listeners.

Review

In 17 and 18, use the equation $5y = 7x - 4$.

17. a. Rewrite the equation in standard form. **$7x - 5y = 4$**
b. Identify the x- and y-intercepts. *(Lesson 3-4)*
x-intercept = 4/7; y-intercept = −4/5
18. a. Rewrite the equation in slope-intercept form. $y = \frac{7}{5}x - \frac{4}{5}$
b. Identify the slope and y-intercept. (This provides a check of Question 17b.) Slope = $\frac{7}{5}$; y-intercept = $\frac{-4}{5}$
c. Graph the equation. *(Lesson 3-2)* See margin.

19. Suppose that the variables H, z, and w are related as illustrated in the graphs at the left. The points on the top graph lie on a line through the origin. The points on the bottom graph lie on or near a hyperbola. Write an equation approximating the relationship between H, z, and w. *(Lessons 2-8, 2-9)* $H = \frac{kz}{w}$

Adapting to Individual Needs

Challenge
In the *Extension* on page 183, students proved that in any linear sequence a, a_5 is the average of a_3 and a_7. Now have them prove a generalization of this statement: in any linear sequence a, if x, y, and z are whole numbers and x is the average of y and z, then a_x is the average of a_y and a_z.

[Sample proof: Given: $x = \frac{y + z}{2}$.

Show that $a_x = \frac{a_y + a_z}{2}$.

$\frac{a_y + a_z}{2} = \frac{a_1 + (y - 1)d + a_1 + (z - 1)d}{2} =$

$\frac{a_1 + yd - d + a_1 + zd - d}{2} =$

$\frac{2a_1 + (y + z)d - 2d}{2} = \frac{2a_1 - 2d}{2} + \frac{y + z}{2}(d) =$

$a_1 - d + xd = a_1 + (x - 1)d = a_x$]

20. The following table gives the percent of the population in the United States aged 65 or over for each census year from 1860 to 1990.

year	1860	1870	1880	1890	1900	1910	1920
% aged 65 or over	2.7	3.0	3.4	3.9	4.1	4.3	4.7
year	1930	1940	1950	1960	1970	1980	1990
% aged 65 or over	5.4	6.8	8.1	9.2	9.8	11.3	12.5

a. Make a scatterplot of these data. **See left.**
b. Find an equation for the regression line. Let x = the number of years after 1860. **about $y = .08x + 1.49$**
c. Separate the data set into two parts:
  (i) the years from 1860 to 1930; and **about $y = .04x + 2.68$**
  (ii) the years from 1940 to 1990. **about $y = .11x - 1.99$**
  Find a linear regression model for each of these data sets.
d. Use the result of part **c** to write a piecewise-linear function to model the given data. **See below left.**
e. Which of the functions, that in part **b** or that in part **d**, do you think is the better predictor of the percent of the U.S. population that will be 65 or over in the year 2010? Explain your reasoning. *(Lessons 3-5, 3-6)* **See below left.**

In 21 and 22, *multiple choice.*   Refer to the graphs below.
(Lessons 2-4, 2-5, 2-6)

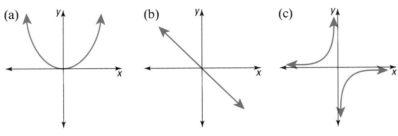

(a)   (b)   (c)

21. Which graph does not represent a direct-variation function? **c**

22. Which graph represents a situation in which the constant of variation is positive? **a**

23. Consider $S = \left\{x: -8 \le x \le -\frac{21}{4}\right\}$
a. Name all integers that are members of S. **-8, -7, -6**
b. Graph S on a number line. *(Previous course, Lesson 1-2)*

23b)

$$-8 \quad -7 \quad -6 \quad -5 \quad -\frac{21}{4} \quad S$$

Exploration

24. Here is a sequence that is *not* an arithmetic sequence.
$$3, 5, 9, 17, 33, 65, 129, 257, 513, \ldots$$
a. What is a possible next term? **1025**
b. Find a recursive formula for the nth term.
c. Find an explicit formula for the nth term. $a_n = 2^n + 1$

b) $\begin{cases} a_1 = 3 \\ a_n = a_{n-1} + 2^{n-1}, \text{ for integers } n \ge 2 \end{cases}$

Lesson 3-8   *Explicit Formulas for Arithmetic Sequences*   **185**

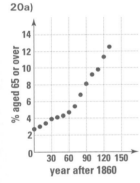

Fit for life. *Exercise classes designed for senior citizens help combat heart disease, high blood pressure, and osteoporosis. More and more of the 31 million people over the age of 65 are taking such classes.*

20a)

(scatterplot: % aged 65 or over vs. year after 1860)

20d) $\begin{cases} y = .04x + 2.68, \\ \qquad 0 \le x \le 70 \\ y = .11x - 1.99, \\ \qquad x \ge 80 \end{cases}$

e) part **d**; people are living longer due to improved medical technology, and the second equation, $y = .11x - 1.99$ reflects this change.

Notes on Questions

Questions 13–16 For these questions, students can think of a sequence or think of the graph of a line.

Question 20 Social Studies Connection The U.S. Census Bureau estimates that there will be 34.9 million Americans over the age of 65 by the year 2000.

Question 23 Note that S is an interval. Notation for describing intervals is used in Lesson 3-9.

Question 24 There is no single algorithm that can be applied to all questions of this type. One way to approach this question is to examine the differences of consecutive terms—this gives 2, 4, 8, 16, . . . , and suggests that the sequence has a formula involving 2^n.

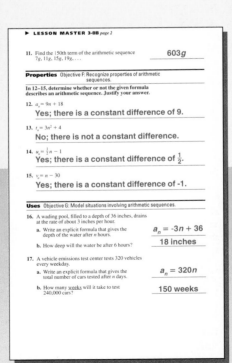

Objectives

C Evaluate expressions based on step functions.
K Model situations leading to step functions.
M Graph or interpret graphs of step functions.

Resources

From the *Teacher's Resource File*
- Lesson Master 3-9A or 3-9B
- Answer Master 3-9
- Teaching Aids
    8 Four-Quadrant Graph Paper
   25 Warm-up
   30 The Greatest Integer Function

Additional Resources
- Visuals for Teaching Aids 8, 25, 30

Teaching Lesson 3-9

Warm-up

Name the greatest integer that is less than or equal to each of the following.

1. 2.99 **2**
2. π **3**
3. $-\frac{8001}{1,000,000}$ **–1**
4. $\sqrt{24}$ **4**
5. 0.77777 **0**
6. –101.1 **–102**
7. $\sqrt{2} + \sqrt{3}$ **3**
8. –6 + .5 **–6**

Upper-level parking. *This is a multi-level parking garage located in Tokyo. To make the best use of space, hydraulic lifts are used to move the buses and cars into their spaces.*

❶ The daily charge to park a car at a city lot is $3.00 for the first half hour and $2.50 for each additional hour or portion of an hour. Thus, the cost of parking is a function of time. The table below gives the cost if a car is parked at 7:00 P.M. and picked up before 1:30 A.M.

time	n = number of minutes since 7:00 P.M.	c = cost (in dollars)
7:00 – 7:30	$0 < n \le 30$	3.00
7:30 – 8:30	$30 < n \le 90$	3.00 + 2.50 = 5.50
8:30 – 9:30	$90 < n \le 150$	5.50 + 2.50 = 8.00
9:30 – 10:30	$150 < n \le 210$	8.00 + 2.50 = 10.50
10:30 – 11:30	$210 < n \le 270$	10.50 + 2.50 = 13.00
11:30 – 12:30	$270 < n \le 330$	13.00 + 2.50 = 15.50
12:30 – 1:30	$330 < n \le 390$	15.50 + 2.50 = 18.00

The graph at the right shows the cost of parking a car for a given number of minutes from 0 to 390. Notice that the graph represents a function. You can verify this with the Vertical-Line Test. The domain consists of any positive real number of minutes less than or equal to the 1440 minutes in a day. The range is the set of costs: {$3.00, $5.50, $8.00, $10.50, . . . , $63.00}.

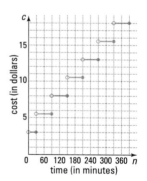

The function is not a linear function, but the graph is piecewise linear. Because the graph looks like a series of steps, this function is called a **step function.** Each step is part of a horizontal line.

Lesson 3-9 Overview

Broad Goals In this lesson, students are introduced to the important class of functions called *step functions*.

Perspective One measure of the importance of these functions is reflected in the number of names they have acquired. The function with equation $y = \lfloor x \rfloor$ is called the *rounding down function*, the *floor function*, or the *greatest integer function*. On computers and calculators, it is usually

denoted by Int or INT. In general, step functions abound in real-life applications, and, more specifically, both the rounding down and rounding up functions are used in computer science.

There are four major points to emphasize: how to calculate values of the greatest integer function, how to translate real situations into the greatest-integer-function language, how to graph the greatest integer function,

and how to use the INT function on a calculator or computer. The four points are presented in that order in the lesson.

When you use function-plotting software or graphics calculators to demonstrate step functions, check ahead of time to see if your technology correctly handles the points of discontinuity. Some packages produce misleading graphs that have "risers," such as the first one shown at the right. You might

The Greatest-Integer Function

The **greatest-integer symbol** $\lfloor \ \rfloor$ is defined as follows.

> **Definition**
> $\lfloor x \rfloor$ = the greatest integer less than or equal to x.

Example 1

Evaluate each of the following.

a. $\left\lfloor 2\frac{3}{4} \right\rfloor$ **b.** $\lfloor 7 \rfloor$ **c.** $\lfloor -3 \rfloor$ **d.** $\lfloor -2.1 \rfloor$

Solution

a. $\left\lfloor 2\frac{3}{4} \right\rfloor$ is the greatest integer less than or equal to $2\frac{3}{4}$. So $\left\lfloor 2\frac{3}{4} \right\rfloor = 2$.

b. $\lfloor 7 \rfloor$ is the greatest integer less than or equal to 7. $\lfloor 7 \rfloor = 7$

c. $\lfloor -3 \rfloor$ is the greatest integer less than or equal to -3. $\lfloor -3 \rfloor = -3$

d. $\lfloor -2.1 \rfloor$ is the greatest integer less than or equal to -2.1. Because $-3 < -2.1 < -2$, The greatest integer less than or equal to -2.1 is $\lfloor -2.1 \rfloor = -3$.

The **greatest-integer function** is the function f with $f(x) = \lfloor x \rfloor$, for all real numbers x. It is sometimes called the **rounding-down function** or **floor function**.

The Graph of the Greatest-Integer Function

Example 2

Graph the function defined by $f(x) = \lfloor x \rfloor$.

Solution

Make a table of values. For all x greater than or equal to 0 but less than 1, the greatest integer less than or equal to x is 0. For all x greater than or equal to 1 but less than 2, the greatest integer less than or equal to x is 1. In a similar manner you can get the other values in the table below. The graph is on the right below.

x	$f(x) = \lfloor x \rfloor$
$-3 \leq x < -2$	-3
$-2 \leq x < -1$	-2
$-1 \leq x < 0$	-1
$0 \leq x < 1$	0
$1 \leq x < 2$	1
$2 \leq x < 3$	2
$3 \leq x < 4$	3

show students the incorrect graph, but make sure they realize it is wrong!

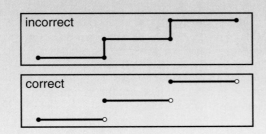

incorrect

correct

❸ A note of caution—on some calculators, INT does not refer to the greatest integer function but to the integer part of a decimal. On these calculators, INT(-2.8) = -2 whereas, for the greatest integer function, INT(-2.8) = ⌊-2.8⌋ = -3. In this text, INT always stands for the greatest integer function.

Additional Examples

1. If $g(x) = 2 + \lfloor x \rfloor$, evaluate each of the following functions.
   a. $g(2.6)$ 4
   b. $g(-3.1)$ -2
   c. $g(\pi)$ 5
2. Graph $f(x) = \lfloor x \rfloor - 1$.

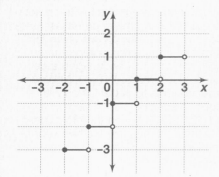

3. Banks often put pennies in rolls of 50. How many full rolls can be made from p pennies? $\lfloor \frac{p}{50} \rfloor$
4. Refer to the BASIC program in Example 4. Suppose line 20 is changed to:
   PRINT 100 * INT((N + 50)/100).
   What is displayed for any number N? **The program rounds to the nearest hundred.**

(Notes on Questions begin on page 191.)

On the graph, the open circles at (1, 0), (2, 1), (3, 2), and so on, indicate that these values are *not* solutions to $f(x) = \lfloor x \rfloor$. At these points, the function value is jumping to the next step. Notice that the domain of the greatest-integer function is the set of real numbers, but the range is the set of integers.

❸ On calculators and computers, the greatest-integer function is often labeled INT. For instance, INT(-6.1) = -7. If your automatic grapher has the INT function, it will graph the greatest-integer function for you. The graph from one automatic grapher is shown below. Because the grapher is programmed to connect successive pixels, it joins successive steps. This makes it appear as if the graph does not represent a function. On some graphers you can get the correct graph by switching from the connected mode to the dot mode.

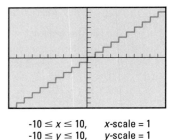

-10 ≤ x ≤ 10,   x-scale = 1
-10 ≤ y ≤ 10,   y-scale = 1

Applications of the Greatest-Integer Function

Formulas with the greatest-integer symbol are often found when function values must be integers but other formulas would give noninteger values.

Example 3

A bottling company prepares flavored water. The bottles are packaged in cartons of 8. Write an equation that gives the number of complete cartons c packaged each day, if the company prepares b bottles each day.

Solution

The number of cartons must be a nonnegative integer because the company cannot package part of a carton. The bottles are packaged in groups of 8, so it seems reasonable to divide the number of bottles by 8. However, $\frac{b}{8}$ may not be an integer. Since we are interested in the number of complete cartons, round the answer down to the nearest integer. Using the greatest-integer function, you can write the equation as

$$c = \left\lfloor \frac{b}{8} \right\rfloor.$$

Check

Substitute values of b. For instance, $\left\lfloor \frac{16}{8} \right\rfloor = \lfloor 2 \rfloor = 2$. Two complete cartons are needed for 16 bottles. Also $\left\lfloor \frac{21}{8} \right\rfloor = \left\lfloor 2\frac{5}{8} \right\rfloor = 2$. When there are 21 bottles, 2 complete cartons will be packaged.

188

Adapting to Individual Needs

Extra Help
The term *greatest integer function* is sometimes confusing to students. Stress the other two possible names—the *rounding down function* or the *floor function*. The latter names may seem more descriptive to some students.

English Language Development
Make sure that students with limited English proficiency are not confused by the definition of the greatest integer function. This function refers to the *greatest* integer that is *less* than or equal to x, not the integer that is greater than x.

Challenge Technology Connection
Computer programmers in your class might be interested in the fact that, by using the formula from **Question 24,** one can print a 12-month calendar for any year. The major challenge of this program is formatting the output. You might have students **work in groups** and try to write such a program. [Responses will vary.]

Step Functions in Calculator or Computer Programs

The greatest-integer function may be used in calculator or computer programs. Consider the two below.

```
BASIC
10 INPUT N
20 PRINT INT(N + .5)
30 GOTO 10
40 END
```

```
CALCULATOR
: Lbl A
: Input N
: Disp int (N + .5)
: Goto A
```

In each program the statement INPUT N prints a ? on the screen, asking the user for a number for N. Then it computes $\lfloor N + .5 \rfloor$ and prints the result. The program then loops back to the beginning and asks the user for another input.

Example 4

Describe what either program above displays for any number N.

Solution

Pick several values of N and evaluate the expression $\lfloor N + .5 \rfloor$.

N	$\lfloor N + .5 \rfloor$
4	$\lfloor 4 + .5 \rfloor = \lfloor 4.5 \rfloor = 4$
4.5	$\lfloor 4.5 + .5 \rfloor = \lfloor 5 \rfloor = 5$
-7	$\lfloor -7 + .5 \rfloor = \lfloor -6.5 \rfloor = -7$
7.49	$\lfloor 7.49 + .5 \rfloor = \lfloor 7.99 \rfloor = 7$
7.6	$\lfloor 7.6 + .5 \rfloor = \lfloor 8.1 \rfloor = 8$

This program seems to take any number, round it to the nearest integer (rounding all halves up), and prints the result.

QUESTIONS

Covering the Reading

In 1 and 2, refer to the parking example on page 186.

1. What would be the cost to park a car for 4 hours and 45 minutes?
   $15.50

2. What is the domain of the function? **{x: 0 ≤ x ≤ 1440}**

3. In your own words, write the meaning of $\lfloor x \rfloor$.
   Sample: $\lfloor x \rfloor$ = the greatest integer that is not bigger than x.

In 4–7, evaluate.

4. $\lfloor 3\frac{1}{2} \rfloor$ **3**   5. $\lfloor 11.9 \rfloor$ **11**   6. $\lfloor -11.7 \rfloor$ **-12**   7. $\lfloor 8 + .5 \rfloor$ **8**

8. a. The function *f* defined by $f(x) = \lfloor x \rfloor$ is called the __?__ or __?__ function. **greatest integer; rounding down or floor**
   b. The range of $f: x \to \lfloor x \rfloor$ is __?__. **the set of integers**
   c. Why are there open circles at (1, 0), (2, 1), (3, 2), and so on in the graph of *f*?
   They indicate that these values are not solutions to $f(x) = \lfloor x \rfloor$.

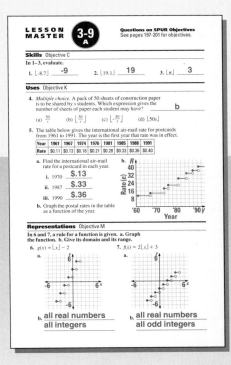

Practice

For more questions on SPUR Objectives, use **Lesson Master 3-9A** (shown on page 189) or **Lesson Master 3-9B** (shown on pages 190–191).

Assessment

Oral/Written Communication
Have students **work in pairs.** Refer to **Example 1** on page 187. Have one student in each pair write a symbol for the greatest integer function, such as $\lfloor -3.2 \rfloor$. Then have the other student read the symbol and give its value. Students can alternate roles and continue for several more examples. [Students demonstrate an understanding of the greatest integer symbol by reading it correctly and then giving the correct value.]

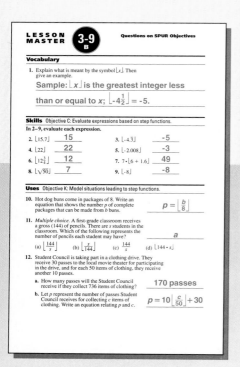

9. Explain why some automatic graphers connect the steps when graphing $y = \lfloor x \rfloor$. Some graphers are programmed to connect successive pixels.

10. Give the domain and range of the function with equation $c = \lfloor\frac{b}{8}\rfloor$ for the situation in the Example 3. domain: the set of nonnegative integers; range: the set of nonnegative integers

11. Suppose a company packaged bottles in cartons of 6. Write an equation that relates the number of bottles b to the number of complete cartons c that can be packaged. $c = \lfloor\frac{b}{6}\rfloor$

12. Refer to the expression INT(N + .5) in Example 4. What will the program display if each of the following is input for N?
    a. 17.3   **b.** 9.99   **c.** -3.29
    17   10   -3

Applying the Mathematics

13. *Multiple choice.* In 1995, the cost to mail a letter first class in the U.S. was 32¢ for up to one ounce, and 23¢ for each additional ounce or fraction thereof. Which is a correct graph for this function? b

(a)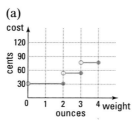
(b)
(c)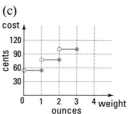
(d)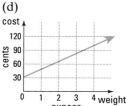

14. *Multiple choice.* An auditorium has 2500 seats available for graduation. There are g graduates. Which of the following represents the number of tickets each graduate may have if each graduate is given the same number of tickets? b
    (a) $\frac{2500}{g}$ (b) $\lfloor\frac{2500}{g}\rfloor$ (c) $\lfloor 2500 \cdot g \rfloor$ (d) $\lfloor\frac{g}{2500}\rfloor$

15. Tyrone's salary is $275 a week plus $75 for each $300 he has in sales that week. a) $500
    a. Find his salary during a week in which he had $1000 in sales.
    b. When he has d dollars in sales, write an equation that gives his weekly earnings. $w = 275 + 75 \cdot \lfloor\frac{d}{300}\rfloor$

16. Consider the BASIC program in Example 4. If line 20 is changed to 20 PRINT 10 * INT((N + 5)/10) a different type of rounding occurs.
    a. Make a table of at least five pairs of input and output for this program. See left.
    b. What kind of rounding is done by this program?
    This program rounds to the nearest 10.

17. The cost C in dollars of making a call lasting m minutes during the day from Chicago, Illinois, to Paris, France, is given by the formula $C = 1.71 - 1.08\lfloor 1 - m \rfloor$.
    a. Evaluate this formula when $m = 2, 7.5$, and 10. $2.79; $9.27; $11.43
    b. Graph this equation for $0 < m \le 10$. See left.

16a) Sample:

N	10*INT((N+5)/10)
13	10
27	30
-11	-10
-55.6	-60
8	10

17b)

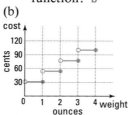

190

191

19a) $\begin{cases} a_1 = 46 \\ a_n = a_{n-1} - 3.5, \\ \text{for integers } n \geq 2 \end{cases}$

22)
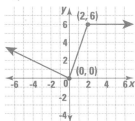

23)

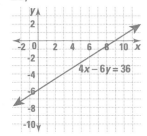

Review

18. Consider the sequence $\begin{cases} a_1 = -x \\ a_n = a_{n-1} + 3x, \text{ for integers } n \geq 2 \end{cases}$.

    a. Write the first four terms of the sequence.   **-x, 2x, 5x, 8x**

    b. Is the sequence arithmetic? How can you tell?

    c. Find an explicit formula for the sequence.   *(Lesson 3-8)*

    $a_n = -x + (n-1) \cdot 3x$ **b)** Yes, there is a constant increase of $3x$.

19. Consider the arithmetic sequence $46, 42.5, 39, 35.5, \ldots$.

    a. Write a recursive formula for the sequence.   **See left.**

    b. Write an explicit formula for the sequence.   *(Lessons 3-7, 3-8)*

    $a_n = 46 - (n-1) \cdot 3.5$

20. Suppose the first term of an arithmetic sequence is -4, and the 15th term is 38. Find the 30th term of the sequence.   *(Lessons 3-7, 3-8)*

    83

21. Write an equation of the line which passes through the points $(3, -1)$ and $(6, 5)$.   *(Lesson 3-5)*   **Sample:** $y + 1 = 2(x - 3)$

22. Graph $4x - 6y = 36$ using the intercepts.   *(Lesson 3-4)*   **See left.**

23. Graph the function defined below.   *(Lessons 3-1, 3-2, 3-5)*   **See left.**

$$f(x) = \begin{cases} 6, & \text{for } x > 2 \\ 3x, & \text{for } 0 \leq x \leq 2 \\ -\frac{1}{2}x, & \text{for } x < 0 \end{cases}$$

Exploration

24. The formula

$$W = d + 2m + \left\lfloor \frac{3(m+1)}{5} \right\rfloor + y + \left\lfloor \frac{y}{4} \right\rfloor - \left\lfloor \frac{y}{100} \right\rfloor + \left\lfloor \frac{y}{400} \right\rfloor + 2$$

gives the day of the week based on our current calendar where

  $d =$ the day of the month of the given date.

  $m =$ the number of the month in the year with January and February regarded as the 13th and 14th months of the previous year; that is, 2/22/1990 is 14/22/1989. The other months are numbered 3 to 12 as usual.

  $y =$ the year.

Once W is computed, divide by 7 and the remainder is the day of the week, with Saturday $= 0$, Sunday $= 1, \ldots,$ Friday $= 6$.

  a. Use the formula to find the day of the week on which you were born.

  b. On what day of the week was the Declaration of Independence adopted?   **Thursday**

  a) **Answers will vary.**

Birth day. *Dolley Madison (top) was born on May 29, 1768. Eleanor Roosevelt (bottom) was born on Oct. 11, 1884. Both of these First Ladies played important roles in American history. On what day of the week was each woman born?*

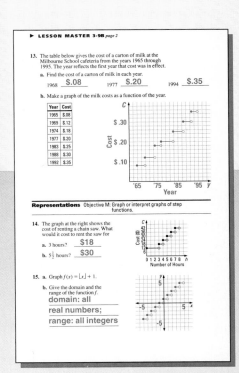

Chapter 3 Projects

Chapter 3 projects relate to the content of the lessons as shown below. They can, however, be used any time after the lessons have been taught. Suggestions for using a project are given in the lesson notes under *Project Update*.

Project	Lesson(s)
1	3-1, 3-4, 3-8
2	3-9
3	3-5, 3-9
4	3-6
5	3-3
6	3-1, 3-5, 3-9

1 A Graphical Investigation
The graphs of the equations in part a are sufficient to reveal the pattern. However, students should supply one or two equations of their own to check their conjectures. Ask students to consider all possibilities, including $A = B = C = 0$.

2 Taxi Meter Students should be clear on the need for the greatest integer function in calculating charges for mileage and wait time. Students should run their programs to see whether they give the correct results for selected test cases.

3 Fines for Speeding Students can gather data for out-of-state speeding fines by consulting travel guides or by contacting motoring associations. Local highway patrols may have information for other states or provinces, especially for those adjacent to their own. Students may find that fines vary not only from state to state but from place to place within the same state.

A project presents an opportunity for you to extend your knowledge of a topic related to the material of this chapter. You should allow more time for a project than you do for typical homework questions.

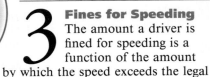

1 A Graphical Investigation
Graphs of equations of the form $Ax + By = C$, where A, B, C are consecutive terms in an arithmetic sequence, share something in common.
a. Graph five equations of this type, for instance,
$$x + 2y = 3$$
$$3x + 5y = 7$$
$$8x + 6y = 4$$
$$-2x - 3y = -4$$
$$3x - y = -5.$$
b. Make a conjecture based on these five graphs.
c. Test your conjecture with a few more graphs.
d. Use the definitions or theorems about arithmetic sequences to verify your conjecture.

---

2 Taxi Meter
If you have ever been in a taxi during a traffic jam, you might have noticed that the meter will "keep running" if there is a charge for miles and waiting time. For instance, a taxi might charge $1.20 as a base rate for the first $\frac{1}{10}$ of a mile, $.20 for each additional $\frac{1}{10}$ of a mile, $0.20 for each full minute waiting time when the taxi isn't moving, and $0.50 for each additional passenger. Find out the taxi rates near where you live. Write a program in which the inputs are the distance traveled, the minutes of waiting time, and the number of additional passengers. Have the output be the amount due to the taxi driver.

192

---

3 Fines for Speeding
The amount a driver is fined for speeding is a function of the amount by which the speed exceeds the legal speed limit. In some states these functions are linear functions; in other states they are piecewise linear.
a. Find out what the fines are for speeding in your state. If they are not the same for cars and trucks, find out both sets of fines. Describe the speeding-fine function using a table and a graph. What are the domain and the range of this function? Does this function belong to any of the types you have studied in this course? If so, what kind of function is it? If possible, find an equation for the speeding fine function.

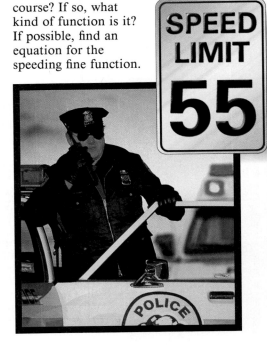

b. Find a state or province that has a different set of fines for speeding than your state. Describe those fines with a table, a graph, and an equation. Describe some ways the two speeding fine functions are alike and the ways they are different.

Possible Responses

1a.
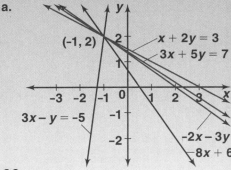

b. It appears that if A, B, and C are consecutive terms of an arithmetic sequence (A, B, and C not all zero), then the graph of $Ax + By = C$ is a line that passes through $(-1, 2)$. If A, B, and C are all zero, then the graph is the entire coordinate plane.
c. The additional equations that students use to check the conjecture will vary. Check to see that A, B, and C are indeed consecutive terms of an arithmetic sequence. Each graph should be a line that passes through $(-1, 2)$.
d. Suppose that A, B, and C are consecutive terms of an arithmetic sequence with common difference d. Then $B = A + d$ and $C = A + 2d$.

4 Time-Series Data

When the value of a dependent variable, such as a world's record in a particular sport, changes over time the data are called *time-series data*.

a. Find an example of time-series data in which the dependent variable appears to vary linearly with time. Make a scatterplot of the data.

b. Use a computer or calculator to find a line of best fit and draw it on the graph with the scatterplot.

c. According to your model, what will the value of the variable be in the years 2000, 2025, 2075, and 3000? Do your predictions seem reasonable? Why or why not?

5 Linear Combinations

Combinations of 23¢ and 32¢ stamps can be used for 55¢ postage, 78¢ postage, and many other amounts. But no combination of 23¢ and 32¢ stamps can be used for 10¢ postage, 30¢ postage, and so on.

a. What is the greatest amount of postage you *cannot* form from 23¢ and 32¢ stamps? Explain how you got your answer.

b. What is the greatest amount of postage you *cannot* form from stamps with denominations x¢ and y¢, if x and y have no common factors? Explain how you got your answer.

6 Graphing Piecewise Functions

Some automatic graphers allow you to use logical statements whose value is 1 if the statement is true and 0 if it is false. These statements can be used to graph an equation over a particular domain. For instance, to graph

$$y = x - 1 \text{ for } x > 1,$$

input $y = (x - 1) \div (x > 1)$. When $x > 1$, the logical statement is true and has a value of 1; so the grapher reads $y = (x - 1) \div (x > 1)$ as $y = x - 1$ and graphs a line. When $x \le 1$, the logical statement $x > 1$ is false and has a value of 0. Because division by 0 is undefined, no graph is displayed.

a. Graph $y = (x - 5) \div (x > 5)$. Describe what is displayed.

b. To graph a function defined by different equations over different domains, enter each equation as a separate function divided by its domain. Make up a piecewise-linear function. Show how to use your grapher to draw this graph.

4 Time-Series Data

Almanacs and books of sports statistics will provide plenty of data of the kind needed for this project. If students are using data from the Olympics, the years 2025 and 2075 would have to be interpolated data; because of the Olympic schedule, the games would not be held in a year ending in 5. Explain that *interpolation* is estimating a value *between* known values of data, while *extrapolation* is estimating a value *beyond* known values of data.

5 Linear Combinations

This project is not as easy as it may look from a casual reading. You might want to have students work in groups and brainstorm possible methods of solution. Remind them that 23 and 32 are relatively prime numbers. You might also suggest that they begin by investigating combinations of smaller pairs of relatively prime numbers and noting, for each pair, the greatest number they cannot make.

6 Graphing Piecewise Functions

This project is not as difficult as it may seem at the first reading. You might want to discuss with students how they would enter an inequality, such as $x > 1$ on their graphics calculator. On the TI-82 they would go to the MATH TEST menu.

Since
$$Ax + By = C,$$
$$Ax + (A + d)y = A + 2d.$$
Now substitute -1 for x and 2 for y.
$$A(-1) + (A + d)(2) = A + 2d.$$
$$A + 2d = A + 2d.$$
Since the last equation is true for all values of a and d, the graph of $Ax + By = C$ contains the point $(-1, 2)$ and, if A and d are not both zero, the graph is a line passing through $(1, 2)$. If $A = d = 0$, then the graph is the entire coordinate plane.

2. Programs may vary, depending on the data gathered. The program the right is for the TI-82 graphics calculator. It uses data given as a sample in the text.

```
PROGRAM: TAXI
: Input "MILES", D
: (.2int(10D)) → M
: Input: "WAIT TIME", T
: (.2int T) → W
: Input: "EXTRA PEOPLE", A
: sA → P
: Disp "TOTAL COST"
: Disp 1.2 + M + W + P
```

(Responses continue on page 194.)

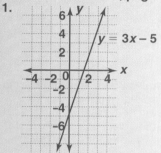
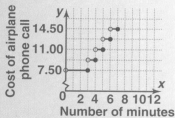
SUMMARY

A linear equation in two variables is one that is equivalent to an equation of the form $Ax + By = C$ where A and B are not both zero. The graph of every linear equation is a line. The form $Ax + By = C$ where $A \neq 0$ and $B \neq 0$ is called the standard form of the equation for a line. If the line is not vertical, then its equation can be put into the form $y = mx + b$, with slope m and y-intercept b. Horizontal lines have slope 0; they have equations of the form $y = b$. Slope is not defined for vertical lines, which have equations of the form $x = h$.

If the slope and one point on a line are known, then the point-slope form of a linear equation can be used to obtain an equation for the line. In many real-world situations, a set of data points is roughly linear. In such cases, a regression line can be used to describe the data and make predictions. The correlation coefficient describes the strength of the linear relationship.

Linear equations result from two basic kinds of situations: constant increase or decrease, and

linear combinations. Sequences with a constant increase or decrease have a constant difference between terms. Their graphs consist of collinear points, and they are called linear or arithmetic sequences. If a_n is the nth term of an arithmetic sequence with constant difference d, then the sequence can be described explicitly as $a_n = a_1 + (n - 1)d$, for integers $n \geq 1$, or recursively as

$$\begin{cases} a_1 \\ a_n = a_{n-1} + d, \text{ for integers } n \geq 2. \end{cases}$$

Some calculators and computers can be programmed to display terms of a sequence defined either explicitly or recursively.

A function whose graph is the union of segments and rays is called piecewise linear. Piecewise-linear functions result from situations in which rates are constant for a while but change at known points. Step functions, in particular the greatest-integer function, are special instances of piecewise-linear functions.

VOCABULARY

Below are the most important terms and phrases for this chapter.
You should be able to give a definition for those terms marked with *.
For all other terms you should be able to give a general description or a specific example.

Lesson 3-1
*y-intercept
initial condition
*slope-intercept form
linear function
constant-increase situation
constant-decrease situation
slope
piecewise-linear graph

Lesson 3-3
linear-combination
   situation

Lesson 3-4
standard form
*x-intercept
vertical line
oblique line
horizontal line

Lesson 3-5
*point-slope form

Lesson 3-6
scatterplot
regression line, line of best
   fit, least squares line
correlation coefficient

Lesson 3-7
constant difference
*arithmetic sequence, linear
   sequence
recursive formula for an
   arithmetic sequence

Lesson 3-8
*explicit formula for an
   arithmetic sequence

Lesson 3-9
step function
*greatest-integer function, $\lfloor x \rfloor$
rounding-down function,
   floor function, INT (x)

194

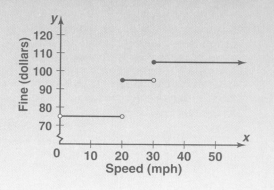

PROGRESS SELF-TEST

See margin for 1, 6, 10, 11a, 12, 14, 16.

Take this test as you would take a test in class. Use graph paper and a ruler. Then check your work with the solutions in the Selected Answers section in the back of the book.

1. Graph the line with equation $y = 3x - 5$.

2. State whether the line determined by $x = -7$ is vertical, horizontal, or oblique. **vertical**

3. Consider the line with equation $4x - 5y = 12$.
   a. What is its slope? $\frac{4}{5}$
   b. What are its x- and y-intercepts? $3;\ \frac{-12}{5}$

4. For what values of m does the equation $y = mx + b$ model a constant-decrease situation? $\{m: m < 0\}$

5. Give an equation for the line through $(4, 2)$ and $(-5, 3)$. **Sample:** $y - 2 = -\frac{1}{9}(x - 4)$

6. Give an equation for the line that contains $(5, -1)$ and is parallel to $y = \frac{5}{3}x + 4$.

7. a. For what kind of lines is slope not defined? **vertical**   b) **horizontal**
   b. Which lines have a slope of zero?

8. A company makes $36''$ and $48''$ shoelaces by cutting off lengths from a spool of cord. Let S be the number of $36''$ laces and L be the number of $48''$ laces made. How much cord will be used in making S short and L long laces? $36S + 48L$ in.

9. A scuba diver is 40 m below the surface. If the diver ascends at a constant rate of 0.8 meters per second, how long will it take to reach a depth of 10 meters? **37.5 sec**

10. Consider the following computer program.

```
10  LET A = 1
20  FOR N = 1 TO 12
30  PRINT A
40  A = A + 5
50  NEXT N
60  END
```

   a. What sequence is generated?
   b. Is the sequence arithmetic? Explain your answer.

11. In 1994, the cost of making a phone call from some airplanes was $7.50 for the first three minutes and $1.75 for each additional minute or portion of a minute.
   a. Graph the function for any call lasting up to 8 minutes. **See margin.**
   b. How much would it cost Isaiah Rich to make a $6\frac{1}{3}$ minute call? **$14.50**

12. Tell whether $8, 5, 2, -3, \ldots$ could be the first four terms of an arithmetic sequence. Justify your answer.

13. Evaluate the expression $10 \cdot \lfloor (x + 5)/10 \rfloor$ when $x = 365$. **370**

14. Celsius temperature and Réaumur temperature are related by a linear equation. Two pairs of corresponding temperatures are $0°C = 0°R$ and $100°C = 80°R$. Write a linear equation relating R and C, and solve it for R.

In 15 and 16, use the fact that $-7, -10, -13, -16, \ldots$ is an arithmetic sequence. **15)** $a_n = -7 - 3(n - 1)$

15. Write an explicit formula for the sequence.

16. Write a recursive formula for the sequence.

17. *Multiple choice.* A store charges for copies as follows:

   For 1–50 copies   5¢ each
        51–200 copies   4¢ each
        more than 200 copies 3¢ each.

   Which graph most closely describes the total cost C for printing n copies? (The scales on all four sets of axes are the same.) **a**

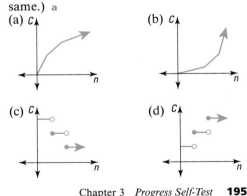

(a) C
(b) C
(c) C
(d) C

Chapter 3 *Progress Self-Test* **195**

Progress Self-Test

For the development of mathemati-cal competence, feedback and cor-rection, along with the opportunity to practice, are necessary. The Progress Self-Test provides the opportunity for feedback and correc-tion; the Chapter Review provides additional opportunities and practice. We cannot overemphasize the importance of these end-of-chapter materials. It is at this point that the material "gels" for many students, allowing them to solidify skills and understanding. In general, student performance should be markedly improved after these pages.

Assign the Progress Self-Test as a one-night assignment. Worked-out *solutions* for all questions are in the Selected Answers section of the stu-dent book. Encourage students to take the Progress Self-Test honestly, grade themselves, and then be pre-pared to discuss the test in class.

Advise students to pay special attention to those Chapter Review questions (pages 197–201) which correspond to questions missed on the Progress Self-Test.

Additional Answers, continued

12. No. An arithmetic sequence must have a constant differ-ence between successive terms.

14. $R = .8C$

16. $\begin{cases} a_1 = -7 \\ a_n = a_{n-1} - 3, \\ \qquad \text{for integers } n \geq 2 \end{cases}$

You can, however, enter and graph the following equation on the TI-82 graphics calculator:
$Y_1 = 75(0 < x \text{ and } x < 20)$
$\quad + 95(20 \leq x \text{ and } x < 30)$
$\quad + 105(30 \leq x \leq 200)$.
For $0 < x \leq 200$, this equation describes a function that coincides with the traffic-fine function. For $x > 200$, the traffic-fine function is

not defined, while the function defined by the equation is defined and has a value of 0. (The inequality symbols and the logical connective "and" are from the MATH and LOGIC menus that can be accessed on the MATH TEST and MATH LOGIC menus.)
   b. Responses will vary.

4. Responses will vary. A sample response is given.
   a. The table and scatterplot on page 196 give Olympic times for the women's 200-meter dash. Times are in seconds. The line on of best fit as calculated in part b.

(Responses continue on page 196.)

Additional Answers, page 197

17b. $\begin{cases} a_1 = 7 \\ a_n = a_{n-1} + 5, \\ \qquad \text{for integers } n \geq 2 \end{cases}$

18b. $\begin{cases} a_1 = 8 \\ a_n = a_{n-1} - 6, \\ \qquad \text{for integers } n \geq 2 \end{cases}$

19. $\begin{cases} a_1 = -9 \\ a_n = a_{n-1} + 2, \\ \qquad \text{for integers } n \geq 2 \end{cases}$

20. $a_n = \frac{1}{2} + (n-1)4$

21b. $\begin{cases} a_1 = 1 \\ a_n = a_{n-1} + 2, \\ \qquad \text{for integers } n \geq 2 \end{cases}$

22a. 1000
   b. 100, 101, 102, 103, 104

23a. 10
   b. 5, 7, 9, 11, 13

PROGRESS SELF-TEST

18. The table and the scatterplot below give the expected years of life left for people in the U.S. at selected ages in 1991.

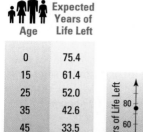

Age	Expected Years of Life Left
0	75.4
15	61.4
25	52.0
35	42.6
45	33.5
55	24.9
65	17.3
75	10.9
85	6.1

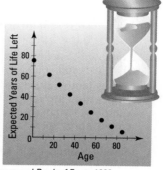

Source: *The World Almanac and Book of Facts 1993*

a. Do the data seem to be linearly related? Explain your answer. **See below.**

b. Find an equation of the regression line for these data. **about** $y = -.83x + 73.07$

c. Use the answer to part **c** to estimate the expected years of life left of someone who is currently 42. **about 38 years**

a) Yes; the points all lie relatively close to a line.

19. The graph below represents the height and horizontal distance moved by a ski lift.

a. What is the slope of the section whose horizontal distance goes from 600 to 900 feet? $\frac{4}{3}$

b. Where is the slope of the lift steepest? **the first 200 feet of horizontal distance**

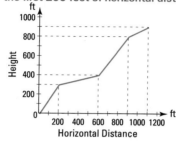

Additional responses, page 193

Year	Time	Year	Time
1948	24.4	1972	22.4
1952	23.7	1976	22.37
1956	23.4	1980	22.03
1960	24.0	1984	21.81
1964	23.0	1988	21.34
1968	22.5	1992	21.81

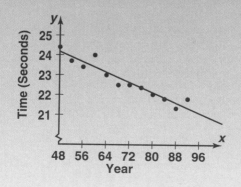

b. An equation for the line of best fit is $y = -0.06355x + 147.92143$. Numbers in the equation have been rounded to five decimal places. The graph of the line is shown on the scatterplot for part a.

CHAPTER REVIEW

Questions on SPUR Objectives

SPUR stands for **S**kills, **P**roperties, **U**ses, and **R**epresentations. The Chapter Review questions are grouped according to the SPUR Objectives for this chapter.

SKILLS DEAL WITH THE PROCEDURES USED TO GET ANSWERS.

Objective A: *Determine the slope and intercepts of a line given its equation.*
(Lessons 3-1, 3-2, 3-4)

In 1–3, an equation for a line is given.
a. Give its slope. **b.** Give its y-intercept.

1. $y = 7x - 2$ a) 7   b) -2
2. $500x + 700y = 1200$ a) $-\frac{5}{7}$ b) $\frac{12}{7}$
3. $y = 4$ a) 0   b) 4

In 4–6, an equation for a line is given.
a. Find its x-intercept. **b.** Find its y-intercept.

4. $3x + 5y = 45$ a) 15   b) 9
5. $x = -4.7$ a) -4.7   b) none
6. $6y = 8x$ a) 0   b) 0

Objective B: *Find an equation for a line given two points on it or given a point on it and its slope.* *(Lessons 3-2, 3-5)*

In 7–12, find an equation for the line satisfying the given conditions. 7) $y - 75 = 8(x - 40)$

7. The line has slope 8 and contains (40, 75).
8. The line has slope -0.25 and goes through the origin. $y = -0.25x$
9. The line contains (2, 4) and (-1, 6).
10. The line contains (5, -9) and (5, 14). $x = 5$
11. The line is parallel to $3x + 2y = 9$ and contains (-1, 2). $y - 2 = -\frac{3}{2}(x + 1)$
12. The line is parallel to $y = 4x$ and contains (11, 0). Sample: $y - 0 = 4(x - 11)$

9) Sample: $y - 4 = -\frac{2}{3}(x - 2)$

Objective C: *Evaluate expressions based on step functions.* *(Lesson 3-9)*

In 13 and 14, evaluate the expression.
13. **a.** $\lfloor 16.2 \rfloor$ 16   **b.** $\lfloor -16.2 \rfloor$ -17

14. **a.** $\lfloor 47.9 \rfloor$ 47   **b.** $\lfloor -47.9 \rfloor$ -48
15. Evaluate $\lfloor N + .5 \rfloor$ when $N = -17$. -17
16. Evaluate 10 INT $((X + 5)/10)$ when $X = 36$. 40

Objective D: *Evaluate or find explicit and recursive formulas for arithmetic sequences.* *(Lessons 3-7, 3-8)* See margin for 17b, 18b, 19, 21b.

In 17 and 18, an arithmetic sequence is given.
a. Find an explicit formula for the nth term.
b. Find a formula for the sequence in recursive form. See margin.
c. Find the 75th term of the sequence.

17. $7, 12, 17, 22, \ldots$ a) $a_n = 7 + (n-1)5$ c) 377
18. $8, 2, -4, -10, \ldots$ a) $a_n = 8 - 6(n-1)$ c) -436
19. Give a recursive description of the sequence whose nth term is $a_n = 2n - 11$.
20. Find an explicit formula for the nth term of the sequence defined below. See margin.
$$\begin{cases} a_1 = \frac{1}{2} \\ a_n = a_{n-1} + 4 \text{ for integers } n \geq 2 \end{cases}$$
21. **a.** Write the first five terms of an arithmetic sequence. Sample: 1, 3, 5, 7, 9
   b. Describe the sequence recursively.
   c. Find an explicit formula for the nth term of your sequence. $a_n = 1 + (n-1)2$

In 22 and 23, a program is given. **a.** Tell how many terms will be printed; **b.** Give the first five terms that will be displayed. See margin.

22.
```
20 LET A = 100
30 FOR N = 1 TO 1000
40 PRINT A
50 A = A + 1
60 NEXT N
70 END
```
23.
```
For (N, 1, 10)
Disp 2 * N + 3
End
```

Additional responses, page 193
c. Predictions will vary. Samples given are rounded to two decimal places.

Year	Predicted Time
2000	20.82 sec
2024	19.30 sec
2076	15.99 sec
3000	−42.73 sec

Taking the limitations of the human body into consideration, the prediction for 2000 seems conceivable and that for 2024 might be possible. The prediction for 2076 seems highly doubtful. the prediction for 3000 is completely impossible, since the time cannot be negative.

5a. 681¢ or $6.81
   $681 = 23 \cdot 32 - 23 - 32$
b. $xy - x - y$ cents

Chapter 3 Review

Resources

From the ***Teacher's Resource File***
■ Answer Masters for Chapter 3 Review
■ Assessment Sourcebook: Chapter 3 Test, Forms A–D Chapter 3 Cumulative Form Comprehensive Test, Chapters 1–3

Additional Resources
■ Quiz and Test Writer

The main objectives for the chapter are organized in the Chapter Review under the four types of understanding this book promotes: Skills, Properties, Uses, and Representations.

Whereas end-of-chapter material may be considered optional in some texts, in UCSMP *Advanced Algebra* we have selected these objectives and questions with the expectation that they will be covered. Students should be able to answer these questions with about 85% accuracy after studying the chapter.

You may assign these questions over a single night to help students prepare for a test the next day, or you may assign the questions over a two-day period. If you work the questions over two days, we recommend assigning the *evens* for homework the first night so that students get feedback in class the next day and then assigning the *odds* the night before the test because answers are provided to the odd-numbered questions.

It is effective to ask students which questions they still do not understand and use the day or days as a total class discussion of the material which the class finds most difficult.

Methods students use to arrive at this response may vary. They might begin with smaller pairs of relatively prime numbers, find various combinations, and note greatest value they cannot make. Then, after studying the greatest values and the two relatively prime numbers, they should come up with a pattern.

(Responses continue on page 198.)

Assessment

Evaluation The *Assessment Sourcebook* provides six forms of the Chapter 3 Test. Forms A and B present parallel versions in a short-answer format. Forms C and D offer performance assessment. The fifth test is Chapter 3 Test, Cumulative Form. About 50% of this test covers Chapter 3, 25% of it covers Chapter 2, and 25% of it covers Chapter 1. In addition to these tests, Comprehensive Test Chapters 1–3 gives roughly equal attention to all chapters covered thus far.

For information on grading, see *General Teaching Suggestions; Grading* in the *Professional Sourcebook,* which begins on page T20 in this Teacher's Edition.

Feedback After students have taken the test for Chapter 3 and you have scored the results, return the tests to students for discussion. Class discussion of the questions that caused trouble for the most students can be very effective in identifying and clarifying misunderstandings. You might want to have them write down the items they missed and work, either in groups or at home, to correct them. It is important for students to receive feedback on every chapter test, and we recommend that students see and correct their mistakes before proceeding too far into the next chapter.

Additional Answers, page 198
27. domain: the set of all real
    numbers
    range: the set of all real
    numbers
36. To form an arithmetic
    sequence, start with the first
    term. Each term after the first
    is found by adding a constant
    difference to the previous
    term.

PROPERTIES DEAL WITH THE PRINCIPLES BEHIND THE MATHEMATICS.

See below for 26, 29, and 30. See margin for 27.

Objective E: *Recognize properties of linear functions.* (Lessons 3-1, 3-2, 3-4, 3-5)

In 24–26, consider the equation $y = mx + b$.

24. When does this equation model a constant-increase situation? when m is positive.

25. What constant represents the initial amount? b

26. What is this form of a linear equation called?

27. Give the domain and range of $f(x) = 3x - 7$.

28. *Multiple choice.* Which of the following does *not* mean a slope of $-\frac{4}{3}$? a

(a) a vertical change of -3 units for a horizontal change of 4 units

(b) a vertical change of -4 units for a horizontal change of 3 units

(c) a vertical change of $-\frac{4}{3}$ units for a horizontal change of 1 unit

(d) a vertical change of $\frac{4}{3}$ units for a horizontal change of -1 unit

29. What is true about the slopes of parallel lines?

In 30–32, refer to the equation $Ax + By = C$.

30. To find the x-intercept, substitute $\underline{?}$ for $\underline{?}$.

31. If $A = 0$ and $B \neq 0$, the graph of this equation is a $\underline{?}$ line. horizontal

32. For what values of A and B does the equation *not* represent a function?
$A \neq 0, B = 0$

26) slope-intercept   29) slopes are equal
30) 0; y

a) horizontal b) oblique c) vertical

33. State whether the line is vertical, horizontal, or oblique.
  a. $y = -4$ **b.** $2x - 3y = 8$ **c.** $4x = 12$

34. Give the point-slope equation for a line.

35. *True or false.* The line with the equation $y - 5 = 3(x - 2)$ goes through the point $(5, 2)$. **False**

34) $y - y_1 = m(x - x_1)$

Objective F: *Recognize properties of arithmetic sequences.* (Lessons 3-7, 3-8)

36. Describe how arithmetic sequences are formed. See margin. 37) See below.

37. Describe the graph of an arithmetic sequence.

In 38–41, tell whether the numbers could be the first four terms of an arithmetic sequence.

38. 1.2, 1.4, 1.6, 1.8 Yes

39. $\pi + 1, \pi + 2, \pi + 3, \pi + 4$ Yes

40. $-9, -11, -13, -15$ Yes   **41.** $4, 2, \frac{1}{2}, \frac{1}{4}$ No

In 42–44, does the formula generate an arithmetic sequence?

42. $\begin{cases} a_1 = 1.5 \\ a_n = a_{n-1} + 13, \text{ for integers } n \geq 2 \end{cases}$ Yes

43. $\begin{cases} a_1 = 9 \\ a_n = 2a_{n-1}, \text{ for integers } n \geq 2 \end{cases}$ No

44. $a_n = 3n^2 + 2$ No

37) The graph is a set of collinear points.

USES DEAL WITH APPLICATIONS OF MATHEMATICS IN REAL SITUATIONS.

Objective G: *Model constant-increase or constant-decrease situations or situations involving arithmetic sequences.* (Lessons 3-1, 3-7, 3-8)

45. A crate weighs 3 kg when empty. It is filled with grapefruit weighing 0.2 kg each.
  a. Write an equation relating the weight w and the number n of grapefruit. $w = 3 + .2n$
  b. Find the weight when there are 22 grapefruit in the crate. 7.4 kg

46. A math teacher has a ream of 500 sheets of graph paper. Each week the advanced algebra class uses about 90 sheets.
  a. About how many sheets are left after w weeks? $500 - 90w$

b. After how many weeks will there be 50 sheets left? 5 weeks

47. The number of feet traveled during each second of free fall is given by the formula $a_n = 16 + 32(n - 1)$. What distance is traveled during the eighth second? 240 ft

48. When Florence Flask joined a laboratory, she was given a $26,000 salary and promised at least an $1800 raise each year. What is the longest time it could take for her salary to reach $35,000? After completing 5 years, she could begin earning $35,000.

Additional responses, page 193
In the samples shown below, note how the greatest number that cannot be made relates to the two relatively prime numbers.
  For 2 and 3: $1 = 2 \cdot 3 - 2 - 3$
  For 2 and 5: $3 = 2 \cdot 5 - 2 - 5$
  For 3 and 5: $7 = 3 \cdot 5 - 3 - 5$
  For 3 and 7: $11 = 3 \cdot 7 - 3 - 7$
  and so on.

This pattern suggests the response given for 23¢ and 32¢ in part a and for x¢ and y¢ in part b. Students can use spreadsheets to show all combinations of 23¢ and 32¢ through, say, 32 stamps of each value. Then, if they arrange the total values in order, they will see that the point after which all values seem to occur is 681.

6a. The grapher draws the part of the line $y = x - 5$ which is above the x-axis.
  b. Sample responses:
$$f(x) = |x| = \begin{cases} x \text{ for } x \geq 0 \\ -x \text{ for } x < 0 \end{cases}$$
  To graph f, enter
  $y_1 = x \div (x \geq 0)$ and
  $y_2 = (-x) \div (x < 0)$.

Objective H: *Model situations leading to linear combinations.* *(Lesson 3-3)*

49. Lubbock Lumber sells 6-foot long 2-by-4 boards for $1.70 each and 8-foot long 2-by-6 boards for $2.50 each. Last week they sold $250 worth of these boards. Let *F* be the number of 2-by-4s and *S* be the number of 2-by-6s. a) $1.7F + 2.5S = 250$.
   a. Write an equation to model this situation.
   b. If 100 2-by-4s were sold, how many 2-by-6s were sold? **32**

50. A maintenance engineer of a swimming pool combines *A* gallons of solution that is 6% chlorine and *B* gallons of solution that is 8% chlorine. a) $A + B$ gal   b) $.06A + .08B$ gal
   a. How much solution is there altogether?
   b. How much chlorine is there altogether?
   c. Two gallons of chlorine are needed in the pool. Write an equation that describes this situation. $.06A + .08B = 2$
   d. List three ordered pairs that are solutions to the equation in part **c.** Sample: (20, 10), (10, 17.5), (5, 21.25)

Objective I: *In a real-world context, find an equation for a line containing two points.* *(Lesson 3-5)*

51. Woody Bench finds that it costs his business $7,600 to make 30 desks and $16,000 to make 100 desks. Assuming a linear relationship exists between the cost and the number of desks, how much will it cost to make 1000 desks? **$124,000**

52. Charlotte finds that the cost of making shoes is linearly related to the number of shoes her company makes. It costs $1450 to make 150 pairs of shoes and $1675 to make 225 pairs of shoes.
   a. Let *C* = the cost of making *p* pairs of shoes. Write a formula relating *C* to *p*.
   b. Rewrite the equation in part **a** in slope-intercept form, and explain what the slope represents in this situation.
   c. How much will it cost to make 500 pairs of shoes? **$2500**

a) Sample: $C - 1450 = 3(p - 150)$
b) $C = 3p + 1000$; The slope is the cost of making one pair of shoes.

Objective J: *Fit lines to data.* *(Lesson 3-6)*

53. The table below gives the percent of the population in 1981–83 in 16 countries who said more emphasis on family life would be good and the percent who said greater respect for authority would be good. a) **See margin.**
   a. Make a scatterplot of these data.
   b. Does it appear that a linear equation would be a good model for this data set? Explain your answer. **See below.**
   c. Find an equation of the linear regression line. about $y = .74x - 9.39$
   d. What is the correlation coefficient? Is it consistent with your answer to part **b**? Explain your answer. .203; This indicates a very bad fit of the data to this line.

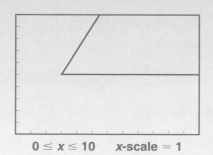

Country	Family emphasis	Respect authority
United States	94.9	85.0
Finland	94.8	29.0
Norway	92.2	36.3
Ireland	90.5	84.4
Australia	90.2	68.3
Canada	90.2	75.6
Denmark	88.0	35.9
France	87.9	56.8
Italy	87.9	56.8
Belgium	84.0	60.0
Sweden	83.7	38.9
Germany	83.5	76.0
Spain	83.5	76.0
United Kingdom	82.1	70.0
Japan	79.7	6.5
Netherlands	70.4	56.9

Source: *We're Number One!* by Andrew L. Shapiro, Vintage Books, 1992

b) **Sample: No;** The data do not seem to lie on a line.

Additional Answers, page 199
53a.

$$g(x) = \begin{cases} 2x - 1 \text{ for } x > 3 \\ 5 \text{ for } x \geq 3 \end{cases}$$

To graph g, enter
$y_1 = (2x - 1) \div (x > 3)$ **and**
$y_2 = (5) \div (x \geq 3)$.
The graph is shown at the right.

$0 \leq x \leq 10$ *x*-scale = 1
$0 \leq y \leq 10$ *y*-scale = 1

Setting Up Lesson 4-1

Homework We recommend that you assign both the reading and some questions in Lesson 4-1 for homework the evening of the test.

Materials If you plan to have students do Question 24 on page 208, they will need a newspaper. If you plan to have students do the *Extension* on page 208, they will need an almanac.

Additional Answers, pages 200–201

54 a.

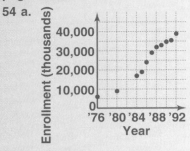

b. Sample: Yes; nearly all of the points seem to lie on a line.

c. about
$y = 2247.57x - 4438976.17$

d. Yes; a correlation coefficient of .976 indicates a very strong linear relationship.

e. about 44925.98 thousands, or 44,925,980 people

55a, b.

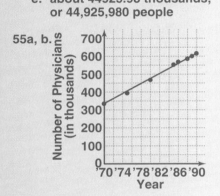

b. Sample:
$y - 334 = 14.07(x - 1970)$

c. Sample: 530,000 physicians

d. about $y = 14.45x - 28144.96$

e. It shows an increase of about 14.45 (thousand) physicians per year.

f. about 523,840 physicians

g. Sample: The correlation coefficient is .998, showing a very strong linear relationship between the regression equation and the data.

57a. $19.62
b. $84.24

58. Sample:

$$C = \begin{cases} .4287t, & 0 < t \le 50 \\ .3432(t - 50) + 21.44, & t > 50 \end{cases}$$

60.

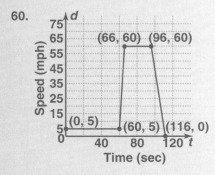

---

54. The table gives the number of people who belong to Health Maintenance Organizations (HMOs). *See margin.*

Year	Enrollment (in thousands)
1976	6,016
1980	9,100
1984	16,743
1985	18,894
1986	23,664
1987	28,587
1988	31,848
1989	32,557
1990	34,663
1991	35,263
1992	38,842

Source: Statistical Abstract of the United States: 1993

a. Make a scatterplot of these data.
b. Does it seem reasonable to fit a line to these data? Explain.
c. Find an equation of the regression line.
d. Does the correlation coefficient suggest that a linear equation is a reasonable way to model these data? Explain.
e. According to this model, what will the HMO enrollment be in 1995?

55. Use the table below. *See margin.*

Year	Number of Physicians (thousands)
1970	334.0
1975	393.7
1980	467.7
1985	552.7
1986	569.2
1988	585.6
1989	600.8
1990	615.4

Source: Statistical Abstract of the United States: 1993

a. Make a scatterplot of these data.
b. Fit a line by eye to these data points and determine the equation of this line.
c. Use the line you drew in part b to estimate the number of physicians in the U.S. in 1984.
d. Find an equation of the line of best fit.
e. Explain what the slope of the regression line means.
f. Use your equation from part d to estimate the number of physicians in the U.S. in 1984.
g. Explain how you know that a linear equation models these data well.

---

56. The display shows the number of public school students (in millions) in the U.S. since 1955. The equation of the regression line is $y = .458x - 856.75$ with $r = .74$.

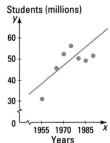

Students (millions)

Source: Statistical Abstract of the United States: 1992

a. There is no data point for 1960. Estimate the number of public school students in 1960. ≈ **41 million**
b. For 1970, **(i)** what is the observed enrollment? **(ii)** what is the predicted enrollment?
c. Estimate the public school enrollment in 2000. ≈ **59.25 million**
b) i) ≈ **52 million** ii) ≈ **45.51 million**

Objective K: *Model situations leading to piecewise-linear functions or to step functions.* (Lessons 3-1, 3-5, 3-9) See margin for 57, 58.

In 57 and 58, a gas company charges $.4287 per therm for the first 50 therms used and $0.3432 per therm for each therm over 50.

57. Find the gas bill for a customer who used **a.** 45.76 therms. **b.** 232.99 therms.

58. Describe this situation algebraically.

59. Refer to the graph below. Cory traveled from her cousin's house to her grandmother's and then back home.

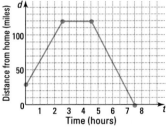

30 mi

a. How far from home did Cory start?
b. How fast did Cory travel during the first two hours? **35 mph**
c. What was the total distance Cory traveled? **210 mi**

63.

64.

65.

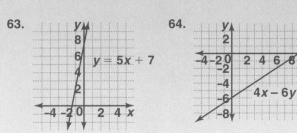

REPRESENTATIONS DEAL WITH PICTURES, GRAPHS, OR OBJECTS THAT ILLUSTRATE CONCEPTS.

See margin for 60.

60. A cheetah trots along at 5 mph for a minute, spies a small deer and accelerates to 60 mph in just 6 seconds. After chasing the deer at this speed for 30 seconds, the cheetah gives up, and over the next 20 seconds, slows to a stop. Graph this situation plotting time on the horizontal axis and speed on the vertical axis.

61. *Multiple choice.* Suppose you earn $5 per hour and the time you work is rounded down to the nearest hour. What is a rule for the function that relates time t in hours to wages w in dollars? c

(a) $w = \lfloor 5t \rfloor$ (b) $w = \left\lfloor \dfrac{t}{5} \right\rfloor$

(c) $w = 5\lfloor t \rfloor$ (d) $w = 5\left\lfloor t - \dfrac{1}{2} \right\rfloor$

62. Evening phone rates, not including taxes, between two cities are 47¢ for the first minute and 33¢ for each additional minute or portion of a minute. How much will it cost to make a 12 minute 10 second phone call between these cities? **$4.43**

Objective L: *Graph or interpret graphs of linear equations.* (Lessons 3-2, 3-4)

63. Graph the line with slope 5 and y-intercept 7.

64. Graph the line $4x - 6y = 36$ using its intercepts. **63–66) See margin.**

65. Graph $x = 3$ in the coordinate plane.

66. Graph $y = -1$ in the coordinate plane.

In 67–69, tell whether the slope of the line is positive, negative, zero, or undefined.

67.   **68.**   **69.**

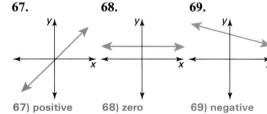

67) positive   68) zero   69) negative

year (y)	1904	1948	1953	1966	1970	1972	1975	1981	1984	1986	1990	1992
fare (f)	.05	.10	.15	.20	.30	.35	.50	.75	.90	1.00	1.15	1.25

70. What is an equation for the line graphed here?
Sample:
$y = -\dfrac{1}{2}x + 2$

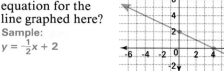

Objective M: *Graph or interpret graphs of piecewise-linear functions or step functions.* (Lessons 3-1, 3-9) See margin for 71–75.

71. Use the function f, where
$$f(x) = \begin{cases} x + 3, & \text{for } x \le 0 \\ 3, & \text{for } x > 0 \end{cases}.$$
   a. Draw a graph of $y = f(x)$.
   b. Find the domain and range of f.

72. Consider the function $g(x) = \lfloor x \rfloor + 4$.
   a. Draw a graph of $y = g(x)$.
   b. Give the domain and range of g.

73. The evening phone rate between two cities is 21¢ for the first minute and 18¢ for each additional minute or fraction thereof. Graph the cost C as a function of the time t for the domain $\{t: 0 \le t \le 10\}$.

74. A salesperson earns a bonus of $270 for every $1000 of merchandise sold. Draw a graph of the bonuses as a function of the value of the merchandise sold.

75. The New York City subway system opened in 1904 with the cost of a one-way ticket being 5¢. In 1948 the fare increased (for the first time) to 10¢. Below is a table of the fares charged and the years these fares took effect.
   a. Make a graph of the fares on the New York City Subway from 1904 to 1994. Let y be the independent variable.
   b. *True or false.* The set of ordered pairs (y, f) for $1904 \le y \le 1992$ is a linear function.

Chapter 3   *Chapter Review*   **201**

72a.

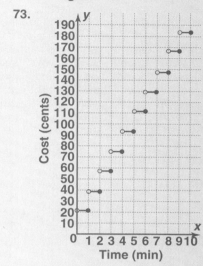

$g(x) = \lfloor x \rfloor + 4$

b. domain: the set of all real numbers range: the set of integers

73.

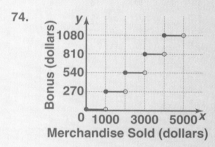

74.

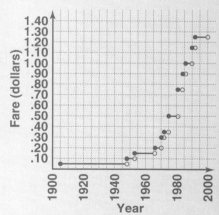

75a.

b. False

66.

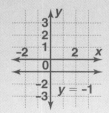

71a.

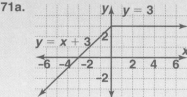

$y = 3$
$y = x + 3$

b. domain: the set of all real numbers range: $\{y: y \le 3\}$

201

Chapter 4 Pacing Chart

Day	Full Course	Minimal Course
1	4-1	4-1
2	4-2	4-2
3	4-3	4-3
4	Quiz*; 4-4	Quiz*; begin 4-4.
5	4-5	Finish 4-4.
6	4-6	4-5
7	4-7	4-6
8	Quiz*; 4-8	4-7
9	4-9	Quiz*; begin 4-8.
10	4-10	Finish 4-8
11	Self-Test	4-9
12	Review	4-10
13	Test*	Self-Test
14		Review
15		Review
16		Test*

*in the Teacher's Resource File

Adapting to Individual Needs

The student text is written for the vast majority of students. The chart at the right suggests two pacing plans to accommodate the needs of your students. Students in the Full Course should complete the entire text by the end of the year. Students in the Minimal Course will spend more time when there are quizzes and more time on the Chapter Review. Therefore, these students may not complete all of the chapters in the text.

Options are also presented to meet the needs of a variety of teaching and learning styles. For each lesson, the Teacher's Edition provides sections entitled: *Video* which describes video segments and related questions that can be used for motivation or extension; *Optional Activities* which suggests activities that employ materials, physical models, technology, and cooperative learning; and *Adapting to Individual Needs* which regularly includes **Challenge** problems, **English Language Development** suggestions, and suggestions for providing **Extra Help.** The Teacher's Edition also frequently includes an **Error Alert,** an **Extension,** and an **Assessment** alternative. The options available in Chapter 4 are summarized in the chart below.

In the Teacher's Edition...

Lesson	Optional Activities	Extra Help	Challenge	English Language Development	Error Alert	Extension	Cooperative Learning	Ongoing Assessment
4-1	●		●	●		●	●	Oral/Written
4-2	●	●	●		●			Written
4-3	●	●	●			●	●	Written
4-4	●	●	●	●		●		Written
4-5	●		●	●		●	●	Oral/Written
4-6	●	●	●	●		●	●	Written
4-7	●	●	●			●	●	Oral/Written
4-8	●	●		●			●	Written
4-9	●	●	●	●		●	●	Written
4-10	●	●	●			●	●	Group

In the Additional Resources...

	In the Teacher's Resource File								
Lesson	Lesson Masters, A and B	Teaching Aids*	Activity Kit*	Answer Masters	Technology Sourcebook	Assessment Sourcebook	Visual Aids**	Technology	Video Segments
4-1	4-1	8, 31, 35		4-1			8, 31, 34, AM		
4-2	4-2	8, 31, 36		4-2			8, 31, 35, 36, AM		
4-3	4-3	32, 37		4-3		Quiz	32, 37, AM		
In-class Activity				4-4			AM		
4-4	4-4	8, 32, 38		4-4			8, 32, 38, AM		
4-5	4-5	8, 32, 38		4-5			8, 32, 38, AM		
4-6	4-6	8, 33, 38	7	4-6			8, 33, 38, AM		4-6
4-7	4-7	8, 33, 40		4-7		Quiz	8, 33, 40, AM		
4-8	4-8	8, 33, 38, 39	8	4-8	Comp 4		8, 33, 38, AM	Spreadsheet	
4-9	4-9	8, 34, 41, 42		4-9	Comp 5		8, 34, 41, 42, AM	GraphExplorer	
4-10	4-10	8, 34, 39		4-10			8, 39, AM		
Summary		38, 39					38, 39		
End of chapter						Tests			

*Teaching Aids are pictured on pages 202C and 202D. The activities in the Activity Kit are pictured on page 202C.

**Visual Aids provide transparencies for all Teaching Aids and all Answer Masters.

Also available is the Study Skills Handbook which includes study-skill tips related to reading, note-taking, and comprehension.

Integrating Strands and Applications

	4-1	4-2	4-3	4-4	4-5	4-6	4-7	4-8	4-9	4-10
Mathematical Connections										
Algebra	●	●	●	●	●	●	●	●	●	●
Geometry	●	●	●	●	●	●	●	●	●	●
Measurement	●			●	●	●	●	●	●	●
Logic and Reasoning						●	●	●	●	●
Statistics/ Data Analysis		●								
Patterns and Functions	●	●	●	●	●	●	●	●	●	●
Interdisciplinary and Other Connections										
Art				●				●	●	
Science	●				●			●		
Social Studies	●	●	●	●	●	●	●		●	●
Multicultural			●				●		●	
Technology		●	●					●	●	
Career		●	●							●
Consumer		●	●							
Sports	●	●	●			●				

Teaching and Assessing the Chapter Objectives

Chapter 4 Objectives (Organized into the SPUR categories—Skills, Properties, Uses, and Representations)	Lessons	Progress Self-Test Questions	Chapter Review Questions	Chapter Test, Forms A and B	Chapter Test, Forms	
					C	**D**
Skills						
A: Add, subtract, and find scalar multiples of matrices.	4-2	5, 6	1–6	6	1	
B: Multiply matrices.	4-3	4	7–12	3, 4	1	
C: Determine equations of lines perpendicular to given lines.	4-9	8	13–16	13	3	
Properties						
D: Recognize properties of matrix operations.	4-2, 4-3, 4-7	3, 7	17–21	3, 5	1	
E: Recognize relationships between figures and their transformation images.	4-4, 4-5, 4-6, 4-8, 4-9, 4-10	11	22–27	14, 18	5	✓
F: Relate transformations to matrices, and vice versa.	4-4, 4-5, 4-6, 4-7 4-8, 4-10	9, 10, 12, 15, 16, 17, 19, 20	28–39	7–12, 16, 17	4, 5	✓
Uses						
G: Use matrices to store data.	4-1	2	40–43	2	2	
H: Use matrix addition, matrix multiplication, and scalar multiplication to solve real-world problems.	4-2, 4-3	13, 14	44–47	19, 20	2	
Representations						
I: Graph figures and their transformation images.	4-1, 4-4, 4-5, 4-6, 4-7, 4-8, 4-10	1, 18	48–52	1, 15	5	✓

In the Teacher's Resource File

Assessment Sourcebook
Quiz for Lessons 4-1 through 4-3
Quiz for Lessons 4-4 through 4-7

Chapter 4 Test, Forms A–D
Chapter 4 Test, Cumulative Form

Quiz and Test Writer

Activity Kit

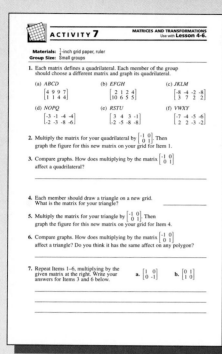

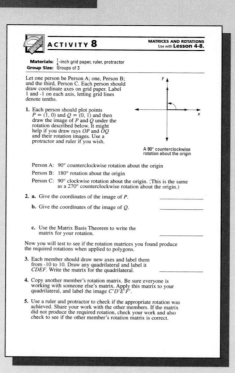

Teaching Aids

Teaching Aid 8, Four-quadrant Graph Paper, (shown on page 4D) can be used with
Lessons 4-1, 4-2, and 4-4 through 4-10.

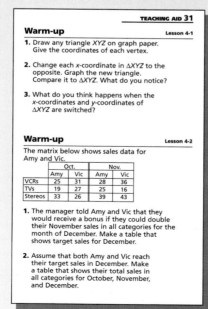

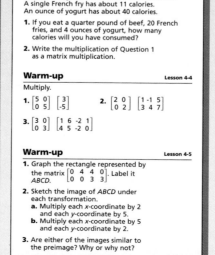

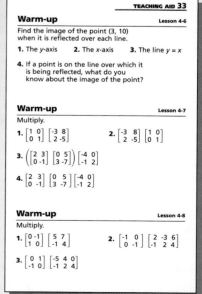

error

202C

Warm-up
Lesson 4-9

Find the slope of the line through the points in each pair.

1. (-6, 2) and (-2, 8)

2. (1, 9) and (7, 5)

3. Graph the lines in Questions 1 and 2. What is true about the lines?

Warm-up
Lesson 4-10

1. Name the matrix representing the rectangle with coordinates $A = (0, 0)$, $B = (6, 0)$, $C = (6, 5)$, and $D = (0, 5)$.

2. Determine the matrix for the coordinates of $A'B'C'D'$ by adding the matrix in Question 1 to
$\begin{bmatrix} 4 & 4 & 4 & 4 \\ 2 & 2 & 2 & 2 \end{bmatrix}$.

3. What relationship exits between $ABCD$ and $A'B'C'D'$?

Additional Examples

1. The high and low Celsius temperatures for six cities on October 11, 1993, were: Beijing, 20, 8; Lima, 19, 16; Moscow, 9, 3; New Delhi, 34, 19; Paris, 16, 9; and Wellington, 12, 7.

   a. Store this information in a matrix.

   b. What are the dimensions of the matrix you made for **part a?**

2. Use the heptagon below.

   a. Write polygon *HEPTAGO* as a matrix.

   b. Write polygon *TAGOHEP* as a matrix.

   c. Are the two matrices in **parts a and b** equal? Why or why not?

Additional Examples

1. Matrices A and B give the production (in thousands) of passenger cars and trucks in selected countries.

A = 1991 Production

	U.S.	Japan	Ger.	France
cars	5439	9753	4809	3188
trucks	3372	3492	391	423

B = 1992 Production

	U.S.	Japan	Ger.	France
cars	5663	9379	4864	3329
trucks	4038	3121	330	438

   a. Find $B - A$.

   b. Which type of vehicle in which country had the greatest increase in production? What was the increase?

2. Find the product.
$3 \begin{bmatrix} 25 & 17 & 50 \\ 30 & 20 & 62 \end{bmatrix}$

Examples of Matrix Multiplication

Example 1

Let $A = \begin{bmatrix} 8 & -2 \\ 4 & 1 \end{bmatrix}$ and $B = \begin{bmatrix} 1 & 3 & 5 \\ 0 & 4 & 2 \end{bmatrix}$. Find AB.
$\quad 2 \times 2 \qquad\qquad 2 \times 3$

$\begin{bmatrix} 8 & -2 \\ 4 & 1 \end{bmatrix} \begin{bmatrix} 1 & 3 & 5 \\ 0 & 4 & 2 \end{bmatrix} = \begin{bmatrix} 8 & — & — \\ — & — & — \end{bmatrix}$

$\begin{bmatrix} 8 & -2 \\ 4 & 1 \end{bmatrix} \begin{bmatrix} 1 & 3 & 5 \\ 0 & 4 & 2 \end{bmatrix} = \begin{bmatrix} 8 & 16 & — \\ — & — & — \end{bmatrix}$

The other four elements are found using

this row ⬜ by column ⬜ pattern.

For instance:
$\begin{bmatrix} 8 & -2 \\ 4 & 1 \end{bmatrix} \begin{bmatrix} 1 & 3 & 5 \\ 0 & 4 & 2 \end{bmatrix} = \begin{bmatrix} 8 & 16 & 36 \\ 4 & 16 & 22 \end{bmatrix}$

Example 2

$\begin{bmatrix} 8 & 10 \end{bmatrix} \left(\begin{bmatrix} 5 & 4 & 3 \\ 6 & 5 & 2 \end{bmatrix} \begin{bmatrix} 4 \\ 2 \\ .50 \end{bmatrix} \right)$

$= \begin{bmatrix} 8 & 10 \end{bmatrix} \begin{bmatrix} 5 \cdot 4 + 4 \cdot 2 + 3 \cdot .50 \\ 6 \cdot 4 + 5 \cdot 2 + 2 \cdot .50 \end{bmatrix}$

$= \begin{bmatrix} 8 & 10 \end{bmatrix} \begin{bmatrix} 29.50 \\ 35 \end{bmatrix}$

$= \begin{bmatrix} 8 \cdot 29.50 + 10 \cdot 35 \end{bmatrix}$

$= \begin{bmatrix} 586 \end{bmatrix}$

Transformations and Their Matrices

Transformations Yielding Images Similar to Preimage

Size change with center (0, 0), magnitude k:
$\begin{bmatrix} k & 0 \\ 0 & k \end{bmatrix}$
$S_k(x, y) = (kx, ky)$

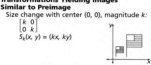

Other Transformations

Scale changes with horizontal magnitude a and vertical magnitude b:
$\begin{bmatrix} a & 0 \\ 0 & b \end{bmatrix}$
$S_{a, b}(x, y) = (ax, by)$

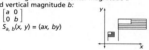

Transformations Yielding Images Congruent to Preimages

Reflections:

over x-axis	over y-axis	over line $x = y$
$\begin{bmatrix} 1 & 0 \\ 0 & -1 \end{bmatrix}$	$\begin{bmatrix} -1 & 0 \\ 0 & 1 \end{bmatrix}$	$\begin{bmatrix} 0 & 1 \\ 1 & 0 \end{bmatrix}$
$r_x(x, y) = (x, -y)$	$r_y(x, y) = (-x, y)$	$r_{y = x}(x, y) = (y, x)$

More Transformations and Their Matrices

Rotations with center (0, 0):

magnitude 90°	magnitude 180°	magnitude 270°
$\begin{bmatrix} 0 & -1 \\ 1 & 0 \end{bmatrix}$	$\begin{bmatrix} -1 & 0 \\ 0 & -1 \end{bmatrix}$	$\begin{bmatrix} 0 & 1 \\ -1 & 0 \end{bmatrix}$
$R_{90}(x, y) = (-y, x)$	$R_{180}(x, y) = (-x, -y)$	$R_{270}(x, y) = (y, -x)$

Translations: No general matrix;
$T_{h,k}(x, y) = (x + h, y + k)$.

Composition of Transformations

$r_{y = x} \circ r_x (\triangle ABC)$

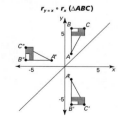

$r_x \qquad A\ B\ C \qquad A'\ B'\ C'$
$\begin{bmatrix} 1 & 0 \\ 0 & -1 \end{bmatrix} \begin{bmatrix} 1 & 1 & 3 \\ 2 & 6 & 6 \end{bmatrix} = \begin{bmatrix} 1 & 1 & 3 \\ -2 & -6 & -6 \end{bmatrix}$

$r_{y = x} \qquad A'\ B'\ C' \qquad A''\ B''\ C''$
$\begin{bmatrix} 0 & 1 \\ 1 & 0 \end{bmatrix} \begin{bmatrix} 1 & 1 & 3 \\ -2 & -6 & -6 \end{bmatrix} = \begin{bmatrix} -2 & -6 & -6 \\ 1 & 1 & 3 \end{bmatrix}$

$r_{y = x} \quad r_x \qquad A\ B\ C \qquad A''\ B''\ C''$
$\begin{bmatrix} 0 & 1 \\ 1 & 0 \end{bmatrix} \left(\begin{bmatrix} 1 & 0 \\ 0 & -1 \end{bmatrix} \begin{bmatrix} 1 & 1 & 3 \\ 2 & 6 & 6 \end{bmatrix} \right) = \begin{bmatrix} -2 & -6 & -6 \\ 1 & 1 & 3 \end{bmatrix}$

Relationships Between Perpendicular and Parallel Lines

	$m \parallel n$	$m \perp n$
$\ell \parallel m$	$\ell \parallel n$	$\ell \perp n$
$\ell \perp m$	$\ell \perp n$	$\ell \parallel n$

Proof of Theorem

If two lines with slopes m_1 and m_2 are perpendicular, then $m_1 \cdot m_2 = -1$.

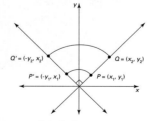

m_1 = slope of $\overleftrightarrow{PQ} = \dfrac{y_2 - y_1}{x_2 - x_1}$

m_2 = slope of $\overleftrightarrow{P'Q'} = \dfrac{x_2 - x_1}{-y_2 - (-y_1)} = \dfrac{x_2 - x_1}{-(y_2 - y_1)} = -\dfrac{x_2 - x_1}{y_2 - y_1}$

$m_1 \cdot m_2 = \dfrac{y_2 - y_1}{x_2 - x_1} \cdot \left(-\dfrac{x_2 - x_1}{y_2 - y_1} \right)$

$= -1$

Chapter Opener

CHAPTER 4

202

Pacing

All lessons in this chapter are designed to be covered in one day. At the end of the chapter, you should plan to spend 1 day to review the Progress Self-Test, 1 to 2 days for the Chapter Review, and 1 day for a test. You may want to spend a day on projects, and a day may be needed for quizzes. Therefore, this chapter should take 13–16 days.

If your students have never encountered geometric transformations, the chapter may take a day or two longer. We recommend that you not spend more than 18 days on this chapter; there is ample opportunity to review ideas in later chapters.

Using pages 202–203

The study of matrices is introduced with a discussion about the need to store data. Many problems in the real world are very complex because they require the manipulation of large quantities of data—sometimes tens of thousands of variables. For example, predictions of how the U.S. economy will perform in the future, or a study of how students are currently performing, or a report dealing with what a sports team did in its previous game, may be based upon the analysis of very large quantities of data. In a printed book, there is usually not enough room to show such large matrices. The matrix showing data regarding the planets was selected because its entries are varied and interesting.

Chapter 4 Overview

Matrices first entered high school mathematics programs with the new-math curricula of the late 1950s and early 1960s. Their appearance was justified by their importance to linear algebra in general and to the study of systems of equations in particular. Now, with the increase in importance of computers, two other important uses have become apparent—first, in the storage of data, and second, in representing geometric

transformations. Thus matrices and their operations should be familiar content.

There are two broad goals for Chapter 4. One goal is to study matrices as a means for storing data and solving problems. A second is to use matrices to review geometric transformations. The language of reflections, rotations, translations, size changes, and scale changes appears again in later chapters. The application to solving

systems appears in Chapter 5. This chapter consists of several groups of lessons. Lessons 4-1 to 4-3 introduce the vocabulary and notation for matrices, their use in storing data, and the operations of matrix addition and multiplication. Lessons 4-4 and 4-5 discuss matrices used for size and scale changes, along with those properties which are preserved or not preserved. Lessons 4-6 to 4-8 introduce matrices used for reflections and rotations. These lessons

MATRICES

A **matrix** is a rectangular arrangement of objects, each of which is called an **element** of the matrix. The plural of "matrix" is "matrices." One use of matrices is to store data. In the matrix below, the elements represent data describing the nine planets in our solar system.

	Mean Distance from Sun (millions of km)	Period of Revolution	Equatorial Diameter (km)
Mercury	57.9	88 days	4,880
Venus	108.2	224.7 days	12,100
Earth	149.6	365.2 days	12,756
Mars	227.9	687 days	6,794
Jupiter	778.3	11.86 years	142,800
Saturn	1,427	29.46 years	120,660
Uranus	2,870	84 years	51,810
Neptune	4,497	165 years	49,528
Pluto	5,900	248 years	2,290

Source: *The 1994 Information Please Almanac*

The brackets [ ] identify the matrix. The titles of the rows and columns are not part of the matrix.

A second use of matrices is to describe transformations of geometric figures. On the graph below, *QUAD* has been reflected over the *x*-axis. The vertices of *QUAD* may be described by a matrix. You will learn that the coordinates of the image *Q'U'A'D'* can be found by multiplying two matrices.

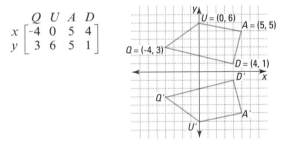

$$\begin{array}{c} \\ x \\ y \end{array} \begin{array}{cccc} Q & U & A & D \\ \left[\begin{array}{cccc} -4 & 0 & 5 & 4 \\ 3 & 6 & 5 & 1 \end{array}\right] \end{array}$$

In this chapter you will study various operations using matrices, and how those operations can be applied to geometric transformations and real-life situations.

203

provide the mathematics necessary to prove the relationship between slopes of perpendicular lines presented in Lesson 4-9. The final lesson deals with matrix addition and its application to the study of translations. A summary at the end of the chapter contains all the transformation matrices presented in Chapter 4.

The matrix content of Chapter 4 will be new to most students, but most of the corresponding transformations will be familiar to students who have studied *Transition Mathematics,* UCSMP *Algebra,* or *Geometry.* Only scale changes will likely be new.

In this chapter, the matrices have numerical entries only. However, many matrices contain *alphanumeric* data—that is, a combination of letters and numerals.

Another use of matrices is shown in the second example, that is, to describe geometric *transformations*. Transformations are not only mathematically interesting, but they also are used to apply the geometry of congruence and similarity to algebra.

The first matrix stores data, and it is not a matrix that we would normally add to or multiply by other matrices. However, the second matrix is one that we can multiply by other matrices, and students will learn how to do so in Lesson 4-3.

Photo Connections

The photo collage makes real-world connections to the content of the chapter: matrices.

Mountains: When mountains are reflected in a lake, the orientation of the image is different from that of the mountains. In geometry, when a figure is reflected, the orientation of the points is changed. Matrices can be used to denote reflections of geometric figures.

Clock with Earth: When the earth rotates on its axis, it takes 24 hours for a complete rotation. The rotation of the earth about the sun takes 365 1/4 days. Matrices can also be used to denote rotations of geometric figures.

Flag: The design of the flag for the United States has changed many times. The present 50-star design was adopted in 1960 after Hawaii became the fiftieth state.

Trumpet: The chief brass instruments in an orchestra are the French horn, the trumpet, the trombone, and the tuba. In Lesson 4-1, matrices are used to describe the number of musical instruments produced by a manufacturer.

Masks: Masks and fancy costumes are an important part of Mardi Gras. In Lesson 4-3, matrix multiplication is used to determine the total cost of costumes that are made from several different materials.

Chapter 4 Projects

At this time you might want to have students look over the projects on pages 261–262.

LESSON 4-1

Storing Data in Matrices

Brass sounds. *Most horns are made of brass. The differences in tubing produce a wide variety of sounds, from the brilliant sound of the trumpet to the mellow sound of the French horn. See Example 1.*

Information is often stored in matrices. The inventory of athletic clothing owned by a high school cross-country team is shown in the matrix below.

	sweat pants	sweat shirts	shorts	
small	9	10	8	row 1
medium	18	20	19	row 2
large	20	24	23	row 3
x-large	11	11	⑫	row 4
	column 1	column 2	column 3	

the element in the 4th row and the 3rd column

❶ Dimensions of a Matrix

The elements of the matrix above are enclosed by large square brackets. (Sometimes, large parentheses are used in place of brackets.) This matrix has 4 *rows* and 3 *columns*. It is said to have the *dimensions* 4 by 3, written 4 × 3. In general, a matrix with *m* rows and *n* columns has **dimensions** $m \times n$.

The entries in spreadsheets also constitute a matrix. Recall that the entries in a spreadsheet are called cells, and the location of a cell is identified by giving its column first (a letter) and row second (a number). Matrices use the reverse order for identifying an element—row first and column second. Matrices, like spreadsheets, can have headings to identify their rows and columns. In matrices, the headings are placed outside the matrix.

204

Lesson 4-1 Overview

Broad Goals This lesson introduces the basic vocabulary of matrices: rows, columns, dimensions, and point matrix.

Perspective The material in this lesson is fairly easy and interesting for most students; it can be covered quickly the day after the Chapter 3 test. Note that we use brackets to designate matrices while some books use large parentheses. Make sure students

realize that the row and column titles are not part of the matrix itself.

If a figure is determined by *n* points, then it can be represented by a matrix. Though **Example 2** shows a matrix representing the polygon *PENTA,* its first three columns could represent ∠*EPN* or △*PNE,* or the circle through *P, N,* and *E,* or any figure determined by those three points.

Example 1

The Matterhorn Company produced 1500 trumpets and 1200 French horns in September; 2000 trumpets and 1400 French horns in October; and 900 trumpets and 700 French horns in November.
a. Store the company's production in a matrix.
b. What are the dimensions of the matrix?

Solution

a. Two matrices can be written. Matrix M_1 has the months as rows, and matrix M_2 has the months as columns. Either matrix is an acceptable way to store the data.

Matrix M_1

	trumpets	French horns
Sept.	1500	1200
Oct.	2000	1400
Nov.	900	700

Matrix M_2

	Sept.	Oct.	Nov.
trumpets	1500	2000	900
French horns	1200	1400	700

b. Matrix M_1 has 3 rows and 2 columns.
   The dimensions of M_1 are 3 × 2.
   Matrix M_2 has 2 rows and 3 columns.
   The dimensions of M_2 are 2 × 3.

Although matrices M_1 and M_2 are both acceptable ways to store the data, the two matrices are not considered equal. Two matrices are **equal matrices** if and only if they have the same dimensions and their corresponding elements are equal.

❸ Matrices and Geometry

Points and polygons can also be represented by matrices. The ordered pair (x, y) is generally represented by the matrix

$$\begin{bmatrix} x \\ y \end{bmatrix}.$$

This 2 × 1 matrix is called a **point matrix.** Notice that the element in the first row is the *x*-coordinate and the element in the second row is the *y*-coordinate. Thus, the point (5, -1) is represented by the matrix

$$\begin{bmatrix} 5 \\ -1 \end{bmatrix}.$$

Similarly, polygons can be written as matrices. The first row of the matrix contains the *x*-coordinates of the vertices in the order in which the polygon is named. The second row contains the corresponding *y*-coordinates. Example 2 illustrates this.

Lesson 4-1 *Storing Data in Matrices* **205**

Notes on Reading

You can use the *Optional Activities* below to introduce this lesson.

❶ It is important for students to understand that the dimensions of a matrix denote the number of rows and columns and that they do not refer to the values of the elements. Point out that, in everyday language, "rows" sometimes refer to both vertical and horizontal arrays, but "columns" usually refer to vertical arrays only.

Sports Connection Since the distance and terrain are different for each cross-country race, there are no national or world records for this event. In the U.S. distances of 1.5 to 3 miles have been established for high school races.

❷ Stress the definition of equality for matrices. Although both M_1 and M_2 are acceptable ways to store the same data, they are not equal.

❸ Representing a plane figure in matrix form is an essential skill for

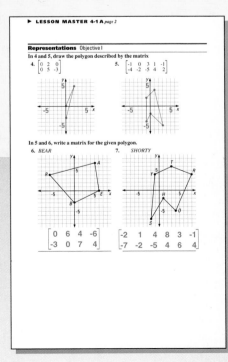

the study of transformations in Lesson 4-4. Note that matrices describing a set of points are of dimension $2 \times n$, where n is the number of points represented by the matrix. Stress that a $2 \times n$ matrix can stand for other things as well; for instance, it could mean n pieces of information related to two people. The context of a problem will determine when a $2 \times n$ matrix is used to describe a polygon.

Additional Examples

1. The high and low Celsius temperatures for six cities on October 11, 1993, were: Beijing, 20, 8; Lima, 19, 16; Moscow, 9, 3; New Delhi, 34, 19; Paris, 16, 9; and Wellington, 12, 7.
   a. Store this information in a matrix.

	High	Low
Beijing	20	8
Lima	19	16
Moscow	9	3
New Delhi	34	19
Paris	16	9
Wellington	12	7

or

	B	L	M	N	P	W
High	20	19	9	34	16	12
Low	8	16	3	19	9	7

   b. What are the dimensions of the matrix you made for **part a?** 6×2 or 2×6

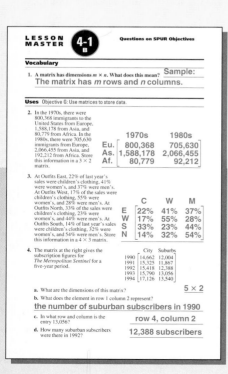

Example 2

a. Write pentagon *PENTA* as a matrix.
b. Write pentagon *NEPAT* as a matrix.
c. Are the two matrices equal? Why or why not?

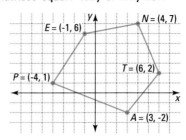

Solution

a. Starting with the coordinates of *P*, write the *x*-coordinates in the first row and the *y*-coordinates in the second row.

$$\begin{array}{c} \quad\ P\ \ \ E\ \ N\ \ \ T\ \ \ A \\ x \begin{bmatrix} -4 & -1 & 4 & 6 & 3 \\ 1 & 6 & 7 & 2 & -2 \end{bmatrix} \\ y \end{array}$$

b. Start with the coordinates of *N* and use the same procedure that was used in part **a.**

$$\begin{array}{c} \quad\ N\ \ \ E\ \ \ P\ \ \ A\ \ \ T \\ x \begin{bmatrix} 4 & -1 & -4 & 3 & 6 \\ 7 & 6 & 1 & -2 & 2 \end{bmatrix} \\ y \end{array}$$

c. **The two matrices are not equal because not all of the corresponding elements are equal. However, both matrices are valid ways to represent the polygon.**

QUESTIONS

Covering the Reading

1. What is a matrix? **a rectangular arrangement of objects**

2. *True or false.* Each element in a matrix must be a number. **False**

In 3 and 4, **a.** Give the number of rows in the indicated matrix. **b.** Give the number of columns. **c.** Give its dimensions.

3. the matrix of basic planetary data from page 203
   a) 9 b) 3 c) 9×3
4. the matrix for pentagon *PENTA* in Example 2
   a) 2 b) 5 c) 2×5

Adapting to Individual Needs

English Language Development
You might draw a rectangle on the board and measure its length and width. Explain that these numbers give the size or *dimensions* of the rectangle. Similarly, the number of rows and columns of a matrix give its size or dimensions. Be sure students understand that for a matrix, the *rows* go across and are read from left to right. The *columns*, like the columns of a building, go up and down and are read from top to bottom.

Challenge
Explain that the two matrices M_1 and M_2 in **Example 1** are *transposes* of one another—that is, the rows of one matrix are the columns of the other matrix. Then have students answer the following questions. If *A* is a matrix, A^T is the transpose of *A*.
1. If *A* is an $m \times n$ matrix, describe the dimensions of A^T. [$n \times m$]
2. What does $(A^T)^T$ mean? [A]

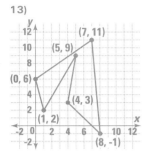

8)
$$\begin{bmatrix} 1500 & 1200 \\ 2000 & 1400 \\ 900 & 700 \\ 2500 & 3800 \end{bmatrix}$$

12)
$$\begin{array}{c} \\ x \\ y \end{array} \begin{array}{ccc} T & R & I \\ \begin{bmatrix} -1 & 2 & -2 \\ -2 & 3 & 4 \end{bmatrix} \end{array}$$

13)
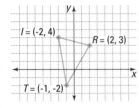

In 5–7, refer to the clothing matrix at the start of this lesson.

5. How many large sweatshirts did the cross-country team have? **24**

6. What does the element in the 2nd row, 3rd column represent?
number of medium shorts

7. What does the sum of the elements in the 3rd column represent?
total number of shorts

8. Refer to Example 1. Suppose the Matterhorn Company produces 2500 trumpets and 3800 French horns in December. Construct a 4 × 2 matrix that gives the company's production through December.
See left.

9. The ordered pair (a, b) can be represented by the matrix __?__ . This matrix is called a __?__ matrix. $\begin{bmatrix} a \\ b \end{bmatrix}$; **point**

10. *Multiple choice.* Which matrix represents the point (-136, 4.9)? **c**
(a) $\begin{bmatrix} -136 & 4.9 \end{bmatrix}$ (b) $\begin{bmatrix} 4.9 & -136 \end{bmatrix}$
(c) $\begin{bmatrix} -136 \\ 4.9 \end{bmatrix}$ (d) $\begin{bmatrix} 4.9 \\ -136 \end{bmatrix}$

11. Refer to Example 2. **See margin.**
a. Write pentagon *EPATN* as a matrix.
b. Are the matrices for *EPATN* and *ENTAP* equal? Why or why not?
c. Do *EPATN* and *ENTAP* both represent the pentagon?

12. Write △*TRI* as a matrix. **See left.**

13. The matrix below describes a hexagon. Graph this hexagon.
See left.
$$\begin{bmatrix} 7 & 8 & 4 & 5 & 1 & 0 \\ 11 & -1 & 3 & 9 & 2 & 6 \end{bmatrix}$$

Applying the Mathematics

14. The matrix below gives the numbers of active-duty U.S. military personnel in 1992.

	Commissioned Officers	Enlisted Personnel
Army	85,953	561,104
Navy	71,826	500,459
Marines	19,132	165,397
Air Force	92,000	394,800

Sources: *1993 and 1994 World Almanacs*

a. What are the dimensions of this matrix? **4 × 2** **See below.**
b. What does the sum of the elements in row 2 represent?
c. What does the sum of the elements in column 1 represent?

15. If $\begin{bmatrix} 7 & 4 \\ y & 2 \end{bmatrix} = \begin{bmatrix} x & 4 \\ 8 & 2 \end{bmatrix}$, then $x =$ __?__ and $y =$ __?__ . **7; 8**

16. If $\begin{bmatrix} 3a + 1 \\ b + 4 \end{bmatrix} = \begin{bmatrix} 7 \\ 4 \end{bmatrix}$, then $a =$ __?__ and $b =$ __?__ . **2; 0**

14b) the total number of active-duty Navy personnel in 1992
c) the total number of commissioned officers in 1992

Heralding the President. *The U.S. Army Herald Trumpets perform at many events—such as this one during the Inaugural festivities in 1993.*

Lesson 4-1 *Storing Data in Matrices* **207**

2. Use the heptagon below.

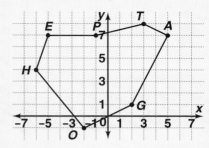

a. Write polygon *HEPTAGO* as a matrix.
$$\begin{array}{ccccccc} H & E & P & T & A & G & O \end{array}$$
$$\begin{bmatrix} -6 & -5 & -1 & 3 & 5 & 2 & -2 \\ 4 & 7 & 7 & 8 & 7 & 1 & -1 \end{bmatrix}$$

b. Write polygon *TAGOHEP* as a matrix.
$$\begin{array}{ccccccc} T & A & G & O & H & E & P \end{array}$$
$$\begin{bmatrix} 3 & 5 & 2 & -2 & -6 & -5 & -1 \\ 8 & 7 & 1 & -1 & 4 & 7 & 7 \end{bmatrix}$$

c. Are the two matrices in **parts a and b** equal? Why or why not? **No; corresponding elements are not equal.**

Notes on Questions

Questions 13 Students will need graph paper or **Teaching Aid 8.**

Questions 15 and 16 Note the application of the definition of equality of matrices.

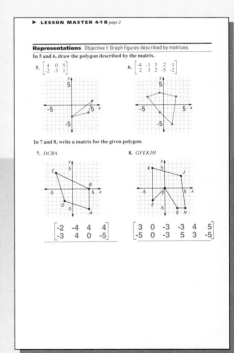

3. Write the transpose of the matrix in **Question 14** and explain how it is different from the original matrix.

$\begin{bmatrix} 85,953 & 71,826 & 19,132 & 92,000 \\ 561,104 & 500,459 & 165,397 & 394,800 \end{bmatrix}$

The elements of the rows and columns have been switched.]

4. Can $A^T = A$? If so, give an example.

[Yes. Sample: $\begin{bmatrix} 2 & 1 & 2 \\ 1 & 3 & 1 \\ 2 & 1 & 4 \end{bmatrix}$]

Additional Answers
11 a.
$$\begin{array}{ccccc} E & P & A & T & N \end{array}$$
$$\begin{bmatrix} -1 & -4 & 3 & 6 & 4 \\ 6 & 1 & -2 & 2 & 7 \end{bmatrix}$$

b. No, the corresponding elements are not equal.

c. Yes

17a) Sample:

	from A	from B	from C
to A	0	2	5
to B	3	0	3
to C	1	4	0

17. Adam, Barbara, and Clem write to each other from time to time. Last year, Adam received 2 letters from Barbara and 5 from Clem. Barbara received 3 from Adam and 3 from Clem. Clem received 1 from Adam and 4 from Barbara.
    a. Organize this information in a 3×3 matrix. (Hint: There are three zeros in the matrix.)
    b. How many letters did each person write?
       Adam, 4; Barbara, 6; Clem, 8

Review

18. Which three of the following describe the graph of $y = -4x^2$?
    (Lesson 2-5) b, c, e
    - (a) hyperbola
    - (b) direct variation
    - (c) parabola
    - (d) inverse variation
    - (e) symmetric to y-axis
    - (f) symmetric to x-axis

19. Write a short paragraph describing the changes in the graph of the line $y = kx$ as k increases from -100 to 100. Include sketches.
    (Lesson 2-4) See margin.

20. Find two more pairs (x, y) in the following function of inverse variation.   *(Lesson 2-1)* Samples: (6, 6), (18, 2)

x	1	2	3	4	5
y	36	18	12	9	7.2

21. Find the area of rectangle $ABCD$.   *(Previous course)*
    $(5 + x)(3 + y) = 15 + 3x + 5y + xy$

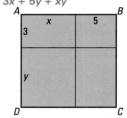

In 22 and 23, state the property.   *(Appendix A)*
22. Commutative Property of Multiplication
    For all real numbers a and b, $ab = ba$.
23. Associative Property of Addition
    For all real numbers a, b, and c, $a + (b + c) = (a + b) + c$.

Exploration

24. Information in newspapers is often organized in matrices. However, newspapers usually don't write square brackets to identify matrices. Find an example of a matrix from a newspaper.
    Samples: sports tables, stock market reports, etc.

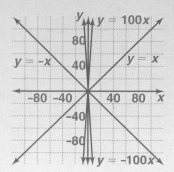

LESSON 4-2

Matrix Addition

How Are Matrices Added?

There are many situations which require adding the information stored in matrices. For instance, suppose matrix C represents the current inventory of the Chic Boutique.

$$
\begin{array}{c}
\text{dresses} \\
\text{suits} \\
\text{skirts} \\
\text{blouses}
\end{array}
\begin{array}{c}
\text{sizes} \\
\begin{array}{ccccc}
8 & 10 & 12 & 14 & 16
\end{array} \\
\left[\begin{array}{ccccc}
5 & 7 & 8 & 10 & 9 \\
3 & 4 & 6 & 2 & 2 \\
15 & 20 & 18 & \boxed{23} & 7 \\
12 & 18 & 14 & 21 & 11
\end{array}\right] = C
\end{array}
\quad \text{Current Inventory}
$$

The quantities of new items received by the boutique are represented by the numbers stored in matrix D.

$$
\begin{array}{c}
\text{dresses} \\
\text{suits} \\
\text{skirts} \\
\text{blouses}
\end{array}
\begin{array}{c}
\text{sizes} \\
\begin{array}{ccccc}
8 & 10 & 12 & 14 & 16
\end{array} \\
\left[\begin{array}{ccccc}
3 & 2 & 4 & 3 & 1 \\
1 & 2 & 3 & 4 & 2 \\
5 & 6 & 4 & \boxed{3} & 5 \\
4 & 3 & 5 & 7 & 6
\end{array}\right] = D
\end{array}
\quad \text{Delivery}
$$

The new inventory is found by taking the sum of matrices C and D. This **matrix addition** is performed according to the following definition.

Definition

If two matrices A and B have the same dimensions, their **sum** $A + B$ is the matrix in which each element is the sum of the corresponding elements in A and B.

For the previously mentioned matrices, the sum $C + D$ is a 4×5 matrix. Add corresponding elements of C and D to find the elements of $C + D$. We have circled one set of corresponding elements: $23 + 3 = 26$.

$$
\begin{array}{c}
\text{dresses} \\
\text{suits} \\
\text{skirts} \\
\text{blouses}
\end{array}
\begin{array}{c}
\text{sizes} \\
\begin{array}{ccccc}
8 & 10 & 12 & 14 & 16
\end{array} \\
\left[\begin{array}{ccccc}
8 & 9 & 12 & 13 & 10 \\
4 & 6 & 9 & 6 & 4 \\
20 & 26 & 22 & \boxed{26} & 12 \\
16 & 21 & 19 & 28 & 17
\end{array}\right] = C + D
\end{array}
\quad \text{New Inventory}
$$

Because addition of real numbers is commutative, *addition of matrices is commutative.* Thus, if two matrices A and B can be added, then $A + B = B + A$. Also, for all matrices A, B, and C, *addition of matrices is associative;* that is, $(A + B) + C = A + (B + C)$.

Lesson 4-2 *Matrix Addition* **209**

Lesson 4-2

Objectives

A Add, subtract, and find scalar multiples of matrices.

D Recognize properties of matrix addition and scalar multiplication.

H Use matrix addition and scalar multiplication to solve real-world problems.

Resources

From the *Teacher's Resource File*
- Lesson Master 4-2A or 4-2B
- Answer Master 4-2
- Teaching Aids
  8 Four-Quadrant Graph Paper
  31 Warm-up
  36 Additional Examples

Additional Resources
- Visuals for Teaching Aids 8, 31, 36
- GraphExplorer

Teaching Lesson 4-2

Warm-up

The matrix below shows sales data for Amy and Vic.

	Oct.		Nov.	
	Amy	Vic	Amy	Vic
VCRs	25	31	28	36
TVs	19	27	25	16
Stereos	33	26	39	43

(Warm-up continues on page 210.)

Lesson 4-2 Overview

Broad Goals This lesson introduces the operations of matrix addition, matrix subtraction, and scalar multiplication of a matrix by a real number.

Perspective Both addition and scalar multiplication of matrices follow conventions that students would expect to be true. In a future lesson, students will learn that multiplying by a scalar k is equivalent to multiplying by S_k, which is a matrix for a size change of k.

The two operations introduced in this lesson are also fundamental operations in linear algebra. Our goal here is simply to introduce them so that (1) students will see (in Lesson 4-10) how matrices can represent translations and (2) the next time these operations are encountered, students will have already had experience with them.

Scalar multiplication helps simplify the writing of inverses of matrices, which students will see in Chapter 5. Matrix addition and scalar multiplication are very easily done on spreadsheets.

1. The manager told Amy and Vic that they would receive a bonus if they could double their November sales in all categories for the month of December. Make a table that shows target sales for December. See below.
2. Assume that both Amy and Vic reach their target sales in December. Make a table that shows their total sales in all categories for October, November, and December.

	Dec.		Total	
	Amy	Vic	Amy	Vic
VCRs	56	72	109	139
TVs	50	32	94	75
Stereos	78	86	150	155

Notes on Reading

Students will need graph paper or **Teaching Aid 8** for this lesson.

Generally, students learn matrix addition without much difficulty. Stress that matrix addition or subtraction may be performed only on two matrices that have the same dimensions. Students should quickly realize that matrix addition is commutative. A proof is featured in the *Challenge* below.

There are some good applications of simple mathematics in this lesson. The use of matrices—as shown at the beginning of the lesson—is exceedingly common in businesses that use computers to maintain inventory.

LESSON MASTER 4-2 A **Questions on SPUR Objectives** See pages 266-269 for objectives.

Skills Objective A

In 1 and 2, express as a single matrix.

1. $\begin{bmatrix} 4 & -2 & 7 \\ 3 & 6 & 0 \end{bmatrix} + \begin{bmatrix} 1 & 4 & -6 \\ 1 & 7 & -3 \end{bmatrix}$ $\begin{bmatrix} 5 & 2 & 1 \\ 4 & 13 & -3 \end{bmatrix}$

2. $\begin{bmatrix} 4 & 1 \\ 5 & -3 \\ -6 & -2 \end{bmatrix} - \begin{bmatrix} 9 & 0 \\ 5 & 2 \\ -6 & 7 \end{bmatrix}$ $\begin{bmatrix} -5 & 1 \\ 0 & -5 \\ 0 & -9 \end{bmatrix}$

In 3–5, let $A = \begin{bmatrix} 1 & 6 & -3 \\ -5 & 4 & -1 \\ 0 & 3 & 5 \end{bmatrix}$ **and** $B = \begin{bmatrix} 1 & 3 & -2 \\ 1 & -7 & -4 \\ 0 & 8 & 2 \end{bmatrix}$. **Calculate.**

3. $A + B$ $\begin{bmatrix} 2 & 9 & -5 \\ -4 & -3 & -5 \\ 0 & 11 & 7 \end{bmatrix}$

4. $4A - B$ $\begin{bmatrix} 3 & 21 & -10 \\ -21 & 23 & 0 \\ 0 & 4 & 18 \end{bmatrix}$

5. $3A + 4B$ $\begin{bmatrix} 7 & 30 & -17 \\ -11 & -16 & -19 \\ 0 & 41 & 23 \end{bmatrix}$

In 6 and 7, solve for *a* and *b*.

6. $\begin{bmatrix} a & 3 \\ -5 & 7 \end{bmatrix} + \begin{bmatrix} 6 & -8 \\ b & 11 \end{bmatrix} = \begin{bmatrix} 10 & -5 \\ 7 & 18 \end{bmatrix}$ $a = 4, b = 12$

7. $5\begin{bmatrix} 1 & -3 \\ -6 & b \end{bmatrix} - 2\begin{bmatrix} a & -7 \\ -1 & 9 \end{bmatrix} = \begin{bmatrix} 3 & -1 \\ -28 & -3 \end{bmatrix}$ $a = 1, b = 3$

Properties Objective D

8. *True or false.* To be added or subtracted, two matrices must have the same dimensions. true

9. *True or false.* Matrix addition is commutative. true

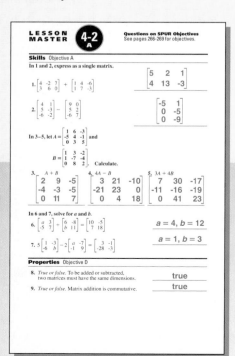

How Are Matrices Subtracted?

Subtraction of matrices is defined like matrix addition is. Given two matrices A and B with the same dimensions, their **difference** $A - B$ is the matrix whose element in each position is the difference of the corresponding elements in A and B.

Example 1

The matrix $W1$ below represents the costs of 1 dozen each of eggs and oranges in three different markets during one week. The matrix $W2$ represents the cost of these same items in the same markets during another week.

$$W1 = \begin{array}{c} \text{market} \\ \begin{array}{ccc} 1 & 2 & 3 \end{array} \\ \begin{bmatrix} .97 & .90 & .95 \\ 1.99 & 1.79 & 1.59 \end{bmatrix} \end{array} \begin{array}{l} \text{eggs} \\ \text{oranges} \end{array} \qquad W2 = \begin{array}{c} \text{market} \\ \begin{array}{ccc} 1 & 2 & 3 \end{array} \\ \begin{bmatrix} .97 & .85 & 1.05 \\ 1.49 & 1.79 & 1.89 \end{bmatrix} \end{array} \begin{array}{l} \text{eggs} \\ \text{oranges} \end{array}$$

a. Find $W2 - W1$.

b. For which of the markets was the change in the price of oranges from Week 1 to Week 2 greatest? What was the change in price?

Solution

a.
$$\overset{W2}{\begin{bmatrix} .97 & .85 & 1.05 \\ 1.49 & 1.79 & 1.89 \end{bmatrix}} - \overset{W1}{\begin{bmatrix} .97 & .90 & .95 \\ 1.99 & 1.79 & 1.59 \end{bmatrix}} = \overset{W2 - W1}{\begin{bmatrix} 0 & -.05 & .10 \\ -.50 & 0 & .30 \end{bmatrix}}$$

b. The changes in prices of oranges are given in row 2 of the matrix $W2 - W1$. The change in price of oranges from week 1 to week 2 was greatest in market 1. The price of oranges decreased $.50 per dozen in this period.

***Egg*-xamination.** *Eggs are collected onto a moving belt that carries them to be washed, rinsed, and dried. They are then* candled—*rolled over bright lights to be graded and inspected for flaws. Once inspected they are weighed, separated according to size, and packed in cartons for shipping.*

Scalar Multiplication

Matrix addition is related to a special multiplication involving matrices called *scalar multiplication.* Consider this repeated addition:

$$\begin{bmatrix} 7 & 8 \\ 4 & 2 \end{bmatrix} + \begin{bmatrix} 7 & 8 \\ 4 & 2 \end{bmatrix} + \begin{bmatrix} 7 & 8 \\ 4 & 2 \end{bmatrix} = \begin{bmatrix} 21 & 24 \\ 12 & 6 \end{bmatrix}$$

Notice that in the final result, every element of the original matrix has been multiplied by 3. With real numbers, we use multiplication as a shorthand for repeated addition; for example, $17 + 17 + 17$ can be written as 3×17. Similarly, we can rewrite the above sum as

$$3\begin{bmatrix} 7 & 8 \\ 4 & 2 \end{bmatrix}.$$

The constant 3 is called a *scalar.* **Scalar multiplication** is defined below.

Definition

The product of a scalar k and a matrix A is the matrix kA in which each element is k times the corresponding element in A.

Optional Activities

Writing After students have completed the questions in *Applying the Mathematics,* you might have them find data relating to their school system as in **Question 8**, information about favorite sports teams as in **Question 9**, or similar information on topics of interest to them. Have students display their data using matrices and write a problem involving adding or subtracting the matrices, or involving scalar multiplication.

Adapting to Individual Needs

Challenge

Ask students to prove that addition of 2×2 matrices is commutative and associative.

[Let $A = \begin{bmatrix} a & b \\ c & d \end{bmatrix}$, $B = \begin{bmatrix} e & f \\ g & h \end{bmatrix}$, $C = \begin{bmatrix} i & j \\ k & l \end{bmatrix}$, where each entry represents a real number.

$A + B =$

$\begin{bmatrix} a+e & b+f \\ c+g & d+h \end{bmatrix} = \begin{bmatrix} e+a & f+b \\ g+c & h+d \end{bmatrix} = B + A,$

Example 2

Find the product $5 \begin{bmatrix} 7 & 2 & -1 \\ 4 & 9 & 11 \end{bmatrix}$.

Solution

Multiply each element in the matrix by 5.

$$5 \begin{bmatrix} 7 & 2 & -1 \\ 4 & 9 & 11 \end{bmatrix} = \begin{bmatrix} 5 \cdot 7 & 5 \cdot 2 & 5 \cdot (-1) \\ 5 \cdot 4 & 5 \cdot 9 & 5 \cdot 11 \end{bmatrix} = \begin{bmatrix} 35 & 10 & -5 \\ 20 & 45 & 55 \end{bmatrix}$$

QUESTIONS

Covering the Reading

1. What must be true about the dimensions of two matrices in order for addition or subtraction to be possible? **They must have the same dimensions.**

In 2 and 3, refer to the clothing matrices C and D at the beginning of this lesson.

2. Does $C + D = D + C$? **Yes**

3. Suppose the shop gets another delivery described by matrix P below. **See margin.**

$$P = \begin{array}{c} \\ \\ \\ \\ \\ \end{array} \overset{\displaystyle \text{sizes}}{\begin{array}{ccccc} 8 & 10 & 12 & 14 & 16 \end{array}} \\ \begin{bmatrix} 5 & 2 & 1 & 0 & 3 \\ 4 & 1 & 1 & 1 & 2 \\ 3 & 6 & 4 & 10 & 5 \\ 4 & 2 & 5 & 11 & 12 \end{bmatrix} \begin{array}{l} \text{dresses} \\ \text{suits} \\ \text{skirts} \\ \text{blouses} \end{array}$$

Find the new inventory matrix $P + C + D$.

4. Refer to Example 1.
   a. In which market did the price of a dozen eggs change the most from Week 1 to Week 2? **market 3**
   b. Was the change an increase or a decrease? **increase**

In 5 and 6, let $A = \begin{bmatrix} 3 & 5 \\ 0 & -3 \end{bmatrix}$, $B = \begin{bmatrix} 4 & -5 \\ -2 & 1 \end{bmatrix}$, and $C = \begin{bmatrix} 1 & -1 \\ -6 & 3 \end{bmatrix}$.

5. a. Find $A - B$. **See left.**
   b. Find $B - A$. **See left.**
   c. *True or false.* Subtraction of matrices is commutative. **False**

6. a. Find $(A + B) + C$. **See left.**
   b. Find $A + (B + C)$. **See left.**
   c. The results of parts **a** and **b** show an instance of which property? **Addition of matrices is associative.**

7. If $M = \begin{bmatrix} 3 & 2 & 5 \\ 4 & 9 & 1 \end{bmatrix}$, what does $10M$ equal?

$$\begin{bmatrix} 30 & 20 & 50 \\ 40 & 90 & 10 \end{bmatrix}$$

5a) $\begin{bmatrix} -1 & 10 \\ 2 & -4 \end{bmatrix}$

b) $\begin{bmatrix} 1 & -10 \\ -2 & 4 \end{bmatrix}$

6a) $\begin{bmatrix} 8 & -1 \\ -8 & 1 \end{bmatrix}$

b) $\begin{bmatrix} 8 & -1 \\ -8 & 1 \end{bmatrix}$

Additional Examples

These examples are also given on **Teaching Aid 36**.

1. Matrices A and B give the production (in thousands) of passenger cars and trucks in selected countries.

   $A = 1991$ Production

	U.S.	Japan	Ger.	France
cars	5439	9753	4809	3188
trucks	3372	3492	391	423

   $B = 1992$ Production

	U.S.	Japan	Ger.	France
cars	5663	9379	4864	3329
trucks	4038	3121	330	438

   a. Find $B - A$.

	U.S.	Japan	Ger.	France
cars	224	-374	55	141
trucks	666	-371	-61	15

   b. Which type of vehicle in which country had the greatest increase in production? What was the increase? **U.S. trucks; 666,000 trucks**

2. Find the product.

   $3 \begin{bmatrix} 25 & 17 & 50 \\ 30 & 20 & 62 \end{bmatrix}$ $\begin{bmatrix} 75 & 51 & 150 \\ 90 & 60 & 186 \end{bmatrix}$

Additional Answers

3.

$$\begin{bmatrix} 13 & 11 & 13 & 13 & 13 \\ 8 & 7 & 10 & 7 & 6 \\ 23 & 32 & 26 & 36 & 17 \\ 20 & 23 & 24 & 39 & 29 \end{bmatrix}$$

► LESSON MASTER 4-2 A *page 2*

Uses Objective H

10. The results of the Eastern Division of the National Conference of the National Football League for 1991 and 1992 are given in the matrices below.

1991	W	L	T
Washington	14	2	0
Dallas	11	5	0
Philadelphia	10	6	0
N.Y. Giants	8	8	0
Phoenix	4	12	0

1992	W	L	T
Washington	9	7	0
Dallas	13	3	0
Philadelphia	11	5	0
N.Y. Giants	6	10	0
Phoenix	4	12	0

a. Subtract the left matrix from the right matrix. Call the difference M. **(See below.)**

b. What is the meaning of the second column of M? **the teams' difference in losses between 1992 and 1991**

c. What is the meaning of the entry in row 2 column 3 of M? **Dallas had the same number of ties in 1991 as in 1992.**

11. The following matrix represents the average daily sales of sandwiches from Shorty's Diner and Cutie's Deli. The various types of sandwiches are referred to as O for open-faced, G for grilled, and C for club.

	O	G	C
Shorty's	35	82	46
Cutie's	49	88	21

During an upcoming festival, both restaurants expect to triple their daily sales. Write a matrix which represents these anticipated sales. **(See below.)**

(#10a)
$$M = \begin{bmatrix} -5 & 5 & 0 \\ 2 & -2 & 0 \\ 1 & -1 & 0 \\ -2 & 2 & 0 \\ 0 & 0 & 0 \end{bmatrix}$$

(#11)
	O	G	C
S	105	246	138
C	147	264	63

Adapting to Individual Needs

since addition of real numbers is commutative. $(A + B) + C =$

$$\begin{bmatrix} (a + e) + i & (b + f) + j \\ (c + g) + k & (d + h) + l \end{bmatrix} =$$

$$\begin{bmatrix} a + (e + i) & b + (f + j) \\ c + (g + k) & d + (h + l) \end{bmatrix} = A + (B + C),$$

since addition of real numbers is associative.]

Extra Help

To find the change in **Example 1**, students must subtract the prices in week 1 from the prices in week 2. This means that they must find the difference matrix $W2 - W1$. When they do this, some of the elements in the difference will be negative. Explain that the sign of each entry in the resulting difference matrix indicates whether there is an increase or a decrease over the given period.

Notes on Questions

Questions 8–9 Error Alert Remind students that when matrices represent real-world data, the matrices must be labeled so that the data are easily identifiable. These questions illustrate appropriate labeling.

Sports Connection The National Hockey League is the major professional hockey league for teams in the United States and Canada. There are also six minor professional leagues.

Question 16 Linear combinations are used in matrix multiplication in the next lesson.

Questions 19–22 The introduction of matrices for these transformations begins in Lesson 4-4.

Question 23 The distance formula is used in Lessons 4-4 and 4-5.

Follow-up **4-2**
for Lesson

Practice

For more questions on SPUR Objectives, use **Lesson Master 4-2A** (shown on pages 210–211) or **Lesson Master 4-2B** (shown on pages 212–213).

Assessment

Written Communication Have students write a paragraph explaining

212

8) $T = \begin{bmatrix} 590 & 570 & 550 & 530 \\ 590 & 575 & 555 & 535 \end{bmatrix}$

Applying the Mathematics

8. The matrices N, C, and S give the enrollments by sex and grade at North, Central, and South High Schools. In each matrix, Row 1 gives the number of boys and Row 2 the number of girls. Columns 1 to 4 give the number of students in grades 9 to 12, respectively. Determine the matrix T that shows the total enrollment by sex and grade in the three schools. **See left.**

$$N = \begin{matrix} & 9 & 10 & 11 & 12 \\ & \begin{bmatrix} 250 & 245 & 240 & 235 \\ 260 & 250 & 240 & 230 \end{bmatrix} & & & \end{matrix} \begin{matrix} \text{boys} \\ \text{girls} \end{matrix}$$

$$C = \begin{bmatrix} 200 & 190 & 180 & 170 \\ 200 & 195 & 190 & 185 \end{bmatrix} \begin{matrix} \text{boys} \\ \text{girls} \end{matrix}$$

$$S = \begin{bmatrix} 140 & 135 & 130 & 125 \\ 130 & 130 & 125 & 120 \end{bmatrix} \begin{matrix} \text{boys} \\ \text{girls} \end{matrix}$$

9. Final standings from the National Hockey League Northeast Division (formerly the Adams Division) for 1992–1993 and 1993–1994 are given in the matrices below. **See margin.**

1992–1993

	W	L	T	Pts
Boston	51	26	7	109
Quebec	47	27	10	104
Montreal	48	30	6	102
Buffalo	38	36	10	86
Hartford	26	52	6	58
Ottawa	10	70	4	24

1993–1994

	W	L	T	Pts
Boston	42	29	13	97
Quebec	34	42	8	76
Montreal	41	29	14	96
Buffalo	43	32	9	95
Hartford	27	48	9	63
Ottawa	14	61	9	37

a. Subtract the left matrix from the right matrix. Call the difference M.
b. What is the meaning of the 4th column of M?
c. What is the meaning of the 1st row of M?

10. A toymaker makes handcrafted toys for children. His output last year is represented by the matrix M below. **See left.**

$$\begin{matrix} & \text{sm} & \text{med} & \text{lg} \\ \text{dolls} & \\ \text{stuffed animals} \end{matrix} \begin{bmatrix} 5 & 10 & 18 \\ 12 & 22 & 9 \end{bmatrix} = M$$

10a) Rounding to the nearest whole number:

$$\begin{bmatrix} 7 & 13 & 23 \\ 16 & 29 & 12 \end{bmatrix}$$

b) $\begin{bmatrix} 10 & 20 & 36 \\ 24 & 44 & 18 \end{bmatrix}$

Sample: the matrix represents the toymaker's output if he doubled his output.

212

a. Suppose he wants to increase his output by 30%. Write the matrix that represents the needed output.
b. Find $2M$ and explain what the matrix represents.

11. Suppose $M = \begin{bmatrix} a & b \\ c & d \end{bmatrix}$. Find kM. $\begin{bmatrix} ka & kb \\ kc & kd \end{bmatrix}$

In 12 and 13, solve for a, b, c, and d.

12. $\begin{bmatrix} 15 & 20 \\ 25 & 30 \end{bmatrix} + \begin{bmatrix} a & b \\ c & d \end{bmatrix} = \begin{bmatrix} 8 & 18 \\ 28 & 38 \end{bmatrix}$

$a = -7$; $b = -2$; $c = 3$; $d = 8$

13. $3\begin{bmatrix} a & -1 \\ c & 4 \end{bmatrix} - 5\begin{bmatrix} 3 & b \\ 11 & -2.5 \end{bmatrix} = \begin{bmatrix} 9 & 0 \\ 8 & d \end{bmatrix}$

$a = 8$; $b = \frac{-3}{5}$; $c = 21$; $d = 24.5$

14. In June, The Faucets & Fixtures Company produced 50 porcelain sinks, 40 stainless steel sinks, and 17 molded plastic sinks. In July, they produced 100 porcelain, 80 stainless steel, and 3 molded plastic sinks. In August they produced 42 porcelain, 58 stainless steel, and 5 molded plastic sinks. Write two different 3 × 3 matrices to store these data. *(Lesson 4-1)* **See margin.**

15. Use the matrix $\begin{bmatrix} 0 & -1 & 0 & 1 \\ 3 & 0 & -3 & 0 \end{bmatrix}$.

  a. Graph the polygon represented by the matrix. **See left.**
  b. What kind of polygon is it? **rhombus**
  c. Graph the image of this polygon under a size change of magnitude 2. *(Previous course, Lesson 4-1)* **See left.**

16. Write an expression to describe the cost of C concert tickets at $20 each, P programs at $3.50 each, and D drinks at $1.50 each. *(Lesson 3-3)* **20C + 3.50P + 1.50D**

17. Consider the function with equation $f(x) = \frac{-3}{x^2}$.
  a. Graph the function. **See margin.**
  b. Identify its domain and range. *(Lesson 2-6)* **domain: set of all real numbers except 0; range: set of all negative real numbers**

18. Write a paragraph explaining some differences and similarities between the functions with equations $y = kx$ and $y = kx^2$. Include some sketches. *(Lessons 2-4, 2-5)* **See margin.**

In 19–22, use the figures at the left. Triangles I, II, III, and IV are congruent. Segments that look parallel are. Fill in the blank with one of the words *translation, rotation,* or *reflection.* *(Previous course)*

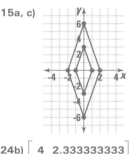

19. IV is a ? image of I. **reflection**

20. III is a ? image of IV. **translation**

21. II is a ? image of IV. **rotation**

22. II is a ? image of III. **rotation**

15a, c)

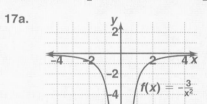

23. Let $P = (-3, 5)$ and $Q = (12, -3)$. Use the Pythagorean Theorem or the distance formula to find PQ. *(Previous course)* **PQ = 17**

Exploration

24. With most graphics calculators you can store data in matrices, add and subtract matrices, and perform scalar multiplication.

24b) $\begin{bmatrix} 4 & 2.333333333 \\ -3 & -6 \end{bmatrix}$

  a. Store $A = \begin{bmatrix} 3 & \frac{1}{3} \\ 0 & -2 \end{bmatrix}$, $B = \begin{bmatrix} 1 & 2 \\ -3 & -4 \end{bmatrix}$, and $C = \begin{bmatrix} -60 \\ 5 \end{bmatrix}$ in a calculator.

c) Sample: the calculator will display an error message.

  b. Find $A + B$ using the calculator. **(b-d) See left.**
  c. What happens when you try to find $A - C$ using the calculator?
  d. Find $7.34B$ using the calculator.

d) $\begin{bmatrix} 7.34 & 14.68 \\ -22.02 & -29.36 \end{bmatrix}$

Lesson 4-2 *Matrix Addition* **213**

Additional Answers, continued

18. Sample: The equation $y = kx$ has the graph of a line, whereas $y = kx^2$ has the graph of a parabola if $k \neq 0$. Both functions have as a domain the set of all real numbers. If $k \neq 0$, the function with the equation $y = kx$ has as a range the set of all real numbers, but the range of the function with equation $y = kx^2$ is either the set of nonnegative reals or the set of nonpositive reals, depending on the sign of k.

18. cont.

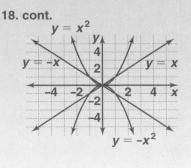

---

how to add matrices and how to multiply a matrix by a scalar. Ask them to include examples in their explanations. [Students demonstrate that they can add matrices, as well as perform scalar multiplication.]

Additional Answers

9a.
$$M = \begin{bmatrix} -9 & 3 & 6 & -12 \\ -13 & 15 & -2 & -28 \\ -7 & -1 & 8 & -6 \\ 5 & -4 & -1 & 9 \\ 1 & -4 & 3 & 5 \\ 4 & -9 & 5 & 13 \end{bmatrix}$$

b. how many more points each team had in 1993–94 than in 1992–93

c. how many more wins, losses, ties, and total points Boston had in 1993–94 than in 1992–93

14.

	porcelain	steel	plastic
June	50	40	17
July	100	80	3
August	42	58	5

	June	July	August
porcelain	50	100	42
steel	40	80	58
plastic	17	3	5

17a.

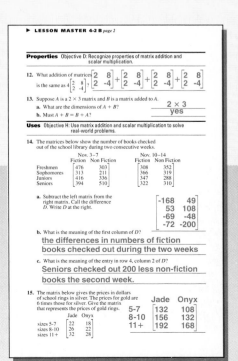

213

Objectives

B Multiply matrices.
D Recognize properties of matrix multiplication.
H Use matrix multiplication to solve real-world problems.

Resources

From the **Teacher's Resource File**
- Lesson Master 4-3A or 4-3B
- Answer Master 4-3
- Assessment Sourcebook: Quiz for Lessons 4-1 through 4-3
- Teaching Aids
  32 Warm-up
  37 Examples of Matrix Multiplication

Additional Resources
- Visuals for Teaching Aids 32, 37

Teaching Lesson **4-3**

Warm-up

Diagnostic
An ounce of ground beef has about 60 calories. A single French fry has about 11 calories. An ounce of yogurt has about 40 calories.

1. If you eat a quarter pound of beef, 20 French fries, and 4 ounces of yogurt, how many calories will you have consumed?
620

2. Write the multiplication of Question 1 as a matrix multiplication.

$$[60 \ 11 \ 40] \begin{bmatrix} 4 \\ 20 \\ 4 \end{bmatrix} = [620]$$

Matrix Multiplication

Reel attractions. *Most movie theaters charge varying admission fees based on age and time of day to attract as many people as possible.*

Row-by-Column Multiplication

In linear-combination applications, it is quite useful to store data in matrices which can then be multiplied. Consider a movie theater which charges $6.00 for adults over 17, $4.00 for students 13–17 years old, and $2.50 for children 12 or under. How much does it cost for a family with 2 adults, 1 student, and 3 children to enter the theater?

The answer is $6.00 \cdot 2 + \$4.00 \cdot 1 + \$2.50 \cdot 3 = \$23.50$. This is the same arithmetic needed to calculate the *product* of these matrices:

$$[6 \quad 4 \quad 2.50] \cdot \begin{bmatrix} 2 \\ 1 \\ 3 \end{bmatrix}$$

cost per category · number of people in each category

Multiplying Two Matrices

More generally, the product $A \cdot B$ or AB of two matrices A and B is found by multiplying rows of A by columns of B. Multiply the first element in the row by the first element in the column, the second element in the row by the second element in the column, and the third element in the row by the third element in the column. In general, multiply the nth element in the row by the nth element in the column. Finally, add the resulting products.

$$[6 \quad 4 \quad 2.50] \cdot \begin{bmatrix} 2 \\ 1 \\ 3 \end{bmatrix} = [6 \cdot 2 + 4 \cdot 1 + 2.50 \cdot 3] = [23.50]$$

The product is the 1×1 matrix $[23.50]$, corresponding to $23.50. If matrix A has 2 rows and matrix B has 3 columns, then there are

---

Lesson 4-3 Overview

Broad Goals This lesson shows how to multiply matrices and gives applications of that operation.

Perspective Matrix multiplication began as a way of keeping track of coefficients in the composition of linear transformations. Today there are four common elementary applications for matrix multiplication: business situations like those given in this lesson; transformation applications as presented

in Lesson 4-4; applications to systems as discussed in Chapter 5; applications to networks, which are not covered in this book.

We purposely delay the systems application —often introduced first—because it does not show the students anything they could not do before. The business applications are a nice surprise.

If you have never taught matrices before, you might think that matrix multiplication is difficult for students to learn. It will not be difficult if you follow the approaches that are given in the lesson and recommended in the *Notes on Reading*.

6 ways to multiply a row by a column. The six products of these rows and columns are the 6 elements of the product matrix AB.

❶ **Example 1**

Let $A = \begin{bmatrix} 8 & -2 \\ 4 & 1 \end{bmatrix}$ and $B = \begin{bmatrix} 1 & 3 & 5 \\ 0 & 4 & 2 \end{bmatrix}$. Find the product AB.

Solution

The product of row 1 of A and column 1 of B is $8 \cdot 1 + -2 \cdot 0 = 8$. This is put in the 1st row and 1st column of the answer. Thus far we have

$$\begin{bmatrix} 8 & -2 \\ 4 & 1 \end{bmatrix}\begin{bmatrix} 1 & 3 & 5 \\ 0 & 4 & 2 \end{bmatrix} = \begin{bmatrix} 8 & - & - \\ - & - & - \end{bmatrix}.$$

The products from row 1 of A and column 2 of B yield $8 \cdot 3 + -2 \cdot 4 = 16$. Now you know the element in the 1st row, 2nd column of the answer.

$$\begin{bmatrix} 8 & -2 \\ 4 & 1 \end{bmatrix}\begin{bmatrix} 1 & 3 & 5 \\ 0 & 4 & 2 \end{bmatrix} = \begin{bmatrix} 8 & 16 & - \\ - & - & - \end{bmatrix}$$

The other four elements of AB are found using this pattern.

row ▨ by column ▨

For instance, the element in the 2nd row, 3rd column of AB is found by multiplying the 2nd row of A by the 3rd column of B, as shown here, along with the final result.

$$\begin{bmatrix} 8 & -2 \\ 4 & 1 \end{bmatrix}\begin{bmatrix} 1 & 3 & 5 \\ 0 & 4 & 2 \end{bmatrix} = \begin{bmatrix} 8 & 16 & 36 \\ 4 & 16 & 22 \end{bmatrix}$$

To multiply matrices with other dimensions, do all possible products using rows from matrix A and columns from matrix B.

> **Definition of Matrix Multiplication**
> Suppose A is an $m \times n$ matrix and B is an $n \times p$ matrix. Then the product $A \cdot B$ (or AB) is the $m \times p$ matrix whose element in row i and column j is the product of row i of A and column j of B.

From the definition, *the product of two matrices A and B exists only when the number of columns of A equals the number of rows of B.* So if A is $m \times n$, B must be $n \times p$ in order for AB to exist.

These matrices can be multiplied.

$$\begin{bmatrix} 8 & -2 \\ 4 & 1 \end{bmatrix}\begin{bmatrix} 1 & 3 & 5 \\ 0 & 4 & 2 \end{bmatrix} = \begin{bmatrix} 8 & 16 & 36 \\ 4 & 16 & 22 \end{bmatrix}$$

2×2 2×3 2×3
equal
dimensions of product

These matrices cannot be multiplied.

$$\begin{bmatrix} 1 & 3 & 5 \\ 0 & 4 & 2 \end{bmatrix}\begin{bmatrix} 8 & -2 \\ 4 & 1 \end{bmatrix}$$

2×3 2×2
not equal

These two cases indicate that, in general, *multiplication of matrices is not commutative.*

Lesson 4-3 *Matrix Multiplication* **215**

Notes on Reading
❶ This example is on **Teaching Aid 37**.

We recommend the following approach when teaching matrix multiplication.
1. Explain the concept of multiplying a row by a column.
2. Point out that, because a row will be multiplied by a column, matrices can be multiplied only when the number of columns for the left matrix equals the number of rows for the right matrix.
3. Show how to determine the dimensions of the product matrix.
4. Find each element of the product matrix as the product of the row and the column that the element is in.

Emphasize the pairing of the elements in a row with the elements in a column. When multiplying

$[4 \; 6 \; 3] \cdot \begin{bmatrix} 2 \\ 9 \\ 1 \end{bmatrix}$, students should see

that every element in the row has a corresponding element in the column. In contrast, if students try to

multiply $[4 \; 6 \; 3 \; 8] \cdot \begin{bmatrix} 2 \\ 9 \\ 1 \end{bmatrix}$, they will find

that they cannot do so because 8 has no corresponding element in the column.

This kind of discussion can help emphasize the importance of a check on dimensions before multiplying matrices. Unless the number of columns of the first matrix equals the number of rows of the second matrix, multiplication cannot be done.

Optional Activities
Cooperative Learning
After completing the lesson, have students **work in groups**. Ask each group to set up two matrices that represent real-world data and that can be multiplied. Be sure that students include the correct headings on all matrices. Finally, have the groups share their data and matrices with the class.

Adapting to Individual Needs
Extra Help
Emphasize that the element in row m, column n of the product matrix is the result of multiplying row m in the left matrix by column n in the right matrix.

Students should now be ready to multiply matrices with more than either 1 row or 1 column. Emphasize that the element in row *m* column *n* of the product matrix is the result of multiplying row *m* in the left matrix by column *n* in the right matrix.

❷ **Example 2** is on **Teaching Aid 37.** In **Example 2,** we could also have set up the problem by using the matrices below.

$$\begin{array}{c} \text{Fabric Ribbon Sequins} \\ [4 \quad 2 \quad .50] \\ \text{unit cost of} \\ \text{materials} \end{array} \begin{bmatrix} 5 & 6 \\ 4 & 5 \\ 3 & 2 \end{bmatrix} \begin{array}{l} \text{Fabric} \\ \text{Ribbon} \\ \text{Sequins} \\ \text{materials for} \\ \text{one costume} \end{array}$$

In both setups, the matrices can be multiplied only in the order shown. In general, point out that problems involving the application of matrix multiplication can often be set up in more than one way.

❸ We encourage you to show students how to multiply matrices by using technology. This will help them realize that although the definition of matrix multiplication may seem strange, it is universally used. However, even if technology is always available, students must also be able to find products by hand. They have to be able to multiply matrices whose elements are variables, and sometimes they have to determine factors from a product.

Setting Up Matrices to Be Multiplied

When matrices arise from real situations you often have several choices for arranging your data. However, when two matrices are to be multiplied, the *number* of columns of the first matrix must match the *number* of rows of the second matrix. In order to set up matrices that can be multiplied, it may help to think about the units involved. That is, the *headings* of the columns of the left matrix must match the *headings* of the rows of the right matrix.

❷ **Example 2**

Costumes have been designed for the school play. Each boy's costume requires 5 yards of fabric, 4 yards of ribbon, and 3 packets of sequins. Each girl's costume requires 6 yards of fabric, 5 yards of ribbon, and 2 packets of sequins. Fabric costs $4 per yard, ribbon costs $2 per yard, and sequins cost $.50 per packet. Use matrix multiplication to find the total cost of the materials for each costume.

Solution

The information about the needed materials for each type of costume can be put in a 2 × 3 matrix. (In the Questions you are asked to start with a 3 × 2 matrix to arrive at the same result.) Then we put the information about the unit cost of each material in a matrix. So that the headings "match," we write this as a 3 × 1 matrix and position it to the right of the original matrix.

$$\begin{array}{c} \quad\quad \text{Fab. Rib. Seq.} \\ \begin{array}{c} \text{Boys} \\ \text{Girls} \end{array} \begin{bmatrix} 5 & 4 & 3 \\ 6 & 5 & 2 \end{bmatrix} \end{array} \quad \begin{array}{c} \quad\quad \text{cost} \\ \begin{array}{c} \text{Fabric} \\ \text{Ribbon} \\ \text{Sequins} \end{array} \begin{bmatrix} 4 \\ 2 \\ .50 \end{bmatrix} \end{array}$$

materials for each costume   unit cost of materials

When we multiply the "materials for each costume" matrix by the "unit cost of materials" matrix we get the total cost of the materials for each costume.

$$\begin{bmatrix} 5 & 4 & 3 \\ 6 & 5 & 2 \end{bmatrix} \begin{bmatrix} 4 \\ 2 \\ .50 \end{bmatrix} = \begin{bmatrix} 5 \cdot 4 + 4 \cdot 2 + 3 \cdot .50 \\ 6 \cdot 4 + 5 \cdot 2 + 2 \cdot .50 \end{bmatrix} = \begin{bmatrix} 29.50 \\ 35 \end{bmatrix}$$

Notice that units work with matrix multiplication as they do with normal multiplication. In Example 2, the units of the original matrices are

$$\begin{array}{c} \quad\quad \text{Fab. Rib. Seq.} \\ \begin{array}{c} \text{Boys} \\ \text{Girls} \end{array} \begin{bmatrix} \quad & \quad & \quad \end{bmatrix} \end{array} \quad \begin{array}{c} \quad\quad \text{cost} \\ \begin{array}{c} \text{Fabric} \\ \text{Ribbon} \\ \text{Sequins} \end{array} \begin{bmatrix} \quad \\ \quad \\ \quad \end{bmatrix} \end{array},$$

so the product has units $\begin{array}{c} \text{cost} \\ \begin{array}{c} \text{Boys} \\ \text{Girls} \end{array} \begin{bmatrix} \quad \\ \quad \end{bmatrix} \end{array}$. Thus the cost of the materials for a boy's costume is $29.50, and for a girl's costume it is $35.00.

Adapting to Individual Needs

Challenge

A matrix whose entries are all between 0 and 1 and whose rows add to 1 is called a *stochastic* matrix. In Exercises 1 and 2, *P* is a stochastic matrix. Have students show that P^2 and P^3 are stochastic matrices. [Responses are shown on page 217.]

1. $P = \begin{bmatrix} .2 & .8 \\ .6 & .4 \end{bmatrix}$

2. $P = \begin{bmatrix} .5 & .3 & .2 \\ .1 & .6 & .3 \\ .3 & .3 & .4 \end{bmatrix}$

3. Both *I* and *P* are stochastic matrices. Have students show that $I \cdot P$ and $I \cdot P^2$ are stochastic matrices.

$I = [.6 \quad .4]$ and $P = \begin{bmatrix} .5 & .5 \\ .2 & .8 \end{bmatrix}$.

4. Prove: If $I = [a \quad b]$ and $P = \begin{bmatrix} c & d \\ e & f \end{bmatrix}$ are stochastic, then *IP* is stochastic.

Multiplying More Than Two Matrices

To multiply more than two matrices, multiply two at a time.

③ Example 3

Find the product below.

$$\left(\begin{bmatrix} 2 & 5 \end{bmatrix} \begin{bmatrix} 3 & 1 & -4 \\ 2 & 0 & 1 \end{bmatrix} \right) \begin{bmatrix} 5 \\ 2 \\ 1 \end{bmatrix}$$

Solution

$$\left(\begin{bmatrix} 2 & 5 \end{bmatrix} \begin{bmatrix} 3 & 1 & -4 \\ 2 & 0 & 1 \end{bmatrix} \right) \begin{bmatrix} 5 \\ 2 \\ 1 \end{bmatrix} = \begin{bmatrix} 16 & 2 & -3 \end{bmatrix} \begin{bmatrix} 5 \\ 2 \\ 1 \end{bmatrix} = \begin{bmatrix} 81 \end{bmatrix}$$

In the Questions, you are asked to verify that changing the way the matrices are grouped does not affect the answer. You are verifying that *matrix multiplication is associative.*

Using Technology to Multiply Matrices

Most graphics calculators and some computer software can be used to multiply matrices. Consult a manual for the specific key sequences needed to input and multiply matrices with your technology.

Activity

Use a graphics calculator or computer software to find *AB*, where

$$A = \begin{bmatrix} 8 & -2 \\ 4 & 1 \end{bmatrix} \text{ and } B = \begin{bmatrix} 1 & 3 & 5 \\ 0 & 4 & 2 \end{bmatrix}. \quad \begin{bmatrix} 8 & 16 & 36 \\ 4 & 16 & 22 \end{bmatrix}$$

This should check Example 1.

QUESTIONS

Covering the Reading

In 1 and 2, multiply the matrices.

1. $\begin{bmatrix} 3 & 5 & 7 \end{bmatrix} \begin{bmatrix} 1 \\ 0 \\ -2 \end{bmatrix}$ [-11]

2. $\begin{bmatrix} 1 & -1 & 1 & -1 \end{bmatrix} \begin{bmatrix} 10 \\ 9 \\ 8 \\ 7 \end{bmatrix}$ [2]

3. Let $M = \begin{bmatrix} 6 & 2 \\ 0 & 3 \end{bmatrix}$ and $N = \begin{bmatrix} 5 & 8 & -2 \\ -4 & 1 & 0 \end{bmatrix}$. Find the product *MN*.
See left.

3) $\begin{bmatrix} 22 & 50 & -12 \\ -12 & 3 & 0 \end{bmatrix}$

4. If *A* has dimensions 11×15 and *B* has dimensions 15×19, what are the dimensions of *AB*? 11 × 19

5. If *A* is $m \times n$ and *B* is $p \times q$, when does *AB* exist? when *n* = *p*

Lesson 4-3 *Matrix Multiplication* **217**

[Each of the following matrices is stochastic.]

1. $P^2 = \begin{bmatrix} .52 & .48 \\ .36 & .64 \end{bmatrix}$; $P^3 = \begin{bmatrix} .392 & .608 \\ .456 & .544 \end{bmatrix}$

2. $P^2 = \begin{bmatrix} .34 & .39 & .27 \\ .2 & .48 & .32 \\ .3 & .39 & .31 \end{bmatrix}$;

$P^3 = \begin{bmatrix} .29 & .417 & .293 \\ .244 & .444 & .312 \\ .282 & .417 & .301 \end{bmatrix}$

3. $I \cdot P = [.38 \quad .62]$; $I \cdot P^2 = [.314 \quad .686]$

4. $IP = [ac + be \quad ad + bf]$;

Now $ac + be + ad + bf$
$= a(c + d) + b(e + f)$
$= a \cdot 1 + b \cdot 1$ since *P* is stochastic
$= a + b$
$= 1$ since *I* is stochastic]

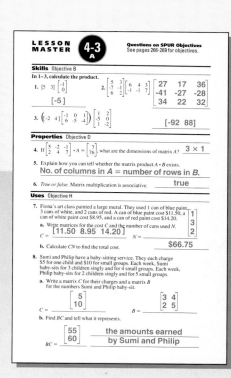
217

Question 10 This question illustrates that, in general, matrix multiplication is not commutative. This result should be stressed because most students are accustomed to believing that all multiplication is commutative.

Question 11 Students may be surprised that matrix multiplication is associative.

Question 14 Discuss this question. The identity matrix is an important matrix both in transformation applications in this chapter and later in the solving of systems.

Question 18 Consumer Connection Transportation equipment, road vehicles, and electric machinery and parts accounted for almost one third of the total U.S. exports from 1987 through 1992. High-technology exports accounted for about 60 percent. The high level of U. S. agricultural exports that occurred during the 1970s has decreased because there are now worldwide food surpluses.

Questions 19, 22–24 Students will use the ideas from these questions in the next lesson — the distance formula in **Question 19**; similar figures in **Question 22**; and radicals in **Questions 23 and 24**.

Question 25 This question expands the identity matrix to dimensions 3×3.

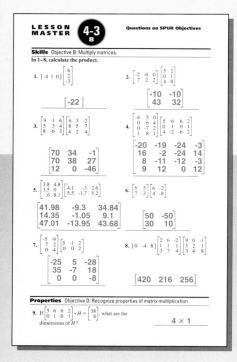

LESSON MASTER 4-3 B Questions on SPUR Objectives

Skills Objective B: Multiply matrices.
In 1–8, calculate the product.

1. $[-4 \ 1 \ 0]\begin{bmatrix} 6 \\ 2 \\ -3 \end{bmatrix}$

$[-22]$

2. $\begin{bmatrix} -2 & -6 & 0 \\ 7 & 2 & 2 \end{bmatrix}\begin{bmatrix} 5 & 2 \\ 0 & 1 \\ 4 & 8 \end{bmatrix}$

$\begin{bmatrix} -10 & -10 \\ 43 & 32 \end{bmatrix}$

3. $\begin{bmatrix} 9 & -1 & 6 \\ 5 & 3 & 4 \\ 8 & -6 & 3 \end{bmatrix}\begin{bmatrix} 6 & 3 & -2 \\ 8 & 5 & 7 \\ 4 & 2 & 4 \end{bmatrix}$

$\begin{bmatrix} 70 & 34 & -1 \\ 70 & 38 & 27 \\ 12 & 0 & -46 \end{bmatrix}$

4. $\begin{bmatrix} -4 & 5 & 0 \\ 0 & 6 & 4 \\ 0 & -7 & 2 \\ 1 & 8 & 1 \end{bmatrix}\begin{bmatrix} 5 & 6 & 6 & 2 \\ 0 & 1 & 0 & 1 \\ 4 & -2 & -6 & 2 \end{bmatrix}$

$\begin{bmatrix} -20 & -19 & -24 & -3 \\ 16 & -2 & -24 & 14 \\ 8 & -11 & -12 & -3 \\ 9 & 12 & 0 & 12 \end{bmatrix}$

5. $\begin{bmatrix} 3.8 & 4.8 \\ 3.5 & 0 \\ .6 & 8.1 \end{bmatrix}\begin{bmatrix} 4.1 & -3 & 2.6 \\ 5.5 & -1.7 & 5.2 \end{bmatrix}$

$\begin{bmatrix} 41.98 & -9.3 & 34.84 \\ 14.35 & -1.05 & 9.1 \\ 47.01 & -13.95 & 43.68 \end{bmatrix}$

6. $\begin{bmatrix} 5 & 5 \\ 7 & -3 \end{bmatrix}\begin{bmatrix} 6 & -2 \\ 4 & -8 \end{bmatrix}$

$\begin{bmatrix} 50 & -50 \\ 30 & 10 \end{bmatrix}$

7. $\begin{bmatrix} -5 & -9 \\ 7 & 2 \\ 0 & 4 \end{bmatrix}\begin{bmatrix} 5 & -1 & 2 \\ 0 & 0 & 2 \end{bmatrix}$

$\begin{bmatrix} -25 & 5 & -28 \\ 35 & -7 & 18 \\ 0 & 0 & -8 \end{bmatrix}$

8. $[0 \ -4 \ 8]\begin{bmatrix} 2 & 6 & -2 \\ 1 & 1 & 1 \\ 3 & 7 & 4 \end{bmatrix}\begin{bmatrix} 9 & 0 & -1 \\ 3 & 2 & 1 \\ 3 & 4 & 8 \end{bmatrix}$

$[420 \ 216 \ 256]$

Properties Objective D: Recognize properties of matrix multiplication.

9. If $\begin{bmatrix} 5 & 6 & 6 & 2 \\ 0 & 1 & 0 & 1 \end{bmatrix} \cdot H = \begin{bmatrix} 38 \\ 8 \end{bmatrix}$, what are the dimensions of H?

4×1

218

6a) 2×3; 2×2
b) No
c) The number of columns in the first matrix does not equal the number of rows in the second matrix.

7a) 3×4; 4×2
b) Yes
c) $\begin{bmatrix} 240 & 160 \\ 41 & 42 \\ -3 & 45 \end{bmatrix}$

From dough to bread.
Shown above is a Native American making fry bread. Fry bread is much like pita bread and is often used to make sandwiches. Below are Mexican sweet breads known as pan dulce. *Sweet breads are generally eaten during the* merienda—*a light supper—with coffee and milk.*

218

In 6 and 7, two matrices are given. **a.** Determine the dimensions of each matrix. **b.** Decide whether the product can or cannot be found. **c.** If the product exists, calculate it; if it does not exist, explain why not. **See left.**

6. $\begin{bmatrix} 8 & 1 & 0 \\ 6 & 3 & -4 \end{bmatrix}\begin{bmatrix} 2 & 8 \\ 5 & 4 \end{bmatrix}$

7. $\begin{bmatrix} 9 & 4 & 8 & 6 \\ 2 & 0 & 3 & 1 \\ 1 & -2 & 5 & 0 \end{bmatrix}\begin{bmatrix} 12 & 2 \\ 15 & 1 \\ 3 & 9 \\ 8 & 11 \end{bmatrix}$

8. Answer the question of Example 2 starting with a 3×2 matrix. **See margin.**

9. Refer to Example 2. How much will it cost to make 8 boys' and 10 girls' costumes? **$586**

10. Suppose $X = \begin{bmatrix} 3 & 0 & 5 \\ -1 & 4 & 2 \end{bmatrix}$ and $Y = \begin{bmatrix} 2 & -2 \\ 0 & 1 \\ -3 & 4 \end{bmatrix}$.

    a. Calculate XY. **See margin.** **b.** Calculate YX. **See margin.**
    c. *True or false.* Matrix multiplication is commutative. **False**

11. **a.** Find the product $[2 \ 5]\left(\begin{bmatrix} 3 & 1 & -4 \\ 2 & 0 & 1 \end{bmatrix}\begin{bmatrix} 5 \\ 2 \\ 1 \end{bmatrix}\right)$. $[81]$

    b. What property is verified in Example 3 and part **a**? **Matrix multiplication is associative.**

Applying the Mathematics

12. The matrix D gives the daily delivery of cases of four bakery products to two restaurants, Pierre's and Pauline's. The matrix C gives the cost per case for each product.

Matrix D:

	wheat bread	white bread	rye bread	English muffins
Pierre's	5	10	3	5
Pauline's	0	15	8	10

Matrix C:

	cost per case
wheat bread	7.00
white bread	7.00
rye bread	6.50
English muffins	8.00

    a. Find DC. **See margin.**
    b. What is the daily cost of these bakery products at Pierre's? **$164.50**
    c. Pierre's restaurant is open 20 days this month and Pauline's is open 25 days. Let $M = [20 \ 25]$. Find the total cost of these bakery items for the month at these two restaurants. **$9215.00**

13. East, Central, and West schools need some new uniforms next year. East needs 10 band uniforms, 20 basketball uniforms, 15 track uniforms, and 10 swimsuits. Central needs 20 band uniforms and 10 track uniforms. West needs 15 band uniforms, 20 basketball uniforms, and 10 swimsuits. A band uniform costs $90, a basketball uniform costs $40, a track uniform costs $50, and a swimsuit costs $25.
    a. Set up a matrix that gives the number of each type of uniform needed by each school. **See margin.**
    b. Use matrix multiplication to find the total cost of uniforms for each school. **See margin.**

Additional Answers

8. cost $[4 \ 2 \ .50]\begin{bmatrix} 5 & 6 \\ 4 & 5 \\ 3 & 2 \end{bmatrix}$ Fab. Rib. Seq. (B G)

   $= [29.50 \ 35]$ cost

10a. $\begin{bmatrix} -9 & 14 \\ -8 & 14 \end{bmatrix}$ b. $\begin{bmatrix} 8 & -8 & 6 \\ -1 & 4 & 2 \\ -13 & 16 & -7 \end{bmatrix}$

12a. $\begin{bmatrix} 164.50 \\ 237.00 \end{bmatrix}$

13a.

	Band	Bask.	Tr.	Sw.
E	10	20	15	10
C	20	0	10	0
W	15	20	0	10

14a) $\begin{bmatrix} a & b \\ c & d \end{bmatrix}$

b) $\begin{bmatrix} a & b \\ c & d \end{bmatrix}$

14. The matrix $\begin{bmatrix} 1 & 0 \\ 0 & 1 \end{bmatrix}$ is called **the 2 × 2 identity matrix** for multiplication.

To see why, calculate the products in parts **a** and **b**. *See left.*

a. $\begin{bmatrix} 1 & 0 \\ 0 & 1 \end{bmatrix}\begin{bmatrix} a & b \\ c & d \end{bmatrix}$ **b.** $\begin{bmatrix} a & b \\ c & d \end{bmatrix}\begin{bmatrix} 1 & 0 \\ 0 & 1 \end{bmatrix}$

c. *True or false.* Matrix multiplication with the identity matrix is commutative. **True**

15. Solve for x. $\begin{bmatrix} 3 & 1 \\ 0 & 2 \end{bmatrix}\begin{bmatrix} x \\ 9 \end{bmatrix} = \begin{bmatrix} 10 \\ 18 \end{bmatrix}$ $x = \frac{1}{3}$

Review

16b) $\begin{bmatrix} 7 & 12 \\ 8 & 10 \end{bmatrix} - \begin{bmatrix} 3 & 7 \\ -1 & 2 \end{bmatrix}$

$= \begin{bmatrix} 7-3 & 12-7 \\ 8-(-1) & 10-2 \end{bmatrix}$

$= \begin{bmatrix} 4 & 5 \\ 9 & 8 \end{bmatrix}$

16. a. Find the matrix M such that $M - \begin{bmatrix} 3 & 7 \\ -1 & 2 \end{bmatrix} = \begin{bmatrix} 4 & 5 \\ 9 & 8 \end{bmatrix}$. $M = \begin{bmatrix} 7 & 12 \\ 8 & 10 \end{bmatrix}$

b. Check your answer. *(Lesson 4-2)* **See left.**

17. A matrix contains the vertices of an *n*-gon. What are the dimensions of the matrix? *(Lesson 4-1)* **2 × n**

18a) $\begin{bmatrix} -1.4 & 7 \\ 4.2 & 4.2 \\ 4.9 & 2.8 \\ 9.5 & 12.2 \\ 5.1 & 13.2 \\ 3.1 & 2.5 \end{bmatrix}$

18. The matrices below represent U.S. exports and imports by region in millions of dollars.
a) See left.

	1992		1991	
	Exports	Imports	Exports	Imports
North Atlantic area	89.2	130.6	90.6	123.6
South Atlantic area	38.7	37.8	34.5	33.6
Gulf area	70.9	70.4	66.0	67.6
Pacific area	129.5	139.5	120.0	127.3
Great Lakes area	85.7	121.3	80.6	108.1
other	33.3	25.3	30.2	22.8

a. Find the difference in exports and imports between 1992 and 1991.
b. From which area did the imports increase the most? *(Lesson 4-2)*
the Great Lakes area

19) The distance between (2, -1) and (7, 6) is $\sqrt{74}$; the distance between (2, -1) and (-5, 4) is $\sqrt{74}$; the distance between (7, 6) and (-5, 4) is $\sqrt{148}$. The triangle is isosceles.

19. The matrix $\begin{bmatrix} 2 & 7 & -5 \\ -1 & 6 & 4 \end{bmatrix}$ can represent a triangle. Use the distance formula to show that this triangle is isosceles. *(Previous course, Lesson 4-1)* **See left.**

20. Solve $3(m + 1) + 5(m + 1) = 40$. *(Lesson 1-5)* **m = 4**

21. Suppose $f: x \rightarrow \dfrac{10}{x}$. What is $f(20)$? *(Lesson 1-3)* $f(20) = \frac{1}{2}$

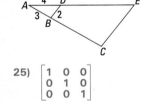

22. In the figure at the left, $\triangle ADB \sim \triangle AEC$. If $DE = 12$, find BC and CE. *(Previous course)* **BC = 9; CE = 8**

23. Simplify $\dfrac{\sqrt{81}}{\sqrt{9}}$.   **24.** Simplify $\dfrac{\sqrt{5}}{\sqrt{80}}$. *(Previous course)*

3 $\frac{1}{4}$

Exploration

25. In Question 14 you used the 2 × 2 identity matrix for multiplication. Find the matrix that is the 3 × 3 identity matrix for multiplication.
See left.

25) $\begin{bmatrix} 1 & 0 & 0 \\ 0 & 1 & 0 \\ 0 & 0 & 1 \end{bmatrix}$

13b.
$\begin{bmatrix} 10 & 20 & 15 & 10 \\ 20 & 0 & 10 & 0 \\ 15 & 20 & 0 & 10 \end{bmatrix}\begin{bmatrix} 90 \\ 40 \\ 50 \\ 25 \end{bmatrix} = \begin{bmatrix} 2700 \\ 2300 \\ 2400 \end{bmatrix}$;

East, $2700; Central, $2300; West, $2400

Setting Up Lesson 4-4

Be sure you have discussed **Question 19** and **Questions 22–24** in this lesson and the In-class Activity on page 220 before assigning Lesson 4-4.

Materials Students will need pictures from magazines for **Question 25** on page 226.

Follow-up for Lesson   **4-3**

Practice

For more questions on SPUR Objectives, use **Lesson Master 4-3A** (shown on page 217) or **Lesson Master 4-3B** (shown on pages 218–219).

Assessment

Quiz A quiz covering Lessons 4-1 through 4-3 is provided in the *Assessment Sourcebook.*

Written Communication Have each student write a real-world problem that can be solved by using matrix multiplication. Students can refer to **Questions 12 and 13** for ideas. [Students write problems that can be solved by applying matrix multiplication.]

Extension

Ask students to describe the multiplicative identity for an *n* × *n* square matrix. [The identity matrix is an *n* × *n* square matrix with 1s on its main diagonal (upper left to lower right) and zeros in every other position.]

Project Update Project 1, *Predicting the Weather*, on page 261, relates to the content of this lesson.

▶ **LESSON MASTER 4-3 B** *page 2*

10. The product of two matrices A and B exists only when the number of ___?___ of A is equal to the number of ___?___ of B. **columns** **rows**

11. Suppose G, H, and M are matrices. If $G \cdot H = M$, the product of row i of G and column j of H is the element located in row ___?___ and column ___?___ of M. **i** **j**

12. a. Calculate $\begin{bmatrix} 0 & -4 & 8 \end{bmatrix}\begin{bmatrix} 2 & 6 & -2 \\ 1 & 1 & 1 \\ 3 & 7 & 4 \end{bmatrix}\begin{bmatrix} 9 & 0 & -1 \\ 3 & 2 & 1 \\ 3 & 4 & 8 \end{bmatrix}$ $\begin{bmatrix} 420 & 216 & 256 \end{bmatrix}$

b. How does your answer compare to your answer in Question 8? What does this illustrate? **It is the same; Associative Prop. for Matrix Multiplication.**

Uses Objective H: Use matrix multiplication to solve real-world problems.

13. A band went to a football game in 2 vans, 6 cars, and one bus. There were 8 band members in each van, 5 in each car, and 38 in the bus. Write V, the vehicle matrix, and N, the matrix showing the number of band members in each vehicle. Calculate VN. Tell what VN represents.

$V = \begin{bmatrix} 2 & 6 & 1 \end{bmatrix}$ $N = \begin{bmatrix} 8 \\ 5 \\ 38 \end{bmatrix}$ $VN = \begin{bmatrix} 84 \end{bmatrix}$

the total number of band members who went to the game

14. Music Boosters ordered sweatshirts that cost $12 for small, $14 for medium, $17 for large, and $20 for extra large. In gray, they ordered 6 S, 8 M, 12 L, and 14 XL. In black, they ordered 2 S, 5 M, 10 L, and 15 XL. Write C, the cost matrix, and N the matrix showing the number ordered. Calculate CN and tell what it represents.

$C = \begin{bmatrix} 12 & 14 & 17 & 20 \end{bmatrix}$ $N = \begin{bmatrix} 6 & 2 \\ 8 & 5 \\ 12 & 10 \\ 14 & 15 \end{bmatrix}$

$CN = \begin{bmatrix} 668 & 564 \end{bmatrix}$ **the total costs for the gray shirts and the black shirts**

219

Resources

From the **Teacher's Resource File**
■ Answer Master 4-4

This activity informally introduces the idea that multiplication by a matrix can perform a transformation on the corresponding geometric figure. The first transformation that is used is a size change with magnitude 3; then a size change with magnitude k is used.

Students who have studied from any of the preceding UCSMP texts will have had lessons dealing with size changes. Therefore, they should understand the algebraic description that says that the image of (x, y) under a size change of magnitude k is (kx, ky). Other students may have studied these transformations but used different terminology (dilations, dilatations, size transformations, expansions, contractions).

Additional Answers

1a.

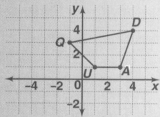

b. $\begin{bmatrix} -1 & 1 & 3 & 4 \\ 3 & 1 & 1 & 4 \end{bmatrix}$

c. $\begin{bmatrix} -3 & 3 & 9 & 12 \\ 9 & 3 & 3 & 12 \end{bmatrix}$

d.

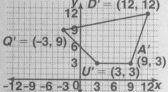

The quadrilateral is similar to *QUAD*, with ratio of similitude 3.

2b. Answers will vary. Each vertex (a, b) of the polygon corresponds to a column with elements a and b of the matrix.

2c. The result should be as if the matrix were multiplied by the scalar k.

Size Changes

IN-CLASS
ACTIVITY

Materials: Each person in the group needs graph paper and a straightedge. Work on this Activity in a small group.

See margin for 1a–d, 2b, c.

1
 a. Draw quadrilateral *QUAD* with $Q = (-1, 3)$, $U = (1, 1)$, $A = (3, 1)$, and $D = (4, 4)$.
 b. Complete the matrix below to represent *QUAD*.

$$\begin{bmatrix} -1 & 1 & \_ & \_ \\ 3 & \_ & \_ & \_ \end{bmatrix}$$

 c. Multiply the matrix for *QUAD* from part **b** by $\begin{bmatrix} 3 & 0 \\ 0 & 3 \end{bmatrix}$.

 d. The answer to part **c** represents a quadrilateral. Draw this quadrilateral. How is it related to the quadrilateral you drew in part **a** above?

2
 a. Draw a polygon of your own choice on graph paper. Answers will vary.
 b. Write a matrix for your polygon.

 c. Multiply the matrix in part **b** by $\begin{bmatrix} k & 0 \\ 0 & k \end{bmatrix}$, where you pick the value of k. Don't pick $k = 0$ or $k = 1$.
 d. The answer to part **c** represents a polygon. Draw this polygon.
 Answers will vary.

3
 Draw conclusions. Look back at the work you and the others in your group did in Questions 1 and 2. What generalization(s) can you make? When you multiply a matrix for a polygon by the matrix $\begin{bmatrix} k & 0 \\ 0 & k \end{bmatrix}$, what happens?

 The polygon is similar to the original, with a ratio of similitude k.

220

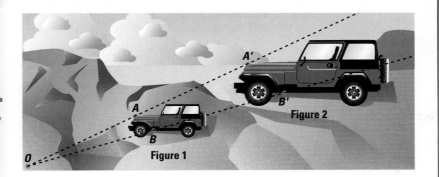

Figure 1

Figure 2

In the drawing above, we began with Figure I and point O. For point A on Figure I, a point A' (read "A prime") was found on Figure II. The position of A' was determined by the following rules: (1) A' is on $\overrightarrow{OA}$, and (2) $\frac{OA'}{OA} = 2$. This procedure was repeated with point B to find B' and with all other points of the smaller car.

Recall from geometry that a **transformation** is a one-to-one correspondence between the points of a preimage and the points of an image. Every point in Figure I above corresponds to exactly one point in Figure II, and vice versa, so a transformation has taken place. Specifically, the above transformation is a size change with center O and magnitude 2. We call Figure I the **preimage** and Figure II the **image** under the transformation. The two figures are similar with the ratio of similitude being 2.

What Is a Size Change?

Consider $\triangle PQR$ with $P = (3, 1)$, $Q = (-4, 0)$, and $R = (-3, -2)$. The size change with center $(0, 0)$ and magnitude 3, denoted S_3, can be performed by multiplying each x- and y-coordinate on $\triangle PQR$ by 3. We write

$$S_3(3, 1) = (9, 3)$$
$$S_3(-4, 0) = (-12, 0)$$
$$S_3(-3, -2) = (-9, -6)$$

and, in general, $\quad S_3(x, y) = (3x, 3y)$.

We read the top line as "A size change of magnitude 3 maps $(3, 1)$ onto $(9, 3)$." Recall that the symbol $\rightarrow$ is often used in mathematics to denote "maps onto"; so the sentence "a size change of magnitude 3 maps (x, y) onto $(3x, 3y)$" can also be written in mapping notation as $S_3: (x, y) \rightarrow (3x, 3y)$.

Definition

For any $k \neq 0$, the transformation that maps (x, y) onto (kx, ky) is called the **size change** with **center** $(0, 0)$ and **magnitude** k, and is denoted S_k.

$$S_k(x, y) = (kx, ky)$$

Lesson 4-4 *Matrices for Size Changes* **221**

Lesson 4-4

Objectives

E Recognize relationships between figures and their size-change images.
F Relate size changes to matrices, and vice versa.
I Graph figures and their size-change images.

Resources

From the **Teacher's Resource File**
■ Lesson Master 4-4A or 4-4B
■ Answer Master 4-4
■ Teaching Aids
  8 Four-Quadrant Graph Paper
  32 Warm-up
  38 Transformations and Their Matrices

Additional Resources
■ Visuals for Teaching Aids 8, 32, 38
■ Magazines and newspapers (Question 25)

Teaching 4-4
Lesson

Warm-up

Multiply.

1. $\begin{bmatrix} 5 & 0 \\ 0 & 5 \end{bmatrix}\begin{bmatrix} 3 \\ -5 \end{bmatrix}$ $\begin{bmatrix} 15 \\ -25 \end{bmatrix}$

2. $\begin{bmatrix} 2 & 0 \\ 0 & 2 \end{bmatrix}\begin{bmatrix} 1 & -1 & 5 \\ 3 & 4 & 7 \end{bmatrix}$ $\begin{bmatrix} 2 & -2 & 10 \\ 6 & 8 & 14 \end{bmatrix}$

3. $\begin{bmatrix} 3 & 0 \\ 0 & 3 \end{bmatrix}\begin{bmatrix} 1 & 6 & -2 & 1 \\ 4 & 5 & -2 & 0 \end{bmatrix}$

   $\begin{bmatrix} 3 & 18 & -6 & 3 \\ 12 & 15 & -6 & 0 \end{bmatrix}$

Lesson 4-4 Overview

Broad Goals This lesson begins a study of relations between transformations and matrices—starting with size changes, the transformations that have the simplest matrices.

Perspective Students should be familiar with size changes from their work in geometry. This should be true for all students who have had a geometry course that dealt with transformations. As a result, this lesson will

provide a breather for students who have studied transformations; it will also provide additional time for students to work with matrix multiplication.

A size change or size transformation is sometimes called a *dilatation* or *dilation,* an *expansion* or *contraction,* or a *homothety.* Because corresponding angle measurements are equal and corresponding lengths of preimage and image are in the same

ratio (size-change magnitude), the preimage and image are similar. Thus, size changes are similarity transformations. The magnitude of the size transformation, the k in S_k, is the ratio of similitude.

221

When students draw preimage and image figures, have them calculate lengths of sides to verify that the ratio of image length to preimage length is the magnitude of the size change. By determining angle measurements and slopes of segments, students can verify that these quantities are preserved under size changes.

In this lesson, discussion of size changes of magnitude k is limited to positive values for k. In the *Extension* on page 225, students can investigate size changes of negative magnitude.

Students should notice that the size transformation S_k can be done on a matrix by multiplying every element of the matrix by k. This is an alternate way of achieving the scalar multiplication introduced in Lesson 4-2.

S_3 transforms $\triangle PQR$. $\triangle PQR$ is the preimage; $\triangle P'Q'R'$ is its image. We also say that S_3 maps $\triangle PQR$ onto $\triangle P'Q'R'$.

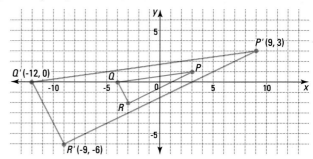

Notice that $\triangle PQR$ and $\triangle P'Q'R'$ are similar with ratio of similitude equal to 3. In general, when two figures are images of each other under a size change, they are similar.

Using Matrices to Perform Size Changes

Size-change images can also be found by multiplying matrices. As you should have seen in the Activity preceding this lesson, when the matrix for the point (x, y) is multiplied by $\begin{bmatrix} k & 0 \\ 0 & k \end{bmatrix}$, the matrix for the point (kx, ky) results.

$$\begin{bmatrix} k & 0 \\ 0 & k \end{bmatrix} \begin{bmatrix} x \\ y \end{bmatrix} = \begin{bmatrix} kx + 0y \\ 0x + ky \end{bmatrix}$$

$$= \begin{bmatrix} kx \\ ky \end{bmatrix}$$

This proves the following theorem.

> **Theorem**
>
> $\begin{bmatrix} k & 0 \\ 0 & k \end{bmatrix}$ is the matrix for S_k.

Example 1

Given $ABCD$ with $A = (0, 3)$, $B = (-2, -4)$, $C = (-6, -4)$, and $D = (-6, 4)$, find the image $A'B'C'D'$ under S_4.

Solution

Write $ABCD$ and S_4 in matrix form and multiply.

$$\begin{matrix} S_4 & A & B & C & D & & A' & B' & C' & D' \end{matrix}$$
$$\begin{bmatrix} 4 & 0 \\ 0 & 4 \end{bmatrix} \begin{bmatrix} 0 & -2 & -6 & -6 \\ 3 & -4 & -4 & 4 \end{bmatrix} = \begin{bmatrix} 0 & -8 & -24 & -24 \\ 12 & -16 & -16 & 16 \end{bmatrix}$$

Thus $A'B'C'D'$ has vertices $A' = (0, 12)$, $B' = (-8, -16)$, $C' = (-24, -16)$, and $D' = (-24, 16)$.

▶

Optional Activities

Art Connection

Materials: Cartoons from newspapers or magazines, graph paper or **Teaching Aid 8**

After completing the lesson, you might have students choose a cartoon from a newspaper or magazine and trace it onto graph paper. Then have them explain how to enlarge the cartoon to $1\frac{1}{2}$ times its original size by using a size-change matrix. [Check

students' responses. The matrix should be $\begin{bmatrix} 1.5 & 0 \\ 0 & 1.5 \end{bmatrix}$ times the matrix for the cartoon.]

Adapting to Individual Needs

Extra Help

Point out that when students use matrix multiplication to designate a size change, the matrix denoting the size change is written to the left. Otherwise, matrix multiplication would not always be possible. For example, in Example 1, if the matrix for S_4 were written on the right, then you would have to multiply a 2 × 4 matrix by a 2 × 2 matrix, and that is impossible.

Check

Graph the preimage and image. They should look similar, and they do.

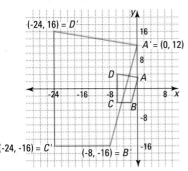

The transformation that maps each point (x, y) onto itself is called the **identity transformation.** When a point matrix $\begin{bmatrix} x \\ y \end{bmatrix}$ is multiplied on the left by $\begin{bmatrix} 1 & 0 \\ 0 & 1 \end{bmatrix}$ each point (x, y) coincides with its image. Thus $\begin{bmatrix} 1 & 0 \\ 0 & 1 \end{bmatrix}$ represents the identity transformation.

$$\begin{bmatrix} 1 & 0 \\ 0 & 1 \end{bmatrix} \begin{bmatrix} x \\ y \end{bmatrix} = \begin{bmatrix} 1 \cdot x + 0 \cdot y \\ 0 \cdot x + 1 \cdot y \end{bmatrix} = \begin{bmatrix} x \\ y \end{bmatrix}$$

The size change of magnitude 1 is the identity transformation.

Properties of Size-Change Images

Since size-change images are similar to preimages, corresponding angles are congruent and ratios of corresponding segments equal the ratio of similitude. This can be verified using the distance formula.

Example 2

Refer to the quadrilaterals in Example 1. Calculate each ratio.

a. $\frac{D'C'}{DC}$ **b.** $\frac{A'B'}{AB}$

Solution

a. $D'C' = 32$ and $DC = 8$. So $\frac{D'C'}{DC} = \frac{32}{8} = 4$.

b. Using the distance formula, we see that

$$AB = \sqrt{(-2 - 0)^2 + (-4 - 3)^2} = \sqrt{53}$$

and $A'B' = \sqrt{(-8 - 0)^2 + (-16 - 12)^2} = \sqrt{848}$.

So $\frac{A'B'}{AB} = \frac{\sqrt{848}}{\sqrt{53}} = 4$, which is the magnitude of the size change.

Additional Examples

1. Given $\triangle PIE$ with $P = (-2, 0)$, $I = (2, 0)$, and $E = (0, 5)$.
   a. Find the image $\triangle P'I'E'$ under S_6. $\begin{bmatrix} -12 & 12 & 0 \\ 0 & 0 & 30 \end{bmatrix}$

   b. Graph the preimage and the image. Are they similar?

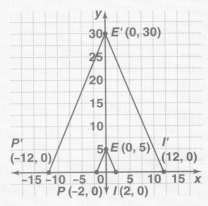

   Yes, the preimage and the image are similar.

2. Refer to the triangles in Additional Example 1. Calculate $\frac{P'I'}{PI}$, $\frac{P'E'}{PE}$, $\frac{I'E'}{IE}$. What do these ratios represent? **Each ratio is 6. The ratios represent the ratio of similitude of the triangles or the magnitude of the size change.**

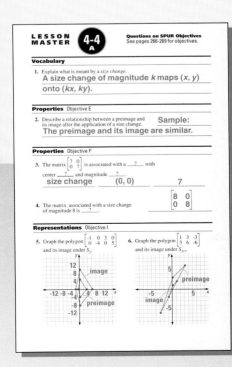

Notes on Questions

Question 15 In **part a**, the verification should be done by using the distance formula, not by measuring. In **part b**, encourage students to make a sketch; it will help them see that the equation of the line is in the form $y = kx$ and that the slope is $\frac{4}{3}$.

Question 18 Some students will be surprised to see the effect of a size change with a negative magnitude. Students of previous UCSMP courses may have seen such size changes before.

(Notes on Questions continue on page 226.)

Follow-up for Lesson 4-4

Practice

For more questions on SPUR Objectives, use **Lesson Master 4-4A** (shown on page 223) or **Lesson Master 4-4B** (shown on pages 224–225).

In general, the size change of magnitude k multiplies distance by $|k|$, so that the ratio of image lengths to preimage lengths is $|k|$. You will prove this in Chapter 7.

QUESTIONS

Covering the Reading

In 1–3, how is the expression read? **See left.**

1) A size change of magnitude 3 maps (3, 1) onto (9, 3).

2) A size change of magnitude 5 maps (2, 1) onto (10, 5).

3) The image triangle P-prime, Q-prime, R-prime

1. $S_3: (3, 1) \rightarrow (9, 3)$ 2. $S_5(2, 1) = (10, 5)$ 3. $\triangle P'Q'R'$

4. **a.** Draw $\triangle ABC$ where $A = (0, 0)$, $B = (-3, 1)$, and $C = (4, 1)$. **See left.**
   b. Draw the image of $\triangle ABC$ under S_2. **See left.**
   c. What is the matrix for the transformation that maps $\triangle ABC$ onto $\triangle A'B'C'$? $\begin{bmatrix} 2 & 0 \\ 0 & 2 \end{bmatrix}$

4a, b)

5. The size-change transformation with center $(0, 0)$ and magnitude k maps (x, y) onto $\underline{\quad?\quad}$. **(kx, ky)**

6. The matrix $\begin{bmatrix} k & 0 \\ 0 & k \end{bmatrix}$ is associated with a(n) $\underline{\quad?\quad}$ change with center $\underline{\quad?\quad}$ of magnitude $\underline{\quad?\quad}$. **size; (0, 0); $k \neq 0$**

In 7–9, refer to Example 1.

7. What are the coordinates of the *image* of point B? **(-8, -16)**

8. What is the magnitude of the size change? **4**

9. Verify that $\frac{A'D'}{AD} = 4$. $\frac{A'D'}{AD} = \frac{\sqrt{592}}{\sqrt{37}} = \sqrt{16} = 4$

14)

10. The identity transformation maps each point onto $\underline{\quad?\quad}$. **itself**

In 11–13, answer *true or false*.

11. Under every size change an angle and its image are congruent. **True**

12. Under every size change a segment and its image are congruent. **False**

13. Under every size change a figure and its image are similar. **True**

15a) $P' = (7.5, 10)$; $OP' = \sqrt{(7.5 - 0)^2 + (10 - 0)^2} = \sqrt{156.25} = 12.5$, and $OP = \sqrt{3^2 + 4^2} = \sqrt{25} = 5$; $\frac{OP'}{OP} = \frac{12.5}{5} = 2.5$

Applying the Mathematics

14. $\triangle ABC$ has matrix $\begin{bmatrix} 6 & -4 & 2 \\ 8 & 2 & -2 \end{bmatrix}$. Graph $\triangle ABC$ and its image $\triangle A'B'C'$ under $S_{\frac{1}{2}}$. **See left.**

15. Suppose $P = (3, 4)$. Let P' be the image of P under the size change with center $O = (0, 0)$ and magnitude 2.5.
    a. Verify that $\frac{OP'}{OP} = 2.5$. **See left.**
    b. Give an equation for the line containing O, P, and P'. $y = \frac{4}{3}x$

224

Additional Answers
18a,c.

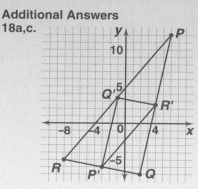

b. $\begin{bmatrix} -3 & -1 & 4 \\ -6 & 3.5 & 2.5 \end{bmatrix}$

d. The lengths of the sides of $\triangle P'R'Q'$ are $\frac{1}{2}$ the lengths of sides of $\triangle PQR$.

e. The area of $\triangle P'Q'R'$ is $\frac{1}{4}$ the area of $\triangle PQR$.

16a) $\begin{bmatrix} 2 & 0 \\ 0 & 2 \end{bmatrix}$

b) $\begin{bmatrix} 2 & 3 & 4 \\ 7 & 6.2 & 8.2 \end{bmatrix}$

16. A 3 × 5 drawing is enlarged to 6 × 10 by using a size change. **See left.**
   a. What is the matrix for the size change?
   b. Suppose $A = (1, 3.5)$, $B = (1.5, 3.1)$, and $C = (2, 4.1)$ are three points located on the smaller drawing. Write a matrix for the location of these points on the enlargement. **See left.**
   c. The skateboard in the enlargement is how many times as long as the skateboard in the original drawing?
   twice as long

Bart Simpson

17. Refer to Example 1.
   a. Find the slope of $\overline{AB}$. $\frac{7}{2}$
   b. Find the slope of $\overline{A'B'}$. $\frac{7}{2}$
   c. Is $\overline{AB}$ parallel to $\overline{A'B'}$? Why or why not?
   Yes, because the slopes are equal.

18. a. Draw $\triangle PQR$ represented by the matrix $\begin{bmatrix} 6 & 2 & -8 \\ 12 & -7 & -5 \end{bmatrix}$.
   b. Find the product $\begin{bmatrix} -\frac{1}{2} & 0 \\ 0 & -\frac{1}{2} \end{bmatrix} \begin{bmatrix} 6 & 2 & -8 \\ 12 & -7 & -5 \end{bmatrix}$.
   c. The matrix in part **b** represents $\triangle P'Q'R'$, the image of $\triangle PQR$ under a size change of magnitude $-\frac{1}{2}$. Draw $\triangle P'Q'R'$.
   d. How are the lengths of the sides of $\triangle P'Q'R'$ related to the lengths of the sides of $\triangle PQR$?
   e. How are the areas of $\triangle PQR$ and $\triangle P'Q'R'$ related?
   See margin for a–e.

Review

20b) Sample:
$\begin{array}{cccc} & Bl & Dr & Sk & Sl \end{array}$
$DM \begin{bmatrix} 38 & 105 & 45 & 44 \end{bmatrix}$

c) $\begin{bmatrix} 3144 & 1680 & 695 \end{bmatrix}$
Berlin: DM3,144,000;
Hamburg: DM1,680,000;
Munich: DM695,000

19. Solve for a and b: $\begin{bmatrix} 2 & a \\ 3 & b \end{bmatrix} \begin{bmatrix} 5 \\ 6 \end{bmatrix} = \begin{bmatrix} 7 \\ 8 \end{bmatrix}$. *(Lesson 4-3)* $a = -\frac{1}{2}$; $b = -\frac{7}{6}$

20. A German clothing manufacturer has factories in Berlin, Hamburg, and Munich. Sales (in thousands of items) can be summarized by the following matrix S.

	Berlin	Hamburg	Munich
Blouses	9	5	3
Dresses	14	7	3
Skirts	12	7	2
Slacks	18	10	4

$= S$

See left for b, c.

   a. What are the dimensions of S? **4 × 3**
   b. The selling price of a blouse is DM38. A dress sells for DM105. A skirt sells for DM45, and a pair of slacks sells for DM44. (DM is the symbol for Deutsche mark, the currency of Germany.) Write a 1 × 4 matrix representing the selling prices of the items.
   c. Use matrix multiplication to determine the total revenue of each factory. *(Lessons 4-1, 4-2)*

Lesson 4-4   *Matrices for Size Changes*   **225**

Adapting to Individual Needs

Challenge
Copy machines often can make size-change copies of originals. Have students carefully draw a figure with measurements as exact as possible. Have them make an enlarged or a reduced copy of their figure. Then have them measure lengths on the copy and divide corresponding lengths to determine the magnitude of the size change. Ask them how close each size-change factor is to the percentage they used to make the copy.

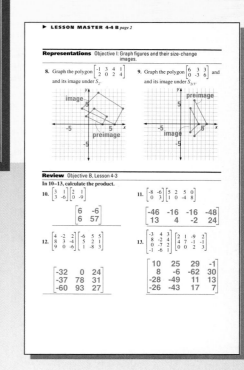
225

Questions 21–22 History Connection As early as the first century, the Romans had lifting platforms that used pulleys operated by human, animal, or water power to lift freight. In 1853 an American, Elisha Graves Otis, made the lifting platforms safe for passenger use. The first passenger elevator was introduced in the Haughwout Department Store in New York City in 1857. Driven by steam power, the elevator climbed five stories in less than a minute. Other improvements followed; the first electric passenger elevator was installed in 1889, push-button controls were introduced in 1894, and power-controlled doors were added in 1915. To provide express service for the upper levels of the new taller buildings, elevator speeds increased to 1,200 feet per minute at the Empire State Building in 1931 and to 1,800 feet per minute at the John Hancock Center, Chicago, in 1970.

Question 23 In geometry, students might answer this question by using one part of what we call the Fundamental Theorem of Similarity: The ratio of areas of similar figures is the square of the ratio of similitude. In this course, you might use the equivalent direct variation formulation: If figures are similar, then their areas vary as the square of lengths of corresponding sides.

Question 24 It is helpful for students to draw graphs when they compute the new areas.

Question 25 Students will need pictures from magazines for this question.

Up-lifting. *Pictured are three glass elevators on the cruise ship* Sovereign of the Seas.

In 21 and 22, refer to the graph below, which shows the location of an elevator over a one-minute period. *(Lessons 1-4, 2-4, 3-1)*

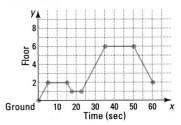

21. When is the elevator on the sixth floor?
from the 35th to the 50th second

22. a. At what rate does the elevator ascend? $\frac{2}{5}$ floor per second
b. Does the elevator descend at the same speed that it ascends? Justify your answer. Yes; the slopes of the lines showing the elevator's descent are -2/5 floor per second.

23. Two figures, *F* and *G*, are similar. The perimeter of *F* is 20 cm, and the perimeter of *G* is 15 cm. If the area of *F* is 100 cm^2, what is the area of *G*? *(Previous course)* 56.25 cm^2

Exploration

24. *ABCD* is the square defined by the matrix $\begin{bmatrix} 0 & 2 & 2 & 0 \\ 0 & 0 & 2 & 2 \end{bmatrix}$.

Transform *ABCD* by multiplying its matrix by each of the following size-change matrices (and by some others of your own choice).

a. $\begin{bmatrix} 2 & 0 \\ 0 & 2 \end{bmatrix}$ **b.** $\begin{bmatrix} 3 & 0 \\ 0 & 3 \end{bmatrix}$ **c.** $\begin{bmatrix} 4 & 0 \\ 0 & 4 \end{bmatrix}$ **d.** $\begin{bmatrix} 5 & 0 \\ 0 & 5 \end{bmatrix}$ See left.

e. Find the area of each image. Enter your results in a table like this one:

Area of Preimage	Matrix	Area of Image
4 units^2	$\begin{bmatrix} 2 & 0 \\ 0 & 2 \end{bmatrix}$	__?__ units^2 16
4 units^2	$\begin{bmatrix} 3 & 0 \\ 0 & 3 \end{bmatrix}$	__?__ units^2 36
4 units^2	?	$\begin{bmatrix} 4 & 0 \\ 0 & 4 \end{bmatrix}$	__?__ 64 units^2
4 units^2	?	$\begin{bmatrix} 5 & 0 \\ 0 & 5 \end{bmatrix}$	__?__ 100 units^2

f. There is a connection between the matrix associated with a size change and the effect the matrix has on the area of a figure. What is this connection? New Area = Original Area × k^2

25. Use the procedure from the beginning of this lesson to make an enlargement of a photo or of a picture from a magazine. Answers will vary.

Original   Horizontal scale change of magnitude 2 (a stretch)   Vertical scale change of magnitude $\frac{1}{3}$ (a shrink)   Horizontal scale change of magnitude 2 and vertical scale change of magnitude $\frac{1}{3}$

What Is a Scale Change?

In contrast to a size change, which you studied in the previous lesson, a *scale change* can transform a figure by stretching or shrinking it in either a horizontal direction, a vertical direction, or both directions at once.

> **Definition**
> For any nonzero numbers *a* and *b*, the transformation that maps (*x*, *y*) onto (*ax*, *by*) is called the **scale change** with **horizontal magnitude** *a* and **vertical magnitude** *b*, and is denoted **S$_{a,b}$**.

When $|a| > 1$ (or $|b| > 1$), the scale change is a *stretch* in the horizontal (or vertical) direction. When $|a| < 1$ (or $|b| < 1$), the scale change is a *shrink* in the horizontal (or vertical) direction.

In mapping notation, we write $S_{a,b}: (x, y) \rightarrow (ax, by)$. In $f(x)$ notation, $S_{a,b}(x, y) = (ax, by)$.

Example 1

Consider quadrilateral *ABCD* with $A = (0, 3)$, $B = (-2, -4)$, $C = (-6, -4)$, and $D = (-6, 4)$. Find its image $A'B'C'D'$ under $S_{2,5}$.

Solution

$S_{2,5}(x, y) = (2x, 5y)$. That is, to find each image point, multiply the *x*-coordinate of the preimage by 2 and the *y*-coordinate of the preimage by 5. So,

$$S_{2,5}(0, 3) = (0, 15),$$
$$S_{2,5}(-2, -4) = (-4, -20),$$
$$S_{2,5}(-6, -4) = (-12, -20), \text{ and}$$
$$S_{2,5}(-6, 4) = (-12, 20).$$

Quadrilateral A'B'C'D' has vertices
A' = (0, 15), B' = (-4, -20), C' = (-12, -20), and D' = (-12, 20). ▶

227

b. Multiply each *x*-coordinate by 5 and each *y*-coordinate by 2. See *A"B"C"D"* below.

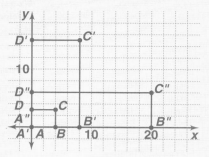

3. Is either of the images similar to the preimage? Why or why not?
No. Ratios of lengths of corresponding sides are not equal; one length is multiplied by 2, and the other is multiplied by 5.

Notes on Reading

You may want to use **Teaching Aid 38** when discussing scale-change transformations.

Stress that a positive magnitude which is less than 1 produces a shrink, and a magnitude which is greater than 1 produces a stretch in that particular direction. The magnitude 1 produces neither a stretch nor a shrink.

❶ Students should easily see that the ratios of lengths of sides of images to lengths of corresponding sides in preimages are not the same. Thus, scale changes are not similarity transformations. However, the size-change transformations that were studied in Lesson 4-4 are special cases of scale-change transformations. They are scale changes with equal horizontal and vertical magnitudes.

► **Check**

Graph the preimage and image.

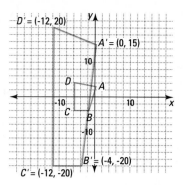

❶ The image of a preimage point on the *y*-axis should be 5 times as far from the origin as the preimage, and the image of a preimage point on the *x*-axis should be 2 times as far from the origin as the preimage. The preimage point $A = (0, 3)$ is 3 units from the origin. The image of (0, 3) is (0, 15), which is 15 units from the origin. For the preimage point (-6, 0), the image is the point (-12, 0), which is twice as far from the origin as its preimage. It checks.

Example 1 shows that a scale-change image is not necessarily similar to its preimage. The ratios of the lengths of corresponding sides in *ABCD* and *A'B'C'D'* are *not* equal. For instance,

$$\frac{D'C'}{DC} = \frac{40}{8} = 5 \qquad \text{(the vertical stretch)}$$

$$\frac{B'C'}{BC} = \frac{8}{4} = 2 \qquad \text{(the horizontal stretch)}$$

and $\frac{A'B'}{AB} = \frac{\sqrt{(-20-15)^2+(-4-0)^2}}{\sqrt{(-4-3)^2+(-2-0)^2}} = \frac{\sqrt{1241}}{\sqrt{53}} \approx 4.84$ (a result of both horizontal and vertical stretches)

Because the ratios of corresponding sides are different, the two quadrilaterals are not similar.

Matrices for Scale Changes

Because a size change has a 2 × 2 matrix, it is reasonable to expect that a scale change also has one. Suppose that $S_{a,b}$ has the matrix

$$\begin{bmatrix} e & f \\ g & h \end{bmatrix}$$

where *e*, *f*, *g*, and *h* are real numbers. Because $S_{a,b}$ maps (x, y) onto (ax, by), we want to find *e*, *f*, *g*, and *h* so that

$$\begin{bmatrix} e & f \\ g & h \end{bmatrix}\begin{bmatrix} x \\ y \end{bmatrix} = \begin{bmatrix} ax \\ by \end{bmatrix}.$$

Notice that by matrix multiplication, $\begin{bmatrix} a & 0 \\ 0 & b \end{bmatrix}\begin{bmatrix} x \\ y \end{bmatrix} = \begin{bmatrix} ax \\ by \end{bmatrix}$. Thus $e = a$, $f = 0$, $g = 0$, and $h = b$. We have proved the following theorem.

Lesson 4-5 Overview, continued

scale change maps the line with equation $x + y = 1$ onto the line with equation $\frac{x}{a} + \frac{y}{b} = 1$. The same scale change maps the graph of $y = \sin x$ onto the graph of $y = b \sin \frac{x}{a}$.

Scale changes are common in statistics. The *scaling* of data by dividing it by the standard deviation is a one-dimensional scale change.

Optional Activities

After completing the lesson, students might enjoy this activity. Tell each student to draw a simple figure (dog, cat, boat, house) in the first quadrant of a coordinate grid. Then have them make a distorted grid, such as the one shown at the right, and transform their figure onto this grid. This is *not* a scale change, but a *distortion*.

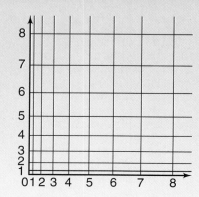

Theorem

$\begin{bmatrix} a & 0 \\ 0 & b \end{bmatrix}$ is a matrix for $S_{a,b}$.

A stretch of the imagination. *The curved mirror shown is performing a horizontal stretch.*

Example 2

Refer to quadrilateral *ABCD* from Example 1. Use matrix multiplication to find its image *A′B′C′D′* under $S_{2,5}$.

Solution

Write $S_{2,5}$ and *ABCD* in matrix form.

$$\begin{array}{cc} & \\ S_{2,5} & \end{array} \quad \begin{array}{cccc} A & B & C & D \end{array} \qquad \begin{array}{cccc} A' & B' & C' & D' \end{array}$$

$$\begin{bmatrix} 2 & 0 \\ 0 & 5 \end{bmatrix} \begin{bmatrix} 0 & -2 & -6 & -6 \\ 3 & -4 & -4 & 4 \end{bmatrix} = \begin{bmatrix} 0 & -4 & -12 & -12 \\ 15 & -20 & -20 & 20 \end{bmatrix}$$

Check

The product matrix gives the same result for quadrilateral *A′B′C′D′* that was found in Example 1.

Notice that a scale change may stretch or shrink by different factors in the horizontal and vertical directions. If the factors are the same in both directions, then the scale-change matrix has the form $\begin{bmatrix} k & 0 \\ 0 & k \end{bmatrix}$ and is really just a size change. Conversely, a size change with magnitude k is a scale change with horizontal magnitude k and vertical magnitude k. Thus *size changes are special types of scale changes.* In symbols, $S_k = S_{k,k}$.

QUESTIONS

Covering the Reading

1. $S_{a,b}$ maps (x, y) onto __?__. *(ax, by)*

2. a. What is the image of $(6, 5)$ under $S_{3,2}$? *(18, 10)*
  b. Describe $S_{3,2}$ in words. *$S_{3,2}$ is a horizontal scale change of magnitude 3 and a vertical scale change of magnitude 2.*

3. If $S_{2,5}(1, -2) = (m, n)$, find m and n. *(2, -10)*

4. If the horizontal and vertical scale changes in the final picture of the clown at the beginning of this lesson were to be done by applying $S_{a,b}$ to the first drawing, what are the values of a and b? *$a = 2$; $b = \frac{1}{3}$*

5a, b)

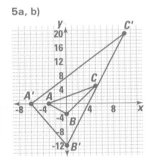

5. a. Draw $\triangle ABC$ with $A = (-3, 0)$, $B = (0, -3)$, and $C = (5, 5)$. **See left.**
  b. Find its image $\triangle A'B'C'$ under $S_{2,4}$ **See left.**
  c. *True or false.* $\triangle ABC$ and $\triangle A'B'C'$ are similar. Justify your answer. **See margin.**

6. a. Find the matrix product $\begin{bmatrix} 100 & 0 \\ 0 & 200 \end{bmatrix} \begin{bmatrix} 7 \\ 9 \end{bmatrix}$. $\begin{bmatrix} 700 \\ 1800 \end{bmatrix}$
  b. You have found the image of __?__ under __?__. *(7, 9)*; $S_{100,200}$

Lesson 4-5 *Matrices for Scale Changes* **229**

Adapting to Individual Needs

English Language Development
Using Physical Models To help students with limited English proficiency understand the words *stretch* and *shrink,* you might use a rubber band. Stretch the rubber band slightly between two tacks on the bulletin board and have students imagine this as an original length. Now expand the rubber band, or *stretch it,* to show a longer length and then relax it altogether, or *shrink it,* to show a shorter length. Explain that a stretch expands a figure or makes it bigger, so the magnitude of the size change for a stretch is greater than 1. A shrink makes a figure smaller, so the magnitude of size change for a shrink is less than 1. Also note that stretches and shrinks can be *vertical* (up or down), *horizontal* (right or left), or both horizontal and vertical.

Additional Examples

1. Consider $\triangle DEF$ with $D = (-3, 0)$, $E = (1, 4)$, and $F = (2, -3)$. Find its image $D'E'F'$ under $S_{3,2}$. $D' = (-9, 0)$, $E' = (3, 8)$, $F' = (6, -6)$

2. Quadrilateral *WXYZ* is represented by the matrix
$\begin{bmatrix} -3 & -1 & 3 & 1 \\ 1 & 5 & 7 & -2 \end{bmatrix}$. Use matrix multiplication to find its image under $S_{5,9}$.

$\begin{bmatrix} 5 & 0 \\ 0 & 9 \end{bmatrix} \begin{bmatrix} -3 & -1 & 3 & 1 \\ 1 & 5 & 7 & -2 \end{bmatrix} = \begin{bmatrix} -15 & -5 & 15 & 5 \\ 9 & 45 & 63 & -18 \end{bmatrix}$

(Notes on Questions begin on page 231.)

Follow-up for Lesson 4-5

Practice

For more questions on SPUR Objectives, use **Lesson Master 4-5A** (shown on page 229) or **Lesson Master 4-5B** (shown on pages 230–231).

Additional Answers
5c. False. Sample: $\dfrac{A'B'}{AB} = \dfrac{\sqrt{180}}{\sqrt{18}} \approx$
3.16, $\dfrac{B'C'}{BC} = \dfrac{\sqrt{1124}}{\sqrt{89}} \approx 3.55$; the
ratios are not equal.

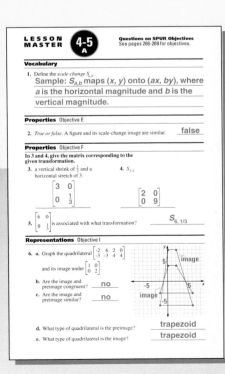

229

230

Assessment

Oral/Written Communication Have students **work in pairs**. Have one student draw a quadrilateral on a coordinate grid. Then have the other student choose a scale transformation of reasonable magnitude and explain how to use matrices to find the image quadrilateral. Students can then change roles. [Students demonstrate an understanding of scale changes and their relation to matrix multiplication.]

Extension

You might have students **work in groups** and use this activity as an extension of **Question 19**. Tell each group to draw rectangle *ABCD* on a coordinate grid and find the area. Then have them find matrices that will transform *ABCD* into a rectangle with an image area that is 16 times that of *ABCD*. [Responses will vary; however, in any scale change $S_{a,b}$ that is used, $ab = 16$.]

Project Update Project 2, *History of Matrices*, on page 261, relates to the content of this lesson.

Additional Answers

10. Since bar graph II is the same height as bar graph I, the vertical scale change is 1. Bar graph II is about 3 times the width of graph I, so the horizontal scale change is 3. Thus graph II is the image of graph I under $S_{3,1}$.

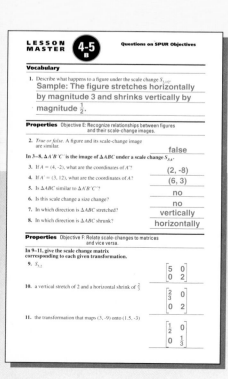

---

9) The slope of $\overline{AB}$ is $\frac{7}{2}$ and the slope of $\overline{A'B'}$ is $\frac{35}{4}$. Since the slopes are different, the lines cannot be parallel.

11d)

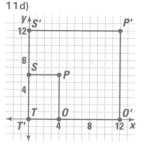

12b)

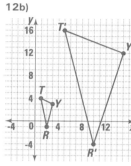

An apple of a pear. *The Japanese pear-apple combines the tastes and textures of both fruits.*

230

---

7. The scale change with matrix $\begin{bmatrix} 0.5 & 0 \\ 0 & 1.5 \end{bmatrix}$ is a horizontal __?__ and a vertical __?__. **shrink; stretch**

8. The size change S_4 can be thought of as the scale change $S_{a,b}$. What are the values of a and b? $a = 4, b = 4$

Applying the Mathematics

9. Refer to Example 1. Prove or disprove: $\overline{AB} \,/\!/\, \overline{A'B'}$. **See left.**

10. I.   II.

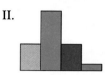

Describe the scale change under which bar graph II is the image of bar graph I. **See margin.**

11. a. Quadrilateral *TOPS* is represented by the matrix $\begin{bmatrix} 0 & 4 & 4 & 0 \\ 0 & 0 & 6 & 6 \end{bmatrix}$. What type of quadrilateral is *TOPS*? **rectangle**
    b. Find the matrix of the image $T'O'P'S'$ of quadrilateral *TOPS* under the scale change represented by $\begin{bmatrix} 3 & 0 \\ 0 & 2 \end{bmatrix}$. $\begin{bmatrix} 0 & 12 & 12 & 0 \\ 0 & 0 & 12 & 12 \end{bmatrix}$
    c. What type of quadrilateral is $T'O'P'S'$? **square**
    d. Graph the preimage *TOPS* and the image $T'O'P'S'$. **See left.**

12. Consider the matrix equation below.

$$\begin{array}{ccc} S_{a,b} & T\ R\ Y & T'\ R'\ Y' \end{array}$$
$$\begin{bmatrix} a & 0 \\ 0 & b \end{bmatrix}\begin{bmatrix} 1 & 2 & 3 \\ 4 & -1 & 3 \end{bmatrix} = \begin{bmatrix} 5 & 10 & 15 \\ 16 & -4 & 12 \end{bmatrix}$$

   a. What scale change is represented by this equation? $S_{5,4}$
   b. Draw the preimage $\triangle TRY$ and the image $\triangle T'R'Y'$. **See left.**
   c. Find $\frac{T'R'}{TR}$ and $\frac{T'Y'}{TY}$. $\frac{T'R'}{TR} \approx 4.04;\ \frac{T'Y'}{TY} \approx 4.82$
   d. Should the ratios be the same? Why or why not? No. The scale change stretches using different factors in the horizontal and vertical directions.

Review

13. The matrix below gives the daily delivery of boxes of apples and pears to two markets.

	Troy's	Abby's
apples	5	4
pears	1	2

a) $S_3 = \begin{bmatrix} 3 & 0 \\ 0 & 3 \end{bmatrix}$

b) $\begin{bmatrix} 3 & 0 \\ 0 & 3 \end{bmatrix}\begin{bmatrix} 5 & 4 \\ 1 & 2 \end{bmatrix} = \begin{bmatrix} 15 & 12 \\ 3 & 6 \end{bmatrix}$

During peak season, the demand for fruit at each market triples.
   a. What size change is needed to meet the increased demand? Represent the size change by a matrix. **See above.**
   b. Multiply the original matrix by the size-change matrix to find the new matrix which meets the increased demand. *(Lesson 4-4)* **See above.**

Adapting to Individual Needs

Challenge
This activity is similar to **Question 19**, but it deals with three-dimensional figures. The rectangular prism at the far right is shown on a three-dimensional coordinate system. The coordinates of the vertices are ordered triples (x, y, z). For instance, $A = (0, 0, 0)$ is the origin, $E = (0, 0, 4)$, and $G = (3, 6, 4)$.

1. Define the prism using a matrix. [Sample: The vertices in the matrix below are listed in alphabetical order.]

$$\begin{bmatrix} 0 & 0 & 3 & 3 & 0 & 0 & 3 & 3 \\ 0 & 6 & 6 & 0 & 0 & 6 & 6 & 0 \\ 0 & 0 & 0 & 0 & 4 & 4 & 4 & 4 \end{bmatrix}$$

2. Replace a, b, and c in this matrix with any positive numbers. $\begin{bmatrix} a & 0 & 0 \\ 0 & b & 0 \\ 0 & 0 & c \end{bmatrix}$

14) $\begin{bmatrix} 9 & 3 & -12 \\ 5 & 3 & -2 \\ -6 & 1 & 12 \end{bmatrix}$

14. Find AX when $X = \begin{bmatrix} 2 & -1 & -2 \\ 0 & 1 & -3 \\ 3 & 4 & 0 \end{bmatrix}$ and $A = \begin{bmatrix} 3 & 2 & 1 \\ 1 & 0 & 1 \\ -3 & -2 & 0 \end{bmatrix}$. *(Lesson 4-3)*
See left.

15. In 1990, about 35 million people in the U.S. did not have health insurance. The four states with the highest percent of uninsured residents were Louisiana (19.7%), Mississippi (19.9%), Texas (21.1%) and New Mexico (22.2%). Their populations in 1990 were as follows: Louisiana, 4,219,973; Mississippi, 2,573,216; Texas, 16,986,510; and New Mexico, 1,515,069. Source: *The 1993 Information Please Almanac* *(Lessons 4-1, 4-3)*
   a. Use matrix multiplication to determine how many people in these four states had no health insurance. **5,263,904**
   b. From this information, which state do you think has the biggest health-insurance problem? Why? **Sample: Texas has the biggest problem because it has the greatest number of uninsured residents.**

16. Evaluate $P_n = 500(2)^{n-1}$ when $n = 1$. *(Lesson 1-7)* $P_1 = 500$

17. *Skill sequence.* Solve the equation. *(Lesson 1-5)*
   a. $\dfrac{x}{\frac{3}{5}} = 15$ $x = 225$
           b. $\dfrac{y}{\frac{3}{9}} = 15$ $y = 25$

18) $\sqrt{(-2-7)^2 + (8-7)^2}$
$= \sqrt{82} = AC$
$\sqrt{(8-7)^2 + (-2-7)^2}$
$= \sqrt{82} = BC$
So $AC = BC$.

18. If $A = (-2, 8)$, $B = (8, -2)$, and $C = (7, 7)$, prove that $AC = BC$.
(Previous course) **See left.**

Exploration

19. Let $ABCD$ be the square defined by the matrix $\begin{bmatrix} 0 & 2 & 2 & 0 \\ 0 & 0 & 2 & 2 \end{bmatrix}$.

Transform $ABCD$ by multiplying its matrix by each of the following matrices (and by some others of your own choice).

  a. $\begin{bmatrix} 3 & 0 \\ 0 & 4 \end{bmatrix}\begin{bmatrix} 0 & 6 & 6 & 0 \\ 0 & 0 & 8 & 8 \end{bmatrix}$ **b.** $\begin{bmatrix} 3 & 0 \\ 0 & 1 \end{bmatrix}\begin{bmatrix} 0 & 6 & 6 & 0 \\ 0 & 0 & 2 & 2 \end{bmatrix}$

  c. $\begin{bmatrix} 3 & 0 \\ 0 & 2 \end{bmatrix}\begin{bmatrix} 0 & 6 & 6 & 0 \\ 0 & 0 & 4 & 4 \end{bmatrix}$ **d.** $\begin{bmatrix} 2 & 0 \\ 0 & 1 \end{bmatrix}\begin{bmatrix} 0 & 4 & 4 & 0 \\ 0 & 0 & 2 & 2 \end{bmatrix}$

  e. Complete the table.

Area of Preimage	Matrix	Area of Image
4 units^2	$\begin{bmatrix} 3 & 0 \\ 0 & 4 \end{bmatrix}$	__?__ units^2 48
4 units^2	$\begin{bmatrix} 3 & 0 \\ 0 & 1 \end{bmatrix}$	__?__ units^2 12
4 units^2 __?__	$\begin{bmatrix} 3 & 0 \\ 0 & 2 \end{bmatrix}$	__?__ 24 units^2
4 units^2 __?__	$\begin{bmatrix} 2 & 0 \\ 0 & 1 \end{bmatrix}$	__?__ 8 units^2

  f. What is the connection between the elements a and b of the scale-change matrix $\begin{bmatrix} a & 0 \\ 0 & b \end{bmatrix}$ and the effect the scale change has on area?
     New Area = Original Area × ab

Lesson 4-5 *Matrices for Scale Changes* **231**

Lesson 4-5 *Matrices for Scale Changes* **231**

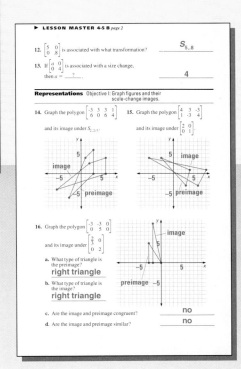

Then transform the prism by multiplying its matrix by this matrix. [See matrix below. Again, vertices are listed in alphabetical order.]

$\begin{bmatrix} 0 & 0 & 3a & 3a & 0 & 0 & 3a & 3a \\ 0 & 6b & 6b & 0 & 0 & 6b & 6b & 0 \\ 0 & 0 & 0 & 0 & 4c & 4c & 4c & 4c \end{bmatrix}$

3. Compare the volume of the preimage prism with the volume of its image. What do you notice? [The volume of the preimage is 72 units^3, and the volume of the image is $72abc$ units^3.]

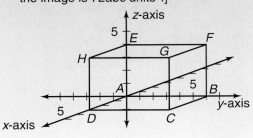

Objectives

E Recognize relationships between figures and their reflection images.
F Relate reflections to matrices, and vice versa.
I Graph figures and their reflection images.

Resources

From the **Teacher's Resource File**
- Lesson Master 4-6A or 4-6B
- Answer Master 4-6
- Activity Kit, Activity 7
- Teaching Aids
   8 Four-Quadrant Graph Paper
   33 Warm-up
   38 Transformations and Their Matrices

Additional Resources
- Visuals for Teaching Aids 8, 33, 38

Teaching Lesson **4-6**

Warm-up

Diagnostic Find the image of the point (3, 10) when it is reflected over each line.
1. The *y*-axis   (–3, 10)
2. The *x*-axis   (3, –10)
3. The line $y = x$ (10, 3)
4. If a point is on the line over which it is being reflected, what do you know about the image of the point? **It is also on the line.**

Mountain reflection. *Shown is Mt. McKinley and its reflection on a lake in Denali National Park in Alaska. The Athabaskan Indians called the mountain* Denali, *The Great One, or The High One.*

What Is a Reflection?

Recall from geometry that the **reflection image of a point *A* over a line *m*** is:

1. the point *A*, if *A* is on *m*;
2. the point *A'* such that *m* is the perpendicular bisector of $\overline{AA'}$, if *A* is not on *m*.

The line *m* is called the **reflecting line** or **line of reflection.**

A **reflection** is a transformation that maps a figure to its reflection image. The figure below shows the *reflection image* of a leaf and the point *A* over the line *m*.

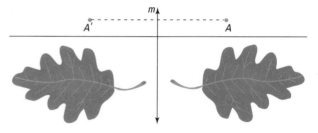

Reflection over the *y*-axis

Suppose that $A = (x, y)$ is reflected over the *y*-axis, as shown below.

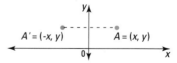

Lesson 4-6 Overview

Broad Goals In this lesson, matrices for reflections over the *x*-axis, *y*-axis, and line $y = x$ are developed. A procedure for remembering the matrices is also given.

Perspective One reason that reflections are such important transformations is that the preimage and image figures are congruent. The image appears backward because its orientation is reversed. Consider the triangles in **Example 1**—if you imagine

walking from *A* to *B* to *C* to *A*, you will travel clockwise; the interior of △*ABC* is on your right. The corresponding walk on the image is counterclockwise from *A'* to *B'* to *C'* to *A'*; the interior of △*A'B'C'* is on your left.

Another reason that reflections are important is that they are intimately connected with bilateral symmetry, which is so common in the real world and in mathematics— it is a property of all the conics and of sine

waves. Also, in this course, the graphs of inverse relations are reflection images of each other over the line $y = x$, something we discuss further in Chapter 8.

Students who have had experience with reflections should find this to be an easy lesson. Still, it will take some effort for the students to learn which matrix is associated with which reflection; for this reason, we give the Matrix Basis Theorem.

Since $\overline{AA'}$ must be perpendicular to the y-axis, it is a horizontal segment. Therefore, the y-coordinate of A' is the same as the y-coordinate of A. Because A' and A are equidistant from the y-axis, and A is x units from the y-axis, the point A' must also be x units from the y-axis. Since A and A' are on opposite sides of the y-axis, this means that the x-coordinate of A' is $-x$. So the reflection image of (x, y) over the y-axis is $(-x, y)$.

Reflection over the y-axis can be denoted $r_{y\text{-axis}}$ or r_y. In this book we use r_y. We write

$$r_y: (x, y) \to (-x, y)$$

This is read "the reflection over the y-axis maps (x, y) onto $(-x, y)$." Or we write

$$r_y(x, y) = (-x, y).$$

This is read "the reflection image of (x, y) over the y-axis is $(-x, y)$."

Notice that $\begin{bmatrix} -1 & 0 \\ 0 & 1 \end{bmatrix} \begin{bmatrix} x \\ y \end{bmatrix} = \begin{bmatrix} -1 \cdot x + 0 \cdot y \\ 0 \cdot x + 1 \cdot y \end{bmatrix} = \begin{bmatrix} -x \\ y \end{bmatrix}$.

This means that there is a matrix for r_y and proves the next theorem.

Theorem

$\begin{bmatrix} -1 & 0 \\ 0 & 1 \end{bmatrix}$ is a matrix for r_y.

Example 1

If $A = (1, 2)$, $B = (1, 4)$, and $C = (2, 4)$, find the image of $\triangle ABC$ under r_y.

Solution
Represent r_y and $\triangle ABC$ as matrices and multiply.

$$\overset{r_y}{\begin{bmatrix} -1 & 0 \\ 0 & 1 \end{bmatrix}} \overset{\triangle ABC}{\begin{bmatrix} 1 & 1 & 2 \\ 2 & 4 & 4 \end{bmatrix}} = \overset{\triangle A'B'C'}{\begin{bmatrix} -1 & -1 & -2 \\ 2 & 4 & 4 \end{bmatrix}}$$

The image $\triangle A'B'C'$ has $A' = (-1, 2)$, $B' = (-1, 4)$, and $C' = (-2, 4)$.

Check
Graph the preimage and image. It checks.

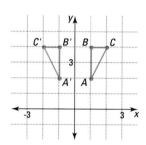

endpoints (1, 0) and (0, 1), that is, to

the segment with matrix $\begin{bmatrix} 1 & 0 \\ 0 & 1 \end{bmatrix}$.

The result is the original matrix. Its left column is the image of (1, 0), and its right column is the image of (0, 1). So, if we want to reconstruct the matrix from the images, we just reverse the process.

Additional Examples

1. If $D = (-3, -1)$, $E = (-3, -4)$, and $F = (-1, -1)$, find the image of $\triangle DEF$ under r_y.

$$\begin{bmatrix} -1 & 0 \\ 0 & 1 \end{bmatrix} \begin{bmatrix} -3 & -3 & -1 \\ -1 & -4 & -1 \end{bmatrix} = $$
$$\begin{bmatrix} 3 & 3 & 1 \\ -1 & -4 & -1 \end{bmatrix}$$

2. Find the reflection image of pentagon *NIFTY* over the line $x = y$ if $N = (-1, 5)$, $I = (7, 2)$, $F = (6, -3)$, $T = (0, -5)$, and $Y = (-5, -5)$.

$$\begin{bmatrix} 0 & 1 \\ 1 & 0 \end{bmatrix} \begin{bmatrix} -1 & 7 & 6 & 0 & -5 \\ 5 & 2 & -3 & -5 & -5 \end{bmatrix} = $$
$$\begin{bmatrix} 5 & 2 & -3 & -5 & -5 \\ -1 & 7 & 6 & 0 & -5 \end{bmatrix}$$

Reflections over Other Lines

Two other important reflecting lines are the *x*-axis and the line with equation $y = x$. Reflection over the *x*-axis is denoted by r_x, and reflection over the line $y = x$ is denoted by $r_{y=x}$.

The following graphs show the effects of r_x and $r_{y=x}$ on $\triangle ABC$ of Example 1.

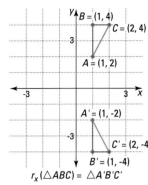

$r_x(\triangle ABC) = \triangle A'B'C'$

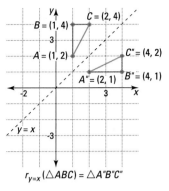

$r_{y=x}(\triangle ABC) = \triangle A''B''C''$

You can verify the following results.

$$r_x: (x, y) \rightarrow (x, -y)$$
$$r_{y=x}: (x, y) \rightarrow (y, x)$$

The matrices for r_x and $r_{y=x}$ also involve only 0s, 1s, and -1s.

Theorem

$\begin{bmatrix} 1 & 0 \\ 0 & -1 \end{bmatrix}$ is the matrix for r_x.

Proof:

$$\begin{bmatrix} 1 & 0 \\ 0 & -1 \end{bmatrix} \begin{bmatrix} x \\ y \end{bmatrix} = \begin{bmatrix} 1 \cdot x + 0 \cdot y \\ 0 \cdot x + -1 \cdot y \end{bmatrix} = \begin{bmatrix} x \\ -y \end{bmatrix}$$

Activity

Use $\triangle ABC$ from Example 1. Give a matrix multiplication that could be used to find the image of $\triangle ABC$ under r_x. $\begin{bmatrix} 1 & 0 \\ 0 & -1 \end{bmatrix} \begin{bmatrix} 1 & 1 & 2 \\ 2 & 4 & 4 \end{bmatrix}$

Theorem

$\begin{bmatrix} 0 & 1 \\ 1 & 0 \end{bmatrix}$ is the matrix for $r_{y=x}$.

Proof:
You are asked to do the proof in Question 13.

Adapting to Individual Needs

Extra Help

If students have difficulty determining which matrix is associated with which reflection, remind them that $r_x: (x, y) \rightarrow (-x, y)$ says that r_y changes the sign of the *x*-coordinate but does not affect the *y*-coordinate. After students become skillful at multiplying by 2 × 2 matrices, they will see that $r_y =$

$\begin{bmatrix} -1 & 0 \\ 0 & 1 \end{bmatrix}$ changes the sign of each element

of the top row of the matrix that is being multiplied and that it does not change the elements in the bottom row. Similarly,

$r_x = \begin{bmatrix} 1 & 0 \\ 0 & -1 \end{bmatrix}$ changes the sign of each

element in the bottom row of the matrix being multiplied and does not change the elements in the top row. This provides a way for students to associate the matrix with the transformation.

For instance, $\begin{bmatrix} 0 & 1 \\ 1 & 0 \end{bmatrix}$ switches the rows of

the matrix being multiplied. Because $r_{y=x}$ switches the coordinates of each point, it is

associated with $\begin{bmatrix} 0 & 1 \\ 1 & 0 \end{bmatrix}$.

Example 2

Find the reflection image of pentagon *WEIRD* over the line $y = x$ if $W = (-1, -1)$, $E = (3, -2)$, $I = (6, 0)$, $R = (6, 5)$ and $D = (-1, 7)$.

Solution

Represent *WEIRD* and $r_{y=x}$ by matrices and multiply.

$$\begin{array}{c} r_{y=x} \\ \begin{bmatrix} 0 & 1 \\ 1 & 0 \end{bmatrix} \end{array} \begin{array}{cccccc} W & E & I & R & D \\ \begin{bmatrix} -1 & 3 & 6 & 6 & -1 \\ -1 & -2 & 0 & 5 & 7 \end{bmatrix} \end{array} = \begin{array}{ccccc} W' & E' & I' & R' & D' \\ \begin{bmatrix} -1 & -2 & 0 & 5 & 7 \\ -1 & 3 & 6 & 6 & -1 \end{bmatrix} \end{array}$$

W'E'I'R'D' is represented by the product matrix.

Check

WEIRD and *W'E'I'R'D'* are graphed at the left.

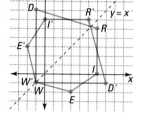

It is important to note one significant way that reflections, size changes, and scale changes differ. All reflections preserve shape and size, so reflection images are always congruent to their preimages. All size changes preserve shape, but only S_1 and S_{-1} yield congruent images. However, size-change images are similar to their preimages. In general, scale-change images are neither congruent nor similar to their preimages.

Remembering Matrices

At this point, you have seen matrices for some size changes, some scale changes, and three reflections. You may wonder: How do I remember them? Here is one way. To write the 2×2 matrix for a particular transformation T, use this rule: The first column is the image of $(1, 0)$ under T. The second column is the image of $(0, 1)$ under T. So, for example, to remember the matrix for r_y, use the picture below. Arrows show the images of $(1, 0)$ and $(0, 1)$ under the transformation r_y.

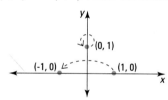

The image of $(1, 0)$ under r_y is $(-1, 0)$.

$$\begin{bmatrix} 1 & 0 \\ 0 & 1 \end{bmatrix} \qquad \begin{bmatrix} -1 & 0 \\ 0 & 1 \end{bmatrix}$$

The image of $(0, 1)$ under r_y is $(0, 1)$.

Lesson 4-6 *Matrices for Reflections* **235**

---

3. Multiply the matrix for $r_{y = x}$ by itself. Explain the result geometrically. $\begin{bmatrix} 0 & 1 \\ 1 & 0 \end{bmatrix} \begin{bmatrix} 0 & 1 \\ 1 & 0 \end{bmatrix} =$

$\begin{bmatrix} 1 & 0 \\ 0 & 1 \end{bmatrix}$. The result of the multiplication is the 2×2 identity matrix. This means that reflecting a figure over $y = x$ and then reflecting the image over $y = x$ yields the original preimage. In general, if a figure is reflected over any line and the image is reflected over that same line, the result is the original figure.

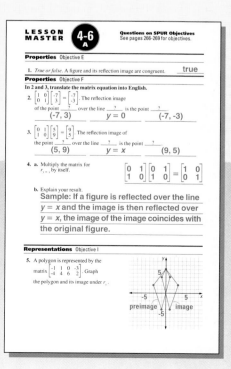

Adapting to Individual Needs

English Language Development
Materials: Mirror

Have students look in a large mirror. Explain that what they see is their *reflection* image. Then put a small mirror on line *m* in the drawing on page 232 so students can see the reflection of the leaf and point *A* in the mirror. Explain that *A'* is the reflection image of point *A*.

235

Students will need graph paper or **Teaching Aid 8** to graph answers.

Question 10 In UCSMP *Geometry*, figures are defined as congruent if and only if one is the image of the other under a composite of reflections. Thus, students of UCSMP *Geometry* may answer "because of the definition of congruence," whereas other students may resort to the justification "same size, same shape."

Question 15 This question is closely related to and touches upon the same concepts as the Exploration questions in Lessons 4-4 and 4-5. But it can be answered without reference to the matrix if students remember that in figures whose ratio of similitude is k, the ratio of the areas is k^2.

(Notes on Questions continue on page 238.)

Additional Answers

13. $$\begin{bmatrix} 0 & 1 \\ 1 & 0 \end{bmatrix}\begin{bmatrix} x \\ y \end{bmatrix} =$$
$$\begin{bmatrix} 0 \cdot x & + & 1 \cdot y \\ 1 \cdot x & + & 0 \cdot y \end{bmatrix} = \begin{bmatrix} y \\ x \end{bmatrix}$$

This rule gives us a way to write matrices for transformations quickly without memorizing them. The rule is called the *Matrix Basis Theorem* because the matrix is *based* on the images of points (1, 0) and (0, 1).

Matrix Basis Theorem
Suppose T is a transformation represented by a 2 × 2 matrix.
If T: (1, 0) → (x_1, y_1) and T: (0, 1) → (x_2, y_2) then T has the matrix
$$\begin{bmatrix} x_1 & x_2 \\ y_1 & y_2 \end{bmatrix}.$$

Proof:
Let $\begin{bmatrix} a & b \\ c & d \end{bmatrix}$ be the matrix representing T. Then, since T: (1, 0) → (x_1, y_1),
$$\begin{bmatrix} a & b \\ c & d \end{bmatrix}\begin{bmatrix} 1 \\ 0 \end{bmatrix} = \begin{bmatrix} x_1 & x_2 \\ y_1 & y_2 \end{bmatrix}$$
or
$$\begin{bmatrix} a \\ c \end{bmatrix} = \begin{bmatrix} x_1 \\ y_1 \end{bmatrix}.$$
Therefore, $a = x_1$ and $c = y_1$. Similarly, since T: (0, 1) → (x_2, y_2),
$$\begin{bmatrix} a & b \\ c & d \end{bmatrix}\begin{bmatrix} 0 \\ 1 \end{bmatrix} = \begin{bmatrix} x_2 \\ y_2 \end{bmatrix}$$
or
$$\begin{bmatrix} b \\ d \end{bmatrix} = \begin{bmatrix} x_2 \\ y_2 \end{bmatrix}.$$
Therefore, $b = x_2$ and $d = y_2$. So the matrix for T is $\begin{bmatrix} x_1 & x_2 \\ y_1 & y_2 \end{bmatrix}$.

QUESTIONS

Covering the Reading

1. Suppose that A is not on line m and that A' is the reflection image of A over m. Then m is the __?__ of $\overline{AA'}$. **perpendicular bisector**

2. **a.** What is the reflection image of a point A over a line m if A is on m? **It is the same point.**
   b. Which vertex of pentagon *WEIRD* in Example 2 shows this? **W**

3. How can the following sentence be read? $r_x(x, y) = (x, -y)$
   The reflection image of (x, y) over the x-axis is (x, −y).

4) $$\begin{bmatrix} 0 & 1 \\ 1 & 0 \end{bmatrix}\begin{bmatrix} 1 & 1 & 2 \\ 2 & 4 & 4 \end{bmatrix}$$
$$= \begin{bmatrix} 2 & 4 & 4 \\ 1 & 1 & 2 \end{bmatrix}$$

4. In Example 1, what matrix multiplication could be used to find the image of $\triangle ABC$ under $r_{y=x}$? **See left.**

In 5–7, *multiple choice.* Choose the matrix which corresponds to the given reflection.

(a) $\begin{bmatrix} 1 & 0 \\ 0 & -1 \end{bmatrix}$ (b) $\begin{bmatrix} -1 & 0 \\ 0 & 1 \end{bmatrix}$ (c) $\begin{bmatrix} -1 & 0 \\ 0 & -1 \end{bmatrix}$ (d) $\begin{bmatrix} 0 & 1 \\ 1 & 0 \end{bmatrix}$ (e) $\begin{bmatrix} 0 & -1 \\ -1 & 0 \end{bmatrix}$

5. r_x **a**   6. r_y **b**   7. $r_{y=x}$ **d**

Adapting to Individual Needs

Challenge
Have students use the rectangular prism shown in the *Challenge* on pages 230–231 of this Teacher's Edition. Challenge them to find the matrix for reflecting the prism over the *xz*-plane. Then have them sketch the reflected image. If students need a hint, tell them to think of the *xz*-plane as a mirror and to find the mirror image. [The matrix is given below. The sketch is shown at the right. Note that a reflection through the *xz*-plane

has the effect of changing the sign of each *y*-coordinate.]
$$\begin{bmatrix} 1 & 0 & 0 \\ 0 & -1 & 0 \\ 0 & 0 & 1 \end{bmatrix}$$

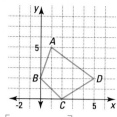

8. a. Write a matrix for quadrilateral *ABCD* shown at the left.
b. Use matrix multiplication to draw *A'B'C'D'*, its reflection image over the *x*-axis. See left for a, b.

9. Refer to Example 2. Find the matrix for *W"E"I"R"D"*, the reflection image of *WEIRD* over the *y*-axis. Graph *WEIRD* and *W"E"I"R"D"*. See left.

10. *True or false.* Reflection images are congruent to their preimages.
True

11. The matrix equation below shows that the reflection image of the point __?__ over the line __?__ is the point __?__. (2, 3); *x* = 0; (-2, 3)

$$\begin{bmatrix} -1 & 0 \\ 0 & 1 \end{bmatrix}\begin{bmatrix} 2 \\ 3 \end{bmatrix} = \begin{bmatrix} -2 \\ 3 \end{bmatrix}$$

8a) $\begin{bmatrix} 1 & 0 & 2 & 5 \\ 5 & 2 & 0 & 2 \end{bmatrix}$

b) $\begin{bmatrix} 1 & 0 \\ 0 & -1 \end{bmatrix}\begin{bmatrix} 1 & 0 & 2 & 5 \\ 5 & 2 & 0 & 2 \end{bmatrix} =$
$\begin{bmatrix} 1 & 0 & 2 & 5 \\ -5 & -2 & 0 & -2 \end{bmatrix}$

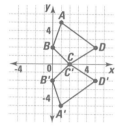

Applying the Mathematics

12. Explain how the Matrix Basis Theorem enables a person to remember the matrix for $r_{y=x}$. See left.

13. Prove that $\begin{bmatrix} 0 & 1 \\ 1 & 0 \end{bmatrix}$ is the matrix for the reflection over the line $y = x$. See margin.

14. Suppose $P = (x, y)$ and $Q = (y, x)$. Let $R = (a, a)$ be any point on the line $y = x$. See margin.

9) *W"E"I"R"D"* =

$\begin{bmatrix} 1 & -3 & -6 & -6 & 1 \\ -1 & -2 & 0 & 5 & 7 \end{bmatrix}$

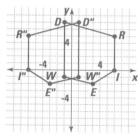

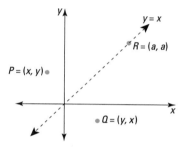

a. Verify that $PR = QR$.
b. From part **a**, what theorem from geometry allows you to conclude that the line $y = x$ is the perpendicular bisector of $\overline{PQ}$?

12) $r_{y=x}$: (1, 0) → (0, 1) and $r_{y=x}$: (0, 1) → (1, 0). By the Matrix Basis Theorem,

$r_{y=x} = \begin{bmatrix} 0 & 1 \\ 1 & 0 \end{bmatrix}$

Review

15. A polygon *P* is represented by the matrix $\begin{bmatrix} 3 & 2 & 5 & -3 \\ 4 & -1 & 0 & 1 \end{bmatrix}$. Find the change in area when *P* is multiplied by $\begin{bmatrix} 3 & 0 \\ 0 & 3 \end{bmatrix}$. *(Lesson 4-4)*
The area is multiplied by 9.

16. Find an equation for the line parallel to $y = 3x - 4$ and containing the point (2, -5). *(Lessons 3-2, 3-5)* $y = 3x - 11$

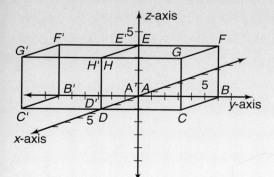

Additional Answers, continued
14a. $PR = \sqrt{(x-a)^2 + (y-a)^2}$
$QR = \sqrt{(y-a)^2 + (x-a)^2}$
So, $PR = QR$
b. Two points (the origin and *R*), equidistant from the endpoints of $\overline{PQ}$, determine the perpendicular bisector of $\overline{PQ}$.

Follow-up
for Lesson **4-6**

Practice

For more questions on SPUR Objectives, use **Lesson Master 4-6A** (shown on page 235) or **Lesson Master 4-6B** (shown on pages 236–237).

Assessment

Written Communication Ask students to write a paragraph that explains how reflections differ from size changes and scale changes. [Students recognize that only reflection images are always congruent.]

Extension

Consumer Connection Reflection-symmetric figures are common in the world of business—many companies have logos or trademarks that are reflection symmetric. You might have students look in newspapers and magazines to find examples of such logos and trademarks.

Project Update Project 2, *History of Matrices*, on page 261, relates to the content of the lesson.

▶ **LESSON MASTER 4-6 B** *page 2*

9. a. Multiply the matrix for r_y by $\begin{bmatrix} 2 & 1 & 6 \\ -3 & 0 & 4 \end{bmatrix}$. $\begin{bmatrix} 2 & 1 & 6 \\ 3 & 0 & -4 \end{bmatrix}$

b. Multiply the matrix for r_x by your answer to Part a. $\begin{bmatrix} 2 & 1 & 6 \\ -3 & 0 & 4 \end{bmatrix}$

c. Explain what happened.
Sample: The reflection of the reflection image coincided with the preimage.

Representations Objective I: Graph figures and their reflection images.

10. Graph the polygon $\begin{bmatrix} 1 & -1 & -7 & -3 \\ 5 & 7 & 5 & 1 \end{bmatrix}$ and its image under r_y.

11. Graph the polygon $\begin{bmatrix} 1 & 6 & 5 \\ 3 & 2 & -2 \end{bmatrix}$ and its image under $r_{y=x}$.

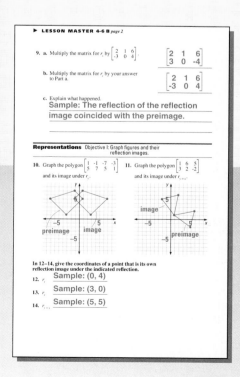

In 12–14, give the coordinates of a point that is its own reflection image under the indicated reflection.

12. r_y Sample: (0, 4)
13. r_x Sample: (3, 0)
14. $r_{y=x}$ Sample: (5, 5)

237

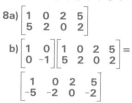

Trick ski. *Snowboards, a type of trick ski, are used to perform tricks and acrobatics.*

17) Factory *X:* $72 for a trick ski, $48 for a slalom ski, $55 for a cross-country ski;   Factory *Y:* $64.50 for a trick ski, $43 for a slalom ski, $49.25 for a cross-country ski

17. A company makes three kinds of skis: trick skis, slalom skis, and cross-country skis. The matrix A represents the time in hours required to make one of each type of ski. The company has two manufacturing plants X and Y in different parts of the country. The hourly rates for each department are given in matrix B.

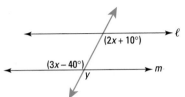

	fabricating department	finishing department
trick	6	1.5
slalom	4	1
cc skis	4.5	1.25

$= A$

	X	Y
fab.	$10	$9
fin.	$8	$7

$= B$

See left.

Find the total labor costs for each ski at each factory.   *(Lesson 4-3)*

18. Refer to the diagram below. Find y given $\ell \,//\, m$.   *(Previous course)*

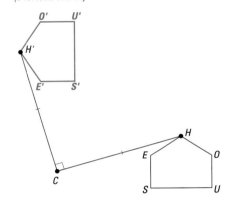

19. Trace the figure below. Point H on pentagon *HOUSE* has been rotated counterclockwise 90° about point C to the position of H'. Rotate the other vertices of *HOUSE* 90° about C and draw $H'O'U'S'E'$.   *(Previous course)*

Exploration

20. Let $r_{y=-x}$ denote reflection over the line $y = -x$.
  a. By graphing and testing points, complete this sentence.
    $r_{y=-x}(x, y) =$ ____. $(-y, -x)$
  b. Find the 2×2 matrix for $r_{y=-x}$. **See left.**

20b)

Video

Wide World of Mathematics
The segment, *Monet Masterpieces,* features the Monet exhibit held at the New Orleans Museum of Art. The segment provides motivation for introducing or extending a lesson on using matrices for reflections. Related questions and an investigation are provided in videodisc stills and in the Video Guide. A related CD-ROM activity is also available.

Videodisc Bar Codes

Search Chapter 19

Play

Setting Up Lesson 4-7

Question 19 involves a 90° rotation, whose matrix is presented in the next lesson.

*Composites of
Transformations*

IN-CLASS
ACTIVITY

Materials: Each member of the group should use graph paper with the same scales on the axes throughout this activity. Work on this Activity in groups of three.

Each person in the group will have a different task to complete. Decide who will be person *X,* who will be person *Y,* and who will be person *Z.* Then, follow the directions accordingly.

1 **Person X** (a–c) See margin.
   a. Draw quadrilateral *ABCD* with *A* = (2, 1), *B* = (3, 3), *C* = (5, 2), and *D* = (4, -2).
   b. Draw the reflection image of *ABCD* over the *x*-axis. Label the image *A'B'C'D'.*
   c. Draw the reflection image of *A'B'C'D'* over the line *y* = *x.* Label the new image *A"B"C"D".*
   d. What single transformation could you apply to *ABCD* to get the image *A"B"C"D"?* a rotation of 90° counterclockwise around the point (0, 0)

   Person Y (a–c) See margin.
   a. Draw quadrilateral *ABCD* with *A* = (2, 1), *B* = (3, 3), *C* = (5, 2), and *D* = (4, -2).
   b. Draw the reflection image of *ABCD* over the line *y* = *x.* Label the image *A'B'C'D'.*
   c. Draw the reflection image of *A'B'C'D'* over the *x*-axis. Label the new image *A"B"C"D".*
   d. What single transformation could you apply to *ABCD* to get the image *A"B"C"D"?* a rotation of 90° clockwise around the point (0, 0)

   Person Z (a–d) See margin.
   a. Draw quadrilateral *ABCD* with *A* = (2, 1), *B* = (3, 3), *C* = (5, 2), and *D* = (4, -2).
   b. Write a matrix to describe this quadrilateral. Call this matrix *Q.*
   c. Multiply *Q* by the matrix $\begin{bmatrix} 0 & -1 \\ 1 & 0 \end{bmatrix}$ and call the image *Q'.*
   d. Graph *Q'.*

2 As a group, summarize what you found.
Sample: Persons X and Z had the same final images. The single transformation is a rotation of 90° with matrix $\begin{bmatrix} 0 & -1 \\ 1 & 0 \end{bmatrix}$.

In-class Activity

Resources

From the *Teacher's Resource File*
■ Answer Master 4-7
■ Teaching Aid 8: Four-Quadrant Graph Paper

Additional Resources
■ Visual for Teaching Aid 8

Students will need graph paper or **Teaching Aid 8** for this activity. This activity introduces students to the composition of transformations on a coordinate plane. It provides the vehicle by which the matrices for rotations in Lessons 4-7 and 4-8 are found.

Person *Z* has the easiest task here—simply multiplying by one matrix. Person *X* has to do two transformations to achieve the same result. Person *Y* gets a different result, but it is still a rotation.

Additional Answers
Person X, a.–c.

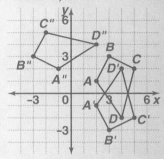

Additional Answers, continued
Person Y, a.–c.

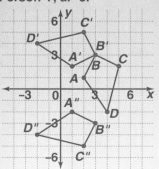

Person Z, a and d.

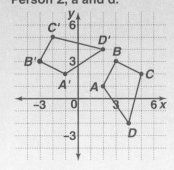

Person Z

b. $\begin{bmatrix} 2 & 3 & 5 & 4 \\ 1 & 3 & 2 & -2 \end{bmatrix} = Q$

c. $\begin{bmatrix} -1 & -3 & -2 & 2 \\ 2 & 3 & 5 & 4 \end{bmatrix} = Q'$

Objectives

D Recognize properties of matrix operations.
F Relate transformations to matrices, and vice versa.
I Graph figures and their transformation images.

Resources

From the *Teacher's Resource File*
- Lesson Master 4-7A or 4-7B
- Answer Master 4-7
- Assessment Sourcebook: Quiz for Lessons 4-4 through 4-7
- Teaching Aids
  - 8 Four-Quadrant Graph Paper
  - 33 Warm-up
  - 40 Composition of Transformations

Additional Resources
- Visuals for Teaching Aids 8, 33, 40

Teaching Lesson 4-7

Warm-up

Multiply.

1. $\begin{bmatrix} 1 & 0 \\ 0 & 1 \end{bmatrix} \begin{bmatrix} -3 & 8 \\ 2 & -5 \end{bmatrix}$ $\begin{bmatrix} -3 & 8 \\ 2 & -5 \end{bmatrix}$

2. $\begin{bmatrix} -3 & 8 \\ 2 & -5 \end{bmatrix} \begin{bmatrix} 1 & 0 \\ 0 & 1 \end{bmatrix}$ $\begin{bmatrix} -3 & 8 \\ 2 & -5 \end{bmatrix}$

3. $\left(\begin{bmatrix} 2 & 3 \\ 0 & -1 \end{bmatrix} \begin{bmatrix} 0 & 5 \\ 3 & -7 \end{bmatrix} \right) \begin{bmatrix} -4 & 0 \\ -1 & 2 \end{bmatrix}$

   $\begin{bmatrix} -25 & -22 \\ 5 & 14 \end{bmatrix}$

Transformations and Matrices

Singapore parade. *Shown are the rotating flags of a flag team in a parade in Singapore. More than 75% of the 2.8 million people who live in Singapore are Chinese. See the Example on page 242.*

Recall that a function is a correspondence between variables such that each value of the first variable corresponds to exactly one value of the second variable. Variables can represent points, so there can be functions that map points to points.

Because transformations are correspondences between sets of points, they are functions. Like other functions, transformations can be described by rules. These rules may be algebraic (a formula), geometric (giving the location of image points), or arithmetic (a matrix). In the preceding three lessons, you have encountered 2×2 matrices for size changes, scale changes, and reflections. Multiplying each of these matrices by a matrix for a polygon results in a transformation image of that polygon. Here we summarize some of the properties of multiplication of 2×2 matrices, and show other ways that matrices are related to transformations.

❶ Properties of Matrix Multiplication

Multiplication of 2×2 matrices has some of the same properties as multiplication of real numbers.

1. Closure: *The set of 2×2 matrices is closed under multiplication. Closure* means: If you multiply two 2×2 matrices, the result is a 2×2 matrix. This property follows from the definition of multiplication of matrices.

2. Associativity: *Multiplication of 2×2 matrices is associative.* In fact, for any three matrices which can be multiplied, it can be shown that $(AB)C = A(BC)$.

Lesson 4-7 Overview

Broad Goals This lesson summarizes the properties of matrix multiplication and culminates with the fundamental relationship between matrices and the transformations they represent—products of matrices correspond to composites of transformations.

Perspective This lesson begins by summarizing the properties of matrix multiplication that students have thus far encountered

and then compares them to the properties of real-number multiplication with which students are familiar.

Then the idea of the *composite* $T_2 \circ T_1$ of two transformations T_1 and T_2 is introduced. A natural question follows: If T_1 has matrix M_1, and T_2 has matrix M_2, what is the matrix for the composite $T_2 \circ T_1$? The answer is just as natural: $M_2 M_1$. In the lesson, an

example is given of this theorem. Here is a general proof: Since T_1 has matrix M_1 and T_2 has matrix M_2, for every point P, $T_1(P) = M_1 \cdot P$ and $T_2 \circ T_1(P) = M_2 \cdot (M_1 \cdot P)$. Since matrix multiplication is associative, $M_2 \cdot (M_1 \cdot P) = (M_2 \cdot M_1) \cdot P$. By the Transitive Property of Equality, $T_2 \circ T_1(P) = (M_2 \cdot M_1) \cdot P$. This means that $T_2 \circ T_1$ can be described by the matrix $M_2 \cdot M_1$.

3. **Identity:** *The matrix* $\begin{bmatrix} 1 & 0 \\ 0 & 1 \end{bmatrix}$ *is the multiplicative identity for 2 × 2 matrices.*

We prove the Identity property below.

> **Proof:**
> Recall that for the real numbers, 1 is the multiplicative identity because for all real numbers a, $1 \cdot a = a \cdot 1 = a$. So we need to show that for all 2 × 2 matrices M,
>
> $$\begin{bmatrix} 1 & 0 \\ 0 & 1 \end{bmatrix} \cdot M = M \cdot \begin{bmatrix} 1 & 0 \\ 0 & 1 \end{bmatrix} = M.$$
>
> Let $M = \begin{bmatrix} a & b \\ c & d \end{bmatrix}$.
>
> Then, $\begin{bmatrix} 1 & 0 \\ 0 & 1 \end{bmatrix}\begin{bmatrix} a & b \\ c & d \end{bmatrix} = \begin{bmatrix} 1 \cdot a + 0 \cdot c & 1 \cdot b + 0 \cdot d \\ 0 \cdot a + 1 \cdot c & 0 \cdot b + 1 \cdot d \end{bmatrix} = \begin{bmatrix} a & b \\ c & d \end{bmatrix}$ and
>
> $\begin{bmatrix} a & b \\ c & d \end{bmatrix}\begin{bmatrix} 1 & 0 \\ 0 & 1 \end{bmatrix} = \begin{bmatrix} a \cdot 1 + b \cdot 0 & a \cdot 0 + b \cdot 1 \\ c \cdot 1 + d \cdot 0 & c \cdot 0 + d \cdot 1 \end{bmatrix} = \begin{bmatrix} a & b \\ c & d \end{bmatrix}$.
>
> (Both multiplications are needed because multiplication is not always commutative.) Thus $\begin{bmatrix} 1 & 0 \\ 0 & 1 \end{bmatrix}$ is the multiplicative identity for 2 × 2 matrices.

Remember that $\begin{bmatrix} 1 & 0 \\ 0 & 1 \end{bmatrix}$, the transformation that maps each point (x, y) onto itself, is the identity transformation. When a point matrix $\begin{bmatrix} x \\ y \end{bmatrix}$ is multiplied on the left by $\begin{bmatrix} 1 & 0 \\ 0 & 1 \end{bmatrix}$, each point (x, y) coincides with its image. Thus $\begin{bmatrix} 1 & 0 \\ 0 & 1 \end{bmatrix}$ represents the identity transformation.

$$\begin{bmatrix} 1 & 0 \\ 0 & 1 \end{bmatrix}\begin{bmatrix} x \\ y \end{bmatrix} = \begin{bmatrix} 1 \cdot x + 0 \cdot y \\ 0 \cdot x + 1 \cdot y \end{bmatrix} = \begin{bmatrix} x \\ y \end{bmatrix}$$

The size change of magnitude 1 is the identity transformation.

Thus the identity for multiplication of matrices represents an identity for transformations as well. One property of multiplication of real numbers that is not true for 2 × 2 matrices is commutativity. That is, there are 2 × 2 matrices A and B with $AB \neq BA$. In the questions, you are asked to find an example of such 2 × 2 matrices.

4. $\begin{bmatrix} 2 & 3 \\ 0 & -1 \end{bmatrix}\left(\begin{bmatrix} 0 & 5 \\ 3 & -7 \end{bmatrix}\begin{bmatrix} -4 & 0 \\ -1 & 2 \end{bmatrix}\right)$

$\begin{bmatrix} -25 & -22 \\ 5 & 14 \end{bmatrix}$

Notes on Reading

❶ Note how the properties of matrices are involved when performing composition of transformations. The first transformation matrix to be applied is the one closest to the preimage point matrix; the last one is the most distant. Since multiplication of 2 × 2 matrices is associative, once the transformation matrices are correctly positioned, either multiplication may be done first.

Reading Mathematics The idea of composition of transformations, which is discussed on page 242, is easy, but the notation is a bit tricky. In English, we normally read from left to right, but in mathematics we sometimes read from right to left. A solution to this problem is to read the symbol ∘ as "following." Thus, $r_{y=x} \circ r_x$ is read "$r_{y=x}$ following r_x", which means that r_x is applied first. This is similar to composition of functions, which students will study in Lesson 8-1: in $(f \circ g)(x) = f(g(x))$, f "follows" g, or f is applied after g.

The terminology for composition of transformations is identical to that which is used for other functions, so being careful now will help students later on. Try to distinguish between the words *composite* and *composition*. *Composite* is the result, and *composition* is the operation; the words are as different as *sum* and *addition*.

Notice that we wrote equal signs between the transformations and the matrices in the preceding paragraph. This can be done because the transformations and the matrices are *isomorphic*. That is, there is a 1-1 correspondence between transformations and matrices so that composition of transformations corresponds to multiplication of matrices. This means that, in these contexts, transformations and matrices are two different languages for discussing the same ideas. The theorem on page 243, which expresses the basic relationship between transformations and matrices, is sometimes called the Matrix-Transformation Isomorphism (MTI) Theorem.

The MTI Theorem makes it possible for you to obtain matrices for composites of transformations if you know the matrices for the individual transformations. The first, and perhaps most important, of these composites is the rotation of 90°—the composite of two reflections over lines that intersect at a 45° angle.

Multiplying the Matrices of Two Transformations

The Example below shows how the product of two transformation matrices is related to the corresponding transformations.

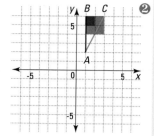

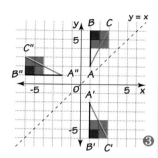

❷ **Example**

A flag has key points at $A = (1, 2)$, $B = (1, 6)$, and $C = (3, 6)$, as shown at the left. Use matrices to reflect this flag over the x-axis. Then reflect its image over the line $y = x$.

Solution

Represent A, B, and C by the matrix $\begin{bmatrix} 1 & 1 & 3 \\ 2 & 6 & 6 \end{bmatrix}$.

To find the first image, multiply this matrix by the matrix for r_x.

$$\overset{r_x}{\begin{bmatrix} 1 & 0 \\ 0 & -1 \end{bmatrix}} \overset{A\ \ B\ \ C}{\begin{bmatrix} 1 & 1 & 3 \\ 2 & 6 & 6 \end{bmatrix}} = \overset{A'\ \ B'\ \ C'}{\begin{bmatrix} 1 & 1 & 3 \\ -2 & -6 & -6 \end{bmatrix}}$$

To find the second image, multiply the matrix for A', B', and C' by the matrix for $r_{y=x}$.

$$\overset{r_{y=x}}{\begin{bmatrix} 0 & 1 \\ 1 & 0 \end{bmatrix}} \overset{A'\ \ \ B'\ \ \ C'}{\begin{bmatrix} 1 & 1 & 3 \\ -2 & -6 & -6 \end{bmatrix}} = \overset{A''\ \ \ B''\ \ \ C''}{\begin{bmatrix} -2 & -6 & -6 \\ 1 & 1 & 3 \end{bmatrix}}$$

❸ The points $A'' = (-2, 1)$, $B'' = (-6, 1)$ and $C'' = (-6, 3)$ enable you to draw the final flag shown at the left.

Composites of Transformations

We call the final flag the image of the original flag under the *composite* of the reflections r_x and $r_{y=x}$. In the In-class Activity on page 239, you found the image of another figure under the composite of these two reflections. In general, any two transformations can be *composed*.

> **Definition**
> Suppose transformation T_1 maps figure F onto figure F', and transformation T_2 maps figure F' onto figure F''. The transformation that maps F onto F'' is called the **composite** of T_1 and T_2, written $T_2 \circ T_1$.

The symbol $\circ$ is read "following." In the Example, r_x came first and then $r_{y=x}$, so we write $r_{y=x} \circ r_x$ and say "$r_{y=x}$ following r_x" or "the composite of $r_{y=x}$ and r_x."

The Composite of $r_{y=x}$ and r_x

To describe $r_{y=x} \circ r_x$ as one transformation, again consider the flags in the Example. The flag containing points A, B, and C is the preimage. The flag containing A', B', and C' is the first image, and the flag containing

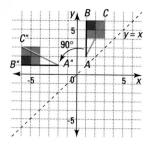

A'', B'', C''' is the final image. Look only at the preimage and the final image as shown at the left. How are the two flags related?

The graph shows that the composite is neither a reflection nor a size or scale change. The composite is the turn, or **rotation** 90° counterclockwise about (0, 0). We denote this rotation by R_{90}. This rotation is the composite of the two reflections:

$$R_{90} = r_{y=x} \circ r_x.$$

Persons X and Z should have found that in the In-class Activity preceding this lesson, the final figure is the image of the original figure under a rotation of 90° counterclockwise.

Matrices and Composites of Transformations

How do we find the matrix associated with R_{90}? Notice that the composite of transformations of the Example led to the following matrix multiplication.

$$\overset{r_{y=x}}{\begin{bmatrix} 0 & 1 \\ 1 & 0 \end{bmatrix}} \overset{r_x}{\begin{bmatrix} 1 & 0 \\ 0 & -1 \end{bmatrix}} \overset{A\ B\ C}{\begin{bmatrix} 1 & 1 & 3 \\ 2 & 6 & 6 \end{bmatrix}} = \overset{A'\ B'\ C'}{\begin{bmatrix} -2 & -6 & -6 \\ 1 & 1 & 3 \end{bmatrix}}$$

Because matrix multiplication is associative, this product can also be computed as follows:

$$\overset{r_{y=x}}{\begin{bmatrix} 0 & 1 \\ 1 & 0 \end{bmatrix}} \overset{r_x}{\begin{bmatrix} 1 & 0 \\ 0 & -1 \end{bmatrix}} \overset{A\ B\ C}{\begin{bmatrix} 1 & 1 & 3 \\ 2 & 6 & 6 \end{bmatrix}} = \begin{bmatrix} 0 & -1 \\ 1 & 0 \end{bmatrix} \overset{A\ B\ C}{\begin{bmatrix} 1 & 1 & 3 \\ 2 & 6 & 6 \end{bmatrix}} = \overset{A''\ B''\ C''}{\begin{bmatrix} -2 & -6 & -6 \\ 1 & 1 & 3 \end{bmatrix}}$$

Observe that multiplying the two reflection matrices gives the single matrix $\begin{bmatrix} 0 & -1 \\ 1 & 0 \end{bmatrix}$. Applying this matrix to A, B, and C results in the final images A'', B'', and C''. Thus, the single matrix $\begin{bmatrix} 0 & -1 \\ 1 & 0 \end{bmatrix}$ is the matrix of the composite $r_{y=x} \circ r_x$. The general idea is summarized below.

❹ **Theorem**

If M_1 is the matrix for transformation T_1 and M_2 is the matrix for transformation T_2, then $M_2 M_1$ is the matrix for $T_2 \circ T_1$.

QUESTIONS

Covering the Reading

1. Explain why every transformation is a function. See left.

2. When a 2 × 2 matrix is multiplied by a 2 × 2 matrix, what are the dimensions of the product matrix? 2 × 2

1) A transformation is a correspondence between two sets of points such that each point in the preimage corresponds to exactly one point in the image.

Additional Examples

1. Rectangle *ALEX* is determined by (3, 1), (3, 2), (6, 2), and (6, 1).
   a. Graph rectangle *ALEX*.
   b. Use matrices to reflect *ALEX* over the line $y = x$. Then graph the image and label it $A'L'E'X'$.

   $$\begin{bmatrix} 0 & 1 \\ 1 & 0 \end{bmatrix} \begin{bmatrix} 3 & 3 & 6 & 6 \\ 1 & 2 & 2 & 1 \end{bmatrix} = \begin{bmatrix} 1 & 2 & 2 & 1 \\ 3 & 3 & 6 & 6 \end{bmatrix}$$

   c. Use matrices to reflect $A'L'E'X'$ over the x-axis. Graph the image. Label it $A''L''E''X''$.

   $$\begin{bmatrix} 1 & 0 \\ 0 & -1 \end{bmatrix} \begin{bmatrix} 1 & 2 & 2 & 1 \\ 3 & 3 & 6 & 6 \end{bmatrix} = \begin{bmatrix} 1 & 2 & 2 & 1 \\ -3 & -3 & -6 & -6 \end{bmatrix}$$

   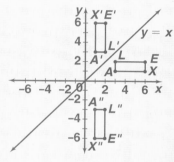

2. If $T_1 = r_x$ and $T_2 = r_y$, find a single matrix to describe the composite transformation $T_2 \circ T_1$.
   $T_2 \circ T_1 = r_y \circ r_x$

   $$\overset{r_y}{\begin{bmatrix} -1 & 0 \\ 0 & 1 \end{bmatrix}} \overset{r_x}{\begin{bmatrix} 1 & 0 \\ 0 & -1 \end{bmatrix}} = \begin{bmatrix} -1 & 0 \\ 0 & -1 \end{bmatrix}$$

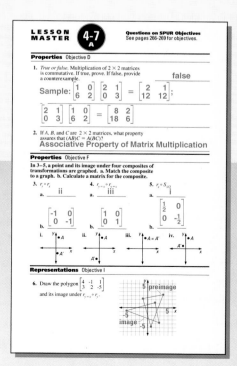

Questions 10, 12–13 Stress that the order in composition of transformations is from right to left.

Question 15a Some students may draw a figure and do the reflection geometrically, some may remember a theorem from geometry, others may use the algebraic rule, and still others may use matrices.

Question 18b This question reviews the concept that reflections are congruence transformations.

Question 24 Students may have to be reminded that the 3×3 identity

matrix is $\begin{bmatrix} 1 & 0 & 0 \\ 0 & 1 & 0 \\ 0 & 0 & 1 \end{bmatrix}$.

Follow-up for Lesson 4-7

Practice

For more questions on SPUR Objectives, use **Lesson Master 4-7A** (shown on page 243) or **Lesson Master 4-7B** (shown on pages 244–245).

Assessment

Quiz A quiz covering Lessons 4-4 through 4-7 is provided in the *Assessment Sourcebook*.

LESSON MASTER 4-7 B Questions on SPUR Objectives

Vocabulary

1. How do we write in symbols the composite of the transformation T_1 followed by the transformation T_2? What does it mean?
$T_2 \circ T_1$; sample: If T_1 maps F onto F', and T_2 maps F' onto F'', then $T_2 \circ T_1$ maps F onto F''.

Properties Objective D: Recognize properties of matrix operations.

2. **a.** Write the identity matrix I. **b.** Show that $I \cdot M = M \cdot I$ for all 2×2 matrices M.
$I = \begin{bmatrix} 1 & 0 \\ 0 & 1 \end{bmatrix}$
b. (See below.)

3. Name two other properties of 2×2 matrices that are shared by multiplication of real numbers.
Associative Property; Closure

Properties Objective F: Relate transformations to matrices and vice versa.

4. Suppose T_1 has matrix $\begin{bmatrix} 4 & 0 \\ 0 & 4 \end{bmatrix}$ and T_2 has matrix $\begin{bmatrix} 1 & 0 \\ 0 & -1 \end{bmatrix}$. $\begin{bmatrix} 4 & 0 \\ 0 & -4 \end{bmatrix}$
a. What is the matrix for $T_2 \circ T_1$?
b. Explain what happens to a figure under $T_2 \circ T_1$.
Sample: The figure undergoes a size change of magnitude 4 and is reflected over the x-axis.

(#2b) $\begin{bmatrix} 1 & 0 \\ 0 & 1 \end{bmatrix}\begin{bmatrix} a & b \\ c & d \end{bmatrix} = \begin{bmatrix} a+0 & b+0 \\ 0+c & 0+d \end{bmatrix} = \begin{bmatrix} a & b \\ c & d \end{bmatrix}$;
$\begin{bmatrix} a & b \\ c & d \end{bmatrix}\begin{bmatrix} 1 & 0 \\ 0 & 1 \end{bmatrix} = \begin{bmatrix} a+0 & 0+b \\ c+0 & 0+d \end{bmatrix} = \begin{bmatrix} a & b \\ c & d \end{bmatrix}$

244

---

3. Let $X = \begin{bmatrix} 1 & -2 \\ 3 & 4 \end{bmatrix}$, $Y = \begin{bmatrix} 0 & 1 \\ 4 & -2 \end{bmatrix}$, and $Z = \begin{bmatrix} \frac{1}{2} & 1 \\ 0 & 1 \end{bmatrix}$.
   a. Show that $(XY)Z = X(YZ)$. See margin.
   b. The answer to part **a** is an instance of what property of matrices? Associative Property

4. **a.** Multiply $\begin{bmatrix} 1 & 0 \\ 0 & 1 \end{bmatrix}$ by $\begin{bmatrix} \pi & \sqrt{2} \\ -3 & \frac{3}{4} \end{bmatrix}$. $\begin{bmatrix} \pi & \sqrt{2} \\ -3 & \frac{3}{4} \end{bmatrix}$
   b. What property of matrix multiplication is illustrated in part **a**? identity property.

5. Find two 2×2 matrices A and B such that $AB = BA$. See margin.

6. Find two 2×2 matrices A and B such that $AB \ne BA$. See margin.

7. The multiplicative-identity matrix for 2×2 matrices is the matrix for what transformation? the identity transformation

8. What property of matrix multiplication justifies this equation?
$\begin{bmatrix} 0 & 1 \\ 1 & 0 \end{bmatrix}\left(\begin{bmatrix} 1 & 0 \\ 0 & -1 \end{bmatrix}\begin{bmatrix} 1 & 1 & 3 \\ 2 & 6 & 6 \end{bmatrix}\right) = \left(\begin{bmatrix} 0 & 1 \\ 1 & 0 \end{bmatrix}\begin{bmatrix} 1 & 0 \\ 0 & -1 \end{bmatrix}\right)\begin{bmatrix} 1 & 1 & 3 \\ 2 & 6 & 6 \end{bmatrix}$?
Associative Property

9. What does the symbol $\circ$ mean? the composite of, or "following"

10. In $r_{y=x} \circ r_x$, which reflection is done first, $r_{y=x}$ or r_x? r_x

11. R_{90} represents a rotation of ? degrees around ? in a(n) ? direction. 90°; the origin; counterclockwise

12. If T_1 has matrix $\begin{bmatrix} -2 & 0 \\ 0 & 2 \end{bmatrix}$ and T_2 has matrix $\begin{bmatrix} 0 & 1 \\ -1 & 0 \end{bmatrix}$, what is a matrix for $T_2 \circ T_1$? $\begin{bmatrix} 0 & 2 \\ 2 & 0 \end{bmatrix}$

14)

15a) (i) identity transformation
(ii) identity transformation
(iii) identity transformation
b) If a point is reflected over a line and then its image is reflected over the same line, the final image is the original point.

Applying the Mathematics

13. **a.** Find the matrix for $r_x \circ r_{y=x}$. $\begin{bmatrix} 0 & 1 \\ -1 & 0 \end{bmatrix}$
    b. To what single transformation is $r_x \circ r_{y=x}$ equivalent? R_{270}
    c. How does your answer to part **b** compare with $r_{y=x} \circ r_x$? not the same; $r_{y=x} \circ r_x = R_{90}$

14. Graph the image of the flag of this lesson under the transformation $S_2 \circ r_y$. See left.

15. **a.** To what single transformation is each of the following equivalent?
    (i) $r_x \circ r_x$ (ii) $r_y \circ r_y$ (iii) $r_{y=x} \circ r_{y=x}$ See left.
    b. Explain the geometric meaning of the results of part **a**.

16. Use $A = \begin{bmatrix} a & b \\ c & d \end{bmatrix}$, $B = \begin{bmatrix} e & f \\ g & h \end{bmatrix}$, and $C = \begin{bmatrix} i & j \\ k & l \end{bmatrix}$.
    Prove that multiplication of 2×2 matrices is associative by calculating the following. See margin.
    a. $(AB)C$ **b.** $A(BC)$

17. Prove that if C is any 2×2 matrix and M_k is the matrix for S_k, then $M_k \cdot C = C \cdot M_k$. See margin.

244

Additional Answers, continued
3a. See page 243.

5. Sample: Let $A = \begin{bmatrix} 1 & 0 \\ 0 & 1 \end{bmatrix}$ and $B = \begin{bmatrix} a & c \\ b & d \end{bmatrix}$. Then $AB = \begin{bmatrix} a & c \\ b & d \end{bmatrix}$.
$BA = \begin{bmatrix} a & c \\ b & d \end{bmatrix}\begin{bmatrix} 1 & 0 \\ 0 & 1 \end{bmatrix} = \begin{bmatrix} a & c \\ b & d \end{bmatrix}$

6. Sample: Let $A = \begin{bmatrix} 1 & 0 \\ 2 & 1 \end{bmatrix}$ and $B = \begin{bmatrix} 2 & 2 \\ 0 & 3 \end{bmatrix}$. Then $AB = \begin{bmatrix} 2 & 2 \\ 4 & 7 \end{bmatrix}$.
$BA = \begin{bmatrix} 2 & 2 \\ 0 & 3 \end{bmatrix}\begin{bmatrix} 1 & 0 \\ 2 & 1 \end{bmatrix} = \begin{bmatrix} 6 & 2 \\ 6 & 3 \end{bmatrix}$

18a) $\begin{bmatrix} 0 & 3 & -1 \\ -5 & 2 & 1 \end{bmatrix}$

19a, d)

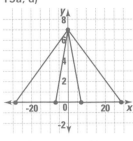

19c) $\begin{bmatrix} -28 & 28 & 0 \\ 0 & 0 & 7 \end{bmatrix}$

International news.
*America's diverse
population reads
newspapers in many
languages. From top to
bottom, these newspapers
are written in Greek,
Chinese, Russian, and
Arabic.*

Review

18. $\triangle BAT$ can be represented by $\begin{bmatrix} 0 & 3 & -1 \\ 5 & -2 & -1 \end{bmatrix}$. *(Lesson 4-6)*

    a. Find a matrix to represent the image $\triangle B'A'T'$ under r_x. **See left.**
    b. *True or false.* $\triangle BAT \cong \triangle B'A'T'$. **True**

19. **a.** Graph the triangle represented by $\begin{bmatrix} -7 & 7 & 0 \\ 0 & 0 & 7 \end{bmatrix}$. **See left.**

    b. What kind of triangle is this? **isosceles triangle**
    c. What matrix describes the image of the triangle in part **a** under

    the transformation given by $\begin{bmatrix} 4 & 0 \\ 0 & 1 \end{bmatrix}$? **See left.**

    d. Graph the image. **See left.**
    e. What special kind of triangle is the image? **isosceles**
    f. Are the triangles in parts **a** and **c** similar? How can you tell? **No.**
       (Lessons 4-1, 4-5) **Sample: the angles at the corresponding vertices do not have the same measure.**

20. Some communication trends in Kenya and New Zealand for the years 1970 and 1990 are given below. "Newspapers" refers to the number of copies of daily newspapers circulated per 1000 people. "TV" refers to the number of televisions owned per 1000 people.

	1970 Newspapers	1970 TV	1990 Newspapers	1990 TV
Kenya	14	1.4	15	9
New Zealand	375	235	324	442

    a. Which country had the greatest change in newspaper circulation?
    b. Name a trend common to both countries. *(Lesson 4-2)* **See below.**
    a) New Zealand

21. During the 1990s, the population of Guatemala has been increasing by about 250,000 per year. In contrast, the population of Hungary has been decreasing by about 11,000 per year. The population of Guatemala in 1990 was about 9,300,000. The population of Hungary in 1990 was about 10,500,000. *(Lessons 3-1, 3-7)*
    a. In what year will the two populations be about the same? **1994**
    b. What will the populations be then? **about 10,450,000**

22. A line has the equation $y - 2 = \frac{1}{2}(x + 3)$. Give the slope of the line and a point it contains. *(Lessons 3-4, 3-5)* **Sample: slope = $\frac{1}{2}$; point = (-3, 2)**

23. *Multiple choice.* Which expression equals $-(x_1 - x_2)$?
    (Previous course) **a**
    (a) $x_2 - x_1$ (b) $x_1 - x_2$ (c) $x_1 + x_2$
    (d) $-x_{-1}$ (e) none of these

20b) The number of televisions owned is increasing in both countries.

Exploration

24. Three properties of multiplication of 2×2 matrices are given in this lesson. Explore whether multiplication of 3×3 matrices has properties identical or similar to these. **See margin.**

Lesson 4-7 *Transformations and Matrices* **245**

245

Oral/Written Communication Have students **work in pairs.** Tell one student to write a 2 × 2 matrix to represent a transformation T_1, and have the other student write a transformation T_2. Then have one student find the matrix for $T_1 \circ T_2$, and the other student find the matrix for $T_2 \circ T_1$. [Students correctly use matrix multiplication to find the composite of two transformations.]

Extension

Have students use the matrices in **Question 16.** For any 2 × 2 matrices A, B, and C, does $A(B + C) = AB + AC$? [Yes]

Project Update Project 2, *History of Matrices*, on page 261, relates to the content of this lesson.

17. $M_k \cdot C = \begin{bmatrix} k & 0 \\ 0 & k \end{bmatrix}\begin{bmatrix} m & n \\ p & q \end{bmatrix} =$

    $\begin{bmatrix} km & kn \\ kp & kq \end{bmatrix}$

    $C \cdot M_k = \begin{bmatrix} m & n \\ p & q \end{bmatrix}\begin{bmatrix} k & 0 \\ 0 & k \end{bmatrix} =$

    $\begin{bmatrix} km & kn \\ kp & kq \end{bmatrix}$

24. Properties are the same with

    $\begin{bmatrix} 1 & 0 & 0 \\ 0 & 1 & 0 \\ 0 & 0 & 1 \end{bmatrix}$ as the identity

    matrix.

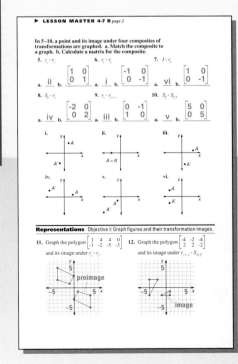

16a. $(AB)C = \left(\begin{bmatrix} a & b \\ c & d \end{bmatrix}\begin{bmatrix} e & f \\ g & h \end{bmatrix}\right)\begin{bmatrix} i & j \\ k & l \end{bmatrix} = \begin{bmatrix} ae + bg & af + bh \\ ce + dg & cf + dh \end{bmatrix}\begin{bmatrix} i & j \\ k & l \end{bmatrix} =$

$\begin{bmatrix} aei + bgi + afk + bhk & aej + bgj + afl + bhl \\ cei + dgi + cfk + dhk & cej + dgj + cfl + dhl \end{bmatrix}$

16b. $\begin{bmatrix} a & b \\ c & d \end{bmatrix}\left(\begin{bmatrix} e & f \\ g & h \end{bmatrix}\begin{bmatrix} i & j \\ k & l \end{bmatrix}\right) = \begin{bmatrix} a & b \\ c & d \end{bmatrix}\begin{bmatrix} ei + fk & ej + fl \\ gi + hk & gj + hl \end{bmatrix} =$

$\begin{bmatrix} aei + afk + bgi + bhk & aej + afl + bgj + bhl \\ cei + cfk + dgi + dhk & cej + cfl + dgj + dhl \end{bmatrix}$

245

Objectives

E Recognize relationships between figures and their rotation images.
F Relate rotations to matrices, and vice versa.
I Graph figures and their rotation images.

Resources

From the *Teacher's Resource File*
- Lesson Master 4-8A or 4-8B
- Answer Master 4-8
- Activity Kit, Activity 8
- Teaching Aids
  8 Four-Quadrant Graph Paper
  33 Warm-up
  38 Transformations and Their Matrices
  39 More Transformations and Their Matrices
- Technology Sourcebook Computer Master 4

Additional Resources
- Visuals for Teaching Aids 8, 33, 38, 39
- Geometry Template

Teaching Lesson 4-8

Warm-up

Multiply.

1. $\begin{bmatrix} 0 & -1 \\ 1 & 0 \end{bmatrix}\begin{bmatrix} 5 & 7 \\ -1 & 4 \end{bmatrix}$ $\begin{bmatrix} 1 & -4 \\ 5 & 7 \end{bmatrix}$

2. $\begin{bmatrix} -1 & 0 \\ 0 & -1 \end{bmatrix}\begin{bmatrix} 2 & -3 & 6 \\ -1 & 2 & 4 \end{bmatrix}$

   $\begin{bmatrix} -2 & 3 & -6 \\ 1 & -2 & -4 \end{bmatrix}$

Matrices for Rotations

Human rotation. *Pictured are members of the Jessie White Tumblers performing the Human Chain. A tumbler rotates 360° while soaring over the backs of up to 20 others. The team, based in Chicago, performs worldwide.*

Rotations are closely related to angles. The arcs used to denote angles suggest turns. Angles with larger measures indicate greater turns. The amount and direction of the turn determine the magnitude of the **rotation.** Counterclockwise turns have positive magnitudes. Clockwise turns have negative magnitudes. The rotation of magnitude x around the origin is denoted by R_x.

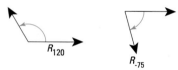

R_{120} R_{-75}

Caution: A rotation is denoted with a capital R, while a reflection is denoted with a lowercase r.

The Composite of Two Rotations

Rotations often occur one after the other, as when going from one frame to another in animated cartoons or in computer generated images.

Lesson 4-8 Overview

Broad Goals This lesson applies the concepts of Lesson 4-7. The matrix for R_{90} is multiplied by itself to obtain a matrix for R_{180}. The matrices for R_{90} and R_{180} are multiplied to obtain the matrix for R_{270}.

Perspective By this time, most students should feel comfortable with transformations and the matrices which represent them. Rotations are interesting examples of

transformations that will give students more practice with matrices. However, this lesson involves more than practice, and it should not be skipped under any circumstances. Rotations are used in the next lesson to prove the theorem which states that the product of slopes of two perpendicular lines is –1. In a later chapter, rotations are used to define cos x and sin x for all real numbers x.

In this lesson, we consider matrices for only rotations whose magnitudes are integral multiples of 90°. But all rotations with center (0, 0) have 2 × 2 matrices; the transformation R_θ has matrix $\begin{bmatrix} \cos\theta & -\sin\theta \\ \sin\theta & \cos\theta \end{bmatrix}$. (Of course, we do not expect students to know this information at this time.) The Matrix Basis Theorem can be used to help students remember the various rotation matrices.

In the frames on page 246, the character undergoes a series of 60° counterclockwise rotations. Notice that figures two frames apart are turned 180°. This is a result of a fundamental property of rotations, which is itself derived from the Angle Addition Postulate in geometry.

> **Theorem**
> A rotation of $b°$ following a rotation of $a°$ with the same center results in a rotation of $(a + b)°$. In symbols: $R_b \circ R_a = R_{a+b}$.

Matrices for Rotations

Can rotations have 2×2 matrices? Notice that $\begin{bmatrix} a & b \\ c & d \end{bmatrix} \begin{bmatrix} 0 \\ 0 \end{bmatrix} = \begin{bmatrix} 0 \\ 0 \end{bmatrix}$.

So any transformation represented by a 2×2 matrix must map $(0, 0)$ onto itself. Thus, the only rotations that can have 2×2 matrices are those with center $(0, 0)$.

In the previous lesson, you learned that $\begin{bmatrix} 0 & -1 \\ 1 & 0 \end{bmatrix}$ is the matrix for the composite $r_{y=x} \circ r_x = R_{90}$. We state this result as a theorem.

> **Theorem**
> $\begin{bmatrix} 0 & -1 \\ 1 & 0 \end{bmatrix}$ is the matrix for R_{90}.

We can verify this theorem using the Matrix Basis Theorem.

The image of $(1, 0)$ is $(0, 1)$.

$$\begin{bmatrix} 1 & 0 \\ 0 & 1 \end{bmatrix} \qquad \begin{bmatrix} 0 & -1 \\ 1 & 0 \end{bmatrix}$$

The image of $(0, 1)$ is $(-1, 0)$.

Matrices for Rotations of Multiples of 90°

By composing two 90° rotations, a matrix for $\boldsymbol{R_{180}}$ can be found.

> **Example**
>
> Find the matrix for R_{180}.
>
> **Solution**
>
> A rotation of 180° can be considered as a 90° rotation followed by another 90° rotation. That is, $R_{90} \circ R_{90} = R_{180}$. In matrix form,
>
> $\begin{bmatrix} 0 & -1 \\ 1 & 0 \end{bmatrix} \begin{bmatrix} 0 & -1 \\ 1 & 0 \end{bmatrix} = \begin{bmatrix} -1 & 0 \\ 0 & -1 \end{bmatrix}$. So $\begin{bmatrix} -1 & 0 \\ 0 & -1 \end{bmatrix}$ is the matrix for R_{180}.

▶

---

3. $\begin{bmatrix} 0 & 1 \\ -1 & 0 \end{bmatrix} \begin{bmatrix} -5 & 4 & 0 \\ -1 & 2 & 4 \end{bmatrix}$
$\begin{bmatrix} -1 & 2 & 4 \\ 5 & -4 & 0 \end{bmatrix}$

Notes on Reading
Graph paper or **Teaching Aid 8** is needed for this lesson.

Reading Mathematics Note that an expression of the form $R_y \circ R_x$ means to rotate by x and then rotate by y; thus, we are reading from right to left instead of left to right, as we would with most expressions. However, composition of rotations with the same center is commutative, so $R_y \circ R_x = R_x \circ R_y$. You can ask students to investigate this commutativity by using the *Challenge* on page 249 of this Teacher's Edition.

If they forget them, students should be able to determine the matrices for R_{90}, R_{180}, and R_{270} by themselves. They can either memorize them, learn the matrix for R_{90} and obtain the others through matrix multiplication, or determine them by examining the images of $(1, 0)$ and $(0, 1)$. The last of these options, using the Matrix Basis Theorem, is quite efficient.

This is also an appropriate time to use **Teaching Aid 39**.

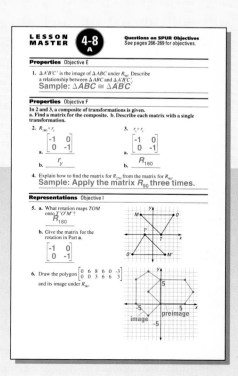

Optional Activities

Activity 1
You should use *Activity Kit, Activity 8* before covering the lesson. In this activity, students use the Matrix Basis Theorem to derive the 2×2 matrices associated with rotations.

Activity 2
Materials: **Teaching Aids 38 and 39**

After discussing the lesson, it is appropriate to summarize the matrices that students have studied thus far. You can use **Teaching Aids 38 and 39** for this activity.

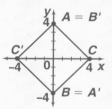
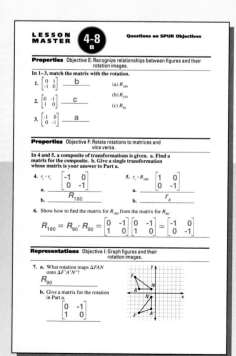
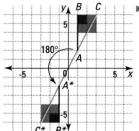

Sample: $R_{180} \circ R_{90} = R_{270}$.
In matrix form,

$$\begin{bmatrix} -1 & 0 \\ 0 & -1 \end{bmatrix}\begin{bmatrix} 0 & -1 \\ 1 & 0 \end{bmatrix} =$$

$$\begin{bmatrix} 0 & 1 \\ -1 & 0 \end{bmatrix}, \text{ which is the}$$

matrix for R_{270}.

▶ **Check**

Apply this matrix to a figure. We use A, B, and C from the last lesson.

$$\begin{array}{cccccc} R_{180} & A & B & C & & A^*\ B^*\ C^* \\ \begin{bmatrix} -1 & 0 \\ 0 & -1 \end{bmatrix} & \begin{bmatrix} 1 & 1 & 3 \\ 2 & 6 & 6 \end{bmatrix} & & = & \begin{bmatrix} -1 & -1 & -3 \\ -2 & -6 & -6 \end{bmatrix}. \end{array}$$

The graph verifies that A, B, and C have been rotated 180°.

Activity

Prove that the matrix for R_{270} is $\begin{bmatrix} 0 & 1 \\ -1 & 0 \end{bmatrix}$. See left.

The image of any figure under a rotation with a negative magnitude can also be found by a clockwise rotation. For instance, R_{-90} represents a 90° turn clockwise. Because a rotation of -90° has the same images for every point as a rotation of 270°, R_{-90} equals R_{270}.

Here is a summary of the rotations of this lesson:

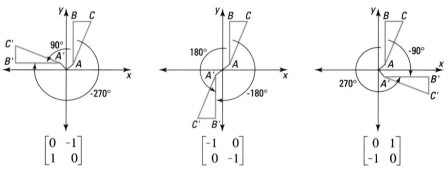

Rotation of 90° or -270°   Rotation of 180° or -180°   Rotation of 270° or -90°

$$\begin{bmatrix} 0 & -1 \\ 1 & 0 \end{bmatrix} \qquad \begin{bmatrix} -1 & 0 \\ 0 & -1 \end{bmatrix} \qquad \begin{bmatrix} 0 & 1 \\ -1 & 0 \end{bmatrix}$$

These matrices make it possible to describe rotation images algebraically. For instance, for R_{90},

$$\begin{bmatrix} 0 & -1 \\ 1 & 0 \end{bmatrix}\begin{bmatrix} x \\ y \end{bmatrix} = \begin{bmatrix} 0 \cdot x + -1 \cdot y \\ 1 \cdot x + 0 \cdot y \end{bmatrix} = \begin{bmatrix} -y \\ x \end{bmatrix}. \text{ Thus, } R_{90}(x, y) = (-y, x).$$

Rotations, being composites of reflections, are transformations that yield images congruent to their preimages.

QUESTIONS

Covering the Reading

1. A rotation of negative magnitude is a turn in which direction?
   clockwise
2. How much of a turn does the character pictured at the bottom of page 246 undergo from the first frame to the fourth frame? 180°

Optional Activities

Activity 3 Technology Connection
In *Technology Sourcebook, Computer Master 4,* students use mapping notation to communicate transformations. Coordinates of vertices of a shape are stored in columns. Operations are performed on these columns and stored in other columns, and preimages and images are compared.

Adapting to Individual Needs

Extra Help
Students may have to be reminded that counterclockwise rotations are positive and clockwise rotations are negative. They may think this is odd, since clock times increase as the clock hands rotate clockwise. Yet the accepted convention in most mathematics is to consider counterclockwise rotations as positive.

11) $\begin{bmatrix} -1 & 0 \\ 0 & -1 \end{bmatrix}\begin{bmatrix} -1 & 0 \\ 0 & -1 \end{bmatrix} =$

$\begin{bmatrix} 1 & 0 \\ 0 & 1 \end{bmatrix}$

$R_{180} \circ R_{180} = R_{360}$, which shows that the matrix for R_{360} is the identity matrix.

13)

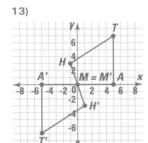

3. The composite of a rotation of 45° and a rotation of 90° is a rotation of __?__. 135°

4. In general, $R_c \circ R_d =$ __?__. R_{c+d}

5. A rotation of -270° is the same as a rotation with what positive magnitude? 90°

In 6–8, *multiple choice.* Identify the matrix for the given rotation. (Hint: Use the Matrix Basis Theorem.)

(a) $\begin{bmatrix} 0 & -1 \\ 1 & 0 \end{bmatrix}$ (b) $\begin{bmatrix} 0 & -1 \\ -1 & 0 \end{bmatrix}$ (c) $\begin{bmatrix} -1 & 0 \\ 0 & -1 \end{bmatrix}$ (d) $\begin{bmatrix} 0 & 1 \\ -1 & 0 \end{bmatrix}$ (e) $\begin{bmatrix} -1 & 0 \\ 0 & 1 \end{bmatrix}$

6. R_{90} a **7.** R_{-90} d **8.** R_{180} c

9. Write your proof from the Activity that $\begin{bmatrix} 0 & 1 \\ -1 & 0 \end{bmatrix}$ is the matrix for R_{270}. See page 248.

10. Find the image of (x, y) under R_{270}. $(y, -x)$

Applying the Mathematics

11. Use matrix multiplication to determine $R_{180} \circ R_{180}$. Write a sentence or two explaining your results. See left.

12. Consider $\triangle DEF$ with $D = (1, -2)$, $E = (3, 5)$, and $F = (-3, -1)$. Use matrix multiplication to find the image of $\triangle DEF$ under R_{90}. See left.

13. Quadrilateral *MATH* has coordinates $M = (0, 0)$, $A = (5, 0)$, $T = (5, 7)$, and $H = (-1, 3)$. Graph *MATH* and its image under R_{180}. See left.

14. a. Calculate a matrix for $R_{180} \circ r_y$. $\begin{bmatrix} 1 & 0 \\ 0 & -1 \end{bmatrix}$
b. To what transformation does the matrix in part **a** correspond? r_x

15. The point (3, 4) lies on the circle with center (0, 0) and radius 5.
a. Rotate this point 90°, 180°, and 270° around (0, 0) to find the coordinates of three other points on this circle. See margin.
b. Graph all four points. See margin.

Review

16–19) See margin.
In 16–19, write the matrix for the transformation. *(Lessons 4-4, 4-5, 4-6, 4-7)*

16. the size change of magnitude 3, center (0, 0)

17. the identity transformation

18. $r_{y=x}$ **19.** $S_{1,3}: (x, y) \rightarrow (x, 3y)$

20. Use the figure at the left. Describe the transformation which maps *ABCDE* onto $A'B'C'D'E'$ *(Lesson 4-6)*
a. in words. The transformation is a reflection over the y-axis.
b. with a matrix. $\begin{bmatrix} -1 & 0 \\ 0 & 1 \end{bmatrix}$
c. using mapping notation. $r_y: (x, y) \rightarrow (-x, y)$

Lesson 4-8 *Matrices for Rotations* **249**

12) $\begin{bmatrix} 2 & -5 & 1 \\ 1 & 3 & -3 \end{bmatrix}$

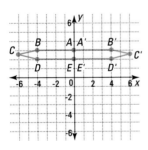

No time for needling.
Shown is a group using rotations of a compass to navigate. They use the angles of the compass to find each checkpoint.

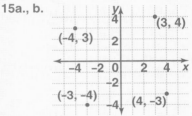
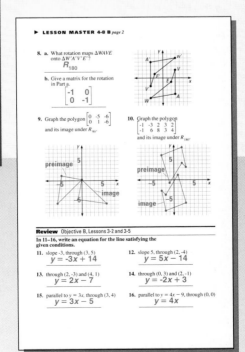
249

Notes on Questions

Question 21 The transformation determined by this matrix is the composite of the reflection r_x and the size change S_2. This fact can be verified by multiplying their matrices.

Questions 27–28 These ideas are utilized in Lesson 4-9.

Question 30 This question is meant to be answered by using a drawing and estimation. Have the students pick a point, use the matrix R_x to find the image point, and use a protractor or their **Geometry Template** to carefully estimate the angle of rotation.

**Follow-up
for Lesson 4-8**

Practice

For more questions on SPUR Objectives, use **Lesson Master 4-8A** (shown on page 247) or **Lesson Master 4-8B** (shown on pages 248–249).

Assessment

Written Communication Have students imagine they have forgotten the matrices for R_{90}, R_{180}, and R_{270}. Then have each student write a paragraph describing a method he or she would use to determine these matrices. [Students demonstrate that they can determine the appropriate matrices for the rotations presented in the lesson.]

Project Update Project 2, *History of Matrices*, on page 261, relates to the content of this lesson.

21a, b)

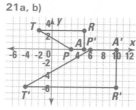

c) reflection about the x-axis and size change of magnitude 2

29) Sample:

$$R_{60} = \begin{bmatrix} \dfrac{1}{2} & \dfrac{-\sqrt{3}}{2} \\ \dfrac{\sqrt{3}}{2} & \dfrac{1}{2} \end{bmatrix}$$

30) about 53°

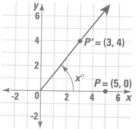

21. Let $T = (-2, 3)$, $R = (5, 3)$, $A = (5, 0)$, and $P = (3, 0)$. *See left.*
   a. Graph polygon *TRAP*.
   b. Graph the image of *TRAP* under the transformation with matrix $\begin{bmatrix} 2 & 0 \\ 0 & -2 \end{bmatrix}$.
   c. Describe the transformation. *(Lessons 4-1, 4-5)*

22. Let $M = \begin{bmatrix} 2 & 1 \\ 0 & -2 \end{bmatrix}$, $N = \begin{bmatrix} -2 & 3 \\ -5 & 0 \end{bmatrix}$, and $P = \begin{bmatrix} 1 & -4 \\ 1 & 2 \end{bmatrix}$.
   a. Compute $M(N + P)$. a) $\begin{bmatrix} -6 & 0 \\ 8 & -4 \end{bmatrix}$ b) $\begin{bmatrix} -6 & 0 \\ 8 & -4 \end{bmatrix}$
   b. Compute $MN + MP$.
   c. Is matrix multiplication distributive over matrix addition in this case? *(Lessons 4-2, 4-3)* Yes

23. What algebraic sentence does $\begin{bmatrix} a & b \end{bmatrix} \cdot \begin{bmatrix} a \\ b \end{bmatrix} = \begin{bmatrix} c^2 \end{bmatrix}$ represent? $a^2 + b^2 = c^2$ *(Lessons 4-1, 4-3)*

In 24–26, two figures are given. **a.** Fill in the blank with one of the following: similar, similar and congruent, or neither similar nor congruent. **b.** Identify the type of transformation that maps the figure on the left to the one on the right. *(Previous course, Lessons 4-3, 4-4, 4-5)*

24.

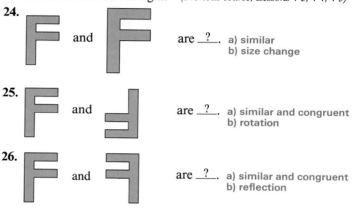

and   are __?__. a) similar
                  b) size change

25.

and   are __?__. a) similar and congruent
                  b) rotation

26.

and   are __?__. a) similar and congruent
                  b) reflection

27. Calculate the slope of the line joining (-4, 6) and (2, 3). *(Lesson 2-4)* $-\dfrac{1}{2}$

28. Give a definition of *perpendicular lines*. *(Previous course)*
   Sample: Perpendicular lines are lines that form a 90° angle.

Exploration

See left.
29. The matrix for R_{30} is $\begin{bmatrix} \dfrac{\sqrt{3}}{2} & \dfrac{-1}{2} \\ \dfrac{1}{2} & \dfrac{\sqrt{3}}{2} \end{bmatrix}$.

   Use this information to determine matrices for some other rotations.

30. $\begin{bmatrix} 0.6 & -0.8 \\ 0.8 & 0.6 \end{bmatrix}$ is a matrix for a rotation R_x about the point (0, 0). By carefully plotting points and their images, estimate x.

Two lines are perpendicular if and only if they form a 90° angle. Thus, if a rotation of magnitude 90° is applied to a line, then the image line is perpendicular to the preimage.

Consider a line passing through points (x_1, y_1) and (x_2, y_2). The line can be represented by the 2×2 matrix $\begin{bmatrix} x_1 & x_2 \\ y_1 & y_2 \end{bmatrix}$. Its slope is $\frac{y_2 - y_1}{x_2 - x_1}$.

Example 1

Consider the line $\overleftrightarrow{AB}$ containing points $A = (-5, -3)$ and $B = (4, 1)$.
a. Represent $\overleftrightarrow{AB}$ as a 2×2 matrix.
b. Calculate the slope of $\overleftrightarrow{AB}$.
c. Find $\overleftrightarrow{A'B'}$, the image of $\overleftrightarrow{AB}$ under R_{90}.
d. Graph $\overleftrightarrow{AB}$ and $\overleftrightarrow{A'B'}$.
e. Calculate the slope of $\overleftrightarrow{A'B'}$.

Solution

a. $\overleftrightarrow{AB}$ can be represented by the matrix $\begin{bmatrix} -5 & 4 \\ -3 & 1 \end{bmatrix}$.

b. slope of $\overleftrightarrow{AB}$ = $\frac{y_2 - y_1}{x_2 - x_1} = \frac{1 - -3}{4 - -5} = \frac{4}{9}$

c. To find $\overleftrightarrow{A'B'}$, multiply the matrix for R_{90} by the matrix for $\overleftrightarrow{AB}$.

$$\overset{R_{90}}{\begin{bmatrix} 0 & -1 \\ 1 & 0 \end{bmatrix}} \overset{(\overleftrightarrow{AB})}{\begin{bmatrix} -5 & 4 \\ -3 & 1 \end{bmatrix}} = \overset{\overleftrightarrow{A'B'}}{\begin{bmatrix} 3 & -1 \\ -5 & 4 \end{bmatrix}}$$

So $\overleftrightarrow{A'B'}$ is the line containing the points $(3, -5)$ and $(-1, 4)$.

d. The preimage $\overleftrightarrow{AB}$ and image $\overleftrightarrow{A'B'}$ are graphed at the right.

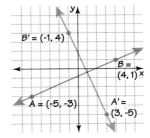

e. slope of $\overleftrightarrow{A'B'}$ = $\frac{4 - -5}{-1 - 3} = \frac{9}{-4} = -\frac{9}{4}$

Notice that the slopes of the lines in Example 1 are negative reciprocals of each other. Their product is -1. The steps of Example 1 can be generalized to prove the following theorem.

Lesson 4-9

Objectives
C Determine equations of lines perpendicular to given lines.
E Recognize relationships between figures and their rotation images.

Resources
From the *Teacher's Resource File*
■ Lesson Master 4-9A or 4-9B
■ Answer Master 4-9
■ Teaching Aids
  8 Four-Quadrant Graph Paper
  34 Warm-up
  41 Relationships Between Perpendicular and Parallel Lines
  42 Proof of Theorem
■ Technology Sourcebook
  Computer Master 5

Additional Resources
■ Visuals for Teaching Aids 8, 34, 41, 42
■ GraphExplorer or other automatic graphers

Teaching Lesson 4-9

Warm-up
Find the slope of the line through the points in each pair.
1. (-6, 2) and (-2, 8) $\frac{3}{2}$
2. (1, 9) and (7, 5) $-\frac{2}{3}$
3. Graph the lines in Questions 1 and 2. What is true about the lines? **They are perpendicular. The graph is shown on page 252.**

Lesson 4-9 Overview

Broad Goals This lesson uses rotations to show why the product of the slopes of two oblique lines is –1 if and only if the lines are perpendicular.

Perspective The major concept of this lesson is the theorem that expresses the relationship between the slopes of two perpendicular lines. The theorem is proved using the rotation of 90°. Although the proof we use is not found in all books, we believe

that it best explains the situation. Since $R_{90}(x, y) = (-y, x)$, R_{90} switches coordinates and changes the sign of the second coordinate. When the same changes are made to the coordinates of the two points (x_1, y_1) and (x_2, y_2) in the formula for the slope m of the original line, the numerator and denominator are switched and one becomes negative. Thus, the slope is changed to the negative reciprocal of the original slope—

namely, $-\frac{1}{m}$. This is the slope of the line that is perpendicular to the original line.

The transformation that maps (x, y) onto $(y, -x)$ also switches coordinates and changes the sign of one of the coordinates. So this transformation also maps lines onto perpendicular lines. This transformation is the rotation of 90° clockwise, which further strengthens the idea found in the proof of the theorem.

251

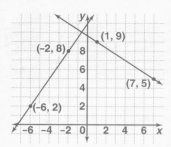

Notes on Reading

Students will need graph paper or **Teaching Aid 8** for the lesson.

Cooperative Learning Discuss **Example 1** to review rotations and to demonstrate the truth of the theorem at the top of page 252. Then discuss the theorem itself. **Teaching Aid 42** contains the drawing in the text and the essence of the proof.

❶ This theorem requires that the two given lines have slopes. Thus, it does not apply to vertical lines—lines that do not have slopes. The statement is often made, "If two lines are perpendicular, then the product of their slopes is -1." This is not accurate, as there are perpendicular lines in which one of the lines does not have a slope.

❷ Students who have studied UCSMP *Geometry* will have encountered this theorem, but they will not have seen a proof. The proof here is algebraic, and it is much simpler than it appears. The basis of the proof is finding the images of points on the perpendicular line by using the matrix for R_{90}, calculating the slopes of the two lines, and showing that the product of their slopes is -1 (or, equivalently, that their slopes are opposite reciprocals).

---

❶ **Theorem**

If two lines with slopes m_1 and m_2 are perpendicular, then $m_1 m_2 = -1$.

❷ **Proof:**

We are given lines with slopes m_1 and m_2. We must show that the product $m_1 m_2$ is -1. The given lines either contain the origin or they are parallel to lines with the same slopes that contain the origin. We prove the theorem for two lines through the origin; this proves the property for perpendicular lines elsewhere.

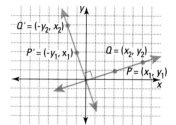

Let $P = (x_1, y_1)$ and $Q = (x_2, y_2)$ be two points on line $\overleftrightarrow{PQ}$ that contains the origin. Then $\overleftrightarrow{PQ}$ can be represented by $\begin{bmatrix} x_1 & x_2 \\ y_1 & y_2 \end{bmatrix}$.

Let $P' = R_{90}(P)$ and $Q' = R_{90}(Q)$. Then

$$R_{90} \left(\overleftrightarrow{PQ} \right) = \overleftrightarrow{P'Q'}.$$

In matrix form, $\begin{bmatrix} 0 & -1 \\ 1 & 0 \end{bmatrix} \begin{bmatrix} x_1 & x_2 \\ y_1 & y_2 \end{bmatrix} = \begin{bmatrix} -y_1 & -y_2 \\ x_1 & x_2 \end{bmatrix}$.

From the matrix, $P' = (-y_1, x_1)$ and $Q' = (-y_2, x_2)$. Let the slope of the preimage be m_1 and the slope of the image be m_2.

$m_1 = $ slope of $\overleftrightarrow{PQ} = \dfrac{y_2 - y_1}{x_2 - x_1}$

$m_2 = $ slope of $\overleftrightarrow{P'Q'} = \dfrac{x_2 - x_1}{-y_2 - (-y_1)} = \dfrac{x_2 - x_1}{-(y_2 - y_1)} = -\dfrac{x_2 - x_1}{y_2 - y_1}$

The product of the slopes is $m_1 m_2 = \left(\dfrac{y_2 - y_1}{x_2 - x_1} \right) \left(-\dfrac{x_2 - x_1}{y_2 - y_1} \right) = -1$.

Example 2

Line n contains (-4, 1) and is perpendicular to line ℓ whose equation is $y = -\frac{3}{2}x + 2$. Find an equation for line n.

Solution

From the equation for line ℓ, we see that its slope is $-\frac{3}{2}$. Since $n \perp \ell$, the slope of n is $\frac{2}{3}$ because the negative reciprocal of $-\frac{3}{2}$ is $\frac{2}{3}$. Now use the point-slope equation for a line. Since line n contains (-4, 1), an equation for n is $y - 1 = \frac{2}{3}(x + 4)$.

▶

Visual Organizer

The table below can be used to summarize **Questions 14–17** on page 254 and can be found on **Teaching Aid 41**.

	$m \,/\!/\, n$	$m \perp n$
$\ell \,/\!/\, m$	$\ell \,/\!/\, n$	$\ell \perp n$
$\ell \perp m$	$\ell \perp n$	$\ell \,/\!/\, n$

Optional Activities

Activity 1 Multicultural Connection
Patterns involving reflections and rotations can be found in cloth, boxes, drums, and statues made by the Bakuba people in Africa. Oroqen people from northeastern China also embroider symmetrical designs on wolf skins and carve similar designs on birch bark boxes. For centuries, American Indians recorded stories and legends in rugs, blankets, baskets, pottery, and jewelry, with much of this art involving repeating

patterns and symmetric designs. Geometric transformations are also found in many American quilt patterns.

Activity 2 Technology Connection
In *Technology Sourcebook, Computer Master 5*, students explore graphs to discover the relationship of the slope and the y-intercept of two perpendicular lines.

Check

Rewrite $y - 1 = \frac{2}{3}(x + 4)$ in slope-intercept form.

$$y - 1 = \frac{2}{3}x + \frac{8}{3}$$
$$y = \frac{2}{3}x + \frac{11}{3}$$

Graph the equations on the same set of axes. The lines are perpendicular, and line n passes through the point $(-4, 1)$.

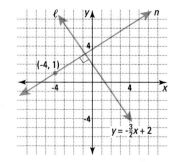

What if line ℓ_1 has slope m_1 and line ℓ_2 has slope m_2, and $m_1 m_2 = -1$? Are ℓ_1 and ℓ_2 always perpendicular? The answer is yes, for the following reason. Any line ℓ_3 perpendicular to ℓ_1 has slope m_3, where $m_1 m_3 = -1$. So $m_1 m_3 = m_1 m_2$, and $m_3 = m_2$. Thus ℓ_3 and ℓ_2 have the same slope. So $\ell_3 \parallel \ell_2$. But $\ell_1 \perp \ell_3$. If a line is perpendicular to one of two parallel lines, it must be perpendicular to the other. So $\ell_1 \perp \ell_2$. We have proved the converse of the previous theorem.

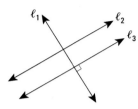

Theorem

If two lines have slopes m_1 and m_2 and $m_1 m_2 = -1$, then the lines are perpendicular.

QUESTIONS

Covering the Reading

1. The line which contains the points (x_1, y_1) and (x_2, y_2) can be represented by the 2×2 matrix __?__. $\begin{bmatrix} x_1 & x_2 \\ y_1 & y_2 \end{bmatrix}$

2. Let $\overleftrightarrow{AB}$ contain points $A = (3, 5)$ and $B = (-1, -6)$.
   a. Find two points on the image of $\overleftrightarrow{AB}$ under R_{90}. **Sample:** $A' = (-5, 3)$, $B' = (6, -1)$
   b. Graph $\overleftrightarrow{AB}$ and its image $\overleftrightarrow{A'B'}$. **See left.**
   c. Find the slopes of $\overleftrightarrow{AB}$ and of $\overleftrightarrow{A'B'}$. $\overleftrightarrow{AB}: \frac{11}{4}$; $\overleftrightarrow{A'B'}: -\frac{4}{11}$
   d. What is the product of the slopes? -1

2b)

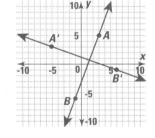

In 3 and 4, *true or false*.

3. If two lines have slopes m_1 and m_2, and $m_1 m_2 = -1$, then the lines are perpendicular. **True**

4. If two lines are perpendicular, and they have slopes m_1 and m_2, then $m_1 m_2 = -1$. **True**

Adapting to Individual Needs

Extra Help
In a problem where two lines are involved, such as **Example 2**, students may switch the slopes of the two lines under consideration. If this happens, encourage students to label the lines and their slopes using subscripts. For example,

L_1: $y = -\frac{3}{2}x + 2$ has slope $m_1 = -\frac{3}{2}$, and
L_2: $y - 1 = \frac{2}{3}(x + 4)$ has slope $m_2 = \frac{2}{3}$.

English Language Development
You might want to review the terms *perpendicular* (which is used in this lesson) and *parallel* (which students will encounter in Lesson 4-10). If your students have not already done so, have them add these terms to their index cards along with illustrations of the concepts.

Additional Examples

1. Consider $\overleftrightarrow{PQ}$, which contains the points $P = (2, 6)$ and $Q = (0, -2)$.
   a. Represent $\overleftrightarrow{PQ}$ as a 2×2 matrix. $\begin{bmatrix} 2 & 0 \\ 6 & -2 \end{bmatrix}$
   b. Calculate the slope of $\overleftrightarrow{PQ}$. 4
   c. Represent $\overleftrightarrow{P'Q'}$, the image of $\overleftrightarrow{PQ}$ under R_{90}, as a 2×2 matrix. $\begin{bmatrix} -6 & 2 \\ 2 & 0 \end{bmatrix}$
   d. Graph $\overleftrightarrow{PQ}$ and $\overleftrightarrow{P'Q'}$.

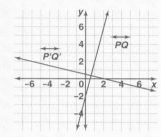

   e. Calculate the slope of $\overleftrightarrow{P'Q'}$. $-\frac{1}{4}$
   f. Are the lines perpendicular? Why or why not? **Yes;** $4 \cdot -\frac{1}{4} = -1$

2. Line n contains $(3, 8)$ and is perpendicular to line m whose equation is $5x + 4y = 7$. Find the equation for line n.
   $y - 8 = \frac{4}{5}(x - 3)$

3. Write an equation for the perpendicular bisector of the segment joining $A = (-6, 7)$ and $B = (-8, -3)$. $y - 2 = -\frac{1}{5}(x + 7)$

LESSON MASTER 4-9 A

Questions on SPUR Objectives See pages 266-269 for objectives.

Skills Objective A

In 1–4, write an equation for the line that goes through the given point and is perpendicular to the given line.

1. $(6, 1)$; $y = 3x - 5$ $y - 1 = -\frac{1}{3}(x - 6)$
2. $(-1, -7)$; $3x + 4y = 7$ $y + 7 = \frac{4}{3}(x + 1)$
3. $(5, 2)$; $x = 12$ $y = 2$
4. $(5, 2)$; $y = 17$ $x = 5$

In 5 and 6, write an equation for the perpendicular bisector of the line segment with the given endpoints.

5. $(-6, 8)$, $(6, -8)$ $y = \frac{3}{4}x$
6. $(8, 16)$, $(24, -12)$ $y - 2 = \frac{4}{7}(x - 16)$

Properties Objective E

7. The slope of a line is 6. What is the slope of the image of this line under R_{90}? $-\frac{1}{6}$
8. Let $\triangle PUT$ be represented by the matrix $\begin{bmatrix} 523 & 23 & -177 \\ -621 & 379 & 79 \end{bmatrix}$. Let $\triangle P'U'T' = R_{90}(\triangle PUT)$.
   a. Find the slope of $\overleftrightarrow{PU}$. -2
   b. Find the slope of $\overleftrightarrow{P'U'}$. $\frac{1}{2}$

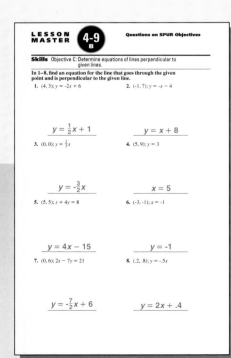

254

8b)

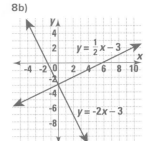

$y = \frac{1}{2}x - 3$

$y = -2x - 3$

13b)

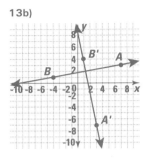

Air lines. *Many airports, like San Francisco's International Airport shown below, have parallel or perpendicular runways and taxiways.*

254

---

5. Find an equation of the line through (6, 1) and perpendicular to the line $y = \frac{4}{3}x - 2$. $y - 1 = -\frac{3}{4}(x - 6)$

6. Find an equation of the line perpendicular to $y = -3x + 7$ passing through the point (-21, 20). $y - 20 = \frac{1}{3}(x + 21)$

Applying the Mathematics

7. Consider the line with equation $2x + 6y = 1$ and the point $P = (7, -2)$.
   a. Find the slope of a line perpendicular to the given line.   3
   b. Find an equation for the line through P and perpendicular to the given line. $y + 2 = 3(x - 7)$

8. Consider the line with equation $y = \frac{1}{2}x - 3$.   a) Sample: $y = -2x - 3$
   a. Find an equation of a line perpendicular to the given line.
   b. Graph the two lines.   See left.

9. Why do the statements of the theorems in this lesson apply only to lines with nonzero slopes?   The reciprocal of 0 is undefined.

10. *Multiple choice.* What is the slope of a line perpendicular to the line with equation $x = 7$?   a
    (a) 0   (b) undefined slope   (c) $\frac{-1}{7}$ (d) 7

11. Find an equation for the line through (6, 2) and perpendicular to $y = 4$. $x = 6$

12. Let $A = (6, 0)$ and $B = (12, 5)$. Find an equation for the perpendicular bisector of $\overline{AB}$. (Hint: First find the midpoint of $\overline{AB}$.) $y - 2.5 = -\frac{6}{5}(x - 9)$

13. Let $A = (7, 3)$ and $B = (-4, 1)$.
    a. Find the coordinates of A' and B' under R_{270}. $A' = (3, -7)$; $B' = (1, 4)$
    b. Graph both $\overleftrightarrow{AB}$ and $\overleftrightarrow{A'B'}$.   See left.
    c. Find the slopes of $\overleftrightarrow{AB}$ and $\overleftrightarrow{A'B'}$. $\overleftrightarrow{AB}$: $\frac{2}{11}$; $\overleftrightarrow{A'B'}$: $\frac{-11}{2}$
    d. What relationship exists between the slopes? What does this tell you about the lines?   Their product is -1; the lines are perpendicular.
    e. A counterclockwise rotation of 270° is the same as a clockwise rotation of __?__.   90°

In 14–17, assume all lines lie in the same plane.
a. Fill each blank with // or ⊥.
b. Draw a picture to illustrate each situation.

14. If ℓ // m and m // n, then ℓ __?__ n.   a) //   b) See margin.

15. If ℓ // m and $m \perp n$, then ℓ __?__ n.   a) ⊥   b) See margin.

16. If $\ell \perp m$ and m // n, then ℓ __?__ n.   a) ⊥   b) See margin.

17. If $\ell \perp m$ and $m \perp n$, then ℓ __?__ n.   a) //   b) See margin.

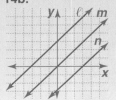
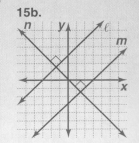

18. **a.** Calculate the matrix of $r_y \circ R_{180}$. $\begin{bmatrix} 1 & 0 \\ 0 & -1 \end{bmatrix}$
    b. In $r_y \circ R_{180}$, which transformation is performed first, R_{180} or r_y? R_{180}
    c. To what transformation does this matrix correspond?
    (Lessons 4-6, 4-7) r_x

19) $M = \begin{bmatrix} \frac{4}{3} & 0 \\ 0 & \frac{3}{4} \end{bmatrix}$

20) $\begin{bmatrix} \frac{2}{3} & 0 \\ 0 & \frac{1}{4} \end{bmatrix}$

In 19 and 20, consider the rectangle $R = \begin{bmatrix} 3 & 3 & 6 & 6 \\ 8 & 0 & 0 & 8 \end{bmatrix}$. *(Lesson 4-5)*

19. Suppose M is a matrix for a scale change and $MR = \begin{bmatrix} 4 & 4 & 8 & 8 \\ 6 & 0 & 0 & 6 \end{bmatrix}$.
    Find M. **See left.**

20. Find the matrix for a scale change that maps the rectangle R onto a square with sides of length 2. **See left.**

21. Matrix D gives the daily delivery of fish to two markets. Matrix C gives the unit cost for each item in the market.

$$\begin{array}{c} \\ \text{Albert's} \\ \text{Carlita's} \end{array} \begin{bmatrix} \overset{\text{cod}}{12} & \overset{\text{perch}}{6} & \overset{\text{grouper}}{20} \\ 8 & 5 & 32 \end{bmatrix} = D \qquad \begin{array}{c} \text{unit cost} \\ \text{cod} \\ \text{perch} \\ \text{grouper} \end{array} \begin{bmatrix} 2.89 \\ 2.59 \\ 1.98 \end{bmatrix} = C$$

   a. Calculate DC. $\begin{bmatrix} 89.82 \\ 99.43 \end{bmatrix}$
   b. What is the cost of the daily delivery of fish at Carlita's? **$99.43**

22. Find an equation for the line passing through the point (16, 50) and parallel to the line $y = -x$. *(Lessons 3-2, 3-5)* $y - 50 = -(x - 16)$

23. **a.** Solve for x: $u + vx = w + yx$. $x = \frac{w - u}{v - y}$
    b. When does the equation in part **a** have no solution?
    (Lessons 1-2, 1-5) **when $v = y$**

24. *Skill sequence.* Use the Distributive Property to rewrite each expression. *(Previous course, Lesson 1-5)*
    a. $x(x + 9)$ — $x^2 + 9x$
    b. $5(x + 9)$ — $5x + 45$
    c. $(x + 5)(x + 9)$ — $x^2 + 14x + 45$

Exploration

25. Rework Example 1, but use R_{180} in place of R_{90}. What general relationship do you find between the slope of the preimage line connecting the two points and the slope of the image line?
    The slopes are equal.

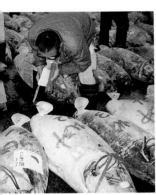

Going once, going twice, sold! *Wholesalers, like this one inspecting whole frozen tuna at the Tsukiji fish market in Tokyo, buy their fish at auction. This market supplies 90% of the fish consumed in Tokyo.*

16b.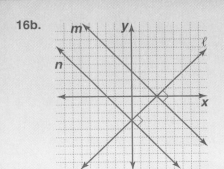

17b.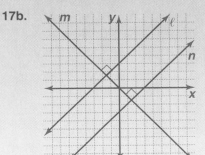

Assessment

Written Communication Have students determine whether the lines with equations (a) $2x - 4y = 1$ and (b) $x - 2y = 2$ are perpendicular, parallel, or neither. Have students include an explanation. [Parallel; students demonstrate an understanding of the fact that parallel lines have the same slope.]

Extension

You might want to have students generalize **Questions 19 and 20.** Suppose a rectangle with vertices (a, b), (c, b), (a, d), and (c, d) is given. What is a matrix for a scale change that maps this rectangle onto a square with sides of length s?

$$\begin{bmatrix} \frac{s}{(c - a)} & 0 \\ 0 & \frac{s}{(d - b)} \end{bmatrix}$$

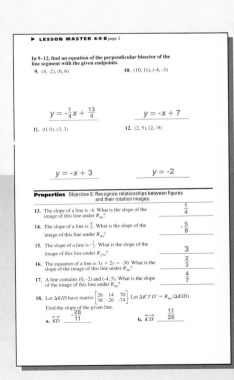

► **LESSON MASTER 4-9 B** *page 2*

In 9–12, find an equation of the perpendicular bisector of the line segment with the given endpoints.
9. (4, -2), (6, 6)   10. (10, 11), (-4, -3)

$y = -\frac{1}{4}x + \frac{13}{4}$ $y = -x + 7$

11. (0, 0), (3, 3)   12. (2, 5), (2, -9)

$y = -x + 3$ $y = -2$

Properties Objective E: Recognize relationships between figures and their rotation images.

13. The slope of a line is -4. What is the slope of the image of this line under R_{90}? — $\frac{1}{4}$

14. The slope of a line is $\frac{8}{5}$. What is the slope of the image of this line under R_{90}? — $-\frac{5}{8}$

15. The slope of a line is $-\frac{1}{3}$. What is the slope of the image of this line under R_{270}? — 3

16. The equation of a line is $3x + 2y = -30$. What is the slope of the image of this line under R_{90}? — $\frac{2}{3}$

17. A line contains (0, -2) and (-4, 5). What is the slope of the image of this line under R_{90}? — $\frac{4}{7}$

18. Let $\triangle KID$ have matrix $\begin{bmatrix} 26 & 14 & 70 \\ 38 & -26 & -74 \end{bmatrix}$. Let $\triangle K'I'D' = R_{90}(\triangle KID)$.
Find the slope of the given line.
a. $\overleftrightarrow{KD}$ — $\frac{28}{11}$ **b.** $\overleftrightarrow{K'D'}$ — $\frac{11}{28}$

255

Objectives

E Recognize relationships between figures and their translation images.

F Relate translations to matrices, and vice versa.

I Graph figures and their translation images.

Resources

From the Teacher's Resource File
■ Lesson Master 4-10A or 4-10B
■ Answer Master 4-10
■ Teaching Aids
  8 Four-Quadrant Graph Paper
  34 Warm-up
  39 More Transformations and Their Matrices

Additional Resources
■ Visuals for Teaching Aids 8, 34, 39

Warm-up

1. Name the matrix representing the rectangle with coordinates $A = (0, 0)$, $B = (6, 0)$, $C = (6, 5)$, and $D = (0, 5)$. $\begin{bmatrix} 0 & 6 & 6 & 0 \\ 0 & 0 & 5 & 5 \end{bmatrix}$

2. Determine the matrix for the coordinates of $A'B'C'D'$ by adding the matrix in Question 1 to $\begin{bmatrix} 4 & 4 & 4 & 4 \\ 2 & 2 & 2 & 2 \end{bmatrix}$. $\begin{bmatrix} 4 & 10 & 10 & 4 \\ 2 & 2 & 7 & 7 \end{bmatrix}$

3. What relationship exists between $ABCD$ and $A'B'C'D'$? **Sample: $A'B'C'D'$ is a rectangle congruent to $ABCD$.**

In this chapter, you have found transformation images by multiplying 2×2 matrices. There is one transformation for which images can be found by *adding* matrices.

Translations

Consider $\triangle ABC$ and $\triangle A'B'C'$ below.

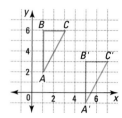

$\triangle A'B'C'$ is a *slide* or *translation image* of the preimage $\triangle ABC$. The matrices M and M' for these triangles are given below.

$\triangle ABC$ has matrix $M = \begin{bmatrix} 1 & 1 & 3 \\ 2 & 6 & 6 \end{bmatrix}$.

$\triangle A'B'C'$ has matrix $M' = \begin{bmatrix} 5 & 5 & 7 \\ -1 & 3 & 3 \end{bmatrix}$.

Calculate $M' - M$.

$M' - M = \begin{bmatrix} 5 & 5 & 7 \\ -1 & 3 & 3 \end{bmatrix} - \begin{bmatrix} 1 & 1 & 3 \\ 2 & 6 & 6 \end{bmatrix} = \begin{bmatrix} 4 & 4 & 4 \\ -3 & -3 & -3 \end{bmatrix}$

In $M' - M$, all the elements in the first row are equal, and all the elements in the second row are equal. Thus, to get the image $\triangle A'B'C'$, add 4 to every x-coordinate and -3 to every y-coordinate of the preimage.

$$\begin{bmatrix} 4 & 4 & 4 \\ -3 & -3 & -3 \end{bmatrix} + \overset{M}{\begin{bmatrix} 1 & 1 & 3 \\ 2 & 6 & 6 \end{bmatrix}} = \overset{M'}{\begin{bmatrix} 5 & 5 & 7 \\ -1 & 3 & 3 \end{bmatrix}}$$

This leads to an algebraic definition of *translation*.

> **Definition**
> The transformation that maps (x, y) onto $(x + h, y + k)$ is a translation of h units horizontally and k units vertically, and is denoted by $T_{h,k}$.

Lesson 4-10 Overview

Broad Goals This lesson completes the study of the basic transformations and matrices, discusses translations, and concurrently gives another application of matrix addition.

Perspective Translations provide the most basic way to modify graphs. After completing this lesson, students should be able to view many of the graphs that they will encounter in mathematics as translation images of basic graphs. The lesson also provides a foundation for the Graph-Translation Theorem, which is introduced in Chapter 6; understanding that theorem requires a knowledge of the algebraic definition of $T_{h,k}$.

It is easier to describe $T_{h,k}$ algebraically than with a matrix, but either way is possible. A problem with the matrix description is that the dimensions of $T_{h,k}$ depend on the dimensions of the preimage polygon, which will have dimensions $2 \times n$, where n is the number of vertices in the polygon.

Notice the three equivalent statements:
• Lines m and n are parallel.
• Lines m and n have the same slope.
• Line n is a translation image of line m.

This information is easily stated because we allow lines to be parallel to themselves.

Using mapping or $f(x)$ notation we can write

$$T_{h,k}: (x, y) \rightarrow (x + h, y + k), \text{ or } T_{h,k}(x, y) = (x + h, y + k).$$

In the figure on page 256, $\triangle A'B'C'$ is the image of $\triangle ABC$ under the translation $T_{4,-3}$.

Matrices for Translations

❶ A given translation cannot be represented by a single matrix because the dimensions of the translation matrix depend on the figure being translated.

For instance, in the Example below, to translate the quadrilateral, you must add a matrix with dimensions 2 by 4.

Example

A quadrilateral has vertices $Q = (-4, 2)$, $U = (-2, 6)$, $A = (0, 5)$ and $D = (0, 3)$.
a. Find its image under the transformation $T_{3,5}$.
b. Graph the image and preimage on the same set of axes.

Solution

a.
$T_{3,5}(x, y) = (x + 3, y + 5)$
$Q' = T_{3,5} (-4, 2) = (-1, 7)$
$U' = T_{3,5} (-2, 6) = (1, 11)$
$A' = T_{3,5} (0, 5) = (3, 10)$
$D' = T_{3,5} (0, 3) = (3, 8)$

In matrix form:

$$\begin{array}{c} T_{3,5} \\ \begin{bmatrix} 3 & 3 & 3 & 3 \\ 5 & 5 & 5 & 5 \end{bmatrix} \end{array} + \begin{array}{c} Q \;\; U \;\; A \;\; D \\ \begin{bmatrix} -4 & -2 & 0 & 0 \\ 2 & 6 & 5 & 3 \end{bmatrix} \end{array} = \begin{array}{c} Q' \;\; U' \;\; A' \;\; D' \\ \begin{bmatrix} -1 & 1 & 3 & 3 \\ 7 & 11 & 10 & 8 \end{bmatrix} \end{array}$$

The image is quadrilateral $Q'U'A'D'$.
b. $Q'U'A'D'$ is the image under a translation 3 units to the right and 5 units up, as expected. The graph is shown below.

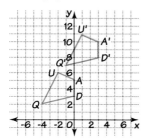

Activity

Consider $\overline{UA}$ and $\overline{U'A'}$ from the Example. It appears that $\overleftrightarrow{UA}$ // $\overleftrightarrow{U'A'}$. Calculate slopes to show that they are parallel. $\overleftrightarrow{UA}: \frac{-1}{2}; \quad \overleftrightarrow{U'A'}: -\frac{1}{2}$

(This is also the convention in *UCSMP Algebra* and *UCSMP Geometry*.) The last of the three statements—the new one in this lesson—is key in graphing. For instance, as a result of the Graph-Translation Theorem, we will have:
- The line $y = mx + b$ is the image of $y = mx$ under $T_{0,b}$.
- The sine curve $y = \sin(x - b)$ is the image of $y = \sin x$ under $T_{b,0}$.

- The parabola $y = a(x - h)^2 + k$ is the image of $y = ax^2$ under $T_{h,k}$.
- The circle $(x - h)^2 + (y - k)^2 = r^2$ is the image of $x^2 + y^2 = r^2$ under $T_{h,k}$.

It is from the last two of these that we have chosen the letters h and k to represent the horizontal and vertical magnitudes in a two-dimensional translation.

Notes on Reading
Students will need graph paper or **Teaching Aid 8** for this lesson.

This is a good time to summarize the ideas of the chapter. See the *Optional Activities on* page 258.

❶ Point out that, unlike the other transformations encountered in this chapter, translations cannot be done by multiplying by a 2 × 2 matrix. Refer to **Teaching Aid 39**. Students should remember that any transformation with a 2 × 2 matrix must map (0, 0) onto itself, and the only translation that does so is $T_{0,0}$.

Additional Examples

1. In $\triangle POD$, $P = (4, 3)$, $O = (3, -1)$, and $D = (6, -4)$.
  a. Find its image under the transformation $T_{-1,1}$.

$$\begin{bmatrix} 3 & 2 & 5 \\ 4 & 0 & -3 \end{bmatrix}$$

  b. Graph the preimage and the image on the same axes.

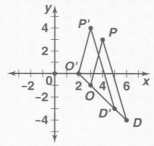

2. What translation undoes $T_{-6,4}$? $T_{6,-4}$

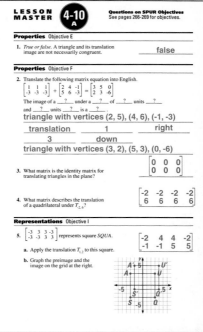

Question 10a Only one point in the preimage and its image are needed to determine the translation. Any preimage point can be used. Students should describe the translation by giving an algebraic rule for it.

Question 11 This question gives an instance of the general theorem that the composite of two translations is a translation.

(Notes on Questions continue on page 260.)

Properties of Translation Images

The Activity provides a special case of the following more general result.

> **Theorem**
> Under a translation, a line is parallel to its image.

Proof:

Let $P = (x_1, y_1)$ and $Q = (x_2, y_2)$ be two different points on the line $\overleftrightarrow{PQ}$. The image of the line under $T_{h,k}$ contains $P' = (x_1 + h, y_1 + k)$ and $Q' = (x_2 + h, y_2 + k)$.

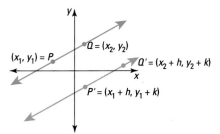

If $\overleftrightarrow{PQ}$ is a vertical line, then $x_1 = x_2$, and so $x_1 + h = x_2 + h$. Then, $\overleftrightarrow{P'Q'}$ is also a vertical line. Thus, in this case $\overleftrightarrow{PQ} \;/\!/\; \overleftrightarrow{P'Q'}$. If $\overleftrightarrow{PQ}$ is not vertical, then $x_1 \neq x_2$, and both $\overleftrightarrow{PQ}$ and $\overleftrightarrow{P'Q'}$ have a slope. Let m_1 be the slope of the preimage and let m_2 be the slope of the image.

$$m_1 = \text{slope of } \overleftrightarrow{PQ} = \frac{y_2 - y_1}{x_2 - x_1}$$

$$m_2 = \text{slope of } \overleftrightarrow{P'Q'} = \frac{(y_2 + k) - (y_1 + k)}{(x_2 + h) - (x_1 + h)} = \frac{y_2 - y_1}{x_2 - x_1}$$

The slopes are equal. So $\overleftrightarrow{PQ} \;/\!/\; \overleftrightarrow{P'Q'}$.

QUESTIONS

Covering the Reading

1. Refer to $\triangle ABC$ and $\triangle A'B'C'$ at the beginning of the lesson.
   a. What translation maps $\triangle ABC$ onto $\triangle A'B'C'$? $T_{4,-3}$
   b. What translation maps $\triangle A'B'C'$ onto $\triangle ABC$? $T_{-4,3}$

2. A translation of the plane is a transformation mapping (x, y) to ?. $(x + h, y + k)$

3. $T_{h,k}$ is a translation of ? units horizontally and ? units vertically. h; k

4. Find the image of the point under $T_{-2, 6}$.
   a. $(0, 0)$ $(-2, 6)$
   b. $(100, -98)$ $(98, -92)$
   c. (a, b) $(a - 2, b + 6)$

258

Optional Activities

Writing Review the fact that transformations may be described *algebraically* with a formula for the image (x', y') in terms of (x, y), *arithmetically* with a matrix, or *geometrically* by indicating the location of image points without using coordinates. Also discuss the strengths and weaknesses of each definition, and why the algebraic definition is preferable with translations. Assign each student a transformation that was studied in this chapter (such as $S_{a,b}$ or R_{90}). Ask each student to write a few paragraphs describing that transformation in as many ways as he or she can. If there is time, students should share their essays with others.

---

5) $\begin{bmatrix} -2 & 13 & 7 \\ -11 & -6 & -6 \end{bmatrix}$

6a) $\begin{bmatrix} 11 & 6 & 5 & 3 & 8 \\ -8 & 3 & -2 & -6 & -15 \end{bmatrix}$

b)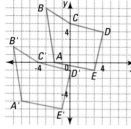

9) No. The contrapositive of the theorem must hold true; that is, if a line is not parallel to its image, then they are not translation images of each other.

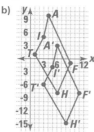

10b) $BB' =$
$\sqrt{(-3 - -7)^2 + (7 - 2)^2}$
$= \sqrt{41}$
$EE' =$
$\sqrt{(3 - -1)^2 + (-1 - -6)^2}$
$= \sqrt{41}$

c) slope of $\overline{BC} = \frac{5 - 7}{0 - -3}$
$= -\frac{2}{3}$, slope of $\overline{B'C'}$
$= \frac{0 - 2}{-4 - -7} = \frac{-2}{3}$

---

5. Consider $\triangle PQR$ represented by the matrix $\begin{bmatrix} 3 & 18 & 12 \\ -5 & 0 & 0 \end{bmatrix}$. Use matrix addition to find $\triangle P'Q'R'$, the image of $\triangle PQR$ under a translation 5 units to the left and 6 units down. **See left.**

6. The matrix $\begin{bmatrix} 9 & 4 & 3 & 1 & 6 \\ -1 & 10 & 5 & 1 & -8 \end{bmatrix}$ represents pentagon *FAITH*. **See left.**

   a. Apply the translation $T_{2,-7}$ to the pentagon.
   b. Graph the preimage and the image on the same set of axes.

In 7 and 8, refer to the Example.

7. a. What is the slope of $\overline{QU}$? **2**   **b.** What is the slope of $\overline{Q'U'}$? **2**

8. Show that $\overleftrightarrow{UA} \parallel \overleftrightarrow{U'A'}$. slope of $\overleftrightarrow{UA} = \frac{5 - 6}{0 - (-2)} = \frac{-1}{2}$; slope of $\overleftrightarrow{U'A'} = \frac{10 - 11}{3 - 1} = \frac{-1}{2}$; so, $\overleftrightarrow{UA} \parallel \overleftrightarrow{U'A'}$

Applying the Mathematics

9. Suppose lines ℓ_1 and ℓ_2 are not parallel. Can they be translation images of each other? Explain your reasoning. **See left.**

10. Refer to the graph at the left.
   a. What translation maps $ABCDE$ onto $A'B'C'D'E'$? $T_{-4,-5}$
   b. Verify that $BB' = EE'$. **See below left.**
   c. Verify that $\overleftrightarrow{BC} \parallel \overleftrightarrow{B'C'}$. **See below left.**

11. $\triangle CUB$ is translated under $T_{4,9}$ to get $\triangle C'U'B'$. $\triangle C'U'B'$ is then translated under $T_{6,5}$ to get $\triangle C''U''B''$. What single translation will give the same result as $T_{6,5} \circ T_{4,9}$? $T_{10,14}$

12. What is the image of the line with equation $y = -3$ under the indicated translation?
   a. $T_{0,5}$ $y = 2$ **b.** $T_{5,0}$ $y = -3$ **c.** $T_{5,5}$ $y = 2$

13. Consider the line whose equation is $y = -2x + 3$. Find an equation for the image of this line under $T_{5,-1}$. $y = -2x + 12$

14. Line ℓ has the equation $y = 3x - 7$. Line ℓ' is the image of ℓ under a translation. If ℓ' contains the point $(0, 5)$, find an equation for ℓ'. $y = 3x + 5$

Review

15. Suppose line ℓ_1 has slope $\frac{2}{3}$, and $\ell_1 \perp \ell_2$. What is the slope of ℓ_2? *(Lesson 4-9)* $-\frac{3}{2}$

16. Find an equation of the perpendicular bisector of $\overline{PQ}$, where $P = (1, 4)$ and $Q = (10, -6)$. *(Lesson 4-9)* $y + 1 = \frac{9}{10}(x - \frac{11}{2})$

17. $H = (5, 1)$ and $I = (-3, -1)$. *(Lessons 4-6, 4-9)*
   a. Find the image $\overline{H'I'}$ under r_y. $H' = (-5, 1)$; $I' = (3, -1)$
   b. Find HI and $H'I'$ and compare the two lengths. **Both equal $\sqrt{68}$**
   c. Are $\overline{HI}$ and $\overline{H'I'}$ perpendicular? Justify your answer. No; the product of their slopes is not -1.

Lesson 4-10 *Translations and Parallel Lines*   **259**

Adapting to Individual Needs

Extra Help
It may help students visualize the image of a figure under the translation $T_{h,k}$ if they think of $T_{h,k}$ as "sliding" the figure h units to the right (to the left if h is negative) and k units upward (downward if k is negative). However, emphasize that there is no physical sliding. The translation, like all other transformations, is simply a correspondence between a figure and its image.

Challenge Art Connection
Many designs created by M. C. Escher are based on geometric tiling of congruent polygons. Many of the designs are examples of translations, reflections, and rotations. You might have interested students find Escher designs that are examples of transformations. Then have them try to create a simple Escher-type design themselves.

Follow-up for Lesson 4-10

Practice
For more questions on SPUR Objectives, use **Lesson Master 4-10A** (shown on page 257) or **Lesson Master 4-10B** (shown on pages 258–259).

Assessment
Group Assessment Have students **work in groups** and take turns drawing figures in the coordinate plane and using matrices to determine various translation images. [Students demonstrate an understanding of how any figure can be translated by applying matrix addition.]

Extension
Show students these matrices:

$\overrightarrow{AB}$: $\begin{bmatrix} a & b \\ c & d \end{bmatrix}$ $\overrightarrow{A'B'}$: $\begin{bmatrix} e & f \\ g & h \end{bmatrix}$

Ask them what they know about corresponding elements in the matrices if: (a) $\overrightarrow{AB}$ and $\overrightarrow{A'B'}$ are parallel, and (b) $\overrightarrow{AB}$ and $\overrightarrow{A'B'}$ are perpendicular.
[Sample: (a) $\frac{d - c}{b - a} = \frac{h - g}{f - e}$
(b) $\frac{d - c}{b - a} = \frac{e - f}{h - g}$]

Project Update Project 2, *History of Matrices*, and Project 4, *Translations using Matrix Multiplication*, on pages 261–262 relate to the content of this lesson.

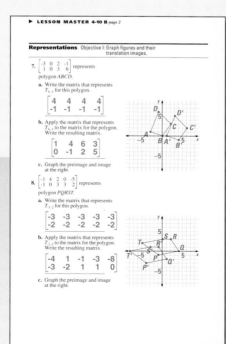

259

Notes on Questions

Question 26 Social Studies Connection In 1992, the average price of a new one-family house in the United States was $144,100—almost double the average price in 1980. However, the cost was down from the all-time highs of $149,800 in 1990 and $147,200 in 1991. Prices in the Northeast were significantly higher than in other regions, while prices in the South were much lower than in other regions.

Question 27 Any transformation with rule $(x, y) \rightarrow (ax + by + c, dx + ey + f)$ is a composite of scale changes, rotations about the origin, and translations. Such a transformation is called an *affine transformation*. In this chapter, students have encountered the building blocks for such transformations.

20a) $\begin{bmatrix} 4 & 0 \\ 0 & 4 \end{bmatrix}$

b) $(4a, 4b)$

21a) $\begin{bmatrix} 1 & 0 \\ 0 & 6 \end{bmatrix}$

b) $(a, 6b)$

23a) $\begin{bmatrix} 0 & 1 \\ 1 & 0 \end{bmatrix}$

b) (b, a)

26a) $\begin{bmatrix} 39 & 275 \\ 51 & 390 \\ 44 & 287 \end{bmatrix}$

The total number of doors and windows in each development

c) $\begin{bmatrix} 30,600 \\ 42,750 \\ 32,430 \end{bmatrix}$

In 18–23, a transformation is given. **a.** Give the matrix for the transformation. **b.** Give the image of (a, b). *(Lessons 4-4, 4-5, 4-6, 4-8)*

18. R_{270} a) $\begin{bmatrix} 0 & 1 \\ -1 & 0 \end{bmatrix}$ b) $(b, -a)$ **19.** r_x a) $\begin{bmatrix} 1 & 0 \\ 0 & -1 \end{bmatrix}$ b) $(a, -b)$

20. a size change of magnitude 4
See left.

21. $S_{1,6}$ See left.

22. $(x, y) \rightarrow (-x, -y)$ a) $\begin{bmatrix} -1 & 0 \\ 0 & -1 \end{bmatrix}$
b) $(-a, -b)$

23. reflection over the line $y = x$
See left.

24. By what matrix must you multiply $\begin{bmatrix} 5 & 0 & -1 \\ 2 & 6 & -4 \end{bmatrix}$ to get $\begin{bmatrix} -10 & 0 & 2 \\ 1 & 3 & -2 \end{bmatrix}$? *(Lesson 4-5)* $\begin{bmatrix} -2 & 0 \\ 0 & 1/2 \end{bmatrix}$

25. Find a single matrix equal to the following. *(Lessons 4-2, 4-3)*

$$\begin{bmatrix} 1 & -1 & 2 \\ 0 & 2 & 1 \end{bmatrix} \begin{bmatrix} 2 & 8 \\ -1 & 0 \\ 1 & -2 \end{bmatrix} - \begin{bmatrix} 5 & 5 \\ 4 & -4 \end{bmatrix} \begin{bmatrix} 0 & -1 \\ -5 & 2 \end{bmatrix}$$

26. A housing contractor builds four model houses—I, II, III, and IV—in three housing developments—Hill, Plain, and Dale. Matrix A gives the number of doors and windows in each model, matrix B gives the number of each model built last year, and matrix C gives the unit cost in dollars of each door and window.

Matrix A

	Doors	Windows
I	2	12
II	2	20
III	3	15
IV	3	20

Matrix B

	I	II	III	IV
Hill	10	5	1	2
Plain	5	10	2	5
Dale	6	4	5	3

Matrix C

	cost
Doors	150
Windows	90

a. Calculate BA and tell what it represents. **See left.**
b. Set up a matrix product that gives the contractor's total cost for doors and windows last year. **Sample: $(BA)C$**
c. Calculate the product in part **b.** *(Lesson 4-3)* **See left.**

Exploration

27. A transformation has the following rule: The image of (x, y) is $(3x, y + 2)$. Find images of a figure of your own choosing. Geometrically describe what the transformation does to a figure.
The figure has a horizontal size change of magnitude 3, and is translated up 2 units.

Chapter 4 Projects

The projects relate to the content of the lessons of this chapter as follows:

Project	Lesson(s)
1	4-3
2	4-4, 4-5, 4-6, 4-7, 4-8, 4-10
3	4-4
4	4-10

1 Predicting the Weather Make sure students write a correct initial matrix, as the entire project depends on this matrix. See the sample answers. Students can switch rows and columns. To obtain a matrix for n days, suggest that students continue the processes beyond Day 4 and seek a trend.

2 History of Matrices Arthur Cayley and James Sylvester are called the "invariant twins" by Eric Temple Bell in his book *Men of Mathematics* (Simon & Schuster Trade, 1986). Two other sources students might use are *A History of Mathematics* by Victor J. Katz (Harper College, 1993) and *An Introduction to the History of Mathematics* by Howard Eves (Saunders College Publishing, 1990).

A project presents an opportunity for you to extend your knowledge of a topic related to the material of this chapter. You should allow more time for a project than you do for typical homework questions.

1 Predicting the Weather

A weather forecaster has collected data to predict whether tomorrow will be sunny (S), cloudy (C), or rainy (R), given today's weather conditions. If today is sunny, then tomorrow the probabilities are 75% for S, 15% for C, and 10% for R. If today is cloudy, then the probabilities for tomorrow are 30% for S, 60% for C, and 10% for R. If today is rainy, then the probabilities for tomorrow are 25% for S, 20% for C, and 55% for R. Represent this information as a 3×3 matrix. Multiply this matrix by itself to calculate predictions of what the weather will be 2 days from now, 3 days from now, 4 days from now, . . . , n days from now, based on today's weather. In general, what can you tell about the weather in the forecaster's area?

2 History of Matrices

Investigate the development of matrices and the early work of Arthur Cayley and James Sylvester in the mid 1800s.
a. What were "matrices" used for before they were given that name?
b. When were matrices first used to describe transformations?
c. What other mathematicians and terms are associated with the history and use of matrices?

Arthur Cayley

James Sylvester

▶

Possible responses

1. The information in the 3×3 matrix is:

tomorrow $\quad S \quad\ C \quad\ R$

$$M = \begin{array}{c} \text{today} \end{array} \begin{array}{c} S \\ C \\ R \end{array} \begin{bmatrix} .75 & .3 & .25 \\ .15 & .6 & .2 \\ .1 & .1 & .55 \end{bmatrix}$$

The matrices for 2, 3, and 4 days from now are given at the right as $M2$, $M3$, and $M4$.

$$M^2 = \begin{bmatrix} .6325 & .43 & .385 \\ .2225 & .425 & .2675 \\ .145 & .145 & .3475 \end{bmatrix}$$

$$M^3 = \begin{bmatrix} .577375 & .48625 & .455875 \\ .257375 & .3485 & .28775 \\ .16525 & .16525 & .256375 \end{bmatrix}$$

$$M^4 = \begin{bmatrix} .55156 & .51055 & .49233 \\ .274081 & .31508 & .29231 \\ .17436 & .17436 & .21537 \end{bmatrix}$$

As n increases without limit, the n-day forecast matrix approaches:

$$M^n = \begin{bmatrix} .529 & .529 & .529 \\ .289 & .289 & .289 \\ .182 & .182 & .182 \end{bmatrix}$$

The area is sunny about 53% of the time, cloudy about 29% of the time, and rainy about 18% of the time.

(Responses continue on page 262.)

3 Overhead Projectors as Size Changers

You might want to have students do this project in pairs; that would allow one student to move the projector while the other student measures the image. Visual microscopes can also be used for the project.

4 Translations using Matrix Multiplication

You might mention that every point $(x, y, 1)$ in three dimensions lies in the plane $z = 1$. In this project students apply the particular 3-dimensional shear transformation with the property that it translates figures in the plane $z = 1$.

(continued)

3 Overhead Projectors as Size Changers

Overhead projectors are used because they project images of figures under a size change. A light source passes through a transparency (preimage), reflects off the mirror and projects a picture onto the screen (image). As you move the projector away from

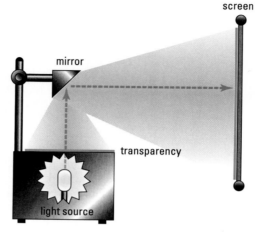

Overhead Projector

the screen, the image gets larger, and as you move the projector closer to the screen, the image gets smaller. Investigate whether the following is true.

$$\frac{\text{length of a line segment on transparency}}{\text{corresponding length of a line segment on screen}} = \frac{\text{distance from transparency to mirror}}{\text{distance from mirror to screen}}.$$

Abbreviated, $\frac{P}{I} = \frac{V}{H}$. (Here, P stands for preimage, I for image, V for vertical, and H for horizontal). Experiment with an overhead projector in your school. Make a table with columns P, I, V, H, $\frac{P}{I}$ and $\frac{V}{H}$ for your data. Does the proportion hold for your data? Write a report explaining your results.

4 Translations using Matrix Multiplication

The translations in this chapter are done using matrix addition. All other transformations of points here are performed using matrix multiplication and a 2×2 matrix particularly chosen for that transformation. A translation cannot be done using multiplication of 2×2 matrices. However, to translate a point using matrix multiplication, first write

the point $\begin{bmatrix} x \\ y \end{bmatrix}$ in *homogeneous form* as $\begin{bmatrix} x \\ y \\ 1 \end{bmatrix}$. In homogeneous form, the translation

$$T_{h,k}: \begin{bmatrix} x \\ y \end{bmatrix} \rightarrow \begin{bmatrix} x + h \\ y + k \end{bmatrix}$$

becomes $T_{h,k}: \begin{bmatrix} x \\ y \\ 1 \end{bmatrix} \rightarrow \begin{bmatrix} x + h \\ y + k \\ 1 \end{bmatrix}$.

a. Multiply $\begin{bmatrix} 1 & 0 & h \\ 0 & 1 & k \\ 0 & 0 & 1 \end{bmatrix} \cdot \begin{bmatrix} x \\ y \\ 1 \end{bmatrix}$ to see how matrix multiplication can be used for translations.

b. When a point is written in homogeneous form, the 2×2 matrices for transformations for size changes, scale changes, reflections, and rotations need to be written as 3×3 matrices in this form. For example,

$$\overset{r_x}{\begin{bmatrix} 1 & 0 \\ 0 & -1 \end{bmatrix}} \overset{(x, y)}{\begin{bmatrix} x \\ y \end{bmatrix}} = \overset{(x, -y)}{\begin{bmatrix} x \\ -y \end{bmatrix}}$$

in homogeneous form becomes

$$\begin{bmatrix} 1 & 0 & h \\ 0 & -1 & k \\ 0 & 0 & 1 \end{bmatrix} \begin{bmatrix} x \\ y \\ 1 \end{bmatrix} = \begin{bmatrix} x + h \\ -y + k \\ 1 \end{bmatrix}.$$

What are the 3×3 matrices for S_k, $S_{a,b}$, R_{90}, and r_y?

c. When translations are represented by 3×3 matrices, you can compose translations with size changes, scale changes, reflections, and rotations. What is the 3×3 matrix for $T_{2,3} \circ R_{90}$?

262

Additional responses, page 261

2. Students' responses might contain the following information.

a. Since the mid 1800s, matrices have been used in solving systems of linear equations, in describing transformations, and in changing variables in the theory of multi-variable integration. The first use of the word *matrix* was by James Joseph Sylvester in 1850.

b. The basic properties of matrices had been established by Augustin Cauchy in 1815 in the development of a theory of determinants. Authur Cayley introduced the inverse of matrices and related them to the solution of linear equations.

c. In 1858, Cayley announced what is now called the Cayley-Hamilton theorem for square matrices of any order. If $M = \begin{bmatrix} a & b \\ c & d \end{bmatrix}$, then the

$$\det \begin{bmatrix} a - M & b \\ c & d - M \end{bmatrix} = 0.$$

SUMMARY

A matrix is a rectangular array of objects. Matrices are frequently used to store data and to represent transformations. Matrices can be added if they have the same dimensions. Addition of matrices can be used to obtain translation images of figures. A matrix can be multiplied by a single number, called a scalar.

The product of two matrices exists only if the number of columns of the left matrix equals the number of rows of the right matrix. The element in the nth row and nth column of AB is the product of the nth row of A and the nth column of B. Matrix multiplication is associative but not commutative.

Matrices with 2 rows can represent points, lines, and other figures in the coordinate plane. Multiplying such a matrix by a 2×2 matrix on its left may yield a transformation image of the figure. Transformations for which 2×2 matrices are given in this chapter include reflections,

rotations, size changes, and scale changes. They are summarized below. The rotation of 90° about the origin is a particularly important transformation. It helps in the proof that two nonvertical lines are perpendicular if and only if the product of their slopes is -1.

The set of 2×2 matrices is closed under multiplication. The identity matrix for multiplying 2×2 matrices is $\begin{bmatrix} 1 & 0 \\ 0 & 1 \end{bmatrix}$. The identity transformation maps any figure onto itself. It can be considered as the size change S_1, the rotation R_0, or the translation $T_{0,0}$.

The Matrix Basis Theorem provides a way for you to remember matrices for transformations. If a transformation T can be represented by a 2×2 matrix, with $T(1, 0) = (x_1, y_1)$ and $T(0, 1) = (x_2, y_2)$, then T has the matrix $\begin{bmatrix} x_1 & x_2 \\ y_1 & y_2 \end{bmatrix}$.

Transformations Yielding Images Congruent to Preimages

Reflections:

over *x*-axis

$\begin{bmatrix} 1 & 0 \\ 0 & -1 \end{bmatrix}$

$r_x: (x, y) \rightarrow (x, -y)$

over *y*-axis

$\begin{bmatrix} -1 & 0 \\ 0 & 1 \end{bmatrix}$

$r_y: (x, y) \rightarrow (-x, y)$

over the line $y = x$

$\begin{bmatrix} 0 & 1 \\ 1 & 0 \end{bmatrix}$

$r_{y=x}: (x, y) \rightarrow (y, x)$

Rotations with center (0, 0):

magnitude 90°

$\begin{bmatrix} 0 & -1 \\ 1 & 0 \end{bmatrix}$

$R_{90}: (x, y) \rightarrow (-y, x)$

magnitude 180°

$\begin{bmatrix} -1 & 0 \\ 0 & -1 \end{bmatrix}$

$R_{180}: (x, y) \rightarrow (-x, -y)$

magnitude 270°

$\begin{bmatrix} 0 & 1 \\ -1 & 0 \end{bmatrix}$

$R_{270}: (x, y) \rightarrow (y, -x)$

Translations:

No general matrix

$T_{h,k}: (x, y) \rightarrow (x + h, y + k)$

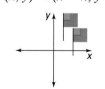

P	I	V	H	$\frac{P}{I}$	$\frac{V}{H}$
.1	1	.4	4	.1	.1
.1	1.7	.3	5	≈.059	≈.06
.3	1.9	.5	3	≈.158	.16
.1	.6	.5	3.5	.$\overline{16}$	≈.143
.2	.5	.8	2	.4	.4
.3	1.6	.7	4	.1875	.175
.15	.7	1.0	4.5	≈.214	.$\overline{2}$
.25	.7	1.0	3	≈.357	.3

(Responses continue on page 264.)

Vocabulary

Terms, symbols, and properties are listed by lesson to provide a checklist of concepts a student must know. Emphasize that students should read the vocabulary list carefully before starting the Progress Self-Test. If students do not understand the meaning of a term, they should refer back to the indicated lesson.

Additional Answers, page 265

1.
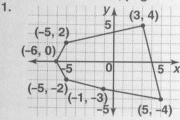

2.

	P	B	G
1st	$\begin{bmatrix} 14 & 3 & 8 \\ 120 & 190 & 250 \end{bmatrix}$		
Econ.			

4. $\begin{bmatrix} 16 & 12 \\ -2 & 16 \end{bmatrix}$ 5. $\begin{bmatrix} -6 & -6 \\ 3 & 3 \end{bmatrix}$

6. $\begin{bmatrix} 14 & 0 \\ 7 & 35 \end{bmatrix}$

7. The result of multiplying any 2 × 2 matrix by $\begin{bmatrix} 1 & 0 \\ 0 & 1 \end{bmatrix}$ is the original matrix.

8. $y + 2.5 = -\frac{1}{5}(x - 3)$

9. $\begin{bmatrix} 0 & 1 \\ 1 & 0 \end{bmatrix}$

12. $\begin{bmatrix} 6 & 4 & 2 & 4 & 6 & 4 \\ 6 & 7 & 4 & 1 & 2 & 4 \end{bmatrix}$

13.   Prices

Los Angeles $\begin{bmatrix} 1378 \\ 1748 \\ 1530 \end{bmatrix}$
Tucson
Santa Fe

The revenues are: $1,378,000 for Los Angeles; $1,748,000 for Tucson; and $1,530,000 for Santa Fe.

SUMMARY

Transformations Yielding Images Similar to Preimages

Size changes with center (0, 0), magnitude k:

$$\begin{bmatrix} k & 0 \\ 0 & k \end{bmatrix}$$

$S_k: (x, y) \rightarrow (kx, ky)$

Other Transformations

Scale change with horizontal magnitude a and vertical magnitude b:

$$\begin{bmatrix} a & 0 \\ 0 & b \end{bmatrix}$$

$S_{a,b}: (x, y) \rightarrow (ax, by)$

VOCABULARY

Below are the most important terms and phrases for this chapter.
You should be able to give a definition for those terms marked with *.
For all other terms you should be able to give a general description or a specific example.

Lesson 4-1
matrix; matrices
element of a matrix
dimensions $m \times n$
row
column
equal matrices
point matrix

Lesson 4-2
*matrix addition
sum of matrices
difference of matrices
scalar multiplication

Lesson 4-3
matrix multiplication
headings
2 × 2 identity matrix

Lesson 4-4
*transformation
*size change, S_k
preimage
image
similar
ratio of similitude
center
magnitude of size change
*identity transformation

Lesson 4-5
*scale change, $S_{a,b}$
horizontal magnitude
vertical magnitude
stretch, shrink

Lesson 4-6
reflection image of a point
   over a line
*reflection image
reflecting line
line of reflection
reflection
r_x, r_y, $r_{y=x}$
Matrix Basis Theorem

Lesson 4-7
closure
*composite of transformations
composed
rotation
R_{90}

Lesson 4-8
rotation
R_x, R_{90}, R_{180}, R_{270}

Lesson 4-10
*translation, $T_{h,k}$
slide or translation image

264

Additional responses, page 262

the transparency to the mirror. The length of a line segment on the image varies directly as the length of the segment on the transparency, and also varies directly as the distance from the mirror to the screen.

4a. $\begin{bmatrix} 1 & 0 & h \\ 0 & 1 & k \\ 0 & 0 & 1 \end{bmatrix} \begin{bmatrix} x \\ y \\ 1 \end{bmatrix} = \begin{bmatrix} x + h \\ y + k \\ 1 \end{bmatrix}$

b. $S_k = \begin{bmatrix} k & 0 & 0 \\ 0 & k & 0 \\ 0 & 0 & 1 \end{bmatrix}$

$S_{a,b} = \begin{bmatrix} a & 0 & 0 \\ 0 & b & 0 \\ 0 & 0 & 1 \end{bmatrix}$

$R_{90} = \begin{bmatrix} 0 & -1 & 0 \\ 0 & 0 & 0 \\ 0 & 0 & 1 \end{bmatrix}$

$r_y = \begin{bmatrix} -1 & 0 & 0 \\ 0 & 1 & 0 \\ 0 & 0 & 1 \end{bmatrix}$

PROGRESS SELF-TEST

Take this test as you would take a test in class. You will need graph paper. Then check your work with the solutions in the Selected Answers section in the back of the book. **1, 2) See margin.**

1. Graph the polygon described by the matrix
$$\begin{bmatrix} 3 & -5 & -6 & -5 & -1 & 5 \\ 4 & 2 & 0 & -2 & -3 & -4 \end{bmatrix}.$$

2. One day on Fruitair flying from Appleburg, there were 14 first-class and 120 economy passengers going to Peachport; 3 first-class and 190 economy passengers bound for Bananasville; and 8 first-class and 250 economy passengers flying to Grapetown. Write a 2 × 3 matrix for this information. **4–9) See margin.**

In 3–6, use matrices A, B, and C below.
$$A = \begin{bmatrix} 5 & -2 \\ 4 & -2 \\ -1 & 0 \end{bmatrix} \quad B = \begin{bmatrix} 2 & 0 \\ 1 & 5 \end{bmatrix} \quad C = \begin{bmatrix} 8 & 6 \\ -2 & 2 \end{bmatrix}$$

3. Which product exists, AB or BA? **AB**
4. Find BC.   5. Find B − C.
6. Calculate 7B.
7. Why is $\begin{bmatrix} 1 & 0 \\ 0 & 1 \end{bmatrix}$ called the identity matrix?
8. Find an equation for the line through (3, -2.5) that is perpendicular to $y = 5x - 3$.
9. Calculate the matrix for $r_x \circ R_{270}$.

In 10–12, refer to the graph at the right.

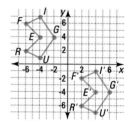

10. What translation maps FIGURE onto F'I'G'U'R'E'? $T_{8,-8}$
11. What is true about $\overleftrightarrow{FI}$ and $\overleftrightarrow{F'I'}$? $\overleftrightarrow{FI} \parallel \overleftrightarrow{F'I'}$
12. Find the image of FIGURE under the transformation r_y. **See margin.**

13–20) See margin.

13. A shoe manufacturer has factories in Los Angeles, Tucson, and Santa Fe. One year's sales (in thousands) can be summarized by the following matrix.

	Deck Shoes	Pumps	Sandals	Boots
Los Angeles	23	8	10	5
Tucson	11	5	10	15
Santa Fe	2	3	15	15

The selling prices of the deck shoes, pumps, sandals, and boots are $18, $58, $12, and $76, respectively. Use matrix multiplication to find the total revenue for each factory.

14. If the matrices below represent two pet store's inventories before they merge, what will be their inventory immediately after the merger?

	Lois's Pet Shop		Doug's Pet Shop	
	Males	Females	Males	Females
Dogs	8	11	10	14
Cats	5	4	11	13
Birds	15	16	7	9
Monkeys	2	0	0	3

In 15 and 16, identify the matrix you might use to perform the given transformation.

15. a horizontal stretch of magnitude 2 and a vertical shrink of magnitude $\frac{1}{4}$
16. $T: (x, y) \rightarrow (y, x)$

In 17 and 18, △ABC has vertices A = (7, 6), B = (-1, 2), and C = (3, -4).

17. Describe the matrix multiplication.
$$\begin{bmatrix} 1 & 0 \\ 0 & -1 \end{bmatrix}\begin{bmatrix} 7 & -1 & 3 \\ 6 & 2 & -4 \end{bmatrix} = \begin{bmatrix} 7 & -1 & 3 \\ -6 & -2 & 4 \end{bmatrix}$$

18. Graph △ABC and R_{90} (△ABC).

19. The translation with matrix $\begin{bmatrix} 3 & 3 \\ 2 & 2 \end{bmatrix}$ is applied to the line $x + 2y = 5$. Find an equation for its image. (Hint: Find two points on the line.)

20. Find the matrix of the image of $\begin{bmatrix} 5 & 2 & -3 \\ -3 & 2 & -5 \end{bmatrix}$
   a. under S_3.   b. under $S_4 \circ S_3$.

Additional Answers, continued

14. $\begin{bmatrix} 18 & 25 \\ 16 & 17 \\ 22 & 25 \\ 2 & 3 \end{bmatrix}$ 15. $\begin{bmatrix} 2 & 0 \\ 0 & \frac{1}{4} \end{bmatrix}$

16. $\begin{bmatrix} 0 & 1 \\ 1 & 0 \end{bmatrix}$

17. **The reflection of △ABC over the x-axis is the image △A'B'C' with vertices A' = (7, -6), B' = (-1, -2), and C' = (3, 4).**

18. A' = (-6, 7), B' = (-2, -1), and C' = (4, 3).

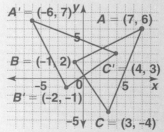

19. $y - 2 = \frac{4-2}{4-8}(x - 8)$ or $y = -\frac{1}{2}x + 6$.

20a. $\begin{bmatrix} 15 & 6 & -9 \\ -9 & 6 & -15 \end{bmatrix}$

b. $\begin{bmatrix} 60 & 24 & -36 \\ -36 & 24 & -60 \end{bmatrix}$

---

c. $T_{2,3} \circ R_{90} = \begin{bmatrix} 1 & 0 & 2 \\ 0 & 1 & 3 \\ 0 & 0 & 1 \end{bmatrix}\begin{bmatrix} 0 & -1 & 0 \\ 1 & 0 & 0 \\ 0 & 0 & 1 \end{bmatrix}$

$= \begin{bmatrix} 0 & -1 & 2 \\ 1 & 0 & 3 \\ 0 & 0 & 1 \end{bmatrix}$

Chapter 4 Review

Resources

From the *Teacher's Resource File*
- Answer Master for Chapter 4 Review
- Assessment Sourcebook: Chapter 4 Test, Forms A–D Chapter 4 Test, Cumulative Form

Additional Resources
- Quiz and Test Writer

The main objectives for the chapter are organized in the Chapter Review under the four types of understanding this book promotes–Skills, Properties, Uses, and Representations.

Whereas end-of-chapter material may be considered optional in some texts, in *UCSMP Advanced Algebra* we have selected these objectives and questions with the expectation that they will be covered. Students should be able to answer these questions with about 85% accuracy after studying the chapter.

You may assign these questions over a single night to help students prepare for a test the next day, or you may assign the questions over a two-day period. If you work the questions over two days, we recommend assigning the *evens* for homework the first night so that students get feedback in class the next day and then assigning the *odds* the night before the test because answers are provided to the odd-numbered questions.

It is effective to ask students which questions they still do not understand and use the day or days as a total class discussion of the material which the class finds most difficult.

CHAPTER REVIEW

Questions on SPUR Objectives

SPUR stands for **S**kills, **P**roperties, **U**ses, and **R**epresentations. The Chapter Review questions are grouped according to the SPUR Objectives for this chapter.

SKILLS DEAL WITH THE PROCEDURES USED TO GET ANSWERS.

Objective A: *Add, subtract, and find scalar multiples of matrices.* (Lesson 4-2)

1–4) See margin.

1. Find a single matrix for $\begin{bmatrix} 8 & 6 \\ 3 & -2 \\ 4 & -1 \end{bmatrix} - \begin{bmatrix} -3 & 0 \\ -1 & 6 \\ -4 & -3 \end{bmatrix}$.

In 2–4, let $A = \begin{bmatrix} 2 & 3 & 4 \\ 7 & 5 & -1 \\ 1 & 2 & 0 \end{bmatrix}$ and $B = \begin{bmatrix} 1 & -6 & 0 \\ 2 & 3 & 1 \\ 4 & 9 & 2 \end{bmatrix}$.

Find the following.

2. $A + B$ 3. $2A + B$ 4. $3A - 4B$

In 5 and 6, solve for a and b.

5. $\begin{bmatrix} a & 16 \\ 10 & b \end{bmatrix} + \begin{bmatrix} .4 & -1 \\ -10 & 3.1 \end{bmatrix} = \begin{bmatrix} 2 & 15 \\ 0 & -7 \end{bmatrix}$ $a = 1.6;$ $b = -10.1$

6. $2\begin{bmatrix} -1 & 9 \\ b & -.5 \end{bmatrix} - \begin{bmatrix} a & 7 \\ -3 & 3 \end{bmatrix} = \begin{bmatrix} 6 & 11 \\ 13 & -4 \end{bmatrix}$ $a = -8;$ $b = 5$

Objective B: *Multiply matrices.* (Lesson 4-3)

In 7–10, calculate the product.

7. $\begin{bmatrix} 6 & -1 & -4 \end{bmatrix} \begin{bmatrix} 8 \\ -3 \\ -2 \end{bmatrix}$ $\begin{bmatrix} 59 \end{bmatrix}$ 8. $\begin{bmatrix} 3 & 5 \\ 4 & 2 \end{bmatrix}\begin{bmatrix} 3 & 5 \\ 4 & 2 \end{bmatrix}$ $\begin{bmatrix} 29 & 25 \\ 20 & 24 \end{bmatrix}$

9. $\begin{bmatrix} -3 & -2 & -1 \\ 0 & 1 & 1 \\ 5 & 0 & 5 \end{bmatrix}\begin{bmatrix} 1 & 2 & 3 \\ 4 & 5 & 6 \\ 7 & 8 & 9 \end{bmatrix}$ $\begin{bmatrix} -18 & -24 & -30 \\ 11 & 13 & 15 \\ 40 & 50 & 60 \end{bmatrix}$

10. $\begin{bmatrix} 1 & 2 & 3 \end{bmatrix}\begin{bmatrix} 4 & 7 \\ 5 & 8 \\ 6 & 9 \end{bmatrix}\begin{bmatrix} 16 & 0 \\ 0 & 4 \end{bmatrix}$ $\begin{bmatrix} 512 & 200 \end{bmatrix}$

In 11 and 12, solve for a and b.

11. $\begin{bmatrix} a & 0 \\ 0 & b \end{bmatrix}\begin{bmatrix} 2 \\ -9 \end{bmatrix} = \begin{bmatrix} 10 \\ 27 \end{bmatrix}$ $a = 5;$ $b = -3$

12. $\begin{bmatrix} 0 & -1 \\ 1 & 0 \end{bmatrix}\begin{bmatrix} a \\ b \end{bmatrix} = \begin{bmatrix} -5 \\ 8 \end{bmatrix}$ $a = 8;$ $b = 5$

13) $y + 1 = 2(x - 3)$

Objective C: *Determine equations of lines perpendicular to given lines.* (Lesson 4-9)

13. Find an equation for the line through $(3, -1)$ and perpendicular to $y = -\frac{1}{2}x + 4$.

14. Find an equation for the line through $(7, 8)$ and perpendicular to $x = -4$. $y = 8$

15. Given $A = (6, 1)$ and $B = (-2, 3)$, find an equation for the perpendicular bisector of $\overline{AB}$. $y - 2 = 4(x - 2)$

16. Let $\triangle SMR$ be represented by the matrix $\begin{bmatrix} 123 & -13 & 43 \\ 65 & 432 & -105 \end{bmatrix}$.

    Let $\triangle S'M'R' = R_{90}(\triangle SMR)$.

    a. What is the slope of $\overleftrightarrow{SR}$? $\frac{17}{8}$

    b. What is the product of the slopes of $\overleftrightarrow{SR}$ and $\overleftrightarrow{S'R'}$? -1

    c. Use your answers to parts **a** and **b** to find the slope of $\overleftrightarrow{S'R'}$. $\frac{-8}{17}$

Additional Answers, pages 266–267

1. $\begin{bmatrix} 11 & 6 \\ 4 & -8 \\ 8 & 2 \end{bmatrix}$ 2. $\begin{bmatrix} 3 & -3 & 4 \\ 9 & 8 & 0 \\ 5 & 11 & 2 \end{bmatrix}$

3. $\begin{bmatrix} 5 & 0 & 8 \\ 16 & 13 & -1 \\ 6 & 13 & 2 \end{bmatrix}$ 4. $\begin{bmatrix} 2 & 33 & 12 \\ 13 & 3 & -7 \\ -13 & -30 & -8 \end{bmatrix}$

17b.
Sample: $\begin{bmatrix} 2 & 3 \\ 1 & -4 \end{bmatrix} + \begin{bmatrix} 1 & 7 \\ 5 & 6 \end{bmatrix} = \begin{bmatrix} 1 & 7 \\ 5 & 6 \end{bmatrix} + \begin{bmatrix} 2 & 3 \\ 1 & -4 \end{bmatrix} = \begin{bmatrix} 3 & 10 \\ 6 & 2 \end{bmatrix}$

18b.
Sample: $\left(\begin{bmatrix} 3 & 2 \\ 5 & 4 \end{bmatrix}\begin{bmatrix} 1 & 3 \\ 7 & 9 \end{bmatrix}\right)\begin{bmatrix} 2 & 6 \\ 9 & 8 \end{bmatrix} = \begin{bmatrix} 3 & 2 \\ 5 & 4 \end{bmatrix}\left(\begin{bmatrix} 1 & 3 \\ 7 & 9 \end{bmatrix}\begin{bmatrix} 2 & 6 \\ 9 & 8 \end{bmatrix}\right) = \begin{bmatrix} 277 & 318 \\ 525 & 606 \end{bmatrix}$

29. $\begin{bmatrix} 1 & 0 \\ 0 & 1 \end{bmatrix}$; it is the identity transformation.

30. Size; (0, 0); 6

PROPERTIES DEAL WITH THE PRINCIPLES BEHIND THE MATHEMATICS.

Objective D: *Recognize properties of matrix operations.*   (Lessons 4-2, 4-3, 4-7)

In 17 and 18, a statement is given. **a.** Is the statement true or false? **b.** Give an example to support your answer. **See margin for part b.**

17. Matrix addition is commutative. **True**

18. Matrix multiplication is associative. **True**

19. Determine whether the product exists.

a. $\begin{bmatrix} 1 & 6 & 4 \end{bmatrix}\begin{bmatrix} 2 \\ 8 \end{bmatrix}$ **No**

b. $\begin{bmatrix} 3 & 1 & 6 \\ 5 & 8 & -2 \end{bmatrix}\begin{bmatrix} 1 & -1 & 0 & 7 \\ 1 & 0 & 0 & 0 \\ 0 & 1 & 5 & 2 \end{bmatrix}$ **Yes**

20. N and T are matrices. N has dimensions $r \times p$ and T has dimensions $q \times r$.

a. Which product must exist, NT or TN? **TN**

b. What are the dimensions of your answer in part **a**? $q \times p$

21. What matrix is the identity for multiplication of 2×2 matrices? $\begin{bmatrix} 1 & 0 \\ 0 & 1 \end{bmatrix}$

Objective E: *Recognize relationships between figures and their transformation images.*
(Lessons 4-4, 4-5, 4-6, 4-8, 4-9, 4-10)

In 22–25, *multiple choice.*
(a) not necessarily similar or congruent
(b) similar, but not necessarily congruent
(c) congruent
(d) parallel

22. A figure and its size-change image are ___?___. **b**

23. A figure and its scale-change image are ___?___. **a**

24. A figure and its reflection image are ___?___. **c**

25. A line and its translation image are ___?___. **d**

26. Consider two lines. One is the image of the other under R_{90}. The slope of one of the lines is -0.2. What is the slope of the other line? **5**

27. Repeat Question 26 if the transformation is the translation $T_{1,2}$. **-0.2**

Objective F: *Relate transformations to matrices, and vice versa.* **29, 30, 31a) See margin.**
(Lessons 4-4, 4-5, 4-6, 4-7, 4-8, 4-10)

28. Translate the following matrix equation into English by filling in the blanks.
$\begin{bmatrix} 0 & 1 \\ 1 & 0 \end{bmatrix}\begin{bmatrix} 5 \\ -2 \end{bmatrix} = \begin{bmatrix} -2 \\ 5 \end{bmatrix}$ (5, -2); $y = x$;   (-2, 5)
The reflection image of the point ___?___ over the line ___?___ is the point ___?___.

29. Multiply the matrix for r_y by itself, and tell what transformation the product represents.

30. The matrix $\begin{bmatrix} 6 & 0 \\ 0 & 6 \end{bmatrix}$ is associated with a ___?___ change with center ___?___ and magnitude ___?___.

31. a. Calculate a matrix for $r_x \circ R_{180}$.
b. What single transformation corresponds to your answer? r_y **32) Sample:** $r_x \circ r_y$

32. Find two reflections whose composite is R_{180}.

33. a. What translation maps *PEAR* onto $P'E'A'R'$, as shown below. $T_{2,-1}$

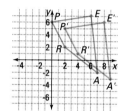

b. Explain how to use a matrix operation to transform *PEAR* to $P'E'A'R'$. **See margin.**

In 34–36, give a matrix for the transformation.
34. $r_{y=x}$ **See below.**   **35.** $S_{4,6}$ **36.** R_{90}

37. Find the image of $\begin{bmatrix} -1 & 0 & 4 & 0 \\ 3 & .5 & -1 & 5 \end{bmatrix}$ under r_y. **See margin.**

38. *GOLD* has coordinates $G(0, 0)$, $O(4, 1)$, $L(3, 5)$, and $D(-1, 4)$. Find the matrix of the image of *GOLD* under R_{270}. **See margin.**

39. Find the matrix of the image of $\begin{bmatrix} 6 & 8 & 2 \\ 0 & 4 & 0 \end{bmatrix}$ under $S_{\frac{1}{2}}$. **See margin.**

34) $\begin{bmatrix} 0 & 1 \\ 1 & 0 \end{bmatrix}$ 35) $\begin{bmatrix} 4 & 0 \\ 0 & 6 \end{bmatrix}$ 36) $\begin{bmatrix} 0 & -1 \\ 1 & 0 \end{bmatrix}$

31a. $\begin{bmatrix} -1 & 0 \\ 0 & 1 \end{bmatrix}$

33b. Because the matrix for PEAR is $\begin{bmatrix} 0 & 6 & 7 & 2 \\ 6 & 7 & -2 & 2 \end{bmatrix}$, the translation matrix has four columns represented by $\begin{bmatrix} 2 & 2 & 2 & 2 \\ -1 & -1 & -1 & -1 \end{bmatrix}$.

33b. continued
Then $\begin{bmatrix} 2 & 2 & 2 & 2 \\ -1 & -1 & -1 & -1 \end{bmatrix} +$
$\begin{bmatrix} 0 & 6 & 7 & 2 \\ 6 & 7 & -2 & 2 \end{bmatrix} = \begin{bmatrix} 2 & 8 & 9 & 4 \\ 5 & 6 & -3 & 1 \end{bmatrix}$
which is the matrix for the vertices of the image $P'E'A'R'$.

37. $\begin{bmatrix} 1 & 0 & -4 & 0 \\ 3 & .5 & -1 & 5 \end{bmatrix}$

38. $\begin{bmatrix} 0 & 1 & 5 & 4 \\ 0 & -4 & -3 & 1 \end{bmatrix}$

39. $\begin{bmatrix} 3 & 4 & 1 \\ 0 & 2 & 0 \end{bmatrix}$

Assessment

Evaluation The *Assessment Sourcebook* provides six forms of the Chapter 4 Test. Forms A and B present parallel versions in a short-answer format. Forms C and D offer performance assessment. The fifth test is Chapter 4 Test, Cumulative Form. About 50% of this test covers Chapter 4, 25% of it covers Chapter 3, and 25% of it covers earlier chapters.

For information on grading, see *General Teaching Suggestions; Grading* in the *Professional Sourcebook*, which begins on page T20 in this Teacher's Edition.

Feedback After students have taken the test for Chapter 4 and you have scored the results, return the tests to students for discussion. Class discussion of the questions that caused trouble for the most students can be very effective in identifying and clarifying misunderstandings. You might want to have them write down the items they missed and work, either in groups or at home, to correct them. It is important for students to receive feedback on every chapter test, and we recommend that students see and correct their mistakes before proceeding too far into the next chapter.

Additional Answers

40.

	oak	pine	maple
tables	5	3	1
chairs	10	12	6

41.

	Boys	Girls
freshmen	490	487
sophomores	402	416
juniors	358	344
seniors	293	300

45. $[270 \ 320 \ 210]\begin{bmatrix} 15 & 6 \\ 10 & 8 \\ 2 & 1 \end{bmatrix} =$

$[7670 \ 4390]$

Factory 1: $7,670,000;
Factory 2: $4,390,000

46a. growth matrix (in thousands):

$$\begin{bmatrix} -60 & -25 & -172 \\ -15 & 12 & -18 \end{bmatrix}$$

48.

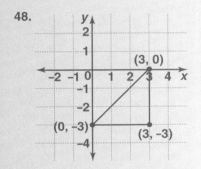

49. $\begin{bmatrix} 1 & 3 & 9 & 6 \\ 1 & 7 & 1 & -6 \end{bmatrix}$

50.

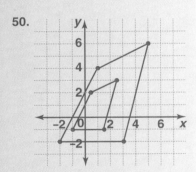

51.

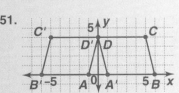

268

USES DEAL WITH APPLICATIONS OF MATHEMATICS IN REAL SITUATIONS.

Objective G: *Use matrices to store data.*
(Lesson 4-1) 40–41) See margin.

40. Chuck makes handcrafted furniture. Last year he made 5 oak tables, 10 oak chairs, 3 pine tables, 12 pine chairs, 1 maple table, and 6 maple chairs. Store this data in a 2×3 matrix.

41. A high school has 490 freshman boys, 487 freshman girls, 402 sophomore boys, 416 sophomore girls, 358 junior boys, 344 junior girls, 293 senior boys, and 300 senior girls. Write a 4×2 matrix to describe the school's enrollment.

In 42 and 43, the matrix below gives the cost of several items at three different markets.

42. Which element gives the cost of plums in Market I? element in 2nd row and 1st column

43. What does the sum of the numbers in the second column represent?

	Market I	Market II	Market III
eggs (12)	.89	.95	.99
plums (lb)	.90	.79	.82
peaches (lb)	1.49	1.50	1.59
bananas (lb)	.33	.28	.25

The price for a dozen eggs, a pound each of plums, peaches, and bananas at Market II

Objective H: *Use matrix addition, matrix multiplication, and scalar multiplication to solve real-world problems.* *(Lessons 4-2, 4-3)*

44. A large pizza costs $12.50, a medium pizza costs $8.90, and a small pizza costs $5.20. An order for a Journalism Club party consists of 7 large pizzas, 2 medium pizzas, and 4 small pizzas. Write matrices C and N for the cost and number ordered, then calculate CN to find the total cost of the order.

$$C = [12.50 \ 8.90 \ 5.20] \quad N = \begin{bmatrix} 7 \\ 2 \\ 4 \end{bmatrix}; \quad CN = \$126.10$$

Making books. *Publishing companies, such as ScottForesman (top), develop and edit manuscripts. Printing companies, such as Donnelley (bottom), print the books.*

268

45. An electronics manufacturer has two factories. Sales (in thousands) can be summarized by the matrix below. The selling price of a VHS recorder is $270, a TV is $320, and a compact disc player is $210. Use matrix multiplication to determine the total revenue for each factory. See margin.

	Factory 1	Factory 2
VHS	15	6
TV	10	8
CD	2	1

46. A printing company has two presses. Print runs for two years are given in the matrices below.

1993

	Textbooks	Novels	Nonfiction
Press 1	250,000	125,000	312,000
Press 2	60,000	48,000	90,000

1994

	Textbooks	Novels	Nonfiction
Press 1	190,000	100,000	140,000
Press 2	45,000	60,000	72,000

a. Calculate the matrix that represents the growth in production of each press from 1993 to 1994. See margin.

b. Which type of book decreased the most in production? nonfiction

52a.

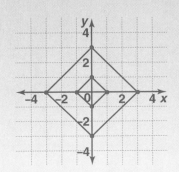

REPRESENTATIONS DEAL WITH PICTURES, GRAPHS, OR OBJECTS THAT ILLUSTRATE CONCEPTS.

47. Normal fares (in $) of an airline to three cities are given in the matrix below. To increase air travel, the airline plans to reduce fares by 40%.

$$\begin{array}{cccc} & \text{city 1} & \text{city 2} & \text{city 3} \\ \text{first class} & \begin{bmatrix} 415 & 672 & 258 \\ \text{economy} & 198 & 394 & 109 \end{bmatrix} \end{array}$$

a. What scalar multiplication will yield the new fares? **0.6**

b. Find the new fares for travel to these three cities.
$$\begin{bmatrix} 249.00 & 403.20 & 154.80 \\ 118.80 & 236.40 & 65.40 \end{bmatrix}$$

Objective I: *Graph figures and their transformation images.* **See margin.**
(Lessons 4-1, 4-4, 4-5, 4-6, 4-7, 4-8, 4-10)

48. Draw the polygon described by the matrix
$$\begin{bmatrix} 3 & 0 & 3 \\ -3 & -3 & 0 \end{bmatrix}.$$

49. Refer to the graph below.
Write quadrilateral *HOPE* as a matrix.

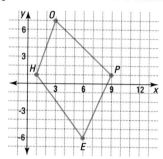

Ideal location. *Pictured is a beach in Cancun, Mexico, a popular destination for airlines.*

52. Consider the quadrilateral defined by the matrix $\begin{bmatrix} 0 & -1 & 0 & 1 \\ 1 & 0 & -1 & 0 \end{bmatrix}.$

a. Graph the quadrilateral and its image under $\begin{bmatrix} 3 & 0 \\ 0 & 3 \end{bmatrix}.$ **See margin.**

b. Are the image and preimage similar? **Yes**

c. Are they congruent? **No**

50. Draw the polygon $\begin{bmatrix} 1 & 5 & 3 & -2 \\ 4 & 6 & -2 & -2 \end{bmatrix}$ and its image under $S_{\frac{1}{2}}$.

51. Trapezoid *ABCD* is represented by $\begin{bmatrix} -1 & 6 & 5 & 0 \\ 0 & 0 & 4 & 4 \end{bmatrix}.$ Graph the preimage and image under r_y.

Setting Up Lesson 5-1
Homework We recommend that you assign reading the Chapter 5 Opener and Lesson 5-1, and some questions from Lesson 5-1 for homework the evening of the test.

Materials For **Question 26,** students will need a health book or an almanac that features a table of normal weights.

Adapting to Individual Needs

The student text is written for the vast majority of students. The chart at the right suggests two pacing plans to accommodate the needs of your students. Students in the Full Course should complete the entire text by the end of the year. Students in the Minimal Course will spend more time when there are quizzes and more time on the Chapter Review. Therefore, these students may not complete all of the chapters in the text.

Options are also presented to meet the needs of a variety of teaching and learning styles. For each lesson, the Teacher's Edition provides sections entitled: *Video* which describes video segments and related questions that can be used for motivation or extension; *Optional Activities* which suggests activities that employ materials, physical models, technology, and cooperative learning; and *Adapting to Individual Needs* which regularly includes **Challenge** problems, **English Language Development** suggestions, and suggestions for providing **Extra Help.** The Teacher's Edition also frequently includes an **Error Alert,** an **Extension,** and an **Assessment** alternative. The options available in Chapter 5 are summarized in the chart below.

Chapter 5 Pacing Chart

Day	Full Course	Minimal Course
1	5-1	5-1
2	5-2	5-2
3	5-3	5-3
4	5-4	5-4
5	Quiz*; 5-5	Quiz*; begin 5-5.
6	5-6	Finish 5-5.
7	5-7	5-6
8	Quiz*; 5-8	5-7
9	5-9	Quiz*; begin 5-8.
10	5-10	Finish 5-8.
11	Self-Test	5-9
12	Review	5-10
13	Test*	Self-Test
14		Review
15		Review
16		Test*

*in the Teacher's Resource File

In the Teacher's Edition...

Lesson	Optional Activities	Extra Help	Challenge	English Language Development	Error Alert	Extension	Cooperative Learning	Ongoing Assessment
5-1	●	●	●	●	●	●	●	Written
5-2	●	●	●	●		●	●	Oral/Written
5-3	●	●	●	●	●	●	●	Written
5-4	●	●	●	●		●	●	Written
5-5	●	●	●	●		●	●	Group
5-6	●	●	●	●		●	●	Written
5-7	●	●	●	●	●	●	●	Written
5-8	●	●	●	●		●	●	Oral/Written
5-9	●	●	●	●		●		Oral
5-10	●	●	●			●	●	Written

In the Additional Resources...

	In the Teacher's Resource File								
Lesson	Lesson Masters, A and B	Teaching Aids*	Activity Kit*	Answer Masters	Technology Sourcebook	Assessment Sourcebook	Visual Aids**	Technology	Video Segments
5-1	5-1	43, 46		5-1			43, 46, AM		5-1
5-2	5-2	8, 19, 43	9	5-2			8, 19, 43, AM	GraphExplorer	
5-3	5-3	8, 19, 43		5-3	Comp 6		8, 19, 43, AM	Spreadsheet	
5-4	5-4	44		5-4	Comp 6	Quiz	44, AM	Spreadsheet	
In-class Activity		8		5-5			8, AM		
5-5	5-5	44	10	5-5			44, AM		
5-6	5-6	44		5-6	Calc 3		44, AM		
5-7	5-7	8, 44, 47-49		5-7		Quiz	8, 44, 47-49, AM		
5-8	5-8	8, 45, 50, 51		5-8	Comp 7		8, 45, 50, 51, AM	GraphExplorer	
5-9	5-9	8, 45, 52		5-9	Comp 7		8, 45, 52, AM	GraphExplorer	
5-10	5-10	8, 45		5-10			8, 45, AM		
End of chapter				Review		Tests			

*Teaching Aids are pictured on pages 270C and 270D. The activities in the Activity Kit are pictured on page 270C.

**Visual Aids provide transparencies for all Teaching Aids and all Answer Masters.

Also available is the Study Skills Handbook which includes study-skill tips related to reading, note-taking, and comprehension.

Integrating Strands and Applications

	5-1	5-2	5-3	5-4	5-5	5-6	5-7	5-8	5-9	5-10
Mathematical Connections										
Number Sense		●					●	●	●	●
Algebra	●	●	●	●	●	●	●	●	●	●
Geometry	●	●	●	●	●	●	●	●	●	●
Measurement	●	●	●							
Logic and Reasoning				●						
Patterns and Functions	●	●	●	●	●	●	●	●	●	
Discrete Mathematics							●	●	●	●
Interdisciplinary and Other Connections										
Art								●		
Science	●		●	●		●			●	●
Social Studies	●			●	●	●	●	●	●	●
Multicultural		●	●		●					
Technology	●	●	●	●		●	●	●		●
Career		●				●		●	●	●
Consumer	●	●	●	●	●	●	●	●		
Sports	●		●				●			

Teaching and Assessing the Chapter Objectives

Chapter 5 Objectives (Organized into the SPUR categories—Skills, Properties, Uses, and Representations)	Lessons	Progress Self-Test Questions	Chapter Review Questions	Chapter Test, Forms A and B	Chapter Test, Forms	
					C	D
Skills						
A: Solve 2 x 2 and 3 x 3 systems using the Linear Combination Method or substitution.	5-3, 5-4	5, 6	1–8	4, 5	2	
B: Find the determinant and the inverse of a square matrix.	5-5	8, 9	9–16	8	1	
C: Use matrices to solve systems of two or three linear equations.	5-6	6, 8	17–20	12	3	
Properties						
D: Recognize properties of systems of equations.	5-2, 5-3, 5-4, 5-6	4	21–30	3, 11	2	
E: Recognize properties of systems of inequalities.	5-8, 5-9	11	31–35	10, 14		✓
Uses						
F: Use systems of two or three linear equations to solve real-world problems.	5-3, 5-4, 5-6	7	36–41	7, 15	5	
G: Use linear programming to solve real-world problems.	5-9, 5-10	12	42, 43	16	5	✓
Representations						
H: Solve and graph linear inequalities in one variable.	5-1	1, 2	44–53	1, 6	4	✓
I: Estimate solutions to systems by graphing.	5-2	3	54–56	2		
J: Graph linear inequalities in two variables.	5-7	10	57–61	9		✓
K: Solve systems of inequalities by graphing.	5-1, 5-8	11	62–66	13		

In the Teacher's Resource File

Assessment Sourcebook
Quiz for Lessons 5-1 through 5-4   Chapter 5 Test, Forms A–D
Quiz for Lessons 5-5 through 5-7   Chapter 5 Test, Cumulative Form

Quiz and Test Writer

Activity Kit

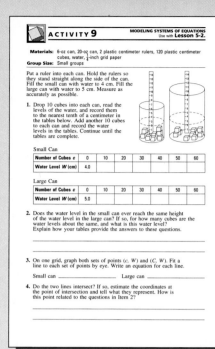

ACTIVITY 9

MODELING SYSTEMS OF EQUATIONS
Use with **Lesson 5-2**.

Materials: 6-oz can, 20-oz can, 2 plastic centimeter rulers, 120 plastic centimeter cubes, water, $\frac{1}{4}$-inch grid paper
Group Size: Small groups

Put a ruler into each can. Hold the rulers so they stand straight along the side of the can. Fill the small can with water to 4 cm. Fill the large can with water to 5 cm. Measure as accurately as possible.

1. Drop 10 cubes into each can, read the levels of the water, and record them to the nearest tenth of a centimeter in the tables below. Add another 10 cubes to each can and record the water levels in the tables. Continue until the tables are complete.

Small Can

Number of Cubes c	0	10	20	30	40	50	60
Water Level W (cm)	4.0						

Large Can

Number of Cubes c	0	10	20	30	40	50	60
Water Level W (cm)	5.0						

2. Does the water level in the small can ever reach the same height of the water level in the large can? If so, for how many cubes are the water levels about the same, and what is this water level? Explain how your tables provide the answers to these questions.

3. On one grid, graph both sets of points (c, W) and (C, W). Fit a line to each set of points by eye. Write an equation for each line.

Small can _____ Large can _____

4. Do the two lines intersect? If so, estimate the coordinates at the point of intersection and tell what they represent. How is this point related to the questions in Item 2?

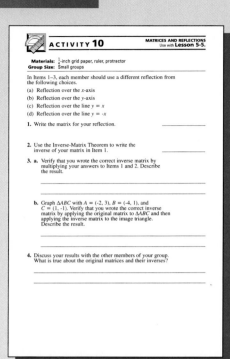

ACTIVITY 10

MATRICES AND REFLECTIONS
Use with **Lesson 5-5**.

Materials: $\frac{1}{4}$-inch grid paper, ruler, protractor
Group Size: Small groups

In Items 1–3, each member should use a different reflection from the following choices.
(a) Reflection over the x-axis
(b) Reflection over the y-axis
(c) Reflection over the line $y = x$
(d) Reflection over the line $y = -x$

1. Write the matrix for your reflection.

2. Use the Inverse-Matrix Theorem to write the inverse of your matrix in Item 1.

3. a. Verify that you wrote the correct inverse matrix by multiplying your answers to Items 1 and 2. Describe the result.

   b. Graph $\triangle ABC$ with $A = (-2, 3)$, $B = (-4, 1)$, and $C = (1, -1)$. Verify that you wrote the correct inverse matrix by applying the original matrix to $\triangle ABC$ and then applying the inverse matrix to the image triangle. Describe the result.

4. Discuss your results with the other members of your group. What is true about the original matrices and their inverses?

▶ **ACTIVITY 10**   page 2

Work independently on Item 5 and compare results with others in your group. Then work together on Item 6.

5. a. The matrix for reflecting a figure over the line $y = \frac{1}{2}x$ is $\begin{bmatrix} .6 & .8 \\ .8 & -.6 \end{bmatrix}$. On a new grid, graph $y = \frac{1}{2}x$ and draw $\triangle ABC$ from Item 3b. Apply this matrix to $\triangle ABC$. Then use paper folding or ruler and protractor to verify that the image triangle is the required reflection image.

   b. What do you predict is the inverse of the matrix from Part a? Why?

   c. Use any method to verify that your prediction from Part c is correct.

6. What do you think can be said about the matrix for any reflection? Do you think the same can be said of the matrix for any rotation? Explain your thinking and try to verify your answer.

Teaching Aids

Teaching Aid 5, Graph Paper, (shown on page 4D) can be used with **Lesson 5-5**.
Teaching Aid 8, Four-quadrant Graph Paper, (shown on page 4D) can be used with **Lessons 5-2, 5-3, and 5-7 through 5-10. Teaching Aid 19, Automatic Grapher Grids,** (shown on page 70D) can be used with **Lessons 5-2 and 5-3.**

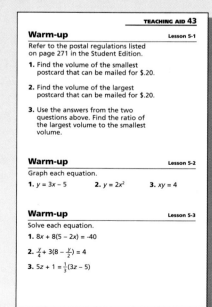

TEACHING AID 43

Warm-up   Lesson 5-1

Refer to the postal regulations listed on page 271 in the Student Edition.

1. Find the volume of the smallest postcard that can be mailed for $.20.

2. Find the volume of the largest postcard that can be mailed for $.20.

3. Use the answers from the two questions above. Find the ratio of the largest volume to the smallest volume.

Warm-up   Lesson 5-2

Graph each equation.

1. $y = 3x - 5$
2. $y = 2x^2$
3. $xy = 4$

Warm-up   Lesson 5-3

Solve each equation.

1. $8x + 8(5 - 2x) = -40$
2. $\frac{y}{4} + 3(8 - \frac{y}{2}) = 4$
3. $5z + 1 = \frac{1}{3}(3z - 5)$

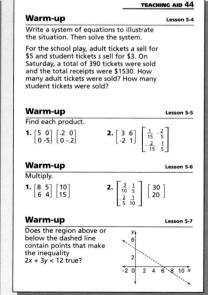

TEACHING AID 44

Warm-up   Lesson 5-4

Write a system of equations to illustrate the situation. Then solve the system.

For the school play, adult tickets a sell for $5 and student tickets s sell for $3. On Saturday, a total of 390 tickets were sold and the total receipts were $1530. How many adult tickets were sold? How many student tickets were sold?

Warm-up   Lesson 5-5

Find each product.

1. $\begin{bmatrix} 5 & 0 \\ 0 & -5 \end{bmatrix} \begin{bmatrix} .2 & 0 \\ 0 & -.2 \end{bmatrix}$
2. $\begin{bmatrix} 3 & 6 \\ -2 & 1 \end{bmatrix} \begin{bmatrix} \frac{1}{15} & -\frac{2}{5} \\ \frac{2}{15} & \frac{1}{5} \end{bmatrix}$

Warm-up   Lesson 5-6

Multiply.

1. $\begin{bmatrix} 8 & 5 \\ 6 & 4 \end{bmatrix} \begin{bmatrix} 10 \\ 15 \end{bmatrix}$
2. $\begin{bmatrix} \frac{3}{10} & \frac{1}{5} \\ \frac{2}{5} & \frac{1}{10} \end{bmatrix} \begin{bmatrix} 30 \\ 20 \end{bmatrix}$

Warm-up   Lesson 5-7

Does the region above or below the dashed line contain points that make the inequality $2x + 3y < 12$ true?

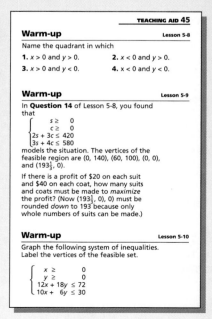

TEACHING AID 45

Warm-up   Lesson 5-8

Name the quadrant in which
1. $x > 0$ and $y > 0$.
2. $x < 0$ and $y > 0$.
3. $x > 0$ and $y < 0$.
4. $x < 0$ and $y < 0$.

Warm-up   Lesson 5-9

In **Question 14** of Lesson 5-8, you found that
$$\begin{cases} s \geq 0 \\ c \geq 0 \\ 2s + 3c \leq 420 \\ 3s + 4c \leq 580 \end{cases}$$
models the situation. The vertices of the feasible region are (0, 140), (60, 100), (0, 0), and ($193\frac{1}{3}$, 0).

If there is a profit of $20 on each suit and $40 on each coat, how many suits and coats must be made to *maximize* the profit? (Now ($193\frac{1}{3}$, 0) must be rounded *down* to 193 because only whole numbers of suits can be made.)

Warm-up   Lesson 5-10

Graph the following system of inequalities. Label the vertices of the feasible set.

$$\begin{cases} x \geq 0 \\ y \geq 0 \\ 12x + 18y \leq 72 \\ 10x + 6y \leq 30 \end{cases}$$

Blank Number Lines

Example 4

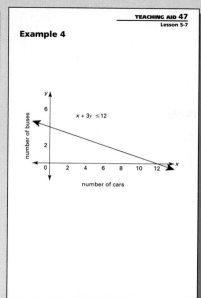

$x + 3y \leq 12$

number of buses

number of cars

Extension

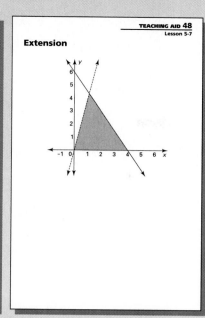

Optional Activities

1.

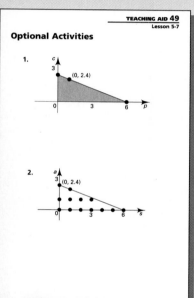

(0, 2.4)

2.

(0, 2.4)

Example 1

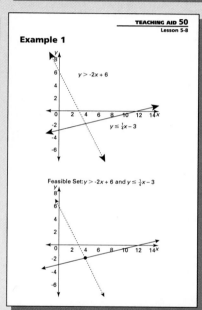

$y > -2x + 6$

$y \leq \frac{1}{4}x - 3$

Feasible Set: $y > -2x + 6$ and $y \leq \frac{1}{4}x - 3$

Example 2

	chairs	desks	total hours available
hrs. of carpentry per piece			
hrs. of finishing per piece			

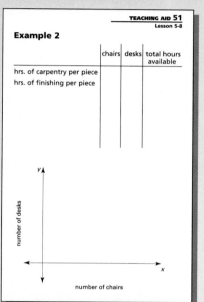

number of desks

number of chairs

Example

	Vitamin A (I. U.)	Potassium (mg)	Iron (mg)	Calories
Fried Chicken (one small piece)				
Corn (ear)				

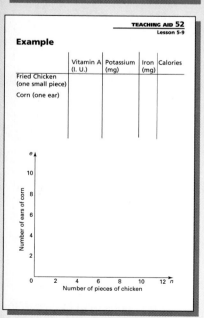

Number of ears of corn

Number of pieces of chicken

CHAPTER 5

Pacing

All of the lessons in this chapter are designed to be covered in one day. However, if your students do not have a good background in solving 2×2 linear systems, at least one extra day will be needed for Lessons 5-3 and 5-4. At the end of the chapter, you should plan to spend 1 day to review the Progress Self-Test, 1–2 days for the Chapter Review, and 1 day for a test. You may want to spend a day on projects, and a day may be needed for quizzes. Therefore, this chapter should take 13–17 days. We strongly recommend that you not spend more than 18 days on this chapter, since the material is reviewed extensively in later chapters.

Using pages 270–271

Ask students to explain what they think of when they hear the word *constraints*. Discuss the fact that constraints are conditions that make it impossible for complete freedom in a situation. Mathematically, constraints are restrictions on the values that variables can take.

Students may be surprised that postal regulations are so complicated. However, these regulations are necessary because most modern-day post offices use automatic sorting machinery that will not take mail of all sizes. Be sure that students realize that the three variables T, h, and l represent the three familiar dimensions length, width, and depth of a box. The system that is described indicates the greatest and least allowable possible sizes of a postcard.

270

Chapter 5 Overview

Chapter 5 reviews and extends methods of solving systems of equations from first-year algebra. Two new concepts are introduced: (1) solving systems using matrices and (2) solving systems of linear inequalities and applying this to linear programming. Linear-programming problems are an important and exciting application, and this chapter is structured so that the students master all the prerequisite skills before they solve such problems.

The first two lessons review the graphing associated with systems. Lesson 5-1 compares and contrasts solutions to compound sentences of one variable connected by *and* or *or* and it relates them to intersections and unions of sets. The graphs in Lesson 5-1 are exclusively on the number line. Lesson 5-2 reviews graphing 2×2 linear systems to find the number of solutions for a system and to estimate the solutions. Lesson 5-2 also extends the graphing method to

nonlinear systems with familiar curves, such as the parabola and the rectangular hyperbola. Additionally, Lesson 5-2 addresses finding solutions by using tables. The algebraic solution of quadratic systems is covered in Chapter 12.

Lessons 5-3 and 5-4 review methods of linear combinations and substitution through some important applications, and extend

SYSTEMS

The 1995 postal regulations describing those post cards that could be sent through the mail at a rate of $.20 are given below.

"Each piece must be rectangular. Additionally each piece

$$\text{must be} \begin{cases} \text{at least 0.007 inches thick,} \\ \text{no more than 0.25 inches thick,} \\ \text{between 3.5 and 4.25 inches high, and} \\ \text{between 5 and 6 inches long.''} \end{cases}$$

Mathematically, if T represents thickness, h represents height, and ℓ stands for length, we could say the *constraints* for a rectangular piece of mail are as follows:

$$T \geq 0.007''$$
$$\text{and } T \leq 0.25''$$
$$\text{and } 3.5'' \leq h \leq 4.25''$$
$$\text{and } 5'' \leq \ell \leq 6''.$$

Notice that each constraint in the system of inequalities involves just one variable. In other situations, constraints may involve more than one variable.

When mathematical conditions are joined by the word *and,* the set of conditions or sentences is called a *system.* Many methods for solving systems of equations were developed in the 19th century. This early work on systems involved some of the greatest mathematicians of all time, including Karl Friedrich Gauss from Germany, Jean Baptiste Joseph Fourier from France, and Arthur Cayley from Great Britain.

Systems have many applications. For instance, in the early 19th century Gauss used systems of equations to calculate the orbits of asteroids from sightings made by a few astronomers. In 1939, the Russian mathematician Leonid Kantorovich was the first to announce that large systems might have applications for production planning in industry. In 1945, the American economist George Stigler used systems to determine a best diet for the least cost. Kantorovich and Stigler each received a Nobel Prize for his work, Kantorovich in 1975 and Stigler in 1982. (Both prizes were in economics; there is no Nobel Prize in mathematics.) In this chapter you will study systems of equations and inequalities; including simplified examples of the kinds of problems studied by Kantorovich and Stigler.

271

The four algebraic sentences in the middle of the page correspond to the four sentences that are stated in words just above them. Because all of the sentences must be satisfied at once, they form a system when taken together. Each inequality involves only one variable, but the problem is 3-dimensional because three variables are involved.

Photo Connections

The photo collage makes real-world connections to the content of the chapter: systems.

Blueberries: Systems of equations are helpful in determining diets that meet the minimum requirements for protein, minerals, and vitamins. Fruits such as blueberries are a source of vitamins.

Watermelon and mango: Both watermelons and mangos are excellent sources of vitamin A and vitamin C. Systems of equations can be used to determine proper dietary combinations.

Ferris wheel: Example 2 in Lesson 5-7 shows how an inequality can be used to illustrate the proper relationship between age and height in meeting safety standards for an amusement ride.

Pencils: Manufacturers of all types of products use systems of inequalities for industrial planning. Every year over 10 billion pencils are manufactured throughout the world.

Tools: Example 2 in Lesson 5-8 illustrates how a system of inequalities could help a furniture maker decide how many desks and chairs to produce.

Chapter 5 Projects

At this time you might want to have students look over the projects on pages 336–337.

these techniques to simple nonlinear systems and to 3×3 linear systems.

Lessons 5-5 and 5-6 introduce solving systems by using matrices. In Lesson 5-5, students are taught how to find the inverse of a 2×2 matrix and then how to use the inverse to solve a system. In Lesson 5-6, 2×2 systems are solved by matrices, and the System-Determinant Theorem helps

students identify the number of solutions to a 2×2 system.

Some 3×3 linear systems are discussed in Lessons 5-3, 5-4, and 5-6. We expect students to solve them using substitution, linear combinations, or technology.

Lessons 5-7 and 5-8 set the stage for the linear programming that is introduced in

Lessons 5-9 and 5-10. Linear inequalities in two variables are graphed in Lesson 5-7. Lesson 5-8 extends the idea of systems of inequalities, which were introduced in Lesson 5-1, to two-dimensional inequalities. Lesson 5-9 introduces the technique for solving linear-programming problems that have already been set up mathematically. In Lesson 5-10, students learn how to set up such problems from information that is given in prose form.

Objectives

H Solve and graph linear inequalities in one variable.
K Solve systems of inequalities in one variable by graphing on a number line.

Resources

From the *Teacher's Resource File*
- Lesson Master 5-1A or 5-1B
- Answer Master 5-1
- Teaching Aids
  43 Warm-up
  46 Blank Number Lines

Additional Resources
- Visuals for Teaching Aids 43, 46
- Table of normal weights (Question 26)

Teaching Lesson 5-1

Warm-up

Refer to the postal regulations listed on page 271.

1. Find the volume of the smallest postcard that can be mailed for $.20. **0.1225 cubic inches**
2. Find the volume of the largest postcard that can be mailed for $.20. **6.375 cubic inches**
3. Use the answers from the two questions above. Find the ratio of the largest volume to the smallest volume. **About 52 to 1**

Notes on Reading

You may want to use **Teaching Aid 46** when discussing **Examples 1 and 2.**

5-1

Inequalities and Compound Sentences

Leaping ahead. *The long jump requires an athlete to run down a runway and leap from a take-off board into a sand pit. The jump is measured from the edge of the take-off board to the place in the sand where the athlete lands.*

Suppose that in order to qualify to compete in the long jump in a track meet, you must jump at least 5 meters. If J is the length of your jump, then you qualify if $J \geq 5$. The *open sentence* $J \geq 5$ is called an **inequality** because it contains one of the symbols $<$, $>$, $\leq$, $\geq$, or $\neq$. There are infinitely many solutions to the sentence $J \geq 5$. Some solutions are 5, 5.2, 5.9, 6, and 6.5. Not all solutions can be listed. One way to describe all possible solutions is to graph them on a number line. A graph of the solutions to $J \geq 5$ is shown below.

❶ The shaded circle means that 5 is included in the solution set. Shaded circles are used in the graphs of inequalities of the form $\leq$ or $\geq$. An open circle at the endpoint indicates that the endpoint is not included in the solution set. Open circles are used for inequalities involving $<$, $>$, or $\neq$. The graph below shows all solutions of $m < -0.2$.

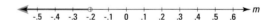

The sets $\{J: J \geq 5\}$ and $\{m: m < -0.2\}$ are *intervals*. The graph of the interval $\{J: J \geq 5\}$ is a ray. The graph of $\{m: m < -0.2\}$ is a ray without its endpoint.

272

Lesson 5-1 Overview

Broad Goals This lesson reviews the graphing of inequalities on the number line, the distinction between the words *and* and *or*, and the symbols for the union and the intersection of sets.

Perspective There are two major reasons why inequalities are discussed along with equations in this book. First, there are analogies between solving equations and solving inequalities that can help students

understand both of these concepts. Second, the application situations, which lead to equations, can almost always lead in the same way to inequalities. For instance, in **Example 4,** if we ask when the ticket agency will have *exactly* 50 tickets left, an equation results. If we ask when the agency will have 50 *or fewer* tickets left, an inequality results.

The content of this lesson should be familiar to students. Solving and graphing solutions to inequalities are topics that most students have seen in a previous algebra course. However, translating application problems into inequalities may be new to students who have not had previous UCSMP courses. This lesson requires attention to detail, and even students who know the concepts will have to pay close attention when answering the questions. Students must be careful

Compound Sentences Using the Word *and*

❷ In English, you can use the words *and* and *or* as conjunctions to join two or more clauses. In mathematics, these two words are used in a similar way. A sentence in which two clauses are connected by the word *and* or by the word *or* is called a **compound sentence.** The sentences below are compound sentences.

$$4 < x \text{ and } x < 8.$$
$$n \text{ is a negative integer and } n > \text{-}5.$$
$$A < 12 \text{ or } A < 65.$$
$$x = 9 \text{ or } x = \text{-}3.$$

The solution set for a compound sentence using *and* is the *intersection* of the solution sets to the individual sentences. Recall that the **intersection** of two sets is the set consisting of those values common to both sets. The graph of the intersection consists of the points common to the graphs of the individual sets.

❸ ### Example 1

On page 271, the post-office regulations for post cards are given. Among these are that a post card must be "at least 0.007 inches thick, no more than 0.25 inches thick." Graph all possible thicknesses for a post card.

Solution

Translate each regulation into an inequality. We let T be the thickness. The first regulation is that $T \geq 0.007$. Here is its graph.

The second regulation is that $T \leq 0.25$. Here is its graph, on the same scale.

The intersection of these two graphs is the graph of allowable thicknesses.

The intersection can be described as an *and* statement, such as "$T \geq 0.007$ and $T \leq 0.25$," or by the single compound sentence $0.007 \leq T \leq 0.25$.

... **wish you were here.**
These leather post cards were mailed in the early 1900s. Cards like these could be mailed today because their dimensions are within the postal regulations.

Recall that the symbol used for intersection is $\cap$. So the intersection of sets A and B is written $A \cap B$. In set notation,

$$\{x: 0.007 \leq x \leq 0.25\} = \{x: x \geq 0.007\} \cap \{x: x \leq 0.25\}.$$

This can be read "the set of numbers from 0.007 to 0.25 equals the intersection of the set of numbers greater than or equal to 0.007 and the set of numbers less than or equal to 0.25."

❶ The distinction between the open circle and the shaded circle seems to bother some students as they graph equations and inequalities. Stress that any time a sentence is being graphed, only those points belonging to the solution set are to be graphed or shaded. The open circle is an efficient way to mark an endpoint of a ray or a segment that is not included in the solution set.

❷ The distinctions between the terms *or* and *and*, and the terms *union* and *intersection* are key concepts in this lesson. To help students understand the difference between union and intersection, suggest that they think of a labor union as wanting as many members as possible and think of a street intersection containing only those points that are on both crossing streets. Also point out that the symbol ∪ looks like a U for union.

Sometimes students are not sure whether a sentence should be graphed on a number line or on a coordinate plane. Point out that when a sentence is expressed in set notation, the variables preceding the colon indicate the dimensions of the solution. For example, the letter s in $\{s: 45 \leq s \leq 55\}$ indicates one dimension and the ordered pair (x, y) in $\{(x, y): x \geq 3\}$ indicates two dimensions.

❸ **Social Studies Connection**
There is a distinction between postal cards (pre-stamped cards issued by the government) and post cards (cards produced privately and requiring stamps). The first postal card was issued on May 1, 1873. It was called a "penny post card" because it cost one cent, including the postage. Except for a two-year period during World War I, the cost of postal cards remained one cent until 1952, when the cost rose to two cents. In 1995, postal-card rates rose to 20 cents.

when they compare and contrast solutions to compound sentences using the words *and* and *or*. Similarly, they must be careful when using set notation and the symbols ∪ and ∩ for union and intersection.

Video

Wide World of Mathematics
The segment, *Saving Ste. Genevieve,* features a town and its struggle as it fights a flood battle against a threatening Mississippi River. The segment provides an excellent tool for introducing a lesson on inequalities. Related questions and an investigation are provided in videodisc stills and in the Video Guide. A related CD-ROM activity is also available.

Videodisc Bar Codes

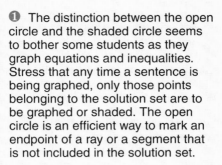

Search Chapter 24

Play

The Americans with Disabilities Act of 1990 requires mass transportation systems to be accessible to people with disabilities.

When describing an interval in words, it is sometimes difficult to know if the endpoints are included. In this book, we use the following language:

"x is from 3 to 4"	means	$3 \le x \le 4$.	The endpoints are included.
"x is between 3 and 4"	means	$3 < x < 4$.	The endpoints are not included.

This is consistent with the use of the word "between" in geometry. When just one endpoint is included, as in "$3 \le x < 4$," you can say "x is 3 or between 3 and 4."

Compound Sentences Using the Word *or*

The solution set for a compound sentence using *or* is the *union* of the solution sets to the individual sentences. Recall that the **union** of two sets is the set consisting of those values in either *one or both* sets. This meaning of *or* is somewhat different from the everyday meaning of *either, but not both*. The symbol often used for union is ∪. The union of sets A and B is written $A \cup B$.

Example 2

People who are either younger than 12 or older than 65 do not pay full fare on a bus.
a. Write this information as a compound inequality.
b. Graph the solution set on a number line.

Solution
a. Let A = the age of the passenger. Then the set of ages A which do not pay full fare on buses is {A: A < 12 or A > 65}.
b. The graph is the union of the graphs of the individual parts.

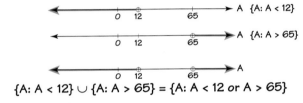

$$\{A: A < 12\} \cup \{A: A > 65\} = \{A: A < 12 \text{ or } A > 65\}$$

Solving Inequalities

The properties of inequality ensure that solving an inequality is very much like solving an equation.

Properties of Inequality
For all real numbers a, b, and c:
If $a < b$, then $a + c < b + c$.   **Addition Property of Inequality**
If $a < b$ and $c > 0$, then $ac < bc$.   **Multiplication Properties of**
If $a < b$ and $c < 0$, then $ac > bc$.   **Inequality**

274

---

④ **Example 3**

Solve $2m + 57 > 113$ and graph the solution set.

Solution

$$2m + 57 > 113$$
$$2m > 56 \qquad \text{Add } -57 \text{ to each side.}$$
$$m > 28 \qquad \text{Multiply each side by } \tfrac{1}{2}.$$

The set of solutions is $\{m: m > 28\}$. The graph of the solution set is a ray without its endpoint.

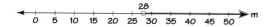

Check

First check the endpoint. Substitute 28 for m in the original sentence. The two sides should be equal. Does $2 \cdot 28 + 57 = 113$? Yes.

Now check the direction of the inequality. Pick a value of m in the solution set. We pick $m = 40$. Is $2 \cdot 40 + 57 > 113$? Yes.

Notice that there are two Multiplication Properties of Inequality. Solving inequalities is different from solving equations only when you multiply or divide each side of an inequality by a negative number. Then you must *reverse* the inequality sign.

There are many applications for inequalities. The words "or less" are clue words for setting up the inequality in Example 4.

Example 4

A ticket agency has 275 tickets to a playoff game. Each caller receives 2 tickets. When there are 50 tickets or less remaining, the agency tries to obtain more tickets. How many callers can be served before more tickets are needed?

Solution

Let $c =$ the number of callers that can be served. Then, after c callers, there will be $275 - 2c$ tickets left. The ticket agency needs to obtain more tickets when c satisfies $275 - 2c \le 50$.

$$275 - 2c \le 50$$
$$-2c \le -225 \qquad \text{Subtract 275 from both sides.}$$
$$\frac{-2c}{-2} \ge \frac{-225}{-2} \qquad \text{Divide each side by } -2, \text{ so reverse the inequality.}$$
$$c \ge 112.5$$

The agency can serve 112 callers before the agency needs to obtain more tickets.

7. $x > 8$ or $x < 4$ [All numbers less than 4 or greater than 8]
8. $x < 8$ or $x > 4$ [All numbers]

Additional Examples

1. As of 1994, recorded temperatures in the state of Michigan have ranged from a low of $-51°F$ in Vanderbilt (1934) to a high of $112°$ in Mio (1936). Graph the range of recorded temperatures T.

2. People from age 16 to 65 can give blood at a Blood Bank.
   a. Write a compound inequality to describe the possible ages A at which blood can be given. $16 \le A \le 65$
   b. Graph the inequality on a number line.

3. Solve $3x - 4 \le 26$ and graph the solution set. $x \le 10$

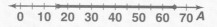

4. An airplane flying at 34,000 feet descends at the rate of 2500 feet per minute. After how many minutes will the plane be below 20,000 feet?
   $34,000 - 2500m < 20,000$; $m > 5.6$. After 5.6 minutes, the plane will be below 20,000 feet.

5. Graph $\{x: x < 3 \text{ or } x \ge \pi\}$

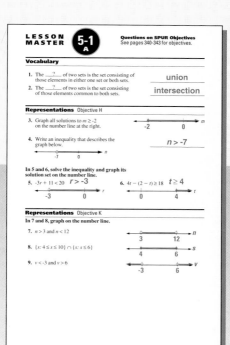

Follow-up 5-1
for Lesson

Practice

For more questions on SPUR Objectives, use **Lesson Master 5-1A** (shown on page 275) or **Lesson Master 5-1B** (shown on pages 276–277).

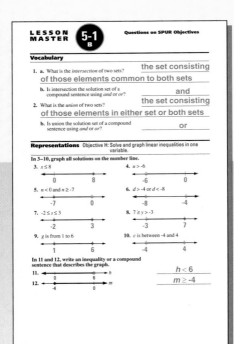

Covering the Reading

In 1 and 2, could a rectangular-shaped piece of mail with the given dimensions have been mailed for 20¢ in 1995?

1. $\frac{1}{10}''$ thick, $4''$ high, and $5''$ long   Yes

2. $\frac{1}{3}''$ thick, $3''$ high, and $5\frac{1}{2}''$ long   No

3. *Multiple choice.* Which inequality is the sentence "x is greater than or equal to 5"?   d
   (a) $x \le 5$ (b) $5 < x$ (c) $5 > x$ (d) $x \ge 5$

4. Write an inequality for the set of numbers graphed below. $r < 15$

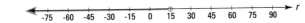

5. The solution set to a compound sentence using *and* is the __?__ of the solution sets to the individual sentences.   intersection

6. The solution set to a compound sentence using *or* is the __?__ of the solution sets to the individual sentences.   union

7. On a number line, graph the solution set to the sentence $n \ge 2.95$ and $n \le 3.005$.   See left.

In 8 and 9, graph the solution set on a number line.   See left.

8. **a.** $x \le -7$ or $x > -2$ **b.** $x \le -7$ and $x > -2$

9. **a.** $x \ge -7$ or $x < -2$ **b.** $x \ge -7$ and $x < -2$

10. Match each set at the left with its graph at the right.
    a. $\{x: x > 1 \text{ and } x < 4\}$ ii   (i)
    b. $\{x: x > 1 \text{ or } x < 4\}$ iv   (ii)
    c. $\{x: x < 1 \text{ or } x > 4\}$ i   (iii)
    d. $\{x: x < 1 \text{ and } x > 4\}$ v   (iv)
                                              (v)

In 11 and 12, solve and graph all solutions.   See left for graphs.

11. $2m < 1.4$ $m < 0.7$

12. $-4n - 5 > 1$ $n < \frac{-3}{2}$

13. Suppose the ticket agency of Example 4 had 300 tickets and sells 4 tickets to each customer. If more tickets are ordered when the supply falls below 75, how many customers can be served?   **56 customers**

276

7)

8a)

b)

9a)

b)

11)

12)

14. When you multiply or divide both sides of an inequality by a negative number, you must __?__ the inequality sign. **reverse**

15. To check that $b \geq 9$ is the simplest sentence equivalent to $5 - \frac{b}{3} \leq 2$, what two values might you pick for b? Why must you pick two values? **Pick $b = 9$ and $b = 10$ (or any number > 9). You select 2 numbers to check both the equality and the inequality.**

Applying the Mathematics

16b)

17a)

20)

16. Louise wants to buy a car. She will spend more than $8000 but less than $11,000 on a new car, or she will buy a good used car for no more than $5000. Let c represent the cost of the car she will buy.
   a. Write a sentence using set notation describing the amount she may spend. **{c: $8000 < c < 11{,}000$} ∪ {c: $0 < c \leq 5000$}**
   b. Graph the possible values of c on a number line. **See left.**

17. Some parts of interstate highways have a maximum speed limit of 55 mph, while the minimum speed is 45 mph.
   a. Graph the possible legal speeds on a number line. **See left.**
   b. Write the set of possible legal speeds in set notation. **{x: $45 \leq x \leq 55$}**

18. A truck weighs 5000 kg when empty. It is used for carrying sacks of pistachio nuts, each sack weighing 50 kg.
   a. Write a sentence for the total weight T of the truck loaded with s sacks of pistachios. **$T = 5000 + 50s$**
   b. How many sacks of pistachios can the truck carry over a bridge with a weight limit of 8000 kg? (Hint: T must be less than or equal to the weight limit.) **60 sacks or fewer**

19. Will solved $x^2 = 4$ and wrote "$x = 2$ *and* $x = -2$." What is wrong with Will's answer? **He should use "or" instead of "and" since "$x = 2$ and $x = -2$" has no solutions.**

20. Solve $4x - 3 \leq 5$ and $8 - 2x < 9$. Then graph the solution set. **$x < 2$ and $x > -\frac{1}{2} = \{x: -\frac{1}{2} < x < 2\}$; See left for graph.**

21. Cheap Rentals rents cars at $10 per day plus 12¢ per mile. Ruby needs a car for four days. How many miles can she drive if the total cost of renting the car is not to exceed $100? **no more than 500 miles**

22. Most programming languages for computers and calculators use the words *and* and *or*. Use either of the programs below.

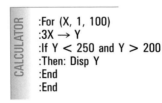

```
BASIC
10 FOR X = 1 TO 100
20 LET Y = 3*X
30 IF Y < 250 AND Y > 200
      THEN PRINT Y
40 NEXT X
50 END
```

```
CALCULATOR
:For (X, 1, 100)
:3X → Y
:If Y < 250 and Y > 200
:Then: Disp Y
:End
:End
```

   a. What numbers will be displayed when these programs are run? **201, 204, 207, 210, . . . 249**
   b. What numbers will be displayed if the word AND in the programs is changed to OR? **3, 6, 9, 12, . . . 300**

Nutty information. *The pistachio nut is the small seed of the pistachio tree. The tree grows in the eastern Mediterranean, southwest Asia, and the southwestern U.S. Often the shells of pistachio nuts are dyed red.*

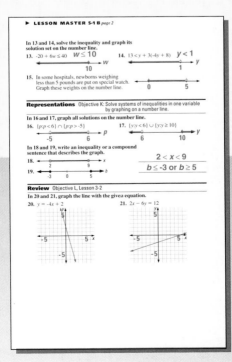

Notes on Questions

Question 23 Use this question to introduce the next lesson. Emphasize that the point of intersection of the two lines is the solution to this system.

Question 24 Ask if any student began by dividing both sides of the equation by 4 to simplify it.

Question 26 Students will need a health book or an almanac to find normal weight-ranges for humans.

Question 27 History Connection
Because Patrick Henry was convinced that war with Great Britain was inevitable, his speech to the Virginia Provincial Convention proposed resolutions that would equip the Virginia militia to fight against the British. He ended with the now-famous words, "I know not what course others may take, but as for me, give me liberty or give me death." The resolutions were granted and Henry commanded the Virginia forces until he became the state's governor in 1776.

Review

23. Write equations for the two lines graphed below. *(Lessons 3-5, 3-6)*
 a) $y = x + 250$
 b) $y = -50$

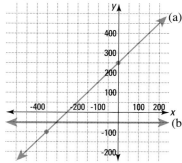

24. Graph the line with equation $8x - 4y = 16$. *(Lessons 3-2, 3-4)*
 See left.

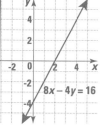

$8x - 4y = 16$

25. If y varies inversely as x^3, how is the value of y changed if x is
 a. quadrupled?
 y is divided by 64
 b. halved? *(Lesson 2-3)*
 y is multiplied by 8

Exploration

26. Normal weights are often given in a table as a range of values depending on height. Find such a table in a health book or almanac. Graph the interval of normal weights for your height.
 Answers may vary.

27. In ordinary usage, replacing *or* by *and* can dramatically change the meaning of a sentence. For instance, "Give me liberty and give me death" differs from Patrick Henry's famous saying by only that one word. Find examples of other sayings whose meanings are changed by replacing "and" with "or," or vice versa.
 Samples: To be and not to be, that is the question.;   truth and consequences;   a government of the people, by the people, or for the people

Outspoken. *This drawing depicts Patrick Henry (1736–1799) who was an American Revolutionary patriot, orator, and statesman. His famous "Give me liberty" speech was given in 1775 before the Virginia Provincial Convention. In 1776 he was elected as the first governor of Virginia.*

278

Setting Up Lesson 5-2

Questions 23 and 24 provide review for the next lesson. They can be used as a lead-in for Lesson 5-2.

LESSON 5-2

Solving Systems Using Tables or Graphs

Remember that a **system** is a set of conditions joined by the word *and*. It is a special kind of compound sentence. A system is often denoted by a brace. Thus, the compound sentence

$$y = 7x - 3 \text{ and } y = 6x + 2$$

can be written as the system $\begin{cases} y = 7x - 3 \\ y = 6x + 2. \end{cases}$

Systems with one or two variables can be represented algebraically (as shown above), graphically, or in a table.

The **solution set for a system** is the intersection of the solution sets for the individual sentences. When the system involves two equations each with two variables, the solution can often be found by making a table of values or a graph.

Finding Solutions with Tables or Graphs

Example 1

Solve the system $\begin{cases} y = 7x - 3 \\ y = 6x + 2. \end{cases}$

Solution 1

Make a table of values for each sentence.

x	y = 7x − 3	x	y = 6x + 2
0	-3	0	2
1	4	1	8
2	11	2	14
3	18	3	20
4	25	4	26
5	32	5	32

The pair of values $x = 5$ and $y = 32$ is in both tables. So $x = 5$, $y = 32$ is a solution to the system. However, we do not know if this is the only solution.

▶

Lesson 5-2

Objectives

D Recognize properties of systems of equations.

I Estimate solutions to systems by graphing.

Resources

From the Teacher's Resource File

- Lesson Master 5-2A or 5-2B
- Answer Master 5-2
- Teaching Aids
  8 Four-Quadrant Graph Paper
  19 Automatic Grapher Grids
  43 Warm-up
- Activity Kit, Activity 9

Additional Resources

- Visuals for Teaching Aids 8, 19, 43
- GraphExplorer

Teaching Lesson 5-2

Warm-up

Graph each equation.

1. $y = 3x - 5$
2. $y = 2x^2$
3. $xy = 4$

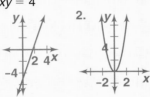

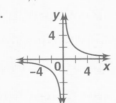

Lesson 5-2 Overview

Broad Goals This lesson discusses how to solve systems of equations with tables and graphs. Examples include linear systems and systems where one equation is not linear.

Perspective In contrast to Lesson 5-1, this lesson focuses only on *systems*, that is, compound sentences using the word *and*. The lesson reviews the idea that the solution to a system is represented by the point(s) of intersection of the graphs of the equations.

In the past, graphing was not the most reliable method for solving a system because it was so difficult to draw an accurate graph. At that time, graphing was used to determine the number of solutions; it was not used to get close to the actual solutions. Automatic graphers have increased the efficiency of graphing.

Technology has also increased the importance of using tables and finding successive approximations to solve systems. The ability of computers to iterate quickly makes these methods practical; they are commonly used in the solution of large systems.

Students who used UCSMP *Algebra* and *Geometry* have already studied linear systems twice. Thus, the content of this lesson and the next two lessons should be review.

279

Teaching Aid 8 or graph paper and Teaching Aid 19 can be used throughout this lesson.

The purpose of the table and graph in **Example 1** is to demonstrate in two concrete ways what solving a system of equations means—that the ordered pair (5, 32) satisfies both equations.

❶ **Example 2** extends the idea of the graphical solution of a system to curves and shows the power of systems. Emphasize how the automatic grapher zooms in on the solution. Point out that the graph of $y_2 = \frac{500}{x}$ is not linear but that it looks like a line because we are seeing so little of it.

❷ It is ironic that we usually find the *intersection* of two or more curves by first graphing their *union*.

Additional Examples

1. Solve the system $\begin{cases} y = 4x + 8 \\ y = 3x + 5. \end{cases}$

   (–3, –4)
2. Fred wants to enclose a 400-square-meter rectangular garden with 70 meters of fencing. To do this, Fred must use one side of his barn as a side of the garden. What can the dimensions of the garden be?

   Let *W* be the dimension along the barn and let *S* be the other dimension: $W + 2S = 70$ and $WS = 400$. The graph shows solutions (*W*, *S*) are near (14, 28) and (56, 7). Closer solutions are (14.4, 27.8) and (55.6, 7.2).

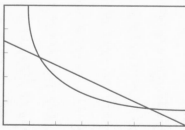

$0 \leq x \leq 70$ *x*-scale = 10
$0 \leq y \leq 50$ *y*-scale = 10

▶ **Solution 2**

Graph the system $\begin{cases} y = 7x - 3 \\ y = 6x + 2 \end{cases}$ by hand.

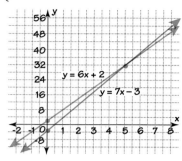

The solution to the system consists of all points of intersection of the two lines. The two lines intersect in only one point, so there is only one solution. The lines seem to intersect when x = 5 and y = 32.

Check

Substitute the point (5, 32) into both sentences.
Is 32 = 7 · 5 − 3? Yes.
Is 32 = 6 · 5 + 2? Yes. This tells us that the solution is exact.
The single solution is the point (5, 32).

Solutions to systems of equations can be described in three ways. For example, the solution to the system of Example 1 could be expressed in any of the following ways.

1. listing the solution: (5, 32)
2. writing the solution set: {(5, 32)}
3. writing a simplified equivalent system: $\begin{cases} x = 5 \\ y = 32 \end{cases}$

Using an Automatic Grapher to Estimate Solutions

Graphing a system can quickly indicate the number of solutions, but if the solutions are not integers, graphing may not give an exact answer. As Example 2 shows, using an automatic grapher gives more precise approximations.

❶ **Example 2**

A family owns land on a straight stretch of the Oldman River. They plan to fence in a rectangular piece of land along the river. They have 80 meters of fencing material, and want to enclose an area of 500 square meters. What can the dimensions of this region be?

Optional Activities

Activity 1
You may use *Activity Kit, Activity 9* before or after covering the lesson. In this activity, students do an experiment to provide a concrete example of systems.

Activity 2
You can use this activity after you have discussed the lesson. Have students **work in groups.** Tell each group to write a system of equations for each solution.

1. (0, 0) [Sample: $y = 5x$, $y = 6x$]
2. (–3, 5) [Sample: $y = x + 8$, $y = 2x + 11$]
3. No solution [Any two equations for parallel lines such as: $y = x + 2$, $y = x + 4$]
4. Infinitely many solutions [Any two equations for the same line such as $y = x + 2$, $2y = 2x + 4$]

Solution

Draw a picture. Let W and S be the width and sides of the rectangle.

The length of the fence is one width plus two sides. So, W + 2S = 80. Since the area is 500 m², WS = 500. The system is

$$\begin{cases} W + 2S = 80 \\ \quad WS = 500. \end{cases}$$

To graph, solve each equation for *W*.

$$\begin{cases} W = 80 - 2S \\ W = \dfrac{500}{S} \end{cases}$$

On an automatic grapher, if we let *S* be the independent variable, these equations become $y_1 = 80 - 2x$ and $y_2 = \dfrac{500}{x}$. Since *W* and *S* represent lengths, they must be positive. Therefore, it is not necessary to draw the third-quadrant branch of the hyperbola.

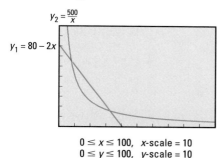

$y_2 = \dfrac{500}{x}$

$y_1 = 80 - 2x$

$0 \le x \le 100, \quad x\text{-scale} = 10$
$0 \le y \le 100, \quad y\text{-scale} = 10$

❷ The graphs intersect at two points, so there are two solutions. Tracing and rounding to the nearest integer gives intersections near (8, 65) and near (32, 15). The family can make the width about 65 m and the other two sides about 8 m, or they can make the width about 15 m and the other two sides 32 m.

Check

Substitute *S* = 8 and *W* = 65 into both sentences.

$$65 + 2 \cdot 8 = 81 \approx 80$$
$$65 \cdot 8 = 520 \approx 500$$

The check shows that (8, 65) is an approximate solution. The check of (32, 15) is left to you in the Questions. The solution set has two ordered pairs, and is approximately {(8, 65), (32, 15)}.

Lesson 5-2 *Solving Systems Using Tables or Graphs* **281**

3a. Solve the system $\begin{cases} y = 5x \\ y = -3x + 1 \end{cases}$ by making a table to estimate the solution. Sample table:

x	y = 5x	x	y = -3x + 1
-2	-10	-2	7
-1	-5	-1	4
0	0	0	1
1	5	1	-2
0.1	0.5	0.1	0.7
0.5	2.5	0.5	-0.5
0.2	1	0.2	0.4

The first four entries indicate that a solution has a value of *x* between 0 and 1. The next two entries indicate that a solution has a value of *x* between 0.1 and 0.5. The final entry suggests that a solution has a value of *x* between 0.1 and 0.2 and a value of *y* between 0.4 and 0.7. The actual solution is *x* = 0.125 and *y* = 0.625.

b. Graph the system. The lines seem to intersect at *x* ≈ 0.12 and *y* ≈ 0.62.

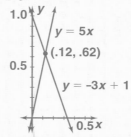

$y = 5x$

(.12, .62)

$y = -3x + 1$

(Additional Examples continue on page 282.)

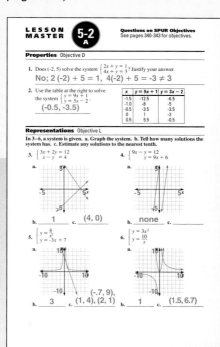

Adapting to Individual Needs

Extra Help

In **Example 2,** students may need a reminder that WS = 500 is an equation of inverse variation and its graph is a hyperbola. However, we graph only one branch of the hyperbola in this case since both W and S must be positive. Point out, however, that some systems might involve hyperbolas in which both branches are used.

English Language Development

To illustrate what it means to *zoom* in on a point on a graph, you might use the zoom feature on a computer or on a camera. Show how the zoom, in each case, enlarges a certain portion of a picture so that the details can be seen more clearly.

4. Use an automatic grapher to solve the system $\begin{cases} y = 3x \\ y = \dfrac{3}{x} \end{cases}$.

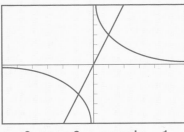

$-6 \le x \le 6 \qquad x\text{-scale} = 1$
$-6 \le y \le 6 \qquad y\text{-scale} = 1$

$(x, y) = (1, 3)$ or $(x, y) = (-1, -3)$

Notes on Questions

Questions 10–12 Point out that exact solutions can be read directly from a graph in some cases, but in many cases solutions read from a graph are just approximations.

Question 15 Make a chart that shows distances from the starting point after each second.

Seconds	Father's distance	Daughter's distance
0	0	40
1	9	45
2	18	50
⋮	⋮	⋮

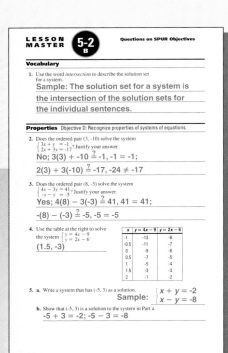

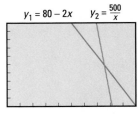

$y_1 = 80 - 2x \qquad y_2 = \dfrac{500}{x}$

$7 \le x \le 8, \qquad x\text{-scale} = .1$
$64 \le y \le 65, \qquad y\text{-scale} = .1$

On an automatic grapher, you can estimate the solution of a system to a high degree of accuracy by *rescaling* or *zooming* in on each point of intersection. With a different window, our automatic grapher shows that a more accurate solution to the system in Example 2 is $S \approx 7.8$ and $W \approx 64.5$.

$$64.5 + 2(7.8) = 80.1 \approx 80$$
$$64.5 \cdot 7.8 = 503.1 \approx 500$$

To get a solution accurate to the nearest hundredth, you can zoom or rescale again.

QUESTIONS

Covering the Reading

1. *Multiple choice.* The solution to a system is **b**
   (a) the union of the solution sets of the individual sentences.
   (b) the intersection of the solution sets of the individual sentences.
   (c) all points satisfying at least one of the individual sentences.

In 2 and 3, consider the system $\begin{cases} y = 3x + 2 \\ y = 20. \end{cases}$

2. *Multiple choice.* The system means **a**
   (a) $y = 3x + 2$ and $y = 20$.
   (b) $y = 3x + 2$ or $y = 20$.

3. **a.** The solution to the system is __?__. (6, 20)
   b. Verify that the ordered pair you found in part a is the solution.
   $20 = 3 \cdot 6 + 2$; $20 = 20$; (6, 20) satisfies both equations.

4. Find a solution to the system $\begin{cases} y = 3x + 6 \\ y = -2x + 16 \end{cases}$ by making a table for each equation for integer values of x from 0 to 5. (2, 12);
   See left for table.

x	y = 3x + 6	y = -2x + 16
0	6	16
1	9	14
2	12	12
3	15	10
4	18	8
5	21	6

5. Solve the system $\begin{cases} y = \frac{1}{2}x - 5 \\ y = 2x - 1 \end{cases}$ by making a graph.
   $\left(\dfrac{-8}{3}, \dfrac{-19}{3}\right) \approx (-2.7, -6.3)$; See left for graph.

In 6–8, refer to Example 2.

6. *Multiple choice.* $WS = 500$ represents a relationship involving **b**
   (a) perimeter.   (b) area.   (c) volume.

7. Why do you not need to draw the third-quadrant branch of the hyperbola? **See margin.**

8. **a.** Show that (32, 15) is an approximate solution to the system.
   b. Show that (32.25, 15.51) is a closer approximate solution to the system than (32, 15) is. **See margin.**

9. Describe one advantage and one disadvantage of graphing to find a solution to a system. **Sample: advantage: easy to see number of solutions; disadvantage: may not give an exact answer**

Adapting to Individual Needs

Challenge
Consumer Connection In business the break-even point occurs when the cost of running a business equals the revenue generated by the business. Have students find the break-even point for Questions 1 and 2 at the right. Students can graph the cost and revenue equations on an automatic grapher and use the trace key to find the break-even point. In both questions, x stands for the number of units produced

and sold and y stands for dollars. Students who have a TI-82 can use the "Intersect" key under the "CALC" menu to find the point of intersection.

1. Cost: $y = 79.50x + 2395$
   Revenue: $y = 105.75x$ [91 units; $9,623]
2. Cost: $y = 2000x + 17000$
   Revenue: $y = 2300x$ [56 units, $128,800]
3. Why need you use only the first quadrant for these graphs? [The units produced and dollar amounts cannot be negative.]

11b) $(2, 1)$, $\left(-\frac{1}{2}, -4\right)$
 c) Check $(2, 1)$: Is
    $2 \cdot 1 = 2$? Yes. Is
    $2 \cdot 2 - 1 = 3$? Yes.
    Check $\left(-\frac{1}{2}, -4\right)$: Is
    $\left(-\frac{1}{2}\right) \cdot (-4) = 2$? Yes. Is
    $2 \cdot \left(-\frac{1}{2}\right) - (-4) = 3$?
    Yes.

12b) $(2, 4)$
 c) Check $(2, 4)$: Is
    $4 = 2^2$? Yes. Is
    $2 \cdot 4 = 8$? Yes.

In 10–12, use the given systems and their graphs.
 a. Tell how many solutions the system has.
 b. Estimate the solutions, if there are any. **See left.**
 c. Verify that your solutions satisfy all equations of the system.
    See left.

10. $\begin{cases} y = x^2 \\ y = x - 5 \end{cases}$
    a) zero solutions

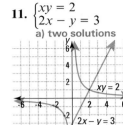

11. $\begin{cases} xy = 2 \\ 2x - y = 3 \end{cases}$
    a) two solutions

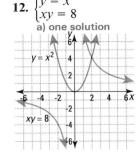

12. $\begin{cases} y = x^2 \\ xy = 8 \end{cases}$
    a) one solution

In 13 and 14 a system is given. **a.** Graph each system. **b.** Tell how many solutions the system has. **c.** Estimate any solutions to the nearest tenth.
a) See margin.

13. $\begin{cases} y = \frac{1}{2}x^2 \\ x + y = 5 \end{cases}$
    b) 2 solutions
    c) $(-4.3, 9.3)$
       $(2.3, 2.7)$

14. $\begin{cases} y = \frac{3}{x^2} \\ y = x + 4 \end{cases}$
    b) 3 solutions
    c) $(-3.8, .2)$,
       $(-1, 3)$, $(.8, 4.8)$

15. The system $\begin{cases} y = 5x + 40 \\ y = 9x \end{cases}$ could represent the following situation:

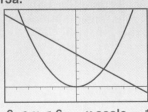

A child challenged her father to a race. The father gave her a head start of 40 m. He ran at 9 meters per second. She ran at 5 meters per second. Let y be distance and x be time in seconds, after the father started.
 a. What equation represents the father's distance from the start after x seconds? **$y = 9x$**
 b. After 1 second, how far was the father from the start? How far was the daughter? **father: 9 m;   daughter: 45 m**
 c. When did the father catch up to his daughter? **10 seconds after he started**
 d. When the father caught up to her, how far from the start were they? **90 m from the start**

16. Use a graph to show that there is no pair of real numbers x and y whose product is 30 and whose sum is 10. **See margin.**

17. Graphing can be the first step in helping to solve more complicated systems by search procedures. Consider the system below.

$$\begin{cases} y = 3x^2 \\ y = 4x + 10 \end{cases}$$

A rough graph shows a solution between $x = -2$ and $x = 0$.
 a. Generate a table or use the zoom features of your automatic grapher to approximate this solution to two decimal places.
 b. The other solution is between $x = 2$ and $x = 3$. Find this solution, correct to two decimal places. **(2.61, 20.44)**
    a) $(-1.28, 4.89)$

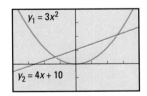

$y_1 = 3x^2$
$y_2 = 4x + 10$

$-4 \le x \le 4$, x-scale $= 1$
$-20 \le y \le 40$, y-scale $= 10$

Lesson 5-2 *Solving Systems Using Tables or Graphs* **283**

Notes on Questions
Question 17 This question shows the need for graphs drawn by hand and graphs generated by automatic graphers. Point out that each method complements the other. The automatic grapher gives a more accurate solution. However, hand graphing initially helps to "zero in" on the solution set and allows us to shorten computer running time.

Additional Answers
7.   *W* and *S* must be positive because they represent length. Any point in the third quadrant would represent negative values for *W* and *S*.
8a. Substitute $(32, 15)$ into both sentences: $15 + 2 \cdot 32 = 79 \approx 80$; $15 \cdot 32 = 480 \approx 500$
 b. $15.51 + 2(32.25) = 80.01 \approx 80$; 80.01 is closer to 80 than 79. $15.51(32.25) = 500.1975 \approx 500$; 500.1975 is closer to 500 than 480.

► **LESSON MASTER 5-2 B** *page 2*

Representations Objective I: Estimate solutions to systems by graphing.
In 6–9, a system is given. a. Graph the system.
b. Tell how many solutions the system has.
c. Estimate any solutions to the nearest tenth.

6. $\begin{cases} 2x + 4y = 6 \\ x + y = -1 \end{cases}$

7. $\begin{cases} 8x - 4y = 12 \\ y = 2x + 3 \end{cases}$

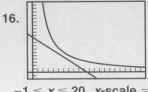

b. **1 solution**

c. **$(-5, 4)$**

b. **no solutions**

c.

8. $\begin{cases} y = \frac{4}{x} \\ y = x \end{cases}$

9. $\begin{cases} y = \frac{2}{x} \\ y = x^2 \end{cases}$

b. **2 solutions**

c. **$(2, 2), (-2, -2)$**

b. **1 solution**

c. **$(1.3, 1.6)$**

Additional Answers, continued
13a.

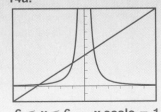

$-6 \le x \le 6$, x-scale $= 1$
$-2 \le y \le 10$, y-scale $= 1$

14a.

$-6 \le x \le 6$, x-scale $= 1$
$-2 \le y \le 10$, y-scale $= 1$

16.

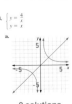

$-1 \le x \le 20$, x-scale $= 1$
$-1 \le y \le 20$, y-scale $= 1$

The graphs do not intersect, so there is no pair of real numbers which satisfy these constraints.

283

Notes on Questions

Question 21 Multicultural Connection Tanzania has about 120 identifiable ethnic groups. The largest group, the Sukuma, constitutes almost 13 percent of the population. Europeans, Asians, and Arabs comprise only about 1 percent of the population. A majority of the people speak Swahili, the official language of the country.

Follow-up for Lesson 5-2

Practice

For more questions on SPUR Objectives, use **Lesson Master 5-2A** (shown on page 281) or **Lesson Master 5-2B** (shown on pages 282–283).

Assessment

Oral/Written Communication
Have each student write a paragraph that explains how an automatic grapher can be helpful when solving a system of equations. Then have students share their responses with the class. [Students demonstrate that they understand (1) the concept of solving a system of two linear equations by graphing and (2) that an automatic grapher can provide more precise approximations of the solution to some systems of equations.]

Extension

Ask students to determine how many solutions are possible for each system described below.
1. Both equations are linear.
   [0, 1, or infinitely many]
2. One equation is linear and the other is quadratic. [0, 1, or 2]
3. Both equations are quadratic.
   [0, 1, 2, or infinitely many]

Project Update Project 3, *Systems Involving a Hyperbola and a Line*, on page 336, relates to the content of this lesson.

---

18)

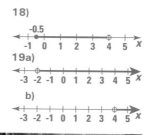

19a)

b)

Shown are school children in Tanzania, a country in Africa with a population of about 31 million.

21b) $S_n = \frac{n(n+1)}{2}$ or
$\begin{cases} t_1 = 1 \\ t_n = t_{n-1} + n, \text{ for integers} \\ \qquad\qquad\qquad n \geq 2 \end{cases}$

22) $h = \frac{T - 2\pi r^2}{2\pi r}$

23a) Yes; all squares are similar. Similar figures with equal areas must be congruent.

b) No; a counter example is a right triangle with length 3 in. and height 4 in. and a right triangle with length 2 in. and height 6 in. Both have area of 6 in². but they are not congruent.

284

Review

18. Graph $\{x: -0.5 \leq x < 4\}$ on a number line. *(Lesson 5-1)* See left.

19. a. Graph $\{x: x > 4 \text{ or } x > -2\}$.
b. Graph $\{x: x > 4 \text{ and } x > -2\}$. *(Lesson 5-1)* See left.

20. Given $a_n = 3 - 5n$, find all n for which $a_n \leq -102$.
(Lessons 1-7, 3-8, 5-1) whole numbers greater than or equal to 21

21. Children in northeastern Tanzania sometimes play a game called *tarumbeta* involving stones or beans arranged in rows like those shown below. Each row has one more stone than the row above it. Older children play the game using more stones.

a. How many stones are needed to form a tarumbeta game with 9 rows? 45
b. Find a formula, either explicit or recursive, for the number S_n of stones in a game with n rows. *(Lessons 1-7, 1-9, 3-8)* See left.

22. An equation relating the total surface area T of a cylinder with height h and radius r is $T = 2\pi r^2 + 2\pi rh$. Solve this equation for h. *(Lesson 1-6)* See left.

23. Suppose two figures of the indicated type have equal area. Must they be congruent? Explain your reasoning. *(Previous course)* See left.
a. squares
b. triangles

24. Solve $x^2 = 121$. *(Previous course)*
$x = 11$ or $x = -11$

Exploration

25. Consider both branches of the hyperbola with equation $y = \frac{1}{x}$. Is there a line that intersects this hyperbola in exactly one point? If there is, give an equation for one such line. If not, explain why not.
Yes; Samples: $y = -x + 2$, $y = 1$, or $x = 1$

Setting Up Lesson 5-3

Materials If you use Activity 1 in the *Optional Activities* in Lesson 5-3, students will need cookbooks.

Making tables and graphing enables you to find solutions to systems, but sometimes these methods do not give exact solutions. To find exact solutions, you usually need to use algebraic techniques. The next several lessons discuss algebraic techniques for solving systems of equations.

The first technique uses the Substitution Property of Equality, which states that if $a = b$, then a may be substituted for b in any arithmetic or algebraic expression. So, if $y = 2 - 10x$, for example, you can substitute $2 - 10x$ for y in any other expression. In this lesson we use the Substitution Property to solve systems with two and three equations.

Solving Systems with Two Linear Equations

❶ Example 1

Solve the system $\begin{cases} 6x + 12y = 5 \\ y = 2 - 10x. \end{cases}$

Solution

Notice that the second equation is solved for y. If you substitute $2 - 10x$ for y in the first equation, the resulting equation will have only one variable. So you can solve it for x.

$6x + 12(2 - 10x) = 5$	Substitute $(2 - 10x)$ for y.
$6x + 24 - 120x = 5$	Apply the Distributive Property.
$-114x = -19$	Add -24 to both sides and add like terms.
$x = \frac{1}{6}$	

Now substitute this value for x back into either equation to find y. We use the second equation because it is already solved for y.

$$y = 2 - 10\left(\frac{1}{6}\right)$$

$$y = 2 - \frac{10}{6}$$

$$y = \frac{2}{6} = \frac{1}{3}$$

So, the solution set is $\left\{\left(\frac{1}{6}, \frac{1}{3}\right)\right\}$.

▶

Lesson 5-3

Objectives

A Solve 2×2 and 3×3 systems using substitution.

D Recognize properties of systems of equations.

F Use systems of two or three linear equations to solve real-world problems.

Resources

From the *Teacher's Resource File*
- Lesson Master 5-3A or 5-3B
- Answer Master 5-3
- Teaching Aids
    8 Four-Quadrant Graph Paper
    19 Automatic Grapher Grids
    43 Warm-up
- Technology Sourcebook
    Computer Master 6

Additional Resources
- Visuals for Teaching Aids 8, 19, 43
- Cookbooks
- Spreadsheet software

Teaching Lesson 5-3

Warm-up

Solve each equation.
1. $8x + 8(5 - 2x) = -40$ **10**
2. $\frac{y}{4} + 3(8 - \frac{y}{2}) = 4$ **16**
3. $5z + 1 = \frac{1}{3}(3z - 5)$ $-\frac{2}{3}$

Notes on Reading

❶ This is a typical example of a linear system for which substitution is a natural choice for solving the system.

Lesson 5-3 Overview

Broad Goals This lesson reviews the substitution method for solving systems of equations and the terminology of consistent and inconsistent systems.

Perspective The use of substitution for 2×2 linear systems should be familiar to students. However, using the substitution method for solving higher-order systems will probably be new content.

Substitution is a more powerful method than the Linear-Combination Method, which will be discussed in Lesson 5-4, but the manipulation can be more complicated. To solve a system with one linear and one nonlinear equation, the substitution method is often the method of choice, as in **Example 3**.

The terms *consistent* and *inconsistent*, as used in mathematics, may be new to

students. If they are confused by a system such as the one in **Example 5**, stress that when one equation is equivalent to another, the system is always consistent.

❷ **Cooperative Learning** Discuss **Example 2** during class. Some students may not have seen a system with more than two equations, or they may not remember seeing such a system. This is an excellent illustration of a system of three equations that is easily solved by substitution.

❸ Relate the solutions of this nonlinear system to the graph of the system. Note that the graph indicates that there are two solutions. Since the graphs of the two equations do not intersect outside the window, there are only two solutions.

Students may use graph paper, **Teaching Aid 8**, or **Teaching Aid 19** throughout this lesson.

Error Alert If students have difficulty using the substitution method, you might want to see the Extra Help in *Adapting to Individual Needs* on page 287.

Additional Examples

1. Solve the system
$$\begin{cases} x + y = 6 \\ y = x + 2. \end{cases}$$
$x = 2, y = 4$

2. The Drama Club printed 1750 tickets for their spring play. They printed twice as many student tickets as adult tickets and half as many children's tickets as adult tickets. Write a system of three equations, and solve the system to find how many tickets of each type were printed. Let A = number of adult tickets, S = number of student tickets, and C = number of children's tickets.
$$\begin{cases} A + S + C = 1750 \\ S = 2A \\ C = \frac{1}{2}A \end{cases}$$
$A = 500, S = 1000, C = 250$

▶ **Check**
Substitute $\frac{1}{6}$ for x and $\frac{1}{3}$ for y in the first equation.
Does $6\left(\frac{1}{6}\right) + 12\left(\frac{1}{3}\right) = 5$? Yes, $1 + 4 = 5$.

Solving Systems with Three or More Linear Equations
Substitution can also be used when there are more than two variables and two conditions, as Example 2 illustrates.

❷ **Example 2**

Suppose a part of a stadium has a seating capacity of 4216. There are four times as many lower-level seats as there are upper-level seats. Also, there are three times as many mezzanine seats as there are upper-level seats. How many seats of each type are there?

Solution
Let L = the number of lower-level seats,
$\quad M$ = the number of mezzanine seats, and
$\quad U$ = the number of upper-level seats.

Then the system to be solved is
$$\begin{cases} L + M + U = 4216 \\ L = 4U \\ M = 3U. \end{cases}$$

Substitute the expressions for L and M given in the last two equations into the first equation.
$$4U + 3U + U = 4216$$
$$8U = 4216$$
$$U = 527$$
Substitute to find L. $\quad L = 4 \cdot 527 = 2108$
Substitute to find M. $\quad M = 3 \cdot 527 = 1581$
There are 527 upper-level seats, 2108 lower-level seats, and 1581 mezzanine seats.

Check
There are 4216 seats. $527 + 2108 + 1581 = 4216$. It checks.

Solving Nonlinear Systems
You may also use the Substitution Property of Equality with a system that has one or more nonlinear equations. Write one equation in terms of a single variable, and substitute the expression into the other equation.

❸ **Example 3**

Solve the system $\begin{cases} y = 3x \\ xy = 48. \end{cases}$ ▶

World's largest soccer stadium. *Maracaña Municipal Stadium in Rio de Janeiro, Brazil has a capacity of 205,000. In 1950, the World Cup final between Brazil and Uruguay drew a record crowd of 199,854. A dry moat, 3 meters wide and more than 1.5 meters deep, separates the players from the spectators.*

Optional Activities

✎ **Activity 1 Writing**
Materials: Cookbooks

As an extension of **Question 14** have students **work in groups** and find a recipe for which they can write a problem that can be solved using a system of equations. Have each group write the recipe and the system on a piece of paper. Then have groups exchange papers and solve the systems.

Activity 2 Technology Connection
You may want to consider using *Technology Sourcebook, Computer Master 6* with Lessons 5-3 and 5-4. Students solve systems of equations using a numerical approach.

Solution

The first equation is already solved for y, so substitute $3x$ for y in the second equation.

$$x(3x) = 48$$
$$3x^2 = 48$$
$$x^2 = 16$$
$$x = 4 \text{ or } x = -4$$

(Note the word *or*. The solution set is the union of all possible answers.) Each value of x yields a value of y. Substitute each value of x into either of the original equations. We substitute into $y = 3x$. If $x = 4$, then $y = 3(4) = 12$. If $x = -4$, then $y = 3(-4) = -12$. The solution set is $\{(4, 12), (-4, -12)\}$.

Check 1

Substitute the coordinates of each point into each equation. For $(4, 12)$, does $12 = 3 \cdot 4$? Yes. Does $4 \cdot 12 = 48$? Yes. In the Questions, you are asked to check the other point.

Check 2

Graph the equations. The graph below shows that there are two solutions. One solution seems near $(4, 12)$; the other near $(-4, -12)$.

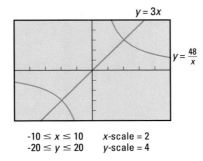

$$-10 \le x \le 10 \qquad x\text{-scale} = 2$$
$$-20 \le y \le 20 \qquad y\text{-scale} = 4$$

Examples 1 to 3 illustrate that substitution may be an appropriate method when at least one of the following applies.

1. At least one of the equations has been or can easily be solved for one of the variables.
2. There are two or more linear equations and two or more variables.
3. The system has one or more nonlinear equations.

Consistent and Inconsistent Systems

Systems are classified into two groups depending on whether or not solutions exist. A system which has *one or more solutions* is called a **consistent** system. Examples 1, 2, and 3 involve consistent systems. A system which has no solutions is called an **inconsistent** system. Example 4 illustrates an inconsistent system.

Lesson 5-3 *Solving Systems by Substitution* **287**

3. Solve the system $\begin{cases} y = 4x \\ xy = 36. \end{cases}$

    (3, 12) and (-3, -12)

In 4–5, describe the graph and the solution.

4. $\begin{cases} y = 4 - 3x \\ 3x + y = 7 \end{cases}$

    The lines are parallel; no solution

5. $\begin{cases} y = 2x^2 \\ 3y = 6x^2 \end{cases}$

    The graphs are the same; infinitely many solutions

6. Determine whether the system is consistent or inconsistent. If it is consistent, tell how many solutions the system has.

    a. $\begin{cases} y = \dfrac{12}{x^2} \\ y = 0 \end{cases}$

    b. $\begin{cases} y = 2x \\ y = \dfrac{3}{x} \end{cases}$

    c. $\begin{cases} 2x - y = -3 \\ 4x - 2y = -6 \end{cases}$

    d. $\begin{cases} x - 2y = 4 \\ 2x - 4y = 6 \end{cases}$

    (a) Inconsistent
    (b) Consistent, two solutions
    (c) Consistent, infinitely many solutions
    (d) Inconsistent

7. Solve the system
    $\begin{cases} 2x - y = -9 \\ 3x - 8y = -7. \end{cases}$
    x = -5, y = -1

(Notes on Questions begin on page 290.)

Adapting to Individual Needs

Extra Help
When using the substitution method, most students will correctly solve for one variable. However, some students will not multiply through by the variable's coefficient after the substitution is made in the second equation. In **Example 1**, for instance, when $2 - 10x$ is substituted for y in $6x + 12y = 5$, students may write the new equation incorrectly as $6x + 2 - 10x = 5$ instead of as $6x + 12(2 - 10x) = 5$.

Students may also have difficulty when the coefficient is negative or the variable is subtracted—they often make errors in signs. Remind them to work carefully.

Practice

For more questions on SPUR Objectives, use **Lesson Master 5-3A** (shown on page 289) or **Lesson Master 5-3B** (shown on pages 290–291).

Assessment

Written Communication
Have each student write a paragraph describing the difference between consistent and inconsistent systems. Then have them give an example of each kind of system. [Students demonstrate that they understand the difference between consistent and inconsistent systems.]

Example 4

Solve the system $\begin{cases} x = 3 - 2y \\ 3x + 6y = 6. \end{cases}$

Solution 1
Substitute $3 - 2y$ for x in the second equation.

$$3(3 - 2y) + 6y = 6$$
$$9 - 6y + 6y = 6 \quad \text{Use the Distributive Property.}$$
$$9 = 6 \quad \text{Add like terms.}$$

What's going on here? We came up with a statement that is never true! This statement indicates that **The system has no solutions.**

Solution 2
Graph this system. We use the intercepts of each line. Notice that the lines are parallel. (If we check the slopes, we see that they are both $-\frac{1}{2}$). Therefore, there are no intersections, and so **The system has no solutions.**

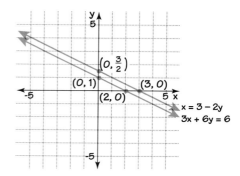

Example 5 illustrates a consistent system with infinitely many solutions.

Example 5

Solve the system $\begin{cases} y = 6 - \frac{x}{6} \\ \frac{x}{3} + 2y = 12. \end{cases}$

Solution 1
Substitute $6 - \frac{x}{6}$ for y in the second equation.

$$\frac{x}{3} + 2\left(6 - \frac{x}{6}\right) = 12$$
$$\frac{x}{3} + 12 - \frac{x}{3} = 12$$
$$12 = 12$$

This statement is *always* true. Thus, this system has an *infinite number of solutions*. The solutions are all ordered pairs satisfying either equation.

▶

288

Adapting to Individual Needs

English Language Development
When discussing the terms *consistent* and *inconsistent* with students who have limited English proficiency, you might point out that the prefix *in* in *inconsistent* sometimes means "not" or "the opposite of." Thus, *inconsistent* is the opposite of *consistent*. In a mathematical context, "consistent" means having one or more solutions, so "inconsistent" means not having one or more solutions; that is, having no solution.

Solution 2

Graph the system. Notice that the two graphs are the same line.

Graphs of $y = 6 - \frac{x}{6}$ and $\frac{x}{3} + 2y = 12$

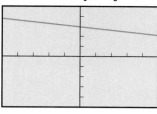

$-10 \le x \le 10$ x-scale = 2
$-10 \le y \le 10$ y-scale = 2

6) Does $-12 = 3(-4)$?
Yes. Does $(-4)(-12) = 48$? Yes.

8a)

$y = 4 - 2x$

$y = \frac{1}{2}(8x - 12)$

b) consistent
c) $\left(\frac{5}{3}, \frac{2}{3}\right)$

9a)

$y = 3x - 1$

$y = \frac{1}{2}(6x - 2)$

b) consistent
c) all pairs (x, y) satisfying $y = 3x - 1$

10a)

$y = 3x - 1$

$y = \frac{1}{2}(6x - 8)$

b) inconsistent
c) The system has no solutions.

QUESTIONS

Covering the Reading

1. Write the Substitution Property of Equality. If $a = b$, then a can be substituted for b in any arithmetic or algebraic expression.

2. Solve the following system using substitution.
$$\begin{cases} y = 3x + 5 \\ 4x - 3y = 12 \end{cases} \left(\frac{-27}{5}, \frac{-56}{5}\right)$$

In 3 and 4, refer to Example 2.

3. After the expressions in the second and third equations were substituted into the first equation, how many variables were in this new equation? one

4. A second part of the stadium was built to the same specifications but has a seating capacity of 6904. How many upper-level seats are there? 863

5. Solve $\begin{cases} 3x + 2y + z = 24 \\ x = 5z - 20 \\ y = -2z. \end{cases}$ (15, -14, 7)

6. Verify that $(-4, -12)$ is a solution to the system of Example 3.
See left.

7. a. Solve the system $\begin{cases} y = 5x \\ xy = 500. \end{cases}$ (10, 50), (-10, -50)

b. Is the system consistent? Yes

In 8–10, a system is given. **a.** Graph the system. **b.** Tell whether the system is consistent or inconsistent. **c.** Solve the system using substitution. See left.

8. $\begin{cases} y = 4 - 2x \\ y = \frac{1}{2}(8x - 12) \end{cases}$

9. $\begin{cases} y = 3x - 1 \\ y = \frac{1}{2}(6x - 2) \end{cases}$

10. $\begin{cases} y = 3x - 1 \\ y = \frac{1}{2}(6x - 8) \end{cases}$

Lesson 5-3 *Solving Systems by Substitution* **289**

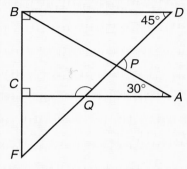

Adapting to Individual Needs

Challenge

Systems that have an infinite number of solutions are called *dependent*. Show students how to use substitution to solve a dependent system in terms of an arbitrary variable. For instance, the solution of

$\begin{cases} 3x + 2y - 5z = 0 \\ x + y - 2z = -1 \end{cases}$ is $(z + 2, z - 3, z)$.

Then have students solve each of the following systems in terms of z and write

four ordered triples that satisfy the system.

1. $\begin{cases} 2x - 3y + z = 19 \\ x + 4y - 5z = -18 \end{cases}$
$[(z + 2, z - 5, z);$ sample triples:
$(2, -5, 0), (3, -4, 1), (4, -3, 2), (5, -2, 3)]$

2. $\begin{cases} 2x - y + z = 5 \\ x + 3y - 2z = 3 \end{cases}$
$[(-\frac{1}{7}z + \frac{18}{7}, \frac{5}{7}z + \frac{1}{7}, z);$ sample triples:
$(\frac{17}{7}, \frac{6}{7}, 1), (\frac{18}{7}, \frac{1}{7}, 0), (\frac{16}{7}, \frac{11}{7}, 2), (\frac{15}{7}, \frac{16}{7}, 3)]$

289

Question 11 To solve $x^2 = x$ algebraically, students may use trial and error, factoring, or the Quadratic Formula. Accept the use of any method. You might inform students who have forgotten how to solve quadratics that Chapter 6 includes a thorough treatment of quadratic equations.

Question 13 When one equation in a system is from a constant-increase or constant-decrease situation, substitution is often a good method of solution.

Question 14 For this situation, many students quickly move to an equation in one variable.

Multicultural Connection For thousands of years lettuce has been eaten as a salad. It was listed as one of the 250 plants grown in the gardens of King Merodach-Baladan of Babylon, and lettuce seeds have been found in Egyptian tombs. Lettuce was a favorite vegetable of the ancient Romans—they usually served it with a dressing. During the Middle Ages, lettuce was a popular vegetable at medieval banquets; and supposedly Columbus himself brought the plant to America. Lettuce is one of the most widely eaten salad plants in the world today.

Questions 17–18 These questions are review for Lesson 5-6.

13a) $\begin{cases} y = .3x \\ y = 2 + .25x \end{cases}$

14a) Let T = amount of tomato juice in cups,
V = amount of vinegar in cups,
L = amount of oil in cups.
Then,
$\begin{cases} 7 = T + V + L \\ V = 3T \\ L = \frac{9}{2}V \end{cases}$

15a)
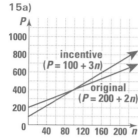

c) Under the incentive plan, anyone selling fewer than 100 gadgets receives a pay cut.

Applying the Mathematics

11. Follow the directions of Questions 8–10 for the system $\begin{cases} y = x^2 \\ y = x. \end{cases}$ See margin.

12. A sports stadium seats 60,000 people. The home team gets 4 times as many tickets as the visiting team. Let H be the number of tickets for the home team and V be the number of tickets for the visiting team.
   a. *Multiple choice.* Which system represents the given conditions? iii
   (i) $\begin{cases} 4H + 4V = 60,000 \\ H = 4V \end{cases}$ (ii) $\begin{cases} H + V = 60,000 \\ V = 4H \end{cases}$ (iii) $\begin{cases} H = 4V \\ H + V = 60,000 \end{cases}$
   b. Solve the correct system for H and V. $H = 48,000$, $V = 12,000$

13. FASTPIC offers to process a roll of film for 30¢ per print with free developing. A competitor, QUALIPRINT, will process a roll for 25¢ per print plus a $2.00 developing charge. Let x = the number of prints made and y = the cost of making x prints.
   a. Set up a system of two equations to describe this situation. See left.
   b. For what number of prints will the cost be the same at FASTPIC and QUALIPRINT? **40 prints**
   c. What is the cost for this number of prints? **$12.00**

14. A recipe which makes 7 cups of French dressing uses tomato juice, vinegar, and olive oil. It calls for 3 times as much vinegar as tomato juice and $4\frac{1}{2}$ times as much olive oil as vinegar.
   a. Set up a system of three equations to describe this situation. See left.
   b. Solve the system to determine how much of each ingredient should be used. **juice: .4 c; vinegar: 1.2 c; oil: 5.4 c**

15. The Buy-A-Gadget company pays sales representatives on a commission basis. The weekly salary P (in dollars) depends on the number n of gadgets sold. When Matt started with the company, the pay scale was $P = 200 + 2n$. In order to encourage higher sales, management decided to change to an incentive scale where $P = 100 + 3n$.
   a. Graph the original pay scale and the incentive scale on the same axes. See left.
   b. At what number of gadgets sold do the two scales pay the same wage? **100**
   c. Interpret the graph in terms of which sales representatives benefit from the incentive plan and which don't. Is anyone hurt by the new plan? See left.
   d. If Matt sells 150 gadgets the first week of June, what would his pay be under the old plan and under the incentive plan? **$500; $550**
   e. Explain why the new pay scale is called an incentive plan. Sample: Salespeople have an incentive to sell more gadgets because they make more money by selling more gadgets.

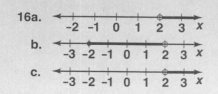

Review

16. Graph on a number line. See margin.
   a. $x > 2$
   b. $-2 \le x$ and $2 > x$
   c. $-2 \le x$ and $2 < x$ *(Lesson 5-1)*

290

Additional Answers
11a.
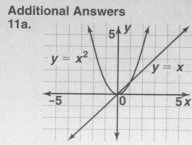
$y = x^2$ $y = x$

b. consistent
c. (0, 0), (1, 1)

16a. -2 -1 0 1 2 3 x
b. -3 -2 -1 0 1 2 3 x
c. -3 -2 -1 0 1 2 3 x

17) $\begin{bmatrix} 58 & 14 & -4 \\ -10 & 7 & -1 \end{bmatrix}$

In 17 and 18, multiply. *(Lesson 4-3)*

17. $\begin{bmatrix} 2 & 4 \\ -3 & 1 \end{bmatrix}\begin{bmatrix} 7 & -1 & 0 \\ 11 & 4 & -1 \end{bmatrix}$

See left.

18. $\begin{bmatrix} a & b \\ c & d \end{bmatrix}\begin{bmatrix} x \\ y \end{bmatrix}\begin{bmatrix} ax + by \\ cx + dy \end{bmatrix}$

19. Kathy has $5 to buy apples and pears for her volleyball team. Let a = number of apples and p = the number of pears.
  a. If apples are 40¢ each and pears are 50¢ each, write an inequality that expresses the combinations of fruits she can get for $5.
  b. List three possible ways for Kathy to spend the entire $5.00.
  (Lesson 3-3) a) $40a + 50p \le 500$ b) 0 apples and 10 pears, 5 apples and 6 pears, or 10 apples and 2 pears

20. Philip David Bayusun fills the bathtub slowly at a constant rate. He turns off the water, then gets in the tub and bathes. After a few minutes he gets out of the tub and pulls the plug. The water drains quickly. Which of the graphs below shows the relation between the height h of water in the tub and time t?   *(Lesson 3-1)* b

(a)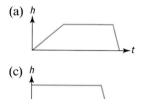

(b)

(c)

(d)

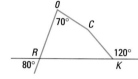

21. Find the measures of all four angles of quadrilateral *ROCK* drawn at the left.   *(Previous course)* m∠ *ROC* = 70°;   m∠ *CKR* = 60°; m∠ *OCK* = 150°;   m∠ *KRO* = 80°

Exploration

22. a. Choose an inconsistent system, such as the one in Example 4. Set up a table with columns for x- and y-values and the differences of the two y-values, such as the one started below. Does the difference column surprise you? Why or why not?
See margin.

x	$y_1 = -.5x + 1.5$	$y_2 = -.5x + 1$	$y_1 - y_2$
0	1.5	1	.5
1	1	.5	.5
2			

b. Make a similar table for the system in Example 5 of this lesson. Explain how the difference column relates to the number of solutions of the system.
c. Make a similar table for a consistent system that has exactly one solution. How does the difference column tell you what the solution to the system is?

Lesson 5-3 *Solving Systems by Substitution* **291**

Objectives

A Solve 2 × 2 and 3 × 3 systems using the Linear Combination Method.
D Recognize properties of systems of equations.
F Use systems of two or three linear equations to solve real-world problems.

Resources

From the *Teacher's Resource File*
■ Lesson Master 5-4A or 5-4B
■ Answer Master 5-4
■ Assessment Sourcebook: Quiz for Lessons 5-1 through 5-4
■ Teaching Aid 44: Warm-up
■ Technology Sourcebook Computer Master 6

Additional Resources
■ Visual for Teaching Aid 44
■ Spreadsheet software

Teaching **5-4**
Lesson

Warm-up

Write a system of equations to illustrate the situation. Then solve the system.
For the school play, adult tickets *a* sell for $5 and student tickets *s* sell for $3. On Saturday, a total of 390 tickets were sold and the total receipts were $1530. How many adult tickets were sold? How many student tickets were sold?

$$\begin{cases} 5a + 3s = 1530 \\ a + s = 390 \end{cases} ; 180, 210$$

In the last lesson, you solved systems using the Substitution Property. To use this method, one of the variables must be solved in terms of the other variables. However, when linear equations are written in standard form, it may be more efficient to solve the system using the Addition and Multiplication Properties of Equality.

Linear Combinations with Systems of Two Equations

Example 1

Solve the system $\begin{cases} x + y = 9 \\ 2x - y = 2. \end{cases}$

Solution

Notice that the coefficients of *y* are 1 and -1, which add to zero. Adding the sides of the two equations gives an equation in one variable.

$$\begin{array}{ll} x + y = 9 & \\ 2x - y = 2 & \\ \hline 3x \quad\quad = 11 & \text{Addition Property of Equality} \end{array}$$

Thus $\quad x \quad = \frac{11}{3}$ or $3\frac{2}{3}$.

Substitute the value of *x* into either of the two original equations, and solve for *y*. We choose the first equation.

$$\frac{11}{3} + y = 9$$

$$y = \frac{16}{3}$$

The solution is $\left(\frac{11}{3}, \frac{16}{3}\right)$.

Check 1

Graph the lines $x + y = 9$ and $2x - y = 2$. Use an automatic grapher's trace feature to determine whether the points of intersection are close to $\left(\frac{11}{3}, \frac{16}{3}\right) = (3.\overline{6}, 5.\overline{3})$. They are.

Check 2

Verify that $\left(\frac{11}{3}, \frac{16}{3}\right)$ satisfies each of the given sentences.
Does $\frac{11}{3} + \frac{16}{3} = 9$? Yes.
Does $2 \cdot \frac{11}{3} - \frac{16}{3} = 2$? Yes, so it checks.

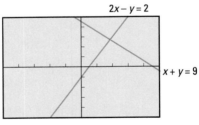

$-10 \le x \le 10, \quad x\text{-scale} = 2$
$-10 \le y \le 10, \quad y\text{-scale} = 2$

Lesson 5-4 Overview

Broad Goals This lesson shows how to use the Addition and Multiplication Properties of Equality to find solutions to certain systems.

Perspective The method of solving systems that is presented in this lesson is called the Linear Combination Method because the resulting equation is a linear combination of the given equations.

In general, given
$$ax + by = e \text{ and } cx + by = f$$
which intersect at a single point, *any* linear combination of these equations
$$m(ax + by) + n(cx + dy) = me + nf$$
will contain that point. In the Linear Combination Method, the multipliers *m* and *n* are chosen so that the resulting combination has only *x* or only *y* in it. That is, the combination will be a horizontal or vertical line that contains the point of intersection.

Some automatic graphers can solve linear systems. You might ask if any students have such graphers. They are particularly useful for systems larger than 2 × 2.

Systems arise in important practical endeavors. During World War II, the United States and many other countries had to ration certain foods. Mathematicians were involved in determining diets that met the minimum requirements of protein, vitamins, and minerals. Here is an example. Notice that we use both the Multiplication Property of Equality and the Addition Property of Equality in its solution.

Example 2

The table shows the protein and calcium contents for a dinner of roast beef and mashed potatoes. How many servings of each are needed to get 29 grams of protein and 61 milligrams of calcium?

	Roast Beef	Mashed Potatoes
protein (g) per serving	25	2
calcium (mg) per serving	11	25

Solution

Let r = the number of servings of roast beef and m = the number of servings of mashed potatoes.
Then for protein, the servings must satisfy $25r + 2m = 29$ and for calcium, the servings must satisfy $11r + 25m = 61$.

The system to be solved is $\begin{cases} 25r + 2m = 29 \\ 11r + 25m = 61. \end{cases}$

To use the addition method of Example 1, the coefficients of the variables must be opposites. Notice that the least common multiple of 2 and 25 (the coefficients of m) is 50. Using the Multiplication Property of Equality, multiply the first equation by 25 and the second equation by –2 to get equivalent equations with opposite coefficients for m.

$25r + 2m\ = 29$ Multiply by 25 to get: $625r + 50m = 725$
$11r + 25m = 61$ Multiply by –2 to get: $\underline{-22r - 50m = -122}$
Then add the resulting equations. $603r\ \ \ \ \ \ = 603$
Solve for r. $r\ \ \ \ \ = 1$
Now substitute $r = 1$ into either equation and solve for m.
We substitute into $25r + 2m = 29$.

$$25(1) + 2m = 29$$
$$m = 2$$

So you need 1 serving of roast beef and 2 servings of potatoes to get the required amounts of protein and calcium.

Check

Substitute $r = 1$ and $m = 2$ into the other sentence, $11r + 25m = 61$.
Does $11(1) + 25(2) = 61$? Yes.

In Example 2, we also could have found the least common multiple for the coefficients of r, which is 275. Then the first equation would be multiplied by 11, and the second equation would be multiplied by -25. Solving the system in this way would result in the same solution.

A rational plan. *Shown are ration coupons from World War II. During the war, the Office of Price Administration set up a rationing program to ensure that scarce goods were distributed fairly. Each family received a book of coupons to be used to purchase such goods as sugar, meat, butter, and gasoline.*

Notes on Reading

Most students will recall from their previous work in algebra the use of the Linear Combination Method to solve 2 × 2 systems. Stress the need to work accurately, and encourage students to organize their work carefully.

Example 1 illustrates a system in which addition of the equations is all that is needed to solve the system. In **Examples 2 and 3**, *both* multiplication and addition are used.

Reading Mathematics We use the phrases "adding equations" and "multiplying an equation by a number." Although these phrases are technically incorrect—we are "adding equals to equals" and "multiplying both sides of an equation by the same number"—the phrases are convenient, and should not lead to misunderstandings.

Optional Activities

Cooperative Learning You might use this activity after discussing the examples. Write a few 2 × 2 systems of equations on the board. Have students **work in small groups.** Ask each group to solve each system in more than one way. Then call on students to identify their preferred method and to tell why they prefer that method.

1. Solve the system.

$$\begin{cases} 3x - 5y = 11 \\ 6x + 5y = 7 \end{cases}$$

$x = 2, y = -1$

2. A school rents its swimming pool for private parties. There is a fixed cost f which remains the same regardless of the number of guests g. There is also a charge per guest. For a party of 40 people, the total charge is $230, and for a party of 125 people, the total charge is $400. Find the fixed cost and the charge per guest.

$$\begin{cases} 40g + f = 230 \\ 125g + f = 400 \end{cases}$$

The fixed cost is $150 and the charge per guest is $2.

3. Solve this system.

$$\begin{cases} 3a + 4b + 5c = 22 \\ 2a - b + 3c = 35 \\ 7a + 3b - c = 26 \end{cases}$$

$(a, b, c) = (7, -6, 5)$

(Notes on Questions begin on page 296.)

Follow-up for Lesson 5-4

Practice

For more questions on SPUR Objectives, use **Lesson Master 5-4A** (shown on page 295) or **Lesson Master 5-4B** (shown on pages 296–297).

Recall that an expression of the form $Ax + By$ is called a *linear combination* of the two variables x and y. The method used in Examples 1 and 2 is often called the **Linear Combination Method** of solving systems because it involves adding multiples of the given equations.

Linear Combinations with Systems of Three Equations

The Linear Combination Method can also be used to solve a system with three linear equations. First, take any pair of equations and eliminate one of the variables; then take another pair of equations and eliminate the same variable. This process results in a system of two equations with two variables. Then the methods of Examples 1 and 2 can be used.

Example 3

Solve the system $\begin{cases} 2x + 3y + z = 13 \\ 5x - 2y - 4z = 7 \\ 4x + 5y + 3z = 25. \end{cases}$

Solution

We choose to eliminate z first. Consider the first two equations. Notice that the coefficients of z in these equations are 1 and -4. To eliminate z from these equations, multiply the first equation by 4 and add the result to the second equation.

$2x + 3y + z = 13$ Multiply by 4 to get: $8x + 12y + 4z = 52.$
$5x - 2y - 4z = 7$ $5x - 2y - 4z = 7$

Add. $13x + 10y = 59$

Now eliminate z from another pair of equations. We choose to use the first and third equations. The least common multiple of 1 and 3, the coefficients of z, is 3.

$2x + 3y + z = 13$ Multiply by -3 to get: $-6x - 9y - 3z = -39.$
$4x + 5y + 3z = 25$ $4x + 5y + 3z = 25$

Add. $-2x - 4y = -14$

We are now left with the following system to solve.

$$\begin{cases} 13x + 10y = 59 \\ -2x - 4y = -14 \end{cases}$$

Use the Linear Combination Method on this system. We eliminate y first.

$13x + 10y = 59$ Multiply by 2 to get: $26x + 20y = 118.$
$-2x - 4y = -14$ Multiply by 5 to get: $-10x - 20y = -70.$

Add. $16x = 48$
                                   $x = 3$

Substitute $x = 3$ into one of the two equations involving just two variables. We substitute into $13x + 10y = 59$.

$$13(3) + 10y = 59$$
$$y = 2$$

Now substitute $x = 3$ and $y = 2$ into one of the original equations of the system. We use $2x + 3y + z = 13$.

$$2(3) + 3(2) + z = 13$$
$$z = 1$$

So **The solution is x = 3, y = 2, and z = 1.** This can be written as the ordered triple (3, 2, 1).

294

Adapting to Individual Needs

Extra Help

When students are asked to solve a system of three equations with three variables, as in **Example 3**, they sometimes are confused about how to pair the equations. For three equations there are three different pairings of equations, that is, equations 1 and 2, equations 1 and 3, or equations 2 and 3. Point out that they can pick any pair of equations and then eliminate any of the three variables from that pair. Once they have decided which variable to eliminate, they must eliminate the *same* variable from another pair of equations.

Check

Substitute $x = 3$, $y = 2$, and $z = 1$ into each equation.
Does $2(3) + 3(2) + 1 = 13$? Yes.
Does $5(3) - 2(2) - 4(1) = 7$? Yes.
Does $4(3) + 5(2) + 3(1) = 25$? Yes.

The equations in the examples are consistent, and each has a unique solution. However, if you use the Linear Combination Method and get a statement such as $0 = -36$, which is always false, the original system is inconsistent and has no solutions.

If, after applying the Linear Combination Method with all the given equations, you get a statement such as $0 = 0$, which is always true, the original system is consistent, and there are infinitely many solutions.

3)
$$\begin{array}{r} 275r + \quad 22m = \quad 319 \\ \underline{-275r - \quad 625m = -1525} \\ -603m = -1206 \\ m = 2 \\ r = 1 \end{array}$$

4a) $\begin{cases} 16s + 2b = 26 \\ 11s + b = 17.5 \end{cases}$

QUESTIONS

Covering the Reading

1. Refer to Example 1. The equation $3x = 11$ is the result of __?__ the two original equations. **adding**

2. Solve the system $\begin{cases} a + b = 14 \\ 3a - b = 50. \end{cases}$ $a = 16, b = -2$

3. Refer to Example 2. Multiply the first equation by 11 and the second equation by -25. Solve the resulting system. **See left.**

4. The table below gives the number of grams of protein and fat in one serving of two foods.

	Beef Stew with Vegetables	Bread
protein (g) per serving	16	2
fat (g) per serving	11	1

Lynne wants to get 26 grams of protein and 17.5 grams of fat from one meal of beef stew and bread.
a. Let s = the number of servings of stew and b = the number of servings of bread. Write a system of equations that describes these conditions. **See left.**
b. How many servings of each does Lynne need to eat? $1\frac{1}{2}$ servings of stew, 1 serving of bread

In 5–8, use the Linear Combination Method to solve the system.

5. $\begin{cases} 5x - 6y = 3 \\ 2x + 12y = 12 \end{cases}$ (1.5, .75)

6. $\begin{cases} a + b = \frac{1}{3} \\ a - b = \frac{1}{4} \end{cases}$ $\left(\frac{7}{24}, \frac{1}{24}\right)$

7. $\begin{cases} p + q = 4 \\ 5p + 6q = 7 \end{cases}$ (17, -13)

8. $\begin{cases} 2x - y + 3z = 9 \\ 4x + 2y - 2z = 10 \\ x - y - z = -5 \end{cases}$ (2, 4, 3)

Lesson 5-4 *Solving Systems Using Linear Combinations* **295**

(Extension continues on page 296.)

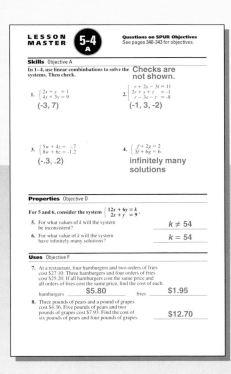

295

3. Linear equations in which the coefficients are multiples of each other, but the constants are not, are inconsistent and have graphs that are parallel lines. Are these systems consistent or inconsistent?

a. $\begin{cases} 3x + 5y = 18 \\ 6x + 10y = 20 \end{cases}$

b. $\begin{cases} 4x + 4y = 20 \\ 3x + 3y = -6 \end{cases}$

[Students should recognize that these systems are inconsistent without doing any algebraic manipulations. The practice of seeing the coefficients as a unit and the constants as a unit will help in Lesson 5-6, where these units are written as separate matrices.]

Notes on Questions

Questions 11–12 These questions can lead to a discussion of the relationship between constants and consistency. A criterion will be discussed in Lesson 5-6. However, you could extend the discussion at this time by using the *Extension* on pages 295–296.

Question 14 This question uses linear combinations in a chemistry application; students may encounter similar problems in their science classes.

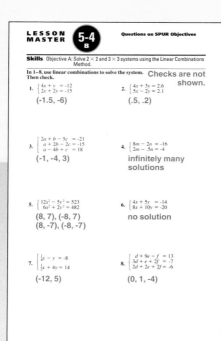

Worth its weight in salt. *Shown is a salt-harvesting machine in France collecting salt obtained from evaporated seawater.*

9. Refer to Example 3.

a. Suppose you want to use the first and second equations to eliminate *y*. If you multiply the first equation by __?__ and the second equation by __?__, then when you add the two equations, you get an equation in *x* and *z* only. 2; 3

b. Suppose you want to use the second and third equations to eliminate *y*. If you multiply the second equation by __?__ and the third equation by __?__, then when you add the two equations, you get an equation in *x* and *z* only. 5; 2

c. The equations resulting from parts **a** and **b** form a system of two equations in two variables. Solve this system. x = 3; z = 1

d. Substitute the values of *x* and *z* from part **c** into one of the original three equations, and solve for *y*. y = 2

e. *True or false.* The method used in parts **a** to **d** gives the same solution as in Example 3. True

10. Morris was solving a system of two equations and got 0 = 0 after adding the equations together. This result means that Morris has what kind of system? a consistent system with infinitely many solutions

In 11 and 12, use the Linear Combination Method to determine whether the system is inconsistent or consistent.

11. $\begin{cases} 2x + 3y = 4 \\ 4x + 6y = 9 \end{cases}$ inconsistent

12. $\begin{cases} 2m + 3n = 4 \\ 4m + 6n = 8 \end{cases}$ consistent

Applying the Mathematics

13. At the zoo, Jay bought 3 slices of vegetable pizza and 1 small lemonade for $5.40. Terri paid $4.80 for 2 slices of vegetable pizza and 2 small lemonades. What is the cost of a small lemonade? 90¢

14. *N* mL of a 60% salt solution are mixed with *S* mL of an 80% salt solution. The result is 35 mL of a 72% salt solution. a) N + S = 35

a. Write an equation relating *N, S,* and the total number of mL.

b. The amount of salt in the 72% solution is 0.72(35), or 25.2 mL. Write an equation relating the amount of salt in the 60%, 80%, and 72% solutions. N(.60) + S(.80) = 25.2

c. Solve the system represented by your answers in parts **a** and **b**. How many mL of the 60% and the 80% solutions are needed? N = 14 mL; S = 21 mL

In 15 and 16, solve by the Linear Combination Method.

15. $\begin{cases} 5u + 4v = -18 \\ 0.04u - 0.12v = 0.16 \end{cases}$ (u, v) = (-2, -2)

16. $\begin{cases} 9x^2 - 6y^2 = 291 \\ 3x^2 + 2y^2 = 197 \end{cases}$ (7, 5), (7, -5), (-7, 5), (-7, -5)

Adapting to Individual Needs

Challenge

Solve the system $\begin{cases} 5^{2x + y} = 125 \\ 2^{x + y} = 16 \end{cases}$.

[(-1, 5)]

Additional Answers

25. Sample: Compare the first and the second conditions. Taking away 2 citrons and adding 2 wood apples gives a total cost which is 6 less than the original. This means that each wood apple must cost 3 less than each citron. So the nine citrons and seven wood apples cost 21 cents less than sixteen citrons. So sixteen citrons cost 128. Thus, the price of a citron is 8. Since the

Designing books. *Shown is Steve Curtis (center), designer of this book, meeting with some of the ScottForesman editorial staff. Designers deal with such issues as how copy is positioned on a page, artwork, and photos.*

17. While checking its records, a publishing company noted the following costs for publishing books.
   Job 1: 60 hr for design, 100 hr for editing, 200 hr for production, total cost = $23,000
   Job 2: 30 hr for design, 300 hr for editing, 400 hr for production, total cost = $49,500
   Job 3: 40 hr for design, 80 hr for editing, 150 hr for production, total cost = $17,400
   How much did the company charge per hour for design, how much for editing, and how much for production?
   design: $50;   editing: $80;   production: $60

Review

18. a. Solve the system $\begin{cases} y = 200 - 2x \\ y = 150 + 1.5x \end{cases}$ by substitution.

b. Make up a question that could be answered by solving this system. *(Lesson 5-3)* **See left.** a) $\left(\frac{100}{7}, \frac{1200}{7}\right) \approx$ **(14.286, 171.429)**

19. *Multiple choice.* A system whose graph is two different parallel lines __?__ has a solution. *(Lesson 5-3)* **c**
   (a) always   (b) sometimes   (c) never

20. Consider the system $\begin{cases} y = \frac{1}{2}x^2 \\ y = \frac{1}{3}x + 1 \end{cases}$.

18b) Sample: Al and Tina have two identical bottles and a spoon. Al begins with 200 mL of water in his bottle and removes two spoonfuls, while Tina begins with 150 mL of water in her bottle and adds $1\frac{1}{2}$ spoonfuls. In the end they both have y mL of water. How much water is this? How much water is in a spoonful?

20a)

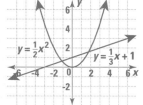

a. Graph the solution set of each sentence. **See left.**
b. Approximate the solutions to the system. *(Lesson 5-2)*
   (1.8, 1.6), (-1.1, .6)

21. Consider the arithmetic sequence 112, 120, 128, 136, ...
   a. Find a recursive formula.
   b. Find an explicit formula. *(Lessons 3-7, 3-8)* $\begin{cases} a_1 = 112 \\ a_n = a_{n-1} + 8, \text{ for} \\ \qquad \text{integers } n \geq 2 \end{cases}$
   $a_n = 112 + (n-1)\,8$ or $a_n = 104 + 8n$
   In 22 and 23, find the product. *(Lesson 4-3)*

22. $\begin{bmatrix} 4 & 7 \\ 2 & 1 \end{bmatrix}\begin{bmatrix} -.1 & .7 \\ .2 & -.4 \end{bmatrix}\begin{bmatrix} 1 & 0 \\ 0 & 1 \end{bmatrix}$ **23.** $\begin{bmatrix} 1 & 0 & 0 \\ 0 & 1 & 0 \\ 0 & 0 & 1 \end{bmatrix}\begin{bmatrix} 7 & 8 & 9 \\ \sqrt{5} & \sqrt{6} & \sqrt{7} \\ -1 & 0 & 1 \end{bmatrix}$ $\begin{bmatrix} 7 & 8 & 9 \\ \sqrt{5} & \sqrt{6} & \sqrt{7} \\ -1 & 0 & 1 \end{bmatrix}$

24. Find the multiplicative inverse of each number. *(Previous course)*
   a. $4\ \frac{1}{4}$ **b.** $-\frac{2}{3}\ \frac{-3}{2}$ **c.** a (when $a \neq 0$) $\frac{1}{a}$ **d.** 0 **does not exist**

Exploration

25. This problem was made up by the Indian mathematician Mahavira and dates from about 850 A.D. "The price of nine citrons and seven fragrant wood apples is 107; again, the mixed price of seven citrons and nine fragrant wood apples is 101. Oh you arithmetician, tell me quickly the price of a citron and a wood apple here, having distinctly separated these prices well." At this time algebra had not yet been developed. How could this question be answered by someone without using algebra?
   See margin.

Lesson 5-4 *Solving Systems Using Linear Combinations* **297**

price of a wood apple is 3 less than a citron, the price of a wood apple is 5.

Setting Up Lesson 5-5

Materials Students will need technology that can perform matrix operations for the In-class Activity on page 298.

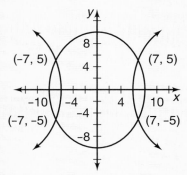
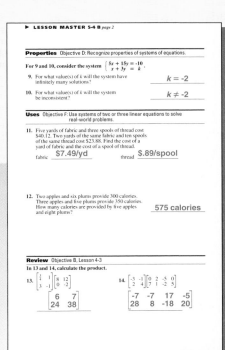

Resources

From the **Teacher's Resource File**
- Answer Master 5-5
- Teaching Aid 8: Four-Quadrant Graph Paper

Additional Resources
- Visual for Teaching Aid 8
- Technology that can perform matrix operations

In this activity, students explore the relation between the matrix for a scale change $S_{a,b}$ and the matrix for the transformation that undoes the change—its inverse $S_{1/a,1/b}$.

On most calculators that perform matrix operations, to find the inverse of a matrix, you must first enter the matrix and store it, say, in location M. Then you either press the inverse key $\boxed{x^{-1}}$ or choose Inverse from the matrix operations menu.

Be sure to discuss students' answers to **Question 4.** You may want to list their responses in a table on the chalkboard or overhead. Ask students to describe the patterns that they see.

Scale Change	$S_{2,5}$	$S_{7,2}$
a. Matrix for scale change		
b. Inverse of Matrix in **a**		
c. Transformation for inverse in **b**		

In Lesson 5-5, students will learn that although all matrices representing reflections, rotations, translations, glide reflections, and scale changes have inverses, not every matrix has an inverse. The lesson also includes a formula for the inverse of a 2×2 matrix.

298

Matrices and Inverses

IN-CLASS
ACTIVITY

Materials: You will need technology that can perform matrix operations. Work on this Activity with a partner.

See margin for 1, 2a-c, 3c

1
  a. Plot quadrilateral *ABCD* with $A = (-2, 1)$, $B = (1, 1)$, $C = (1, -2)$, and $D = (-2, -2)$.
  b. Plot $A'B'C'D'$, the image of *ABCD* under $S_{2,5}$.
  c. Plot $A''B''C''D''$, the image of $A'B'C'D'$ under $S_{\frac{1}{2},\frac{1}{5}}$.
  d. Describe how $A''B''C''D''$ and *ABCD* are related.

2
  a. Write the matrix for $S_{2,5}$.
  b. Write the matrix for $S_{\frac{1}{2},\frac{1}{5}}$.
  c. Find the product of the matrices in parts **a** and **b**.
  d. What is the matrix in part **c** called? **2 × 2 identity matrix**

3 Two matrices whose product is the identity matrix are called **inverse matrices.** Most graphics calculators and some computer programs can find the inverse of some matrices. Check with your teacher, a friend, or the manual for your technology.
  a. Enter the matrix for $S_{2,5}$ on a calculator. **a, b) Keystrokes will vary.**
  b. Use the calculator to find the inverse of the matrix in part **a**.
  c. What transformation does the matrix in part **b** represent?
4a, b)Answers will vary.   c) The inverse of the matrix in part a.

4
  a. Write the matrix for some scale change other than $S_{2,5}$ and $S_{\frac{1}{2},\frac{1}{5}}$.
  b. Use the calculator to find the inverse of the matrix in part **a**.
  c. What transformation does the matrix in part **b** represent?
  d. Do the transformations represented by the matrices in parts **a** and **b** undo each other? How can you tell? **Yes; when multiplied together, the result is the identity matrix.**

298

Additional Answers
1a-c.

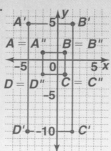

d. *A''B''C''D''* and *ABCD* are identical images.

2a. $\begin{bmatrix} 2 & 0 \\ 0 & 5 \end{bmatrix}$

b. $\begin{bmatrix} \frac{1}{2} & 0 \\ 0 & \frac{1}{5} \end{bmatrix}$

c. $\begin{bmatrix} 1 & 0 \\ 0 & 1 \end{bmatrix}$

3c. $S_{\frac{1}{2},\frac{1}{5}}$ represents the inverse of the matrix in part a.

So far in this chapter, you have seen three methods for solving systems: graphing, substitution, and linear combination. A fourth method involves matrices and their inverses.

In the Activity on page 298, you saw that the scale-change matrix $\begin{bmatrix} 2 & 0 \\ 0 & 5 \end{bmatrix}$ has an inverse $\begin{bmatrix} \frac{1}{2} & 0 \\ 0 & \frac{1}{5} \end{bmatrix}$ because

$$\begin{bmatrix} 2 & 0 \\ 0 & 5 \end{bmatrix} \begin{bmatrix} \frac{1}{2} & 0 \\ 0 & \frac{1}{5} \end{bmatrix} = \begin{bmatrix} 1 & 0 \\ 0 & 1 \end{bmatrix} \text{ and}$$

$$\begin{bmatrix} \frac{1}{2} & 0 \\ 0 & \frac{1}{5} \end{bmatrix} \begin{bmatrix} 2 & 0 \\ 0 & 5 \end{bmatrix} = \begin{bmatrix} 1 & 0 \\ 0 & 1 \end{bmatrix}.$$

What Are Inverse Matrices?

In general, 2×2 matrices M and N are **inverse matrices** if and only if their product is the 2×2 identity matrix for multiplication, that is, if and only if

$$MN = NM = \begin{bmatrix} 1 & 0 \\ 0 & 1 \end{bmatrix}.$$

All the transformation matrices you saw in Chapter 4 have inverses. But not all matrices represent transformations, and not all matrices have inverses. In general, only **square matrices,** those with the same number of rows and columns, can have inverses.

When a matrix M represents a transformation, its inverse represents a transformation that undoes the effect of M. For instance, $\begin{bmatrix} 4 & 0 \\ 0 & 3 \end{bmatrix}$ is the matrix for the scale change $S_{4,3}$, and $\begin{bmatrix} \frac{1}{4} & 0 \\ 0 & \frac{1}{3} \end{bmatrix}$ is the matrix for the scale change $S_{1/4,1/3}$. As shown below, $S_{1/4,1/3}$ undoes the effect of $S_{4,3}$ on $\triangle ABC$. The product of the matrices for $S_{4,3}$ and $S_{1/4,1/3}$ is the identity matrix. The composite of the transformations is the identity transformation, and so the final image is identical to the preimage.

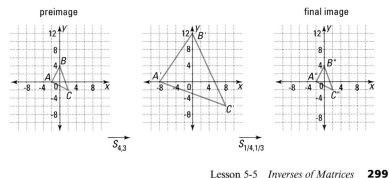

Lesson 5-5 *Inverses of Matrices* **299**

Lesson 5-5

Objectives
B Find the determinant and the inverse of a square matrix.

Resources
From the *Teacher's Resource File*
■ Lesson Master 5-5A or 5-5B
■ Answer Master 5-5
■ Teaching Aid 44: Warm-up
■ Activity Kit, Activity 10

Additional Resources
■ Visual for Teaching Aid 44

Teaching 5-5
Lesson

Warm-up
Find each product.

1. $\begin{bmatrix} 5 & 0 \\ 0 & -5 \end{bmatrix} \begin{bmatrix} .2 & 0 \\ 0 & -.2 \end{bmatrix} \begin{bmatrix} 1 & 0 \\ 0 & 1 \end{bmatrix}$

2. $\begin{bmatrix} 3 & 6 \\ -2 & 1 \end{bmatrix} \begin{bmatrix} \frac{1}{15} & -\frac{2}{5} \\ \frac{2}{15} & \frac{1}{5} \end{bmatrix} \begin{bmatrix} 1 & 0 \\ 0 & 1 \end{bmatrix}$

Notes on Reading
Point out that the inverse of a 2×2 matrix is also a 2×2 matrix, so the two matrices may be multiplied in either order. Normally, multiplication of matrices is not commutative, but it is always commutative when the matrices are inverses. Have students verify the matrix multiplication in the proof of the Inverse Matrix Theorem.

Lesson 5-5 Overview

Broad Goals Lessons 5-5 and 5-6 relate the matrix concepts that were studied in Chapter 4 to systems of equations. In this lesson, the inverse of a 2×2 matrix is found. In the next lesson, the inverse is used to solve systems of linear equations.

Perspective A system of linear equations can be considered as a *single* matrix equation $AX = B$, where A is a matrix of coefficients, X is a matrix of variables, and B is a matrix of constants. The equation $AX = B$ is solved by multiplying both sides by the multiplicative inverse of the matrix A. This process, being analogous to the process of solving the linear equation $ax = b$, reinforces earlier work. The only difficulty in the process is finding the inverse of A. As one might expect from the process of matrix multiplication, the formula for the inverse under this operation is not at all obvious. Because many students are amazed at

how this process works, this lesson and the next one can be intriguing lessons.

In the Activity you saw two other pairs of inverse scale-change matrices.

Example 1

Verify that the inverse of $\begin{bmatrix} 2 & 5 \\ 3 & 8 \end{bmatrix}$ is $\begin{bmatrix} 8 & -5 \\ -3 & 2 \end{bmatrix}$.

Solution

We multiply the matrices. The product is the identity matrix.

$$\begin{bmatrix} 8 & -5 \\ -3 & 2 \end{bmatrix}\begin{bmatrix} 2 & 5 \\ 3 & 8 \end{bmatrix} = \begin{bmatrix} 8(2) + -5(3) & 8(5) + -5(8) \\ -3(2) + 2(3) & -3(5) + 2(8) \end{bmatrix} = \begin{bmatrix} 1 & 0 \\ 0 & 1 \end{bmatrix}$$

Activity 1

Multiply the matrices in reverse order. Do you get the identity matrix?
Yes, see left.

$$\begin{bmatrix} 2 & 5 \\ 3 & 8 \end{bmatrix}\begin{bmatrix} 8 & -5 \\ -3 & 2 \end{bmatrix} = \begin{bmatrix} 1 & 0 \\ 0 & 1 \end{bmatrix}$$

Recall that the multiplicative inverse of a real number x is sometimes written as x^{-1}. Similarly, the multiplicative inverse of a matrix M can be written as M^{-1}. Thus, from Example 1 we can write

$$\begin{bmatrix} 2 & 5 \\ 3 & 8 \end{bmatrix}^{-1} = \begin{bmatrix} 8 & -5 \\ -3 & 2 \end{bmatrix}.$$

Finding the Inverse of a 2 × 2 Matrix

❶ The following theorem tells when an inverse matrix exists, and gives you a formula to find it.

Inverse Matrix Theorem

If $ad - bc \neq 0$, the inverse of $\begin{bmatrix} a & b \\ c & d \end{bmatrix}$ is $\begin{bmatrix} \frac{d}{ad-bc} & \frac{-b}{ad-bc} \\ \frac{-c}{ad-bc} & \frac{a}{ad-bc} \end{bmatrix}$.

Proof:

We need to show that the product of the two matrices in either order is the identity matrix. Below, we show one order. In the Questions, you are asked to verify the multiplication in the reverse order.

$$\begin{bmatrix} a & b \\ c & d \end{bmatrix}\begin{bmatrix} \frac{d}{ad-bc} & \frac{-b}{ad-bc} \\ \frac{-c}{ad-bc} & \frac{a}{ad-bc} \end{bmatrix} = \begin{bmatrix} \frac{ad}{ad-bc} + \frac{-bc}{ad-bc} & \frac{-ab}{ad-bc} + \frac{ab}{ad-bc} \\ \frac{cd}{ad-bc} + \frac{-cd}{ad-bc} & \frac{-bc}{ad-bc} + \frac{ad}{ad-bc} \end{bmatrix}$$

$$= \begin{bmatrix} \frac{ad-bc}{ad-bc} & \frac{0}{ad-bc} \\ \frac{0}{ad-bc} & \frac{ad-bc}{ad-bc} \end{bmatrix} = \begin{bmatrix} 1 & 0 \\ 0 & 1 \end{bmatrix}$$

❷ The formula in the Inverse Matrix Theorem is programmed into most graphics calculators. However, when the numbers in a 2×2 matrix are integers, it is often quicker to calculate the inverse matrix by hand than to find it with a calculator.

Example 2

Find the inverse of the matrix $\begin{bmatrix} 0 & -2 \\ 2 & 1 \end{bmatrix}$.

Solution

Use the Inverse Matrix Theorem. In $\begin{bmatrix} 0 & -2 \\ 2 & 1 \end{bmatrix}$, $a = 0$, $b = -2$, $c = 2$, and $d = 1$. So $ad - bc = 0(1) - (-2)(2) = 4$.

Substitute into the formula to get

$\begin{bmatrix} \frac{1}{4} & \frac{2}{4} \\ \frac{-2}{4} & \frac{0}{4} \end{bmatrix}$, which can be written as $\begin{bmatrix} \frac{1}{4} & \frac{1}{2} \\ -\frac{1}{2} & 0 \end{bmatrix}$.

Check

Does $\begin{bmatrix} 0 & -2 \\ 2 & 1 \end{bmatrix}\begin{bmatrix} .25 & .5 \\ -.5 & 0 \end{bmatrix} = \begin{bmatrix} 1 & 0 \\ 0 & 1 \end{bmatrix} = \begin{bmatrix} .25 & .5 \\ -.5 & 0 \end{bmatrix}\begin{bmatrix} 0 & -2 \\ 2 & 1 \end{bmatrix}$?

Yes, it checks.

Activity 2

Verify Example 2 by storing the matrix $A = \begin{bmatrix} 0 & -2 \\ 2 & 1 \end{bmatrix}$ on a computer or calculator and using the technology to find A^{-1}.

Determinants and Inverses

The formula in the Inverse Matrix Theorem can be simplified by using scalar multiplication. When $ad - bc \neq 0$,

$$\begin{bmatrix} \dfrac{d}{ad-bc} & \dfrac{-b}{ad-bc} \\ \dfrac{-c}{ad-bc} & \dfrac{a}{ad-bc} \end{bmatrix} = \dfrac{1}{ad-bc}\begin{bmatrix} d & -b \\ -c & a \end{bmatrix}.$$

Not all square matrices have inverses. You can see that the inverse of $\begin{bmatrix} a & b \\ c & d \end{bmatrix}$ exists only if $ad - bc \neq 0$. Because the number $ad - bc$ determines whether or not a matrix has an inverse, it is called the **determinant** of the matrix. We abbreviate the word *determinant* as *det*. Thus, the Inverse Matrix Theorem can be written:

Let $M = \begin{bmatrix} a & b \\ c & d \end{bmatrix}$. $M^{-1} = \dfrac{1}{\det M}\begin{bmatrix} d & -b \\ -c & a \end{bmatrix}$ if and only if $\det M \neq 0$.

In 3–4, explain why the matrix does or does not have an inverse.

3. $\begin{bmatrix} 5 & 0 \\ -2 & 1 \end{bmatrix}$ 4. $\begin{bmatrix} 6 & -4 \\ 3 & -2 \end{bmatrix}$

3. **An inverse exists since $5 \cdot 1 - -2 \cdot 0 \neq 0$.**
4. **An inverse does not exist since $6 \cdot -2 - 3 \cdot -4 = 0$**

(Notes on Questions begin on page 303.)

Follow-up for Lesson 5-5

Practice

For more questions on SPUR Objectives, use **Lesson Master 5-5A** (shown on page 301) or **Lesson Master 5-5B** (shown on pages 302–303).

Assessment

Group Assessment Have students **work in groups.** First have one student write a 2 × 2 matrix. Have another student find the determinant of the matrix and have a third student find the inverse if it exists. Finally have a fourth student check the results by multiplying. Students can switch roles and repeat the activity. [Students demonstrate that they understand how to find the determinant of a 2 × 2 matrix and use the determinant to write the inverse matrix if it exists.]

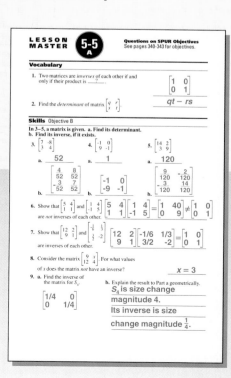

Adapting to Individual Needs

Extra Help
Here is a way to help students remember the Inverse Matrix Theorem. To find the inverse of a 2 × 2 matrix $M = \begin{bmatrix} a & b \\ c & d \end{bmatrix}$, proceed as follows: (1) Find det M. If det $M = 0$, the inverse of M does not exist. (2) Reverse the positions of a and d. (3) Take the opposites of b and c. Divide each element by det M. This forms the new matrix.

English Language Development
Remind students with limited English proficiency that new words in this chapter are listed on page 338. Encourage them to write the words on index cards along with a definition that they understand. If appropriate, suggest that students include an example along with their definition. At this time, you might have students **work in pairs** and discuss the new vocabulary.

Extension

The proof of the Inverse Matrix Theorem doesn't tell how we knew in advance that the matrix

$$\begin{bmatrix} \dfrac{d}{ad-bc} & \dfrac{-b}{ad-bc} \\ \dfrac{-c}{ad-bc} & \dfrac{a}{ad-bc} \end{bmatrix}$$ is indeed the

inverse of $\begin{bmatrix} a & b \\ c & d \end{bmatrix}$. You might want

to show students that the inverse can be derived by using a generalization of the technique that is illustrated in **Question 16**.

If the inverse of $\begin{bmatrix} a & b \\ c & d \end{bmatrix}$ exists, it

must be a 2×2 matrix; therefore, we can multiply it on either the left or

the right. Call the inverse $\begin{bmatrix} w & x \\ y & z \end{bmatrix}$.

Now we have to find w, x, y, and z

such that $\begin{bmatrix} a & b \\ c & d \end{bmatrix}\begin{bmatrix} w & x \\ y & z \end{bmatrix} = \begin{bmatrix} 1 & 0 \\ 0 & 1 \end{bmatrix}$

and $\begin{bmatrix} w & x \\ y & z \end{bmatrix}\begin{bmatrix} a & b \\ c & d \end{bmatrix} = \begin{bmatrix} 1 & 0 \\ 0 & 1 \end{bmatrix}$.

Multiplying the matrices on the left and equating the entries yields this

system: $\begin{cases} aw + by = 1 \\ ax + bz = 0 \\ cw + dy = 0 \\ cx + dz = 1. \end{cases}$

*Gottfried Leibniz
(1646–1716)*

Example 3

Determine whether $\begin{bmatrix} 3 & 2 \\ -5 & 4 \end{bmatrix}$ has an inverse.

Solution

Evaluate the determinant of the matrix.

$\det \begin{bmatrix} 3 & 2 \\ -5 & 4 \end{bmatrix} = 3 \cdot 4 - 2 \cdot \text{-}5 = 22 \neq 0.$

So the matrix has an inverse.

Example 4

Explain why $\begin{bmatrix} 3 & 1 \\ 6 & 2 \end{bmatrix}$ does not have an inverse.

Solution 1

Suppose $\begin{bmatrix} 3 & 1 \\ 6 & 2 \end{bmatrix}$ had an inverse $\begin{bmatrix} e & f \\ g & h \end{bmatrix}$. Then by the definition of

inverses, $\begin{bmatrix} 3 & 1 \\ 6 & 2 \end{bmatrix}\begin{bmatrix} e & f \\ g & h \end{bmatrix} = \begin{bmatrix} 3e + 9 & 3f + h \\ 6e + 2g & 6f + 2h \end{bmatrix} = \begin{bmatrix} 1 & 0 \\ 0 & 1 \end{bmatrix}.$

This leads to two systems:

$\begin{cases} 3e + g = 1 \\ 6e + 2g = 0 \end{cases}$ and $\begin{cases} 3f + h = 0 \\ 6f + 2h = 1 \end{cases}.$

Both of these systems are inconsistent.
Therefore, the matrix can have no inverse.

Solution 2

$\det \begin{bmatrix} 3 & 1 \\ 6 & 2 \end{bmatrix} = 3 \cdot 2 - 1 \cdot 6 = 0,$ so the matrix has no inverse.

Determinants were first used by the Japanese mathematician Seki Kowa in 1683, and independently ten years later by the German mathematician Gottfried Leibniz (1646–1716). Formulas for inverses of 3×3 or larger matrices exist, but are quite complicated. Calculators and computers can often find inverses of square matrices larger than 2×2.

QUESTIONS

Covering the Reading

1. **a.** If a and b are real numbers and multiplicative inverses of each other, what does ab equal? 1
   b. If M and N are 2×2 matrices and multiplicative inverses of each other, what does MN equal? $\begin{bmatrix} 1 & 0 \\ 0 & 1 \end{bmatrix}$

302

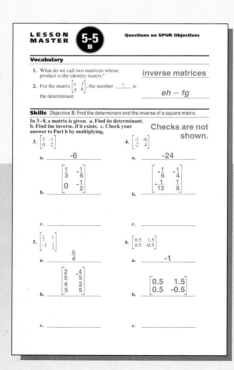

Additional Answers

4. $\begin{bmatrix} \dfrac{d}{ad-bc} & \dfrac{-b}{ad-bc} \\ \dfrac{-c}{ad-bc} & \dfrac{a}{ad-bc} \end{bmatrix}\begin{bmatrix} a & b \\ c & d \end{bmatrix} =$

$\begin{bmatrix} \dfrac{ad}{ad-bc} + \dfrac{-bc}{ad-bc} & \dfrac{bd}{ad-bc} + \dfrac{-bd}{ad-bc} \\ \dfrac{-ac}{ad-bc} + \dfrac{ac}{ad-bc} & \dfrac{-bc}{ad-bc} + \dfrac{ad}{ad-bc} \end{bmatrix} =$

$\begin{bmatrix} \dfrac{ad-bc}{ad-bc} & 0 \\ 0 & \dfrac{ad-bc}{ad-bc} \end{bmatrix} = \begin{bmatrix} 1 & 0 \\ 0 & 1 \end{bmatrix}$

3) $\begin{bmatrix} 12 & 13 \\ 2 & 3 \end{bmatrix}\begin{bmatrix} .3 & -1.3 \\ -.2 & 1.2 \end{bmatrix} =$

$\begin{bmatrix} 1 & 0 \\ 0 & 1 \end{bmatrix};$

$\begin{bmatrix} .3 & -1.3 \\ -.2 & 1.2 \end{bmatrix}\begin{bmatrix} 12 & 13 \\ 2 & 3 \end{bmatrix} =$

$\begin{bmatrix} 1 & 0 \\ 0 & 1 \end{bmatrix}.$

10)

$\begin{bmatrix} 2 & 5 \\ 3 & 8 \end{bmatrix}\begin{bmatrix} 8 & -5 \\ -3 & 2 \end{bmatrix} = \begin{bmatrix} 1 & 0 \\ 0 & 1 \end{bmatrix}$

12c)

$\begin{bmatrix} 1 & -2 \\ -1 & \frac{5}{2} \end{bmatrix}\begin{bmatrix} 5 & 4 \\ 2 & 2 \end{bmatrix} = \begin{bmatrix} 1 & 0 \\ 0 & 1 \end{bmatrix}$

$= \begin{bmatrix} 5 & 4 \\ 2 & 2 \end{bmatrix}\begin{bmatrix} 1 & -2 \\ -1 & \frac{5}{2} \end{bmatrix}$

13c)

$\begin{bmatrix} -\frac{2}{5} & \frac{3}{20} \\ -\frac{1}{5} & -\frac{1}{20} \end{bmatrix}\begin{bmatrix} -1 & -3 \\ 4 & -8 \end{bmatrix} =$

$\begin{bmatrix} \frac{2}{5}+\frac{3}{5} & \frac{6}{5}-\frac{6}{5} \\ \frac{1}{5}-\frac{1}{5} & \frac{3}{5}+\frac{2}{5} \end{bmatrix} = \begin{bmatrix} 1 & 0 \\ 0 & 1 \end{bmatrix} =$

$\begin{bmatrix} -1 & -3 \\ 4 & -8 \end{bmatrix}\begin{bmatrix} -\frac{2}{5} & \frac{3}{20} \\ -\frac{1}{5} & -\frac{1}{20} \end{bmatrix}$

15) Sample: $\begin{bmatrix} 2 & 6 \\ 1 & 3 \end{bmatrix}$

16a) $e = \frac{1}{6}, f = \frac{1}{3}, g = \frac{-1}{2},$

$h = 0$, or $\begin{bmatrix} \frac{1}{6} & \frac{1}{3} \\ -\frac{1}{2} & 0 \end{bmatrix}$

---

2. a. Find the inverse of $M = \begin{bmatrix} 5 & 0 \\ 0 & 3 \end{bmatrix}.$ $\begin{bmatrix} \frac{1}{5} & 0 \\ 0 & \frac{1}{3} \end{bmatrix}$

   b. What transformation does M represent? $S_{5,3}$

   c. What transformation does the inverse of M represent? $S_{\frac{1}{5},\frac{1}{3}}$

3. *True or false.* $\begin{bmatrix} 12 & 13 \\ 2 & 3 \end{bmatrix}$ and $\begin{bmatrix} .3 & -1.3 \\ -.2 & 1.2 \end{bmatrix}$ are inverses of each other. Justify your answer. **True; see left.**

4. Verify the second part of the proof of the Inverse-Matrix Theorem. That is, show that the identity matrix is the product of the two matrices in the reverse order. **See margin.**

In 5 and 6, *true or false.*

5. Only square matrices have inverses. **True**

6. All square matrices have inverses. **False**

7. Give an expression for $\det \begin{bmatrix} a & b \\ c & d \end{bmatrix}.$ **$ad - bc$**

8. M is a matrix with nonzero determinant. What does M^{-1} denote? **the inverse of M**

9. If A is a 2×2 matrix and A^{-1} exists, what does $A^{-1}A$ equal? $\begin{bmatrix} 1 & 0 \\ 0 & 1 \end{bmatrix}$

10. Show the result you obtained for Activity 1 in this lesson. **See left.**

11. What did you need to do to complete Activity 2 in this lesson? **Answers will vary.**

In 12–14, a matrix is given. **a.** Find its determinant. **b.** Find its inverse, if it has one. **c.** Check your answer to part **b** by multiplying. **c) See left.**

12. $\begin{bmatrix} 5 & 4 \\ 2 & 2 \end{bmatrix}$
a) 2 b) $\begin{bmatrix} 1 & -2 \\ -1 & \frac{5}{2} \end{bmatrix}$

13. $\begin{bmatrix} -1 & -3 \\ 4 & -8 \end{bmatrix}$
a) 20 b) $\begin{bmatrix} -\frac{2}{5} & \frac{3}{20} \\ -\frac{1}{5} & -\frac{1}{20} \end{bmatrix}$

14. $\begin{bmatrix} \frac{1}{2} & \frac{1}{2} \\ \frac{1}{2} & \frac{1}{2} \end{bmatrix}$
a) 0 b) It has no inverse.

Applying the Mathematics

15. Give an example of a matrix not mentioned in this lesson that does not have an inverse. **See left.**

16. The inverse of a 2×2 matrix can also be found by solving a pair of systems. Here is how. If the inverse of $\begin{bmatrix} 0 & -2 \\ 3 & 1 \end{bmatrix}$ is $\begin{bmatrix} e & f \\ g & h \end{bmatrix},$

then $\begin{bmatrix} 0 & -2 \\ 3 & 1 \end{bmatrix}\begin{bmatrix} e & f \\ g & h \end{bmatrix} = \begin{bmatrix} 1 & 0 \\ 0 & 1 \end{bmatrix}.$

This yields the systems $\begin{cases} 0e - 2g = 1 \\ 3e + g = 0 \end{cases}$ and $\begin{cases} 0f - 2h = 0 \\ 3f + h = 1. \end{cases}$

   a. Solve these two systems and determine the inverse matrix. **See left.**

   b. Check your answer to part **a** by finding the inverse matrix using the Inverse Matrix Theorem. **See margin.**

Lesson 5-5 *Inverses of Matrices* **303**

By using linear-combination techniques, we can solve for *w, x, y,* and *z*. For instance, if we multiply the first equation by *c* and the third by *–a*, and then add the resulting equations, we can solve for *y* :

$$y = \frac{c}{bc - ad} = \frac{-c}{ad - bc}.$$

Other linear combinations will allow you to find *w, x,* and *z.* We do not suggest you do the complete derivation for all four variables, but some students might enjoy working through the complete derivation on their own.

Project Update Project 2, *Inverses of 3 × 3 Matrices,* and Project 5, *Using Matrices to Code and Decode Messages,* on pages 336–337, relate to the content of this lesson.

Notes on Questions

Question 16 If it exists, the inverse of a matrix can always be found using the method shown in this question. However, using the Inverse Matrix Theorem is faster.

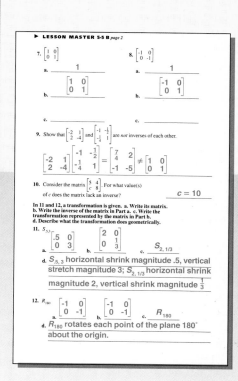

16b. Since the determinant $(0)(1) - (-2)(3) = 6 \neq 0$, the inverse of

$\begin{bmatrix} 0 & -2 \\ 3 & 1 \end{bmatrix}$ is $\begin{bmatrix} \frac{1}{6} & \frac{2}{6} \\ -\frac{3}{6} & \frac{0}{6} \end{bmatrix} = \begin{bmatrix} \frac{1}{6} & \frac{1}{3} \\ -\frac{1}{2} & 0 \end{bmatrix}.$

Adapting to Individual Needs

Challenge
Fill in the blank.

$\begin{bmatrix} 2 & 3 \\ 1 & 2 \end{bmatrix} \cdot \underline{\quad} = \begin{bmatrix} 11 \\ 6 \end{bmatrix}$ $\begin{bmatrix} 4 \\ 1 \end{bmatrix}$

303

Notes on Questions

Question 19 To lead into the next lesson, you might want to check this question using the matrix solution. Equations that are set up for linear combinations are also set up for matrices.

Multicultural Connection Bread has been a important food since ancient times. A bread made from crushed grain mixed with water is known to have existed 12,000 years ago. Today, flat breads are popular in Central America and in parts of Asia and Africa. Raised breads are preferred in the United States, Canada, and Europe. Flat breads include millet cakes and chapaties from India, corn tortillas from Latin America, and Jewish matzoth. Raised breads probably originated in ancient Egypt when Egyptians discovered that if bread dough were allowed to ferment before baking, a lighter and expanded loaf of bread would form. Today this fermentation is produced by adding yeast to the bread dough.

Question 20 This question can lead to the discussion of some interesting topics, such as: modeling of a constant-increase situation, domain, intersection or equal-cost point, and the significance of a portion of one line being "above" the other line on this graph.

Question 22 Point out that the product of the two matrices can represent two linear combinations of x and y. In the next lesson, the process is reversed. That is, two linear combinations of x and y are given to be represented as a product of two matrices.

20a)

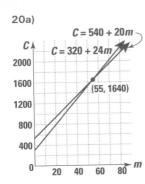

Shown are volunteers filling sandbags during the Midwest floods of 1993.

24b) Samples:

$A = \begin{bmatrix} -1 & 3 \\ -3 & 5 \end{bmatrix}$, $B = \begin{bmatrix} -4 & 4 \\ 3 & 4 \end{bmatrix}$

det $A = 4$; det $B = -28$; det $AB = -112$;

$A = \begin{bmatrix} 1 & 2 \\ 2 & 3 \end{bmatrix}$, $B = \begin{bmatrix} 8 & 5 \\ 7 & 4 \end{bmatrix}$

det $A = -1$, det $B = -3$, det $AB = 3$

304

17. a. Find the inverse of the matrix for R_{90}. $\begin{bmatrix} 0 & 1 \\ -1 & 0 \end{bmatrix}$
  b. Explain the result to part a geometrically.
  Sample: The matrix in part a represents R_{270} or R_{-90}. Geometrically, R_{-90} and R_{90} are opposite transformations.

Review

18. Solve the system $\begin{cases} 5x + y + 6z = 3 \\ x - y + 10z = 9 \\ 5x + y - 2z = -9. \end{cases}$ *(Lesson 5-4)* $\left(-2, 4, \frac{3}{2}\right)$

19. A chef reports that with 5 kilograms of flour, 12 loaves of bread and 6 pizza crusts can be made. With 2 kilograms of flour, 1 loaf of bread and 10 pizza crusts can be made. How much flour is needed to make one loaf of bread? How much is needed for one pizza crust? *(Lesson 5-4)* $\frac{1}{3}$ kg for bread, $\frac{1}{6}$ kg for pizza crust

20. Alan Aska wanted to purchase a new air conditioner. One brand costs $540 to purchase and $20 a month to operate. A less efficient brand costs $320 to purchase and $24 a month to operate. See left.
  a. Plot the costs over time of both brands on a single graph.
  b. What does the point of intersection of the graphs denote?
  (Lessons 3-1, 5-2, 5-3) The point of intersection denotes the total costs are the same. In 55 months, costs are the same.

21. Solve $\begin{cases} y = 4x \\ 3x + 2y = 22. \end{cases}$ *(Lessons 5-2, 5-3)* (2, 8)

22. Multiply $\begin{bmatrix} 1 & -2 \\ 4 & 5 \end{bmatrix} \begin{bmatrix} x \\ y \end{bmatrix}$. *(Lesson 4-3)* $\begin{bmatrix} x - 2y \\ 4x + 5y \end{bmatrix}$

23. During a flood watch, a group of volunteers filled sandbags at a rate of 500 sandbags an hour. In how many hours will the group have prepared at least 10,000 sandbags? *(Lesson 5-1)* in 20 hours

Exploration

24. a. If $A = \begin{bmatrix} -7 & 4 \\ -9 & -4 \end{bmatrix}$ and $B = \begin{bmatrix} 3 & 3 \\ 0 & 3 \end{bmatrix}$, find det A, det B, and det (AB). 64; 9; 576
  b. Pick two other 2×2 matrices A and B with nonzero determinants. Find det A, det B, and det (AB). See left.
  c. Generalize the results of parts **a** and **b.** (det A) · (det B) = det AB

25. a. Find the area of the triangle with vertices (0, 0), (-3, 0), and (-7, 8). 12 sq units
  b. Calculate $\frac{1}{2}$ det $\begin{bmatrix} -3 & -7 \\ 0 & 8 \end{bmatrix}$. -12
  c. Find the area of the triangle with vertices (0, 0), (5, 2), and (4, 0). 4 sq units
  d. Calculate $\frac{1}{2}$ det $\begin{bmatrix} 5 & 4 \\ 2 & 0 \end{bmatrix}$. -4
  e. Make a conjecture based on parts **a–d.** See margin.
  f. Test your conjecture with another example. See margin.

Additional Answers
25e. Sample: The area of the triangle with vertices (0, 0), (a, b), and (c, d) is equal to the absolute value of

$\frac{1}{2}$ det $\begin{bmatrix} a & c \\ b & d \end{bmatrix}$.

f. The area of a triangle with vertices (0, 0), (12, 1), and (0, 5) is $\frac{1}{2} \cdot 5 \cdot 12$

$= 30$ or $\frac{1}{2}$ det $\begin{bmatrix} 12 & 0 \\ 1 & 5 \end{bmatrix} = 30$.

Setting Up Lesson 5-6
Discuss **Question 22** to prepare students for the next lesson.

Taking stock. *Pictured are parts of the stock certificates an investor receives when purchasing stocks. Superimposed are stock prices. A large system of equations could be used to plan an investment portfolio. See Example 2.*

Using Matrices to Solve 2 × 2 Linear Systems

In the middle of the nineteenth century, the British mathematician Arthur Cayley developed a way to solve systems of linear equations by using matrices. To see how this method works, we begin with an example. Notice that

$$\begin{bmatrix} 1 & 3 \\ 2 & -1 \end{bmatrix} \begin{bmatrix} x \\ y \end{bmatrix} = \begin{bmatrix} x + 3y \\ 2x - y \end{bmatrix}.$$

Thus, we can represent the system $\begin{cases} x + 3y = 22 \\ 2x - y = 2 \end{cases}$

by the matrix equation $\begin{bmatrix} 1 & 3 \\ 2 & -1 \end{bmatrix} \begin{bmatrix} x \\ y \end{bmatrix} = \begin{bmatrix} 22 \\ 2 \end{bmatrix}.$

This is called the **matrix form of a system.** The matrix $\begin{bmatrix} 1 & 3 \\ 2 & -1 \end{bmatrix}$ contains the coefficients of the variables, so it is called the **coefficient matrix.** The matrix $\begin{bmatrix} 22 \\ 2 \end{bmatrix}$ contains the constants on the right sides of the equations. It is called the **constant matrix.**

To solve a system in matrix form, multiply each side of the matrix equation by the inverse of the coefficient matrix.

Lesson 5-6

Objectives

C Use matrices to solve systems of two or three linear equations.
D Recognize properties of systems of equations.
F Use systems of two or three linear equations to solve real-world problems.

Resources

From the **Teacher's Resource File**
■ Lesson Master 5-6A or 5-6B
■ Answer Master 5-6
■ Teaching Aids 44: Warm-up
■ Technology Sourcebook Calculator Master 3

Additional Resources
■ Visual for Teaching Aid 44

Teaching 5-6
Lesson

Warm-up

Multiply.

1. $\begin{bmatrix} 8 & 5 \\ 6 & 4 \end{bmatrix} \begin{bmatrix} 10 \\ 15 \end{bmatrix}$ $\begin{bmatrix} 155 \\ 120 \end{bmatrix}$

2. $\begin{bmatrix} \frac{3}{10} & \frac{1}{5} \\ -\frac{2}{5} & \frac{1}{10} \end{bmatrix} \begin{bmatrix} 30 \\ 20 \end{bmatrix}$ $\begin{bmatrix} 13 \\ -10 \end{bmatrix}$

Lesson 5-6 Overview

Broad Goals This lesson illustrates how to solve 2 × 2 and 3 × 3 linear systems by representing the system as a matrix equation, and then multiplying each side of the matrix equation by the inverse of the coefficient matrix.

Perspective For 2 × 2 linear systems students can use the Inverse Matrix Theorem from Lesson 5-5 to find the inverse of the coefficient matrix, if it exists.

For 3 × 3 linear systems, students are either given the inverse of the coefficient matrix, or are expected to find the inverse using technology. Finding the inverse of a 3 × 3 matrix by hand is not an objective of this course. (See *Optional Activities,* page 306.)

The availability of both calculator and computer technology that can find inverses of

matrices has greatly increased the use of matrix methods for solving systems.

The matrix method of solving a system of equations is especially useful for applications in which the coefficients of the variables remain the same while the constants change.

(Overview continues on page 306.)

History Connection In 1863, Arthur Cayley was elected to the new Sadlerian chair of pure mathematics at Cambridge University in England. From that time on, he was constantly engaged in mathematical investigation, and he played a leading role in the founding of the modern British school of pure mathematics. He was also influential in changing admission requirements to allow women to enroll at Cambridge.

Cooperative Learning You might want to read through this lesson with the students. If you have students read the lines aloud, you may find that some students still do not know how to read a matrix orally. Point out that matrices are read row by row.

For instance, $\begin{bmatrix} 1 & 3 \\ 2 & -1 \end{bmatrix}$ is read "the matrix 1, 3, 2, –1."

Students may ask why they are using matrices to solve systems that they could solve by other means. You can give them many reasons: (1) these methods generalize the solving of systems with many equations and many variables; (2) these methods are used by computers; (3) these methods indicate exactly when a system has a solution; and (4) the System-Determinant Theorem extends to any linear system of n equations and n variables.

Example 1

Use matrices to solve $\begin{cases} x + 3y = 22 \\ 2x - y = 2. \end{cases}$

Solution

Write the matrix form of the system.

$$\begin{bmatrix} 1 & 3 \\ 2 & -1 \end{bmatrix} \begin{bmatrix} x \\ y \end{bmatrix} = \begin{bmatrix} 22 \\ 2 \end{bmatrix}$$

Use the Inverse Matrix Theorem to find the inverse of the coefficient matrix.

The inverse of $\begin{bmatrix} 1 & 3 \\ 2 & -1 \end{bmatrix}$ is $\begin{bmatrix} \frac{-1}{-7} & \frac{-3}{-7} \\ \frac{-2}{-7} & \frac{1}{-7} \end{bmatrix} = \begin{bmatrix} \frac{1}{7} & \frac{3}{7} \\ \frac{2}{7} & \frac{-1}{7} \end{bmatrix}$.

Multiply both sides of the matrix equation by the inverse. Because matrix multiplication is not commutative, the inverse matrix must be *at the left on each side* of the equation.

$$\begin{bmatrix} \frac{1}{7} & \frac{3}{7} \\ \frac{2}{7} & \frac{-1}{7} \end{bmatrix} \begin{bmatrix} 1 & 3 \\ 2 & -1 \end{bmatrix} \begin{bmatrix} x \\ y \end{bmatrix} = \begin{bmatrix} \frac{1}{7} & \frac{3}{7} \\ \frac{2}{7} & \frac{-1}{7} \end{bmatrix} \begin{bmatrix} 22 \\ 2 \end{bmatrix}$$

Multiply the matrices. $\begin{bmatrix} 1 & 0 \\ 0 & 1 \end{bmatrix} \begin{bmatrix} x \\ y \end{bmatrix} = \begin{bmatrix} 4 \\ 6 \end{bmatrix}$

The presence of the identity matrix verifies that the inverse matrix was calculated correctly. Thus

$$\begin{bmatrix} x \\ y \end{bmatrix} = \begin{bmatrix} 4 \\ 6 \end{bmatrix}.$$

So, x = 4 and y = 6.

Check

Substitute $x = 4$ and $y = 6$ into the original equations.
Does $4 + 3(6) = 22$? Does $2(4) - 6 = 2$? Yes, it checks.

In general, to solve the system $\begin{cases} ax + by = e \\ cx + dy = f \end{cases}$ using matrices, first rewrite the system as the matrix equation

$$\begin{bmatrix} a & b \\ c & d \end{bmatrix} \begin{bmatrix} x \\ y \end{bmatrix} = \begin{bmatrix} e \\ f \end{bmatrix}.$$

This equation is of the form $A \begin{bmatrix} x \\ y \end{bmatrix} = B$, where A is the coefficient matrix and B is the constant matrix. As long as $ad - bc \neq 0$, A^{-1} exists. To solve this equation, multiply each side by A^{-1}.

$$A^{-1} A \begin{bmatrix} x \\ y \end{bmatrix} = A^{-1} B$$

$$\begin{bmatrix} 1 & 0 \\ 0 & 1 \end{bmatrix} \begin{bmatrix} x \\ y \end{bmatrix} = A^{-1} B$$

▶

(Lesson 5-6 Overview, continued.)

To create M^{-1} for a 3 × 3 matrix without using technology, begin with

$$M = \begin{bmatrix} a_{11} & a_{12} & a_{13} \\ a_{21} & a_{22} & a_{23} \\ a_{31} & a_{32} & a_{33} \end{bmatrix}.$$

The cofactor C_{ij} of the component a_{ij} in a 3 × 3 matrix is the product of $(-1)^{i+j}$ and the determinant of the 2 × 2 submatrix of M determined by deleting the ith row and jth column. Calculate the cofactor of each element and then calculate det $M = a_{11}C_{11} + a_{12}C_{12} + a_{13}C_{13}$. The inverse M^{-1} of the matrix exists if and only if det $M \neq 0$. And if det $M \neq 0$, then

$$M^{-1} = \begin{bmatrix} \frac{C_{11}}{\det M} & \frac{C_{21}}{\det M} & \frac{C_{31}}{\det M} \\ \frac{C_{12}}{\det M} & \frac{C_{22}}{\det M} & \frac{C_{32}}{\det M} \\ \frac{C_{13}}{\det M} & \frac{C_{23}}{\det M} & \frac{C_{33}}{\det M} \end{bmatrix}.$$

Generalizations of these formulas to higher-order systems can be found in linear-algebra texts.

► So,
$$\begin{bmatrix} x \\ y \end{bmatrix} = A^{-1}B$$

The last equation shows that the solution to the system is the product of the inverse of the coefficient matrix and the constant matrix.

Example 2

Ku invested $25,000, some in a savings account and the rest in bonds. If the return on his savings account was 4% last year and the return on his bonds was 6%, how did Ku divide his investments if the total interest was $1300?

Solution 1

Let s be the amount invested in savings and b be the amount invested in bonds. Because the total invested was $25,000, one equation to be satisfied is

$$s + b = 25,000.$$

The interest on savings was $.04s$ and the interest on the bonds was $.06b$. Because the total interest was $1300, a second equation to be satisfied is

$$.04s + .06b = 1300.$$

Now write the matrix equation for this system.

$$\begin{bmatrix} 1 & 1 \\ .04 & .06 \end{bmatrix} \begin{bmatrix} s \\ b \end{bmatrix} = \begin{bmatrix} 25,000 \\ 1300 \end{bmatrix}$$

Find the inverse of the coefficient matrix. It is $\begin{bmatrix} \frac{.06}{.02} & \frac{-1}{.02} \\ \frac{-.04}{.02} & \frac{1}{.02} \end{bmatrix}$ or $\begin{bmatrix} 3 & -50 \\ -2 & 50 \end{bmatrix}$.

Multiply both sides of the matrix equation *on the left* by this matrix.

$$\begin{bmatrix} 3 & -50 \\ -2 & 50 \end{bmatrix} \begin{bmatrix} 1 & 1 \\ .04 & .06 \end{bmatrix} \begin{bmatrix} s \\ b \end{bmatrix} = \begin{bmatrix} 3 & -50 \\ -2 & 50 \end{bmatrix} \begin{bmatrix} 25,000 \\ 1300 \end{bmatrix}$$

$$\begin{bmatrix} 1 & 0 \\ 0 & 1 \end{bmatrix} \begin{bmatrix} s \\ b \end{bmatrix} = \begin{bmatrix} 10,000 \\ 15,000 \end{bmatrix}$$

So the solution is $s = 10,000$ and $b = 15,000$. Ku invested $10,000 in a savings account and $15,000 in bonds.

Solution 2

Set up the system $\begin{cases} s + b = 25,000 \\ .04s + .06b = 1300 \end{cases}$ as in Solution 1.

Use the Linear Combination Method to solve the system. (You are asked to do this in the Questions.)

Check

Does $10,000 + 15,000 = 25,000$? Yes.
Does $.04(10,000) + .06(15,000) = 1300$? Yes.

Lesson 5-6 Solving Systems Using Matrices **307**

Additional Examples

1. Use matrices to solve:
$$\begin{cases} 2x + 3y = 7 \\ 3x - y = 5 \end{cases}.$$

$$\begin{bmatrix} \frac{1}{11} & \frac{3}{11} \\ \frac{3}{11} & \frac{-2}{11} \end{bmatrix} \begin{bmatrix} 7 \\ 5 \end{bmatrix} = \begin{bmatrix} \frac{22}{11} \\ \frac{11}{11} \end{bmatrix} = \begin{bmatrix} 2 \\ 1 \end{bmatrix}$$

$x = 2$, $y = 1$

2. A painter has two kinds of paint. Paint A is 1 part white and 3 parts red. Paint B is 2 parts white and 1 part red. How much of each paint is needed to make one liter of paint that is half white and half red? (Hint: First change the given information into the fractions of red in each paint.) Let A = amount of Paint A needed and let B = the amount of Paint B needed.
$A + B = 1$; $\frac{3}{4}A + \frac{1}{3}B = \frac{1}{2}$; $(A, B) = (\frac{2}{5}, \frac{3}{5})$

3. How many solutions does the system $\begin{cases} 8x - 12y = 20 \\ 2x + 3y = 4 \end{cases}$ have? Justify your answer.
No solution; the determinant of the coefficient matrix is zero, and a solution to the first equation does not work in the second equation.

4. Solve: $\begin{cases} x + y + 2z = 1 \\ 2x + y = 2 \\ x + 2y + 2z = 3 \end{cases}$,

using $\begin{bmatrix} \frac{1}{2} & \frac{1}{2} & \frac{-1}{2} \\ -1 & 0 & 1 \\ \frac{3}{4} & \frac{-1}{4} & \frac{-1}{4} \end{bmatrix}$ for the inverse of the coefficient matrix.
$x = 0$, $y = 2$, $z = -\frac{1}{2}$

Optional Activities

Activity 1 In this chapter students solved systems by substitution, by using linear combinations, and by using matrices. After completing this lesson, you might have students **work in groups** and discuss each method. Suggest that they give examples of systems they would solve using each method. [Students should recognize that for systems like the first one shown at the right, solving the system involves merely substituting 4 for y in the first equation and solving for x:

$$\begin{cases} 8x + 12y = 16 \\ 3y = 12 \end{cases}$$

Students probably would solve this system using linear combinations:

$$\begin{cases} 8x + 12y = 20 \\ 2x + 3y = 4 \end{cases}$$

Matrices are often used when systems are solved using graphics calculators or computers.]

Activity 2 Technology Connection
You may wish to assign *Technology Sourcebook, Calculator Master 3*. This activity reinforces the process of solving systems with matrices that is presented in this lesson.

307

The Number of Solutions to a 2 × 2 Linear System

Matrices can be used to determine the number of solutions to a 2 × 2 linear system. Consider the system $\begin{cases} ax + by = e \\ cx + dy = f \end{cases}$. When the determinant $ad - bc$ of the coefficient matrix is not 0, the inverse of the coefficient matrix exists, and the system has exactly one solution.

When $ad - bc = 0$, the coefficient matrix has no inverse. Thus, when the determinant of the coefficient matrix is 0, the system has infinitely many solutions or none at all. This is summarized in the next theorem.

> **System-Determinant Theorem**
> A 2 × 2 system has exactly one solution if and only if the determinant of the coefficient matrix is *not* zero.

To determine whether there are no solutions or infinitely many solutions, find an ordered pair that satisfies one of the equations and test it in the other one. If it satisfies the other equation, the two equations represent the same line and there are infinitely many solutions. If the given ordered pair does not satisfy the other equation, the two lines are parallel and there are no solutions.

Example 3

How many solutions does the system $\begin{cases} 6x - 9y = 12 \\ 2x - 3y = 4 \end{cases}$ have?

Solution 1

The determinant is $ad - bc = 6 \cdot (-3) - (-9) \cdot (2) = 0$.
So either the two equations describe the same line, or they describe two parallel lines. Find an ordered pair that satisfies one equation. The point $(2, 0)$ satisfies the first equation. Does it satisfy the second? Does $2 \cdot 2 - 3 \cdot 0 = 4$? Yes. Thus, the system has infinitely many solutions. The two equations describe the same line.

Solution 2

Use the Linear Combination Method. Multiply each side of the second equation by -3, and add the resulting equations.

$$6x - 9y = 12 \qquad\qquad 6x - 9y = 12$$
$$-3(2x - 3y) = -3 \cdot 4 \qquad \underline{-6x + 9y = -12}$$
$$0 = 0$$

There are infinitely many solutions.

Solution 3

Multiplying both sides of the first equation by $\frac{1}{3}$ gives the second equation. Thus, the two given equations are equivalent. So their graphs are identical, and the system has infinitely many solutions.

Using Matrices to Solve 3 × 3 Linear Systems

Matrices can be used to solve $n \times n$ linear systems whenever the inverse of the coefficient matrix exists. In the next example, we solve a system of three equations with three unknowns using 3×3 matrices.

The identity matrix for 3×3 matrices is $\begin{bmatrix} 1 & 0 & 0 \\ 0 & 1 & 0 \\ 0 & 0 & 1 \end{bmatrix}$. The calculation of the inverse of a 3×3 matrix by hand is complicated, so use a graphics calculator or computer software to find the inverse of a 3×3 matrix whenever it is needed.

Example 4

Solve the system $\begin{cases} x - y + 3z = 9 \\ x + 2z = 3 \\ 2x + 2y + z = 10. \end{cases}$

Solution

First, rewrite each equation in standard form if necessary. The second equation becomes $1 \cdot x + 0 \cdot y + 2 \cdot z = 3$. Then rewrite the system as a matrix equation. To the right of the solution steps below, we have given the general form of the steps.

$$\begin{bmatrix} 1 & -1 & 3 \\ 1 & 0 & 2 \\ 2 & 2 & 1 \end{bmatrix} \begin{bmatrix} x \\ y \\ z \end{bmatrix} = \begin{bmatrix} 9 \\ 3 \\ 10 \end{bmatrix} \qquad A \begin{bmatrix} x \\ y \\ z \end{bmatrix} = B$$

Multiply each side by the inverse of the coefficient matrix, then simplify. Use technology to obtain the inverse.

$$\begin{bmatrix} 1 & 0 & 0 \\ 0 & 1 & 0 \\ 0 & 0 & 1 \end{bmatrix} \begin{bmatrix} x \\ y \\ z \end{bmatrix} = \begin{bmatrix} 4 & -7 & 2 \\ -3 & 5 & -1 \\ -2 & 4 & -1 \end{bmatrix} \begin{bmatrix} 9 \\ 3 \\ 10 \end{bmatrix} \qquad A^{-1}A \begin{bmatrix} x \\ y \\ z \end{bmatrix} = A^{-1}B$$

You should find that

$$\begin{bmatrix} x \\ y \\ z \end{bmatrix} = \begin{bmatrix} 35 \\ -22 \\ -16 \end{bmatrix} \qquad \begin{bmatrix} x \\ y \\ z \end{bmatrix} = A^{-1}B$$

So the solution is x = 35, y = -22, and z = -16.

Check

Substitute $x = 35$, $y = -22$, and $z = -16$ into each equation of the system. You are asked to do this in the Questions.

Note that on many calculators and computers you can compute $A^{-1}B$ without actually finding the elements in matrix A^{-1}.

In general, to solve a linear system using matrices, first rewrite the system so that all equations are in standard form. Then set up the coefficient matrix as matrix A and the constant matrix as matrix B. The solution is given by $A^{-1}B$. If the system is 2×2 you can compute $A^{-1}B$ by hand. For larger systems you will probably need to use a graphics calculator or computer software.

Lesson 5-6 *Solving Systems Using Matrices* **309**

Adapting to Individual Needs

Challenge

Have students use matrices to find a formula for the solution to this system of equations:

$$ac + by = c$$
$$dx + ey = f$$

If students need a hint, tell them to use the matrix formula $X = A^{-1} \cdot B$, where

$A = \begin{bmatrix} a & b \\ d & e \end{bmatrix}$ and $B = \begin{bmatrix} c \\ f \end{bmatrix}$.

$[x = \dfrac{ec - bf}{ae - bd}, \ y = \dfrac{af - dc}{ae - bd}]$

309

Notes on Questions

Questions 6, 7, and 11 Emphasize that the inverse matrix must be to the *left* of the constant matrix in order to multiply.

Question 11 Students with graphics calculators can use this question to check whether they know how to use technology to obtain the inverse of a matrix.

Practice

For more questions on SPUR Objectives, use **Lesson Master 5-6A** (shown on page 309) or **Lesson Master 5-6B** (shown on pages 310–311).

Assessment

Written Communication Have each student write a paragraph that summarizes the procedure he or she would follow to solve a 2 × 2 linear system of equations using matrices. [Students demonstrate that they understand the steps in using matrices to solve a 2 × 2 linear system.]

3a) $\begin{bmatrix} a & b \\ d & e \end{bmatrix}\begin{bmatrix} x \\ y \end{bmatrix} = \begin{bmatrix} c \\ f \end{bmatrix}$

b) $\begin{bmatrix} a & b \\ d & e \end{bmatrix}$

4) Multiply the top equation by -.04 and add it to the second equation. The result is .02*b* = 300, so *b* = 15,000 and *s* = 10,000.

6) $\left(\frac{-25}{12}, \frac{20}{9}\right)$ or $\begin{bmatrix} -2.08\overline{3} \\ 2.\overline{2} \end{bmatrix}$

7) $\left(\frac{8}{17}, \frac{2}{17}\right)$ or $\begin{bmatrix} \approx.471 \\ \approx.118 \end{bmatrix}$

11b)
Does 4(1) − 2(3) + 3(1) = 1? Yes.
Does 8(1) − 3(3) + 5(1) = 4? Yes.
Does 7(1) − 2(3) + 4(1) = 5? Yes.
It checks.

In 1 and 2, refer to the system in Example 1.

1. What does the matrix $\begin{bmatrix} 1 & 3 \\ 2 & -1 \end{bmatrix}$ represent? **the coefficients of the variables**

2. Noel found the inverse $\begin{bmatrix} \frac{1}{7} & \frac{3}{7} \\ \frac{2}{7} & \frac{-1}{7} \end{bmatrix}$ and multiplied as shown here.

$$\begin{bmatrix} 1 & 3 \\ 2 & -1 \end{bmatrix}\begin{bmatrix} \frac{1}{7} & \frac{3}{7} \\ \frac{2}{7} & \frac{-1}{7} \end{bmatrix}\begin{bmatrix} x \\ y \end{bmatrix} = \begin{bmatrix} 22 \\ 2 \end{bmatrix}\begin{bmatrix} \frac{1}{7} & \frac{3}{7} \\ \frac{2}{7} & \frac{-1}{7} \end{bmatrix}$$

Did Noel find a solution? Explain.
No; he multiplied the inverse on the right rather than on the left.

3. **a.** Rewrite the system $\begin{cases} ax + by = c \\ dx + ey = f \end{cases}$ in matrix form.

   b. What matrix in part **a** is the coefficient matrix for the system?
   See left.

In 4 and 5, refer to Example 2.

4. Use the Linear Combination Method to finish Solution 2.
   See left.

5. Suppose the return on Ku's savings account was 3% and the return on his bonds was 5%. How did Ku invest his money if he received a total of $1200 interest? **$2500 in savings and $22,500 in bonds**

In 6 and 7, solve each system using matrices. **See left.**

6. $\begin{cases} -8x - 3y = 10 \\ 4x + 6y = 5 \end{cases}$ 7. $\begin{cases} 4x + y = 2 \\ 9x - 2y = 4 \end{cases}$

See margin for 8, 9.
In 8 and 9, how many solutions does the system have? Justify your answer.

8. $\begin{cases} 10x + 15y = 30 \\ 4x + 6y = 12 \end{cases}$ 9. $\begin{cases} 30p - 18q = 42 \\ 35p - 21q = 76 \end{cases}$

10. Complete the check of Example 4. **See margin.**

11. **a.** Solve the system $\begin{cases} 4x - 2y + 3z = 1 \\ 8x - 3y + 5z = 4 \\ 7x - 2y + 4z = 5 \end{cases}$ using matrices. **(1, 3, 1)**

    b. Check your answer. **See left.**

Applying the Mathematics

12. **a.** Solve this matrix equation: $\begin{bmatrix} 1 & 2 \\ 3 & 4 \end{bmatrix}\begin{bmatrix} w & x \\ y & z \end{bmatrix} = \begin{bmatrix} 5 & 6 \\ 7 & 8 \end{bmatrix}$
    w = -3, x = -4, y = 4, z = 5

    b. What two systems does part **a** simultaneously solve?
    $\begin{cases} w + 2y = 5 \\ 3w + 4y = 7 \end{cases}$ and $\begin{cases} x + 2z = 6 \\ 3x + 4z = 8 \end{cases}$

---

13. A bicycle, three tricycles, and an unicycle cost $561. Seven bicycles and a tricycle cost $906. Five unicycles, two bicycles and seven tricycles cost $1758.
  a. Set up a system of equations that can be used to find the cost of each item. *See left.*
  b. Use matrices to solve the system.
      unicycle: $183;   bicycle: $117;   tricycle: $87

In 14 and 15, determine all values of n that satisfy the condition.

14. $\begin{cases} 2x + 4y = n \\ x + 2y = 7 \end{cases}$ has infinitely many solutions. $n = 14$

15. $\begin{cases} 4x - 6y = 5 \\ 2x + ny = 2 \end{cases}$ has no solution. $n = -3$

Review

16. If the determinant of a 2×2 matrix is 0, what can you conclude about the inverse of the matrix? *(Lesson 5-5)* **The matrix has no multiplicative inverse.**

17. a. Find a 2×2 matrix whose determinant equals 1.
  b. Find the inverse of the matrix in part **a.** *(Lesson 5-5)*
    See left.

In 18–20, solve using any method. *(Lessons 5-2, 5-3, 5-4, 5-5)*

18. $\begin{cases} y = |x| \\ y = 9 \end{cases}$ **19.** $\begin{cases} x + y = 10 \\ x + 2y = 3 \end{cases}$ **20.** $\begin{cases} 3x - 2y = z \\ x = y + 9 \\ z = 8x \end{cases}$

(9, 9), (-9, 9)   (17, -7)   **See left.**

In 21 and 22, use the facts that whole milk is 4% butterfat, and some low fat milk is 1% butterfat.

21. If you mix one quart (32 oz) of each of these two types of milk, how many ounces of butterfat are in the result?
  (Previous course, Lesson 3-3) **1.6 oz**

22. How much of each type of milk must you mix to get one quart of milk that is 2% butterfat? *(Lessons 5-4, 5-5)* $\frac{32}{3}$ **oz whole milk and** $\frac{64}{3}$ **oz low fat milk**

23. Graph on a number line: $\{x: x > 11\} \cap \{x: x > 12\}$. *(Lesson 5-1)*
  See left.

24. In the coordinate plane, graph the line with equation $x = -3$.
  (Lesson 3-6) **See left.**

Exploration

25. a. Show how the *two* systems
  $\begin{cases} -3w + 4y = 5 \\ w + 2y = 0 \end{cases}$ $\begin{cases} -3x + 4z = 1 \\ x + 2z = 3 \end{cases}$
  can be rewritten as a single matrix equation with three 2×2 matrices. **See left.**
  b. When can two 2×2 systems be rewritten as in part **a?** **See left.**
  c. Can three 2×2 systems ever be rewritten as a single matrix equation? Explain your answer. **See margin.**

Lesson 5-6   *Solving Systems Using Matrices*   **311**

Who needs two wheels?
Unicycles first appeared in the late 1800s as part of circus acts and similar entertainment.

13a) $\begin{cases} u + b + 3t = 561 \\ 7b + t = 906 \\ 5u + 2b + 7t = 1758 \end{cases}$

17a) Sample: $\begin{bmatrix} 2 & 3 \\ 3 & 5 \end{bmatrix}$

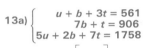

b) Sample: $\begin{bmatrix} 5 & -3 \\ -3 & 2 \end{bmatrix}$

20) $\left(\frac{18}{7}, \frac{-45}{7}, \frac{144}{7} \right)$

23)
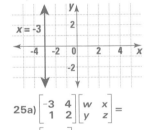

24)

b) **When the coefficient matrices are equal**

25a) $\begin{bmatrix} -3 & 4 \\ 1 & 2 \end{bmatrix} \begin{bmatrix} w & x \\ y & z \end{bmatrix} = \begin{bmatrix} 5 & 1 \\ 0 & 3 \end{bmatrix}$

Extension

Have students solve the following system using matrices and a graphics calculator.
$$a + b + 2c - d = 1$$
$$a + 2b - c + d = 1$$
$$3a + 4c - d = 10$$
$$a - b + 3c - 2d = 1$$
$[a = 1, b = -1, c = 3,$ and $d = 5]$

Project Update Project 2, *Inverses of 3 × 3 Matrices,* on page 336, relates to the content of the lesson.

Additional Answers
8. Infinitely many solutions; the determinant of the coefficient matrix is zero, and the point (0, 2) satisfies both equations.
9. No solutions; the determinant of the coefficient matrix is zero, and the ordered pair (2, 1) satisfies the first but not the second equation.
10. Does $1(35) - 1(-22) + 3(-16) = 9$? Yes. Does $1(35) + 2(-16) = 3$? Yes. Does $2(35) + 2(-22) + 1(-16) = 10$? Yes; it checks.

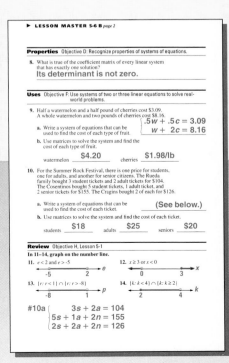

311

Teaching Lesson 5-7

Warm-up

Does the region above or below the dashed line contain points that make the inequality $2x + 3y < 12$ true?

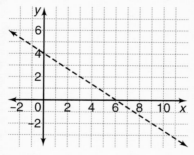

Below the line

Can you ride? _Ferris wheels, roller coasters, and other rides may have height restrictions for riders. See Example 2._

As you learned in Lesson 5-1, solutions to compound sentences with inequalities involving only one variable can be graphed on a number line. Before studying compound sentences with inequalities with two or more variables, we must study the graphs of inequalities in the plane.

When a line is drawn in a plane, the line separates the plane into two distinct regions called **half-planes.** The line itself is the **boundary** of the two regions. The boundary does not belong to either half plane.

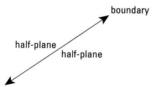

Inequalities with Horizontal or Vertical Boundaries

Inequalities with one variable can be graphed either on a number line or in the coordinate plane.

❶ Example 1

Graph the solutions to $x > 5$
a. on a number line.   **b.** in the coordinate plane.

Solution

a. Plot all points on a number line with x-coordinate greater than 5. These are the points to the right of $x = 5$. Use an open circle to show that 5 is not included in the solution set.

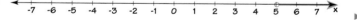

Lesson 5-7 Overview

Broad Goals This lesson expands the idea of graphing inequalities on a number line (which was discussed in Lesson 5-1) to graphing inequalities in the coordinate plane.

Perspective The graphing of half-planes will be review for students who have had UCSMP _Algebra_ or _Geometry_. The idea is usually not difficult for students to master.

The graphing of linear inequalities is critical for the graphing of systems of inequalities later in this chapter. It also provides a review of the graphing encountered in Chapter 3.

The boundary for a linear inequality separates the coordinate plane into three disjoint sets of points: the points on either side of the boundary line and the points on the boundary line itself. This idea will be used

later when students graph inequalities relating to circles and parabolas, so it is important to stress the idea at this time.

Each example serves a different purpose. **Example 1** illustrates the difference between graphing an inequality on a number line and graphing it in the coordinate plane. **Example 2** shows a half-plane of a horizontal line and its boundary. **Example 3** contains a half-plane of an oblique line.

b. Plot all points in the coordinate plane with *x*-coordinate greater than 5. The line with equation $x = 5$ is the boundary for the half-plane that is the solution set. Draw a dashed line because the points on this line are not part of the solution set. The solution set consists of all points to the right of $x = 5$. It is shaded below.

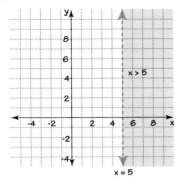

Check

b. Pick a point in the shaded region. We pick (7, 2). Its coordinates should satisfy $x > 5$. Is $7 > 5$? Yes. So (7, 2) is in the solution set. If you pick a point in the unshaded region, its coordinates should not satisfy the inequality. We pick (1, 4). Is $1 > 5$? No. So (1, 4) is not in the solution set.

Riding tall. Shown is a sign at a children's ride at an amusement park in Australia.

Some applications use these kinds of simple inequalities in the plane.

❷ **Example 2**

A person's safety on many amusement park rides depends on the person's size rather than age. So someone may need to be 4 feet tall to go on a ride, regardless of age. Graph the constraint ''A person must be 4 feet tall or taller, regardless of age.'' Let H = the height of a person and A = the person's age.

Solution

Let A be the independent variable. Notice that age is always positive. So the solution is the set of points (A, H) such that $H \geq 4$ and $A > 0$. These are the points in the first quadrant on or above the line $H = 4$. Since points on the line are in the solution set, draw the part of the line in the first quadrant with a solid line. Mark the points in the solution set as shown by the shaded region below.

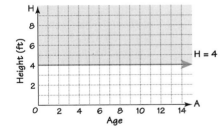

Lesson 5-7 *Graphing Inequalities in the Coordinate Plane* **313**

 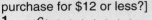
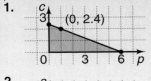 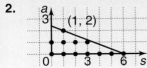

❸ Students should read $y > 2x + 7$ as "the set of all points whose y-coordinates are greater than $2x + 7$." Reading inequalities this way helps students realize that the half-plane of the solution set is the half-plane where the y-values are greater than the x-values—that is, the half-plane above the boundary.

Students may use **Teaching Aid 8** or graph paper throughout the lesson.

❹ This situation can be interpreted as an introduction to a simple system of inequalities, namely

$$\begin{cases} x \geq 0 \\ y \geq 0 \\ x + 3y \leq 12 \end{cases}$$

where x and y are integers. Caution students to be aware of the domains of the variables; the domains determine if the graph is a discrete set of points or if it consists of all points in a region.

A portion of the graph in **Example 4** is shown on **Teaching Aid 47**. You may want to use **Teaching Aid 47** as you discuss **Example 4** with the class.

Additional Examples

1. Graph the solutions to $y < 3$
   a. on a number line.
   b. in the coordinate plane.

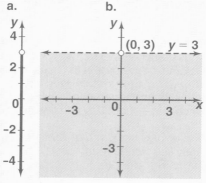

Half-Planes with Oblique Boundaries

All half-planes are easily described by inequalities. The half-planes determined by the line $y = mx + b$ are described by $y > mx + b$ and $y < mx + b$.

❸ | **Example 3**

Graph the linear inequality $y > 2x + 7$.

Solution

Step 1: Graph the boundary $y = 2x + 7$. These points must be connected with a dashed line because the boundary points do not satisfy the inequality. This line is shown below at the left.

Step 2: To determine which half-plane contains the solutions to the inequality, test a point not on the boundary. Usually $(0, 0)$ is an easy point to test. Does $(0, 0)$ satisfy $y > 2x + 7$? To find out, substitute $(0, 0)$ into $y > 2x + 7$. Is $0 > 2(0) + 7$? No. So $(0, 0)$ is not on the graph of $y > 2x + 7$. Thus the solutions to the inequality are all ordered pairs in the half-plane on the side of the line *not* containing $(0, 0)$. Shade the solution set as shown below at the right.

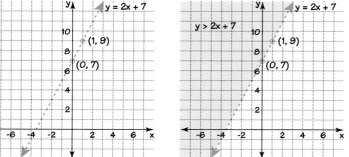

Check

Pick a point in the shaded region. We pick $(-3, 6)$. Do the coordinates satisfy $y > 2x + 7$? Is $6 > 2(-3) + 7$? Yes.

Notice that in Examples 1 to 3, the domain of all variables is the set of real numbers or the set of real numbers greater than a certain constant. In such cases, the graph of an inequality consists of all points in a region, which we indicate by shading. However, in some situations the domain of the variables consists of only integers. Then, the solution set consists of points whose coordinates are integers, called **lattice points.** If there are not too many lattice point solutions, you should indicate each with a dot on the plane, rather than with a shaded region.

314

Adapting to Individual Needs

Extra Help
Encourage students to use $(0, 0)$ as a test point for inequalities because it is easy to substitute $(0, 0)$ in most inequalities. However, stress that $(0, 0)$ should not be used when it is on the boundary, since a point on the boundary will not help the student determine which half-plane is in the solution set.

Beats swimming.
Pictured is a large ferry at Horseshoe Bay in Vancouver, British Columbia.

④ **Example 4**

A ferryboat transports cars and buses across a river. It has space for 12 cars, and a bus takes up the space of 3 cars. Draw a graph showing all possible combinations of cars and buses that can be taken in one crossing.

Solution

This is a linear-combination situation. A car occupies 1 space, so x cars need x spaces. A bus occupies 3 spaces, so y buses need 3y spaces. The ferry has only 12 spaces, so a sentence describing the situation is

$$x + 3y \leq 12.$$

First note that $x \geq 0$ and $y \geq 0$. So only points in the first quadrant or its boundary rays need to be considered. Since x and y are integers, only lattice points are possible. Next, graph the boundary $x + 3y = 12$. Five points on this line, including (0, 4) and (12, 0), are lattice points. They satisfy the inequality.

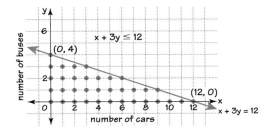

To determine the half-plane in which the solutions lie, try an ordered pair not on the boundary. Substituting (0, 0) gives $0 + 3(0) \leq 12$. This is true; so all solutions lie below $x + 3y = 12$. Thus the graph consists of only those points on or below the line $x + 3y = 12$ whose coordinates are whole numbers. The solutions are represented by the dots in the graph above. Thirty-five combinations of cars and buses can be taken by the ferry in one crossing.

Check

To check that the correct half-plane was chosen, pick a point on the *other* side of the boundary. It should not satisfy the inequality. We choose (10, 5). Substitute into the inequality. Is $10 + 3(5) \leq 12$? No. So the solution checks.

In summary, to graph a linear inequality in the coordinate plane:

1. Graph the appropriate boundary line, either a dashed or solid line, to the corresponding linear equation.

2. Test a point in one half-plane to see if the point satisfies the inequality. If it does not lie on the boundary, the point (0, 0) is often used.

3. Shade the half-plane that satisfies the inequality, or plot points if the situation is discrete.

Lesson 5-7 *Graphing Inequalities in the Coordinate Plane* **315**

2. The price of a general-admission ticket at the ball park depends on a person's age rather than height. A person 12 years old and older pays the adult price for a ticket. Graph the constraint "A person 12 years old and older pays the adult rate for a general-admission ticket, regardless of height." Let H = the height of a person and A = the person's age.

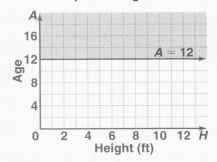

3. Graph the linear inequality $y \geq \frac{4}{3}x + 5$.

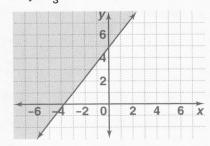

(Additional Examples continue on page 316.)

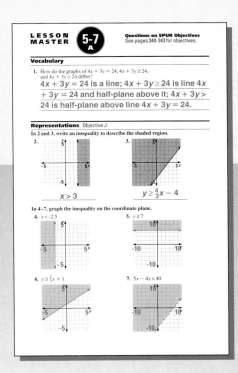

Adapting to Individual Needs

English Language Development

To help students with limited English proficiency understand the term *boundary,* name a boundary that is familiar to students. For instance, "The river is the *boundary* between the north side of town and the south side of town," means that the river separates the town into these two regions. Then use a string on a desk to illustrate that a line can separate a plane into two regions or *half-planes.* Explain that the string is the boundary between the left side of the desk and the right side. Put objects on the desk and have students tell if they are in the left region, the right region, or on the boundary itself.

4. Leo has at most $1.50 in his pocket.

   a. Draw a graph showing all possible combinations of dimes and quarters that Leo could have.

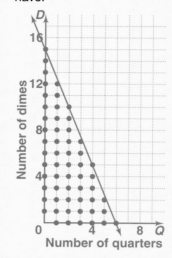

   b. How many possible combinations of dimes and quarters could Leo have? **57**

2a)

b)

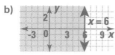

5)

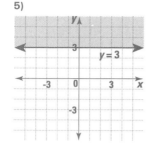

9)

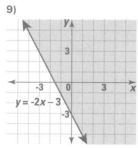

10)

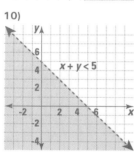

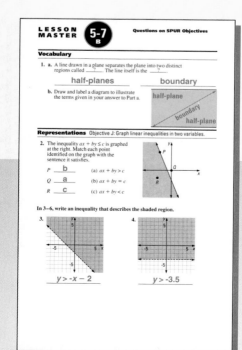

QUESTIONS

Covering the Reading

1. a. A line separates a plane into two distinct regions called __?__ .
  b. The line itself is called the __?__ of these regions. **boundary**
   a) half-planes

2. Graph the solutions to $x \le 6$: **a.** on a number line. **b.** in the coordinate plane. **See left.**

3. Could a 42-year-old man, whose height in inches matches his age in years, go on the ride in Example 2? **No**

4. The graph in the plane of all solutions to $x < -2$ consists of points to one side of the line $x = -2$. Which side? **left side**

5. Graph the set of all ordered pairs (x, y) that satisfy $y \ge 3$. **See left.**

In 6–8, refer to Example 3. Justify your answer.

6. *True or false.* The ordered pair $(-4, 3)$ is a solution to the inequality. **True; $3 > 2(-4) + 7$**

7. Why is the boundary line dashed rather than solid?
  The symbol > does not include the equality of y and 2x + 7.

8. How would the graph change if the inequality were $y < 2x + 7$?
  The right side of the dashed line is shaded.

In 9 and 10, graph the inequality. **See left.**

9. $y \ge -2x - 3$

10. $x + y < 5$

11. What is a lattice point? **a point with integer coordinates**

In 12–14, refer to Example 4.

12. Why are there no points in the solution set in the second, third, or fourth quadrants?
  The number of cars and the number of buses must be nonnegative.

13. a. In how many ways can all the spaces be filled for one ferry crossing? **5**
  b. List them. **(0, 4), (3, 3), (6, 2), (9, 1), (12, 0)**
  c. On which part of the graph are these solutions found?
  on the boundary line x + 3y = 12

14. a. In how many ways can less than the twelve spaces be filled? **30**
  b. List four of them. **Sample: (0, 3), (3, 2), (6, 1), (9, 0)**
  c. Where are these solutions found on the graph?
  in the region bounded by the two axes and the graph of the line x + 3y = 12

Adapting to Individual Needs

Challenge

Have students graph these inequalities.

1. $y \ge x^2 + 2x - 3$ **2.** $y \le \sqrt{x^2 - 4}$
3. $x^2 + y^2 \le 16$ **4.** $y \le |x + 3|$

[See graphs on pages 316–317.]

1.

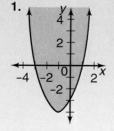

$y \ge x^2 + 2x - 3$

2.

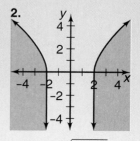

$y \le \sqrt{x^2 - 4}$

Applying the Mathematics

In 15 and 16, write an inequality that describes the shaded region.

15.

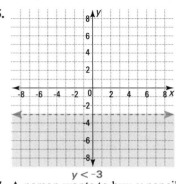

$y < -3$

16.

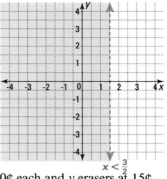

$x < \frac{3}{2}$

17. A person wants to buy x pencils at 10¢ each and y erasers at 15¢ each and spend less than 75¢.
  a. Write an inequality with x and y describing this situation.
  b. Graph all solutions. **See left.** $10x + 15y < 75$
  c. How many solutions are there? **24 solutions**

17b)

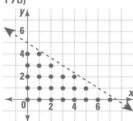

18. In order to make the playoffs, the Dunkers basketball team must win at least twice as many of its 38 games as it loses. Graph the set of points (L, W) which satisfy these conditions. Plot L on the horizontal axis. **See left.**

18)

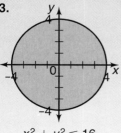

19. Write an inequality which describes the shaded region below.
$y \le \frac{-3}{4}x - 4$

20. Explain why the sentence $y > 2x + 7$ does not describe a function.
Because one value of x can be paired with many values of y

Review

21. a. What linear system is represented by the matrix equation

$$\begin{bmatrix} 3 & 4 \\ 1 & 2 \end{bmatrix} \begin{bmatrix} x \\ y \end{bmatrix} = \begin{bmatrix} 0 \\ -2 \end{bmatrix}? \quad \begin{cases} 3x + 4y = 0 \\ x + 2y = -2 \end{cases}$$

  b. Solve this system.   *(Lesson 5-6)* **(4, -3)**

Lesson 5-7 *Graphing Inequalities in the Coordinate Plane* **317**

3.

$x^2 + y^2 \le 16$

4.

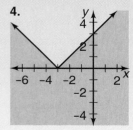

$y \le |x + 3|$

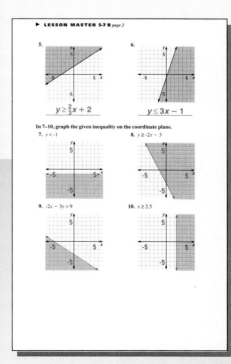

317

Practice

For more questions on SPUR Objectives, use **Lesson Master 5-7A** (shown on page 315) or **Lesson Master 5-7B** (shown on pages 316–317).

Assessment

Quiz A quiz covering Lessons 5-5 through 5-7 is provided in the *Assessment Sourcebook.*

Written Communication Have students **work in pairs.** First have each student write a linear inequality. Then have the students exchange inequalities and draw the graph of the inequality in the coordinate plane. Have students exchange papers and correct each other's work. [Students correctly draw the graphs of linear inequalities in the coordinate plane.]

Extension

Have students write a system of inequalities that represents the system shown on the graph. The graph below can be found on **Teaching Aid 48.**

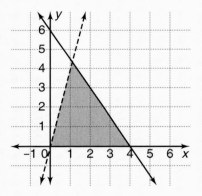

$$\begin{bmatrix} x > 0 \\ y \geq 0 \\ y \leq -\frac{3}{2}x + 6 \\ y < 4x \end{bmatrix}$$

Helping hands. *Shown are American Red Cross workers aiding flood victims in Iowa. More than 135 nations have Red Cross societies. The name* Red Cross *comes from the organization's flag—honoring Switzerland, where the Red Cross was founded in 1863. Most Muslim countries use a red crescent for their symbol. In Israel, the symbol is a red Star of David.*

22a)
$$\begin{cases} 10c + 10t + 40h = 1950 \\ 20c + \quad\quad 20h = 1800 \\ 10c + \quad 5t + 20h = 1350 \end{cases}$$

26d)
Solve the system
$$\begin{cases} y + 9 = -2(x - 9) \\ y - 3 = -2(x - 3). \end{cases}$$
Solving both equations for y gives
$$\begin{cases} y = -2x + 9 \\ y = -2x + 9. \end{cases}$$ Thus, both equations represent the same line.

22. A relief organization supplies cots, tables, and chairs to victims of floods, fires, or other natural disasters. Recently the organization purchased the following items.

	Number of cots	Number of tables	Number of chairs	Total cost ($)
January	10	10	40	1950
February	20	0	20	1800
March	10	5	20	1350

The unit cost of cots, tables, and chairs was constant during this period.
   a. Write a system of equations that can be used to determine the cost of one cot, one table, or one chair. **See left.**
   b. Solve the system. *(Lessons 5-4, 5-6)* **cot: $75; table: $60; chair: $15**

23. Let $M = \begin{bmatrix} 3 & 15 \\ -20 & x \end{bmatrix}$. For what value(s) of x does M^{-1} not exist? *(Lesson 5-5)* **-100**

In 24 and 25, refer to the following systems. *(Lessons 5-3, 5-4)*
   (a) $\begin{cases} y = 3x + 1 \\ 4x - 3y = 12 \end{cases}$
   (b) $\begin{cases} 5x - 7y = 12 \\ -12x + 8y = 19 \end{cases}$
   (c) $\begin{cases} 3x + 2y + z = -22 \\ x = 15z \\ y = -12z \end{cases}$
   (d) $\begin{cases} x + 5y = 12 \\ 2x + 5y = 8 \end{cases}$

24. Which systems are written in a form which is convenient to be solved using linear combinations? **b and d**

25. Which systems can be solved conveniently using substitution? **a and c**

26. Consider the translation $T_{3,1}$ applied to the point $(6, -10)$ on the line $y = -2x + 2$. *(Lessons 3-5, 4-10)*
   a. What is the image of $(6, -10)$ under the translation? **(9, -9)**
   b. What is the equation of the line through this image, parallel to $y = -2x + 2$? **$y + 9 = -2(x - 9)$**
   c. Repeat parts **a** and **b** with the point $(0, 2)$. **a) (3, 3) b) $y - 3 = -2(x - 3)$**
   d. Show that the lines in **b** and **c** are the same line. **See left.**
   e. What is the image of the line $y = -2x + 2$ under the translation $T_{3,1}$? **$y = -2x + 9$**

Exploration

27. Earlier in this chapter you encountered many lines that arise from real situations. **Answers will vary.**
   a. Pick one of the situations and modify it so that it leads to an inequality.
   b. Graph the inequality.

Setting Up Lesson 5-8
Materials If you use Activity 1 in the *Optional Activities* for Lesson 5-8, students will need overhead-projector transparencies and colored markers.

Because the graph of a linear inequality in two variables is a half-plane, the graph of the solution to a system of linear inequalities is the intersection of half-planes. The set of solutions to a system of linear inequalities is often called the **feasible set** or **feasible region** for that system. The boundaries are always parts of lines. The intersections of the boundaries are called **vertices** of the feasible set.

Example 1

Graph the feasible set for the system $\begin{cases} y > -2x + 6 \\ y \le \frac{1}{4}x - 3. \end{cases}$

Solution

Graph each inequality on the same set of axes. The graph of $y > -2x + 6$ is the set of points above and to the right of the line with equation $y = -2x + 6$. In the graphs below, this set is indicated by the shading ▢. The graph of $y \le \frac{1}{4}x - 3$ consists of points on or below the line with equation $y = \frac{1}{4}x - 3$, indicated by the shading ▨. The part of the plane shaded ▨ is the feasible set for this system. As shown in the graph below to the right, the feasible set for this system is the union of the interior of an angle and one of the rays of the angle except for the vertex.

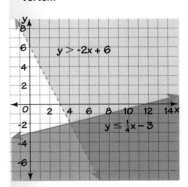

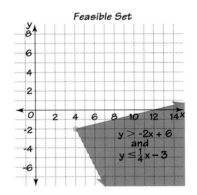

Feasible Set

Check

First find the vertex of the feasible set by solving the system of equations

$$\begin{cases} y = -2x + 6 \\ y = \frac{1}{4}x - 3. \end{cases}$$

▶

Lesson 5-8 Overview

Broad Goals This lesson teaches students to solve systems of linear inequalities using their knowledge of graphs of inequalities and their knowledge of systems of equations (Lessons 5-2 through 5-4). It introduces the words *feasible set* or *feasible region* for the solution set of a system of inequalities and lays the groundwork for the solution of problems using the linear programming method discussed in Lessons 5-9 and 5-10.

Perspective We devote three lessons to the discussion of systems of linear inequalities for a number of reasons. First and foremost, this is important mathematics—linear programming is used by many corporations. Second, it provides an opportunity to review and solidify concepts related to linear equations. Third, it opens students' eyes to the entire subject of optimization, an important topic in both pure and applied mathematics.

Example 1 presents a typical system of linear inequalities. The solution set is the union of an angle and its interior, but with one side removed. **Example 2** presents the kind of translation problem that is required in a linear programming situation.

Lesson **5-8**

Objectives
E Recognize properties of systems of inequalities.
K Solve systems of inequalities by graphing.

Resources
From the *Teacher's Resource File*
■ Lesson Master 5-8A or 5-8B
■ Answer Master 5-8
■ Teaching Aids
   8 Four-Quadrant Graph Paper
   45 Warm-up
   50 Example 1
   51 Example 2
■ Technology Sourcebook
   Computer Master 7

Additional Resources
■ Visuals for Teaching Aids 8, 45, 50, 51
■ Overhead-projector transparencies, colored markers
■ GraphExplorer or other automatic graphers

Teaching **5-8**
Lesson

Warm-up
Name the quadrant in which
1. $x > 0$ and $y > 0$. **1st quadrant**
2. $x < 0$ and $y > 0$. **2nd quadrant**
3. $x > 0$ and $y < 0$. **4th quadrant**
4. $x < 0$ and $y < 0$. **3rd quadrant**

Notes on Reading
Students may use graph paper or **Teaching Aid 8** throughout this lesson.

We usually find the intersection of the solution sets by graphing their union first, just as we did for graphing lines and curves in Lesson 5-7. However, point out to students that in this lesson, the feasible region is highlighted by redrawing the graph with only the points that belong to the intersection. Students do not have to draw two figures as is done in **Example 1**; the first drawing is sufficient as long as the shading is clear.

The graphs from **Example 1,** without shaded regions, can be found on **Teaching Aid 50.** You may want to use this Teaching Aid to work through the necessary shading with your class.

❶ **Cooperative Learning** Discuss **Example 2** in class. First, have students explain how the inequalities are derived. Then have them graph the feasible set and use what they know about solving systems of equations to find the vertices. Emphasize that the feasible set includes *all* the points that satisfy the conditions stated in the inequalities and *only* those points. **Teaching Aid 51** provides the table and the grid from **Example 2** that you can complete during your classroom discussion.

Students may not have used the word "feasible" before in mathematics and therefore think it relates to a totally new concept. Emphasize that the feasible set is simply the intersection of the solution sets of the individual inequalities. Its name comes from its application, not from any new mathematical idea.

Hand-crafted. *Shown is a woodworker in a furniture plant in Winchester, Virginia.*

This vertex is (4, -2), which checks with the graph. Second, pick a point in the shaded region, such as (8, -5), and substitute it into each inequality.

Is -5 > -2(8) + 6? Yes.

Is $-5 \leq \frac{1}{4}(8) - 3$? Yes. So the solution checks.

You should also try points outside the region to show that they do not satisfy both inequalities.

Many automatic graphers can graph inequalities and systems of inequalities. If your grapher has this capability, you should repeat Example 1 using your grapher.

The applications of systems to production planning in industry, discovered by Kantorovich in 1939, may involve systems with thousands of variables. Computers are needed to solve these problems. But simple examples can be done by hand. Here is a simplified example of a business application.

❶ **Example 2**

The Biltrite Furniture Company makes wooden desks and chairs. Carpenters and finishers work on each item. On the average, the carpenters spend four hours working on each chair and eight hours on each desk. There are enough carpenters for up to 8000 worker-hours per week. The finishers spend about two hours on each chair and one hour on each desk. There are enough finishers for a maximum of 1300 worker-hours per week. Given these constraints, find the feasible region for the number of chairs and desks that can be made per week.

Solution

Make a table to organize this information.

	chairs	desks	total hours available
hrs. of carpentry per piece	4	8	8000
hrs. of finishing per piece	2	1	1300

Let x = the number of chairs that can be made per week and y = the number of desks that can be made per week.

Write sentences for each constraint. Because *x* and *y* represent pieces of furniture, they must be nonnegative integers; that is,

$x \geq 0$ and $y \geq 0$, and (x, y) is a lattice point.

The carpentry hours must satisfy $4x + 8y \leq 8000$.

The finishing hours must satisfy $2x + y \leq 1300$.

Thus, the feasible region for this situation is the set of lattice-point solutions of the system

$$\begin{cases} x \geq 0 \\ y \geq 0 \\ 4x + 8y \leq 8000 \\ 2x + y \leq 1300. \end{cases}$$

Optional Activities

Activity 1 Art Connection
Materials: Transparencies for the overhead projector, colored markers, and **Teaching Aid 8**

As they read the examples and exercises, interested students might enjoy making overhead-projector overlays to illustrate the situations. Then, when you discuss the examples and exercises in class, these students could demonstrate the problems.

For instance, to illustrate **Example 2**, students might use 4 transparencies with identical four-quadrant coordinate graphs. They would graph $x \geq 0$ on one transparency, $y \geq 0$ on another, $4x + 8y \leq 8000$ on a third, and $2x + y \leq 1300$ on the fourth, using a different kind of shading for each graph.

Activity 2 Technology Connection
You may want to consider using *Technology Sourcebook, Computer Master 7* with Lessons 5-8 and 5-9. Students are led through an entire linear programming exercise.

Now graph the solution to the system. The first two inequalities indicate all solutions are in the first quadrant or on the positive axes. So it is sufficient to examine solutions to the last two inequalities only in the first quadrant. The graph is shown below.

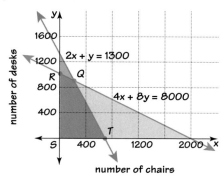

The feasible region is the set of lattice points in the quadrilateral QRST and its interior.

You can find the coordinates of each vertex of *QRST* by solving a system of equations. For instance, *Q* is the solution to the system

$$\begin{cases} 4x + 8y = 8000 \\ 2x + y = 1300. \end{cases}$$

Notice that even though only integer values are solutions, shading is used because it would be too difficult to show all the dots.

Check

Choose a point in the feasible region and see if it is a solution of each inequality of the system. We choose (400, 200).
Is $400 \geq 0$? Yes.
Is $200 \geq 0$? Yes.
Is $4(400) + 8(200) \leq 8000$? Yes.
Is $2(400) + 200 \leq 1300$? Yes.
So one option available to the Biltrite Furniture Company is to make 400 chairs and 200 desks per week.

As a further check, choose a point just outside the feasible region, such as (700, 400), and show that there is at least one inequality which is not satisfied by this point.

Additional Examples
1. Graph the feasible set for the system below and give the coordinates of its vertices.

$$\begin{cases} x + 2y \leq 12 \\ 2x + y \leq 12 \\ x \geq 0 \\ y \geq 0 \end{cases}$$

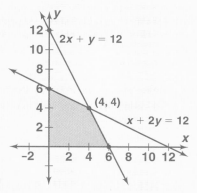

Vertices are (0, 6), (6, 0), (4, 4) and (0, 0).

(Additional Examples continue on page 322.)

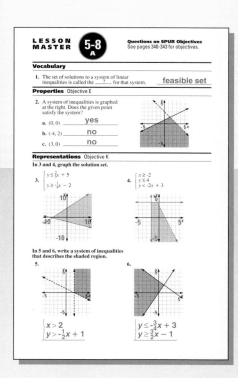

Adapting to Individual Needs
Extra Help
Students may find the feasible region easier to identify if the region represented by each inequality is highlighted with vertical and horizontal lines rather than shading.

321

Additional Example 2 is adapted from the CPA (Certified Public Accountant) exam given in May, 1975.

2. The Random Company manufactures two products, Zeta and Beta. Each product must pass through two processing operations. Zeta requires one hour for each process, and Beta requires 2 hours for process I and 3 hours for process II. Process I has a total capacity of 1000 hours per day and process II has a total capacity of 1275 hours per day.

a. Make a table to organize the information.

Process	Hours for Zeta	Hours for Beta	Total Hours per day
I	1	2	1000
II	1	3	1275

b. Identify the variables.
Let x = number of Zetas to be made each day. Let y = number of Betas to be made each day.

c. Write sentences to model each step in the process.
$$\begin{cases} x + 2y \le 1000 \\ x + 3y \le 1275 \\ x \ge 0 \\ y \ge 0 \end{cases}$$

---

5) Does $-2 = -2 (4) + 6$? Yes. Does $-2 = \frac{1}{4}(4) - 3$? Yes, so this is a vertex of the feasible set.

9) $\begin{cases} 4x + 8y = 8000 \\ x = 0 \end{cases}$

11a)

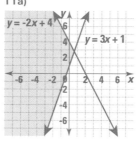

12a)

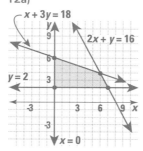

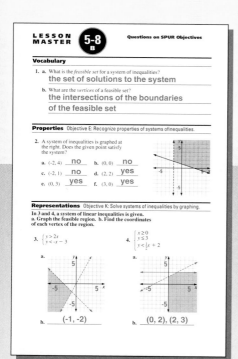

QUESTIONS

Covering the Reading

1. The solution to a system of linear inequalities can be represented by the __?__ of half-planes. intersection

2. The solution to a system of linear inequalities is often called the __?__. feasible set or feasible region

In 3–5, refer to Example 1. Verify the following statements. 3-4) See below

3. (10, -6) is a solution to the system.

4. (5, 0) is *not* a solution to the system.

5. (4, -2) is the vertex of the feasible set for the system. See left.

In 6–10, refer to Example 2.

6. Which inequality expresses the amount of time that the company can have its finishers working? $2x + y \le 1300$

7. Why is it sufficient to consider only the first quadrant in graphing the feasible set? The number of pieces of furniture will be nonnegative.

8. Find the coordinates of vertex Q. (200, 900)

9. What system of equations gives vertex R as its solution? See left.

10. Could the company manufacture 600 chairs and 200 desks per week under the given operating conditions? Justify your answer.
No; (600, 200) fails to satisfy the inequality $2x + y \le 1300$.

In 11 and 12, a system of inequalities is given. **a.** Graph the feasible region. **b.** Find the coordinates of each vertex of the region.
See left for graphs.

11. $\begin{cases} y \ge 3x + 1 \\ y \le -2x + 4 \end{cases}$ **12.** $\begin{cases} x + 3y \le 18 \\ 2x + y \le 16 \\ x \ge 0 \\ y \ge 2 \end{cases}$ b) (0, 2), (0, 6), (7, 2), (6, 4)

b) $\left(\frac{3}{5}, \frac{14}{5}\right)$

3) Is $-6 > -2(10) + 6$? Yes. Is $-6 \le \frac{1}{4}(10) - 3$? Yes, so the solution checks.

Applying the Mathematics

13. Refer to the graph at the left.
   a. Write a system of inequalities which is represented by this feasible set. See below.
   b. *True or false.* The point (3, 4) is in the feasible region. True
   c. Find the coordinates of vertex C. (4, 5)

   a) $\begin{cases} x \ge 0 \\ y \le x + 1 \\ y \le \frac{1}{2}x + 3 \\ x \le 6 \\ y \ge 0 \end{cases}$

4) Is $0 > -2(5) + 6$? Yes. Is $0 \le \frac{1}{4}(5) - 3$? No, so this is not a solution.

Adapting to Individual Needs

English Language Development
When discussing **Question 24,** note that convex figures "curve out," and concave figures "curve in."

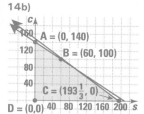
14. A clothier makes women's suits and coats from nylon lining and wool tweed. Each suit requires 2 yards of nylon lining and 3 yards of wool tweed. Each coat requires 3 yards of nylon lining and 4 yards of wool tweed. A total of 420 yards of nylon lining and 580 yards of wool are in stock.

   a. Let s be the number of suits and c be the number of coats. Complete the translation of this situation into a system of inequalities.

$$\begin{cases} s \geq \underline{\ ?\ } \ 0 \\ c \geq \underline{\ ?\ } \ 0 \\ 2s + 3c \leq \underline{\ ?\ } \ 420 \\ \underline{\ ?\ } \leq 580 \ \ 3s + 4c \end{cases}$$

   b. Graph the feasible region of points (s, c) for this system and label the vertices. **See left.**

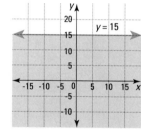
15. An electronics firm makes two kinds of televisions: black-and-white and color. The firm has enough equipment to make as many as 1000 black-and-white sets per month or 600 color sets per month. It takes 20 worker-hours to make a black-and-white set and 30 worker-hours to make a color set. The firm has up to 24,000 worker-hours of labor available each month. Let x be the number of black-and-white TVs and y be the number of color TVs made in a month. **See left.**

   a. Translate this situation into a system of inequalities.

   b. Graph the feasible set for this system, and label the vertices.

Review

16. Write an inequality to describe the region shaded below. *(Lesson 5-7)*
$y \leq 15$

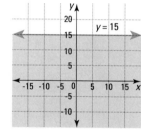

y
20
$y = 15$
15
10
5
-15 -10 -5 | 0 | 5 10 15 x
-5
-10

17. Jack has a savings account from which to pay his share of the rent at college for 9 months. The account must also cover a security deposit of $200.

    a) $R \leq \dfrac{D - 200}{9}$

   a. If the account contains D dollars, write an inequality that expresses the monthly rent R he can afford without running out of money.

   b. If Jack's account has $1500 dollars in it, what is the maximum monthly rent he can afford? *(Lesson 5-7)* **$144.44**

18. Solve the following matrix equation. *(Lesson 5-6)*

$$\begin{bmatrix} -1 & 2 \\ 3 & 4 \end{bmatrix} \begin{bmatrix} x \\ y \end{bmatrix} = \begin{bmatrix} -6 \\ 8 \end{bmatrix} \quad (4, -1)$$

d. Graph the solution to the system.

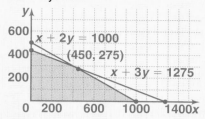

y
600   $x + 2y = 1000$
400   $(450, 275)$
200   $x + 3y = 1275$
0   200   600   1000 1400 x

e. Identify the vertices of the feasible region. **(0, 425), (0, 0), (1000, 0), (450, 275)**

Notes on Questions

Questions 14–15 Stress the importance of using a table to illustrate the information in each problem. Mathematical prose is often very dense, and the use of a table helps to separate and clarify the given information.

The *Warm-up* on page 325 of this teacher's edition refers to **Question 14.**

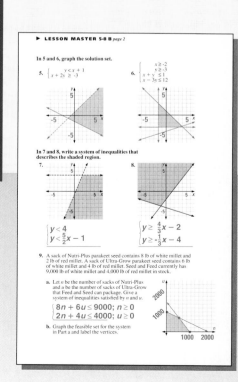

Adapting to Individual Needs

Challenge
You might have students solve this problem. A company manufactures two models of frames for CD players. Each Model M requires 12 units of black plastic and 8 units of gray plastic. Each Model N requires 7 units of black plastic and 9 units of gray plastic. There are at most 840 units of black plastic and 720 units of gray plastic available each day.

Is the given level of production possible on a daily basis?
  1. 45 Model Ms and 35 Model Ns [Yes]
  2. 60 Model Ms and 30 Model Ns [No]
  3. 49 Model Ms and 37 Model Ns [No]
  4. 0 Model Ms and 80 Model Ns [Yes]

[Let $m =$ the number of Model Ms and let $n =$ the number of Model Ns. Then graphing $m \geq 0$, $n \geq 0$, $12m + 7n \leq 840$, and $8m + 9n \leq 720$ gives the feasible region.]

323

Notes on Questions

Question 24 The definition of *convex region* is contained in this question. The concept is an important one in preparation for the Linear Programming Theorem to be discussed in Lessons 5-9 and 5-10. Every feasible region of a system of linear inequalities is convex. In general, the intersection of two convex sets is a convex set. Students who have studied UCSMP *Geometry* have seen this language.

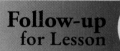

Follow-up for Lesson 5-8

Practice

For more questions on SPUR Objectives, use **Lesson Master 5-8A** (shown on page 321) or **Lesson Master 5-8B** (shown on pages 322–323).

Assessment

Oral/Written Communication
Have students **work in pairs.** First have one student draw the graph of a linear equation in the form $y = mx + b$. Have the other student draw the graph of another similar equation so that there are two intersecting lines in the coordinate plane. Then have students take turns shading in one of the four regions determined by the intersecting lines. The other student must determine the system of linear inequalities that is represented by the shaded region. Then have each pair of students share their work with the class. [Students demonstrate that they understand the graphing technique for finding the intersection of the solution sets for two linear inequalities.]

Extension

The feasible region for a system is the set of points on and bounded by a triangle with vertices $(0, 6)$, $(6, 0)$, and $(4, -2)$. Write a system for this situation.

[Sample system: $\begin{cases} x + y \le 6 \\ x - y \le 6 \\ 2x + y \ge 6 \end{cases}$]

Long live the king. *It is believed that chess originated in India around 600 A.D. It soon spread to Persia and later to Europe. The term "checkmate" derives from the Persian* shah mat, *meaning "the king is dead."*

25a)

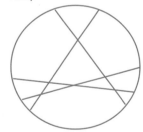

In 19 and 20, solve each system. *(Lessons 5-2, 5-3, 5-4, 5-5)*

19. $\begin{cases} y = \frac{8}{x} \\ y = x^2 \end{cases}$
(2, 4)

20. $\begin{cases} x + 2y - z = -11 \\ 4x + 3y + 2z = -39 \\ 2x - y + 3z = -17 \end{cases}$
(-9, -1, 0)

21. If a toy manufacturer makes $5 profit on each board game and $8 profit on each video game, how much profit will be earned from x board games and y video games? *(Lesson 3-3)* **5x + 8y dollars**

22. What is the slope of the line with equation $5x + 8y = 1000$? *(Lesson 3-2)* $\frac{-5}{8}$

23. *Skill sequence.* Multiply and simplify where possible. *(Previous course)*
a. $8(n + 8)$ **8n + 64**
b. $n(n + 8)$ $n^2 + 8n$
c. $(n + 8)(n + 8)$ $n^2 + 16n + 64$
d. $(n + 8)^2$ $n^2 + 16n + 64$

24. A region of the plane is said to be **convex** if and only if any two points of the region can be connected by a line segment which is itself entirely within the region. The pentagon below is convex but the quadrilateral is not.

Convex   Not convex

Tell whether or not the shaded region is convex. *(Previous course)*

a. **b.** **c.** **d.**

Yes   No   Yes   Yes

Exploration

25. Refer to Question 24.
a. At most how many pieces can you get out of a circular pie with 4 straight cuts? How many of these pieces are convex? Draw a picture to illustrate this situation. **11, 11; See left.**
b. At most, how many pieces can you get out of a circular pie with n straight cuts? How many of these pieces are convex? $\frac{n^2 + n + 2}{2}$; **all of them**

Setting Up Lesson 5-9

Discuss **Example 2** and **Questions 14** and **21** in some detail before assigning Lesson 5-9. In each of these situations, there are choices of quantities to produce, so the question one might ask is, "Which quantity maximizes the profit?" The expression in **Question 21** is the type of expression that will be maximized. Explain that this type of situation will be discussed in Lesson 5-9.

In Example 2 of Lesson 5-8, a system of linear inequalities describes constraints of the manufacturing operations of the Biltrite Furniture Company. The feasible set describes various combinations of chairs and desks that the company can make with the given constraints. Now suppose that the company also knows that it earns a profit of $15 on each chair and $20 on each desk it makes. Given these known constraints, how can the production schedule be set to maximize the profit?

If x chairs and y desks are sold, the profit P is given by the formula

$$15x + 20y = P.$$

For instance, the solutions to

$$15x + 20y = 3000$$

are ordered pairs that will yield a $3000 profit.

The shaded region in the figure below again shows the feasible set for Biltrite's system of inequalities. The figure also shows the graphs of some lines that result from substituting different values of P into the profit formula.

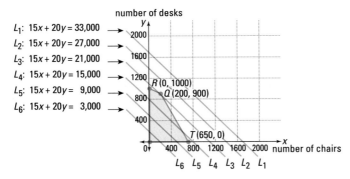

L_1: $15x + 20y = 33,000$
L_2: $15x + 20y = 27,000$
L_3: $15x + 20y = 21,000$
L_4: $15x + 20y = 15,000$
L_5: $15x + 20y = 9,000$
L_6: $15x + 20y = 3,000$

number of desks

R (0, 1000)
Q (200, 900)
T (650, 0)
number of chairs

All lines with equations of the form $15x + 20y = P$ are parallel because each has slope $-\frac{3}{4}$. Some of these lines intersect the feasible region and some do not. In the figure above, the lines above L_3 do not intersect the feasible set. Lines such as L_3 and L_4 that do intersect the feasible region indicate possible profits. The greatest profit will occur when the line with equation $15x + 20y = P$ is as high as possible, but still intersects the feasible region. This will happen when the profit line passes through vertex $Q = (200, 900)$. This is the line L_3. Thus to maximize profits, the company should manufacture 200 chairs and 900 desks per week. The maximum profit under these conditions is $21,000.

Lesson 5-9 *Linear Programming I* **325**

Lesson 5-9

Objectives
E Recognize properties of systems of inequalities.
G Use linear programming to solve real-world problems.

Resources
From the **Teacher's Resource File**
■ Lesson Master 5-9A or 5-9B
■ Answer Master 5-9
■ Teaching Aids
   8 Four-Quadrant Graph Paper
   45 Warm-up
   52 Example
■ Technology Connection
   Computer Master 7

Additional Resources
■ Visuals for Teaching Aids 8, 45, 52
■ GraphExplorer or other automatic graphers

Teaching 5-9
Lesson

Warm-up
Diagnostic The system

$$\begin{cases} s \geq 0 \\ c \geq 0 \\ 2s + 3c \leq 420 \\ 3s + 4c \leq 580 \end{cases}$$

models the situation described in **Question 14** on page 323. The vertices of the feasible region are (0, 140), (60, 100), (0, 0), and $(193\frac{1}{3}, 0)$.

If there is a profit of $20 on each suit and $40 on each coat, how many suits and coats must be made to *maximize* the profit? (Now $(193\frac{1}{3}, 0)$ must be rounded *down* to 193 because only whole numbers of suits can be made.) **The maximum profit occurs at (0, 140). At that point, $P = 5600$.**

Lesson 5-9 Overview

Broad Goals This is the first of two lessons devoted to linear programming. In this lesson, the expression whose value is to be maximized or minimized is introduced.

Perspective Initially, linear programming problems may seem formidable to students. However, when students realize how the mathematics they know can be applied to solve such seemingly complex problems, they usually enjoy these lessons.

The Linear Programming Theorem gives a numerical shortcut for finding the maximum or minimum value of an expression without graphing a family of lines. The linear combination expression to be maximized or minimized is often called the *objective function.*

Linear programming problems take a great deal of time to do. We suggest giving no more than two such problems in an assignment.

Students may use graph paper or **Teaching Aid 8** throughout this lesson.

You may want to use **Teaching Aid 52** during your classroom discussion of the **Example.**

❶ **Health Connection** The chart shows the amount of vitamin A, potassium, and iron in chicken and corn. The human body uses vitamin A for building bones and maintaining healthy skin, iron is part of hemoglobin in the body's red blood cells (the oxygen-carrying molecules), and potassium helps the body change food into energy and new tissue.

Additional Examples

Use linear programming to solve the following problem. Jeano's candy factory packages bags of mixed nuts. Jeano has 75 pounds of cashews and 120 pounds of peanuts. They will be mixed in 1-pound packages in the following ways: a lower-grade package that contains 4 ounces of cashews and 12 ounces of peanuts and a higher-grade mixture that contains 8 ounces of cashews and 8 ounces of peanuts. A profit of $0.35 per package can be made on the lower-grade mixture, and a profit of $0.55 per package can be made on the higher-grade mixture. How many packages of each mixture should Jeano make to obtain the maximum profit?

An amazing building.
Shown is Mitchell Corn Palace in Mitchell, South Dakota. The building is decorated with murals made of different colors of ears of corn. The decorations are replaced every September. Concerts, dances, and many other events are held there.

Problems such as this one, which lead to systems of linear inequalities, are called **linear-programming problems.** The word "programming" does not refer to a computer; it means that the solution gives a "program," or course of action, to follow. The most profitable program for Biltrite Furniture Company is to make 200 chairs and 900 desks per week.

In 1826, the French mathematician Jean Baptiste Joseph Fourier proved the following theorem.

> **Linear-Programming Theorem**
> The feasible region of every linear-programming problem is convex, and the maximum or minimum quantity is determined at one of the vertices of this feasible region.

The Linear-Programming Theorem tells you where to look for the greatest or least value of a linear combination expression in a linear-programming situation, without having to draw many lines through the feasible region.

In 1945, George Stigler (then at Columbia University, later at the University of Chicago) was looking for the least expensive diet that would provide a person's daily needs of calories, protein, and various vitamins and minerals. Here is a simplified diet problem of the type first considered by Stigler.

Example

Here is a table with some of the nutritional value of fried chicken and corn on the cob.

	Vitamin A (I.U.)	Potassium (mg)	Iron (mg)	Calories
Fried Chicken (one small piece)	100	0	1.2	122
Corn (one ear)	310	151	1.0	70

Suppose you want at least 1000 units of vitamin A, 200 mg of potassium, 6 mg of iron, and at least 600 calories of energy from these foods. Let n = the number of pieces of chicken and e = the number of ears of corn.

$$\begin{cases} n \geq 0 \\ e \geq 0 \\ 100n + 310e \geq 1000 & \text{(at least 1000 units vitamin A)} \\ 151e \geq 200 & \text{(at least 200 mg potassium)} \\ 1.2n + e \geq 6 & \text{(at least 6 mg iron)} \\ 122n + 70e \geq 600 & \text{(at least 600 calories)} \end{cases}$$

A graph of this system is shown on the next page.

Optional Activities

You might want to use this activity after students do the *Warm-up.* Explain that by changing the assumption about the profit made on individual items, you can show how the optimal choice of what to produce may vary. Have students refer to the problem in the *Warm-up* (which is based on **Question 14** in Lesson 5-8). Tell them to use other values for the coat and suit profits and see if this changes the vertex at which the maximum profit occurs.

[Sample: If the profit on each suit is $20 and the profit on each coat is $25, the point (193, 0) yields the greatest profit of $3860. But if the profit on each suit is $20 and the profit on each coat is $30, both (0, 140) and (60, 100) maximize the profit at $4200. In fact, in the latter case all points on the line segment joining (0, 140) and (60, 100) yield the same profit.]

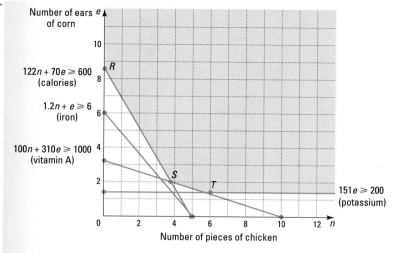

Number of ears e of corn

$122n + 70e \geq 600$ (calories)

$1.2n + e \geq 6$ (iron)

$100n + 310e \geq 1000$ (vitamin A)

$151e \geq 200$ (potassium)

Number of pieces of chicken

a. Find the vertices of the feasible set.

b. Now suppose that each piece of chicken costs \$.80 and each ear of corn costs \$.50. Determine the values of n and e which will meet the nutritional requirements above at the lowest cost C.

Solution

a. There are three vertices R, S, and T. To find R, let $n = 0$ in the equation $122n + 70e = 600$.

$$122(0) + 70e = 600$$
$$e \approx 8.6$$

So the coordinates of R are about (0, 8.6).

Vertex S is the intersection of lines with equations $122n + 70e = 600$ and $100n + 310e = 1000$. So solve this system. We find $e \approx 2$ and $n \approx 3.8$. So the coordinates of S are about (3.8, 2).

Finally, T is the intersection of $100n + 310e = 1000$ and $151e = 200$. Solve the second equation for e and substitute into the first. The coordinates of T are about (6, 1.3).

b. The cost formula is $C = .80n + .50e$. The Linear-Programming Theorem says that the minimum value of C occurs at a vertex of the feasible region. So evaluate C at each vertex to see which combination of n and e gives the minimum cost. Because n and e are integers and the feasible set has no values less than those found at the vertices, the coordinates of each vertex must be rounded up to the nearest integer. Thus we use (0, 9) for R, (4, 2) for S, and (6, 2) for T.

$$\text{at } (0, 9): \quad C = .80(0) + .50(9) = 4.50$$
$$\text{at } (4, 2): \quad C = .80(4) + .50(2) = 4.20$$
$$\text{at } (6, 2): \quad C = .80(6) + .50(2) = 5.80$$

Thus the minimum cost satisfying the given constraints is \$4.20. To satisfy this nutritional need for the lowest cost, you should eat 4 pieces of chicken and 2 ears of corn.

Lesson 5-9 *Linear Programming I* **327**

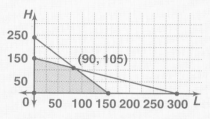

	Cashews	Peanuts
Lower-grade Mix	4 oz	12 oz
Higher-grade Mix	8 oz	8 oz
Maximum Available	1200 oz	1920 oz

Let L = number of packages of lower-grade mix. Let H = number of packages of higher-grade mix.

Then
$$\begin{cases} 4L + 8H \leq 1200 \\ 12L + 8H \leq 1920 \\ L \geq 0 \\ H \geq 0 \end{cases}$$

$P = .35L + .55H$

(90, 105)

Vertices of the feasible region are (0, 0), (0, 150), (160, 0) and (90, 105). The maximum profit of \$89.25 is at (90, 105).

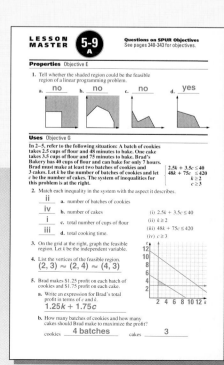
Adapting to Individual Needs

Extra Help

Point out to students that linear programming problems often fall into two categories. In one type the object is to maximize profits, as in the opening example for Lesson 5-9. In the other type the object is to minimize costs as in **Question 16**.

Notes on Questions

We recommend that you discuss the questions in the order given.

(Notes on Questions continue on page 330.)

(Notes on Questions continue on page 330.)

Follow-up for Lesson 5-9

Practice

For more questions on SPUR Objectives, use **Lesson Master 5-9A** (shown on page 327) or **Lesson Master 5-9B** (shown on pages 328–329).

(shown on page 327) or **Lesson Master 5-9B** (shown on pages 328–329).

Assessment

Oral Communication Have students refer to **Question 15.** Then have them suggest values other than $75 and $85 for profits per acre from corn and soybeans, and determine if these values change the vertex at which the maximum profit occurs. Have students justify their answers. [Students demonstrate that they understand that the maximum profit will always occur at a vertex of the feasible region.]

LESSON MASTER 5-9 B Questions on SPUR Objectives

Properties Objective E: Recognize properties of systems of inequalities.

1. *Multiple choice.* List all of the following shaded regions that could be the feasible region of a linear-programming problem. Explain your answer.

(a) (b) (c) (d)

b, c; the feasible region must be convex.

In 2 and 3, use the graph at the right. It shows the feasible region of a linear-programming problem.

2. Name the points which could be solutions to the linear-programming problem.
B, C, D

3. Find the point in the feasible region that minimizes $P = 2.8x + 1.5y$.
C

Uses Objective G: Use linear programming to solve real-world problems.

In 4–8, refer to the following situation: Justine makes jewelry to sell at a flea market. She can currently make a pair of earrings with 20 beads in 30 minutes and a necklace with 30 beads in 30 minutes. She plans to use no more than 600 beads, work a maximum of 12 hours (720 minutes), and make at least 5 pairs of earrings and 5 necklaces. Let e be the number of pairs of earrings and n be the number of necklaces she can make. The system of inequalities for this problem is below.

$$\begin{cases} 20e + 30n \le 600 \\ 30e + 30n \le 720 \\ e \ge 5 \\ n \ge 5 \end{cases}$$

Stigler originally considered 70 possible foods and found that the lowest-cost diet satisfying an adult's need for calories, protein, calcium, vitamin A, thiamine, riboflavin, niacin, and ascorbic acid was a combination of wheat flour, cabbage, and pork liver. By eating just these three foods, a person was thought to be able to live in good health in 1945 for $59.88 a year. Costs today are higher, so it might now cost about $500 a year for that diet.

Of course many other vitamins, minerals, and foods are now taken into account by dietitians planning well-balanced meals. Stigler could not consider a greater number of possible foods nor consider more health needs because computers were not available in 1945. Today it is possible to consider hundreds of foods and many more daily needs.

QUESTIONS

Covering the Reading

In 1–5, refer to the discussion of the Biltrite Furniture Company at the beginning of this lesson.

1. What is the company trying to maximize? **profit**

2. What do the numbers 15 and 20 represent in the profit equation? **profit per chair, profit per desk**

3. *True or false.* If a line with equation $15x + 20y = P$ intersects the feasible region for the system of inequalities, it is possible for Biltrite to make a profit of P dollars. **True**

4. **a.** What is the maximum weekly profit Biltrite can earn? **$21,000**
   b. How many chairs and how many desks must the company produce to make this profit? **200 chairs and 900 desks**

5. Find the profit if 199 chairs and 899 desks are made. **$20,965**

6. To what does the word "program" refer in a linear-programming problem? **a course of action to follow**

7. In a linear-programming problem, why is it necessary to find the vertices of the feasible region? **The maximum or minimum quantity is determined at one of the vertices of the feasible region.**

In 8 and 9, refer to the Example in this lesson.

8. **a.** Which linear combination must be minimized? $C = .80n + .50e$
   b. What is the minimum value of C satisfying the constraints of the problem? **$4.20**
   c. At which vertex does the maximum cost occur? T

9. If 10 mg of iron were needed in this diet, the constraint for iron would be $1.2n + e \ge 10$.
   a. Regraph the feasible region of the system with this new iron requirement. **See left.**
   b. In the new feasible region, which vertex yields the minimum cost? **(0, 10)**

9a)

Adapting to Individual Needs

English Language Development
Show students the program for a play. Explain that the program shows how the play will progress. Similarly, the word *program* in Linear Programming, refers to a way to proceed, or a course of action to follow. Alternatively, you could present a student's program of classes, or any other similar schedule.

11) *T.* Sample: The following table shows the values of *P* corresponding to each of the vertices of the feasible region. The profit value is the greatest at vertex *T.* By the Linear-Programming Theorem, this vertex maximizes profit over the feasible set.

Vertex	P
Q	250
R	460
S	580
T	680
U	660
V	610

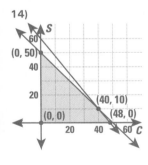

Harvest time. *Shown is a combine harvesting a soybean crop in Iowa. The combine cuts the plants, and threshes and cleans the seeds in one operation. Soybeans are usually harvested in late summer or early fall.*

14)

---

10. a. A diet problem like the one in the Example was first modeled mathematically by whom and in what year? **George Stigler, 1945**
   b. Why can more variables be dealt with now than could be considered when these diet problems were first studied? **Computers can handle more variables, and computers were not available in 1945.**

Applying the Mathematics

11. Use the feasible set graphed at the right. Which vertex maximizes the profit equation $P = 3x + 4y + 250$? Justify your answer. **See left.**

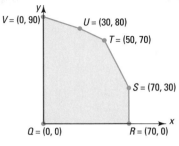

V = (0, 90)   *U* = (30, 80)
T = (50, 70)
S = (70, 30)
Q = (0, 0)   *R* = (70, 0)

12. Refer to Question 15 in Lesson 5-8. Suppose the electronics firm earns a profit of $25 on each black-and-white TV and $40 on each color TV.
   a. Write a formula for the monthly profit earned. **$P = 25x + 40y$**
   b. What combination of black-and-white and color TVs will maximize profit? **(300, 600) for $31,500 profit**

In 13–15, suppose that a farmer has no more than 50 acres for planting either corn or soybeans or both and has a maximum of $12,000 to spend on the planting. Further suppose that it costs $250 per acre to plant corn and $200 per acre to plant soybeans. If *C* is the number of acres of corn and *S* is the number of acres of soybeans that the farmer plants, the system for this problem is given below.

$$\begin{cases} C + S \le 50 \\ 250C + 200S \le 12{,}000 \\ C \ge 0 \\ S \ge 0 \end{cases}$$

(Source: USDA, 1991)

13. Match each inequality in the system with its meaning.
   a. $C + S \le 50$ ii
   b. $250C + 200S \le 12{,}000$ iii
   c. $C \ge 0$ iv
   d. $S \ge 0$ i

   (i) The number of acres of soybeans is not negative.
   (ii) The total number of acres is not more than 50.
   (iii) The cost of planting must be no more than $12,000.
   (iv) The least number of acres of corn is zero.

14. Graph the feasible region of points (*C*, *S*). **See left.**

15. Suppose the profit per acre for corn is $75 and for soybeans is $85.
   a. Find the vertices of the feasible region. **(0, 0), (0, 50), (40, 10), (48, 0)**
   b. State the profit formula. **$P = 75C + 85S$**
   c. At which vertex is *P* maximized? **(0, 50)**

Lesson 5-9   *Linear Programming I*   **329**

Extension

✎ **Consumer Connection**
Writing Remind students that for **Questions 13–15** they graphed a system of inequalities and found a feasible region as well as a maximum profit. Have them write a brief explanation of what would happen to the feasible region if the farmer can increase the number of acres that would be available for planting. Then ask students to explain how they would advise the farmer if there is a glut of soybeans on the market and to justify their recommendations. [Answers will vary. Make sure that the students substantiate what they say with data.]

Project Update Project 1, *Nutritious and Cheap?* and Project 4, *History of Linear Programming,* on page 336, relate to the content of this lesson.

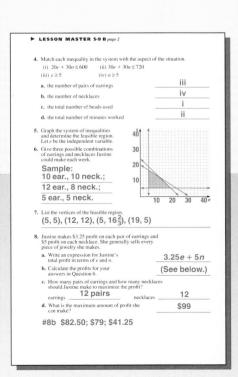

▶ **LESSON MASTER 5-9 B** *page 2*

4. Match each inequality in the system with the aspect of the situation.
   (i) $20e + 30n \le 600$ (ii) $30e + 30n \le 720$
   (iii) $e \ge 5$ (iv) $n \ge 5$
   a. the number of pairs of earrings — iii
   b. the number of necklaces — iv
   c. the total number of beads used — i
   d. the total number of minutes worked — ii

5. Graph the system of inequalities and determine the feasible region. Let *e* be the independent variable.

6. Give three possible combinations of earrings and necklaces Justine could make each week.
   Sample:
   10 ear., 10 neck.;
   12 ear., 8 neck.;
   5 ear., 5 neck.

7. List the vertices of the feasible region.
   (5, 5), (12, 12), (5, 16⅔), (19, 5)

8. Justine makes $3.25 profit on each pair of earrings and $5 profit on each necklace. She generally sells every piece of jewelry she makes.
   a. Write an expression for Justine's total profit in terms of *e* and *n*. — $3.25e + 5n$
   b. Calculate the profits for your answers in Question 6. — (See below.)
   c. How many pairs of earrings and how many necklaces should Justine make to maximize the profit?
      earrings — **12 pairs** necklaces — **12**
   d. What is the maximum amount of profit she can make? — $99

   #8b $82.50; $79; $41.25

Adapting to Individual Needs

Challenge
Show students the following linear programming problems. Ask them to explain why the first problem has no solutions and why the second problem has two solutions.

1. Maximize $z = 2x + 5y$ on the feasible

   region defined by $\begin{cases} 5x + y \ge 10 \\ 2x + 3y \ge 12 \\ x \ge 0 \\ y \ge 0 \end{cases}$

[The region is unbounded and produces no maximum.]

2. Maximize $z = x + 5y$ on the feasible

   region defined by $\begin{cases} x + 5y \le 40 \\ 3x + 3y \le 36 \\ x \ge 0 \\ y \ge 0 \end{cases}$

[There are two vertices, (0, 8) and (10, 6), that each give the maximum value of *z*.]

329

16a)

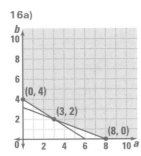

16. A landscaping contractor uses a combination of two brands of fertilizers, each containing different amounts of phosphates and nitrates, as shown in the table below.

	Phosphate Content per Package	Nitrate Content per Package
Brand *A*	4 lb	2 lb
Brand *B*	6 lb	5 lb

A certain lawn requires a mixture of at least 24 lb of phosphates and at least 16 lb of nitrates. If a is the number of packages of Brand A and b is the number of packages of Brand B, then the constraints of the problem are given by the following system of inequalities.

$$\begin{cases} a \geq 0 \\ b \geq 0 \\ 4a + 6b \geq 24 \\ 2a + 5b \geq 16 \end{cases}$$

a. Graph the feasible region. **See left.**
b. If a package of Brand A costs $6.99 and a package of Brand B costs $17.99, which pair (a, b) in the feasible region gives the lowest cost? **(8, 0)**

Review

17. *Multiple choice.* Which of the following systems describes the graph at the left? *(Lesson 5-8)* **b**

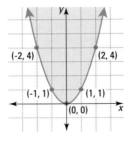

(a) $\begin{cases} 2y + x \geq 6 \\ y - 3x \leq 4 \end{cases}$ (b) $\begin{cases} 2y + x \leq 6 \\ y - 3x \geq 4 \end{cases}$ (c) $\begin{cases} 2y + x < 6 \\ y - 3x > 4 \end{cases}$

18. Evaluate $\det \begin{bmatrix} x & -3 \\ 2 & y \end{bmatrix}$. *(Lesson 5-5)* $xy + 6$

19. Find the inverse of the matrix for S_{-3}. *(Lessons 4-4, 5-5)* $S_{-\frac{1}{3}} = \begin{bmatrix} -\frac{1}{3} & 0 \\ 0 & -\frac{1}{3} \end{bmatrix}$

20. Find an equation for the line through the points $(-2, -4)$ and $(5, 7)$. *(Lesson 3-5)* $y - 7 = \frac{11}{7}(x - 5)$

21. At the left is a graph of the function $f(x) = x^2$. Write an inequality to describe the shaded region. *(Lesson 5-7)* $y \geq x^2$

22. The strength S of a rectangular beam varies directly as its width w and the square of its depth d, and varies inversely as its length L. Suppose a beam can support 1750 pounds, and its dimensions are $w = 4''$, $d = 8''$, and $L = 20$ feet. What is the strength of a beam of the same material with $w = 4''$, $d = 8''$, and $L = 25$ feet? *(Lesson 2-9)* **1400 lb**

Exploration

23. Suppose $a + b + c + d = 100$, and a, b, c, and d are all nonnegative. What are the largest and smallest possible values of $abcd$? **See margin.**

Setting Up Lesson 5-10

Materials If you plan to use the *Extension* in Lesson 5-10, you will need software that solves linear programming problems.

Golden touch. *Although most jewelry today is made by machine, many people make jewelry as a hobby. This woman is working with brass wires to make jewelry to be sold at a local craft fair. See the Example on page 332.*

In Lesson 5-9, you practiced using the Linear-Programming Theorem for a given feasible region and linear combination expression to be maximized or minimized. In this lesson you will learn to solve linear-programming problems from scratch. To solve a linear-programming problem, follow these steps.

1. Identify the variables.
2. Identify the constraints, and translate them into a system of inequalities relating the variables. If necessary, make a table.
3. Graph the system of inequalities; find the vertices of the feasible set.
4. Write a formula or an expression to be maximized or minimized.
5. Apply the Linear-Programming Theorem.
6. Interpret the results.

Because linear-programming problems are long and involved, you must organize your work and write neatly. We illustrate the entire process in the following Example.

Lesson 5-10 *Linear Programming II* **331**

Lesson 5-10

Objectives
G Use linear programming to solve real-world problems.

Resources
From the *Teacher's Resource File*
■ Lesson Master 5-10A or 5-10B
■ Answer Master 5-10
■ Teaching Aids
 8 Four-Quadrant Graph Paper
45 Warm-up

Additional Resources
■ Visuals for Teaching Aids 8, 45
■ Software to solve linear-programming problems

Teaching
Lesson **5-10**

Warm-up
Graph the following system of inequalities. Label the vertices of the feasible set.

$$\begin{cases} x \geq 0 \\ y \geq 0 \\ 12x + 18y \leq 72 \\ 10x + 6y \leq 30 \end{cases}$$

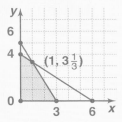

Lesson 5-10 Overview

Broad Goals The goal of this lesson is for students to be able to give a complete solution to a linear programming problem, given adequate information in prose.

Perspective In Lessons 5-8 and 5-9, most situations presented to students included a set of inequalities. In this lesson, in order to solve a problem, students must translate a given situation into a system of inequalities in which each inequality represents a constraint of the problem, and an expression to be maximized or minimized.

Notes on Reading

Students may use graph paper or **Teaching Aid 8** throughout this lesson.

If you have discussed several examples from Lessons 5-8 and 5-9 in class, students will probably not need any additional examples before reading Lesson 5-10. What they will need now is time to work either individually or in small groups on the questions in this lesson.

Pacing Notice that there are only two *Applying the Mathematics* questions. We have found that it takes time to discuss the example and that two complete linear-programming problems and some shorter questions make a reasonable assignment for students at this level.

Additional Examples

A pet-food company wants to mix two kinds of pet food. Brand A provides .3 units of iron per ounce and .9 units of calcium per ounce. Brand B provides .4 units of iron and .5 units of calcium per ounce. The mixture is to have at least 12 units of iron and 29.7 units of calcium. If Brand A costs 8¢ per ounce to produce and Brand B costs 6¢ per ounce to produce, how many ounces of each food should be used in the mixture to meet these requirements while keeping costs to a minimum? What is the minimum cost? **28 oz of Brand A and 9 oz of Brand B; $2.78**

Example

Some students make necklaces and bracelets in their spare time and sell all that they make. Every week they have available 10,000 g of metal and 20 hours to work. It takes 50 g of metal to make a necklace and 200 g to make a bracelet. Each necklace takes 30 minutes to make and each bracelet takes 20 minutes. The profit on each necklace is $3.50, and the profit on each bracelet is $2.50. The students want to earn as much money as possible. Because you are taking this course, they ask you to give them advice. What numbers of necklaces and bracelets should they make each week? How much profit can they make?

Solution

1. Identify the variables.
   Let x = the number of necklaces to be made per week and y = the number of bracelets to be made per week.
2. Identify the constraints, and translate them into a system of inequalities. Negative numbers cannot be used; thus

$$x \geq 0$$
$$y \geq 0.$$

The following table summarizes the information about production.

	Metal Used	Time to Make
for each necklace	50 g	30 min
for each bracelet	200 g	20 min
Total available	10,000 g	20 hours (or 1200 min)

The amount of metal (in grams) used satisfies

$$50x + 200y \leq 10,000.$$

The amount of time (in minutes) needed satisfies

$$30x + 20y \leq 1200.$$

3. Graph the system and find the vertices. Only the feasible set is shown.

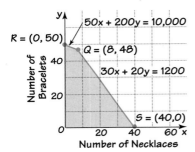

The vertices $R = (0, 50)$, $Q = (8, 48)$, and $S = (40, 0)$ are found by solving systems of equations. For instance, Q is found by solving $50x + 200y = 10,000$ and $30x + 20y = 1200$. The vertices are labeled on the graph.

4. Write a formula to be maximized or minimized.
   The profit formula is $P = 3.50x + 2.50y$. P is to be maximized.

Noble prize. *Shown are Tjalling Koopmans (top) and Leonid Kantorovich. The Nobel Prize, named for Alfred Nobel, was first awarded in 1901. There are six categories—physics, chemistry, physiology (medicine), literature, economic sciences, and international peace.*

5. Apply the Linear-Programming Theorem. Substitute the coordinates of each vertex into the profit formula.
For (0, 0): $P = 3.5(0) + 2.5(0) = 0$.
For (40, 0): $P = 3.5(40) + 2.5(0) = 140$.
For (8, 48): $P = 3.5(8) + 2.5(48) = 148$.
For (0, 50): $P = 3.5(0) + 2.5(50) = 125$.
6. Interpret the results. The maximum profit of $148 occurs at vertex $Q = (8, 48)$. To earn the maximum weekly profit of $148, the students should make 8 necklaces and 48 bracelets each week.

Linear programming is often used in industries in which all the competitors make the same product (such as gasoline, paper, appliances, clothing, and so on). Efficiency in the use of labor and materials determines the amount of profit. These situations can involve as many as 5000 variables and 10,000 inequalities. Although we use graphing to solve linear-programming problems in this book, more efficient methods of solution are used by computers and calculators. The most efficient procedure for most linear-programming problems is the *simplex algorithm* invented in 1947 by the econometrician Leonid Hurwicz and the mathematicians George Dantzig and Tjalling Koopmans, all from the United States. It is for this work that Koopmans shared the Nobel Prize with Kantorovich in 1975.

QUESTIONS

Covering the Reading

In 1–5, refer to the Example in this lesson.

1. What are the students trying to find? **the maximum profit and the number of necklaces and bracelets needed to maximize profits**

2. What is the *x*-intercept of the equation which limits the amount of metal to be used? Is it in the feasible region? **200; no**

3. How much more profit do the students make with the linear combination at (8, 48) than at the next best vertex? **$8.00**

4. a. What would be the profit if the students made 9 necklaces and 47 bracelets? **$149.00**
   b. Why can they not do this?
      The point does not satisfy the time constraint.

5. Suppose the students in the Example decide to put semiprecious gems in their jewelry: six in each necklace and one in each bracelet. They can use 150 gems each week.
   a. Translate this constraint into an inequality. **$6x + y \le 150$**
   b. The entire system, including this new constraint, is graphed at the left. Find the new vertices, *T* and *U*. **$T = (20, 30)$, $U = (25, 0)$**
   c. If the students will now earn $6.50 profit on each necklace and $3.00 profit on each bracelet, do they need to change their program to keep profits at a maximum? Justify your answer.
   Yes; The profit at the new vertex *T* (for $P = 220$) exceeds the profit at *Q*, so *T* maximizes profit rather than *Q*.

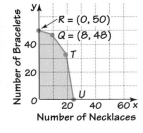

Lesson 5-10 *Linear Programming II* **333**

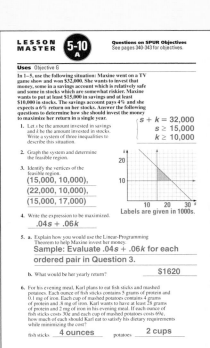

Question 7 This question combines all the concepts and skills of Lessons 5-8, 5-9, and 5-10. Note that steps **a** through **f** are worded in a way that provides direction to the insecure students. Encourage these students to do as complete a solution as possible on their own.

Question 8 Emphasize that the solution for this question (a maximization problem) should follow the same steps used for **Question 7** (a minimization problem).

Question 13 Science Connection About 8% of the earth's crust is made up of aluminum, making it the third most common element in the crust—greater amounts of only oxygen and silicon can be found. Pure aluminum is soft and weak, but it becomes hard and strong when it is mixed with silicon and iron. Aluminum and aluminum alloys are used in aircraft and building construction, consumer products, packaging materials, electrical conductors and processing equipment.

Question 16 This skill sequence reviews solving simple quadratic equations in preparation for Chapter 6.

7a) *h*: oz of hamburger;
p: number of medium potatoes

b) $\begin{cases} .8h + 1.1p \geq 5 \\ 10h \geq 30 \\ 6.5h + 4p \geq 35 \\ h \geq 0 \\ p \geq 0 \end{cases}$

c)
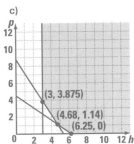

9a)
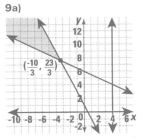

---

6. **a.** Name a method for solving linear-programming problems without graphing. **The simplex algorithm**
   b. Who developed this method, and when?
   Hurwicz, Dantzig, Koopmans; 1947

Applying the Mathematics

7. Some parents shopping for their family want to know how much hamburger and how many potatoes to buy. From a nutrition table, they find that one ounce of hamburger has 8 mg of iron, 10 units of Vitamin A, and 6.5 grams of protein. One medium potato has 1.1 mg of iron, 0 units of Vitamin A, and 4 grams of protein.

   For this meal the parents want each member of the family to have at least 5 mg of iron, 30 units of Vitamin A, and 35 grams of protein. One potato costs $0.10 and 1 ounce of hamburger costs $0.15. The parents want to be economical (minimize their costs), yet meet daily requirements. They need a program for the quantities of hamburger and potatoes to buy for the family. **a–c) See left.**
   a. Identify the variables for this problem.
   b. Translate the constraints of the problem into a system of inequalities. (You should have five inequalities; a table may help.)
   c. Graph the system of inequalities in part **b**, and find the vertices of the feasible set. (Note: Usually the variable that comes first in the alphabet is plotted on the horizontal axis.)
   d. Write an expression for the cost to be minimized. **.15h + .10p**
   e. Apply the Linear-Programming Theorem to determine which vertex minimizes the cost expression of part **d**. **(4.68, 1.14)**
   f. Interpret your answer to part **e**. What is the best program for this family? **4.68 oz of hamburger and 1.14 oz of potatoes per person give the proper nutrition for the lowest cost.**

8. A company makes two kinds of tires: model R (regular) and model S (snow). Each tire is processed on three machines, A, B, and C. To make one model R tire requires $\frac{1}{2}$ hour on machine A, 2 hours on B, and 1 hour on C. To make one model S tire requires 1 hour on A, 1 hour on B, and 4 hours on C. During the next week, machine A will be available for at most 20 hours, machine B for at most 60 hours, and machine C for at most 60 hours. If the company makes a $10 profit on each model R tire and a $15 profit on each model S tire, how many of each tire should be made to maximize the company's profit? (Hint: Use the six steps suggested in this lesson.) **26 regular and 7 snow tires**

Review

9. **a.** Graph the feasible set of the system $\begin{cases} x + 2y \geq 12 \\ 2x + y \leq 1 \\ x \leq 4 \\ y \geq 0. \end{cases}$
   See left.
   b. What are the coordinates of its vertices? *(Lesson 5-9)*
   $\left(\frac{-10}{3}, \frac{23}{3}\right)$

Adapting to Individual Needs

Challenge
Have students solve this problem. A company installs captain seats and benches in vans. Each seat requires 20 feet of plastic, 1 pound of foam, and 2 square yards of fabric. Each bench requires 100 feet of plastic, 50 pounds of foam, and 20 square yards of fabric. The company has in stock 1900 feet of plastic, 500 pounds of foam, and 240 yards of fabric. If seats are sold for a profit of $20 each and benches are sold for a profit of $300 each, how many of each should the company produce to yield the greatest income? [Sample answer: The mathematical solution is 25 seats and 9.5 benches, but this is not feasible. The company might make 25 seats and 9 benches for a profit of $3200. Or, the company might get more materials and make a 10th bench, but then the cost of the additional materials would cut down on the profit from the 10th bench.]

10. a. Graph all solutions to the system $\begin{cases} x > -4 \\ y < 6 \end{cases}$. *See left.*

b. Is the point (-7, 2) in the solution set? How can you tell?
(Lessons 5-7, 5-8)
No;   since -7 < -4, the point (-7, 2) lies outside the shaded region.

11. Solve the following system by using matrices.   *(Lessons 5-5, 5-6)*
x = -1, y = 4
$$\begin{cases} 5x + 3y = 7 \\ 2x - 7y = -30 \end{cases}$$

12. Does the matrix $\begin{bmatrix} 4 & -6 \\ -6 & 9 \end{bmatrix}$ have an inverse? How can you tell?
(Lesson 5-5)   No. Since the determinant is zero, it has no inverse.

13. An alloy containing 65% aluminum is made by melting together two alloys that are 25% aluminum and 75% aluminum. How many kilograms of each alloy must be used to produce 160 kilograms of the 65% alloy?
(Lesson 5-4)
32 kg of 25% aluminum;   128 kg of 75% aluminum

14. Solve $12 - 5x < 16$.   *(Lesson 5-1)* $x > \frac{-4}{5}$

15. A formula for the nth term of a sequence is $a_n = 10 - .5(n - 1)$.
a. Write the first three terms.   10;   9.5;   9
b. Write a recursive formula for this sequence.   *See left.*
c. Solve the explicit formula for n. $-2a_n + 21 = n$
d. One term of the sequence is -39. Which term is it?
(Lessons 1-5, 1-7, 3-3, 3-4)   99th term

16. *Skill sequence.*   Solve.   *(Previous course)*
a. $x^2 = 49$
$x = 7$ or $x = -7$
b. $x^2 + 2 = 51$
$x = 7$ or $x = -7$
c. $x^2 + 2 = 49$
$x = \sqrt{47}$ or $x = -\sqrt{47}$

Exploration

17. In this lesson and in the last lesson six situations are described that lead to linear-programming problems. For instance, one situation is found in the Example of this lesson and another is in Question 7 of this lesson. Make up another situation that would lead to this kind of problem.   Answers may vary.

Plainly aluminum. *Shown is a McDonnell-Douglas MD-80 series jet. This jet contains approximately 18,000 kilograms of aluminum.*

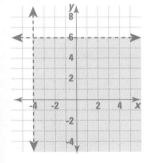

10a)

15b)
$\begin{cases} a_1 = 10 \\ a_n = a_{n-1} - .5, \text{ for} \\ \quad \text{integers } n \geq 2 \end{cases}$

Lesson 5-10   *Linear Programming II*   **335**

Follow-up
for Lesson   **5-10**

Practice

For more questions on SPUR Objectives, use **Lesson Master 5-10A** (shown on page 333) or **Lesson Master 5-10B** (shown on pages 334–335).

Assessment

Written Communication Have students write a paragraph explaining some of the techniques that they have found useful in solving linear programming problems. [Students write meaningful paragraphs that demonstrate an understanding of linear programming techniques.]

Extension

Technology Connection Software exists that will solve linear programming problems. You might demonstrate such software. In the business world, virtually all linear programming problems are solved using technology.

Project Update Project 1, *Nutritious and Cheap?* and Project 4, *History of Linear Programming*, on page 336, relate to the content of this lesson.

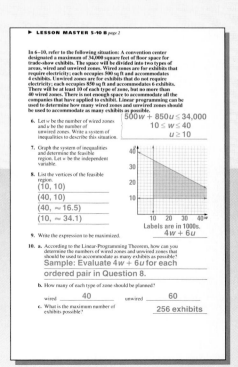

► **LESSON MASTER 5-10 B** *page 2*

In 6–10, refer to the following situation: A convention center designated a maximum of 34,000 square feet of floor space for trade-show exhibits. The space will be divided into two types of areas, wired and unwired zones. Wired zones are for exhibits that require electricity; each occupies 500 sq ft and accommodates 4 exhibits. Unwired zones are for exhibits that do not require electricity; each occupies 850 sq ft and accommodates 6 exhibits. There will be at least 10 of each type of zone, but no more than 40 wired zones. There is not enough space to accommodate all the companies that have applied to exhibit. Linear programming can be used to determine how many wired zones and unwired zones should be used to accommodate as many exhibits as possible.

6. Let w be the number of wired zones and u be the number of unwired zones. Write a system of inequalities to describe this situation.
$\begin{cases} 500w + 850u \leq 34,000 \\ 10 \leq w \leq 40 \\ u \geq 10 \end{cases}$

7. Graph the system of inequalities and determine the feasible region. Let w be the independent variable.

8. List the vertices of the feasible region.
(10, 10)
(40, 10)
(40, ≈ 16.5)
(10, ≈ 34.1)

Labels are in 1000s.

9. Write the expression to be maximized. $4w + 6u$

10. a. According to the Linear-Programming Theorem, how can you determine the numbers of wired zones and unwired zones that should be used to accommodate as many exhibits as possible?
Sample: Evaluate $4w + 6u$ for each ordered pair in Question 8.

b. How many of each type of zone should be planned?
wired   40   unwired   60

c. What is the maximum number of exhibits possible?   256 exhibits

Chapter 5 Projects

The projects relate chiefly to the content of the lessons of this chapter as follows:

1 Nutritious and Cheap Students can find recommended daily dietary allowance in almanacs, health books, and encyclopedias.

2 Inverses of 3 × 3 Matrices If students do not have access to an advanced mathematics book which describes how to find the inverse of a 3 × 3 matrix, see the method suggested in the *Overview* for Lesson 5-6 on pages 305–306.

3 Systems Involving a Hyperbola and a Line This is a straightforward activity. Some students might want to try to prove their conjectures.

4 History of Linear Programming There are many books devoted to linear programming, including one by George Dantzig, one of the founders of the subject.

5 Using Matrices to Code and Decode Messages Students should be able to find information on secret codes in the library. The book *Sophisticated Ciphers*, by Josephine P. Andree and Richard V. Andree of the University of Oklahoma (and later distributed by Mu Alpha Theta) explains the use of matrices for codes in detail.

A project presents an opportunity for you to extend your knowledge of a topic related to the material of this chapter. You should allow more time for a project than you do for typical homework questions.

PROJECTS 5 CHAPTER FIVE

1 Nutritious and Cheap?

a. Look up the recommended daily allowance (RDA) of protein, vitamin A, vitamin C, and calcium for someone your age.

b. Name some foods that contain these nutrients, and find the cost of one serving of each of these foods.

c. Use linear programming to find out how many servings of these foods you would need to eat each day in order to get the RDA of these nutrients at the lowest possible cost.

d. Make up some other problem about nutrients that can be solved using a system of equations or inequalities. Solve your problem.

2 Inverses of 3 × 3 Matrices

Find a book that tells how to find the inverse of a 3 × 3 matrix by hand.

a. Write an explanation of the method using a matrix of your own choosing.

b. Apply the method to solve a 3 × 3 system.

c. Tell what 3 × 3 matrices do not have inverses.

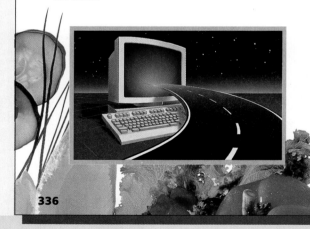

336

3 Systems Involving a Hyperbola and a Line

In Lesson 5-2 you found the intersection points of a hyperbola and line. Use an automatic grapher to examine the possible intersections of all systems written in the form below.

$$\begin{cases} y = mx + b \\ y = \dfrac{n}{x} \end{cases}$$

Make conjectures, if you can, about the following situations.

a. If m and n are both positive and constant, how does varying b affect the number of intersections? What are the numbers of intersections possible? (Try positive and negative values for b.)

b. Repeat part **a** with m and n both negative.

c. Repeat part **a** with m and n having opposite signs. Does it make any difference which is positive and which negative? How do the graphs compare?

4 History of Linear Programming

Throughout the chapter, there have been brief references to the history of linear programming. Research the work of the mathematicians mentioned in this chapter and their contributions to the development of linear-programming techniques. Also, find out more about recent developments using computers to solve such problems, such as work done by Karmarkar in 1984. Write a report that summarizes your findings.

Possible responses

1. **a.** Recommended daily allowances (15–18 years old):

	Male	Female
Protein	59 g	44 g
Vitamin A	1000 RE*	800 RE*
Vitamin C	60 mg	60 mg
Calcium	1200 mg	1200 mg

*retinol equivalents

b. Sample foods are listed. The cost of one serving will vary.
Protein: meat, poultry, fish, dry beans, eggs, nuts, peanut butter
Vitamin A: green and yellow vegetables, cereals, milk
Vitamin C: fruits, potatoes
Calcium: milk, yogurt, cheese, cream soups, spinach

c. Responses will vary.

d. Responses will vary.

2. Sample responses given.
a. One method is described in the *Overview* for Lesson 5-6.

b. Consider
$$\begin{aligned} x + 2y + 3z &= 4 \\ 3x + y - z &= -3 \\ x - 2y + z &= 4. \end{aligned}$$

$$M = \begin{bmatrix} 1 & 2 & 3 \\ 3 & 1 & -1 \\ 1 & -2 & 1 \end{bmatrix} \quad M^{-1} = \begin{bmatrix} \frac{1}{30} & \frac{8}{30} & \frac{5}{30} \\ \frac{4}{30} & \frac{2}{30} & -\frac{10}{30} \\ \frac{7}{30} & -\frac{4}{30} & \frac{5}{30} \end{bmatrix}$$

5 Using Matrices to Code and Decode Messages

Between 1929 and 1931, the mathematician Lester Hill devised a method of encoding messages using matrices. Every integer is assigned a letter according to the scheme:

$1 = A, 2 = B, 3 = C, \ldots, 25 = Y, 26 = Z,$
$27 = A, 28 = B, \ldots,$ and $0 = Z,$
$-1 = Y, \ldots, -24 = B, -25 = A, -26 = Z \ldots.$

a. To code or encipher the word FOUR, follow these steps.

Step 1 Put the letters into a 2×2 matrix four at a time. With $6 = F, 15 = O, 21 = U, 18 = R$, use the matrix

$$\begin{bmatrix} 6 & 15 \\ 21 & 18 \end{bmatrix}.$$

Step 2 Choose a 2×2 coding or key matrix, such as $\begin{bmatrix} 0 & 1 \\ 1 & 2 \end{bmatrix}$. Multiply each 2×2 matrix by the coding matrix. For instance,

$$\begin{bmatrix} 0 & 1 \\ 1 & 2 \end{bmatrix}\begin{bmatrix} 6 & 15 \\ 21 & 18 \end{bmatrix} = \begin{bmatrix} 21 & 18 \\ 48 & 51 \end{bmatrix}.$$

Step 3 Change the resulting matrix $\begin{bmatrix} 21 & 18 \\ 48 & 51 \end{bmatrix}$ back to letters to write the coded message: URVY.

Step 4 Repeat this as many times as necessary to encode a longer message. Code MEET ME AT NOON using the key $\begin{bmatrix} 0 & 1 \\ 1 & 2 \end{bmatrix}$.

b. To decode or decipher a message, follow these steps.

Step 1 Break the message up into groups of four letters and write as matrices using the corresponding numbers. Each letter-group matrix should be:

$$\begin{bmatrix} \text{1st letter} & \text{2nd letter} \\ \text{3rd letter} & \text{4th letter} \end{bmatrix}.$$

Step 2 Find the inverse of the key matrix and multiply each letter-group matrix by the inverse. The following message was also encoded using the key $\begin{bmatrix} 0 & 1 \\ 1 & 2 \end{bmatrix}$:

YTKOFOTISBGVITWKOULO.
What is the original message?

c. Make up a coding matrix and a coded message of your own. (Note: In order for Hill's method to work the determinant of your coding matrix must be 1 or -1.)

$$\begin{bmatrix} \frac{1}{30} & \frac{8}{30} & \frac{5}{30} \\ \frac{4}{30} & \frac{2}{30} & -\frac{10}{30} \\ \frac{7}{30} & -\frac{4}{30} & \frac{5}{30} \end{bmatrix}\begin{bmatrix} 4 \\ -3 \\ 4 \end{bmatrix} = \begin{bmatrix} 0 \\ -1 \\ 2 \end{bmatrix}$$

So, $x = 0, y = -1$, and $z = 2$.

c. If the determinant is 0, there is no inverse.

3. Sample conjectures are given.

a. When $m > 0$ and $n > 0$, varying b does not affect the number

of intersections; there are two intersections for every value of b.

b. When $m < 0$ and $n < 0$ varying b does not affect the number of intersections; there are two intersections for every value of b.

(Responses continue at the top of the next column.)

Additional responses, page 336

3c. When m and n have opposite signs, there can be 0, 1, or 2 intersections, depending on the value of b. It does not matter which number is positive and which is negative. When m is positive and n is negative, the line has a positive slope and the hyperbola occupies Quadrants II and IV. Otherwise the line has a negative slope and the hyperbola occupies Quadrants I and III.

4. Sample information students might include in their reports is given. Jean Baptiste Fourier was the first person to systematically study linear inequalities. In 1826, he conceived that the region of solutions to a system of linear inequalities is a convex polygon. He was also the first person to introduce the idea of finding an optimal solution to the system by comparing the vertices of the polygon. The mathematician George Dantzig first used linear programming to solve an economics problem in 1947. He showed how to optimize the achievement of various goals of the U. S. Air Force by comparing different plans to fulfill these goals. Using the suggestions of T. C. Koopman, Dantzig and Leonid Hurwicz created the simplex method for solving linear programming problems. The method uses Fourier's idea of moving along the edges of a polygon and comparing vertices. The simplex method remained the most effective method for solving linear programming problems until the work of Narendra Karmarkar in 1984. When at Bell Laboratories, Karmarkar introduced what is called the projective method. Where the simplex method moves along the edges of a polygon, Karmarkar's method takes a short cut through the polygon to arrive at an optimal solution, and is more efficient in some cases.

(Responses continue on page 338.)

Additional Answers
Progress Self-Test, page 339

1. $n > -2$

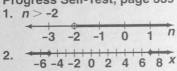

2.
```
←+++|+++|+++|+++|+++|+++|+++→ x
 -6 -4 -2 0  2  4  6  8
```

4. a. inconsistent
   b. The graphs of these equations are both vertical lines, but they have different x-intercepts. Since the lines do not intersect, the system is inconsistent.

5. Sample: In the third equation, substitute r with $t + 11$ and s with $4t$. This gives $3(t + 11) - 8(4t) = 4$. Solve this equation to get $t = 1$. Substitute $t = 1$ into the original system's first and second equation; $s = 4(1) = 4$, $r = 1 + 11 = 12$; $(r, s, t,) = (12, 4, 1)$

SUMMARY

When two or more sentences are joined by the words *and* or *or,* a compound sentence results. The solution set to *A or B* is the union of the solution sets of *A* and *B*. If the word joining them is *and,* the compound sentence is called a system. The solution set to *A and B* is the intersection of the solution sets of *A* and *B*.

Systems have many applications and may contain any number of variables. If the system contains one variable, then its solutions may be graphed on a number line or in the plane, depending on the situation. If the system contains two variables, then its solutions may be graphed in the plane. Graphing in the plane often tells you the number of solutions but may not yield the exact solutions.

In using algebra to solve systems of linear equations you may use linear combinations, substitutions, or matrices. The matrix method converts a system of n equations in n unknowns to a single matrix equation. To get the solution to the system, both sides of the equation are multiplied by the inverse of the coefficient matrix.

The graph of a single linear inequality in two variables is a half-plane or a half-plane with its boundary. For a system of two linear inequalities, if the boundary lines intersect, then the graph is the interior of an angle plus perhaps one or both of its sides.

Systems with two variables but more than two inequalities arise in linear-programming problems. In a linear-programming problem, you look for a solution to the system that maximizes or minimizes the value of a particular expression or formula. To solve such a problem, first find the set of solutions to the system. This feasible set is always a convex region. The Linear-Programming Theorem states that the desired point must be a vertex of the feasible set, so all vertices must be tested. Applications of linear programming are a relatively recent development in mathematics and are quite important in industry.

VOCABULARY

Below are the most important terms and phrases for this chapter. You should be able to give a definition for those terms marked with *. For all other terms you should be able to give a general description and a specific example.

Lesson 5-1
constraint
system
open sentence
interval
compound sentence
* union of sets, *or*
* intersection of sets, *and*
inequality
Addition Property of Inequality
Multiplication Properties
   of Inequality

Lesson 5-2
system
* solution for a system
rescale, zoom

Lesson 5-3
consistent system
inconsistent system

Lesson 5-4
Linear Combination Method

Lesson 5-5
* inverse of a matrix M, M^{-1}
Square matrix
Inverse Matrix Theorem
* determinant of a 2 × 2
   matrix M
det M

Lesson 5-6
matrix form of a system
coefficient matrix
constant matrix
System-Determinant Theorem
3 × 3 identity matrix

Lesson 5-7
half-plane
boundary
lattice point

Lesson 5-8
* feasible set, feasible region
* vertices of feasible region
convex region

Lesson 5-9
linear-programming problem
Linear-Programming Theorem

338

Additional Responses, page 337

5. a. Code MEET MEAT NOON.

$$\begin{bmatrix} 0 & 1 \\ 1 & 2 \end{bmatrix}\begin{bmatrix} 13 & 5 \\ 5 & 20 \end{bmatrix} = \begin{bmatrix} 5 & 20 \\ 23 & 45 \end{bmatrix}$$

So, MEET → ETWS.

$$\begin{bmatrix} 0 & 1 \\ 1 & 2 \end{bmatrix}\begin{bmatrix} 13 & 5 \\ 1 & 20 \end{bmatrix} = \begin{bmatrix} 1 & 20 \\ 15 & 45 \end{bmatrix}$$

So, MEAT → ATOS.

$$\begin{bmatrix} 0 & 1 \\ 1 & 2 \end{bmatrix}\begin{bmatrix} 14 & 15 \\ 15 & 14 \end{bmatrix} = \begin{bmatrix} 15 & 14 \\ 44 & 43 \end{bmatrix}$$

So, NOON → ONRQ.

The code for MEET ME AT NOON is ETWSATOSONRQ.

b. To decode YTKOFOTISBGVITWKOULO, multiply the matrix for each group of four letters (YTKO FOTI SBGV ITWK OULO) by $\begin{bmatrix} -2 & 1 \\ 1 & 0 \end{bmatrix}$, the inverse of the coding matrix.

$$\begin{bmatrix} -2 & 1 \\ 1 & 0 \end{bmatrix}\begin{bmatrix} 25 & 20 \\ 11 & 15 \end{bmatrix} = \begin{bmatrix} -39 & -25 \\ 25 & 20 \end{bmatrix}$$

So, YTKO → MAYT.

$$\begin{bmatrix} -2 & 1 \\ 1 & 0 \end{bmatrix}\begin{bmatrix} 6 & 15 \\ 20 & 9 \end{bmatrix} = \begin{bmatrix} 8 & -21 \\ 6 & 15 \end{bmatrix}$$

So, FOTI → HEFO.

$$\begin{bmatrix} -2 & 1 \\ 1 & 0 \end{bmatrix}\begin{bmatrix} -19 & 2 \\ 7 & 22 \end{bmatrix} = \begin{bmatrix} -31 & 18 \\ 19 & 2 \end{bmatrix}$$

So, SBGVI → URSB.

PROGRESS SELF-TEST

Take this test as you would take a test in class. Use graph paper and a calculator. Then check your work with the solutions shown in the Selected Answers section in the back of the book.

1. Solve and graph the solution set to $-3n + 16 < 22$ on a number line. **See margin.**

2. On a number line, graph $\{x: x \le -5 \text{ or } x \ge 7\}$. **See margin.**

3. A graph of the system $\begin{cases} y = .5x - 2 \\ y = -x^2 \end{cases}$
is shown below. Estimate the solutions to the system, to the nearest tenth.
$(-1.7, -2.8), (1.2, -1.4)$

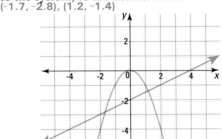

4. Consider the system $\begin{cases} 2x - 9 = 8 \\ 2x - 9 = -7. \end{cases}$ **See margin.**
   a. Is this system consistent or inconsistent?
   b. Explain how you can tell.

In 5 and 6, solve each system. Show your work, or explain how you used technology to find the solution. **See margin.**

5. $\begin{cases} s = 4t \\ r = t + 11 \\ 3r - 8s = 4 \end{cases}$ 6. $\begin{cases} -3x + 3y = 2 \\ -4x - 2y = 3 \end{cases}$

7. At Eggs-N-Links Restaurant you can get a Double Duo Breakfast of 2 eggs with 2 sausage links for $2.78 and a Triple Quad Breakfast of 3 eggs with 4 sausage links for $4.99. From this information, use a system of equations to determine what Eggs-N-Links might charge for 1 egg. Be sure to identify what each variable represents. **See margin.**

8. Consider the system $\begin{cases} 8x + 3y = 41 \\ 6x + 5y = 39. \end{cases}$ **See margin.**
   a. What is the coefficient matrix?
   b. Find the inverse of the coefficient matrix.
   c. Use a matrix equation to solve the system.

9. a. Give an example of a 2×2 matrix that does not have an inverse.
   b. How can you tell that the inverse does not exist? **a, b) See margin.**

10. Graph the solution set of $y < -2x + 6$. **See margin.**

11. *Multiple choice.* The graph at the right shows the feasible set for which system? **c**

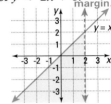

(a) $\begin{cases} y \le 3x \\ x \ge 2 \end{cases}$ (b) $\begin{cases} y > x \\ x \le 2 \end{cases}$

(c) $\begin{cases} y \le x \\ x < 2 \end{cases}$ (d) $\begin{cases} y < x \\ x < 2 \end{cases}$

12. A furniture manufacturer makes upholstered chairs and sofas. On the average it takes carpenters 7 hours to build a chair and 4 hours to build a sofa. There are enough carpenters for no more than 133 worker-hours per day. Upholsterers average 2 hours per chair and 6 hours per sofa. There are enough upholsterers for no more than 72 worker-hours per day. The profit per chair is $80 and the profit per sofa is $70. How many sofas and chairs should be made per day to maximize the profit? **See margin.**
   a. Translate the constraints into a system of linear inequalities. Call the variables c and s.
   b. Graph the system of inequalities and find the vertices of the feasible set.
   c. Apply the Linear-Programming Theorem and interpret the results.

Progress Self-Test

For the development of mathematical competence, feedback and correction, along with the opportunity to practice, are necessary. The Progress Self-Test provides the opportunity for feedback and correction; the Chapter Review provides additional opportunities and practice. We cannot overemphasize the importance of these end-of-chapter materials. It is at this point that the material "gels" for many students, allowing them to solidify skills and understanding. In general, student performance should be markedly improved after these pages.

Assign the Progress Self-Test as a one-night assignment. Worked-out *solutions* for all questions are in the Selected Answers section of the student book. Encourage students to take the Progress Self-Test honestly, grade themselves, and then be prepared to discuss the test in class.

Advise students to pay special attention to those Chapter Review questions (pages 340–343) which correspond to questions missed on the Progress Self-Test.

6. **Sample:**
   $-3x + 3y = 2$ **(multiply by 2)**
   $-4x - 2y = 3$ **(multiply by 3)**
   _____ **(add)**

   $-6x + 6y = 4$
   $-12x - 6y = 9$
   _____
   $-18x = 13$
   $x = -\frac{13}{18}$

   Substitute $x = -\frac{13}{18}$ **into the first equation;** $-3(-\frac{13}{18}) + 3y = 2$;
   $y = -\frac{1}{18}$; $(-\frac{13}{18}, -\frac{1}{18})$

   (Additional Answers continued, page 343.)

$\begin{bmatrix} -2 & 1 \\ 1 & 0 \end{bmatrix}\begin{bmatrix} 9 & 20 \\ 23 & 11 \end{bmatrix} = \begin{bmatrix} 5 & -29 \\ 9 & 20 \end{bmatrix}$

So, ITWK → EWIT.

$\begin{bmatrix} -2 & 1 \\ 1 & 0 \end{bmatrix}\begin{bmatrix} 15 & 21 \\ 12 & 15 \end{bmatrix} = \begin{bmatrix} -18 & -27 \\ 15 & 21 \end{bmatrix}$

So, OULO → HYOU.
The decoded message is MAY THE FOURS BE WITH YOU.
c. **Messages and codes will vary. In the sample that follows, HELP US AT MIDNIGHT is coded**

using the matrix: $\begin{bmatrix} 1 & -2 \\ 0 & 1 \end{bmatrix}$.

$\begin{bmatrix} 1 & -2 \\ 0 & 1 \end{bmatrix}\begin{bmatrix} 8 & 5 \\ 12 & 16 \end{bmatrix} = \begin{bmatrix} -16 & -27 \\ 12 & 16 \end{bmatrix}$

So, HELP → JYLP.

$\begin{bmatrix} 1 & -2 \\ 0 & 1 \end{bmatrix}\begin{bmatrix} 21 & 19 \\ 1 & 20 \end{bmatrix} = \begin{bmatrix} 19 & -21 \\ 1 & 20 \end{bmatrix}$

So, USAT → SEAT.

$\begin{bmatrix} 1 & -2 \\ 0 & 1 \end{bmatrix}\begin{bmatrix} 13 & 9 \\ 4 & 14 \end{bmatrix} = \begin{bmatrix} 5 & -19 \\ 4 & 14 \end{bmatrix}$

So, MIDN → EGDN.

$\begin{bmatrix} 1 & -2 \\ 0 & 1 \end{bmatrix}\begin{bmatrix} 9 & 7 \\ 8 & 20 \end{bmatrix} = \begin{bmatrix} -7 & -33 \\ 8 & 20 \end{bmatrix}$

So, IGHT → SSHT.
The coded message is JYLPSEATEGDNSSHT.

339

Chapter 5 Review

Resources

From the Teacher's Resource File
- Answer Master for
  Chapter 5 Review
- Assessment Sourcebook:
  Chapter 5 Test, Forms A–D
  Chapter 5 Test, Cumulative Form

Additional Resources
- Quiz and Test Writer

The main objectives for the chapter are organized in the Chapter Review under the four types of understanding this book promotes—Skills, Properties, Uses, and Representations.

Whereas end-of-chapter material may be considered optional in some texts, in UCSMP *Advanced Algebra* we have selected these objectives and questions with the expectation that they will be covered. Students should be able to answer these questions with about 85% accuracy after studying the chapter.

You may assign these questions over a single night to help students prepare for a test the next day, or you may assign the questions over a two-day period. If you work the questions over two days, we recommend assigning the *evens* for homework the first night so that students get feedback in class the next day and then assigning the *odds* the night before the test because answers are provided to the odd-numbered questions.

It is effective to ask students which questions they still do not understand and use the day or days as a total class discussion of the material which the class finds most difficult.

CHAPTER REVIEW

Questions on SPUR Objectives

SPUR stands for **S**kills, **P**roperties, **U**ses, and **R**epresentations. The Chapter Review questions are grouped according to the SPUR Objectives for this chapter.

SKILLS DEAL WITH THE PROCEDURES USED TO GET ANSWERS.
See margin for 9–12, 15, 16b.

Objective A: *Solve 2 × 2 and 3 × 3 systems using the Linear Combination Method or substitution.* *(Lessons 5-3, 5-4)*

1. *Multiple choice.* After which of the following does the system $\begin{cases} 2x + 3y = 19 \\ 4x - y = 17 \end{cases}$ yield $-7y = -21$? a
   a. Multiply the first equation by -2 and add.
   b. Multiply the second equation by 3 and add.
   c. Multiply the first equation by 2, the second equation by -1, and then add.
   d. Multiply the second equation by 3 and subtract.

2. Consider the system $\begin{cases} y = 5x \\ -3x + 2y = -28. \end{cases}$
   a. Which method do you prefer to use to solve this system? Sample: substitution
   b. Solve and check the system using the method you prefer. See margin.

In 3–8, solve and check. See margin.

3. $\begin{cases} 2a - 4b = 18 \\ .5a - b = 22 \end{cases}$

4. $\begin{cases} 3m + 10n = 16 \\ m = -6n \end{cases}$

5. $\begin{cases} y = x - 4 \\ 2x - y = -2.5 \end{cases}$

6. $\begin{cases} 3x + 6y = -3 \\ -5x - 8y + 22 = 0 \end{cases}$

7. $\begin{cases} 2r + 15t = 6 \\ r = 3s \\ t = \frac{2}{5}s \end{cases}$

8. $\begin{cases} a = 3b - 2 \\ b = 4c + 5 \\ c = 5a + 1 \end{cases}$

Objective B: *Find the determinant and inverse of a square matrix.* *(Lesson 5-5)*

In 9–12, a matrix is given. **a.** Calculate its determinant. **b.** Write the inverse, if it exists.

9. $\begin{bmatrix} 2 & 0 \\ 0 & 1 \end{bmatrix}$

10. $\begin{bmatrix} 6 & 4 \\ -3 & 2 \end{bmatrix}$

11. $\begin{bmatrix} 2 & -4 \\ 5 & -10 \end{bmatrix}$

12. $\begin{bmatrix} a & b \\ c & d \end{bmatrix}$

13. Suppose $M = \begin{bmatrix} 1 & 9 \\ -7 & 6 \end{bmatrix}$. Find M^{-1}. $\begin{bmatrix} \frac{6}{69} & \frac{-9}{69} \\ \frac{7}{69} & \frac{1}{69} \end{bmatrix}$

14. If the inverse of $\begin{bmatrix} p & q \\ r & s \end{bmatrix}$ does not exist, what must be true about its determinant? It equals 0.

15. Explain why the matrix $\begin{bmatrix} 3 & 2 \\ 6 & 4 \end{bmatrix}$ does not have an inverse.

16. **a.** Find $\begin{bmatrix} -1 & 2 & 3 \\ 4 & 5 & 6 \\ 7 & 8 & 9 \end{bmatrix}^{-1}$ using a calculator or a computer.
    b. Check your result.
    a) $\begin{bmatrix} -.5 & 1 & -.5 \\ 1 & -5 & 3 \\ -.5 & 3.\overline{6} & -2.1\overline{6} \end{bmatrix}$

Objective C: *Use matrices to solve systems of two or three linear equations.* *(Lesson 5-6)*

In 17–20, solve each system using matrices.

17. $\begin{cases} 2x - 9y = 14 \\ 6x - y = 42 \end{cases}$ (7, 0)

18. $\begin{cases} 4a - 5b = -19 \\ 3a + 7b = 18 \end{cases}$ $a = -1, b = 3$

19. $\begin{cases} 3m = 4n + 5 \\ 2m = 3n - 6 \end{cases}$ $m = 39, n = 28$

20. $\begin{cases} 36 = 3x - 4y + 2z \\ 3 = x + 8y \\ 20 = 2x - y + 6z \end{cases}$ (11, -1, -.5)

Additional Answers

2b. (-4, -20); -20 = 5(-4) and -3(-4) + 2(-20) = -28

3. inconsistent or no solutions

4. $m = 12, n = -2; 3(12) + 10(-2) = 16$ and $12 = (-6)(-2)$

5. (-6.5, -10.5); -10.5 = -6.5 - 4 and 2(-6.5) + 10.5 = -2.5

6. (26, -13.5); 3(26) + 6(-13.5) = -3 and -5(26) - 8(-13.5) + 22 = 0

7. $(\frac{3}{2}, \frac{1}{2}, \frac{1}{5})$; $2(\frac{3}{2}) + 15(\frac{1}{5}) = 6, \frac{3}{2} = 3(\frac{1}{2})$, and $\frac{1}{5} = \frac{2}{5}(\frac{1}{2})$

8. $(-\frac{25}{59}, \frac{31}{59}, -\frac{66}{59})$; $\frac{-25}{59} = \frac{3(31)}{59} - \frac{118}{59}$, $\frac{31}{59} = \frac{4(-66)}{59} + \frac{295}{59}$, and $\frac{-66}{59} = \frac{5(-25)}{59} + \frac{59}{59}$

9a. 2

b. $\begin{bmatrix} \frac{1}{2} & 0 \\ 0 & 1 \end{bmatrix}$

10a. 24

b. $\begin{bmatrix} \frac{1}{12} & -\frac{1}{6} \\ \frac{1}{8} & \frac{1}{4} \end{bmatrix}$

11a. 0

b. The inverse does not exist.

12a. $ad - bc$

b. $\begin{bmatrix} \frac{d}{ad - bc} & \frac{-b}{ad - bc} \\ \frac{-c}{ad - bc} & \frac{a}{ad - bc} \end{bmatrix}$

15. Since the determinant, $3 \cdot 4 - 6 \cdot 2$, equals zero, the matrix has no inverse.

16b. The two matrices multiply to $\begin{bmatrix} 1 & 0 & 0 \\ 0 & 1 & 0 \\ 0 & 0 & 1 \end{bmatrix}$.

PROPERTIES DEAL WITH THE PRINCIPLES BEHIND THE MATHEMATICS.

Objective D: *Recognize properties of systems of equations.* (Lessons 5-2, 5-3, 5-4, 5-6) **21, 22)**
See below.

21. Are the systems $\begin{cases} 3x - y = 19 \\ 5x + 2y = 39 \end{cases}$ and

$\begin{cases} x = 7 \\ x + y = 9 \end{cases}$ equivalent? Why or why not?

22. Give the simplest system equivalent to $3x = 6$ and $x + y = 10$.
inconsistent

23. What is a system with no solutions called?

In 24–27, a system is given. **a.** Identify the system as inconsistent or consistent.
b. Determine the number of solutions. **See margin.**

24. $\begin{cases} 3x + 5y = 15 \\ 3x + 5y = 45 \end{cases}$ 25. $\begin{cases} 6m - 4n = 9 \\ -3m = -2n - \frac{9}{2} \end{cases}$

26. $\begin{cases} 8a - 5b = 40 \\ 2a + b = -6 \end{cases}$ 27. $\begin{cases} y = -x^2 \\ y = x - 5 \end{cases}$

28. For what value of k does $\begin{cases} 2x + ky = 6 \\ 14x + 7y = 42 \end{cases}$
have infinitely many solutions? **1**

29. For what value of t does $\begin{cases} 3x + 9y = t \\ 4x + 12y = 7 \end{cases}$
have infinitely many solutions? **$\frac{21}{4}$**

30. Suppose the determinant of the coefficient matrix of a system of equations is not zero. What can you conclude about the system?
The system has exactly one solution.

Objective E: *Recognize properties of systems of inequalities.* (Lessons 5-8, 5-9)

31. *True or false.* The boundaries are included in the graph of the solution set of **False.**
$\begin{cases} y > 2 \\ y < 4 - x. \end{cases}$

21) Yes, the solution (7, 2) satisfies both systems.

22) $\begin{cases} x = 2 \\ y = 8 \end{cases}$

32) See margin.

32. A system of inequalities was graphed as shown below. Tell whether the point is a solution to the system. Justify your answer.
 a. (3, 2)   **b.** (6, 3)

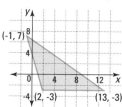

33. Which two of the shaded regions could be feasible sets in a linear-programming situation? **a, c**

(a)   (b)   (c)   (d)

34) at the vertices

34. Where in a feasible set are the possible solutions to a linear programming problem?

35. Does the point M in the region at the right represent a possible solution to a linear programming problem? Why or why not? **Yes; it is one of the vertices of the feasible region.**

USES DEAL WITH APPLICATIONS OF MATHEMATICS IN REAL SITUATIONS.

Objective F: *Use systems of two or three linear equations to solve real-world problems.*
(Lessons 5-3, 5-4, 5-6)

36. At Kit's Kitchen, it costs $4.20 for two hamburgers and one order of fries. It costs $14.40 for six hamburgers and six orders of fries. At these prices, how much should one hamburger cost? **$1.80**

37. Billy likes to mix two cereals for breakfast. He wants to reduce his sugar intake without giving up Sugar-O's, his favorite cereal. Sugar-O's contains 20% sugar while Health-Nut contains 5% sugar. How much of each cereal does he need to fill a small bowl with a 25 g mixture that is 10% sugar?
Sugar-O's: $8\frac{1}{3}$ g;   Health-Nut: $16\frac{2}{3}$ g

Chapter 5   *Chapter Review*   **341**

24a. **inconsistent**
  b. **no solutions**
25a. **consistent**
  b. **infinitely many solutions**
26a. **consistent**
  b. **one solution**
27a. **consistent**
  b. **two solutions**
32a. **Yes, (3, 2) is in the feasible region.**
  b. **No, (6, 3) is not in the feasible region.**

Assessment

Evaluation The *Assessment Sourcebook* provides five forms of the Chapter 5 Test. Forms A and B present parallel versions in a short-answer format. Forms C and D offer performance assessment. The fifth test is Chapter 5 Test, Cumulative Form. About 50% of this test covers Chapter 5, 25% of it covers Chapter 4, and 25% of it covers earlier chapters.

For information on grading, see *General Teaching Suggestions; Grading* in the *Professional Sourcebook*, which begins on page T20 in this Teacher's Edition.

Feedback After students have taken the test for Chapter 5 and you have scored the results, return the tests to students for discussion. Class discussion of the questions that caused trouble for the most students can be very effective in identifying and clarifying misunderstandings. You might want to have them write down the items they missed and work, either in groups or at home, to correct them. It is important for students to receive feedback on every chapter test, and we recommend that students see and correct their mistakes before proceeding too far into the next chapter.

Setting Up Lesson 6-1

Homework We recommend that you assign the Chapter 6 Opener and Lesson 6-1, both reading and some questions, for homework the evening of the test.

341

Additional Answers, pages 342–343

42a. Let r = number of rings made per week, p = number of pendants made per week,

$$\begin{cases} 5r + 20p \le 500 \\ 1.5r + p \le 80 \\ r \ge 0 \\ p \ge 0 \end{cases}$$

b.

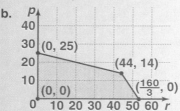

c. $90r + 40p$

d. The maximum profit is $4770 obtained from 53 rings and no pendants.

47. $x < -\frac{5}{2}$

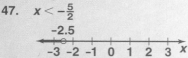

48. $n \ge 9$

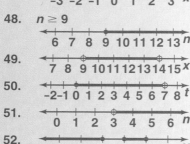

49.

50.

51.

52.

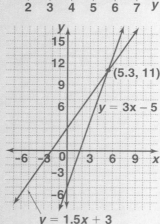

54.

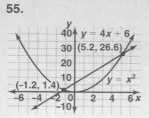

---

38. One night at the circus, the big top attraction sold out, selling all 3,050 seats. There are four times as many lower-level seats as upper-level seats. How many upper-level seats are there? **610 upper-level seats**

39. A farm worker can earn $5.00 per hour plus $.30 per bag picking cucumbers at one farm and $5.40 per hour and $.24 per bag at another farm. Suppose a worker picks cucumbers for 8 hours each day.

a. How many bags of cucumbers must the worker pick in order to earn the same daily wage at each farm? **about 53**

b. How many bags of cucumbers must the worker pick daily in order to earn more at the first farm? **more than 53**

40. After two tests Barbara's average in math was 76. After three tests it was 83. If the teacher drops Barbara's lowest test score, Barbara's average will be 88. What are Barbara's three test scores? **73, 79, 97**

41. A travel agent books three charter groups to go on a weekend cruise. A group of surgeons reserves 9 first-class, 22 business-class, and 15 tourist-class rooms for $30,760. A group of journalists reserves 4 first-class, 13 business-class, and 8 tourist-class rooms for $16,660. A teacher's association reserves 5 first-class, 7 business-class, and 25 tourist-class rooms for $22,600. What is the weekend charge for each class of room? **$790 for first-class, $700 for business-class, and $550 for tourist-class**

Objective G: *Use linear programming to solve real-world problems.* *(Lessons 5-9, 5-10)*

42. Jocelyn's Jewelry Store makes rings and pendants. Every week the staff uses at most 500 g of metal and spends at most 80 hours making jewelry. It takes 5 g of metal to make a ring and 20 g to make a pendant. Each ring takes 1.5 hours to make and each pendant takes 1 hour. The profit on each ring is $90 and the profit on each pendant $40. The store wants to earn as much profit as possible.

a. Identify the variables and translate the constraints into a system of inequalities.

b. Graph the system and find the vertices of the feasible set.

c. Write an expression to be maximized.

d. Apply the Linear-Programming Theorem and interpret the results. **See margin for a–d**

43. Surehold Shelving company produces two types of decorative shelves. The Olde English style takes 20 minutes to assemble and 10 minutes to finish. The Cool Contemporary style takes 10 minutes to assemble and 20 minutes to finish. Each day, there are 48 worker-hours of labor available in the assembly department and 64 worker-hours of labor available in the finishing department. To fulfill its commitments, the company must produce at least 200 shelving units per day. The cost of materials for the Olde English shelf is $2.00 each. The cost of materials for the Cool Contemporary shelf is $2.50 each. How many of each type of shelf should the company produce to minimize the cost of materials and still meet its production commitments? **88 Olde English shelves;   112 Cool Contemporary shelves**

55.

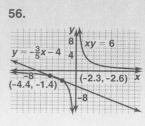

56.

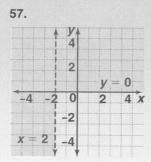

57.

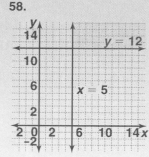

58.

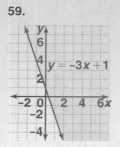

59.

REPRESENTATIONS DEAL WITH PICTURES, GRAPHS, OR OBJECTS THAT ILLUSTRATE CONCEPTS.

Objective H: *Solve and graph linear inequalities in one variable.* *(Lesson 5-1)*

44. Graph all solutions to $y \leq 6$ on a number line. **See below.**

45. *Multiple choice.* Which inequality is graphed below? **c**
(a) $x > -7$ (b) $x < -7$ (c) $x \geq -7$ (d) $x \leq -7$

46. Write an inequality that describes the graph below. $t < 4$

In 47 and 48, solve the inequality and graph its solution set. **See margin.**

47. $-4x + 12 > 22$

48. $3n + 6(n - 12) \geq 9$

In 49–52, graph. **See margin.**

49. $\{x: x > 9 \text{ and } x < 14\}$

50. $\{t: -2 \leq t < 7\} \cap \{t: t \geq 0\}$

51. $\{n: n > 5\} \cup \{n: n > 3\}$

52. $\{y: y \leq 4 \text{ or } 5 \leq y \leq 6\}$

53. Write the compound sentence graphed below.

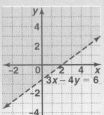

$x \leq -1 \text{ or } x > 3$

Objective I: *Estimate solutions to systems by graphing.* *(Lesson 5-2)* **See margin.**

In 54–56, estimate all solutions by graphing.

54. $\begin{cases} y = 3x - 5 \\ y = 1.5x + 3 \end{cases}$ **55.** $\begin{cases} 4x - y = -6 \\ y = x^2 \end{cases}$

56. $\begin{cases} 3x + 5y = -20 \\ xy = 6 \end{cases}$

Objective J: *Graph linear inequalities in two variables.* *(Lesson 5-7)* **See margin.**

In 57–60, graph on a coordinate plane.

57. $x < -2 \text{ or } y \geq 0$ **58.** $x \geq 5 \text{ and } y \geq 12$

59. $y \geq -3x + 1$ **60.** $3x - 4y < 6$

44)
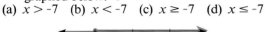

61. Write an inequality to describe the shaded region at the right.
$y \geq \frac{-5}{8}x + 5$

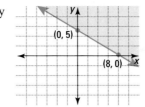

Objective K: *Solve systems of inequalities by graphing.* *(Lessons 5-1, 5-8)*

In 62–64, graph the solution set. **See margin.**

62. $\begin{cases} x \geq 2 \\ y \leq -3 \end{cases}$ **63.** $\begin{cases} 7c + 3d < 21 \\ 7c - 3d > -1 \end{cases}$

64. $\begin{cases} 5x \geq -10 \\ 3(x + y) \leq 6 \\ 6 > y - 4x \end{cases}$

65. Use a compound sentence to describe the region below. $y \leq -1 \text{ and } x \leq -3$

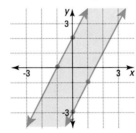

66. *Multiple choice.* Which of the following systems describes the region below? **c**

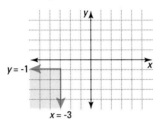

(a) $\begin{cases} y < \frac{1}{2}x + 2 \\ y < \frac{1}{2}x - 3 \end{cases}$ (b) $\begin{cases} y > 2x + 2 \\ y < 2x - 3 \end{cases}$

(c) $\begin{cases} y \leq 2x + 2 \\ y \geq 2x - 3 \end{cases}$ (d) $\begin{cases} y \leq 2x - 1 \\ y \geq 2x + 1.5 \end{cases}$

60.
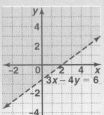

62.
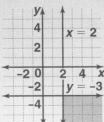

63.
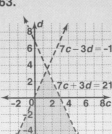

64.
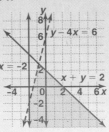

Additional Answers
Progress Self-Test, page 339

7. Let $e =$ the price for 1 egg; let $s =$ the price for one sausage link. The system $\begin{cases} 2e + 2s = 2.78 \\ 3e + 4s = 4.99 \end{cases}$ describes our situation. They might charge 57¢ for one egg.

8a. $\begin{bmatrix} 8 & 3 \\ 6 & 5 \end{bmatrix}$ **b.** $\begin{bmatrix} \frac{5}{22} & \frac{-3}{22} \\ \frac{-6}{22} & \frac{8}{22} \end{bmatrix}$

c. $\begin{bmatrix} \frac{5}{22} & \frac{-3}{22} \\ \frac{-6}{22} & \frac{8}{22} \end{bmatrix} \begin{bmatrix} 8 & 3 \\ 6 & 5 \end{bmatrix} \begin{bmatrix} x \\ y \end{bmatrix} =$

$\begin{bmatrix} \frac{5}{22} & \frac{-3}{22} \\ \frac{-3}{11} & \frac{4}{11} \end{bmatrix} \begin{bmatrix} 41 \\ 39 \end{bmatrix}; \begin{bmatrix} x \\ y \end{bmatrix} = \begin{bmatrix} 4 \\ 3 \end{bmatrix}$.

9a. Sample: $\begin{bmatrix} 2 & 4 \\ 1 & 2 \end{bmatrix}$

b. The determinant of the matrix is $2 \cdot 2 - 4 \cdot 1 = 0$.

10.
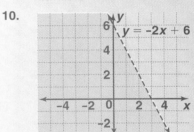

12a. $\begin{cases} 7c + 4s \leq 133 \\ 2c + 6s \leq 72 \\ c \geq 0 \\ s \geq 0 \end{cases}$

b.
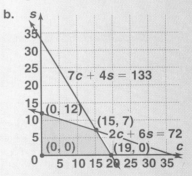

c. We know that $P = 80c + 70s$ and P is maximized at one of the vertices. Check the vertices to find the maximum value.
$80(0) + 70(12) = 840$
$80(0) + 70(0) = 0$
$80(19) + 70(0) = 1520$
$80(15) + 70(7) = 1690$
P is maximized at the point (15, 7). The manufacturer can maximize profits, earning $1690, by producing 15 chairs and 7 sofas per day.

Chapter 6 Planner

Adapting to Individual Needs

The student text is written for the vast majority of students. The chart at the right suggests two pacing plans to accommodate the needs of your students. Students in the Full Course should complete the entire text by the end of the year. Students in the Minimal Course will spend more time when there are quizzes and more time on the Chapter Review. Therefore, these students may not complete all of the chapters in the text.

Options are also presented to meet the needs of a variety of teaching and learning styles. For each lesson, the Teacher's Edition provides sections entitled: *Video* which describes video segments and related questions that can be used for motivation or extension; *Optional Activities* which suggests activities that employ materials, physical models, technology, and cooperative learning; and *Adapting to Individual Needs* which regularly includes **Challenge** problems, **English Language Development** suggestions, and suggestions for providing **Extra Help.** The Teacher's Edition also frequently includes an **Error Alert,** an **Extension,** and an **Assessment** alternative. The options available in Chapter 6 are summarized in the chart below.

Chapter 6 Pacing Chart

Day	Full Course	Minimal Course
1	6-1	6-1
2	6-2	6-2
3	6-3	6-3
4	6-4	6-4
5	Quiz*; 6-5	Quiz*; begin 6-5.
6	6-6	Finish 6-5.
7	6-7	6-6
8	Quiz*; 6-8	6-7
9	6-9	Quiz*; begin 6-8.
10	6-10	Finish 6-8.
11	Self-Test	6-9
12	Review	6-10
13	Test*	Self-Test
14		Review
15		Review
16		Test*

*in the Teacher's Resource File

In the Teacher's Edition...

Lesson	Optional Activities	Extra Help	Challenge	English Language Development	Error Alert	Extension	Cooperative Learning	Ongoing Assessment
6-1	•	•	•	•		•	•	Oral/Written
6-2	•	•	•	•		•	•	Written
6-3	•	•				•	•	Written
6-4	•	•	•			•	•	Written
6-5	•	•	•	•	•	•	•	Oral/Written
6-6	•	•	•	•		•	•	Oral/Written
6-7	•	•	•	•		•	•	Oral/Written
6-8	•	•	•		•	•	•	Written
6-9	•	•	•		•	•	•	Oral
6-10	•	•	•			•	•	Written

In the Additional Resources...

Lesson	In the Teacher's Resource File								
	Lesson Masters, A and B	Teaching Aids*	Activity Kit*	Answer Masters	Technology Sourcebook	Assessment Sourcebook	Visual Aids**	Technology	Video Segments
6-1	6-1	8, 53, 56, 57		6-1			8, 53, 56, 57, AM		
6-2	6-2	8, 53		6-2			8, 53, AM		
In-class Activity		19		6-3			19, AM		
6-3	6-3	8, 19, 53, 58–60	11	6-3	Comp 8		8, 19, 53, 58–60, AM	GraphExplorer	
6-4	6-4	8, 19, 54		6-4		Quiz	8, 19, 54, AM		6-4
6-5	6-5	8, 19, 54		6-5	Comp 9		8, 19, 54, AM	Symbol Manipulator	
6-6	6-6	8, 19, 54	12	6-6	Comp 10		8, 19, 54, AM	StatExplorer	
6-7	6-7	8, 19, 55, 61		6-7		Quiz	8, 19, 55, 61, AM		
6-8	6-8	55		6-8			55, AM		
6-9	6-9	8, 55, 62, 63		6-9			8, 55, 62, 63, AM		
In-class Activity		64		6-10			64, AM		
6-10	6-10	8, 19, 55		6-10			8, 19, 55, AM		
End of chapter				Review		Tests			

*Teaching Aids are pictured on pages 344C and 344D. The activities in the Activity Kit are pictured on page 344C.

**Visual Aids provide transparencies for all Teaching Aids and all Answer Masters.

Also available is the Study Skills Handbook which includes study-skill tips related to reading, note-taking, and comprehension.

Integrating Strands and Applications

	6-1	6-2	6-3	6-4	6-5	6-6	6-7	6-8	6-9	6-10
Mathematical Connections										
Algebra	●	●	●	●	●	●	●	●	●	●
Geometry	●	●	●	●	●	●	●	●		●
Measurement	●	●	●	●	●	●	●	●		●
Logic and Reasoning							●			
Statistics/Data Analysis						●			●	
Patterns and Functions	●	●	●	●	●	●	●	●	●	●
Interdisciplinary and Other Connections										
Art										●
Science	●			●	●	●	●	●	●	●
Social Studies	●	●	●	●		●		●	●	●
Multicultural					●			●		●
Technology		●	●	●	●	●				●
Career	●			●						
Consumer	●	●		●						
Sports	●	●			●		●			●

Teaching and Assessing the Chapter Objectives

Chapter 6 Objectives (Organized into the SPUR categories—Skills, Properties, Uses, and Representations)	Lessons	Progress Self-Test Questions	Chapter Review Questions	Chapter Test, Forms A and B	Chapter Test, Forms C	D
Skills						
A: Expand squares of binomials.	6-1	17, 18	1–6	17	1	
B: Transform quadratic equations from vertex form to standard form, and vice versa.	6-4, 6-5	1, 2, 25	7–12	7, 10	5	
C: Solve quadratic equations.	6-2, 6-7, 6-8, 6-10	3, 11,12, 13	13–26	19, 20	2, 5	
D: Perform operations with complex numbers.	6-8, 6-9	4, 5, 6, 7, 8	27–46	2–5, 18	3	
Properties						
E: Apply the definition of absolute value and the Absolute Value–Square Root Theorem.	6-2	14	47–52	13	2	
F: Use the discriminant of a quadratic equation to determine the nature of the solutions to the equation.	6-10	16	53–57	1, 6	5	
Uses						
G: Use quadratic equations to solve area problems or problems dealing with velocity and acceleration.	6-1, 6-2, 6-4, 6-7	19, 20, 21, 22	58–62	14, 16	6	
H: Fit a quadratic model to data.	6-6	24	63, 64	15		✓
I: Use the Graph-Translation Theorem to interpret equations and graphs.	6-3	9, 23	65–71	8, 9	4	
Representations						
J: Graph quadratic functions or absolute value functions and interpret them.	6-2, 6-3, 6-4	10	72–80	12	4	
K: Use the discriminant of a quadratic equation to determine the number of x-intercepts of the graph.	6-10	15	81–84	8	5	

In the Teacher's Resource File

Assessment Sourcebook
Quiz for Lessons 6-1 through 6-4
Quiz for Lessons 6-5 through 6-7
Chapter 6 Test, Forms A–D
Chapter 6 Test, Cumulative Form
Comprehensive Test, Chapters 1-6

Quiz and Test Writer

Activity Kit

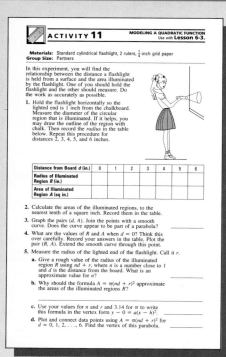

Materials: Standard cylindrical flashlight, 2 rulers, $\frac{1}{4}$-inch grid paper
Group Size: Partners

In this experiment, you will find the relationship between the distance a flashlight is held from a surface and the area illuminated by the flashlight. One of you should hold the flashlight and the other should measure. Do the work as accurately as possible.

1. Hold the flashlight horizontally so the lighted end is 1 inch from the chalkboard. Measure the diameter of the circular region that is illuminated. If it helps, you may draw the outline of the region with chalk. Then record the *radius* in the table below. Repeat this procedure for distances 2, 3, 4, 5, and 6 inches.

Distance from Board d (in.)	0	1	2	3	4	5	6
Radius of Illuminated Region R (in.)							
Area of Illuminated Region A (sq in.)							

2. Calculate the areas of the illuminated regions, to the nearest tenth of a square inch. Record them in the table.

3. Graph the pairs (d, A). Join the points with a smooth curve. Does the curve appear to be part of a parabola?

4. What are the values of R and A when $d = 0$? Think this over carefully. Record your answers in the table. Plot the pair (R, A). Extend the smooth curve through this point.

5. Measure the radius of the lighted end of the flashlight. Call it r.

   a. Give a rough value of the radius of the illuminated region R using $nd + r$, where n is a number close to 1 and d is the distance from the board. What is an approximate value for n? _____

   b. Why should the formula $A = \pi(nd + r)^2$ approximate the areas of the illuminated regions R? _____

   c. Use your values for n and r and 3.14 for π to write this formula in the vertex form $y - 0 = a(x - h)^2$. _____

   d. Plot and connect data points using $A = \pi(nd + r)^2$ for $d = 0, 1, 2, \ldots, 6$. Find the vertex of this parabola. _____

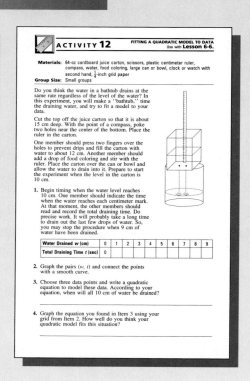

Materials: 64-oz cardboard juice carton, scissors, plastic centimeter ruler, compass, water, food coloring, large can or bowl, clock or watch with second hand, $\frac{1}{4}$-inch grid paper
Group Size: Small groups

Do you think the water in a bathtub drains at the same rate regardless of the level of the water? In this experiment, you will make a "bathtub," time the draining water, and try to fit a model to your data.

Cut the top off the juice carton so that it is about 15 cm deep. With the point of a compass, poke two holes near the center of the bottom. Place the ruler in the carton.

One member should press two fingers over the holes to prevent drips and fill the carton with water to about 12 cm. Another member should add a drop of food coloring and stir with the ruler. Place the carton over the can or bowl and allow the water to drain into it. Prepare to start the experiment when the level in the carton is 10 cm.

1. Begin timing when the water level reaches 10 cm. One member should indicate the time when the water reaches each centimeter mark. At that moment, the other members should read and record the total draining time. Do precise work. It will probably take a long time to drain out the last few drops of water. So, you may stop the procedure when 9 cm of water have been drained.

Water Drained w (cm)	0	1	2	3	4	5	6	7	8	9
Total Draining Time t (sec)	0									

2. Graph the pairs (w, t) and connect the points with a smooth curve.

3. Choose three data points and write a quadratic equation to model these data. According to your equation, when will all 10 cm of water be drained?

4. Graph the equation you found in Item 3 using your grid from Item 2. How well do you think your quadratic model fits this situation?

Teaching Aids

Teaching Aid 8, Four-quadrant Graph Paper, (shown on page 4D) can be used with **Lessons 6-1 through 6-10. Teaching Aid 19, Automatic Grapher Grids,** (shown on page 70D) can be used with **Lessons 6-3 and 6-7** and the In-class Activity preceding **Lesson 6-3.**

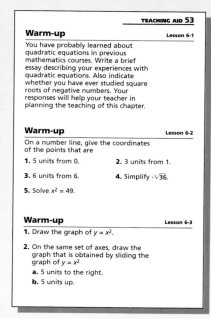

Warm-up Lesson 6-1

You have probably learned about quadratic equations in previous mathematics courses. Write a brief essay describing your experiences with quadratic equations. Also indicate whether you have ever studied square roots of negative numbers. Your responses will help your teacher in planning the teaching of this chapter.

Warm-up Lesson 6-2

On a number line, give the coordinates of the points that are

1. 5 units from 0.   2. 3 units from 1.

3. 6 units from 6.   4. Simplify $-\sqrt{36}$.

5. Solve $x^2 = 49$.

Warm-up Lesson 6-3

1. Draw the graph of $y = x^2$.

2. On the same set of axes, draw the graph that is obtained by sliding the graph of $y = x^2$
   a. 5 units to the right.
   b. 5 units up.

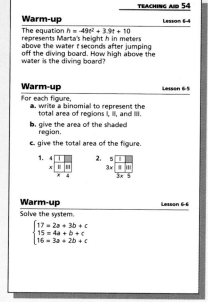

Warm-up Lesson 6-4

The equation $h = -49t^2 + 3.9t + 10$ represents Marta's height h in meters above the water t seconds after jumping off the diving board. How high above the water is the diving board?

Warm-up Lesson 6-5

For each figure,
   a. write a binomial to represent the total area of regions I, II, and III.
   b. give the area of the shaded region.
   c. give the total area of the figure.

Warm-up Lesson 6-6

Solve the system.
$$\begin{cases} 17 = 2a + 3b + c \\ 15 = 4a + b + c \\ 16 = 3a + 2b + c \end{cases}$$

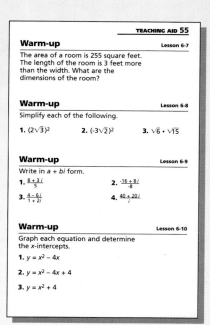

Warm-up Lesson 6-7

The area of a room is 255 square feet. The length of the room is 3 feet more than the width. What are the dimensions of the room?

Warm-up Lesson 6-8

Simplify each of the following.

1. $(2\sqrt{3})^2$ 2. $(-3\sqrt{2})^2$ 3. $\sqrt{6} \cdot \sqrt{15}$

Warm-up Lesson 6-9

Write in $a + bi$ form.

1. $\frac{8 + 3i}{5}$ 2. $\frac{-16 + 8i}{-8}$

3. $\frac{4 - 6i}{1 + 2i}$ 4. $\frac{40 + 20i}{i}$

Warm-up Lesson 6-10

Graph each equation and determine the x-intercepts.

1. $y = x^2 - 4x$

2. $y = x^2 - 4x + 4$

3. $y = x^2 + 4$

Additional Examples

1. The senior class at Ravine High School is holding a Cutest-Baby Picture Contest. The bulletin board they will use to display the pictures measures 8 ft by 3 ft. The decorating committee plans to put a border of the school colors all around the interior edge of the bulletin board. The border will be b inches wide. Write an expression for the area that is available for the pictures and expand the expression using the Distributive Property.

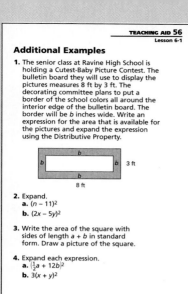

2. Expand.
  a. $(n - 11)^2$
  b. $(2x - 5y)^2$

3. Write the area of the square with sides of length $a + b$ in standard form. Draw a picture of the square.

4. Expand each expression.
  a. $(\frac{1}{2}a + 12b)^2$
  b. $3(x + y)^2$

Optional Activity

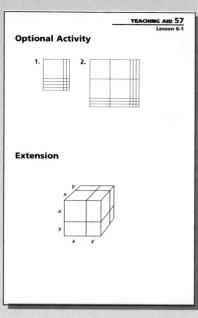

1.   **2.**

Extension

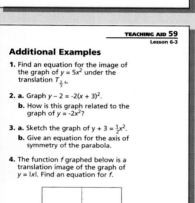

Examples 1 and 2

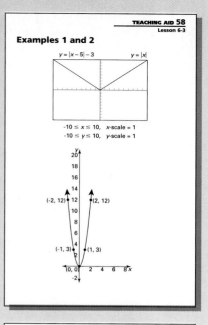

$y = |x - 5| - 3$ $y = |x|$

$-10 \le x \le 10$, x-scale = 1
$-10 \le y \le 10$, y-scale = 1

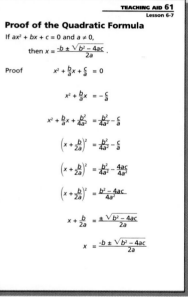

(-2, 12)   (2, 12)
(-1, 3)   (1, 3)

Additional Examples

1. Find an equation for the image of the graph of $y = 5x^2$ under the translation $T_{\frac{2}{3}, 6}$.

2. a. Graph $y - 2 = -2(x + 3)^2$.
  b. How is this graph related to the graph of $y = -2x^2$?

3. a. Sketch the graph of $y + 3 = \frac{1}{2}x^2$.
  b. Give an equation for the axis of symmetry of the parabola.

4. The function f graphed below is a translation image of the graph of $y = |x|$. Find an equation for f.

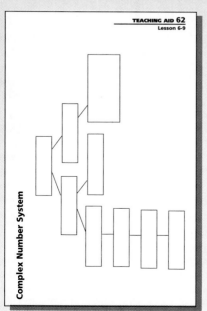

$-4 \le x \le 4$, x-scale = 1
$-3 \le y \le 6$, y-scale = 1

Optional Activity 3

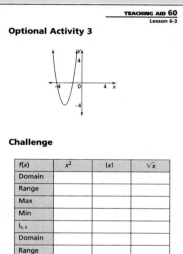

Challenge

$f(x)$	x^2	$|x|$	$\sqrt{x}$
Domain			
Range			
Max			
Min			
$I_{h, k}$			
Domain			
Range			
Max			
Min			

Proof of the Quadratic Formula

If $ax^2 + bx + c = 0$ and $a \ne 0$,

then $x = \dfrac{-b \pm \sqrt{b^2 - 4ac}}{2a}$.

Proof $x^2 + \dfrac{b}{a}x + \dfrac{c}{a} = 0$

$x^2 + \dfrac{b}{a}x = -\dfrac{c}{a}$

$x^2 + \dfrac{b}{a}x + \dfrac{b^2}{4a^2} = \dfrac{b^2}{4a^2} - \dfrac{c}{a}$

$\left(x + \dfrac{b}{2a}\right)^2 = \dfrac{b^2}{4a^2} - \dfrac{c}{a}$

$\left(x + \dfrac{b}{2a}\right)^2 = \dfrac{b^2}{4a^2} - \dfrac{4ac}{4a^2}$

$\left(x + \dfrac{b}{2a}\right)^2 = \dfrac{b^2 - 4ac}{4a^2}$

$x + \dfrac{b}{2a} = \dfrac{\pm \sqrt{b^2 - 4ac}}{2a}$

$x = \dfrac{-b \pm \sqrt{b^2 - 4ac}}{2a}$

Complex Number System

Venn Diagram of Complex Number System

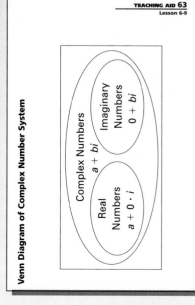

Complex Numbers
$a + bi$

Imaginary Numbers
$0 + bi$

Real Numbers
$a + 0 \cdot i$

Table for Recording Results

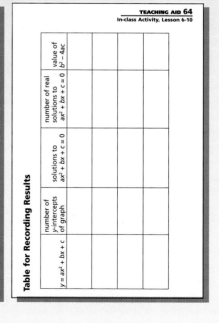

$y = ax^2 + bx + c$	number of y-intercepts of graph	solutions to $ax^2 + bx + c = 0$	number of real solutions to $ax^2 + bx + c = 0$	value of $b^2 - 4ac$			

Chapter Opener

CHAPTER 6

Pacing

All lessons in this chapter are designed to be covered in one day. At the end of the chapter, you should plan to spend 1 day to review the Progress Self-Test, 1–2 days for the Chapter Review, and 1 day for a test. You may want to spend a day on projects, and a day may be needed for quizzes. Therefore, this chapter should take 13–16 days. We strongly advise you not to spend more than 17 days on this chapter; there is ample opportunity to review ideas in later chapters.

Using Pages 344–345

Some of the vocabulary students will encounter in the chapter is introduced here: quadratic expression, quadratic function, parabola, and square roots of negative numbers.

The simplest quadratic equations are $A = s^2$ and $A = xy$, which students have seen before. Perhaps the most common application of quadratics, other than to area, is to the paths of projectiles, including the projecting of water from a hose. You might have students graph $y = x^2$ on automatic graphers and zoom in and out of this graph near its vertex to get an idea of the shape of a parabola.

Automatic graphers are used extensively throughout this chapter. They are also used for the In-class Activities preceding Lessons 6-3 and 6-10.

344

Chapter 6 Overview

This chapter continues the study of quadratic equations introduced in Chapter 2, with the discussion of $y = kx^2$. We present the traditional paper-and-pencil skills of manipulating expressions and solving equations, and balance these skills with an analysis of the relationship between parameters of equations and the properties of graphs.

The first two lessons of the chapter provide the basic underpinnings for the skills of the chapter. In Lesson 6-1, students use rectangles and squares in situations that lead to quadratic expressions, and they review the squares of binomials. In Lesson 6-2, the absolute value function is defined and then used to solve equations of the form $ax^2 = k$ by applying the theorem $\sqrt{x^2} = |x|$.

Lessons 6-3 through 6-7 deal with the graphing of quadratic functions and the solving of quadratic equations. The Graph-Translation Theorem is introduced in Lesson 6-3 to derive the vertex form of the parabola, $y - k = a(x - h)^2$. Lesson 6-4 is devoted to graphing equations of the form $y = ax^2 + bx + c$ and to applications involving distance, time, velocity, and acceleration. In Lesson 6-5, students complete the square for the equation $y = ax^2 + bx + c$

QUADRATIC FUNCTIONS

The word quadratic comes from the Latin word *quadratus,* which means "to make square."

Many situations lead to quadratic functions. You studied direct-variation quadratic functions of the form $f(x) = kx^2$ in Chapter 2. The area formulas $A = s^2$ (for a square) and $A = \pi r^2$ (for a circle) are equations for quadratic functions. The area of a rectangle with length x and width y is xy, a quadratic expression in the two variables x and y.

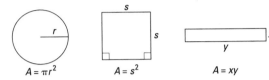

$$A = \pi r^2 \qquad A = s^2 \qquad A = xy$$

Quadratic functions also arise from studying the paths of objects. The path traveled by a baseball or a basketball closely follows the path of a parabola. The paths of the jets of a fountain also outline parabolas. All parabolas can be described by quadratic equations.

In this chapter, you will study many uses of quadratic expressions and functions. You also will learn how to solve all quadratic equations, including those whose solutions involve square roots of negative numbers.

Few realistic applications are modeled by equations that are solved by factoring over the rationals. Therefore, in this chapter, quadratic equations are not solved by factoring trinomials. Instead, we teach students problem-solving strategies that generalize easily. Factoring trinomials and the Factor Theorem are discussed in Chapter 11.

Photo Connections

The photo collage makes real-world connections to the content of the chapter: quadratic functions.

Taj Mahal: Writings of Indian mathematicians in 800 to 1200 A. D. indicate that they could solve quadratic equations centuries before the Taj Mahal was completed in 1654.

Water Ripples: When a stone falls into still water, ripples form in concentric circles. The formula for the area of a circle is the equation for a quadratic function.

Rows of Squares: Squares occur in art, architecture, and design. The formula for the area of a square is also an equation for a quadratic function.

Man in Square/Circle: The interior of any circle can be rearranged to form a square region.

Highway: In Lesson 6-6 a quadratic equation relates the braking distance of a car to its speed.

Chapter 6 Projects

At this time you might want to have students look over the projects on pages 408–409.

in order to write it in vertex form. Lesson 6-6 shows how to find a parabola to approximate or fit data. In Lesson 6-7, the Quadratic Formula is derived by completing the square, and then it is used to solve equations.

The last three lessons of the chapter embed quadratic equations in the larger domain of complex numbers. Lessons 6-8 and 6-9 introduce imaginary numbers and complex numbers, respectively, paving the way for Lesson 6-10, in which the Quadratic Formula is used to solve all types of quadratic equations with real coefficients.

For students who have studied UCSMP *Algebra,* graphing the equation $y = ax^2 + bx + c$ and solving quadratics using the Quadratic Formula should be review; completing the square, fitting quadratics to data, and operating with nonreal numbers will be new material.

Objectives

A Expand squares of binomials.
G Use quadratic equations to solve area problems.

Resources

From the Teacher's Resource File
- Lesson Master 6-1A or 6-1B
- Answer Master 6-1
- Teaching Aids
  8 Four-Quadrant Graph Paper
  53 Warm-up
  56 Additional Examples
  57 Optional Activities and Extension

Additional Resources
- Visuals for Teaching Aids 8, 53, 56, 57
- Algebra tiles

Teaching Lesson 6-1

Warm-up

Writing You have probably learned about quadratic equations in previous mathematics courses. Write a brief essay describing your experiences with quadratic equations. Also indicate whether you have ever studied square roots of negative numbers. Your responses will help your teacher in planning the teaching of this chapter.

LESSON 6-1

Quadratic Expressions, Rectangles, and Squares

Pooling resources. *International swim meets are held in pools that are 50 m long and are divided into 6, 8, or 10 lanes, each 2.1 or 2.4 m wide. The water must be at least 1.2 m deep and have a temperature of about 26°C.*

The word *quadratic* in today's mathematics refers to expressions, equations, and functions that involve sums of constants and first and second powers of variables and no higher powers. That is, they are of degree 2. Specifically, when $a \neq 0$:

$ax^2 + bx + c$ is the general **quadratic expression** in the variable x,
$ax^2 + bx + c = 0$ is the general **quadratic equation** in the variable x, and
$f: x \rightarrow ax^2 + bx + c$ is the general **quadratic function** in the variable x.

We call $ax^2 + bx + c$ the **standard form of a quadratic.** Some expressions, equations, and functions of degree 2 are not in standard form, but they can be rewritten in standard form. We still call them quadratic.

There can also be quadratics in two or more variables. The general quadratic expression in two variables is $Ax^2 + Bxy + Cy^2 + Dx + Ey + F$, and there are corresponding equations and functions of two variables. These are the subject of Chapter 12.

The simplest quadratic expression, x^2, equals the product of the simplest linear expressions x and x. More generally, the product of any two linear expressions $ax + b$ and $cx + d$ is a quadratic expression. Since all area formulas involve the product of two lengths, they all involve quadratic expressions.

Quadratic Expressions from Rectangles

Example 1

Suppose a rectangular swimming pool 50 m by 20 m is to be built with a walkway around it. If the walkway is *w* meters wide, write the total area of the pool and walkway in standard form.

▶

Lesson 6-1 Overview

Broad Goals This lesson reviews the concepts reflected in its title. These concepts are basic to the study of quadratic functions.

Perspective Even in the same class, students may differ widely in their experiences with, and their retained knowledge about, quadratic equations. Students' responses to the *Warm-up* for this lesson can help you plan your teaching of this chapter.

The opening paragraphs on this page provide an opportunity for you to help students distinguish between expressions, equations, and functions. You should be aware that some software does not distinguish between expressions and equations. For example, some software solves the equation $x^2 - 5 = 0$ if asked to solve the expression $x^2 - 5$.

The first concept reviewed in the lesson is the relation between quadratic expressions and areas of rectangles. This generates a type of walkway or border problem which recurs throughout the chapter.

The second main idea presented is a review of the Binomial Square Theorem. Although this theorem is used in Lesson 6-5 for completing the square, it will be of help to students in each lesson of this chapter.

▶ **Solution**

Draw a picture. The pool with walkway occupies a rectangle with length 50 + 2w meters and width 20 + 2w meters. The area of this rectangle is (50 + 2w)(20 + 2w) square meters.

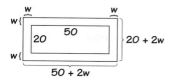

❶

Apply the Distributive Property several times to find the product of (50 + 2w)(20 + 2w).

$$(50 + 2w)(20 + 2w) = (50 + 2w) \cdot 20 + (50 + 2w) \cdot 2w$$
$$= 1000 + 40w + 100w + 4w^2$$
$$= 1000 + 140w + 4w^2$$

The total area of the pool and the walkway is $4w^2 + 140w + 1000$ square meters.

Check

Suppose the walkway is 3 meters wide. The width of the pool with the walkway is 20 + 2(3) = 26 m and the length is 50 + 2(3) = 56 m. So the area is 26 · 56 = 1456 m². Does 1456 = 1000 + 140(3) + 4(3²)? 1456 = 1000 + 420 + 36. Yes, it checks.

Notice in Example 1 that the expression $4w^2 + 140w + 1000$ is of the form $ax^2 + bx + c$, with $w = x$, $a = 4$, $b = 140$, and $c = 1000$.

Quadratic Expressions from Squares

When a linear expression is multiplied by itself, the result, its square, is a quadratic expression. In Example 2, the linear expression $(x + 7)$ is squared. It is taken to the 2nd power. Writing this power as a quadratic expression is called *expanding* the power.

❷ **Example 2**

Expand $(x + 7)^2$.

Solution

Use the definition of the second power. Then apply the Distributive Property several times.

$$(x + 7)^2 = (x + 7)(x + 7)$$
$$= (x + 7)x + (x + 7)7$$
$$= x^2 + 7x + 7x + 49$$
$$= x^2 + 14x + 49$$

Check

Let $x = 5$. Then $(x + 7)^2 = (5 + 7)^2 = 12^2 = 144$. Also, $x^2 + 14x + 49 = 5^2 + 14 \cdot 5 + 49 = 144$. It checks.

Lesson 6-1 *Quadratic Expressions, Rectangles, and Squares* **347**

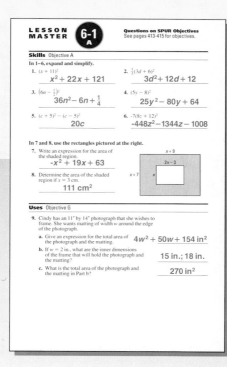

Optional Activities

Using Physical Models
Materials: Algebra tiles, **Teaching Aid 57**

You might demonstrate **Example 2** using algebra tiles and then have students use tiles to expand other binomials. You might also show students rectangles made from algebra tiles—like those at the right—and have students express each total area as a product of binomials and in standard form.

1. 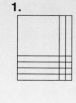   2.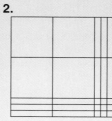

$[1. (x + 2)(x + 4) = x^2 + 6x + 8$
$2. (2x + 3)^2 = 4x^2 + 12x + 9]$

1. The senior class at Ravine High School is holding a Cutest-Baby-Picture Contest. The bulletin board they will use to display the pictures measures 8 ft by 3 ft. The decorating committee plans to put a border of the school colors all around the interior edge of the bulletin board. The border will be b inches wide. Write an expression for the area that is available for the pictures and expand the expression using the Distributive Property.

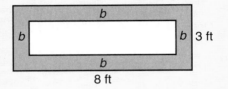

$A = (96 - 2b)(36 - 2b) = 3456 - 264b + 4b^2$

2. Expand.
   a. $(n - 11)^2$ $n^2 - 22n + 121$
   b. $(2x - 5y)^2$ $4x^2 - 20xy + 25y^2$

3. Write the area of the square with sides of length $a + b$ in standard form. Draw a picture of the square.
$(a + b)^2 = a^2 + 2ab + b^2$

	a	b
a	a^2	ab
b	ab	b^2

The square of a binomial can be thought of as the area of a square whose side is the binomial.

Example 3

Write the area of the square with sides of length $x + y$ in standard form.

Solution 1

Draw a picture of the square. Notice that its area is the sum of the four smaller areas: a square of area x^2, two rectangles, each with area xy, and a square of area y^2. So the area of the square is $x^2 + 2xy + y^2$.

Solution 2

The area of a square with side $x + y$ is $(x + y)^2$.
Expand $(x + y)^2$.

$$
\begin{aligned}
(x + y)^2 &= (x + y)(x + y) && \text{definition of 2nd power} \\
&= (x + y)x + (x + y)y && \text{Distributive Property} \\
&= x^2 + yx + xy + y^2 && \text{Distributive Property} \\
&= x^2 + 2xy + y^2 && \text{Commutative Property} \\
&&& \text{of Multiplication and} \\
&&& \text{Distributive Property}
\end{aligned}
$$

The area of the square is $x^2 + 2xy + y^2$.

Squares of binomials occur so often that their expansions are identified as a theorem.

> **Binomial Square Theorem**
> For all real numbers x and y,
> $$(x + y)^2 = x^2 + 2xy + y^2 \text{ and}$$
> $$(x - y)^2 = x^2 - 2xy + y^2.$$

The proof of the second part of the theorem is left to you. Of course, the theorem holds for *any* numbers or expressions. It is important for you to be able to apply it automatically.

Example 4

Expand $\left(3m - \dfrac{k}{4}\right)^2$.

Solution

Use the Binomial Square Theorem with $x = 3m$ and $y = \dfrac{k}{4}$.

$$
\begin{aligned}
(x - y)^2 &= x^2 - 2 \cdot x \cdot y + y^2 \\
\left(3m - \frac{k}{4}\right)^2 &= (3m)^2 - 2(3m)\left(\frac{k}{4}\right) + \left(\frac{k}{4}\right)^2 \\
&= 9m^2 - \frac{3k}{2}m + \frac{k^2}{16}
\end{aligned}
$$

348

Adapting to Individual Needs

Extra Help
The most common error that students make in squaring a binomial is to assume that powers are distributive over addition and subtraction. That is, they assume that $(x + y)^2 = x^2 + y^2$. By applying the Binomial Square Theorem directly, students will avoid this difficulty.

English Language Development
There are many terms in this lesson. Students have seen the individual terms— *quadratic, equation, expression, function,* and *standard form* — but may not have seen them applied to quadratics. If students with limited English proficiency have made index cards, they need to add the specific terms to their list.

Check

Let $m = 3$ and $k = 8$. The left side is then 7^2 or 49. The right side is

$$9 \cdot 3^2 - \frac{3 \cdot 8}{2} \cdot 3 + \frac{8^2}{16} = 81 - 36 + 4 = 49.$$

QUESTIONS

Covering the Reading

1. *Multiple choice.* Which is *not* a quadratic equation? d
(a) $y = \frac{1}{2}x^2$ (b) $xy = 4$ (c) $x^2 + y^2 = 10$ (d) $y = 2x$

2. Is $x^2 - \sqrt{3}x + 4$ a quadratic expression? Explain your answer.
Yes; it is of the form $ax^2 + bx + c$, where $a \neq 0$.

3. What kind of path does a thrown baseball follow?
the path of a parabola

4. A swimming pool 50 m by 25 m is to be built with a walkway w meters wide around it. Write the total area of the pool and walkway in the form $ax^2 + bx + c$. $4w^2 + 150w + 1250$ m^2

In 5–8, multiply and simplify.

5. $(4x + y)(2x + 3y)$ $8x^2 + 14xy + 3y^2$
6. $(x + 1)(x - 2)$ $x^2 - x - 2$
7. $(2 - y)(3 - y)$ $6 - 5y + y^2$
8. $(12 + a)(5 + a)$ $60 + 17a + a^2$

9. Expand.
a. $(10 + 2)^2$ 144
b. $(n + 2)^2$ $n^2 + 4n + 4$
c. $(n + q)^2$ $n^2 + 2nq + q^2$

10. Expand $(x - 5)^2$ and check your work.
$x^2 - 10x + 25$; See left for check.

11. Describe two different ways to find the area of a square with side of length $p + 3$. See left.

12. Prove the second part of the Binomial Square Theorem.
See margin.

In 13–16, rewrite the expression in the form $ax^2 + bx + c$.

13. $(5a + b)^2$ $25a^2 + 10ab + b^2$
14. $(a - 8)^2$ $a^2 - 16a + 64$
15. $\left(2w - \frac{1}{2}\right)^2$ $4w^2 - 2w + \frac{1}{4}$
16. $(7e + 3f)^2$ $49e^2 + 42ef + 9f^2$

10) Check: Sample: Let $x = 7$. The left side is 2^2 or 4. The right side is $7^2 - 10 \cdot 7 + 25 = 49 - 70 + 25 = 4$. It checks.

11) Sample:

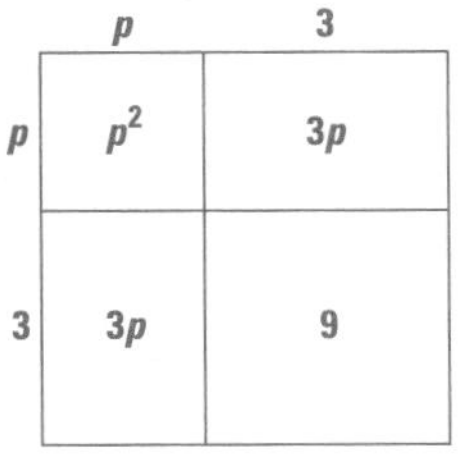

p
3
p
p^2
3p
3
3p
9

The total area is the sum of the 4 smaller areas as shown:
$A = p^2 + 3p + 3p + 9 = p^2 + 6p + 9$.
The area is also the side length squared: $A = (p + 3)^2 = p^2 + 6p + 9$.

Applying the Mathematics

17. Refer to the walkway around the swimming pool mentioned in Example 1. What is the area of the walkway? $140w + 4w^2$ m^2

18. Refer to the rectangles at the left. What is the area of the shaded region? $x^2 + 13x + 12$

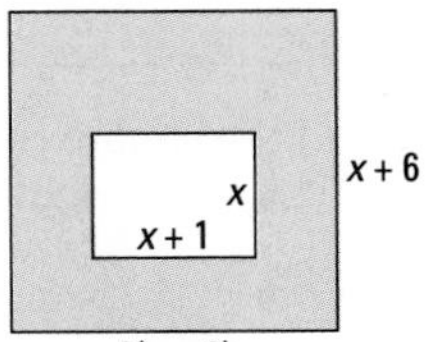

x
x + 1
x + 6
2(x + 1)

In 19–21, expand and simplify.

19. $\frac{1}{2}n(n + 1)^2$ $\frac{1}{2}n^3 + n^2 + \frac{1}{2}n$
20. $(x + y)^2 - (x - y)^2$ $4xy$
21. $-3(x - 2)^2$ $-3x^2 + 12x - 12$

Additional Answers

12. $(x - y)^2 = (x - y)(x - y)$ definition of 2nd power
$= (x - y)x - (x - y)y$ Distributive Property
$= x^2 - yx - xy + y^2$ Distributive Property
$= x^2 - 2xy + y^2$ Commutative Property of Multiplication and Distributive Property

24a, b, page 350

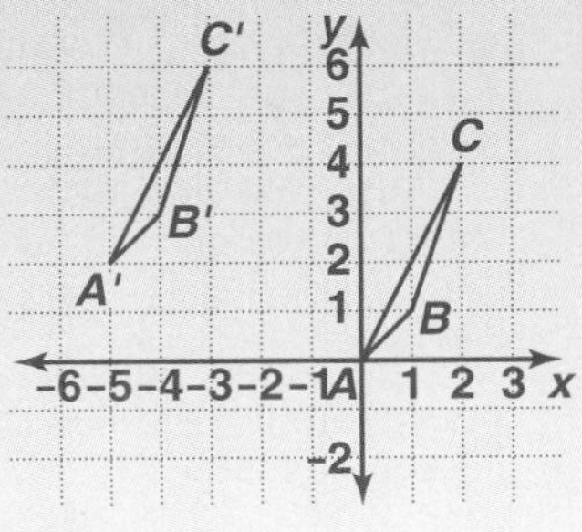

C'
C
B'
B
A'
A
y
x
6
5
4
3
2
1
-6 -5 -4 -3 -2 -1
1 2 3
-2

4. Expand each expression.
a. $(\frac{1}{2}a + 12b)^2$ $\frac{1}{4}a^2 + 12ab + 144b^2$
b. $3(x + y)^2$ $3x^2 + 6xy + 3y^2$

Notes on Questions

Question 4 Sports Connection The Fédération Internationale de Natation Amateur, which regulates international swimming events, recognizes swimming records set only in *long-distance* pools. These pools are 164 feet long and contain 6, 8, or 10 eight-foot lanes. The water in the pool must be at least 4 feet deep and must be kept at about 70°F.

Questions 9–10 Not all students will notice the similarity among **parts a, b,** and **c.** Note that knowing the numerical value in **part a**, 144, can help students remember the middle term in the expansion of the other binomials. Students who tend to forget the middle term should be encouraged to do a numerical check such as $(10 + 2)^2$.

When discussing $(n + 2)^2$, $(n + q)^2$, or $(x - 5)^2$, ask students whether any real-number values of the variables give a negative value to the expression. [No; the square of any real number is nonnegative.] Point out that another mathematical idea that involves nonnegative values is absolute value, which is part of the content of the next lesson.

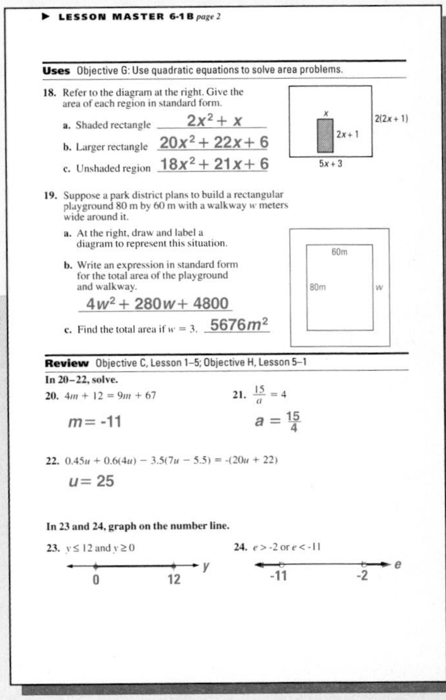

LESSON MASTER 6-1 B *page 2*

Uses Objective G: Use quadratic equations to solve area problems.

18. Refer to the diagram at the right. Give the area of each region in standard form.
a. Shaded rectangle $2x^2 + x$
b. Larger rectangle $20x^2 + 22x + 6$
c. Unshaded region $18x^2 + 21x + 6$

x
2x + 1
2(2x + 1)
5x + 3

19. Suppose a park district plans to build a rectangular playground 80 m by 60 m with a walkway w meters wide around it.
a. At the right, draw and label a diagram to represent this situation.
b. Write an expression in standard form for the total area of the playground and walkway.
$4w^2 + 280w + 4800$
c. Find the total area if $w = 3$. $5676m^2$

60m
80m
w

Review Objective C, Lesson 1–5; Objective H, Lesson 5–1

In 20–22, solve.

20. $4m + 12 = 9m + 67$ $m = -11$
21. $\frac{15}{a} = 4$ $a = \frac{15}{4}$
22. $0.45u + 0.6(4u) - 3.5(7u - 5.5) = -(20u + 22)$ $u = 25$

In 23 and 24, graph on the number line.

23. $y \leq 12$ and $y \geq 0$
24. $e > -2$ or $e < -11$

0
12
y
-11
-2
e

Questions 22–23 and 28 These questions are preparation for Lesson 6-5, where students have to be able to recognize perfect square binomials in order to complete the square.

Question 24 Translations in the coordinate plane are preparation for the Graph-Translation Theorem in Lesson 6-3.

Question 26 Fitting a line to data is preparation for fitting a quadratic expression to data in Lesson 6-6.

Question 27 Cooperative Learning Properties of the general quadratic $y = ax^2 + bx + c$ are studied, beginning in Lesson 6-3. This question can serve as a stimulus for group discussion.

Follow-up for Lesson 6-1

Practice

For more questions on SPUR Objectives, use **Lesson Master 6-1A** (shown on page 347) or **Lesson Master 6-1B** (shown on pages 348–349).

Assessment

Oral/Written Communication Have students **work in pairs**. First have one student name a binomial. Have the other student apply the Binomial Square Theorem and write the trinomial that is equivalent to the square of the binomial. Then have students switch roles. [Students demonstrate that they can correctly apply the Binomial Square Theorem.]

Extension

Have students extend **Example 3** by writing the volume of a cube with edge $x + y$ in standard form. **Teaching Aid 57** contains the diagram of the cube.

$[(x + y)^3 = x^3 + 3x^2y + 3xy^2 + y^3]$

Project Update Project 5, *History of Quadratics*, on page 409, relates to the content of this lesson.

350

In 22 and 23, solve for h.

22. $x^2 + 50x + 625 = (x + h)^2$
$h = 25$

23. $x^2 - 2x + 1 = (x + h)^2$
$h = -1$

Review

24. a. Draw $\triangle ABC$ with vertices $A = (0, 0)$, $B = (1, 1)$, $C = (2, 4)$.
  b. Draw $\triangle A'B'C'$, its image under the transformation $(x, y) \rightarrow (x - 5, y + 2)$. **See margin on page 349 for a, b.**
  c. Describe the effect of this transformation on $\triangle ABC$. *(Lesson 4-10)*
  $\triangle ABC$ is translated 5 units to the left and 2 units up.

In 25 and 26, use the following data about the United States National Parks. *(Lessons 2-5, 3-7)*

Located in Crater Lake National Park in Oregon, Crater Lake is the deepest lake in the U.S. with a depth of 1932 feet. The lake was formed when the top of Mount Mazama, an inactive volcano, collapsed and left a huge bowl that gradually filled with water.

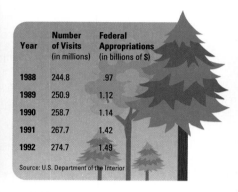

Year	Number of Visits (in millions)	Federal Appropriations (in billions of $)
1988	244.8	.97
1989	250.9	1.12
1990	258.7	1.14
1991	267.7	1.42
1992	274.7	1.49

Source: U.S. Department of the Interior

25. Find the rate of change from 1988 to 1992 for each of the following.
  a. number of visits
  7.475 million visitors/year
  b. federal appropriations
  0.13 billion dollars/year

26. a. Find an equation for the line of best fit describing the number of visits as a function of the year using only the years 1988, 1990, 1992. Let x be the number of years after 1988. $y = 7.475x + 244.45$
  b. How well does the line of best fit predict the values for 1991? **See below.**

27. a. Graph $y = \frac{1}{2}x^2$ and $y = -2x^2$ on the same set of axes. **See left.**
  b. Describe two properties that apply to both graphs. *(Lesson 2-5)* **See left.**

28. Which numbers between 100 and 200 are perfect squares? *(Previous course)* **121, 144, 169, 196**

26b) $7.475 \cdot 3 + 244.45 = 266.875$; It seems that the equation predicts the number of visitors very well.

27a)
$y = \frac{1}{2}x^2$
$y = -2x^2$

b) They have the same vertex (0, 0) and they are both symmetric to the y-axis.

29a) $100^2 = 10,000$; add 100 and 101 to 10,000; so $101^2 = 10,000 + 100 + 101 = 10,201$
b) $(x + 1)^2 = x^2 + 2x + 1 = x^2 + x + (x + 1)$

Exploration

29. If you know the square of an integer, you can find the square of the next higher integer in your head. For instance, since 70^2 is known to be 4900, add 70 and 71 to 4900 to find 71^2.
  a. How could you find 101^2 in your head? **See left.**
  b. Explain why this procedure works for any integer x. **See left.**

350

Adapting to Individual Needs

Challenge
Have students give quadratic expressions for the areas described below.

1. The largest possible circle inside a rectangle whose shorter side is x and whose longer side is y. [The radius of the circle is $\frac{1}{2}x$, so $A = \pi(\frac{1}{2}x)^2 = \frac{1}{4}\pi x^2$.]

2. The largest possible circle inside a square whose side is x. [See the answer for Question 1.]

3. The largest possible square inside a circle whose radius is x. [The length of the diagonal of the square is $2x$ so the length of each side is $\sqrt{2}x$ and $A = (\sqrt{2}x)^2 = 2x^2$.]

4. The smallest possible circle surrounding a square whose side is x. [The diameter of the circle is $\sqrt{2}x$, so $A = \pi(\frac{1}{2}\sqrt{2}x)^2 = \frac{1}{2}\pi x^2$.]

Alge-robics. *These students are doing function "exercises." The graphs formed by their arms represent absolute value functions. See page 352.*

The Absolute Value Function

Geometrically, the absolute value of a number n, written $|n|$, is the distance of n from 0 on the number line. For instance, $|27| = 27$ and $|{-27}| = 27$. Both 27 and -27 are 27 units away from zero.

Algebraically, the **absolute value** of a number can be defined piecewise as
$$|x| = \begin{cases} x, \text{ for } x \geq 0 \\ -x, \text{ for } x < 0. \end{cases}$$

Examine the definition carefully. Because $-x$ is the opposite of x, $-x$ is positive when x is negative. For instance, $|{-18}| = -(-18) = 18$. Thus, $|x|$ and $|{-x}|$ are never negative, and in fact, $|x| = |{-x}|$.

Example 1

Solve for x: $|x - 2| = 5.3$

Solution 1

Use the algebraic definition of absolute value.
Either $\quad x - 2 = 5.3 \quad$ or $\quad x - 2 = -5.3$.
So $\qquad\quad x = 7.3 \quad$ or $\qquad\quad x = -3.3$.

Solution 2

Think of distance on the number line. $|x - 2|$ represents the distance between the points with coordinates x and 2. This distance equals 5.3. So measure 5.3 units from 2 in each direction.

Check

The solutions are -3.3 or 7.3. $|7.3 - 2| = |5.3| = 5.3$ and $|{-3.3} - 2| = |{-5.3}| = -(-5.3) = 5.3$. It checks.

Lesson 6-2

Objectives

C Solve quadratic equations.
E Apply the definition of absolute value and the Absolute Value–Square Root Theorem.
G Use quadratic equations to solve area problems.
J Graph absolute value functions and interpret them.

Resources

From the **Teacher's Resource File**
■ Lesson Master 6-2A or 6-2B
■ Answer Master 6-2
■ Teaching Aids
  8 Four-Quadrant Graph Paper
  53 Warm-up

Additional Resources
■ Visuals for Teaching Aids 8, 53

Teaching Lesson 6-2

Warm-up

On a number line, give the coordinates of the points that are
1. 5 units from 0. **5, –5**
2. 3 units from 1. **–2, 4**
3. 6 units from 6. **0, 12**
4. Simplify $-\sqrt{36}$. **–6**
5. Solve $x^2 = 49$. **7, –7**

Lesson 6-2 Overview

Broad Goals This lesson reviews the relationship between square roots and absolute value: $\sqrt{x^2} = |x|$.

Perspective Students first saw piecewise definitions of functions in Chapter 1. The absolute value function is perhaps the most familiar example of a piecewise-linear function. Students should be familiar with absolute value from both algebra and geometry, although they may not have

been introduced to the function aspect of absolute value.

The Absolute Value–Square Root Theorem $\sqrt{x^2} = |x|$ is used later in the derivation of equations of parabolas from their distance definition. The theorem also lets us change an expression that is defined piecewise (as absolute value) into one that is related to powers and roots.

Students who have studied from UCSMP *Geometry* are likely to have been introduced to rational and irrational numbers. They should recall that the two sets are disjoint, and they have seen at least one proof that $\sqrt{2}$ is irrational.

Students will need graph paper or **Teaching Aid 8** throughout this lesson.

Reading Mathematics As you discuss the reading, stress that when x is positive, the symbol $\sqrt{x}$ is often called *the* square root of x, but it really is only the *positive* square root. To denote the negative root of a positive number, we use $-\sqrt{x}$. You may want to anticipate Lessons 6-8 and 6-9 on complex numbers by mentioning that later in the chapter we will discuss what $\sqrt{x}$ means when x is negative.

❶ Another way of showing the Absolute Value–Square Root Theorem is to have students graph $y = \sqrt{x^2}$ with an automatic grapher using the domain $\{x: -10 \leq x \leq 10\}$. Many students are surprised to see the graph of the absolute value function appear.

❷ **Example 3 History Connection** The collective contribution of the Greek mathematicians was the development of mathematics as a theoretical discipline. That is, mathematics was developed as a system in which mathematical statements are general, and the statements are confirmed by proof, which is derived, using logic, from an initial set of assumed propositions.

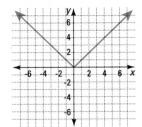

Because every real number has exactly *one* absolute value, $f: x \rightarrow |x|$ is a function.

The graph of $f(x) = |x|$ is shown at the left. When $x \geq 0$ the graph is a ray with slope 1 and endpoint $(0, 0)$. This is the ray in the first quadrant. When $x < 0$, the graph is the ray with slope -1 and endpoint $(0, 0)$. This is the ray in the second quadrant. The graph of $f(x) = |x|$ is the union of two rays, so the graph of $f(x) = |x|$ is an angle.

This function is called the **absolute value function.** Its domain is the set of real numbers, and its range is the set of nonnegative real numbers.

On many automatic graphers and spreadsheets and in many calculator and computer languages, the absolute value function is denoted ABS or abs. That is, $\text{ABS}(x) = |x|$. Parentheses must usually be used to indicate the argument of the absolute value function. For example, to evaluate $|x - 3|$, you need to enter $\text{ABS}(x - 3)$, not $\text{ABS } x - 3$.

Absolute Value and Square Roots

❶ Recall that the square root or radical sign $\sqrt{}$ stands for only the *nonnegative* square root of a real number. Thus, $\sqrt{16} = 4$. To write the negative square root, you need to write $-\sqrt{16}$.

Activity 1

1. Evaluate each of the following. Use your calculator if necessary. $\sqrt{4^2}$, $\sqrt{(-4)^2}$, $\sqrt{9.3^2}$, $\sqrt{(-9.3)^2}$ 4; 4; 9.3; 9.3
2. Find a value of x that is a solution to $\sqrt{x^2} = x$. **Sample: $x = 4$**
3. Find a value of x that is not a solution to $\sqrt{x^2} = x$. **Sample: $x = -4$**

As you should have noticed from Activity 1, $\sqrt{x^2}$ cannot always be simplified to x.

If x is positive, then $\sqrt{x^2} = x$.
If $x = 0$, then $\sqrt{x^2} = 0$.
If x is negative, then $\sqrt{x^2} = -x$, which is a positive number.

This proves a surprising relationship between square roots and absolute value.

x	x^2	$\sqrt{x^2}$	$|x|$
-17	289	17	17
-3.14	9.8596	3.14	3.14
-1	1	1	1
$-\frac{2}{3}$	$\frac{4}{9}$	$\frac{2}{3}$	$\frac{2}{3}$
0	0	0	0
$\frac{2}{3}$	$\frac{4}{9}$	$\frac{2}{3}$	$\frac{2}{3}$
1	1	1	1
3.14	9.8596	3.14	3.14
10	100	10	10

Absolute Value–Square Root Theorem
For all real numbers x, $\sqrt{x^2} = |x|$.

You can verify this theorem by making a table of values like the one shown at the left. Notice how the values in the last two columns are always equal.

Solving Some Quadratic Equations

The simplest quadratic equations are of the form $x^2 = k$. As you know, if $k \geq 0$, the solutions to $x^2 = k$ are the **square roots** of k, namely $\sqrt{k}$ and $-\sqrt{k}$.

The Absolute Value-Square Root Theorem can be used to solve some quadratic equations.

Example 2

Solve $x^2 = 40$.

Solution

Take the positive square root of each side.

$$\sqrt{x^2} = \sqrt{40}.$$

Use the Absolute Value-Square Root Theorem.

$$|x| = \sqrt{40}$$

So either $x = \sqrt{40}$ or $x = -\sqrt{40}$.

Check

Use your calculator to evaluate $(\sqrt{40})^2$ and $(-\sqrt{40})^2$. Each equals 40.

Questions about squares intrigued the ancient Greek mathematicians. They wondered: What should be the radius of a circle if it is to have the same area as a given square? With algebra, it is possible to find it.

 ### Example 3

A square and a circle have the same area. The square has side 10. What is the radius of the circle?

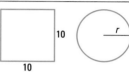

10

10

r

Solution

The area of the square is 100. Let r be the radius of the circle.

$$\pi r^2 = 100$$

$$r^2 = \frac{100}{\pi} \qquad \text{Divide by } \pi.$$

$$|r| = \sqrt{\frac{100}{\pi}} \qquad \text{Take the square root of each side.}$$

$$r = \pm \sqrt{\frac{100}{\pi}}$$

The $\pm$ sign here means there are two solutions, one with the $+$ sign, one with the $-$ sign. In this situation we can ignore the negative solution because the radius can never be negative. Using a calculator, $\sqrt{\frac{100}{\pi}} \approx 5.64$. The radius of the circle is approximately 5.64 units.

Check

The diameter of the circle should be greater than the side of the square. (Do you see why?) Since $d = 2r$, $d \approx 11.28$, which is greater than 10.

Lesson 6-2 *Absolute Value, Square Roots, and Quadratic Equations* **353**

Adapting to Individual Needs

Extra Help
You may want to help students break down the complex name of the Absolute Value–Square Root Theorem. Explain that the name is a shorthand reminder that the square root of a squared expression $\sqrt{x^2}$ is the absolute value of that expression, $|x|$.

English Language Development
Point out that *rational* has *ratio* as its root word, and that a rational number is a number that can be written as a ratio of two integers. Although a rational number may not always appear in the $\frac{a}{b}$ form, it can always be written in this form. For example, $\sqrt{169} = 13 = \frac{13}{1}$. So $\sqrt{169}$ is rational.

353

Additional Examples

1. Solve for y: $|34 - 2y| = 12$
   $y = 11$ or $y = 23$
2. Solve $3x^2 = 18$. $x = \pm\sqrt{6}$
3. A square and a triangle have the same area. The triangle has base 7 cm and altitude 6 cm. What is the length of a side of the square? **The area of the triangle is $\frac{1}{2}(7)(6) = 21$ sq cm. If s is the side of the square, $s^2 = 21$ so $s = \sqrt{21} \approx 4.58$ cm.**

Notes on Questions

Question 11 If students give $|x|$ as an answer to this question, ask them what $|x|$ equals when $x < 0$. Emphasize that $-x$ is positive when x is negative.

Question 26 Encourage students to make a sketch of a circle and a rectangle for this question.

Question 27 Remind students that equations of the form $x^2 + a = b$ always have two solutions when $a < b$. Emphasize that the solution of an equation includes all numbers from the domain that make the original sentence true.

The Greek mathematicians also wondered if square roots could be expressed as simple fractions. For instance, they knew that $\sqrt{40}$ was between 6 and 7, because $\sqrt{36} = 6$ and $\sqrt{49} = 7$. But was it some number like $\frac{13}{2}$, which as a mixed number is $6\frac{1}{2}$? No, $\left(6\frac{1}{2}\right)^2 = 42\frac{1}{4}$, so $6\frac{1}{2} > \sqrt{40}$.

Activity 2

a. Square $6\frac{8}{25}$.
   39.9424

b. Is $6\frac{8}{25}$ more or less than $\sqrt{40}$?
   less than

Recall from Lesson 1-2 that a *rational number* is a number that can be written in the form $\frac{a}{b}$, where a and b are integers and $b \neq 0$. So the Greeks were asking: Is $\sqrt{40}$ a rational number? Around 430 B.C., they proved that unless an integer was a perfect square (like 49, or 625, or 10,000), its square root was an *irrational number*. An **irrational number** is a real number that cannot be written as a simple fraction. You may have seen proofs that certain square roots are irrational in an earlier course. In general, irrational numbers are exactly those numbers which have infinite non-repeating decimal expansions.

QUESTIONS

Covering the Reading

1. Evaluate $|17.8|$. **17.8**   2. Evaluate $|-11|$. **11**
3. a. Evaluate $|x + 2|$ when $x = -3$. **1**
   b. Compare your answer in part **a** to the value of $|x| + 2$ when $x = -3$. **See left.**
4. Solve $|x - 6| = 4.5$. **$x = 10.5$ or $x = 1.5$**   5. Solve $|n + 1.8| = 5$. **$n = 3.2$ or $n = -6.8$**
6. State the domain and range of the function f with $f(x) = |x|$. **See left.**
7. Is the graph of $f(x) = |x|$ piecewise linear? Justify your answer. **See left.**
8. The square roots of 25 are _?_ and _?_. **5; -5**
9. Give your answers to the questions in Activity 1. **See page 352.**
10. Give your answers to the questions in Activity 2. **See above.**
11. When $x < 0$, what does $\sqrt{x^2}$ equal? **$-x$**
12. When $x < 0$, what does $|x|$ equal? **$-x$**
13. Solve $t^2 = 720$. **$t = \pm 12\sqrt{5} \approx \pm 26.83$**
14. A circle has the same area as a square of side 6. What is the radius of the circle? **$\sqrt{\frac{36}{\pi}} \approx 3.39$**
15. About how many years ago was it first shown that certain numbers are irrational? **about 2430 years**

(margin notes:)
3b) When $x = -3$,
$|x + 2| = 1$ and
$|x| + 2 = 5$; so
$|x + 2| \neq |x| + 2$.

6) domain: the set of all real numbers;
range: the set of all nonnegative real numbers

7) Yes, since $f(x) = |x|$ can be described by linear equations over different domains:
$f(x) = \begin{cases} x, \text{ when } x \geq 0 \\ -x, \text{ when } x < 0 \end{cases}$.

Adapting to Individual Needs

Challenge
Have students determine if each statement is *True* or *False*. If the statement is false, have them give a counterexample.

1. $|ab| = |a||b|$ [True]
2. $|a + b| = |a| + |b|$ [False.
   Sample: $|-2 + 4| = |2| = 2$;
   $|-2| + |4| = 2 + 4 = 6$]
3. $|a^2| = |a|^2$ [True]

4. $\sqrt{a^2 + b^2} = \sqrt{a} + \sqrt{b}$ [False.
   Sample: $\sqrt{2^2 + 3^2} = \sqrt{13}$;
   $\sqrt{2^2} + \sqrt{3^2} = 2 + 3 = 5$]
5. $\sqrt{a^2 + b^2} = a + b$ [False.
   Sample: $\sqrt{(-3)^2 + 4^2} = \sqrt{25} = 5$;
   $-3 + 4 = 1$]

23a)

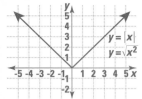

In 16–21, tell whether the number is rational or irrational. If rational, write the number as a simple fraction.

16. $\sqrt{10}$ irrational   **17.** $\sqrt{100}$ rational; $\frac{10}{1}$ **18.** -5 rational; $\frac{-5}{1}$

19. $\frac{203}{317}$ rational; $\frac{203}{317}$ **20.** $\sqrt{2} - \sqrt{2}$ rational; $\frac{0}{1}$ **21.** π irrational

---

Applying the Mathematics

22. Suppose the ideal length of an item is I units. If the item is actually p units long, then the formula $e = |p - I|$ gives the error e in the length of the item. When constructing a swimming pool for international competitions the contractor aims for a length of 50.015 meters with an acceptable value of e of no more than .015 m.
　a. Write a mathematical sentence satisfied by the possible lengths p of pools in this situation. $|p - 50.015| \leq 0.015$
　b. What are the possible solutions to this sentence? $50 \leq p \leq 50.030$

23. a. Graph on the same set of axes: $f(x) = \sqrt{x^2}$ and $g(x) = |x|$.   **See left.**
　b. How are the two graphs related?   **They coincide everywhere.**

24. a. Graph the function d with $d(x) = -|x|$.   **See left.**
　b. State the domain and the range of d.   **domain: the set of all real numbers; range: the set of nonpositive real numbers**

25. If $\sqrt{(x - 3)^2} = |k|$, then $k = \underline{\quad?\quad}$. $x - 3$ or $3 - x$

26. On a brand-name pizza box, the directions read: "Spread dough to edges of pizza pan or onto a 10″ by 14″ rectangular cookie sheet." How big a circular pizza could you make with this dough, assuming it is spread the same thickness as for the rectangular pizza?
6.7″ radius

27. Solve.
　a. $x^2 + 36 = 49$ $\pm\sqrt{13}$　　　**b.** $x^2 + 36 = 50$ $\pm\sqrt{14}$

Review

28. *Skill sequence.*   Expand and simplify.   *(Lesson 6-1)*
　a. $(x - 10)^2$　　**b.** $(3x_2 - 10)^2$　　**c.** $3(x - 10)^2$
　　$x^2 - 20x + 100$　　$9x_2^2 - 60x + 100$　　$3x^2 - 60x + 300$

29. *True or false.* $(n + 11)^2 = n^2 + 11^2$. Justify your answer.   *(Lesson 6-1)*
See left.

30. Find the area of the shaded region determined by the rectangles at the left.   *(Lesson 6-1)* $17a + 64$

31. Consider the graph of $y = 3x^2$. Find an equation for its image under r_x and under r_y.   *(Lesson 4-6)*   under r_x: $y = -3x^2$; under r_y: $y = 3x^2$

Exploration

Sample: 6,324,555/1,000,000

32. a. Find a simple fraction within .000001 of $\sqrt{40}$.
　b. How close to 40 is the square of your number?
less than 4.1×10^{-6} away

Lesson 6-2   *Absolute Value, Square Roots, and Quadratic Equations*   **355**

Shown is the beginning of a 100-meter race with U.S. record holder Mary T. Meagher in the foreground. International swimming competitions are held annually.

24a)

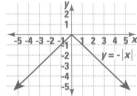

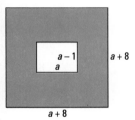

$a + 8$

29) False: for instance, when $n = 1$, $(1 + 11)^2 = 144$ and $1^2 + 11^2 = 122$; so $(n + 11)^2 = n^2 + 11^2$ is not true.

Setting Up Lesson 6-3
Be sure to use the In-class Activity on page 356 before assigning Lesson 6-3.

Follow-up for Lesson   6-2

Practice
For more questions on SPUR Objectives, use **Lesson Master 6-2A** (shown on page 353) or **Lesson Master 6-2B** (shown on pages 354–355).

Assessment
Written Communication Have students write a paragraph explaining how they can determine if a given square root is rational or irrational. [Students demonstrate that they understand the concept of perfect squares and that the square roots of perfect squares are rational.]

Extension
In **Example 1,** absolute value is interpreted as the distance between two points on a number line. Have students apply this meaning to inequalities by solving problems like $|x - 2| < 5.3$. [The distance between x and 2 is less than 5.3 units.]

Project Update Project 5, *History of Quadratics*, on page 409, relates to the content of this lesson.

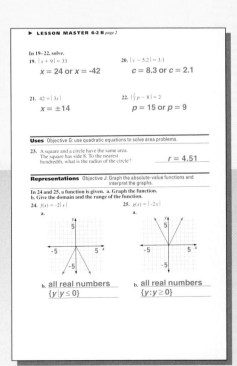

Resources

From the Teacher's Resource File
- Answer Master 6-3
- Teaching Aid 19: Automatic Grapher Grids

Additional Resources
- Visual for Teaching Aid 19

This In-class Activity is designed to provide concrete experiences for Lesson 6-3.

For **Questions 3 and 6**, make certain that each person in the group chooses a different value of *h* and *k*, respectively. **Question 7** is easy if the students can graph the parabola using an automatic grapher. You might challenge groups to predict the vertex without graphing, and then use the graph as a check.

Students may use **Teaching Aid 19** to draw the graphs that they generate on their automatic graphers.

Additional Answers

1a.

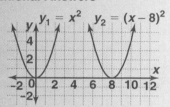

2a.

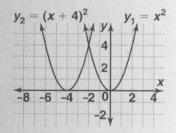

3a. The translation that maps $y_1 = x^2$ onto the graph of $y_2 = (x - h)^2$ is a horizontal translation *h* units to the right.
b. Answers will vary.

Graphs and Translations

IN-CLASS
ACTIVITY

Materials: Use an automatic grapher.
Work in small groups. Clear the screen of your grapher after you have answered each question.

In 1 and 2, equations for two functions are given. **a.** Draw the graphs of both functions on the same set of axes. **b.** What transformation maps the graph of the first function onto the graph of the second?

1 $y_1 = x^2$, $y_2 = (x - 8)^2$ a) See margin.
b) It is a horizontal translation 8 units to the right.

2 $y_1 = x^2$, $y_2 = (x + 4)^2$ a) See margin.
b) It is a horizontal translation 4 units to the left.

3 **a.** Make a conjecture describing the transformation that maps the graph of $y_1 = x^2$ onto the graph of $y_2 = (x - h)^2$. See margin.
b. Test your conjecture with another value of *h*. See margin.
In 4 and 5, follow the directions of Questions 1 and 2.

4 $y_1 = x^2$, $y_2 = x^2 + 3$ a) See margin.
b) It is a vertical translation 3 units up.

5 $y_1 = x^2$, $y_2 = x^2 - 6$ a) See margin.
b) It is a vertical translation 6 units down.

6 **a.** Make a conjecture describing the transformation that maps the graph of $y_1 = x^2$ onto the graph of $y_2 = x^2 + k$.
b. Test your conjecture with another value of *k*. a, b) See margin.

7 Find the vertex of the parabola $y = (x - 2)^2 + 4$. (2, 4)

8 Find an equation for a parabola congruent to $y = x^2$ with vertex at (-6, 3). $y = (x + 6)^2 + 3$

4a.

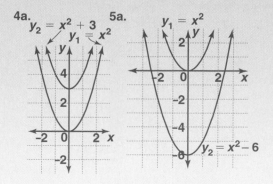

5a.

6a. Sample: The translation that maps $y_1 = x^2$ onto $y_2 = x^2 + k$ is a vertical translation *k* units up.
b. Answers will vary.

Shown is a multi-exposure print which illustrates the Graph-Translation Theorem.

What Is the Graph-Translation Theorem?

Consider the graphs of the equations $y_1 = x^2$ and $y_2 = (x - 8)^2$ that you made in the preceding In-class Activity.

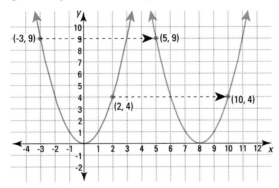

As the arrows indicate, the graph of $y = (x - 8)^2$ can be obtained from the graph of $y = x^2$ by a translation 8 units to the right. Thus, replacing x by $x - 8$ in the equation for the function translates its graph 8 units to the right.

In general, replacing x by $x - h$ in a sentence translates its graph h units to the right.

Similarly, vertical translations of graphs result from replacing y by $y - k$. For example, you saw that the graph of the equation $y = x^2 + 3$ is 3 units above the graph of $y = x^2$. Note that we can rewrite this equation as $y - 3 = x^2$. Thus, replacing y by $y - 3$ in the equation for a function translates its graph 3 units up. In general, replacing y by $y - k$ in a sentence translates its graph k units up.

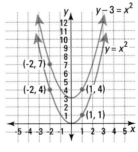

Lesson 6-3 *The Graph-Translation Theorem* **357**

Lesson 6-3

Objectives
I   Use the Graph-Translation Theorem to interpret equations and graphs.
J   Graph parabolas and interpret the graphs.

Resources

From the ***Teacher's Resource File***
■ Lesson Master 6-3A or 6-3B
■ Answer Master 6-3
■ Teaching Aids
  8 Four-Quadrant Graph Paper
  19 Automatic Grapher Grids
  53 Warm-up
  58 Examples 1 and 2
  59 Additional Examples
  60 Optional Activity 3 and
    Challenge
■ Activity Kit, Activity 11
■ Technology Sourcebook
  Computer Master 8

Additional Resources
■ Visuals for Teaching Aids 8, 19, 53, 58, 59, 60
■ GraphExplorer or other automatic grapher

Teaching 6-3
Lesson

Warm-up

1. Draw the graph of $y = x^2$.
2. On the same set of axes, draw the graph that is obtained by sliding the graph of $y = x^2$
   a. 5 units to the right.
   b. 5 units up.

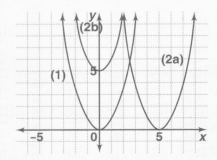

Lesson 6-3 Overview

Broad Goals This lesson presents the Graph-Translation Theorem and applies it to parabolas and absolute value functions.

Perspective The Graph-Translation Theorem is very powerful, and it can be used repeatedly in students' later work in mathematics. Here are a few of the instances of this theorem that appear elsewhere in the study of mathematics.

1. Find the equation of circle with center (h, k) and radius r by applying $T_{h,k}$ to $x^2 + y^2 = r^2$; image: $(x - h)^2 + (y - k)^2 = r^2$.
2. Find the point-slope equation of line with slope m through (x_0, y_0) by applying T_{x_0,y_0} to $y = mx$; image: $y - y_0 = m(x - x_0)$.
3. Find the equation of $y = \sin x$ after a phase shift of π units to the right by applying $T_{\pi,0}$; image: $y = \sin(x - \pi)$.

(Overview continues on page 358.)

Graph paper, **Teaching Aid 8**, and **Teaching Aid 19** will be used throughout the lesson.

You might want to use Activity 1 in *Optional Activities* on page 359 before discussing **Example 1**.

Teaching Aid 58 contains the preimage graphs of the translations discussed in **Examples 1 and 2.** You may want to use **Teaching Aid 58** to draw the image graphs as you discuss **Examples 1 and 2** with your class.

The window that is used on an automatic grapher limits the view of a graph and can distort the viewer's perception of the graph. For instance, some students may think that the graphs in **Example 1** are not congruent. Have these students view the graphs in a different window by zooming out. Also have them describe the angle made by the two rays and note that each angle is a right angle.

For **Example 2,** there is no substitute for substitution. Use any point on $y = 3x^2$; for instance, pick $(-2, 12)$ and verify that $(4, 19)$, the corresponding point, is on the graph of the equation $y - 7 = 3(x - 6)^2$. With actual substitution, the Graph-Translation Theorem can seem reasonable and even obvious. Students should see that the subtractions of h and k compensate for the different values that are substituted for x and y.

You might mention that the Graph-Translation Theorem will be used many times in this course and in other math courses the students may take.

Recall that the translation $T_{h,k}$ slides a figure h units to the right and k units up at the same time. Thus we can translate horizontally and vertically at the same time. We can summarize these examples as follows.

> **Graph-Translation Theorem**
> In a relation described by a sentence in x and y, the following two processes yield the same graph:
> (1) replacing x by $x - h$ and y by $y - k$;
> (2) applying the translation $T_{h,k}$ to the graph of the original relation.

The Graph-Translation Theorem applies to all relations that can be described by a sentence in x and y.

Example 1

Find an equation for the image of the graph of $y = |x|$ under the translation $T_{5,-3}$.

Solution

Applying $T_{5,-3}$ is equivalent to replacing x by $x - 5$ and y by $y - -3$ or $y + 3$ in the equation for the preimage. An equation for the image is $y + 3 = |x - 5|$ or $y = |x - 5| - 3$.

Check

Graph $y = |x|$ and $y = |x - 5| - 3$ on the same set of axes. As shown at the left, the graph of the second equation is the image of the graph of the first equation under a translation 5 units to the right and 3 units down.

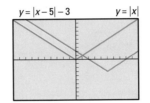

$y = |x - 5| - 3$ $y = |x|$

$-10 \leq x \leq 10$, x-scale = 1
$-10 \leq y \leq 10$, y-scale = 1

Applying the Graph-Translation Theorem to Graph Parabolas

Recall from Chapter 2 that the graph of $y = ax^2$ is a parabola. If we replace x by $x - h$ and y by $y - k$ in the equation $y = ax^2$, we obtain $y - k = a(x - h)^2$. Since any figure is congruent to its translation image, the image is also a parabola.

This argument proves the following *corollary* to the Graph-Translation Theorem. (Recall that a **corollary** is a theorem that follows immediately from another theorem.)

> **Corollary**
> The image of the parabola $y = ax^2$ under the translation $T_{h,k}$ is the parabola with the equation
> $$y - k = a(x - h)^2.$$

Lesson 6-3 Overview, continued

In this lesson we emphasize the application of the Graph-Translation Theorem to parabolas. From their work in Chapter 2, students know that the curve with equation $y = ax^2$ is a parabola with the vertex at $(0, 0)$ and the y-axis ($x = 0$) as the line of symmetry. When we translate $y = ax^2$ h units to the right and k units up, we get the curve with equation $y - k = a(x - h)^2$.

That equation represents a parabola with vertex (h, k) and line of symmetry $x = h$.

The Graph-Translation Theorem is presented at this time so we can develop the vertex form of the equation of a parabola. However, the theorem applies to any curve, and it tells how the two equations that represent the image and preimage are related. A proof of the Graph-Translation Theorem is as follows: Under $T_{h,k}$, $(x', y') = (x + h, y + k)$.

Thus $x' = x + h$ and $y' = y + k$, from which $x = x' - h$ and $y = y' - k$. If we know a relationship between x and y (which we do, if we have a sentence describing a graph), then we can substitute $x' - h$ for x and $y' - k$ for y. The result is a relationship involving the coordinates of the image points under this translation. This is exactly what happens; the only reason we do not see the x' and y' in the image is that we customarily drop the prime symbols.

Example 2

Sketch the graph of $y - 7 = 3(x - 6)^2$.

Solution

The equation is the result of replacing x by $x - 6$ and y by $y - 7$ in $y = 3x^2$. So its graph is the image of $y = 3x^2$ under the translation $T_{6,7}$. Thus, the graph is a parabola with vertex $(6, 7)$. Because $y = 3x^2$ opens up, so does the graph of $y - 7 = 3(x - 6)^2$. To find some other points on the graph, find some solutions to $y = 3x^2$ and then find their images under $T_{6,7}$. For example,

$$\begin{array}{ccc}
\text{preimage} & \rightarrow & \text{image} \\
(-2, 12) & \rightarrow & (4, 19) \\
(-1, 3) & \rightarrow & (5, 10) \\
(1, 3) & \rightarrow & (7, 10) \\
(2, 12) & \rightarrow & (8, 19)
\end{array}$$

The graph is shown below.

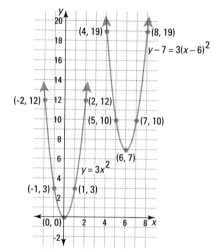

Check

Use an automatic grapher to draw the graph. Trace to verify that $(6, 7)$ is the vertex.

You know that $(0, 0)$ is the vertex of the parabola $y = ax^2$. The translation image of $(0, 0)$ is $T_{h,k}(0, 0) = (0 + h, 0 + k) = (h, k)$. So, the vertex of the parabola with equation $y - k = a(x - h)^2$ is (h, k). For this reason, the equation $y - k = a(x - h)^2$ is called the **vertex form of an equation for a parabola.** The line with equation $x = h$ is the line of symmetry or **axis of symmetry** of the parabola. If $a > 0$, then the parabola opens up and the y-coordinate of the vertex is the **minimum** y-value. If $a < 0$, then the parabola opens down and the graph has a **maximum** y-value. When the equation for a parabola is in vertex form, the parabola can be graphed quickly even if you do not have an automatic grapher.

Lesson 6-3 *The Graph-Translation Theorem* **359**

Teaching Aid 60 contains the graph in Activity 3 in *Optional Activities* on page 360 and the chart from the *Challenge* on page 362.

Additional Examples

These examples are also given on **Teaching Aid 59.**

1. Find an equation for the image of the graph of $y = 5x^2$ under the translation $T_{-\frac{2}{3}, 6}$.

   $y - 6 = 5(x + \frac{2}{3})^2$

2. **a.** Graph $y - 2 = -2(x + 3)^2$.

   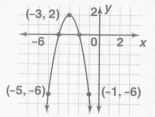

   b. How is this graph related to the graph of $y = -2x^2$?

   It is the image under $T_{-3,2}$.

3. **a.** Sketch the graph of $y + 3 = \frac{1}{2}x^2$.

   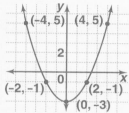

   b. Give an equation for the axis of symmetry of the parabola.

   $x = 0$

(Additional Examples continue on page 360.)

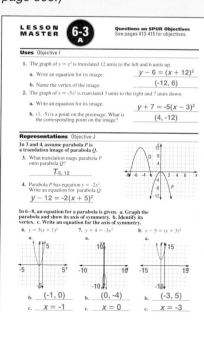

Optional Activities

Activity 1

Before students read **Example 1,** and as preparation for translating a figure, you might have them translate individual points. For example, ask them to give the images of $(5, -3)$, $(6, 2)$, and (m, n) under the translation $T_{1,-3}$. [$(6, -6)$, $(7, -1)$, and $(m + 1, n - 3)$, respectively]

Activity 2

In *Activity Kit, Activity 11* students gather data relating the distance a flashlight is held from a surface and the illuminated area. The graph of the data approximates a parabola of the form $y = a(x - h)^2$. This activity can be used as a follow-up to the lesson.

4. The function f graphed below is a translation image of the graph of $y = |x|$. Find an equation for f.

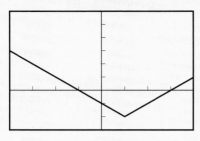

$-4 \le x \le 4, \quad x\text{-scale} = 1$
$-3 \le y \le 6, \quad y\text{-scale} = 1$
$y + 2 = |x - 1| \text{ or } y = |x - 1| - 2$

Notes on Questions

Questions 3b, 5, and 12–13
Encourage students to check their answers by graphing.

Questions 10–11 Have students describe in their own words how they could predict the answers to **parts a, b, and c** just by looking at the equation.

Example 3

a. Sketch the graph of $y = -\frac{1}{2}(x + 3)^2$.
b. Give an equation for the axis of symmetry of the parabola.

Solution

a. Rewrite the equation in vertex form: $y - 0 = -\frac{1}{2}(x - -3)^2$. The graph is the image of the parabola $y = -\frac{1}{2}x^2$ under $T_{-3,0}$. Thus it opens down and its vertex is $(-3, 0)$. Find other points by substituting values into $y = -\frac{1}{2}(x + 3)^2$. Use some values of x less than -3 and some values greater than -3. A table and a graph are shown below.

x	y
-7	-8
-5	-2
-3	0
-1	-2
1	-8

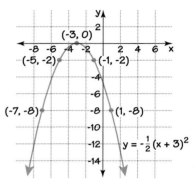

$y = -\frac{1}{2}(x + 3)^2$

b. The axis of symmetry is the vertical line through the vertex. The axis of symmetry has equation $x = -3$.

Finding Equations for Parabolas

You can apply the Graph-Translation Theorem to a known parabola to find an equation for its image under a given translation.

Example 4

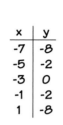

$-5 \le x \le 5, \quad x\text{-scale} = 1$
$-5 \le y \le 10, \quad y\text{-scale} = 1$

Consider the parabolas at the left. The one that passes through the origin has equation $y = 2x^2$. The other is its image under a translation. Find an equation for the image.

Solution

The translation image appears to be 3 units to the left and 4 units up from the preimage. So the translation is $T_{-3,4}$. Applying $T_{-3,4}$ is equivalent to replacing x by $x + 3$ and y by $y - 4$ in the equation for the preimage. An equation for the image is $y - 4 = 2(x + 3)^2$ or $y = 2(x + 3)^2 + 4$.

Check

Use an automatic grapher. Plot $y = 2x^2$ and $y = 2(x + 3)^2 + 4$ on the same set of axes. You should see that the graph of the second equation is the image of the graph of the first under a translation 3 units left and 4 units up.

Optional Activities

Activity 3
Materials: **Teaching Aid 60**

You might give this problem to students after they have completed the lesson. Show them the graph at the right, which is on **Teaching Aid 60.** Ask if it is correct to say that since the parabola has the same shape as $y = 2x^2$, its equation is $y = 2(x - 3)^2 - 4$. Then ask why or why not. [It is incorrect. The vertex is $(-3, -4)$, so the equation is $y = 2(x + 3)^2 - 4$.]

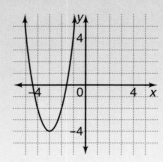

In 1 and 2, tell how the graphs of the two equations are related.

1. $y_1 = x^2$ and $y = (x - 8)^2$ The graph of $y = (x - 8)^2$ is the image of the graph of $y_1 = x^2$ under $T_{8,0}$.

2. $y_1 = x^2$ and $y - 3 = x^2$ The graph of $y - 3 = x^2$ is the image of the graph of $y_1 = x^2$ under $T_{0,3}$.

3. a. What is the image of (x, y) under $T_{6,0}$? $(x + 6, y)$
   b. Under $T_{6,0}$, what is an equation for the image of the graph of $y = x^2$? $y = (x - 6)^2$

4. a. On the same axes, draw the graphs of $y = |x|$ and $y + 3 = |x - 5|$.
   b. Describe how the two graphs are related.
      See left.

5. Suppose the parabola with equation $y = \frac{4}{7}x^2$ undergoes the translation $T_{2,-3}$. Find an equation for its image. $y = \frac{4}{7}(x - 2)^2 - 3$

6. The graph of $y - k = a(x - h)^2$ is __?__ units above and __?__ units to the right of the graph of $y = ax^2$. k, h

7. *True or false.* The graphs of $y = ax^2$ and $y = a(x - h)^2 + k$ are congruent. True

8. What is the vertex of the parabola with equation $y - k = a(x - h)^2$?
   (h, k)

9. Refer to Example 2.
   a. Give an equation of the axis of symmetry of $y = 3x^2$. $x = 0$
   b. Give an equation of the axis of symmetry of $y - 7 = 3(x - 6)^2$.
      $x = 6$

In 10 and 11, an equation for a parabola is given.
   a. Give the coordinates of the vertex of the parabola. 10) (-7, -2) 11) (2, 6)
   b. Give an equation for the axis of symmetry. 10) $x = -7$ 11) $x = 2$
   c. Tell whether the parabola opens up or down. 10) down 11) up
   d. Graph the solution set to the equation. See left.

10. $y + 2 = -3(x + 7)^2$ 11. $y = (x - 2)^2 + 6$

12. Find an equation for the translation image of $y = |x|$ graphed at the left below. $y + 1 = |x - 2|$

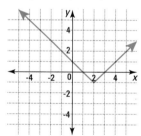

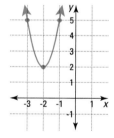

13. The parabola graphed at the right above is a translation image of $y = 3x^2$. What is an equation for this parabola? $y - 2 = 3(x + 2)^2$

4a)

$y_1 = |x|$

$y_2 + 3 = |x - 5|$

b) The graph of $y + 3 = |x - 5|$ is the image of the graph of $y = |x|$ under $T_{5,-3}$.

10d)

$y + 2 = -3(x + 7)^2$

11d)

$y = (x - 2)^2 + 6$

Practice
For more questions on SPUR Objectives, use **Lesson Master 6-3A** (shown on page 359) or **Lesson Master 6-3B** (shown on pages 360–361).

Assessment
Written Communication Have students write a letter to another student who has not yet studied Chapter 6, and in the letter explain how to describe the graph of $y = a(x - h)^2 + k$ without actually plotting points or using an automatic grapher. [Students demonstrate an understanding of the Graph-Translation Theorem.]

Extension
Ask students what single translation of the graph of $y = x^2$ is equivalent to translating the graph of $y = x^2$ by $T_{5,-3}$ and then translating the image by $T_{-2,5}$. [$T_{3,2}$]

Project Update Project 3, *The Graph-Translation Theorem and Other Functions*, on page 408, relates to the content of this lesson.

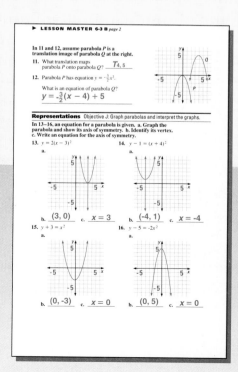

Adapting to Individual Needs

Activity 4 Technology Connection
You may wish to assign *Technology Sourcebook, Computer Master 8.* Students are led through exercises that allow them to discover the Graph-Translation Theorem.

Extra Help
Emphasize that the corollary to the Graph-Translation Theorem states how to graph any parabola that is a translation image of $y = ax^2$. Point out that in the vertex form there are three constants: h, k, and a. The graphs of $y = ax^2$ and of $y - k = a(x - h)^2$ are congruent. The magnitude of a determines the "width" of the parabola, and its sign determines whether the parabola opens up or down.

362

Notes on Questions

Question 16 Cooperative Learning This question can lead to rich discussion and many connections. Encourage students to describe how they solved the problem. There are several ways they may do it: (1) use purely numerical strategies, such as mentally finding 10 and –10 as solutions to **part a**, and adding 3 to each number to get 13 and –7 for **part b**; (2) use the Absolute Value–Square Root Theorem to take the square roots to obtain $|x - 3| = 10$, an equation that can be solved; (3) expand the square and use the Quadratic Formula; (4) graph $y = (x - 3)^2$ and $y = 100$ and find the points of intersection graphically. (Method 4 is discussed in Lesson 6-10.)

Question 17 When discussing this question, point out that the second equation is identical to the first except that x has been replaced by $x - 4$. This translates the solutions four units to the right, so the solutions to the second equation are 4 greater than the solutions to the first equation.

Question 18 This question applies the Graph-Translation Theorem to obtain the point-slope equation for a line that students saw in Chapter 3.

Question 21 Social Studies Connection A builder's permit is a legal authorization to construct a building. The main purpose of a permit is to allow city officials to decide if the proposed structure meets community standards and zoning laws. Zoning laws regulate the heights and sizes of buildings. Zoning committees also try to keep buildings that are used for the same purpose, such as commercial, residential, or industrial, grouped together.

16c) The solutions to part **b** are 3 greater than the solutions to part **a**, which corresponds to the translation $T_{3,0}$ applied to the solution set of part **a**.

19) Does $|2(-0.25) + 1| = 0.5$? Yes. Does $|2(-0.75) + 1| = 0.5$? Yes. It checks.

20) Does $(\sqrt{39})^2 - 17 = 22$? Yes. Does $(-\sqrt{39})^2 - 17 = 22$? Yes. It checks.

26a) Sample: (0, 0), (1, 1), (1, -1), (4, 2), (4, -2)

b)

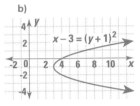

$x - 3 = (y + 1)^2$

Applying the Mathematics

14. A parabola congruent to $y = 7x^2$ has vertex $(2, -5)$ and opens down. What is an equation for the parabola? $y + 5 = -7(x - 2)^2$

15. Consider the graph of $y = -1.4x^2$. Write an equation for its translation image. **a.** with vertex $(0, 3)$. **b.** with vertex $(3, 0)$.
$y - 3 = -1.4x^2$ $y = -1.4(x - 3)^2$

16. **a.** Solve $x^2 = 100$. $x = 10, x = -10$
    b. Solve $(x - 3)^2 = 100$. $x = 13, x = -7$
    c. How are the solutions in parts **a** and **b** related to the Graph-Translation Theorem? See left.

17. One solution to $x^2 + 5x + 3 = 87$ is 7. Use this information to find a solution to $(x - 4)^2 + 5(x - 4) + 3 = 87$. $x = 11$

18. The point-slope form of a line, $y - y_1 = m(x - x_1)$, can be thought of as the image of the line with equation ___?___ under the translation $T_{h,k}$ where $h = $ ___?___ and $k = $ ___?___. $y = mx$; x_1; y_1

Review

In 19 and 20, solve and check. *(Lesson 6-2)* See left for checks.

19. $|2n + 1| = 0.5$ 20. $x^2 - 17 = 22$ $x = \pm\sqrt{39} \approx \pm6.24$
$n = -0.25$ or -0.75

21. A 100'-by-60' rectangular lot is located in a town that allows no building closer than 5 feet to the edge of a lot.
    a. How much room is there to build? 4500 sq ft
    b. If no building were allowed to be closer than x feet to the edge of the lot, how much room would there be to build? *(Lesson 6-1)*
    $6000 - 320x + 4x^2$ sq ft

22. A student claims that the graphs of $y_1 = (x - 9)^2$ and $y_2 = x^2 - 18x + 81$ coincide. How can you tell without graphing whether the student is right? *(Lesson 6-1)* Expanding $(x - 9)^2$ yields $x^2 - 18x + 81$. Therefore, the two expressions are equivalent and their graphs coincide.

23. Expand and simplify.
    a. $2(x + 4)^2$ **b.** $2(x + 4)^2 + 3$ *(Lesson 6-1)*
    $2x^2 + 16x + 32$ $2x^2 + 16x + 35$

24. **a.** Find an equation of the line through the points $(-2, 8)$ and $(1, 17)$.
    b. Find a point on this line which lies in the third quadrant.
    (Lesson 3-5) a) $y = 3x + 14$ b) Sample: $(-5, -1)$

25. A school has buses that hold 40 students each. If s students are to be transported, how many buses are needed? *(Lessons 1-1, 3-9)* $\left\lfloor \frac{s - 0.5}{40} \right\rfloor + 1$; or $\left\lfloor \frac{s}{40} \right\rfloor + 1$ when s is not a multiple of 40, $\left\lfloor \frac{s}{40} \right\rfloor$ when s is a multiple of 40

Exploration

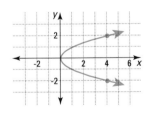

26. The parabola with equation $x = y^2$ is graphed at the left.
    a. Give the coordinates of five points on this parabola. See left.
    b. Graph its image under the translation $T_{3,-1}$. See left.
    c. Write an equation for the image. $x - 3 = (y + 1)^2$
    d. Does the Graph-Translation Theorem hold for parabolas that open to the side? Yes.

362

Adapting to Individual Needs

Challenge
Materials: **Teaching Aid 60**

Have students investigate the effects of translations on domains, ranges, maximum values, and minimum values by completing the following chart, which is on **Teaching Aid 60**.

$f(x)$	x^2	$|x|$	$\sqrt{x}$
Domain	[set of reals]	[set of reals]	[{x: x ≥ 0}]
Range	[{y: y ≥ 0}]	[{y: y ≥ 0}]	[{y: y ≥ 0}]
Max	[none]	[none]	[none]
Min	[0]	[0]	[0]
$T_{h,k}$	$[(x - h)^2 + k]$	$[|x - h| + k]$	$[\sqrt{x - h} + k]$
Domain	[set of reals]	[set of reals]	[x ≥ h]
Range	[{y: y ≥ k}]	[{y: y ≥ k}]	[{y: y ≥ k}]
Max	[none]	[none]	[none]
Min	[k]	[k]	[k]

LESSON 6-4

Graphing $y = ax^2 + bx + c$

Natural curve. *Shown are Manabezho Falls at the Porcupine Mountains State Wilderness Park in the Upper Peninsula of Michigan. The path of the water forms part of a parabola.*

Standard Form for the Equation of a Parabola

In general, any parabola whose equation can be written in vertex form $y - k = a(x - h)^2$ can be rewritten in the standard form $y = ax^2 + bx + c$. Here we show how.

Example 1

Show that the two formulas $y = 2(x + 3)^2 - 8$ and $y = 2x^2 + 12x + 10$ are equivalent.

Solution

Begin with $y = 2(x + 3)^2 - 8$. Expand the binomial, and simplify the right side of the equation.

$$y = 2(x^2 + 6x + 9) - 8$$
$$y = 2x^2 + 12x + 18 - 8$$
$$y = 2x^2 + 12x + 10$$

So the two formulas are equivalent.

❶ Check

Graph $y = 2(x + 3)^2 - 8$ and $y = 2x^2 + 12x + 10$.
The graphs are the same.
Each looks like the graph shown here.

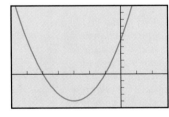

$-7 \leq x \leq 3$, x-scale = 1
$-10 \leq y \leq 20$, y-scale = 2

Lesson 6-4

Objectives

B Transform quadratic equations from vertex form to standard form.
G Use quadratic equations to solve problems dealing with velocity and acceleration.
J Graph quadratic functions and interpret them.

Resources

From the ***Teacher's Resource File***
- Lesson Master 6-4A or 6-4B
- Answer Master 6-4
- Assessment Sourcebook: Quiz for Lessons 6-1 through 6-4
- Teaching Aids
  8 Four-Quadrant Graph Paper
  19 Automatic Grapher Grids
  54 Warm-up

Additional Resources
- Visuals for Teaching Aids 8, 19, 54

Teaching 6-4
Lesson

Warm-up

The equation $h = -49t^2 + 3.9t + 10$ represents Marta's height h in meters above the water t seconds after jumping off the diving board. How high above the water is the diving board? **10 meters**

Notes on Reading

❶ Students may wonder how to determine *where the parabola turns*—that is, the location of its vertex. In this lesson, they should estimate this point from the graph;

Lesson 6-4 Overview

Broad Goals This lesson relates the graph of the equation $y = ax^2 + bx + c$ to the vertex form $y = a(x - h)^2 + k$ and investigates the classic application of quadratics to the heights of projectiles and to their actual paths.

Perspective Applications of projectile motion apply to those situations in which the moving object is subject to constant vertical acceleration; that is, objects whose height h at time t is given by an equation of the form
$$h = -\frac{1}{2}gt^2 + v_0t + h_0.$$
These applications were first analyzed by Tartaglia and Galileo in the 16th century. They are historically of great importance as the applications which led to the invention of calculus by Newton and Leibniz, and thus paved the way for modern physics and mechanics. Newton, as the lesson indicates, used the term *gravity* as the force attracting objects to Earth.

The analysis of the graph of $y = ax^2 + bx + c$ is facilitated by translating the equation $y = ax^2 + bx + c$ into vertex form. This provides what often is a surprise to students: regardless of the values of the real numbers $a \neq 0$, b, and c, the graph of the equation $y = ax^2 + bx + c$ is a parabola. The application of this idea has a subtlety which is mentioned in the lesson. Consider

(Overview continues on page 364.)

a method to find the exact value will be covered in Lesson 6-5.

At this time, we also expect students to estimate *x*-intercepts from the graph and to check these estimates by substitution. After studying the Quadratic Formula in Lesson 6-7, students should be able to determine the *x*-intercepts precisely.

When we look at the graph of a parabola, our perception is affected by the scales on the axes. Congruent parabolas may not look congruent when they are graphed with different scales. The confusion is due to two different aspects of *point,* to which students of UCSMP *Geometry* were introduced in the first chapter of that book. In looking at drawings, we think of points as locations, and a parabola is a set of ordered pairs. Changing the scale on a graph may change the drawing, but it does not change the set of ordered pairs.

❷ **History Connection** Galileo left medical school when he discovered he had a talent for mathematics. He became a professor of mathematics and is credited with developing original ways to approach scientific problems. Galileo first reduced problems to the simplest terms on the basis of everyday experience and common-sense logic. Then he analyzed and resolved the problems according to simple mathematical descriptions.

Students will use graph paper, **Teaching Aid 8,** or **Teaching Aid 19** throughout this lesson.

Galileo (1564–1642), an Italian astronomer and physicist, conducted research on motion consistent with a moving Earth. From this research he developed the law of falling bodies and the law of the pendulum.

In general, to change vertex form to standard form, proceed as follows.

$$y - k = a(x - h)^2$$
$$y = a(x - h)^2 + k \qquad \text{Add } k \text{ to each side.}$$
$$y = a(x^2 - 2hx + h^2) + k \qquad \text{Square the binomial}$$
$$y = ax^2 - 2ahx + ah^2 + k \qquad \text{Use the Distributive Property}$$

This is in standard form, with $b = -2ah$ and $c = ah^2 + k$. With these substitutions, the equation becomes

$$y = ax^2 + bx + c.$$

Because the parabola determined by the equation $y - k = a(x - h)^2$ is a translation image of the parabola determined by the equation $y = ax^2$, the two parabolas are congruent.

> **Theorem**
> The graph of the equation $y = ax^2 + bx + c$ is a parabola congruent to the graph of $y = ax^2$.

Recall that any function f with an equation that can be put in the form $f(x) = ax^2 + bx + c$, where $a \neq 0$, is a quadratic function. Thus the graph of every quadratic function is a parabola, with *y*-intercept at $f(0) = c$. Unless otherwise specified, the domain of a quadratic function is the set of real numbers. The range is determined by examining the graph of the function.

The vertex form of a parabola is useful because it provides a quick way to visualize or sketch its graph, and it tells you the axis of symmetry and the vertex of the parabola. The standard form of a parabola is important because it has many applications in the real world, and because it tells you the *y*-intercept of the graph.

Applications of Quadratic Functions

❷ Some applications of quadratic functions have been known for centuries. In the 16th century, Galileo described the motion of objects in free fall using mathematics. In the 17th century, Isaac Newton formulated his laws of motion and the law of universal gravitation. According to these laws, a ball thrown straight up at a velocity of 44 feet per second (30 mph) would go up

$$44t \text{ feet}$$

t seconds after it was released if there were no force acting to pull the ball downward. However, objects in free fall near the surface of the earth are acted upon by a force which he called *gravity* that acts to pull the object downward. After the first t seconds, gravity decreases the height of the ball by $16t^2$ feet. Thus, after t seconds the height h of the ball would be

$$44t - 16t^2 \text{ feet.}$$

Lesson 6-4 Overview, continued

Example 2. The formula $h = -\frac{1}{2}gt^2 + v_0 t + h_0$ gives the height of the ball at a particular time. The graph is *not* congruent to the graph of the path of the ball because the ball loses velocity due to air friction. However, both graphs are parabolas because the loss of speed over time is linear.

Students of UCSMP *Algebra* will have seen applications of projectiles earlier.

Video

Wide World of Mathematics
The segment, *High Diving,* discusses the sport of diving and the effects of height and gravity on the diver. This segment may be used to introduce quadratic functions. Related questions and an investigation are provided in videodisc stills and in the Video Guide. A related CD-ROM activity is also available.

Videodisc Bar Codes

Search Chapter 29

Play

If the ball is released from a point 5 feet above ground level, then the height of the ball above the ground after the first t seconds is

$$44t - 16t^2 + 5 \text{ feet.}$$

Letting h be the height after t seconds, we can write $h = -16t^2 + 44t + 5$. By substituting values for t, the height h can be found after any number of seconds. The pairs (t, h) can be graphed.

Example 2

Suppose $h = -16t^2 + 44t + 5$.
a. Find h when $t = 0, 1, 2,$ and 3.
b. Explain what each pair (t, h) tells you about the height of the ball.
c. Graph the pairs (t, h) over the domain of the function.

Solution

a. At $t = 0$, $h = -16 \cdot 0^2 + 44 \cdot 0 + 5 = 5$
At $t = 1$, $h = -16 \cdot 1^2 + 44 \cdot 1 + 5 = 33$
At $t = 2$, $h = -16 \cdot 2^2 + 44 \cdot 2 + 5 = 29$
At $t = 3$, $h = -16 \cdot 3^2 + 44 \cdot 3 + 5 = -7$

b. The pair $(0, 5)$ means that at 0 seconds, the time of release, the ball is 5 feet above the ground. The pair $(1, 33)$ means the ball is 33 feet high after 1 second. The pair $(2, 29)$ means the ball is 29 feet high after 2 seconds. (It is already on its way down.) The pair $(3, -7)$ means that after 3 seconds, the ball is 7 feet below ground level. Unless the ground is not level, it has already hit the ground.

c. The points in part **a** are plotted below on the left. The points do not tell much about the shape of the graph. More points are needed to show the parabola.

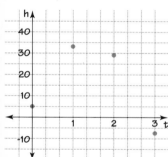
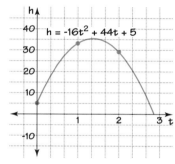

By calculating $h(t)$ for other values of t, or by using an automatic grapher, you can obtain a graph similar to the one above on the right.

In fact, because of the theorem on page 364, we know that, if $h = -16t^2 + 44t + 5$ is graphed for all real numbers t, it is a translation image of the graph of $y = -16x^2$.

Sir Isaac Newton (1642–1727) published his discoveries on the laws of motion and theories of gravitation in 1687 in Philosophiae Naturalis Principia Mathematica. This publication is considered one of the greatest single contributions in the history of science. Queen Anne of Great Britain knighted him in 1705.

Additional Examples

1. Are these two equations equivalent? Why or why not?
   $y = 3(x + 1)^2 - 4$
   $y = 3x^2 + 6x - 1$
   Yes. Samples: $3(x + 1)^2 - 4 = 3(x^2 + 2x + 1) - 4 = 3x^2 + 6x + 3 - 4 = 3x^2 + 6x - 1$. Or graph $y = 3(x + 1)^2 - 4$ and $y = 3x^2 + 6x - 1$ on the same window and notice that the graphs coincide.

2. **a.** From the graph of the equation $h = -16t^2 + 44t + 5$ on page 365, estimate at what time(s) the height of the ball is 20 ft. **Approximately 0.4 and 2.35 seconds after being thrown**
   b. Use the formula to determine the height of the ball one-half second after it was thrown. **23 feet**

3. Suppose a toy rocket is launched so that its height h in meters after t seconds is given by $h = -4.9t^2 + 20t + 1.5$.
   a. How high is the rocket after one second? **16.6 m**
   b. How high is the rocket when launched? **At launching, $t = 0$, so height is 1.5 m.**
   c. How high is the rocket after 12 seconds? **When $t = 12$, $h = -464.1$, so the rocket is no longer in the air. It has returned to the ground.**

(Additional Examples continue on page 366.)

Optional Activities

✎ **Activity 1 Writing**
After students have completed the lesson, have them **work in groups** to discuss the meaning of each term and then write a definition of the term. [Sample responses are given.]
1. Gravity [The force that causes objects to move toward the center of the earth]
2. Parabola [A plane curve formed by all points equally distant from a fixed line and from a fixed point not on that line]

3. Acceleration due to gravity [The rate of change in velocity of a freely falling body, caused by the force of gravity]
4. Quadratic equation [An equation of the form $y = ax^2 + bx + c$; an equation involving a square or squares, but no higher powers of the unknown quantity or quantities]
5. Congruent [Having the same size and shape; two figures in which one is the image of the other under an isometry]

Activity 2 Science Connection
After discussing the lesson, you might have students **work in groups** to find the answer to this problem: As a hose shoots a stream of water in a horizontal direction, a drop of water drips from the nozzle. Which hits the ground first, the stream or the drip? [The only vertical force acting on the stream or the drip is gravity. Both will hit the ground at the same time.]

365

4. Graph $y = x^2 + 2x - 1$ for values of x between -3 and 3. Use the graph to write the vertex form of the equation.

The vertex is (-1, -2) so the vertex form is $y + 2 = (x + 1)^2$.

(Notes on Questions begin on page 368.)

Practice

For more questions on SPUR Objectives, use **Lesson Master 6-4A** (shown on pages 366–367) or **Lesson Master 6-4B** (shown on pages 368–369).

LESSON MASTER **6-4** A

Questions on SPUR Objectives
See pages 413-415 for objectives.

Skills Objective B

In 1–3, write the equation in standard form.

1. $y = 2(x + 5)^2 - 7$ 2. $y + 5 = -2(x - 6)^2$ 3. $y - 3 = \frac{1}{4}(x - 2)^2$
   $y = 2x^2 + 20x + 43$ $y = -2x^2 + 24x - 77$ $y = \frac{1}{4}x^2 - x + 4$

Uses Objective G

4. Suppose a ball is thrown upward from a height of 5 feet with an initial velocity of 30 ft/sec.
   a. Write an equation relating the time t in seconds and the height h of the ball in feet. $h = -16t^2 + 30t + 5$
   b. Find the height of the ball after 1.5 seconds. 14 ft

5. Suppose a ball is dropped from the top of a 79-foot-tall tree.
   a. Write an equation that describes the relationship between h, the height in feet of the ball above the ground, and time t in seconds.
   $h = -16t^2 + 79$
   b. On the grid at the right, graph the height h after t seconds.
   c. Estimate how long it would take the ball to reach the ground. Explain your reasoning.
   Sample: About 2.2 seconds; this is the approximate value of t when $h = 0$.

6. Johanna threw a water balloon upward at a speed of 10m/sec while standing on the roof of a building 12 meters high.
   a. What was the height of the balloon after 2 seconds? 12.4 m
   b. Assume that the balloon did not land on the roof, and estimate how long it took the balloon to reach the ground. ≈ 2.9 sec

---

Two natural questions about the thrown ball are related to questions about this parabola:

1. How high does the ball get? That asks for the largest possible value of h. From the graph, it seems to be about 35 feet.

2. When does the ball hit the ground? That asks for the larger t-intercept of the graph. It is between 2 and 3 seconds, nearer 3.

In later lessons, you will learn how to determine more precise answers to these questions.

The equation in Example 2 is a special case of a general formula for the height h of an object at time t with an initial upward velocity v_0 and initial height h_0 that was discovered by Newton. That formula is

$$h = -\frac{1}{2}gt^2 + v_0t + h_0$$

where g is a constant measuring the **acceleration due to gravity.** Recall that *velocity* is the rate of change of position with respect to time. Velocity is measured in units such as miles per hour, feet per second, or meters per second. Acceleration is a measure of how fast the velocity changes. This "rate of a rate" is measured in units like feet per second per second (or feet per second^2). The acceleration due to gravity varies depending on how close the object is to the center of a massive object. Near the surface of Earth, g is about $32\frac{\text{ft}}{\text{sec}^2}$, or $9.8\frac{\text{m}}{\text{sec}^2}$. In Example 2, $v_0 = 44$ and the height $h_0 = 5$.

Caution! The equation

$$h = -\frac{1}{2}gt^2 + v_0t + h_0$$

represents the height h of the ball off the ground at time t. It *does not* describe the path of the ball. However, the actual path of a ball thrown up into the air at any angle except straight up or straight down is almost parabolic, and an equation for its path is quadratic.

The paths of some objects in free fall can be described with simpler equations. For instance, when a ball is dropped (not thrown downward), its initial velocity is 0. So $v_0 = 0$ in the formula $h = -\frac{1}{2}gt^2 + v_0t + h_0$ and there is one less term. Example 3 illustrates such a situation.

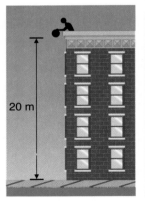

20 m

366

Example 3

A ball is dropped from the top of a 20 meter tall building.
a. Find an equation describing the relation between h, the ball's height above the ground, and time t.
b. Graph its height h after t seconds.
c. Estimate how much time it takes the ball to fall to the ground. Explain your reasoning.

Solution

a. Because the unit of height is meters, use $g = 9.8$ m/sec^2. The ball is dropped, so $v_0 = 0$. Because the ball started 20 meters up, $h_0 = 20$. So the height in this situation is determined by the equation at the top of page 367. ▶

Adapting to Individual Needs

Extra Help

It is important that students understand the exact definition of each variable in the general formula $h = -\frac{1}{2}gt^2 + v_0t + h_0$. List the variables on the chalkboard with a written identification of each. Stress that the subscript 0, as used in v_0 and h_0, indicates a condition at time 0, an initial state or condition—in this case, the initial velocity and the initial height.

English Language Development

Many of the applications in this lesson use context clues to indicate that the problem involves the formula for projectile motion. You might want to help students with limited English proficiency identify contexts that are applications of that formula, such as juggling, hitting a baseball, free fall, and projectiles.

$$h = -\frac{1}{2}(9.8)t^2 + (0)t + 20$$

This equation is equivalent to $h = -4.9t^2 + 20$.

b. Negative values of t are not in the domain of t because a negative value of t would refer to something that had happened before the ball is dropped. Thus, the graph is entirely to the right of the y-axis. Negative values of h are not in the range because the ball is never below the ground, so the graph is entirely above the x-axis.

t	$h = -4.9t^2 + 20$
0	20
0.5	18.775
1	15.1
1.5	8.975
2	0.4
2.5	-10.625

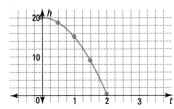

c. At $t = 2$ the ball is 0.4 m above the ground; at $t = 2.5$, according to the equation, the ball will be about 10.6 m below ground. Therefore, the ball hits the ground between 2 and 2.5 seconds after the ball is dropped.

Notice in Example 3 that the curve becomes steeper and steeper as t increases from 0 to 2. This reflects the increasing speed of the ball as it falls.

QUESTIONS

Covering the Reading

1. Give the standard form for the equation of a parabola.
$y = ax^2 + bx + c$
In 2 and 3, rewrite the equation in standard form.

2. $y = (x + 6)^2$
$y = x^2 + 12x + 36$

3. $y = -2(x + 3)^2 + 4$
$y = -2x^2 - 12x - 14$

4. *True or false.* For any values of a, b, and c, the graph of $y = ax^2$ is congruent to the graph of $y = ax^2 + bx + c$. **True**

In 5–7, use the equation $h = -\frac{1}{2}gt^2 + v_0t + h_0$ for the motion of a body in free fall.

5a) height above ground at time t
b) initial height
c) initial velocity
d) time
e) the constant measuring acceleration due to gravity

5. Give the meaning of each of the following variables. **See left.**
   a. h **b.** h_0 **c.** v_0 **d.** t **e.** g

6. If v_0 is measured in meters per second, what value of g should be used? **9.8 m/sec^2**

7. What is the value of v_0 if a ball is dropped? **0**

In 8–10, refer to the graph of Example 2.

8. About how high is the ball after 2.5 seconds? **15 ft**

9. When the ball hits the ground, the value of h is __?__. **0**

Lesson 6-4 *Graphing* $y = ax^2 + bx + c$ **367**

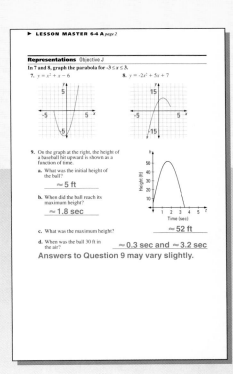

368

Notes on Questions

Question 16 If students have difficulty writing the equation for **part a**, remind them of the meaning of the constants in the height formula. In this case v_0, the initial velocity, is 10 m/sec and h_0, the initial height, is 1 m. **Part d** can be answered by numerical or graphical techniques.

Question 17 If students have difficulty writing the equation for **part a**, remind them of the meaning of the constants in the height formula. In this case v_0, the initial velocity, is 0 and h_0, the initial height, is 6700 m. In **part c**, to solve the equation for t, students can use the fact that the value of h, upon landing, is zero.

Additional Answers

13.

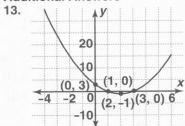

14.

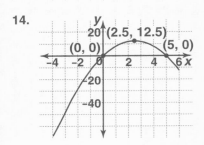

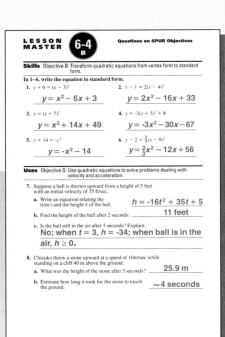

10. About when will the ball in Example 2 be 10 feet from the ground? (There are two answers.) $t \approx 0.12$ sec or $t \approx 2.63$ sec

In 11 and 12, refer to Example 3.

11. What point corresponds to the time the ball is dropped? (0, 20)

12. Tell whether the ball is above or below ground at $t = 2.1$. Justify your answer.
It is below ground at $t = 2.1$ because $(-4.9)(2.1)^2 + 20 = -1.609$.

Applying the Mathematics

In 13 and 14, graph the given equation for $-4 \le x \le 6$. On your sketch of the graph, label the vertex and the x- and y-intercepts. See margin.

13. $y = x^2 - 4x + 3$ **14.** $y = -2x^2 + 10x$

15. Consider the function defined by the equation $f(x) = x^2 - 5x - 6$.
 a. Sketch the graph of the function. See margin.
 b. Give an equation for the line of symmetry of the graph. $x = 2.5$
 c. Estimate the coordinates of the lowest point on the graph. (2.5, -12.25)

16. Suppose a juggler throws an object from his hand at a height of 1 meter with an initial upward velocity of 10 meters per second.
 a. Write an equation to describe the height of the object after t seconds. $h = -4.9t^2 + 10t + 1$
 b. How high is the object after 1 second? 6.1 meters
 c. Graph the equation from part **a**. See margin.
 d. Estimate the maximum height the object reaches. about 6.1 meters

17. I.M. Chisov of the USSR set a record in January 1942 for the highest altitude from which someone survived after bailing out of an airplane without a parachute. He bailed out at about 6700 meters.
 a. Write an equation describing his height at t seconds. $h = -4.9t^2 + 6700$
 b. Graph the equation in part **a**. See margin.
 c. About how long did his fall take? ≈ 37 seconds

18. Consider the parabolas with equations $y = \frac{1}{2}x^2 + \frac{x}{2}$ and $y = \frac{1}{2}(x + 1)^2$.
 a. Are the parabolas congruent? Why or why not? See below.
 b. Do the parabolas coincide? Why or why not? See below.

19. Find an equation in standard form for the image of the graph of $y = -.5x^2$ under the translation $T_{-2,4}$. $y = -.5x^2 - 2x + 2$

Review

In 20 and 21, **a.** Draw the graph of both equations on the same set of axes. **b.** Describe in a sentence or two how the graphs are related. *(Lessons 6-1, 6-3)*

20. $y = x^2$ and $y = (x - 2)^2$ See margin.

21. $y = |x|$ and $y + 4 = |x - 5|$ See margin.

18a) Yes, they are both congruent to $y = \frac{1}{2}x^2$.
 b) No, the point (0, 0) is on $y = \frac{1}{2}x^2 + \frac{1}{2}x$ and is not on $y = \frac{1}{2}(x + 1)^2$.

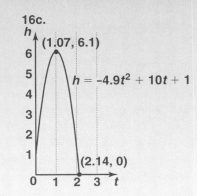

Up in the air. *Juggling is throwing and catching more than one object in one hand, or three or more objects in two hands. Juggling helps to develop hand-eye coordination and is often taught in elementary school.*

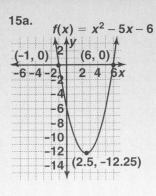

15a.
$f(x) = x^2 - 5x - 6$
(-1, 0)   (6, 0)
(2.5, -12.25)

16c.
h
(1.07, 6.1)
$h = -4.9t^2 + 10t + 1$
(2.14, 0)

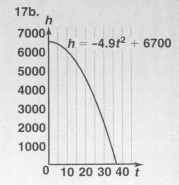

17b.
h
$h = -4.9t^2 + 6700$

22. A half-gallon of paint is supposed to cover an area of 450 square feet. Find the diameter of the largest circle that can be painted with this paint. *(Lesson 6-2)* ≈ **23.94 ft**

23. A mat w inches wide is to surround a picture that is 8″ by 12″. A thin frame surrounds the mat.
 a. What is the area of the picture with its mat? **96 + 40w + 4w² sq in.**
 b. What is the inner perimeter of the frame surrounding the mat?
  (Lesson 6-1) **40 + 8w in.**

24a) 0.5 b) 0.5
c) −0.5 d) 0.25
e) −0.25 f) 0.25
g) 0.5 h) −0.5

24. Evaluate when $x = -0.5$. *(Lessons 1-2, 6-1, 6-2)* **See left.**
 a. $|x|$ **b.** $|-x|$ **c.** $-|x|$ **d.** x^2
 e. $-x^2$ **f.** $(-x)^2$ **g.** $\sqrt{x^2}$ **h.** $-\sqrt{x^2}$

25. Solve for a: $x^2 + 24x + 144 = (x + a)^2$. *(Lesson 6-1)*
 a = 12

26. Given the feasible region at the right, find the vertex at which $80x + 120y = P$ is maximized. *(Lesson 5-9)* **(15, 30)**

27. The table below gives the book value of a 1986 Chevrolet S-10 pickup truck from the year of its purchase until 1993.

Year	1987	1988	1990	1993
Value	5825	5450	4225	3425

a) $y \approx -411x + 823{,}031$
b) $\approx \$2675$

 a. Find an equation for the line of best fit for the data.
 b. Use the equation to predict the value of a 1986 S-10 pickup in 1996.
 c. Why is it not a good idea to use this equation to predict the value of the truck in the year 2006? *(Lesson 3-8)* **The truck does not continue to depreciate in value at the same rate. In this case, one gets a negative value for the truck in year 2006 if the line of best fit is used.**

Exploration

28. Draw a dot and a line on a large piece of plain paper. Now fold the paper so that the dot falls on a point of the line. Then unfold the paper. Do this 25 times, each time with a different point on the line, and describe what happens. **The creases in the paper are all tangents to the same parabola, and together they outline it.**

Lesson 6-4 *Graphing* $y = ax^2 + bx + c$ **369**

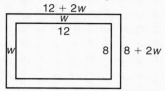
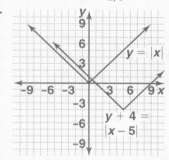
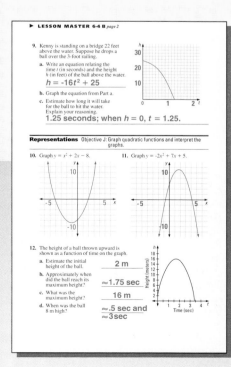
20a.

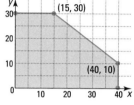

$y = x^2$ $y = (x - 2)^2$

369

Objectives

B Transform quadratic equations from standard form to vertex form.

Resources

From the Teacher's Resource File
- Lesson Master 6-5A or 6-5B
- Answer Master 6-5
- Teaching Aids
  8 Four-Quadrant Graph Paper
  19 Automatic Grapher Grids
  54 Warm-up
- Technology Sourcebook
  Computer Master 9

Additional Resources
- Visuals for Teaching Aids 8, 19, 54
- Symbol Manipulator

Teaching **6-5**
Lesson

Warm-up

For each figure,
a. write a binomial to represent the total area of regions I, II, and III.
b. give the area of the shaded region.
c. give the total area of the figure.

1.   **2.**

1. $x^2 + 8x$; 16; $x^2 + 8x + 16$
2. $9x^2 + 30x$; 25; $9x^2 + 30x + 25$

LESSON 6-5

Completing the Square

You have now seen two forms for an equation of a parabola.

$$y = ax^2 + bx + c \qquad \text{standard form}$$
$$y - k = a(x - h)^2 \qquad \text{vertex form}$$

Because each form is useful, converting from one form to the other is helpful. Lesson 6-4 covered how to convert from vertex form to standard form. In this lesson, you will learn to convert from standard form to vertex form.

Completing the Square Geometrically

One method for converting from standard form to vertex form is called *completing the square*. Remember that $(x + h)^2 = x^2 + 2hx + h^2$. The trinomial $x^2 + 2hx + h^2$ is called a **perfect-square trinomial** because it is the square of a binomial. You can picture the equation

$$(x + h)^2 = x^2 + 2hx + h^2$$

as shown below.

	x	h	
h	hx	h^2	
x	x^2	hx	

$(x + h)^2 = x^2 + 2hx + h^2$

Lesson 6-5 Overview

Broad Goals In this lesson, students convert quadratic expressions from standard form to vertex form so they can determine the vertex of the graph of a parabola.

Perspective A first reason for the technique called *completing the square* is to find the vertex of a parabola whose equation is in standard form, as shown in **Example 2.** Now, with knowledge of the exact vertex, students can graph a parabola more

accurately, and certain maximum or minimum problems can be solved (see **Questions 11–12**).

A second reason for completing the square is to derive the Quadratic Formula, which is done in Lesson 6-7. A third reason is to find key points on graphs of circles and other quadratic relations. These topics will be covered later in this course.

Solving specific quadratic equations by completing the square is not an objective either in this book or in UCSMP *Algebra*. The Quadratic Formula is the general theorem. It would be a poor use of algebraic proof to derive individual cases again and again as if the general theorem did not exist. This is analogous to proving the Pythagorean Theorem each time we wanted to find the distance between two points in the plane.

What number should be added to $x^2 + 10x$ to make a perfect-square trinomial?

Solution 1

Draw a picture to represent $x^2 + 10x$.

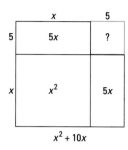

$$x^2 + 10x$$

Think: What is the area of the missing square in the upper right corner that allows you to complete the larger square? (This is the reason this process is called "completing the square.") A square with area 25 would complete the larger square. So, 25 must be added to $x^2 + 10x$ to make a perfect square.

Solution 2

Compare $x^2 + 10x + \underline{\ ?\ }$ with the perfect-square trinomial $x^2 + 2hx + h^2$. The first terms, x^2, are identical. To make the second terms equal, set

$$10x = 2hx.$$

So

$$h = 5.$$

The term added should be h^2 or 25.

Check

Apply the Binomial Square Theorem: $(x + 5)^2 = x^2 + 10x + 25$.

To generalize Example 1, consider the expression

$$x^2 + bx + \underline{\ ?\ }.$$

What must be put in the blank so the result is a perfect-square trinomial?

$$x^2 + bx + \underline{\ ?\ } = x^2 + 2hx + h^2$$

Because $b = 2h$, $h = \frac{1}{2}b$. Then $h^2 = \left(\frac{1}{2}b\right)^2$. This proves the following theorem.

Theorem

To complete the square on $x^2 + bx$, add $\left(\frac{1}{2}b\right)^2$.

$$x^2 + bx + \left(\frac{1}{2}b\right)^2 = \left(x + \frac{1}{2}b\right)^2 = \left(x + \frac{b}{2}\right)^2$$

Lesson 6-5   *Completing the Square*   **371**

Notes on Reading

Students will use graph paper, **Teaching Aid 8,** or **Teaching Aid 19** throughout this lesson.

❶ You might begin this lesson by having students guess the number that needs to be added to expressions such as $x^2 + 8x$, $x^2 - 2x$, or $x^2 + 30x$ to make a perfect square. [$x^2 + 8x + 16$, $x^2 - 2x + 1$, $x^2 + 30x + 225$] Ask students if they see a pattern. If so, have them verbalize the pattern by giving the term needed to complete $x^2 + 7x$. [$\frac{49}{4}$]

The odd-number coefficient of 7 will force students to isolate the steps in the method they use to find the term $\left(\frac{b}{2}\right)^2$.

Optional Activities

Activity 1 Here is an alternate algorithm for writing a quadratic equation in vertex form. You might use this activity after you discuss **Example 3.**
Consider $y = 5x^2 - 150x + 1185$.
1. Rewrite the equation so that the right side contains only terms with the variable x: $y - 1185 = 5x^2 - 150x$.

2. Use the Distributive Property to rewrite the right-hand side so x^2 appears in an expression with a coefficient of 1: $y - 1185 = 5(x^2 - 30x)$.
3. Complete the square of the expression in parentheses.
   a. Rewrite the equation as
   $y - 1185 + \underline{\ } = 5(x^2 - 30x + \underline{\ })$
   b. To fill in the blank on the right side, find $(\frac{1}{2}b)^2$, which in this case is 225.

c. Write 225 in the blank on the right side. Note that $5 \cdot 225$ is actually being added to the right side, so add 1125 to the left side. Now the equation is:
$y - 1185 + 1125 = 5(x^2 - 30x + 225)$.
4. Simplify the left side and write the right side as the square of a binomial.
$y - 60 = 5(x - 15)^2$

Additional Examples

1. What number should be added to $x^2 + 5x$ to make a perfect-square trinomial? $\frac{25}{4}$

2. Rewrite each equation in vertex form. Then identify the vertex of the parabola.
   a. $y = x^2 + 18x + 90$
   $y - 9 = (x + 9)^2$; (-9, 9)
   b. $y = x^2 - 11x + 4$
   $y + \frac{105}{4} = (x - \frac{11}{2})^2$;
   $(\frac{11}{2}, -\frac{105}{4})$
   c. $y = 3x^2 - 12x + 1$
   $y + 11 = 3(x - 2)^2$; (2, -11)
   d. $y = -5x^2 + 4x - 3$
   $y + \frac{11}{5} = -5(x - \frac{2}{5})^2$; $(\frac{2}{5}, -\frac{11}{5})$

3. Suppose a ball is thrown straight up from a height of 4 feet with an initial velocity of 50 feet per second. What is the maximum height of the ball? $\approx$ **43 feet**

(Notes on Questions begin on page 374.)

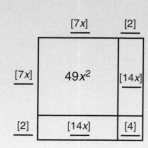

A toss up. *Shown is Lindsey Davenport at the 1994 U.S. Open. In a tennis serve, the player throws the ball straight up before hitting it.*

372

The theorem on page 371 can be used to transform an equation of a parabola from standard form into vertex form.

Example 2

a. Rewrite the equation $y = x^2 + 10x + 8$ in vertex form.
b. Locate the vertex of the parabola.

Solution

a. Rewrite the equation so that only terms with x are on one side.

$$y - 8 = x^2 + 10x + \underline{\ ?\ }$$

Here $b = 10$, so $\left(\frac{1}{2}b\right)^2 = 25$.   Complete the square on x.

$$y - 8 + 25 = x^2 + 10x + 25$$ Add 25 to both sides.
$$y + 17 = x^2 + 10x + 25$$ Simplify the left side.
$$y + 17 = (x + 5)^2$$ Apply the Binomial Square Theorem.

b. The vertex of the parabola is (-5, -17).

Check 1

Use an automatic grapher. Draw graphs of $y = x^2 + 10x + 8$ and $y = (x + 5)^2 - 17$ on the same set of axes. They appear to be identical. Tracing verifies that the vertex is near (-5, -17).

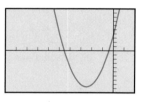

$-20 \leq x \leq 4$, x-scale = 2
$-20 \leq y \leq 20$, y-scale = 2

Check 2

To check the vertex, try x-values on either side of -5. When $x = -4$, $y = -16$ and when $x = -6$, $y = -16$. Because those values are equal, and because of the symmetry of the parabola, the vertex must be midway between $x = -4$ and $x = -6$.

Example 2 involves a parabola in which the coefficient of x^2 is 1. Example 3 shows how to complete the square on a quadratic expression if the coefficient of x^2 is not 1. This kind of expression occurs in describing paths of projectiles.

Example 3

Suppose a ball is thrown straight up from a height of 5 ft with an initial velocity of 60 ft/sec. The height h after t seconds is given by the equation

$$h = -16t^2 + 60t + 5.$$

Find the maximum height of the ball.

▶

	[7x]	[2]
[7x]	$49x^2$	[14x]
[2]	[14x]	[4]

Solution

We need to find the vertex of the parabola that describes the height. Subtract 5 from each side to remove the constant from the right side.

$$h - 5 = -16t^2 + 60t$$

Divide each side by -16, the coefficient of t^2.

$$\frac{h-5}{-16} = t^2 - \frac{15}{4}t$$

Now we can complete the square on the right side. Here $b = -\frac{15}{4}$. So

$$\left(\frac{b}{2}\right)^2 = \left(\frac{-15}{8}\right)^2 = \frac{225}{64}.$$

Add $\frac{225}{64}$ to each side. $\quad \frac{h-5}{-16} + \frac{225}{64} = t^2 - \frac{5}{4}t + \frac{225}{64}$

Rewrite the perfect-square trinomial as the square of a binomial.

$$\frac{h-5}{-16} + \frac{225}{64} = \left(t - \frac{15}{8}\right)^2$$

Thus the maximum height occurs when $t = \frac{15}{8}$. To put the equation in vertex form, multiply each side by -16, the original coefficient of t^2.

$$h - 5 - \frac{225}{4} = -16\left(t - \frac{15}{8}\right)^2$$

Simplify the left side. $\quad h - \frac{245}{4} = -16\left(t - \frac{15}{8}\right)^2.$

The vertex of this parabola is $\left(\frac{15}{8}, \frac{245}{4}\right)$. *So the maximum height of the ball is $\frac{245}{4} = 61.25$ feet.*

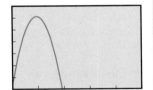

$0 \le x \le 10, \quad x\text{-scale} = 2$
$0 \le y \le 70, \quad y\text{-scale} = 10$

Check 1

Graph $y = -16x^2 + 60x + 5$. Trace to locate the vertex. Using the window at the left, our grapher shows the vertex to be between the points (1.80, 61.1) and (1.89, 61.2) on the curve. It checks.

Check 2

Make a table. We checked values of x from 1.80 to 1.90 in the table below. The values are symmetric to $x = 1.875$. So the axis of symmetry must be $x = 1.875$, and hence the vertex is (1.875, 61.25). It checks.

x	$y = -16x^2 + 60x + 5$
1.80	61.16
1.81	61.1824
1.82	61.2016
1.83	61.2176
1.84	61.2304
1.85	61.24
1.86	61.2464
1.87	61.2496
1.88	61.2496
1.89	61.2464
1.90	61.24

Lesson 6-5 *Completing the Square* **373**

Adapting to Individual Needs

English Language Development
Students with limited English proficiency may be confused by the geometric and the algebraic uses of the word *square.* You may want to point out how the two meanings are interrelated by drawing a square on the board and noting that all sides are the same length. Then use **Example 1** to relate this idea to *completing the square* and making a *perfect-square trinomial.*

Follow-up for Lesson **6-5**

Practice

For more questions on SPUR Objectives, use **Lesson Master 6-5A** (shown on page 373) or **Lesson Master 6-5B** (shown on pages 374–375).

Assessment

Oral/Written Communication Have students **work in pairs.** First have one student write a binomial of the form $ax^2 + bx$, $a \ne 1$. Then have the other student add an expression to complete the square and write the resulting trinomial as the square of a binomial. [Students demonstrate that they can complete the square for binomials of the form $ax^2 + bx$, $a \ne 1$, and write the result as the square of a binomial.]

Extension

Question 22 can be extended by having students substitute numbers for a, b, and c and expand expressions such as $(3x - 4y + 5)^2$.
$[(3x - 4y + 5)^2 = 9x^2 + 16y^2 + 25 - 24xy + 30x - 40y]$

Project Update Project 5, *History of Quadratics*, on page 409, relates to the content of this lesson.

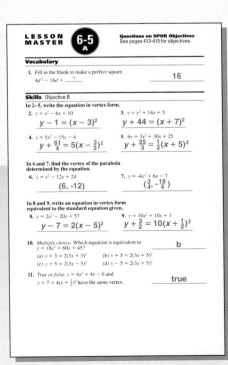

LESSON MASTER 6-5 A

Questions on SPUR Objectives
See pages 413-415 for objectives.

Vocabulary

1. Fill in the blank to make a perfect square.
$4d^2 - 16d + \underline{\quad ? \quad}$ **16**

Skills Objective B

In 2–5, write the equation in vertex form.

2. $y = x^2 - 6x + 10$
$\quad y - 1 = (x - 3)^2$

3. $y = x^2 + 14x + 5$
$\quad y + 44 = (x + 7)^2$

4. $y = 5x^2 - 15x - 4$
$\quad y + \frac{61}{4} = 5\left(x - \frac{3}{2}\right)^2$

5. $6y = 3x^2 + 30x + 25$
$\quad y + \frac{25}{3} = \frac{1}{2}(x + 5)^2$

In 6 and 7, find the vertex of the parabola determined by the equation.

6. $y = x^2 - 12x + 24$
$\quad (6, -12)$

7. $y = -4x^2 + 6x - 7$
$\quad \left(\frac{3}{4}, -\frac{19}{4}\right)$

In 8 and 9, write an equation in vertex form equivalent to the standard equation given.

8. $y = 2x^2 - 20x + 57$
$\quad y - 7 = 2(x - 5)^2$

9. $y = 10x^2 + 10x + 1$
$\quad y + \frac{3}{2} = 10\left(x + \frac{1}{2}\right)^2$

10. *Multiple choice.* Which equation is equivalent to $y = 18x^2 + 60x + 45$?   **b**
(a) $y + 3 = 2(3x + 3)^2$ (b) $y + 5 = 2(3x + 5)^2$
(c) $y + 5 = 2(3x - 5)^2$ (d) $y - 5 = 2(3x + 5)^2$

11. *True or false.* $y = 4x^2 + 4x - 6$ and $y + 7 = 4(x + \frac{1}{2})^2$ have the same vertex.   **true**

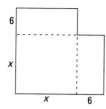

1b) 36

c) In the diagram we need to put in a missing square of side 6 (area 36) to complete the larger square.

7a) $y + 75 = (x + 9)^2$
b) $(-9, -75)$

8a) $y - 1 = (x - 2)^2$
b) $(2, 1)$

9a) $y + 5 = 4(x + 8)^2$
b) $(-8, -5)$

10a) $y - 5 = -2(x + 3)^2$
b) $(-3, 5)$

Completing the square helps to find key points on graphs involving quadratic expressions. But perhaps its most important application is in the proof of the *Quadratic Formula,* which you shall study in Lesson 6-7.

QUESTIONS

Covering the Reading

1. **a.** Give the sum of the areas of the three rectangles at the left. $x^2 + 12x$
   b. What number must be added to this sum to complete the square?
   c. Interpret your answer to part **b** geometrically. **b, c) See left.**

In 2–5, find a number to write in the blank to make the expression a perfect square trinomial.

2. $x^2 + 18x + \underline{\ ?\ }$ 81
3. $x^2 - 6x + \underline{\ ?\ }$ 9
4. $z^2 - 3z + \underline{\ ?\ }$ $\frac{9}{4}$
5. $x^2 + bx + \underline{\ ?\ }$ $\frac{b^2}{4}$

6. Find an equation in vertex form equivalent to $y = x^2 + 40x + 10$.
   $y + 390 = (x + 20)^2$

In 7–10, an equation in standard form is given. **a.** Rewrite the equation in vertex form. **b.** Find the vertex of the parabola represented by each equation. **See left.**

7. $y = x^2 + 18x + 6$
8. $y = x^2 - 4x + 5$
9. $y = 4x^2 + 64x + 251$
10. $y = -2x^2 - 12x - 13$

11. **a.** Find the vertex of the parabola $h = -16t^2 + 44t + 5$ graphed in Lesson 6-4. $\left(\frac{11}{8}, \frac{141}{4}\right)$
    b. Write a sentence describing what the vertex tells you about the height of the ball. **The maximum height of the ball is $\frac{141}{4}$ = 35.25 ft which occurs after $\frac{11}{8}$ seconds.**

Applying the Mathematics

12c)

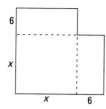

12. Suppose a ball is thrown straight up from a height of 4 ft with an initial upward velocity of 22 ft/sec.
    a. Write an equation to describe the height h of the ball after t seconds. $h = -16t^2 + 22t + 4$
    b. How high is the ball after 1 second? **10 ft**
    c. Graph your equation from part **a.** **See left.**
    d. Determine the maximum height attained by the ball by completing the square. $h - \frac{185}{16} = -16\left(t - \frac{11}{16}\right)^2$; $h \approx 11.56$

13. Suppose $f(x) = 3x^2 + 12x + 16$.
    a. What is the domain of f? **the set of all real numbers**
    b. What is the vertex of its graph? **$(-2, 4)$**
    c. What is the range of f? **$\{y: y \geq 4\}$**

14. What term must be added to the expression $x^2 + \frac{b}{a}x + \underline{\ ?\ }$ to make a perfect square trinomial? $\frac{b^2}{4a^2}$

374

Adapting to Individual Needs

Challenge
Have students prove that the vertex of the parabola $y = ax^2 + bx + c$ is (h, k) where $h = \frac{-b}{2a}$ and $k = \frac{4ac - b^2}{4a}$. (If they need a hint, have them substitute the values given above in the equation $y - k = a(x - h)^2$, and show that this simplifies to $y = ax^2 + bx + c$.)

[Sample proof:
$$y - k = a(x - h)^2$$
$$y - \frac{4ac - b^2}{4a} = a\left(x - \frac{-b}{2a}\right)^2$$
$$y = a\left(x + \frac{b}{2a}\right)^2 + \frac{4ac - b^2}{4a}$$
$$= a\left(x^2 + \frac{b}{a}x + \frac{b^2}{4a^2}\right) + \frac{4ac - b^2}{4a}$$
$$= ax^2 + bx + \frac{b^2}{4a} + \frac{4ac - b^2}{4a}$$
$$= ax^2 + bx + \frac{4ac}{4a} = ax^2 + bx + c]$$

15. The KTHI-TV transmitting tower between Fargo and Blanchard, North Dakota is about 629 meters tall.
  a. If a tennis ball were dropped from the top, what would its height be after t seconds? $h = -4.9t^2 + 629$
  b. In about how many seconds would it hit the ground? *(Lesson 6-4)* **about 11.3 seconds**

16. A student stated that $x^2 - 6x + 9 = (x - 3)^2$. Another student stated that $x^2 - 6x + 9 = (3 - x)^2$. Who is right? Justify your answer. *(Lessons 6-1, 6-4)* **They are both right, because $(x - 3)^2 =$ $[-1(3 - x)]^2 = (-1)^2 (3 - x)^2 = (3 - x)^2$.**

17. Consider the function with equation $\frac{y}{6} = \left(x + \frac{1}{2}\right)^2$.
  a. Convert the equation to standard form. $y = 6x^2 + 6x + \frac{3}{2}$
  b. Graph the function. **See left.**
  c. What is the y-intercept of the graph? *(Lessons 6-3, 6-4)* $\left(0, 1\frac{1}{2}\right)$

17b)

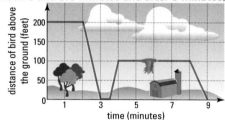

18. Find an equation for the image of the graph of $y = (x + 1)^2$ under the translation $T_{4,0}$. *(Lesson 6-3)* $y = (x - 3)^2$

19. Solve $y^2 = 20$. *(Lesson 6-2)* $y = \pm\sqrt{20} \approx \pm4.47$

20. Refer to the graph of a bird's flight shown below. *(Lessons 1-4, 2-4, 3-1)*
  a. When was the bird on the ground?
  b. What was the bird's average speed during its first descent?
  a) between 3 and 3.5 minutes and after 9 minutes; b) 200 ft/min

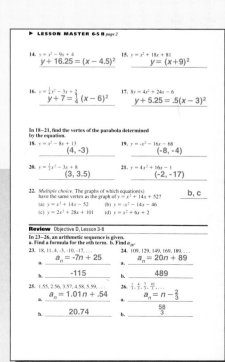

distance of bird above the ground (feet) vs. time (minutes)

21. Simplify $\dfrac{-11 + \sqrt{121 - 96}}{6}$. *(Previous course)* **-1**

Exploration

22. *PONM* is a square of sides $a + b + c$. The areas of three regions inside have been given.
  a. Find the areas of the other six rectangles.
  b. Use the drawing to expand $(a + b + c)^2$. $a^2 + b^2 + c^2 + 2ab + 2ac + 2bc$
  c. Show a drawing to expand $(a + b + c + d)^2$. **See left.**

	P		O
c	ac	bc	c^2
b	ab	b^2	bc
a	a^2	ab	ac
	M a	b	c N

22c)

	a	b	c	d
a	a^2	ab	ac	ad
b	ab	b^2	bc	bd
c	ac	bc	c^2	cd
d	ad	bd	cd	d^2

$(a + b + c + d)^2 = a^2 + b^2 + c^2 + d^2 + 2ab + 2ac + 2ad + 2bc + 2bd + 2cd$

Lesson 6-5 *Completing the Square* **375**

Notes on Questions

Question 15 Multicultural Connection Tribes of Plains Indians, especially the Mandan and the Hidatsa, lived in North Dakota before European settlers came to the region. The earliest white settlers included Norwegians and Germans. Today the Sioux, Ojibwa, Arikara, Hidatsa, and Mandan Indians continue to maintain their folk traditions, and the Norwegian language is taught at the University of North Dakota.

Question 20 Technology Connection Graphs are natural aids in analyses of data of these types. Signal-sending transmitters have been attached to birds to collect data like these (but more complicated), and computers analyze the data from the signals. The same idea is used with airplanes and space vehicles.

Question 21 This question reviews order of operations with an expression like the ones students will encounter when applying the Quadratic Formula in Lesson 6-7.

Objectives

H Fit a quadratic model to data.

Resources

From the Teacher's Resource File
- Lesson Master 6-6A or 6-6B
- Answer Master 6-6
- Teaching Aids
   8 Four-Quadrant Graph Paper
   19 Automatic Grapher Grids
   54 Warm-up
- Activity Kit, Activity 12
- Technology Sourcebook
   Computer Master 10

Additional Resources
- Visuals for Teaching Aids 8, 19, 54
- StatExplorer

Teaching Lesson **6-6**

Warm-up

Solve the system.

$$\begin{cases} 17 = 2a + 3b + c \\ 15 = 4a + b + c \\ 16 = 3a + 2b + c \end{cases}$$

$a = 3$, $b = 4$, $c = -1$

Notes on Reading

Students will need graph paper, **Teaching Aid 8**, or **Teaching Aid 19** throughout this lesson.

❶ **Example 1** uses the relationship between the numbers of sides and diagonals of a polygon—a relationship that we expect students have seen before. The purpose of this example is to exhibit the method of

---

Fitting a Quadratic Model to Data

Using diagonals. *Sticks placed along the diagonals of a kite provide its support. Kites are the oldest form of aircraft, probably originating in China almost 3000 years ago.*

In Chapter 3, you studied how to find an equation for the line through two points, and how to find a linear model for data that lie approximately on a straight line. In this lesson you will learn how to find an equation for a parabola that passes through three points. You will apply the techniques of solving systems of equations you learned in the last chapter.

An Example from Geometry

Some students could not remember the formula for the number of diagonals in a polygon. So, they decided to try to rediscover it. They drew some polygons and their diagonals. In the figures below, n is the number of sides and d is the number of diagonals.

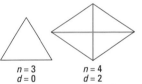

$n = 3$	$n = 4$	$n = 5$	$n = 6$	$n = 7$
$d = 0$	$d = 2$	$d = 5$	$d = 9$	$d = 14$

Using n as the independent variable, they plotted the ordered pairs (n, d) to get the graph at the right. From the graph they could see that the points do not lie on a line. The points look as if they might lie on a parabola. So they decided to see if a *quadratic model* would fit these data.

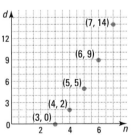

Lesson 6-6 Overview

Broad Goals This lesson gives examples of data that can be described either exactly or approximately by quadratic functions.

Perspective Some kinds of data fit a quadratic model. Three kinds are found in this chapter: area situations, motion situations involving acceleration and deceleration, and counting connections.

There is exactly one quadratic function $f: x \rightarrow ax^2 + bx + c$ through three non-collinear points. If more than three points are given, one must choose which three points to use. This is directly analogous to the fitting of a linear function to data, as found in Lesson 3-6. The method used in the Examples of this lesson to find the values of a, b, and c is to solve a system of three linear equations in three variables.

Another way to find a quadratic model is to use quadratic regression, a feature on many automatic graphers. This method is suggested on page 379 in the student edition.

Show that the ordered pairs graphed on page 376 satisfy an equation of the form

$$d = an^2 + bn + c.$$

Solution

Because the ordered pairs (n, d) are solutions of the equation $d = an^2 + bn + c$, they can be substituted to produce equations with a, b, and c. To find the three numbers, three equations must be used. Substitute the first three data points to get the system below.

When $n = 3$, $d = 0$: $0 = a(3)^2 + b(3) + c$.
When $n = 4$, $d = 2$: $2 = a(4)^2 + b(4) + c$.
When $n = 5$, $d = 5$: $5 = a(5)^2 + b(5) + c$.

So a, b, and c are solutions to the following system.

$$\begin{cases} 0 = 9a + 3b + c \\ 2 = 16a + 4b + c \\ 5 = 25a + 5b + c \end{cases}$$

This 3-by-3 system can be solved using linear combinations, substitution, or matrices. We use linear combinations. Subtract each equation from the one below it to eliminate c. This results in the 2-by-2 system below.

$$\begin{cases} 2 = 7a + b \\ 3 = 9a + b \end{cases}$$

Solve the 2-by-2 system by subtracting the top equation from the one below it to solve for a.

$$1 = 2a \quad \Rightarrow \quad a = \frac{1}{2}$$

Substitute $\frac{1}{2}$ for a in the top equation of the 2-by-2 system to find b.

$$2 = 7\left(\frac{1}{2}\right) + b \quad \Rightarrow \quad b = -\frac{3}{2}$$

Substitute $\frac{1}{2}$ for a and $-\frac{3}{2}$ for b into $0 = 9a + 3b + c$ to get

$0 = 9\left(\frac{1}{2}\right) + 3\left(-\frac{3}{2}\right) + c$. Thus, $c = 0$. So, a quadratic equation which models the students' data is $d = \frac{1}{2}n^2 - \frac{3}{2}n$.

Check

Compare the actual number of diagonals with the number of diagonals predicted by the formula.

n	d (actual)	$d = \frac{1}{2}n^2 - \frac{3}{2}n$ (predicted)
3	0	0
4	2	2
5	5	5
6	9	9
7	14	14

The predicted and actual values for d are the same. The model here turns out to be exact.

solving a 3 × 3 system to find the coefficients of the quadratic that fits the data.

Because the relationship between sides and diagonals is exact, any three points on the parabola could be selected to obtain the three equations of the system. However, in order to obtain a system in which successive subtractions enable one to find one of the variables, the three domain values must form an arithmetic sequence. This is why the values 3, 4, and 5, chosen in the solution to **Example 1**, work so well.

History Connection The fitting of a quadratic relation to a set of points is a significant event in the history of mathematics and statistics. Shortly after the first asteroid, Ceres, was discovered in 1801 by Giuseppe Piazzi, it could not be found in the night skies. Five points determine an ellipse in space. Based on the assumption that it went around the sun, the orbit of Ceres had to be an ellipse (with suitable adjustments for the gravities of bodies near it). It was determined that Ceres had been seen and noted by others. Through these observations, more than five data points became available, but these did not give precisely the same orbit. Gauss, the greatest mathematician of his time, tackled the problem of how to calculate the best estimate to the real orbit of Ceres. In the process, he discovered the normal distribution that is often called by his name.

377

378

② **Example 2** uses a relationship from physics. It is not exact, so the model will be slightly different, depending on which points are used. This situation is analogous to the situation for linear regression in Lesson 3-6. Quadratic regression will give a *quadratic of best fit*. This is analogous to the line of best fit discussed in Lesson 3-6.

Additional Examples

1. The number *h* of handshakes needed for everyone in a group of *n* people, $n \geq 2$, to shake the hands of every other person is a quadratic function of *n*. Find three points of the function relating *h* and *n*. Use these points to find a formula for this function. When $n = 2$, $h = 1$; when $n = 3$, $h = 3$; when $n = 4$, $h = 6$. $h = \frac{1}{2}n^2 - \frac{1}{2}n$

2. A batter hit a ball when it was 2 feet off the ground directly above home plate. It was about 12 feet off the ground when it passed over the pitcher's head—about 60 feet away from home plate. It was caught 4 feet off the ground by an outfielder 300 feet away from home plate. Find a quadratic equation relating the height *h* of the ball to its distance *d* from home plate. $h = -18d^2 + 258d - 444$

(*Notes on Questions begin on page 380.*)

Follow-up for Lesson 6-6

Practice

For more questions on SPUR Objectives, use **Lesson Master 6-6A** (shown on page 379) or **Lesson Master 6-6B** (shown on pages 380–381).

On the road again.
Shown is Cascade Lakes Highway Scenic Byway in the Deschutes National Forest in Cascade Range, Oregon.

An Example from Physics

Many physical relationships, such as that between car speed and braking distance, or between time elapsed and distance fallen in a free fall, can be modeled by quadratic functions. The following example shows how.

② **Example 2**

Based on tests, here are the distances in feet it takes to stop a certain car in minimum time under emergency conditions.

Speed (mph)	10	20	30	40	50	60	70
Distance (ft)	19	42	73	116	173	248	343

a. Construct a scatterplot of these data.
b. Fit a quadratic model to these data using the points (10, 19), (20, 42), and (30, 73).
c. Graph the equation found in part **b** on top of the scatterplot of part **a**.

Solution

a. Let *s* be the speed in mph, and let *d* be the distance in ft. Use *s* as the independent variable. A scatterplot is given below. The scatterplot suggests that the data may be quadratic.

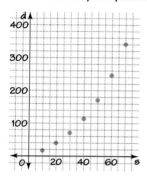

b. A quadratic model will be of the form $d = as^2 + bs + c$. To solve for *a, b,* and *c,* you need three equations. Substitute.
When $s = 10$, $d = 19$: $19 = a(10)^2 + b(10) + c$.
When $s = 20$, $d = 42$: $42 = a(20)^2 + b(20) + c$.
When $s = 30$, $d = 73$: $73 = a(30)^2 + b(30) + c$.
Solve the system.

$$\begin{cases} 19 = 100a + 10b + c \\ 42 = 400a + 20b + c \\ 73 = 900a + 30b + c \end{cases} \Rightarrow \begin{cases} 23 = 300a + 10b \\ 31 = 500a + 10b \end{cases} \Rightarrow 8 = 200a$$

From the equation $8 = 200a$, $a = .04$.
Now substitute .04 for *a* in $23 = 300a + 10b$ to get $23 = 300(.04) + 10b$. Thus, $b = 1.1$. Now substitute .04 for *a* and 1.1 for *b* in $19 = 100a + 10b + c$ to get $19 = 100(.04) + 10(1.1) + c$. Thus, $c = 4$. Therefore, the equation

$$d = .04s^2 + 1.1s + 4$$

models these data. ▶

378

Optional Activities

Activity 3 Technology Connection

You might assign *Technology Sourcebook, Computer Master 10.* Data are provided on height versus time, for an object thrown in the air. If a calculator or computer based lab is available, you may want to collect your own data. Both matrices and quadratic regression are used for developing models.

Adapting to Individual Needs

Extra Help

Remind students that two points determine a line that will satisfy the equation $ax + by = c$. Only three points are needed to determine a parabola whose equation is $y = ax^2 + bx + c$. Stress that the values of *a, b,* and *c* will be the same no matter which three points are used. However, the system of three equations that is used to determine *a, b,* and *c* will vary.

English Language Development

You may want to point out that the word *model* (like the word *form* in Lessons 6-1 and 6-3) has a special meaning in mathematics as a noun. In this lesson, a "mathematical model" is a function whose values approximate those of a real situation.

c. Below, a graph of $d = .04s^2 + 1.1s + 4$ is superimposed on the scatterplot.

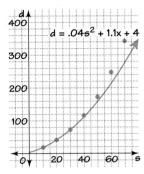

Notice that although the model goes through the points (10, 19), (20, 42), and (30, 73), it does not fit the other data exactly. However, because it passes close to the other data points, it seems to be a reasonably good model.

Two points not on a vertical line determine a linear function. Analogously, three noncollinear points, no two on the same vertical line, determine a quadratic function. If the data you are modeling can be described exactly with a quadratic function as in Example 1, any three points you use will lead to the same equation. However, if the data are only approximately quadratic, as in Example 2, the model will change. In either case, if you use three points whose x-values are equally spaced, for instance $x = 1, 2, 3$, or $x = 10, 20, 30$, the computation for the solution of the system of equations will be simpler.

Activity

Find the model for the braking-distance data obtained by using the data points (10, 19), (40, 116), and (70, 343). Draw a graph of the parabola determined by your equation. Do you think this is a better model than the one in the example? Why or why not? $d \approx .072s^2 - .378s + 15.56$
See left for graph.

Some computer software and some graphics calculators will find an equation of the parabola which in some sense is a best fit for the data set. This equation uses all of the data points. Our technology gave us

$$d \approx .072s^2 - .490s + 19.71$$

for the best quadratic fit to the braking-distance data. If you have technology with a *quadratic regression* feature, you may wish to learn how to use it.

Give me a *brake*. *Braking distances should be increased in poor weather conditions, such as snow, rain, or fog.*

Graph for Activity:

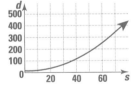

Lesson 6-6 *Fitting a Quadratic Model to Data* **379**

Lesson 6-6 *Fitting a Quadratic Model to Data* **379**

Assessment

Oral/Written Communication
Have students **work in groups.** Have one student graph three points in the coordinate plane. Then have the students take turns substituting the three ordered pairs in the equation $y = ax^2 + bx + c$ until they have a 3×3 system of equations. Next have the students work together to solve the system of equations for a, b, and c. [Students demonstrate an understanding of the method presented in this lesson for fitting a quadratic model to data.]

Extension

Ask students to extend the data in **Example 1** to show the differences of the numbers of diagonals:

Number of Sides	Number of Diagonals	Difference
3	0	
4	2	2
5	5	3
6	9	4
7	14	5
8	[20]	[6]
9	[27]	[7]
10	[35]	[8]

Students can use the pattern in the third column to predict values for polygons with 8 or more sides.

(Follow-up continues on page 380.)

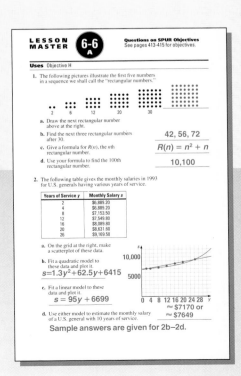

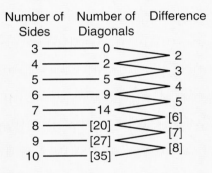

Challenge Technology Connection
Have students learn to use the QuadReg option under the STAT Calc Menu on their TI-82 graphics calculator. Then have them find the quadratic function of best fit for each of the following sets of points.
1. (2, 5), (4, 18), (6, 35), (8, 70)
  [$y = 1.375x^2 - 3.15x + 6.5$]
2. (37, 1440), (40, 1680), (45, 2115), (51, 2705), (56, 3250)
  [$y = .9853x^2 + 3.605x - 41.696$]

Setting Up Lesson 6-7

Questions 9c and **9d** require students to solve quadratic equations, and they help set up the next lesson.

Notes on Questions

Question 7 You might ask students to explain their answers. [This question shows that the equations modeling the stopping distances do not apply to all situations.]

Questions 17–21 These questions review simplifying radicals in preparation for the next lesson.

Additional Answers

3. Sample: when
$n = 3$, $d = 0$:
$0 = a(3)^2 + b(3) + c$
$n = 5$, $d = 5$:
$5 = a(5)^2 + b(5) + c$
$n = 7$, $d = 14$:
$14 = a(7)^2 + b(7) + c$

$$\begin{cases} 0 = 9a + 3b + c \\ 5 = 25a + 5b + c \\ 14 = 49a + 7b + c \end{cases}$$

$$\begin{cases} 5 = 16a + 2b \\ 9 = 24a + 2b \end{cases}$$

Subtracting gives $4 = 8a$, so
$a = \frac{1}{2}$. Substituting $a = \frac{1}{2}$ in
$5 = 16a + 2b$ gives $b = -\frac{3}{2}$.
Substituting $a = \frac{1}{2}$ and $b = -\frac{3}{2}$
in $0 = 9a + 3b + c$ gives
$c = 0$. So, $d = \frac{1}{2}n^2 - \frac{3}{2}n$.

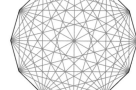

5) Yes; $\dfrac{n(n-3)}{2} = \dfrac{n^2 - 3n}{2}$
$= \frac{1}{2}n^2 - \frac{3}{2}n.$

8a) The point (0, 0) should be part of these data because a car traveling at 0 mph needs 0 feet to stop.

t (sec)	h (ft)
1	364
2	371
3	346
4	289
5	200
6	79

380

QUESTIONS

Covering the Reading

In 1–5, refer to Example 1.

1. How many diagonals does a heptagon (a polygon with seven sides) have? **14**

2. Explain why the students thought it inappropriate to fit a linear model to their data. **A linear model is inappropriate because the rate of change between points is not constant.**

3. Use three points different from those the students used to show that these points also lead to the model $d = \frac{1}{2}n^2 - \frac{3}{2}n$. **See margin.**

4. How many diagonals does the dodecagon pictured at the left have? **54**

5. Some geometry books give the formula $d = \dfrac{n(n-3)}{2}$ for the number of diagonals of an n-gon. Is this formula equivalent to the one developed by the students? Explain why or why not. **See left.**

In 6 and 7, refer to Example 2 about braking distance.

6. **a.** Use the equation $d = .04s^2 + 1.1s + 4$ found in Example 2 to determine the stopping distance of a car traveling 60 mph. **214 ft**
   b. What equation did you obtain in the Activity? $d \approx .072s^2 - .378s + 15.56$
   c. Use your equation to determine the stopping distance of a car traveling 60 mph. **≈ 252.08 ft**
   d. Use the quadratic regression equation $d \approx .072s^2 - .490s + 19.71$ to determine the stopping distance of a car traveling 60 mph. **≈249.51 ft**
   e. Which model comes closest to the observed distance? **the quadratic regression equation**

7. Find the predicted stopping distance for a car traveling at 0 mph using
   a. the equation of the Activity. **≈15.56 ft**
   b. the equation of Example 2. **4 ft**
   c. the quadratic regression equation. **≈19.71 ft**

Applying the Mathematics

8. Refer to Example 2.
   a. Explain why (0, 0) should be a point in this data set. **See left.**
   b. Add (0, 0) to the data set. Fit a new quadratic model to this enlarged data set. **Best quadratic fit: $d = .064s^2 + .249s + 5.75$**

9. A ball is thrown off the top of a tall building. The table at the left shows the height h in feet of the ball above ground.
   a. Fit a quadratic model to these data. **Sample: $h = -16t^2 + 55t + 325$**
   b. How tall is the building? **325 ft**
   c. When will the ball be 100 feet above the ground? **≈5.8 sec**
   d. When will the ball hit the ground? **≈6.5 sec**

Additional Answers, continued

15. $\begin{bmatrix} 100 & 10 & 1 \\ 400 & 20 & 1 \\ 900 & 30 & 1 \end{bmatrix} \begin{bmatrix} a \\ b \\ c \end{bmatrix} = \begin{bmatrix} 19 \\ 42 \\ 73 \end{bmatrix}$; $\begin{bmatrix} 1 & 0 & 0 \\ 0 & 1 & 0 \\ 0 & 0 & 1 \end{bmatrix} \begin{bmatrix} a \\ b \\ c \end{bmatrix} = \begin{bmatrix} \frac{1}{200} & -\frac{1}{100} & \frac{1}{200} \\ -\frac{1}{4} & \frac{2}{5} & -\frac{3}{20} \\ 3 & -3 & 1 \end{bmatrix} \begin{bmatrix} 19 \\ 42 \\ 73 \end{bmatrix}$;

$\begin{bmatrix} a \\ b \\ c \end{bmatrix} = \begin{bmatrix} \frac{1}{25} \\ \frac{11}{10} \\ 4 \end{bmatrix} = \begin{bmatrix} .04 \\ 1.1 \\ 4 \end{bmatrix}$

22a. The main reason for the census was the need to decide how many seats each state would have in the House of Representatives. (Ref. Article 1, Section 2 of the original U.S. Constitution.)

11a) $(x + 3)(x + 7)$
b) $x^2 + 10x + 21$

16a) $\begin{cases} a_1 = 7 \\ a_n = a_{n-1} + 3, \text{ for} \\ \quad \text{integers } n \geq 2 \end{cases}$

10. Consider the sums of the integers from 1 to n.

		n	$S = 1 + 2 + 3 + \ldots + n$
	$1 + 2 = 3$	2	3
	$1 + 2 + 3 = 6$	3	6
	$1 + 2 + 3 + 4 = 10$	4	10
		5	? 15
		6	? 21

a. Complete the table of the sum S as a function of n.
b. Fit a quadratic model to the data in part **a.** $S = \frac{1}{2}n^2 + \frac{1}{2}n$
c. Use your model to find the sum of the first 1000 positive integers.
500,500

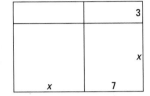

Review

11. Express the area of the largest rectangle at the left **a.** as a product of binomials, and **b.** in the form $ax^2 + bx + c$. *(Lessons 6-1, 6-4)*
See left.

12. Rewrite $y - 18 = -2(x - 2)^2$ in the standard form of a parabola. *(Lesson 6-4)* $y = -2x^2 + 8x + 10$

13. Consider the equation $y = 2x^2 + 24x - 20$. *(Lessons 6-3, 6-4, 6-5)*
a. Without making a graph, identify the y-intercept of the graph. (0, -20)
b. Rewrite the equation in vertex form. $y + 92 = 2(x + 6)^2$
c. Without making a graph, identify the vertex of the graph. (-6, -92)

14. Solve $\sqrt{(x + 2)^2} = 5$. *(Lesson 6-2)* $x = -7$ or $x = 3$

15. Use matrices to solve the 3-by-3 system in Example 2. *(Lesson 5-7)*
See margin.

16. Consider the sequence 7, 10, 13, 16, ...
a. Write a recursive formula for this sequence. See left.
b. Write an explicit formula for this sequence. $a_n = 4 + 3n$
c. What is the 200th term of the sequence? 604
d. Which term of the sequence is 1966? *(Lessons 1-7, 1-9, 3-3, 3-4)* 654

In 17–19, recall that for all nonnegative real numbers a and b, $\sqrt{a}\sqrt{b} = \sqrt{(ab)}$. Simplify each expression. *(Previous course)*

17. $\sqrt{3}\sqrt{12}$ 6

18. $\sqrt{20}\sqrt{50}$ $10\sqrt{10}$

19. $(\sqrt{17})^2$ 17

In 20 and 21, *true or false.* Justify your answer. *(Previous course)*

20. $\sqrt{50} = 5\sqrt{10}$ False; $\sqrt{50} = \sqrt{25 \cdot 2} = \sqrt{25} \cdot \sqrt{2} = 5\sqrt{2}$

21. $\dfrac{4 \pm \sqrt{12}}{6} = \dfrac{2 \pm \sqrt{3}}{3}$ True; $\dfrac{4 \pm \sqrt{12}}{6} = \dfrac{4 \pm 2\sqrt{3}}{6} = \dfrac{2 \pm \sqrt{3}}{3}$

Exploration

22. The U.S. Constitution states that a census must be taken every ten years.
a. Why did the framers of the Constitution include such a requirement?
b. The first census was in 1790. Find the U.S. population for each census from 1790 to 1990.
c. Draw a scatterplot of these data and fit a quadratic model to the data.
d. Use your model to estimate the U.S. population in
(i) 1975. **(ii)** 2000. **(iii)** 2090.
See margin.

Lesson 6-6 *Fitting a Quadratic Model to Data* **381**

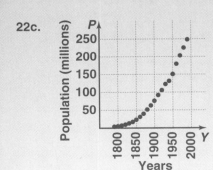

Coming to your census.
Shown is interviewer Marie Cioffi collecting data from Margaret Napolitana in New York City for the 1930 census. Since 1960 the Census Bureau has used a combination of interviewers and individuals filling out the census forms themselves.

22b.

Year	Population (millions)
1790	3.929
1800	5.308
1810	7.240
1820	9.638
1830	12.866
1840	17.069
1850	23.192
1860	31.443
1870	39.818
1880	50.156
1890	62.948
1900	75.995
1910	91.972
1920	105.711
1930	122.775
1940	131.669
1950	150.697
1960	179.323
1970	203.302
1980	226.546
1990	248.710

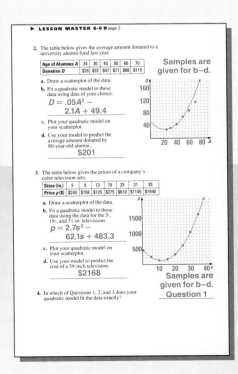

22c.

Population (millions) vs. Years (1800, 1850, 1900, 1950, 2000)

Sample: The quadratic regression equation
$P \approx .00651y^2 - 23.38y + 21010.7$
if P is in millions.

d. i Sample: ≈ 228.269 million
ii Sample: ≈ 290.70 million
iii Sample: ≈ 582.831 million

381

Objectives

C Solve quadratic equations.
G Use quadratic equations to solve problems.

Resources

From the Teacher's Resource File

■ Lesson Master 6-7A or 6-7B
■ Answer Master 6-7
■ Assessment Sourcebook: Quiz for Lessons 6-5 through 6-7
■ Teaching Aids
   8 Four-Quadrant Graph Paper
   19 Automatic Grapher Grids
   55 Warm-up
   61 Proof of Quadratic Formula

Additional Resources

■ Visuals for Teaching Aids 8, 19, 55, 61

Teaching **6-7**
Lesson

Warm-up

The area of a room is 255 square feet. The length of the room is 3 feet more than the width. What are the dimensions of the room? **length:** ≈ 17.55 ft; **width:** ≈ 14.55 ft

---

6-7

The Quadratic Formula

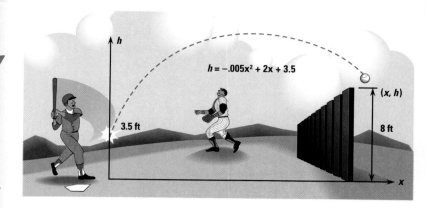

$$h = -.005x^2 + 2x + 3.5$$

3.5 ft

(x, h)

8 ft

❶ Pop Fligh, the famous baseball player, hit a pitch that was 3.5 ft high. The ball traveled towards the outfield along a nearly parabolic path. Let x be the distance along the ground (in feet) of the ball from home plate, and let $h(x)$ be the height (in feet) of the ball at that distance. Then the path of his ball can be described by the function h, where

$$h(x) = -.005x^2 + 2x + 3.5.$$

Suppose we want to know where the ball was 8 feet high. Because we wish to know the horizontal distance x when the height was 8, we substitute 8 for $h(x)$ in the equation above.

$$8 = -.005x^2 + 2x + 3.5$$

By adding -8 to each side, you can put the equation into the standard form $ax^2 + bx + c = 0$.

$$0 = -.005x^2 + 2x - 4.5.$$

This equation can be solved by rewriting it in vertex form. But the arithmetic is messy. It is much easier to solve the equation by using the **Quadratic Formula.** This formula is very important—*if you have not learned it before, you should memorize it now.* The Quadratic Formula is a theorem; that is, it can be proved using the basic properties of algebra.

What Is the Quadratic Formula?

> **Quadratic Formula Theorem**
> If $ax^2 + bx + c = 0$ and $a \neq 0$, then
> $$x = \frac{-b \pm \sqrt{b^2 - 4ac}}{2a}.$$

Our proof of the Quadratic Formula relies on completing the square.

Lesson 6-7 Overview

Broad Goals This lesson provides motivation, a proof, and two applications of the Quadratic Formula.

Perspective In this lesson, we emphasize that (1) the solutions to $ax^2 + bx + c = 0$, when $a \neq 0$, are given by the formula
$$x = \frac{-b \pm \sqrt{b^2 - 4ac}}{2a},$$
and (2) any quadratic equation may be solved using this formula. Because the

Quadratic Formula solves any quadratic equation, and many situations can be represented by quadratic equations, it is one of the most important theorems in this course. Students should memorize it.

Students who have studied UCSMP *Algebra* and *Geometry* have worked with the Quadratic Formula, but they have not been expected to derive it. In this course, they should understand how the formula is

derived. Note that in going from Step 5 to Step 6 in the derivation given on page 383, there are technically two square roots for the left side also, namely $x + \frac{b}{2a}$ and $-(x + \frac{b}{2a})$. However, the $\pm$ sign on the right side of the equation accounts for both roots. Similarly, from Step 7 to Step 8, the $\pm$ sign accounts for all the possibilities when we take the square root of a fraction by taking the square root of the numerator and denominator.

❷ **Proof**

Given: the equation $ax^2 + bx + c = 0$, where $a \neq 0$.

1. $x^2 + \frac{b}{a}x + \frac{c}{a} = \frac{0}{a}$ First divide both sides by a so the coefficient of x^2 is 1.

2. $x^2 + \frac{b}{a}x = -\frac{c}{a}$ Add $-\frac{c}{a}$ to each side.

3. $x^2 + \frac{b}{a}x + \frac{b^2}{4a^2} = \frac{b^2}{4a^2} - \frac{c}{a}$ Complete the square by adding $\left(\frac{1}{2} \cdot \frac{b}{a}\right)^2$ to both sides.

4. $\left(x + \frac{b}{2a}\right)^2 = \frac{b^2}{4a^2} - \frac{c}{a}$ Write the left side as a binomial squared.

5. $\left(x + \frac{b}{2a}\right)^2 = \frac{b^2 - 4ac}{4a^2}$ Add the fractions on the right side.

6. $x + \frac{b}{2a} = \pm\sqrt{\frac{b^2 - 4ac}{4a^2}}$ Take the square roots of both sides.

7. $x + \frac{b}{2a} = \frac{\pm\sqrt{b^2 - 4ac}}{2a}$ Use the definition of square root.

8. $x = \frac{-b \pm \sqrt{b^2 - 4ac}}{2a}$ Add $-\frac{b}{2a}$ to both sides.

Using the Quadratic Formula

Example 1

Solve $3x^2 + 11x - 4 = 0$.

Solution

To use the Quadratic Formula, you need to know the values of a, b, and c. Here $a = 3$, $b = 11$, and $c = -4$. Write the formula. Then substitute for a, b, and c.

$$x = \frac{-b \pm \sqrt{b^2 - 4ac}}{2a}$$

$$= \frac{-11 \pm \sqrt{11^2 - 4 \cdot 3 \cdot -4}}{2 \cdot 3}$$

$$= \frac{-11 \pm \sqrt{121 - -48}}{6}$$

$$= \frac{-11 \pm \sqrt{169}}{6}$$

$$= \frac{-11 \pm 13}{6}$$

So $x = \frac{-11 + 13}{6}$ or $x = \frac{-11 - 13}{6}$

$x = \frac{1}{3}$ or $x = -4$

▶

Lesson 6-7 *The Quadratic Formula* **383**

Notes on Reading

Students may use graph paper, **Teaching Aid 8,** or **Teaching Aid 19** throughout this lesson.

❶ **Sports Connection** To be eligible for the Baseball Hall of Fame, a player must have played in the major leagues for at least 10 years and be retired for at least five years. Players can be elected by receiving 75 percent of the votes cast by members of the Baseball Writers Association of America. Also, a special committee considers all players who have been retired for a minimum of 25 years and who may have been overlooked when they were first eligible. In 1971, a committee was set up to consider ballplayers who played in the old Negro Leagues.

❷ This proof of the Quadratic Formula is on **Teaching Aid 61.**

Optional Activities

Activity 1 Cooperative Learning After discussing the lesson, you might have students **work in groups** and make up another example like the one involving Pop Fligh. They should begin with three points that they want to be on the flight of the ball and derive an equation from those three points. Then they should use the vertex form to determine the highest point the ball reached and apply the quadratic formula to find out how far the ball traveled.

Activity 2 After students complete the lesson, you might give them the following quadratic equations to solve by using the quadratic formula. Discuss their responses. [In each case, $b^2 - 4ac = 0$ and there is only one solution to the equation.]

1. $x^2 + 8x + 16 = 0$ $[x = -4]$
2. $9x^2 - 30x + 25 = 0$ $[x = \frac{5}{3}]$
3. $\frac{1}{4}x^2 - 3x + 9 = 0$ $[x = 6]$

The major benefit of having a formula for solving a quadratic is that many problems lead to quadratics. Two rather typical problems are given as examples: **Example 2** is a problem about the path of a baseball and **Example 3** is a problem from geometry involving the Pythagorean Theorem. **Example 2** is particularly significant because both solutions to the quadratic have meaning.

The lesson provides a good opportunity to review how to simplify expressions with square roots and to help students use their calculators efficiently. For example, using the Quadratic Formula on $x^2 - x - 1 = 0$ yields $x = \frac{1 \pm \sqrt{5}}{2}$, and using it on the equivalent $3x^2 - 3x - 3 = 0$ yields $x = \frac{3 \pm \sqrt{45}}{6}$. Students can use calculators or algebraic techniques to realize that these answers are identical. You can make up other examples of this type by multiplying both sides of an equation by an integer and not reducing before applying the formula.

Check

Each solution should be checked.

Does $3 \cdot \left(\frac{1}{3}\right)^2 + 11 \cdot \frac{1}{3} - 4 = 0$? Yes, $\frac{1}{3} + \frac{11}{3} - 4 = 0$.

Does $3 \cdot (-4)^2 + 11 \cdot -4 - 4 = 0$? Yes, $48 - 44 - 4 = 0$.

In Example 1, since the number $b^2 - 4ac$ under the radical sign is a perfect square, the solutions are integers. In applications, however, the numbers are not always so nice. The Quadratic Formula still works, but you may need a calculator to estimate the solutions. Here is the problem posed at the beginning of this lesson.

Example 2

Find out when the ball hit by Pop Fligh was 8 feet high.

Solution

We need to solve $-.005x^2 + 2x - 4.5 = 0$. In this situation $a = -.005$, $b = 2$, and $c = -4.5$. Substitute into the formula.

$$x = \frac{-2 \pm \sqrt{2^2 - 4 \cdot (-.005) \cdot (-4.5)}}{2 \cdot (-.005)}$$

$$= \frac{-2 \pm \sqrt{4 - .09}}{-.01}$$

$$= \frac{-2 \pm \sqrt{3.91}}{-.01}$$

Use a calculator to estimate the square root. Separate the two solutions.

$$x \approx \frac{-2 + 1.977}{-.01} \text{ or } x \approx \frac{-2 - 1.977}{-.01}$$

So $x \approx 2.3$ or $x \approx 397.7$.

As you might expect, There are two places where the ball is 8 ft high. The first is when the ball is about 2.3 ft away from home plate and on the way up. The second is when the ball is about 398 ft away from home plate and on the way down.

Check

Graph $h(x) = -.005x^2 + 2x + 3.5$ with an automatic grapher. Use the trace feature to find the value of y when x is about 2.3 or 397.7. The value of y should be close to 8.

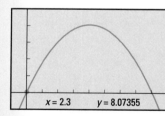

$x = 2.3$ $y = 8.07355$

$-50 \leqslant x \leqslant 450$, x-scale = 50
$-50 \leqslant y \leqslant 250$, y-scale = 50

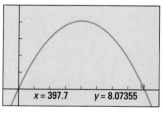

$x = 397.7$ $y = 8.07355$

$-50 \leqslant x \leqslant 450$, x-scale = 50
$-50 \leqslant y \leqslant 250$, y-scale = 50

Adapting to Individual Needs

Extra Help

Stress to students that when they use the Quadratic Formula Theorem, one side of the equation must be zero. This discourages students from incorrectly applying the formula. Stress that the ± sign in the formula means that there are always two (possibly equal) solutions. Encourage students to separate the solutions as is done in the examples for this lesson.

An equation of the form $ax^2 + bx + c = 0$, with $a \neq 0$, is said to be in the **standard form of a quadratic equation.** If a quadratic equation is not in standard form, use the properties of algebra to rewrite it in that form before applying the Quadratic Formula. Example 3 illustrates this.

Example 3

The 3-4-5 right triangle has sides which are consecutive integers. Are there any other right triangles with this property?

Solution

If n is an integer, then n, n + 1, and n + 2 are consecutive integers. By the Pythagorean Theorem,

$$n^2 + (n + 1)^2 = (n + 2)^2.$$

Therefore, $n^2 + n^2 + 2n + 1 = n^2 + 4n + 4.$
$$2n^2 + 2n + 1 = n^2 + 4n + 4$$

Rewrite this equation in standard form by adding $-n^2 - 4n - 4$ to each side.

$$n^2 - 2n - 3 = 0$$

Use the Quadratic Formula with $a = 1$, $b = -2$, and $c = -3$.

$$n = \frac{-(-2) \pm \sqrt{(-2)^2 - 4(1)(-3)}}{2(1)}$$

$$= \frac{2 \pm \sqrt{16}}{2}$$

$$= \frac{2 \pm 4}{2}$$

So $n = \frac{2 + 4}{2} = 3$ or $n = \frac{2 - 4}{2} = -1$.

When $n = 3$, then $n + 1 = 4$ and $n + 2 = 5$. This is the 3-4-5 triangle. The value $n = -1$ must be rejected because a side of a triangle must have positive length. Thus The only right triangle with consecutive integer sides is the 3-4-5 right triangle.

QUESTIONS

Covering the Reading

1. If $ax^2 + bx + c = 0$, and $a \neq 0$, give the two values of x in terms of a, b, and c. See left.

1) $x = \dfrac{-b + \sqrt{b^2 - 4ac}}{2a}$

$x = \dfrac{-b - \sqrt{b^2 - 4ac}}{2a}$

2. *Multiple choice.*   The Quadratic Formula is a a
(a) theorem.   (b) postulate.   (c) definition.

In 3–6, refer to the proof of the Quadratic Formula.

3. Why is it necessary to divide both sides by a in Step 1? Before completing the square, it is necessary to make sure the coefficient of x^2 is 1.

4. Write $x^2 + \dfrac{b}{a}x + \dfrac{b^2}{4a^2}$ as the square of a binomial. $\left(x + \dfrac{b}{2a}\right)^2$

5. Write $\dfrac{b^2}{4a^2} - \dfrac{c}{a}$ as a single fraction. $\dfrac{b^2 - 4ac}{4a^2}$

Lesson 6-7   *The Quadratic Formula*   **385**

Follow-up for Lesson **6-7**

Practice

For more questions on SPUR Objectives, use **Lesson Master 6-7A** (shown on page 385) or **Lesson Master 6-7B** (shown on pages 386–387).

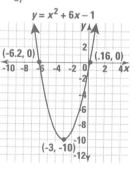

---

6) The variable *a* appears in the denominator, and division by zero is undefined.

8) $v = \frac{5 - \sqrt{97}}{12} \approx -0.404$ or $\frac{5 + \sqrt{97}}{12} \approx 1.237$

19a) $x = -3 + \sqrt{10} \approx .16$ or $x = -3 - \sqrt{10} \approx -6.16$; x-intercepts

c)

$y = x^2 + 6x - 1$

(-6.2, 0) (.16, 0)

(-3, -10)

---

6. Why can't *a* equal 0 in the Quadratic Formula? **See left.**

In 7–10, a quadratic equation is given. Solve the equation using the Quadratic Formula.

7. $10x^2 + 13x + 3 = 0$ $x = -1$ or $\frac{-3}{10}$ **8.** $6v^2 - 5v - 3 = 0$ **See left.**

9. $x^2 + 2x - 15 = 0$ $x = -5$ or 3 **10.** $2n^2 - 11n = 0$ $n = 0$ or $\frac{11}{2}$

In 11–13, consider the equation $h(x) = -.005x^2 + 2x + 3.5$ and the situation at the start of this Lesson.

11. What do x and $h(x)$ represent? **x: distance along the ground from home plate; h(x): height above home plate at that distance**

12. Manny Walker pitched the ball that Pop hit. How high was the ball when it passed over Manny's head, 60 ft from home plate? **105.5 ft**

13. Where was Pop's hit 100 ft high? **56.13 ft and 343.87 ft from home plate**

14. In Example 2, we could have multiplied both sides of the equation by -1 and solved $.005x^2 - 2x + 4.5 = 0$. Find the solutions to this equation to the nearest tenth. **x = 397.7 or 2.3**

15. Refer to Example 3. If n is the first of three consecutive integers, what are the other two? **n + 1, n + 2**

Stingy on runs. *Shown is Greg Maddux of the Atlanta Braves. In 1994, Maddux had a league low 1.56 earned run average.*

Applying the Mathematics

16. Find all right triangles whose sides are consecutive *even* integers n, $n + 2$, and $n + 4$. **The only such triangle is one with sides 6, 8, 10.**

In 17 and 18, solve.

17. $n^2 + 9 = 6n$ $n = 3$

18. $4(m^2 - 3m) = -9$ $m = \frac{3}{2}$

19. Consider the parabola with equation $y = x^2 + 6x - 1$. **See left for a, c.**
  a. Find the values of x if $y = 0$. What are these points called?
  b. Find the vertex of this parabola. **(-3, -10)**
  c. Graph the parabola.
  d. Give an equation for its axis of symmetry. **x = -3**

20. As shown below, the graphs of $y = -\frac{1}{2}x^2 + 4x$ and $y = 4$ intersect at two points.
  a. Find the coordinates of the points of intersection without graphing.
  b. Check by using an automatic grapher.
  a, b) $(4 + 2\sqrt{2}, 4) \approx (6.83, 4)$; $(4 - 2\sqrt{2}, 4) \approx (1.17, 4)$

$y = -\frac{1}{2}x^2 + 4x$

$y = 4$

-2 ≤ x ≤ 10, x-scale = 2
-2 ≤ y ≤ 10, y-scale = 2

Adapting to Individual Needs

Challenge
Have students find a number such that 1 less than the number divided by the reciprocal of the number is equal to 1.

$\left[\frac{x - 1}{\frac{1}{x}} = 1 \right.$, so $x^2 - x - 1 = 0$ and

$x = \frac{1 \pm \sqrt{5}}{2}$. The larger value of x is called the Golden Ratio.]

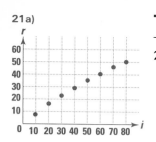

21a)

Review

21. When a beam of light in air strikes the surface of water it is *refracted*, or bent. Below are the earliest known data on the relation between *i*, the angle of incidence in degrees, and *r*, the angle of refraction in degrees. The measurements are recorded in the *Optics* of Ptolemy, a Greek scientist who lived in the second century A.D.

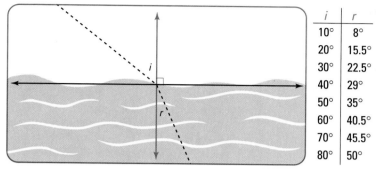

i	*r*
10°	8°
20°	15.5°
30°	22.5°
40°	29°
50°	35°
60°	40.5°
70°	45.5°
80°	50°

a. Draw a scatterplot of these data. **See left.**
b. Fit a quadratic model to these data. **Sample:** $r = -.0025i^2 + .825i$
c. Fit a linear model to these data. **Sample:** $r = .6i + 3.75$
d. Decide which model seems more appropriate. Explain why you made that decision. *(Lessons 3-6, 6-6)* **See left.**

21d) Sample: The quadratic model is more appropriate because the points are closer to the quadratic model than to the linear model.

22) Complete the square on $3x^2 + 24x$ to change $y = 3x^2 + 24x + 50$ from standard form to vertex form. If the result is $y - 2 = 3(x + 4)^2$, the graphs are the same.

22. Explain how you can tell without graphing whether or not the equations $y = 3x^2 + 24x + 50$ and $y - 2 = 3(x + 4)^2$ have the same graph. *(Lesson 6-5)* **See left.**

23. a. Graph the solution sets to $y = \frac{36}{x}$ and $y + 2 = \frac{36}{x}$ on the same axes. **See left.**
b. Find equations for the lines of symmetry for the image and preimage. *(Lessons 2-6, 6-3)* **preimage:** $y = x, y = -x$; **image:** $y = x - 2, y = -x - 2$

24. For what values of *x* is it true that $\sqrt{x^2} = x$? *(Lesson 6-2)* **for all nonnegative values of x**

25. A door $36'' \times 78''$ is surrounded by a wooden frame of width *w* inches on three sides. $2808 + 192w + 2w^2$ in²
a. What is the total area of the door and frame?
b. If $w = 4$, find the total area of the door and frame. *(Lesson 6-1)* **3608 in²**

23a)

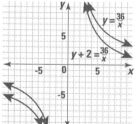

26. Find the slope of the line through $(1, -4)$ and parallel to the *x*-axis. *(Lessons 3-1, 3-2)* **0**

Exploration

27. For Question 14, we multiplied both sides of the equation $-.005x^2 + 2x - 4.5 = 0$ by -1 and asked you to solve it. Multiply both sides of this equation by 1000 and solve it. Compare your results with the solutions in Example 2 and Question 14. Write a few sentences explaining your results. **See margin.**

Lesson 6-7 *The Quadratic Formula* **387**

Additional Answers
27. $1000 \cdot (-.005x^2 + 2x - 4.5) = 1000 \cdot 0$
$-5x^2 + 2000x - 4500 = 0$
$$x = \frac{-2000 \pm \sqrt{2000^2 - 4 \cdot (-5) \cdot (-4500)}}{-10}$$
$x \approx 397.7$ or $x \approx 2.3$
The results are the same because multiplying both sides of the equation by a nonzero number yields an equivalent equation, and equivalent equations have the same solutions.

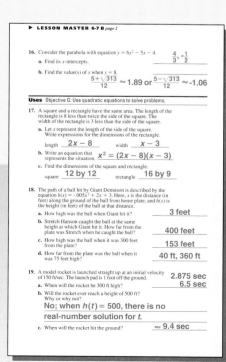

Objectives

C Solve quadratic equations.
D Perform operations with complex numbers.

Resources

From the *Teacher's Resource File*
■ Lesson Master 6-8A or 6-8B
■ Answer Master 6-8
■ Teaching Aid 55: Warm-up

Additional Resources
■ Visual for Teaching Aid 55

Teaching Lesson 6-8

Warm-up

Simplify each of the following.

1. $(2\sqrt{3})^2$ 12
2. $(-3\sqrt{2})^2$ 18
3. $\sqrt{6} \cdot \sqrt{15}$ $3\sqrt{10}$

Square Roots and Imaginary Numbers

Consider the equation $t^2 = 400$. You can solve it for t as follows.

$$t^2 = 400$$
$$\sqrt{t^2} = \sqrt{400} \quad \text{Take square roots.}$$
$$|t| = 20 \quad \text{Use the Absolute Value-Square Root Theorem}$$
$$t = \pm 20. \quad \text{Solve the absolute value equation.}$$

But now consider the equation $t^2 = -400$. You know that this equation has no real solutions because the square of a real number is never negative. However, if you followed the solution above you might write

$$t^2 = -400$$
$$\sqrt{t^2} = \sqrt{-400}$$
$$|t| = ?$$

So far, $\sqrt{x}$ has been defined only for $x \geq 0$. If you try to evaluate $\sqrt{-400}$ on most calculators, an error message will be displayed.

Until the 1500s, mathematicians were also puzzled by square roots of negative numbers. They knew that if they solved certain quadratics, they would get negative numbers under the radical sign. They did not know, however, what to do with them.

❶ One of the first to work with these numbers was Girolamo Cardano. In a book called *Ars Magna* ("Great Art") published in 1545, Cardano reasoned as follows: When k is positive, the equation $x^2 = k$ has two solutions, $\sqrt{k}$ and $-\sqrt{k}$. If we solve the equation $x^2 = -k$ in the same way, then the two solutions are $\sqrt{-k}$ and $-\sqrt{-k}$. These, then, are symbols for the square roots of negative numbers.

> **Definition**
> When $k > 0$, the two solutions to $x^2 = -k$ are denoted $\sqrt{-k}$ and $-\sqrt{-k}$.

By the definition, $(\sqrt{-k})^2 = -k$. This means that we can say, for *all* real numbers r,

$$\sqrt{r} \cdot \sqrt{r} = r.$$

Cardano called these square roots of negatives "fictitious numbers." In the 1600s, Descartes called them **imaginary numbers** in contrast to the numbers everyone understood, which he called "real numbers." In his book *De Formulis Differentialibus Angularibus,* written in 1777, Euler wrote, "In the following I shall denote the expression $\sqrt{-1}$ by the letter i so that $i\,i = -1$."

Lesson 6-8 Overview

Broad Goals This lesson introduces i and its multiples, and it explores the fundamental operations with them.

Perspective For many years, the concept of imaginary numbers was difficult for mathematicians to accept and explain logically, even though they were able to devise rules that made computation with such numbers relatively easy. Now imaginary numbers are considered as acceptable and explainable as real numbers.

The use of "imaginary" to describe the square root of a negative number is unfortunate, for these numbers have numerous real-world applications. Be sure to emphasize that the term *imaginary number* is used to describe only the nonreal numbers that can be written in the form bi, where b is any nonzero real number. The term *complex*

number is broader, describing all numbers that can be written in the form $a + bi$, where a and b are nonzero reals. The latter term is introduced in Lesson 6-9.

Some texts use "pure imaginary number" for the numbers we here call "imaginary." Where this usage is in place, the term *imaginary number* may apply to any complex number.

Definition

$i = \sqrt{-1}$

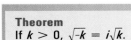

The number i is the **imaginary unit**.

❷ Putting these two definitions together, we conclude that i and $-i$ are the two solutions to

$$x^2 = -1. \text{ That is, } i^2 = -1 \text{ and } (-i)^2 = -1.$$

Now consider multiples of i, such as $5i$. By the definition of i, $5i = 5\sqrt{-1}$. If we assume that multiplication of imaginary numbers is commutative and associative, then

$$
\begin{aligned}
(5i)^2 &= 5i \cdot 5i \\
&= 5^2 \cdot i^2 \\
&= 25 \cdot {-1} \\
&= -25.
\end{aligned}
$$

So $5i$ is a square root of -25. We write $5i = \sqrt{-25}$ and then $-5i = -\sqrt{-25}$. The following theorem generalizes this result.

Theorem

If $k > 0$, $\sqrt{-k} = i\sqrt{k}$.

Thus all square roots of negative numbers are multiples of i.

Example 1

Solve $t^2 = -400$.

Solution

Apply the first definition in this Lesson.

$$t = \sqrt{-400} \quad \text{or} \quad t = -\sqrt{-400}$$

Now use the theorem above.

$$t = i\sqrt{400} \quad \text{or} \quad t = -i\sqrt{400}$$

Simplify.

$$t = 20i \quad \text{or} \quad t = -20i$$

Example 2

Show that $i\sqrt{3}$ is a square root of -3.

Solution

Multiply $i\sqrt{3}$ by itself.

$$
\begin{aligned}
i\sqrt{3} \cdot i\sqrt{3} &= i \cdot i \cdot \sqrt{3} \cdot \sqrt{3} \\
&= i^2 \cdot 3 \\
&= -1 \cdot 3 \\
&= -3
\end{aligned}
$$

The other square root of -3 is $-i\sqrt{3}$.

Lesson 6-8 *Imaginary Numbers* **389**

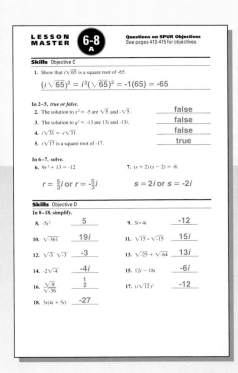

Notes on Reading

By this time, most students have heard of the number i, even though they may not know anything about it. They will be curious about its properties and may think it is far more difficult to work with than it is.

❶ **History Connection** Girolamo Cardano, an Italian physician, mathematician, and astrologer, was considered the most renowned mathematician of his time, and his book *Ars Magna* is considered a fundamental work in the history of algebra.

Reading Mathematics This lesson provides an appropriate opportunity to remind students that a word's *technical* meaning in mathematics may be quite different from the word's *general* meaning in everyday use. For example, there is nothing "irrational" about irrational numbers. Nor is there anything "negative" about negative numbers. Similarly, there is nothing "imaginary" about imaginary numbers.

❷ Emphasize the paragraph at the top of this page. You may want to read it with the students.

Optional Activities

You can use this activity after discussing **Question 35.** Ask students to write some general rules for evaluating powers of i. [Any power of i generalizes to one of four numbers—1, i, -1, $-i$. The number can be determined by dividing the exponent by 4 and considering the remainder, rather than the quotient. If the remainder is 0, the evaluated power of i is 1; if the remainder is 1, the evaluated power of i is i; if the remainder is 2, the evaluated power of i is -1; if the remainder is 3, the evaluated power of i is $-i$. Or, if n is any integer, $i^{4n} = 1$, $i^{4n+1} = i$, $i^{4n+2} = -1$, and $i^{4n+3} = -i$.]

1. Solve $2x^2 + 100 = 0$.
   $\pm 5\sqrt{2}i = \pm 5i\sqrt{2}$
2. Show that $i\sqrt{7}$ is a square root of -7. $i\sqrt{7} \cdot i\sqrt{7} = i^2 \cdot 7 = -1(7) = -7$
3. Simplify.
   a. $(8i)^2$ -64
   b. $-3\sqrt{-49}$ $-21i$
   c. $\sqrt{-9} + \sqrt{-121}$ $14i$
   d. $\frac{\sqrt{-144}}{\sqrt{16}}$ $3i$
4. Simplify $\sqrt{-9} \cdot \sqrt{-121}$. -33

Follow-up for Lesson 6-8

Practice

For more questions on SPUR Objectives, use **Lesson Master 6-8A** (shown on page 389) or **Lesson Master 6-8B** (shown on pages 390–391).

Assessment

Written Communication Have students write a short essay explaining why the terms "imaginary numbers" and "real numbers" may be misleading. [Students demonstrate an understanding that imaginary numbers are just as useful and important as real numbers.]

LESSON MASTER **6-8 B**   Questions on SPUR Objectives

Vocabulary

1. What are *imaginary numbers*?
   square roots of negative numbers

2. a. What symbol is used to designate the imaginary unit? i
   b. What is the value of the imaginary unit? $\sqrt{-1}$

Skills Objective C: Solve quadratic equations.
In 3–12, solve.

3. $x^2 = -900$
   $x = \pm 30i$

4. $y^2 = -14$
   $y = \pm i\sqrt{14}$

5. $a^2 + 8 = -28$
   $a = \pm 6i$

6. $b^2 - 12 = -13$
   $b = \pm i$

7. $5d^2 = -20$
   $d = \pm 2i$

8. $-8g^2 = 24$
   $g = \pm i\sqrt{3}$

9. $3h^2 + 17 = -130$
   $h = \pm 7i$

10. $x^2 + 3x + 8 = 0$
    $x = \frac{-3 \pm i\sqrt{23}}{2}$

11. $(k - 1)^2 + 20 = 5$
    $k = 1 \pm i\sqrt{15}$

12. $(m + 5)(m - 5) = -31$
    $m = \pm i\sqrt{6}$

Due to the long history of quadratic equations, solutions to them are described in different ways. The following all refer to the same numbers.

the solutions to $x^2 = -3$
the square roots of -3
$\sqrt{-3}$ and $-\sqrt{-3}$
$i\sqrt{3}$ and $-i\sqrt{3}$

Operations with Imaginary Numbers

All the Field Postulates listed in Appendix B, including the commutative, associative, and distributive properties of addition and multiplication, hold for imaginary numbers, as do all theorems based on these postulates. Consequently, you can use them when working with multiples of i, just as you would when working with multiples of any real numbers.

Example 3

Simplify the following.
a. $(2i)(5i)$ b. $\sqrt{-9} - \sqrt{-25}$ c. $\sqrt{-27} + \sqrt{-3}$ d. $\frac{\sqrt{-9}}{\sqrt{-25}}$

Solution
a. $(2i)(5i) = 10i^2 = 10 \cdot -1 = -10$
b. $\sqrt{-9} - \sqrt{-25} = 3i - 5i = -2i$
c. $\sqrt{-27} + \sqrt{-3} = 3i\sqrt{3} + i\sqrt{3} = 4i\sqrt{3}$
d. $\frac{\sqrt{-9}}{\sqrt{-25}} = \frac{3i}{5i} = \frac{3}{5}$

The next example shows how to multiply imaginary numbers expressed in radical form. Notice that the order of operations must be followed. Take square roots before multiplying.

Example 4

Simplify $\sqrt{-16}\,\sqrt{-25}$.

Solution
Convert to multiples of i.
$$\sqrt{-16} \cdot \sqrt{-25} = i\sqrt{16} \cdot i\sqrt{25}$$
$$= 4i \cdot 5i$$
$$= 20i^2$$
$$= -20$$

Adapting to Individual Needs

Extra Help
To help students avoid errors, encourage them to write out all the steps when multiplying or dividing square roots of negative numbers, as shown in **Examples 3 and 4**.

Even after discussing **Example 4**, you may need to stress several times that imaginary numbers are different from real numbers, and thus we cannot assume that all properties which hold true for real numbers will also hold true for imaginary numbers. In particular, $\sqrt{a}\,\sqrt{b} \neq \sqrt{ab}$ and $\frac{\sqrt{a}}{\sqrt{b}} \neq \sqrt{\frac{a}{b}}$ when a and b are negative.

You are familiar with the property $\sqrt{ab} = \sqrt{a}\sqrt{b}$ for *nonnegative* real numbers a and b. Does this property hold when a and b are negative? Consider Example 4. If we assume that $\sqrt{a}\sqrt{b} = \sqrt{ab}$ for negative values of a and b, then

$$\sqrt{-16}\sqrt{-25} = \sqrt{(-16)(-25)}$$
$$= \sqrt{400}$$
$$= 20.$$

Clearly, this is different from the answer of Example 4. This counterexample shows that the property $\sqrt{a}\sqrt{b} = \sqrt{ab}$ does not hold when a and b are both negative numbers.

QUESTIONS

Covering the Reading

1. *Multiple choice.* About when did mathematicians begin to use roots of negative numbers as solutions to equations? **c**
   (a) sixth century   (b) twelfth century
   (c) sixteenth century   (d) twentieth century

2. *True or false.* Not all negative numbers have square roots. **False**

3. Write the solutions to $x^2 = -1$. **$x = i$ or $x = -i$**

4. Who first used the term "imaginary number"? **Descartes**

5. Who was the first person to suggest using i for $\sqrt{-1}$? **Euler**

6. *Multiple choice.* $\sqrt{-b} \neq i\sqrt{b}$ when b __?__ 0. **c**
   (a) >   (b) =   (c) <

7a) $x = \pm 4\sqrt{-1}$, $x = \pm 4i$
b) $x = \pm\sqrt{16}$, $x = \pm 4$

7. Solve for x. Write the solutions to each equation with a radical sign, and without a radical sign. **See left.**
   a. $x^2 + 16 = 0$ b. $x^2 - 16 = 0$

8. *True or false.* $i\sqrt{5}$ is a square root of -5. Justify your answer.
   True; $(i\sqrt{5})(i\sqrt{5}) = i^2 \cdot 5 = -5$

9. Show that $-3i$ is a square root of -9. **$(-3i)(-3i) = 9i^2 = -9$**

In 10–12, simplify.

10. $\sqrt{-7}$ **$i\sqrt{7}$**   11. $\sqrt{-144}$ **12i**   12. $-\sqrt{96}$ **$-4\sqrt{6}$**

In 13–18, perform the indicated operations. Give answers as real numbers or as multiples of i.

13. $3i + 4i$ **7i**   14. $8i - i$ **7i**   15. $(9i)(8i)$ **–72**

16. $2\sqrt{-9} + \sqrt{-49}$ **13i**   17. $\dfrac{\sqrt{-16}}{\sqrt{-4}}$ **2**   18. $-\sqrt{25} + \sqrt{-25}$ **–5 + 5i**

In 19–21, simplify the product.

19. $\sqrt{-3} \cdot \sqrt{-3}$ **–3**   20. $\sqrt{-6} \cdot \sqrt{-3}$ **$-3\sqrt{2}$**   21. $\sqrt{-2} \cdot \sqrt{2}$ **2i**

22. When does $\sqrt{xy} \neq \sqrt{x}\sqrt{y}$? **when $x < 0$ and $y < 0$**

Lesson 6-8   *Imaginary Numbers*   **391**

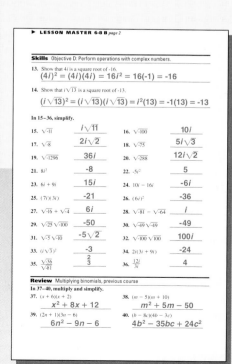

Adapting to Individual Needs

English Language Development
Using the word *imaginary* to describe the numbers in this lesson might confuse students who are just learning English. Explain that at one time people did not understand these numbers, nor did they know how to represent them. Since the numbers were not real numbers, the term *imaginary numbers* was given to them. Stress, however, that imaginary numbers do exist.

Questions 25–26 Remind students that providing a counterexample is an easy way to prove a statement false.

Question 29 Students should use the solutions to **part a** to solve **part b**. You may want to point out that the solutions to **part b** are neither real numbers nor imaginary numbers.

You might also use the *Extension* on page 391 to show that when the graph of $y = ax^2 + bx + c$ is symmetric to the y-axis and does not intersect the x-axis, the equation $ax^2 + bx + c = 0$ has imaginary solutions. When the graph does not intersect the x-axis and is not symmetric to the y-axis, the equation has complex solutions that are not imaginary. This idea is covered in Lessons 6-9 and 6-10.

Question 34b Error Alert Some students will not notice that the units given for r and h are different. Ask students how they solved this problem. Those who use the results of **part a** to do **part b** have to do much less arithmetic than those who substitute numerical values for r and h before finding the difference between the circumferences.

27) $x = \dfrac{-0 \pm \sqrt{0^2 - 4 \cdot 1 \cdot 1}}{2 \cdot 1}$

$= \dfrac{\pm\sqrt{-4}}{2} = \pm\dfrac{2i}{2} = \pm i$

Concentric circles in design. *Shown is a shell gorget with a snake motif, a Native American artifact from 4000–3000 B.C. The gorget is from a mound in Hamilton County, Tennessee.*

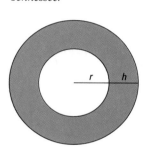

Applying the Mathematics

In 23 and 24, simplify.

23. $\sqrt{-434{,}281}$ 659i

24. $\dfrac{2i + 3i}{i}$ 5

In 25 and 26, *true or false.* If false, give a counterexample.

25. The sum of two imaginary numbers is imaginary. False; Sample: $2i + (-2i) = 0$

26. The product of two imaginary numbers is imaginary. False; Sample: $(2i)(3i) = -6$

27. Verify your solutions to $x^2 = -1$ in Question 3 by using the Quadratic Formula to solve $x^2 + 0x + 1 = 0$. See left.

28. Solve $4x^2 + 25 = 0$ using the Quadratic Formula. $x = \pm\frac{5}{2}i$

29. Solve for x.

  a. $x^2 + 15 = 6$ $x = \pm 3i$
  b. $(x - 3)^2 + 15 = 6$ $x = 3 \pm 3i$

Review

In 30 and 31, solve.   *(Lesson 6-7)*

30. $4m^2 - 4m + 1 = 0$. $m = \frac{1}{2}$
31. $2 - x^2 = 12x$. $x = -6 \pm \sqrt{38}$

32. A ball is thrown upwards from a height of 3 feet with an initial velocity of 28 feet per second.
  a. What is the height of the ball after t seconds? $h = -16t^2 + 28t + 3$
  b. What is the maximum height of the ball? 15.25 ft
  c. When does the ball hit the ground?   *(Lessons 6-3, 6-5, 6-7)*
  after 1.85 seconds

In 33 and 34, use the two concentric circles shown at the left. The smaller circle has radius r; the larger circle has radius $r + h$. *(Previous course)*

33. Find the area of the shaded region. $2\pi rh + \pi h^2$

34. a. How much greater is the circumference of the larger circle than the circumference of the smaller. $2\pi h$
  b. The Earth's equator is nearly a circle with a radius of about 3963 miles. If a rope were held up along the equator 6 feet above ground level, how much longer would the rope be than the equator? $12\pi \approx 37.70$ ft

Exploration

35. By definition, $i^2 = -1$. So $i^3 = i^2 \cdot i = -1 \cdot i = -i$ and $i^4 = i^3 \cdot i = -i \cdot i = -i^2 = -(-1) = 1$.
  a. Continue this pattern to evaluate and simplify each power of i: i^5, i^6, i^7, and i^8. $i^5 = i, i^6 = -1, i^7 = -i, i^8 = 1$
  b. Generalize your result to predict the values of i^{1995}, i^{1996}, and i^{2000}. $i^{1995} = -i, i^{1996} = 1, i^{2000} = 1$

Adapting to Individual Needs

Challenge
Factor each expression completely.
1. $x^2 + 4$ $[(x + 2i)(x - 2i)]$
2. $x^2 + 9$ $[(x + 3i)(x - 3i)]$
3. $x^2 + 25$ $[(x + 5i)(x - 5i)]$
4. $y^2 + 49$ $[(y + 7i)(y - 7i)]$
5. $x^4 + 34x^2 + 225$
   $[(x + 3i)(x - 3i)(x + 5i)(x - 5i)]$
6. $x^4 + 53x^2 + 196$
   $[(x + 2i)(x - 2i)(x + 7i)(x - 7i)]$

Setting Up Lesson 6-9

Be sure to discuss **Question 29b** as an introduction to Lesson 6-9 on complex numbers.

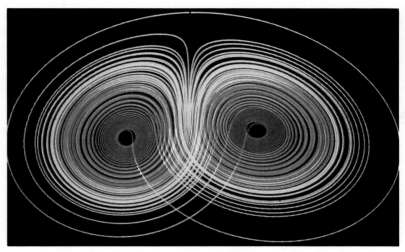

Strange Attractor. *Shown is the Lorenz Attractor, discovered in the early 1960s by MIT meteorologist Edward Lorenz. This shape shows that chaotic behavior can arise from simple dynamical systems. See page 395.*

What Are Complex Numbers?

The set of numbers of the form bi, where b is a real number, are the imaginary numbers. When a real number and an imaginary number are added, the sum is called a **complex number.**

> **Definition**
> A complex number is a number of the form $a + bi$, where a and b are real numbers and $i = \sqrt{-1}$; a is called the real part and b is called the imaginary part.

For example, $-3 + 4i$ is a complex number. The *real part* of $-3 + 4i$ is -3 and the *imaginary part* is 4 (not $4i$).

Two complex numbers $a + bi$ and $c + di$ are **equal** if and only if their real parts are equal and their imaginary parts are equal. That is, $a + bi = c + di$ if and only if $a = c$ and $b = d$. For example, if $x + yi = 2i - 3$, then $x = -3$ and $y = 2$.

Operations with Complex Numbers

> **Postulate**
> All postulates for real numbers except those for inequalities (see Appendix A) also hold for the set of complex numbers.

Thus, you can use the properties to operate with complex numbers in a manner consistent with the way you operate with real numbers.

Lesson 6-9 *Complex Numbers* **393**

Objectives

D Perform operations with complex numbers.

Resources

From the *Teacher's Resource File*
- Lesson Master 6-9A or 6-9B
- Answer Master 6-9
- Teaching Aids
  8 Four-Quadrant Graph Paper
  55 Warm-up
  62 Complex Number System
  63 Venn diagram of Complex Number System

Additional Resources
- Visuals for Teaching Aids 8, 55, 62, 63

Teaching 6-9
Lesson

Warm-up

Diagnostic Write in $a + bi$ form.

1. $\frac{8 + 3i}{5}$ $\frac{8}{5} + \frac{3}{5}i$

2. $\frac{-16 + 8i}{-8}$ $2 - i$

3. $\frac{4 - 6i}{1 + 2i}$ $-\frac{8}{5} - \frac{14}{5}i$

4. $\frac{40 + 20i}{i}$ $20 - 40i$

Notes on Reading

We have not stated nor proved a rule for the sum or product of two complex numbers because the proofs follow so easily from the field properties. You might want to use *Optional Activities* on page 394 and have students develop a rigorous proof for the sum or product of complex numbers.

Lesson 6-9 Overview

Broad Goals This lesson defines and introduces operations on the set of complex numbers. Addition, subtraction, multiplication, and division of complex numbers are covered.

Perspective Many books *define* addition and multiplication of complex numbers and then deduce their properties. We take another approach: we *assume*, as we did with real numbers, that addition and

multiplication in the set of complex numbers satisfy the customary (field) properties, and from those assumptions deduce the operations of complex-number addition and multiplication.

It is customary to write the answer to a complex-number computation in the form of $a + bi$, so that the real and imaginary parts of the complex number are evident.

Error Alert Students often have difficulty with opposite signs when doing problems such as in **Example 3**. Encourage students to write down all the steps and to first write i^2. Then in the next step they should change i^2 to –1. This should help them avoid careless errors.

History Connection At age 22, Karl Gauss earned his doctorate with a thesis that developed the concept of complex numbers and proved the Fundamental Theorem of Algebra. Two years later, he published a treatise on the theory of numbers, one of the most brilliant achievements in the history of mathematics.

The term *complex conjugate* is also used in Lesson 6-10, so it should be discussed here in **Example 4**.

When discussing the various kinds of complex numbers listed on page 396, emphasize that each type of number in the hierarchy is an example of any higher type and has special cases of a lower type. (Examples: the rational number $\frac{a}{b}$ is a real number and is an integer if $b = 1$; the complex number $a + bi$ is an imaginary number if $a = 0$.) Students of UCSMP *Geometry* will be familiar with hierarchical diagrams of this type based on inclusion. They will have seen them for the various types of angles, triangles, and quadrilaterals. You may want to use the *Visual Organizer* of the complex number system described below for this discussion. This visual organizer can also be found on **Teaching Aid 62**.

Teaching Aid 63 contains a Venn diagram of the complex number system.

Example 1

Add and simplify: $(3 + 4i) + (7 + 8i)$.

Solution

Use the Associative and the Commutative Properties of addition to regroup the real parts together and the imaginary parts together.

$(3 + 4i) + (7 + 8i) = (3 + 7) + (4i + 8i)$

Then use the Distributive Property to add the multiples of i.

$$= 10 + (4 + 8)i$$
$$= 10 + 12i$$

The Distributive Property can also be used to multiply a complex number by a real number or by an imaginary number.

Example 2

Simplify $2i(8 + 5i)$.

Solution

$2i(8 + 5i)$	$= 2i(8) + 2i(5i)$	Distributive Property
	$= 16i + 10(i^2)$	Associative and Commutative Properties of Multiplication
	$= 16i + 10(-1)$	Definition of i
	$= -10 + 16i$	Commutative Property of Addition

In Example 2, notice that i^2 was simplified using the fact that $i^2 = -1$. Generally, all answers to complex-number computations should be put in the form $a + bi$. This makes it easy to identify the real and imaginary parts.

To multiply complex numbers, think of complex numbers as linear expressions in i, and multiply using the Distributive Property. Then use $i^2 = -1$ to simplify your answer.

Example 3

Multiply and simplify: $(8 - 3i)(4 + 5i)$.

Solution

$(8 - 3i)(4 + 5i)$	$= 32 + 40i - 12i - 15i^2$	Distributive Property
	$= 32 + 28i - 15i^2$	Distributive Property (like terms)
	$= 32 + 28i - 15(-1)$	Definition of i
	$= 47 + 28i$	Arithmetic

394

Visual Organizer
Materials: **Teaching Aid 62**

You may wish to use a diagram like the one at the right to illustrate the relationship between number systems. Ask students to give examples of each kind of number in the diagram.

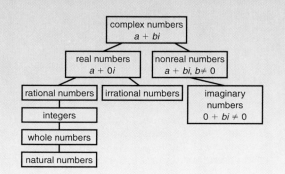

Optional Activities

After you discuss **Examples 1 and 2**, you might have students **work in groups** and go through these proofs for the sum and product of two complex numbers. Have students assign one or more of the following justifications for each step.

(1) Commutative Property of Addition
(2) Associative Property of Addition
(3) Commutative Property of Multiplication
(4) Associative Property of Multiplication

Applications of Complex Numbers

The first use of the term "complex number" is generally credited to Karl Friedrich Gauss. Gauss applied complex numbers to the study of electricity. Later in the 19th century, applications using complex numbers were found in geometry and acoustics. In the 1970s, a new field called *dynamical systems* arose in which complex numbers play a pivotal role.

Here is a situation arising from electricity. The *impedance* in an alternating-current (AC) circuit is the amount by which the circuit resists the flow of electricity. Impedance is described by a complex number. Two electrical circuits may be connected *in series* or *in parallel*.

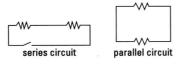

series circuit   parallel circuit

The total impedance Z_T of a circuit is a function of the impedances Z_1 and Z_2 of the individual circuits. In a series circuit, $Z_T = Z_1 + Z_2$. In a parallel circuit, $Z_T = \dfrac{Z_1 Z_2}{Z_1 + Z_2}$. Thus, to find the total impedance in a parallel circuit, division of complex numbers is needed.

Shown are electrical engineers aligning elements of the OPAL particle detector at CERN, the European centre for particle physics near Geneva, Switzerland. Electrical engineers deal with the development, production, and testing of electrical and electronic devices and equipment.

Example 4

Find the total impedance in a parallel circuit if $Z_1 = 3 - i$ ohms and $Z_2 = 3 + i$ ohms.

Solution

Substitute into the impedance formula for parallel circuits, and evaluate.

$$
\begin{aligned}
Z_T &= \frac{Z_1 Z_2}{Z_1 + Z_2} \\
&= \frac{(3 - i)(3 + i)}{(3 - i) + (3 + i)} \\
&= \frac{9 + 3i - 3i - i^2}{6} \\
&= \frac{9 - (-1)}{6} \\
&= \frac{10}{6} \\
&= \frac{5}{3}
\end{aligned}
$$

The total impedance is $\frac{5}{3}$ ohms.

The complex numbers $3 - i$ and $3 + i$ given in Example 4 are *complex conjugates* of each other. Notice that the product $(3 - i)(3 + i)$ in the numerator of the fraction in Example 4 is a real number. In general, the **complex conjugate** of $a + bi$ is $a - bi$. In the Questions, you are asked to prove that the product of any two complex conjugates is a real number.

Lesson 6-9   *Complex Numbers*   **395**

---

(5) Distributive Property
(6) Multiplication Property of –1
(7) Definition of i
(8) Definition of subtraction

$$
\begin{aligned}
(a + bi) + (c + di) &= a + (bi + c) + di && [2] \\
&= a + (c + bi) + di && [1] \\
&= (a + c) + (bi + di) && [2] \\
&= (a + c) + (b + d)i && [5] \\
(a + bi)(c + di) &= (a + bi)c + (a + bi)di && [5]
\end{aligned}
$$

$$
\begin{aligned}
&= c(a + bi) + di(a + bi) && [3] \\
&= (ca + cbi) + ((di)a + (di)(bi)) && [5] \\
&= ca + cbi + dia + dibi && [2 \text{ and } 4] \\
&= ac + adi + bci + bdii && [4 \text{ and } 3] \\
&= ac + adi + bci + bd(-1) && [7] \\
&= ac + adi + bci + -bd && [6] \\
&= ac + -bd + adi + bci && [2 \text{ and } 1] \\
&= ac + -bd + (ad + bc)i && [5 \text{ and } 3] \\
&= ac - bd + (ad + bc)i && [8] \\
&= (ac - bd) + (ad + bc)i && [2]
\end{aligned}
$$

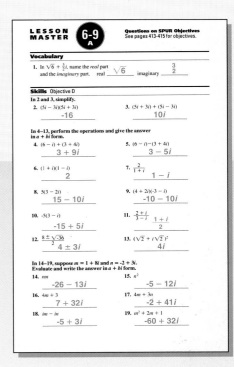

Notes on Questions

Questions 10, 20–21 Students are expected to recognize names of properties when they do these questions.

Question 15 You may wish to generalize **parts a and b** to ask: What is the result (in $x + yi$ form) when $a + bi$ is divided by $c + di$?

$[\frac{ac + bd}{c^2 + d^2} + \frac{bc - ad}{c^2 + d^2}i]$

(Notes on Questions continue on page 398.)

Follow-up for Lesson **6-9**

Practice

For more questions on SPUR Objectives, use **Lesson Master 6-9A** (shown on page 395) or **Lesson Master 6-9B** (shown on pages 396–397).

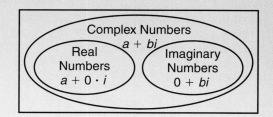

Complex conjugates are useful when dividing complex numbers. To divide two complex numbers, multiply both numerator and denominator by the conjugate of the denominator. When the denominator is multiplied by its complex conjugate, the result is a real number. Then divide each term in the numerator by this real number.

Example 5

Write $\frac{3 - 4i}{2 + 5i}$ in $a + bi$ form.

Solution

The complex conjugate of $2 + 5i$ is $2 - 5i$, so multiply both the numerator and the denominator by $\frac{2 - 5i}{2 - 5i}$, and divide the numerator by the real number that results.

$$\frac{3 - 4i}{2 + 5i} = \frac{3 - 4i}{2 + 5i} \cdot \frac{2 - 5i}{2 - 5i} \qquad \text{Identity Property of Multiplication}$$

$$= \frac{6 - 15i - 8i + 20i^2}{4 - 10i + 10i - 25i^2} \qquad \text{Distributive Property}$$

$$= \frac{6 - 23i + 20i^2}{4 - 25i^2} \qquad \text{Distributive Property (like terms)}$$

$$= \frac{6 - 23i + 20(-1)}{4 - 25(-1)} \qquad \text{Definition of } i$$

$$= \frac{-14 - 23i}{29}$$

$$= \frac{-14}{29} - \frac{23}{29}i \qquad \text{Distributive Property (adding fractions)}$$

The Various Kinds of Complex Numbers

Because $a + 0i = a$, every real number a is a complex number. Thus, the set of real numbers is a subset of the set of complex numbers. Likewise, every imaginary number bi equals $0 + bi$, so the set of imaginary numbers is also a subset of the set of complex numbers.

The diagram below shows how various kinds of complex numbers are related.

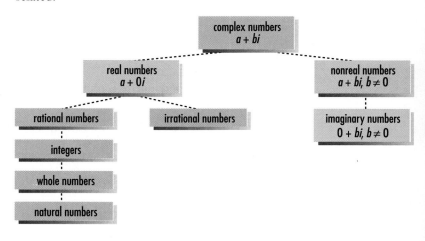

Adapting to Individual Needs

Extra Help
A Venn diagram can help illustrate the relationship among complex, real, and imaginary numbers. **Teaching Aid 63** contains this Venn diagram.

QUESTIONS

Covering the Reading

1. A complex number is a number of the form $a + bi$ where a and b are __?__ numbers. **real**

In 2–4, give the real and imaginary parts of the complex number.

2. $14 + 5i$
   $a = 14, b = 5$

3. $3 - i\sqrt{2}$
   $a = 3, b = -\sqrt{2}$

4. i **$a = 0, b = 1$**

5. If $x + 12i = 7 - yi$, find x and y. **$x = 7, y = -12$**

In 6–9, perform the operation and write your answer in $a + bi$ form.

6. $(11 - 4i) + (18 - 3i)$ **$29 - 7i$**

7. $3i(2 + 9i)$ **$-27 + 6i$**

8. $(2 - i)(2 + i)$ **5**

9. $(-8 + i)(5 - 3i)$ **$-37 + 29i$**

10a) Distributive Property
b) Distributive Property (like terms)
c) definition of i
d) Commutative Property of Addition

10. Provide reasons for each step. **See left.**

$$
\begin{aligned}
(12 + 7i)(8 + 4i) &= 96 + 48i + 56i + 28i^2 && \text{a. } \underline{\quad?\quad} \\
&= 96 + 104i + 28i^2 && \text{b. } \underline{\quad?\quad} \\
&= 96 + 104i + 28(-1) && \text{c. } \underline{\quad?\quad} \\
&= 96 + -28 + 104i && \text{d. } \underline{\quad?\quad} \\
&= 68 + 104i
\end{aligned}
$$

11. Who is thought to be the first to use the term "complex number"? **Karl Friedrich Gauss**

12. What are the complex numbers $3 + 7i$ and $3 - 7i$ called? **complex conjugates**

13. Given two electrical circuits with impedances $Z_1 = 10 + 5i$ ohms and $Z_2 = 10 - 5i$ ohms, find the total resistance if these two circuits are connected as described.
    a. in series **20 ohms**
    b. in parallel **6.25 ohms**

14. Name two fields in which complex numbers are applied. **electricity, acoustics**

15. Write in $a + bi$ form.
    a. $\dfrac{6 - 2i}{5}$ **$\frac{6}{5} - \frac{2}{5}i$**
    b. $\dfrac{5}{6 - 2i}$ **$\frac{3}{4} + \frac{1}{4}i$**

In 16–18, write in $a + bi$ form.

16. $\dfrac{3 + i}{4 - 7i}$ **$\frac{1}{13} + \frac{5}{13}i$**

17. $\dfrac{4 + i}{-2 - 5i}$ **$\frac{-13}{29} + \frac{18}{29}i$**

18. $\dfrac{20 + 15i}{5i}$ **$3 - 4i$**

19. *True or false.* Every real number is also a complex number. **True**

Applying the Mathematics

20. Write the additive identity for the complex numbers in $a + bi$ form. **$0 + 0i$**

21. Write the multiplicative identity for the complex numbers in $a + bi$ form. **$1 + 0i$**

22. Write $\sqrt{-9}$ in $a + bi$ form. **$0 + 3i$**

Lesson 6-9 *Complex Numbers* **397**

Assessment

Oral Communication Choose one of the categories of numbers from the chart on page 396 and ask students for an example of that type of number. Also give students examples of various types of numbers and have them name the categories on the chart to which the number belong. [Students correctly give examples of various types of numbers and also correctly classify numbers according to type.]

Extension

A group of students can follow up **Question 31** by graphing integral powers of other complex numbers. [Students should see that generally the powers fall in a spiral; the spiral is best seen if the original complex number (a, b) is just above or just below the x-axis and if $a^2 + b^2 = 1$; integral powers of the complex number lie on a circle with radius 1 and center at the origin. If $a^2 + b^2 < 1$, a spiral of decreasing radius is formed by increasing powers of the complex number.]

Project Update Project 5, *History of Quadratics*, on page 409, relates to the content of this lesson.

▶ **LESSON MASTER 6-9 B** *page 2*

In 20–31, perform the operations and write the answer in $a + bi$ form.

20. $(12 + 3i) - (2 + 6i)$
    $10 - 3i$

21. $(7 + i)(3 - 4i)$
    $25 - 25i$

22. $(8 - i)(8 + i)$
    $65 + 0i$

23. $(4 - 3i) + (10 + 2i)$
    $14 - i$

24. $5(6 - 4i)$
    $30 - 20i$

25. $7i(1 + 5i)$
    $-35 + 7i$

26. $(3 + 9i)(3 - 9i)$
    $90 + 0i$

27. $(5 - 2i)(1 - 3i)$
    $-1 - 17i$

28. $(4 - i)^2$
    $15 - 8i$

29. $(7i + 2)^2$
    $-45 + 28i$

30. $(\sqrt{3} + i)^2$
    $2 + 2i\sqrt{3}$

31. $(\sqrt{3} + i\sqrt{3})^2$
    $0 + 6i$

In 32–37, suppose $p = 4 + i$ and $q = -3 - 2i$. Evaluate and write the answer in $a + bi$ form.

32. $2p - iq$
    $6 + 5i$

33. pq
    $-10 - 11i$

34. q^2
    $5 + 12i$

35. iq
    $2 - 3i$

36. $p^2 + 2p - 3$
    $20 + 10i$

37. $(ip)^2 - (iq)^2$
    $-10 + 4i$

397

Notes on Questions

Question 25 This question should be discussed, since it leads into the ideas of Lesson 6-10.

Question 27 If you have access to a symbol manipulator, use it to do this question. Students are often amazed at the ability of symbol-manipulator technology to do complex arithmetic.

Question 29 Each side of this equation may be divided by 2 before the Quadratic Formula is used. Although it is not necessary to do so, most students prefer to work with integers of the smallest possible magnitude.

Question 31 Students may use graph paper or **Teaching Aid 8** to graph complex numbers.

24) $a^2 + b^2$; since a and b are real numbers, a^2 and b^2 are real.

30a

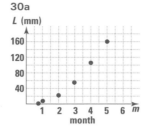

In 23 and 24, consider the complex numbers $a - bi$ and $a + bi$.

23. Calculate their sum. $2a$

24. Find their product and explain why it is a real number. **See left.**

25. a. Solve $x^2 - 2x + 5 = 0$ using the Quadratic Formula. Write your solutions in $a + bi$ form. $1 \pm 2i$
   b. Check your answer(s).

   b) $(1 + 2i)^2 - 2(1 + 2i) + 5 = 0$? $1 + 4i - 4 - 2 - 4i + 5 = 0$? $0 = 0$? Yes.
   $(1 - 2i)^2 - 2(1 - 2i) + 5 = 0$? $1 - 4i - 4 - 2 + 4i + 5 = 0$? $0 = 0$? Yes.

Review

26. *Multiple choice.* Which is not a square root of -9? *(Lesson 6-8)* c
   (a) $-3i$ (b) $3i$ (c) -3 (d) $\sqrt{-9}$

In 27 and 28, suppose each letter of the English alphabet except for i is a variable representing a real number, and $i^2 = -1$. *(Lesson 6-8)*

27. Simplify Mississippi. Ms^4p^2

28. Name a state that represents an imaginary number. **Sample: Florida**

29. Solve $4a^2 = 2 + 4a$. *(Lesson 6-7)* $\dfrac{1 \pm \sqrt{3}}{2}$

crown-rump length

30. The size of a human embryo is often measured by calculating its *crown-rump length,* as shown by segment $\overline{CR}$ at the left. The table below gives the average crown-rump length L in millimeters of a human embryo m months after conception.

m	.75	1	2	3	4	5
L	2	5	23	56	112	160

   a. Make a scatterplot of the data. **See left.**
   b. Find a quadratic equation to model these data. **See below.**
   c. According to your model, about how long is the average human embryo 2.5 months after conception? ≈ 40.79 mm
   d. At full term (9 months after conception) the average crown-rump length of a human fetus is 350 mm. Does the model in part **b** overestimate or underestimate this length? *(Lesson 6-6)* overestimates
   b) Sample: $L = 6.15m^2 + 2.76m - 4.55$

Exploration

31a, b)

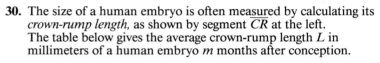

31. A complex number $a + bi$ is graphed as the point (a, b) with the x-axis as the real axis and the y-axis as the imaginary axis.
   a. Graph $z = 1 + i$ as the point $(1, 1)$. **See left.**
   b. Compute and graph z^2, z^3, and z^4. **See left.**
   c. What pattern emerges? Can you predict where z^5 will be?
   The points appear to be on a spiral; $z^5 = (-4, -4)$

Adapting to Individual Needs

Challenge
Have students prove the following two statements.

1. Prove that $\sqrt{i} = \dfrac{\sqrt{2}}{2} + \dfrac{\sqrt{2}}{2}i$ and give another square root of i.

$[(\dfrac{\sqrt{2}}{2} + \dfrac{\sqrt{2}}{2}i)^2 = (\dfrac{\sqrt{2}}{2} + \dfrac{\sqrt{2}}{2}i)(\dfrac{\sqrt{2}}{2} + \dfrac{\sqrt{2}}{2}i)$

$= \dfrac{1}{2} + \dfrac{1}{2}i + \dfrac{1}{2}i + \dfrac{1}{2}i^2 = \dfrac{1}{2} + i + -\dfrac{1}{2} = i$

Another square root of i is $-\dfrac{\sqrt{2}}{2} - \dfrac{\sqrt{2}}{2}i$.]

2. Prove that no quadratic equation with real coefficients can have one real solution and one nonreal solution.
[If one solution is $a + bi$, then $a - bi$ is also a solution. Therefore, the solutions both have to be real or they both have to be nonreal.]

Setting Up Lesson 6-10

Use **Question 25** to lead into the In-class Activity, which in turn prepares students for Lesson 6-10. Be sure students complete the activity before you assign Lesson 6-10.

398

Predicting the Number of Real Solutions to a Quadratic Equation

IN-CLASS ACTIVITY

Materials: Automatic grapher
Work on this activity in a small group.

Record your results in a table like the one below.

$y = ax^2 + bx + c$	number of x-intercepts of graph	solutions to $ax^2 + bx + c = 0$	number of real solutions to $ax^2 + bx + c = 0$	value of $b^2 - 4ac$
a. $y = 2x^2 - 12x + 18$	1	$x = 3$	1	0
b. $y = 2x^2 - 12x + 13$	2	$x = 3 \pm \frac{1}{2}\sqrt{10}$	2	40
c. $y = 2x^2 - 12x + 23$	0	no real solution	0	-40

1 Use an automatic grapher to sketch a graph of the quadratic function. Identify the number of x-intercepts.
a. $y = 2x^2 - 12x + 18$ (a-c) See margin for graphs. See table above for
b. $y = 2x^2 - 12x + 13$ x-intercepts.
c. $y = 2x^2 - 12x + 23$

2 Solve the equations using the Quadratic Formula, and tell how many of the solutions are real. (a-c) See table above.
a. $2x^2 - 12x + 18 = 0$
b. $2x^2 - 12x + 13 = 0$
c. $2x^2 - 12x + 23 = 0$

3 Discuss with others in your group any patterns you notice in the table so far. See margin.

4 When $ax^2 + bx + c = 0$, the value of the expression $b^2 - 4ac$ can be used to predict the number of real solutions to the quadratic equation. Calculate the value of $b^2 - 4ac$ for each of the equations in Question 2, and record it in your table. See table above.

5 Each person in the group should do the following.
a. Make up an equation of the form $y = ax^2 + bx + c$, where a, b, and c are real numbers and $a \neq 0$. Answers may
b. Sketch a graph of $y = ax^2 + bx + c$. vary.
c. Complete the table for your equation.

6 Look again at the entries in the table. See margin.
a. If $b^2 - 4ac > 0$, what conclusion(s) can you draw?
b. If $b^2 - 4ac = 0$, what seems to be true?
c. If $b^2 - 4ac < 0$, what conclusion(s) can you draw?

399

In-class Activity
Resources
From the *Teacher's Resource File*
■ Answer Master 6-10
■ Teaching Aid 64: Table for Recording Results

Additional Resources
■ Visual for Teaching Aid 64

By doing this activity, students see that the number of x-intercepts of a quadratic function with equation $y = ax^2 + bx + c$ is the number of real solutions to the corresponding quadratic equation $ax^2 + bx + c = 0$, and that these numbers are determined by the value of $b^2 - 4ac$.

This is a long activity, but if it is done and discussed in class, you will have introduced most of the major ideas in Lesson 6-10.

Use **Teaching Aid 64**. When most students have finished the activity, have one member of each group announce the equation that group used, as well as other entries. Discuss the conclusions students drew as responses to **Question 6.**

Additional Answers, continued
3. Sample: The number of x-intercepts in the graph is equal to the number of real solutions.
6a. The graph has two x-intercepts and the equation has two real solutions.
b. The graph has one x-intercept and the equation has exactly one real solution.
c. The graph has no x-intercept and the equation has no real solution.

Additional Answers
1a.
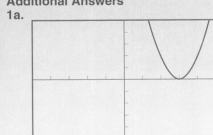

−5 ≤ x ≤ 5,   x-scale = 1
−5 ≤ y ≤ 5,   y-scale = 1

1b.
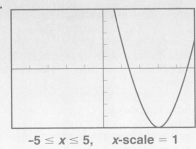

−5 ≤ x ≤ 5,   x-scale = 1
−5 ≤ y ≤ 5,   y-scale = 1

1c.
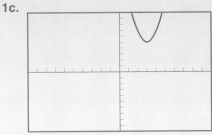

−10 ≤ x ≤ 10,   x-scale = 1
−10 ≤ y ≤ 10,   y-scale = 1

Objectives

C Solve quadratic equations.

F Use the discriminant of a quadratic equation to determine the nature of the solutions to the equation.

K Use the discriminant of a quadratic equation to determine the number of x-intercepts of the graph.

Resources

From the *Teacher's Resource File*
- Lesson Master 6-10A or 6-10B
- Answer Master 6-10
- Teaching Aids
  8 Four-Quadrant Graph Paper
  19 Automatic Grapher Grids
  55 Warm-up

Additional Resources
- Visuals for Teaching Aids 8, 19, 55

Teaching Lesson **6-10**

Warm-up

Graph each equation and determine the x-intercepts.

1. $y = x^2 - 4x$ 0, 4
2. $y = x^2 - 4x + 4$ 2
3. $y = x^2 + 4$ None

Graphs are shown at the top of page 401.

Analyzing Solutions to Quadratic Equations

Stamps of approval. *Many countries have issued stamps to honor great mathematicians and their works. The mathematicians shown are Descartes (top), al-Khowarizmi (left), and Gauss (right).*

❶ A Brief History of Quadratics

As early as 1700 B.C., ancient mathematicians considered problems that today we would solve using quadratic equations. The Babylonians even described solutions to these problems using words that indicate that they had general procedures for finding solutions that were like the Quadratic Formula. However, the ancients had neither our modern notation nor the notion of complex numbers. The history of the solving of quadratic equations helped lead to the acceptance of irrational numbers, negative numbers, and complex numbers.

The Pythagoreans in the 5th century B.C. thought of x^2 as the area of a square with side x. So if $x^2 = 2$, as in the square pictured below, then $x = \sqrt{2}$. These Greek mathematicians proved that $\sqrt{2}$ was an irrational number, and so they realized that irrational numbers have meaning. But they never considered the negative solution to the equation $x^2 = 2$, because lengths could not be negative.

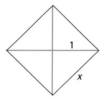

Lesson 6-10 Overview

Broad Goals This lesson serves three purposes. It gives students another day to practice obtaining solutions to quadratic equations. It introduces the concept of the discriminant and how the discriminant determines the number and the nature of the roots of a quadratic equation. And it serves to put together earlier ideas of the chapter concerning graphs of quadratic functions.

Perspective This lesson helps students connect the symbolic and graphical solutions to quadratic equations. By working through the In-class Activity on page 399, many students will "discover" the Discriminant Theorem.

The Quadratic Formula may be applied to any quadratic equation. However, in this lesson we restrict our attention to those quadratic equations with real coefficients.

Only when there are real coefficients does the Discriminant Theorem hold.

Writings of Indian and Arab mathematicians from the years 800 A.D. to 1200 A.D. indicate that they could solve quadratic equations. In 825 A.D., the Arab mathematician al-Khowarizmi, in his book *Hisab al-jabr w'al muqabala* (from which we get the word "algebra"), solved quadratics like the Babylonians did. His contribution is that he did not think of the unknown as having to stand for a length. Thus the unknown became an abstract quantity. Around 1200, al-Khowarizmi's book was translated into Latin by Fibonacci, and European mathematicians had a method for solving quadratics.

The first to use letters and coefficients the way we do was François Viète, a French lawyer and mathematician in the late 1500s. For $a^2 - 3a = 10$, Viète would write "1AQ–3A aequatur 10". (The Q stands for "quadratus.") Our modern notation with exponents is first found in a book by René Descartes published in 1637. These symbols forced European mathematicians to consider negative solutions to quadratic equations.

In the 16th century, mathematicians began using complex numbers because these numbers arose as solutions to equations. In the 19th century, Gauss brought both geometric and physical meaning to complex numbers. The geometric meaning, which you will encounter in later mathematics courses, uses the coordinate plane of Descartes. You have seen one of the physical meanings of complex numbers, the representation of impedance, in Lesson 6-9. In 1848, Gauss was the first to allow the *coefficients* in his equations to be complex numbers.

Finding Real Solutions by Graphing

Descartes' coordinate system provides a graphical way to find real-number solutions to quadratic equations, one that you have seen many times in this book. To solve $x^2 - 3x = 10$, notice that the graphs of $y = x^2 - 3x$ and $y = 10$ intersect at the two points $(-2, 10)$ and $(5, 10)$. This verifies that the solutions to $x^2 - 3x = 10$ are -2 and 5. This is shown on the graph below.

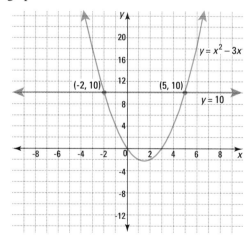

Lesson 6-10 *Analyzing Solutions to Quadratic Equations* **401**

Notes on Reading
Students may use graph paper, **Teaching Aid 8,** or **Teaching Aid 19** throughout this lesson.

❶ **Multicultural Connection**
When you discuss the history of quadratics, emphasize the span of time and the various cultures involved in the development of the concepts. Activity 1 in *Optional Activities* below relates to the information given in the text.

Optional Activities

Activity 1 History Connection
You can use this activity after students read the opening paragraphs on "A Brief History of Quadratics." Suggest that students **work in groups** and make time lines using the information given in the text. Encourage students to do additional research on quadratics and also include that information on their time lines. To give their time lines a historical perspective, students might decorate the paper to reflect other events taking place at various times along the line, such as the building of the pyramids, the eruption of Mt. Vesuvius, and the invention of the printing press.

❷ Emphasize that when the coefficients of $ax^2 + bx + c = 0$ are real, such as in **Example 1**, any complex roots are complex conjugates. However, when the coefficients are not all real, complex roots are not necessarily complex conjugates. For instance, the solutions to $x^2 + ix + 6 = 0$ are $-3i$ and $2i$.

Stress the connection between the nature of the solutions to the quadratic equation $ax^2 + bx + c = 0$ and the x-intercepts of the graph of $y = ax^2 + bx + c$.

Students should realize that they are now able to solve any quadratic equation, although if an equation has complex coefficients they will not always be able to simplify the solutions.

Another graphical way to solve the same equation is shown below. We have converted the equation $x^2 - 3x = 10$ to the standard form $x^2 - 3x - 10 = 0$. Now we look for intersections of the graphs of $y = x^2 - 3x - 10$ and $y = 0$. The graphs intersect at the two points $(-2, 0)$ and $(5, 0)$. This is shown below.

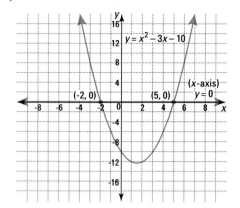

There is an advantage to the second graphical method. By converting the equation to standard form, all real-number solutions can be found by examining the x-axis. The x-intercepts of the graph of $y = ax^2 + bx + c$ indicate the real-number solutions to $ax^2 + bx + c = 0$. You should have seen in the In-class Activity that the number of real-number solutions to each quadratic equation was the same as the number of x-intercepts.

How Many Real Solutions Does a Quadratic Equation Have?

Now consider the general quadratic equation. When a, b, and c are real numbers and $a \neq 0$, the Quadratic Formula indicates that the two solutions to $ax^2 + bx + c = 0$ are

$$x = \frac{-b \pm \sqrt{b^2 - 4ac}}{2a}.$$

Because a and b are real numbers, the numbers $-b$ and $2a$ are real, so only $\sqrt{b^2 - 4ac}$ could possibly be nonreal. There are now three possibilities:

(1) If $b^2 - 4ac$ is positive, then $\sqrt{b^2 - 4ac}$ is a positive number. There will then be two real solutions.

(2) If $b^2 - 4ac$ is zero, then $\sqrt{b^2 - 4ac} = \sqrt{0} = 0$. Then $x = \frac{-b \pm 0}{2a} = \frac{-b}{2a}$, and there is only one real solution.

(3) If $b^2 - 4ac$ is negative, then $\sqrt{b^2 - 4ac}$ is an imaginary number. There will then be two nonreal solutions. Furthermore, since these solutions are of the form $m + ni$ and $m - ni$, they are complex conjugates.

Furthermore, if a, b, and c are rational numbers, and if $b^2 - 4ac$ is a perfect square, then the solutions to the equation will also be rational.

402

Optional Activities
Activity 2
This activity can be used after students have completed the *Extension* on page 405. Ask students to use the fact that the sum of the roots of a quadratic is $-\frac{b}{a}$, and find the axis of symmetry for $y = ax^2 + bx + c$. [The axis of symmetry is halfway between the roots. Half the sum of the roots is $\frac{-b}{2a}$, so the axis of symmetry is $y = -\frac{b}{2a}$.]

Because of the three properties on page 402, the number $b^2 - 4ac$ is called the **discriminant** of the quadratic equation. It determines the *nature of the solutions* to the equation.

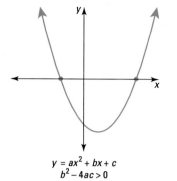

$y = ax^2 + bx + c$
$b^2 - 4ac > 0$
two real solutions

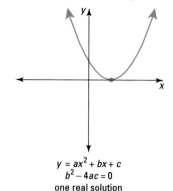

$y = ax^2 + bx + c$
$b^2 - 4ac = 0$
one real solution

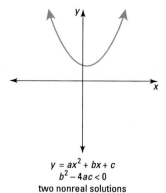

$y = ax^2 + bx + c$
$b^2 - 4ac < 0$
two nonreal solutions

Geometrically, the graph of $y = ax^2 + bx + c$ intersects the x-axis in two points in situation (1), in one point in situation (2), and in no points in situation (3). Above are drawn these situations when a is positive, so the parabolas open up. The results you found from the In-class Activity should be consistent with this theorem.

> **Discriminant Theorem**
> Suppose a, b, and c are real numbers with $a \neq 0$.
> Then the equation $ax^2 + bx + c = 0$ has
> (i)   two real solutions if $b^2 - 4ac > 0$.
> (ii) one real solution if $b^2 - 4ac = 0$.
> (iii) two complex conjugate solutions if $b^2 - 4ac < 0$.

Solutions to quadratic (and other) equations are sometimes called **roots**. The number i allows square roots of negative numbers to be considered as complex solutions.

In Example 1, we let D stand for the discriminant. This shortens some of the writing.

❷ **Example 1**
Determine the nature of the roots of the following equations. Then solve.
a. $4x^2 - 12x + 9 = 0$
b. $2x^2 + 3x + 4 = 0$
c. $2x^2 - 3x - 9 = 0$

Solution
a. Use the Discriminant Theorem. Here $a = 4$, $b = -12$, and $c = 9$.
$$D = b^2 - 4ac = (-12)^2 - 4(4)(9) = 0$$
Thus, the equation has one real solution or root.
By the quadratic formula, $x = \dfrac{12 \pm \sqrt{0}}{8} = \dfrac{3}{2} = 1.5$ ▶

Lesson 6-10 *Analyzing Solutions to Quadratic Equations* **403**

Adapting to Individual Needs
Extra Help
Be sure that students note that the discriminant of $ax^2 + bx + c = 0$ is $b^2 - 4ac$ and *not* the expression $\sqrt{b^2 - 4ac}$. Explain to students that in order for the equation to have two rational roots, the coefficients must be rational and the discriminant must be a perfect square.

Additional Examples
1. Determine the nature of roots of the following equations. Then solve the equations.
   a. $3x^2 + 3x + 8 = 0$ Two complex roots; $-\frac{1}{2} \pm \frac{\sqrt{87}}{6} i$
   b. $15x^2 + 2x - 1 = 0$ Two real roots; $\frac{1}{5}, -\frac{1}{3}$
   c. $16x^2 - 72x + 81 = 0$ One real root; $\frac{9}{4}$
   d. $x^2 + 7x + 1 = 0$ Two real roots; $\frac{-7 \pm 3\sqrt{5}}{2}$
2. A ball is thrown from a height of 5 feet with a vertical velocity of 40 feet per second. Will this ball ever reach a height of 50 feet? Why or why not? No; the discriminant of the quadratic equation $50 = -16t^2 + 40t + 5$ is negative.
3. Does the graph of the equation $y = 6x^2 + 5x - 2$ have any x-intercepts? Yes; $b^2 - 4ac > 0$ so there are two intercepts.
4. Does $10x^2 - x - 3 = 0$ have any rational solutions? If so, find them. Yes; $b^2 - 4ac = 121$, which is a perfect square. The solutions are $x = \frac{3}{5}$ and $x = -\frac{1}{2}$.

(Notes on Questions begin on page 406.)

Practice

For more questions on SPUR Objectives, use **Lesson Master 6-10A** (shown on page 405) or **Lesson Master 6-10B** (shown on pages 406–407).

Assessment

Written Communication Have students use the Discriminant Theorem to determine three different quadratic equations—one with two real solutions, one with one real solution, and one with two nonreal solutions. [Students correctly provide three quadratic equations with the following characteristics:
In the first, $b^2 - 4ac > 0$.
In the second, $b^2 - 4ac = 0$.
In the third, $b^2 - 4ac < 0$.]

b. Here $a = 2$, $b = 3$, and $c = 4$,
so $D = b^2 - 4ac = 9 - 4 \cdot 2 \cdot 4 = -23 < 0$.
The equation has two complex conjugate roots.

By the quadratic formula, $x = \frac{-3 \pm \sqrt{-23}}{4}$.

So $x = \frac{-3}{4} + \frac{\sqrt{23}}{4}\, i$ or $x = \frac{-3}{4} - \frac{\sqrt{23}}{4}\, i$.

c. Here $a = 2$, $b = -3$, and $c = -9$;
so $D = b^2 - 4ac = (-3)^2 - 4 \cdot 2\,(-9) = 81 > 0$.
The equation has two real roots. Because D is a perfect square, the roots are rational.

By the quadratic formula, $x = \frac{3 \pm \sqrt{81}}{4} = \frac{3 \pm 9}{4}$.

So $x = 3$ or $x = -\frac{6}{4} = -\frac{3}{2} = -1.5$

Applying the Discriminant Theorem

The number of real solutions to a quadratic equation can tell us something about the situation that led to the equation. For instance, recall the formula

$$h(x) = -.005x^2 + 2x + 3.5$$

describing the height of the baseball hit by Pop Fligh. When we let $h(x) = 8$, we solved

$$8 = -.005x^2 + 2x + 3.5$$

and found two solutions. These solutions indicated that the ball was 8 feet above the ground in two places. You can use the Discriminant Theorem to determine whether the ball ever reached a particular height.

Example 2

Does Pop Fligh's ball ever reach a height of 40 feet?

Solution

Pop Fligh's ball will reach a height of 40 feet if there are real values of x with

$$40 = -.005x^2 + 2x + 3.5.$$

To calculate the discriminant of this equation, first rewrite the equation in standard form:

$$0 = -.005x^2 + 2x - 36.5$$

The discriminant is

$$D = b^2 - 4ac = 2^2 - 4 \cdot (-.005) \cdot (-36.5) = 3.27.$$

Since D is positive, there are two real-number solutions to this equation. This means that the ball gets to a height of 40 feet twice. One of these times is on the way up, the other on the way down.

Adapting to Individual Needs

English Language Development
This lesson can provide an opportunity to discuss how different terms are used and interrelated, such as the *roots of an equation*, the *zeros of a function*, and the *solutions to an equation*.

QUESTIONS

Covering the Reading

1. Match the idea at the left with the estimated length of time it has been known.
   a. today's notation for quadratics
   b. problems leading to quadratics

   a) v

   b) i

   (i) about 3700 years
   (ii) about 2300 years
   (iii) about 1750 years
   (iv) about 1150 years
   (v) about 350 years

2. The word *algebra* stems from a word in which language?   Arabic

3. Why did the Pythagoreans think there was only one solution to $x^2 = 2$?
   They viewed x as the side of a square; since length is positive, x is positive.

4. Consider the equation $ax^2 + bx + c = 0$, where a, b, and c are real.
   a. What is its discriminant?   b. What are its roots?   See left.
   $b^2 - 4ac$

5. The discriminant of an equation $ax^2 + bx + c = 0$ is -1000. What does this indicate about the graph of $y = ax^2 + bx + c$?   It does not intersect the x-axis.

In 6 and 7, use the discriminant to determine the nature of the roots to the equation.   See left.

6. $3x^2 - 4x + 5 = 0$ 7. $5y^2 - 10y + 5 = 0$
                                                                    See left.

8. a. Solve $3x^2 + 4x + 5 = 0$, and write the solutions in $a + bi$ form.
   b. *True or false.*   The roots of this equation are complex conjugates.
   True

In 9 and 10, the graph of a quadratic function $f(x) = ax^2 + bx + c$ is shown.
   a. Tell whether the value of $b^2 - 4ac$ is positive, negative, or zero.
   b. Tell how many real roots the equation $f(x) = 0$ has.

9.

10.

a) negative   b) none   a) positive   b) two

11. Without drawing a graph, tell whether the x-intercepts of $y = -4x^2 + 2x + 1$ are rational or irrational.   irrational

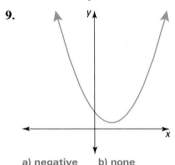

In the colorized medieval wood art shown, Pythagoras is producing music from carefully graduated bells and water glasses. Until they discovered irrational numbers, the Pythagoreans thought that all things could be described by whole numbers or ratios of them.

4b) $x = \dfrac{-b \pm \sqrt{b^2 - 4ac}}{2a}$

6) $D = -44 < 0$;   no real roots

7) $D = 0$;   1 real root

8a) $\dfrac{-2}{3} \pm \dfrac{\sqrt{11}}{3}i$

Lesson 6-10   *Analyzing Solutions to Quadratic Equations*   **405**

Adapting to Individual Needs

Challenge Writing
The discriminant of a quadratic equation with real coefficients can be used to tell whether or not the quadratic is factorable. Explain how this could be done. [If the discriminant is zero or a perfect square, the roots are rational and so the quadratic is factorable.]

Extension

When the solutions to a quadratic equation are rational, they can be checked by substitution without much difficulty. But when the solutions are of the form $m \pm \sqrt{n}$, then because they are either complex or irrational conjugates, there is a much simpler check. The sum of the roots is $2m$, which should equal $-\dfrac{b}{a}$, and the product of the roots is $m^2 - n^2$ (if n is positive) or $m^2 + n^2$ (if n is negative), which should equal $\dfrac{c}{a}$. Ask students to apply these criteria to the quadratic equations of this lesson.

See Activity 2 in *Optional Activities* on page 402 for another use of the sum of the roots.

Project Update Project 1, *Projectile Motion*, Project 2, *Sum and Product of Roots*, and Project 5, *History of Quadratics*, on pages 408–409, relate to the content of this lesson.

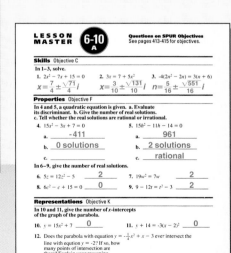

405

Question 12 This question uses the Discriminant Theorem in a practical way. When students find that the value of the discriminant is positive, they should realize that the ball was 200 feet high at two different times. If the value of the discriminant had been zero, there would have been a single such time, the highest point of the path. Students can check their answers by graphing.

Questions 16–17 Technology Connection At first glance, it may seem to students the program does not handle the case $b^2 - 4ac \geq 0$. But finding that the conditional in line 250 is false is equivalent to stating that the discriminant is greater than zero, and the program continues to line 300. When you run the program, use values for A, B, and C that cover all cases of the Discriminant Theorem, for instance,

1. $x^2 + 4x - 21 = 0$
   $[x = -7 \text{ or } x = 3]$
2. $4x^2 + 20x + 25 = 0$
   $[x = -2.5]$
3. $x^2 - 12x = -46$
   [no real solutions]

Explain to students that running the program without line 250 and with the values A = 1, B = -12, C = 46 will result in an error message because most computers cannot calculate nonreal roots. Students may also get an error message when they try to use the Quadratic Formula with these values on their calculators. Stress that the "error" is

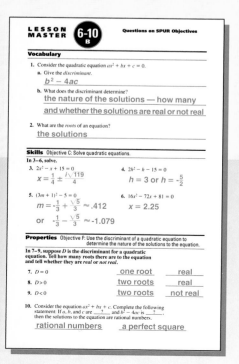

12. Pop Fligh wanted to know if the ball he hit went higher than the top of the stadium, 200 feet high. Was the ball ever 200 feet high? Justify your answer. Yes. The discriminant for $200 = -.005x^2 + 2x + 3.5$ is 0.07, which is greater than 0, so there are real values of x.

Applying the Mathematics

13. The three graphs on page 403 cover the possible cases when the parabolas open up. Draw the three graphs corresponding to $b^2 - 4ac > 0$, $b^2 - 4ac = 0$, and $b^2 - 4ac < 0$ when the parabolas open down. See left.

In 14 and 15, *true or false.*   If true, prove the statement; if false, give a counterexample.

14. Every parabola which has an equation of the form $y = ax^2 + bx + c$ has a y-intercept. True;   the graph must contain (0, c)

15. Whenever a parabola has one x-intercept, it also has a second x-intercept.
False;   if the discriminant = 0, the graph has exactly one x-intercept.
In 16 and 17, the following program in BASIC uses the discriminant to solve quadratic equations of the form $ax^2 + bx + c = 0$.

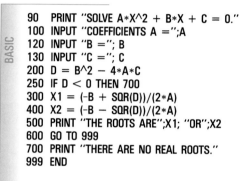

```
90   PRINT "SOLVE A*X^2 + B*X + C = 0."
100  INPUT "COEFFICIENTS A =";A
120  INPUT "B ="; B
130  INPUT "C ="; C
200  D = B^2 - 4*A*C
250  IF D < 0 THEN 700
300  X1 = (-B + SQR(D))/(2*A)
400  X2 = (-B - SQR(D))/(2*A)
500  PRINT "THE ROOTS ARE";X1; "OR";X2
600  GO TO 999
700  PRINT "THERE ARE NO REAL ROOTS."
999  END
```

BASIC

13)
$b^2 - 4ac > 0$

$b^2 - 4ac = 0$

$b^2 - 4ac < 0$

17a) error message in line 300
b) add lines:
110 IF A = 0, THEN 610
610 PRINT "NOT A QUADRATIC EQUATION"
620 GO TO 999

16. Check to see that this BASIC program gives the correct solutions to the following equations. (Or translate this program to your calculator's language.)
   a. $-2x^2 + 40x = 0$ **b.** $5x^2 - 150x + 1185 = 0$
      $x = 0 \text{ or } x = 20$ There are no real roots.
17. a. Describe what happens when you input $a = 0$.
   b. Modify the program so it tests whether a is 0, and prints "NOT A QUADRATIC EQUATION" when $a = 0$.
   See left.

406

18b)

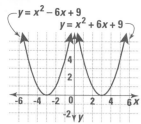

$y = x^2 - 6x + 9$
$y = x^2 + 6x + 9$

27b)

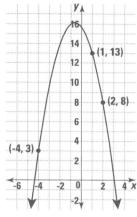

(1, 13)

(2, 8)

(-4, 3)

28) Sample: Yes. By the
Multiplication
Property of Equality,
if each side of
$n^2 - 5n + \frac{25}{4} = 0$
is multiplied by 4,
the products
$4n^2 - 20n + 25$ and
0 are equal.
Since the equations
are equivalent,
they must have
the same roots.

18. a. Find the value(s) of k for which the graph of the equation $y = x^2 + kx + 9$ will have exactly one x-intercept. (Hint: When is the discriminant zero?) $k = 6$ or $k = -6$
 b. Check your answers by graphing. See left.

Review

In 19–24, perform the operation(s), and write the result in $a + bi$ form.
(Lessons 6-8, 6-9)

19. $(i \cdot 3i)^2$ 9

20. $\sqrt{-64} + \sqrt{-36}$ 14i

21. $\sqrt{-64} \cdot \sqrt{-36}$ -48

22. $(6i + 1)(6i - 1)$ -37

23. $\frac{3 + 5i}{i}$ 5 − 3i

24. $\frac{6 + i}{2 - 3i}$ $\frac{9}{13} + \frac{20}{13}i$

25. For an electrical circuit, the formula $V = ZI$ gives the voltage V in volts in terms of the impedance Z in ohms and the current I in amps. Find the voltage if the current is $10 + 2i$ amps and the impedance is $5 - 3i$ ohms. *(Lesson 6-9)* 56 − 20i

26. Solve $-7 - 3n^2 = 5n$. *(Lesson 6-7)* $\frac{-5 \pm \sqrt{59}\,i}{6}$

27. The graph of a quadratic function f passes through the points (-4, 3), (2, 8), and (1, 13).
 a. Find an equation for this graph. $y = \frac{-7}{6}x^2 - \frac{3}{2}x + \frac{47}{3}$
 b. Check your work by graphing the equation in part **a.**
  (Lessons 6-4, 6-6) See left.

28. Janice didn't want to deal with the fraction $\frac{25}{4}$ when solving $n^2 - 5n + \frac{25}{4} = 0$ so she multiplied each side by 4 and solved $4n^2 - 20n + 25 = 0$ instead. Do both equations have the same roots? Why or why not? *(Lessons 1-6, 6-6)* See left.

Exploration

Samples are given.

29. a. Find two nonreal complex numbers that are not complex conjugates and whose sum is a real number. $1 + i$ and $2 - i$
 b. Find two nonreal complex numbers that are not complex conjugates and whose product is a real number. i and $2i$
 c. Find two nonreal complex numbers that are not complex conjugates and whose quotient is a real number. $3i$ and i

not a mathematical error, but an error in asking the calculator or computer to perform an operation for which it is not equipped. In order to keep this program short, we have omitted a test for A = 0. This case is discussed in **Question 17.** We also calculate the square root of the discriminant twice, so the program is not as efficient as it might be. If you have discussed programming skills with your students, you may want to discuss revising this program to make it "crash-proof" and more efficient.

Chapter 6 Projects

The projects relate chiefly to the content of the lessons of this chapter as follows:

Project	Lesson(s)
1	6-4, 6-7, 6-10
2	6-7, 6-10
3	6-3
4	6-6
5	6-1, 6-2, 6-4, 6-5, 6-6, 6-7, 6-8, 6-9, 6-10
6	6-6

1 Projectile Motion A projectile is any object that is thrown, hurled, or shot into the air. Any projectile that is subject to nearly constant gravity will have a nearly parabolic path.

2 Sum and Product of Roots Students should look at solutions of several quadratic equations, including equations with rational solutions, irrational solutions, and nonreal solutions. Since a proof of the generalizations may be difficult for some students, you might suggest that they work in groups to write the proofs.

3 The Graph-Translation Theorem and Other Functions This is a straightforward project, and it is easier than it appears. Students may draw their graphs by hand or with the use of an automatic grapher.

4 Quadratic Models Students need not limit their data search to the sources mentioned in the project description; however, they should clearly identify their sources. Encourage students to inspect data in a general way before they make scatterplots or find regression equations.

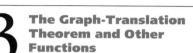

A project presents an opportunity for you to extend your knowledge of a topic related to the material of this chapter. You should allow more time for a project than you do for typical homework questions.

PROJECTS 6 CHAPTER SIX

1 Projectile Motion
Paths of objects other than batted baseballs are almost parabolic. Find out about other objects that travel in parabolic paths. Make a poster or write a brief report illustrating and describing these paths. Find equations for some of the paths.

2 Sum and Product of Roots
Checking solutions to quadratic equations can be tedious, but there is an easier way to check than by substitution. The method checks the sum and the product of the roots. Look back over some quadratic equations you have solved. Let r_1 and r_2 be the roots of the equation $ax^2 + bx + c = 0$. For each equation calculate $r_1 + r_2$ and $r_1 \cdot r_2$. What patterns do you notice? Can you prove your generalizations hold for all quadratics? Use your results to check some of the solutions to quadratic equations in this chapter.

3 The Graph-Translation Theorem and Other Functions
The Graph-Translation Theorem applies to graphs of all functions, not just the quadratic and absolute value functions used in this chapter. Consider the family of inverse variation functions.

a. Graph the "parent" function $y = \frac{1}{x}$.

b. Graph 3 or 4 "offspring" whose equations have the form $y = \frac{1}{x - h}$.

c. Graph 3 or 4 "offspring" whose equations have the form $y = \frac{1}{x} + k$.

d. Graph 3 or 4 "offspring" whose equations have the form $y = \frac{1}{x - h} + k$.

e. Write a brief report summarizing the patterns you observe.

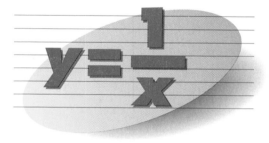

408

Possible responses

1. Examples of projectiles are balls thrown into the air, firecrackers, bullets, rockets, and leaping dolphins. For instance, the path of a particular bottle rocket might be modeled by the function $h(t) = -16t^2 + 117t + 5$ where t represents the number of seconds that have elapsed and $h(t)$ represents the height of the rocket in feet. When a dolphin leaps, the path of its center of gravity is a parabola; its height h above the water (in feet) could be given by $h = -16t^2 + 35.2t$ where t is time (in seconds).

2. The table at the right shows r_1, r_2, $r_1 + r_2$ and $r_1 \cdot r_2$ for sample equations a–d.
   (a) $x^2 - 3x - 4 = 0$
   (b) $6x^2 - 13x - 5 = 0$
   (c) $x^2 - 5x + 3 = 0$
   (d) $x^2 - 4x + 5 = 0$

	r_1	r_2	$r_1 + r_2$	$r_1 \cdot r_2$
a	4	-1	3	-4
b	$-\frac{1}{3}$	$\frac{5}{2}$	$\frac{13}{6}$	$-\frac{5}{6}$
c	$\frac{5 + \sqrt{13}}{2}$	$\frac{5 - \sqrt{13}}{2}$	5	3
d	$2 + i$	$2 - i$	4	5

4 Quadratic Models

Look through an almanac or the *Statistical Abstract of the United States.* Find some current data for which x and y appear to be related by a quadratic model. Find an equation for a quadratic function that models the data. What seems to be a reasonable domain and range for this function? Why do you believe that a quadratic model fits the data set better than a linear model?

5 History of Quadratics

Throughout this chapter we have mentioned people who have contributed to our understanding of quadratic functions and equations. Make a time line marking important dates in this history. Consult a book on the history of mathematics and other references to find out about others who contributed to this history, and include their work on your time line.

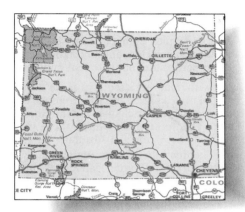

6 Predicting the Areas of States or Countries

In a square with area A and side s, $s^2 = A$ exactly. The length of a side of shapes that are close to Squares can be a good predictor of area, even if the prediction is not exact. Use an atlas to find the lengths of sides of several states in the United States or countries in the world that are fairly close to being square. On a map measure the length and width of the state or country with a ruler, and use the scale of the map to translate these distances into miles or kilometers. For each state or country you measure, look up its area in an atlas or encyclopedia. Fit a model to the data and compare the predicted and actual areas. Write a report which includes a table, graph, your model, an explanation of how you arrived at the model, and the conclusions you made.

409

The pattern that emerges is that
$r_1 + r_2 = \frac{-b}{a}$ and $r_1 \cdot r_2 = \frac{c}{a}$.
One possible proof is as follows:
the two roots of $ax^2 + bx + c = 0$ are
$r_1 = \frac{-b + \sqrt{b^2 - 4ac}}{2a}$ and $r_2 = \frac{-b + \sqrt{b^2 - 4ac}}{2a}$.

Therefore, $r_1 + r_2 = \frac{-b + \sqrt{b^2 - 4ac}}{2a} +$

$\frac{-b + \sqrt{b^2 - 4ac}}{2a} = \frac{-2b}{2a} = \frac{-b}{a}$.

$r_1 \cdot r_2 = \frac{-b + \sqrt{b^2 - 4ac}}{2a} \cdot \frac{-b + \sqrt{b^2 - 4ac}}{2a} =$
$\frac{b^2 - (b^2 - 4ac)}{4a^2} = \frac{4ac}{4a^2} = \frac{c}{a}$.

(Responses continue in the middle of the next column.)

5 History of Quadratics
Students may find information in reference books or history of mathematics books under headings such as complex numbers, quadratic equations, irrational numbers, imaginary numbers, number systems, and so on.

6 Predicting the Areas of States or Countries
For each selected state or country, suggest that students measure its length and width on a map and use the map scale. Then, to approximate the dimensions of the square, suggest that they use the average of the length and width of the state for the length of the sides of the square.

Additional Responses, page 408
3a.

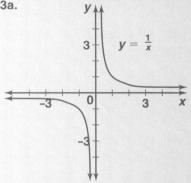

3b–d. Graphs will vary. You might suggest that students write each equation alongside its graph and tell what values they used for *h* and *k*. You might also suggest that they use a colored pencil to draw horizontal and vertical asymptotes.

e. Sample information students might include in their report: Graphs whose equations have the form $y = \frac{1}{x-h} + k$ are congruent to the graph of $y = \frac{1}{x-h}$. The parent function has asymptotes $y = 0$ and $x = 0$, whereas the graphs having undergone a translation of $T_{h,k}$ have asymptotes $y = k$ and $x = h$.

(Responses continue on page 410.)

SUMMARY

Quadratic expressions are those which involve one or more terms in x^2, y^2, or xy, but no higher powers of x or y. If $k > 0$, the equation $x^2 = k$ has two real solutions, $\sqrt{k}$ and $-\sqrt{k}$. When $k < 0$, the solutions are the imaginary numbers $i\sqrt{k}$ and $-i\sqrt{k}$, where, by definition, $\sqrt{-1} = i$. Any number of the form $a + bi$, where a and b are real, is a complex number. Complex numbers are added, subtracted, and multiplied using the field properties that apply to real numbers.

Work with quadratics requires some skill in manipulating squares and square roots. Among the theorems in this chapter are the Binomial Square Theorem: for all x and y, $(x + y)^2 = x^2 + 2xy + y^2$, and the Absolute Value-Square Root Theorem: for all real numbers x, $\sqrt{x^2} = |x|$. Additionally, for all nonnegative real numbers x and y, $\sqrt{xy} = \sqrt{x}\,\sqrt{y}$. This last theorem does not hold when x and y are both negative.

Areas, paths of projectiles, and relations between the initial velocity of an object and its height over time lead to problems involving quadratic equations and functions. If data involving two variables are graphed, and the scatterplot appears to be part of a parabola, you can use three points on the graph to set up a system of equations that will allow you to find a, b, and c in the equation $y = ax^2 + bx + c$.

When a, b, and c are real numbers and $a \neq 0$, the graph of the equation $y = ax^2 + bx + c$ is a parabola. Using the process known as completing the square, this equation can be rewritten in vertex form $y - k = a(x - h)^2$. This parabola is a translation image of the parabola $y = ax^2$ you studied in Chapter 2. Its vertex is (h, k), its line of symmetry is $x = h$, and it opens up if $a > 0$ and opens down if $a < 0$.

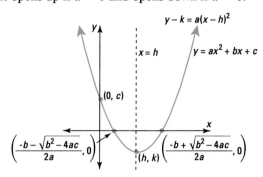

Its x-intercepts, the values of x for which $ax^2 + bx + c = 0$, can be found by the famous Quadratic Formula

$$x = \frac{-b \pm \sqrt{b^2 - 4ac}}{2a}$$

The expression $b^2 - 4ac$ is the discriminant of the quadratic equation, and reveals the nature of its roots. If $b^2 - 4ac > 0$, there are two real solutions. That is the situation pictured above. If $b^2 - 4ac = 0$, there is exactly one solution and the vertex of the parabola is on the x-axis. If a, b, and c are rational numbers and the discriminant is a perfect square, then the solutions are rational numbers. If $b^2 - 4ac < 0$, there are no real solutions and the parabola does not intersect the x-axis. The solutions are complex conjugates.

410

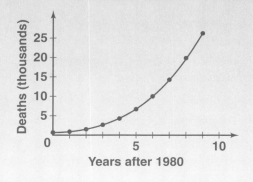

VOCABULARY

Below are the most important terms and phrases for this chapter.
You should be able to give a definition for those terms marked with a *.
For all other terms you should be able to give a general description or
a specific example.

Lesson 6-1
quadratic
quadratic expression
quadratic equation
quadratic function
standard form of a quadratic
Binomial Square Theorem

Lesson 6-2
absolute value
absolute value function
Absolute Value-Square Root Theorem
square root
simple fraction
irrational number

Lesson 6-3
*Graph-Translation Theorem
corollary
vertex form of an equation of a parabola
axis of symmetry
minimum, maximum

Lesson 6-4
standard form of an equation of a parabola
acceleration due to gravity
$h = -\frac{1}{2}gt^2 + v_0 t + h_0$
velocity

Lesson 6-5
completing the square
perfect-square trinomial

Lesson 6-6
quadratic model
quadratic regression

Lesson 6-7
*Quadratic Formula
standard form of a quadratic equation

Lesson 6-8
*$\sqrt{-k}$
*$\sqrt{-1}$, i
imaginary number

Lesson 6-9
*complex number
*real part, imaginary part
*equal complex numbers
impedance
circuit in series, in parallel
*complex conjugate
hierarchy

Lesson 6-10
*discriminant of a quadratic equation
nature of the solutions
*root of an equation
Discriminant Theorem

Additional responses, page 409

  d. Around 250 B. C. Euclid included the solutions to some quadratics in his *Elements*—written with the geometric idea of completing the square.
  e. Around 250 A. D. Diophantus gave some general solutions of problems that lead to quadratics.
  f. Aryabhata (around 476 A. D.) and Brahmagupta (a century later), knew the Quadratic Formula and recognized that a quadratic with real solutions has two formal roots. They gave what we would write today as the algebraic solution of quadratic equations by the familiar method of completing the square. These ideas were written down by Al-Khwarizmi around 825, and his Islamic texts made their way into Europe.
  g. By the early 1500s, German Christoff Rudolff and Portuguese Pedro Nuñez wrote symbolic solutions.
  h. In the 1540s, Girolamo Cardano considered complex number solutions.
  i. Our current notation originated with Francois Viète in the 1590s.
6. Students' responses will vary considerably. Sample data for six states is shown in the first three columns of the table on page 412. The accompanying graph on page 413 shows a scatterplot with estimated average side lengths and actual areas. The more the length and width of a state differ, the less accurate is the prediction. One calculator gives the following quadratic model for the data in the scatterplot:
    $y = 0.76268x^2 - 4.42949x + 22561.15$
    The last column in the table shows the area predicted by the equation model. This quadratic model has limited usefulness as a predictor of actual area. For example, when the estimated average side length is 50 miles, the predicted area is not realistic.

(*Responses continue on page 412.*)

---

5. There is a great deal of material in this chapter that could be included in a time line. Some additional information follows.
   a. About 1700 B. C. the Babylonians solved the equivalent of this quadratic equation: $x^2 - px = q$:
      $x = \sqrt{(\frac{p}{2})^2 + q} + \frac{p}{2}$.

   b. The Chinese manuscript *Jiuzhang* (from about 1000 B. C.) contains some quadratics and their solutions.
   c. Between 600 and 450 B. C., the Pythagorean geometric solution regarding the methods of proportions and applications appeared.

(*Responses continue at the top of the next column.*)

Progress Self-Test

For the development of mathematical competence, feedback and correction, along with the opportunity to practice, are necessary. The Progress Self-Test provides the opportunity for feedback and correction; the Chapter Review provides additional opportunities and practice. We cannot overemphasize the importance of these end-of-chapter materials. It is at this point that the material "gels" for many students, allowing them to solidify skills and understanding. In general, student performance should be markedly improved after these pages.

Assign the Progress Self-Test as a one-night assignment. Worked-out *solutions* for all questions are in the Selected Answers section of the student book. Encourage students to take the Progress Self-Test honestly, grade themselves, and then be prepared to discuss the test in class.

Advise students to pay special attention to those Chapter Review questions (pages 413–415) which correspond to questions missed on the Progress Self-Test.

Additional Answers, page 412

10.

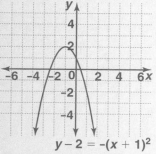

$y - 2 = -(x + 1)^2$

24a.

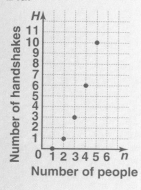

PROGRESS SELF-TEST

Take this test as you would take a test in class. Use graph paper and a calculator. Then check your work with the solutions in the Selected Answers section in the back of the book.
8) $1 - 9i$

In 1–3, consider the parabola with equation $y = x^2 - 8x + 12$. 1) $y + 4 = (x - 4)^2$
1. Rewrite the equation in vertex form.
2. What is the vertex of this parabola? $(4, -4)$
3. What are the x-intercepts of this parabola?
   2; 6

In 4–7, perform the operations and simplify.
4. $2i \cdot i$ -2
5. $\sqrt{-8} \cdot \sqrt{-2}$ -4
6. $\frac{4 + \sqrt{-8}}{2}$ $2 + i\sqrt{2}$
7. $(3i + 2)(6i - 4)$ -26
8. If $z = 2 - 4i$ and $w = 1 + 5i$, what is $z - w$?
9. *Multiple choice.* How does the graph of $y - 2 = -(x + 1)^2$ compare with the graph of $y = -x^2$? c
   (a) It is 1 unit to the right and 2 units below.
   (b) It is 1 unit to the right and 2 units above.
   (c) It is 1 unit to the left and 2 units above.
   (d) It is 1 unit to the left and 2 units below.
10. Graph the solution set to $y - 2 = -(x + 1)^2$.
    See margin.

In 11–13, find all solutions.
11. $3x^2 + 14x - 5 = 0$ $\frac{1}{3}$ or -5
12. $(m + 40)^2 = 2$ $-40 \pm \sqrt{2}$
13. $3x^2 + 15 = 18x - 60$ $3 \pm 4i$
14. *True or false.* $\sqrt{x^2} = |x|$ for all real values of x. True

In 15 and 16, use the equation $y = ax^2 + bx + c$, assuming $a \neq 0$ and a, b, and c are real numbers.
15. How many x-intercepts does the graph have
    a. if its discriminant is 0? one
    b. if its discriminant is 1? two
16. If $y = 0$, describe the nature of the roots
    a. if its discriminant is 0. There is one real root.
    b. if its discriminant is -5.
       There are two complex conjugate roots.

17) $2a^2 + 18$ 18) $64v^2 + 16v + 1$
In 17 and 18, expand.
17. $(a - 3)^2 + (a + 3)^2$ 18. $(8v + 1)^2$
19. A ball is thrown upward from an initial height of 20 meters at an initial velocity of 10 meters per second. Write an equation for the height h of the ball t seconds after being thrown. $h = -4.9t^2 + 10t + 20$

In 20 and 21, the height in feet h of a ball at time t is given by $h = -16t^2 + 12t + 4$.
20. How high is the ball .5 second after it is thrown? 6 ft
21. When does the ball hit the ground? after 1 se
22. A rectangular piece of metal is 40 cm by 30 cm. A strip s cm wide is cut parallel to each side of the metal. What is the area of the remaining rectangle in terms of s?
23. *Multiple choice.* Which parabola is not congruent to the others? a
    (a) $y = 2x^2$ (b) $y = x^2 + 2$
    (c) $y = (x + 2)^2$ (d) $y + 2 = x^2$
24. There is a pattern to the number of handshakes needed in a group of people if everyone shakes hands with everybody else exactly once. Examine the table below.

Number of people n	1	2	3	4	5
Number of handshakes	0	1	3	6	10

   a. Draw a scatterplot of these data. See margi
   b. Fit a quadratic model to these data. See below.
   c. How many handshakes would be needed if 100 people shake hands with each other exactly once? 4950
25. $y = 2x^2 - 6x + 4$ is written in standard form. Rewrite this equation in vertex form, and write a sentence detailing information about the graph you can obtain just by looking at the equation in this form. $y + \frac{1}{2} = 2\left(x - \frac{3}{2}\right)^2$
   It opens upward, has the vertex $\left(\frac{3}{2}, -\frac{1}{2}\right)$ and has an axis of symmetry $x = \frac{3}{2}$.

22) $4s^2 - 140s + 1200$
24b) $H = \frac{1}{2}n^2 - \frac{n}{2}$

Additional responses, page 409

State	Estimated average side length (mi)	Estimated area (mi²)	Actual area (mi²)	Predicted area (by model mi²)
Arizona	350	122,500	113,510	114,439
Arkansas	200	40,000	52,082	52,182
Colorado	333	110,889	103,598	105,659
Kansas	323	104,329	81,783	100,700
New Mexico	330	108,900	121,336	104,155
Wyoming	305	93,025	96,988	92,158

CHAPTER REVIEW

Questions on SPUR Objectives

SPUR stands for **S**kills, **P**roperties, **U**ses, and **R**epresentations. The Chapter Review questions are grouped according to the SPUR Objectives for this chapter.

SKILLS DEAL WITH THE PROCEDURES USED TO GET ANSWERS.

Objective A: *Expand squares of binomials.*
(Lesson 6-1) 1) $a^2 + 2ax + x^2$ 3) $9x^2 + 24x + 16$

In 1–6, expand.

1. $(a + x)^2$ **2.** $(y - 11)^2$ $y^2 - 22y + 121$

3. $(3x + 4)^2$ **4.** $2(x - 2)^2$ $2x^2 - 8x + 8$

5. $9(t - 5)^2$ **6.** $3(a + b)^2 - 4(a - b)^2$
$9t^2 - 90t + 225$ $-a^2 + 14ab - b^2$

Objective B: *Transform quadratic equations from vertex form to standard form, and vice versa.*
(Lessons 6-4, 6-5) 7) $y = 3x^2 + 12x + 12$ 8) $y = \frac{1}{2}x^2 - 4x$

In 7 and 8, transform into standard form.

7. $y = 3(x + 2)^2$ **8.** $y + 8 = \frac{1}{2}(x - 4)^2$

In 9 and 10, transform each equation into vertex form. 9) $y + 31 = (x + 5)^2$ 10) $y + \frac{11}{2} = 2\left(x - \frac{3}{2}\right)^2$

9. $y = x^2 + 10x - 6$ **10.** $y = 2x^2 - 6x - 1$

11. Find an equation in vertex form equivalent to $y = 3x^2 - 30x + 12$. $y + 63 = 3(x - 5)^2$

12. *Multiple choice.* Which equation is equivalent to $y = 2x^2 - 4x + 3$? b
  (a) $y - 1 = 2(x + 2)^2$
  (b) $y - 1 = 2(x - 1)^2$
  (c) $y - 3 = 2(x + 1)^2$
  (d) $y - 2 = 2(x - 1)^2$

Objective C: *Solve quadratic equations.*
(Lessons 6-2, 6-7, 6-8, 6-10)

In 13–26, solve. $d = \pm 4\sqrt{3}$

13. $(x - 3)^2 = 0$ $x = 3$ **14.** $d^2 - 48 = 0$

15. $z^2 = -8$ $z = \pm 2i\sqrt{2}$ **16.** $w^2 = -9$
                    $w = \pm 3i$

17) $x = -1/2 \pm \sqrt{5}/2$ 18) $y = -7/2 \pm \sqrt{29}/2$

17. $x^2 + x - 1 = 0$ **18.** $1 - y^2 - 7y = 6$

19. $z^2 - 8z + 11 = -5$ **20.** $0 = 4a^2 + 3a + 2$

21. $k^2 = 4k + 2$ $k = 2 \pm \sqrt{6}$ 19) $z = 4$

22. $3x^2 + 2x + 6 = 2x^2 + 4x - 3$ $x = 1 \pm 2i\sqrt{2}$

23. $x^2 + 25 = 0$ $x = \pm 5i$ **24.** $x(x + 1) = 1$

25. $3 = 5p + 2p^2$ **26.** $2(3n^2 + 2) = 4(n - 9)$
$p = \frac{1}{2}$ or -3 20, 24, 26) See below.

Objective D: *Perform operations with complex numbers.*   *(Lessons 6-8, 6-9)*

In 27–34, simplify.

27. $-i^2$ 1   **28.** $\sqrt{-36}$ $6i$

29. $\sqrt{-16} \cdot \sqrt{-49}$ -28 **30.** $\sqrt{2} \cdot \sqrt{-2}$ $2i$

31. $10\sqrt{-50}$ $50i\sqrt{2}$ **32.** $3i \cdot i$ -3

33. $\frac{4 \pm \sqrt{-80}}{2}$ $2 \pm 2i\sqrt{5}$ **34.** $\frac{-5 \pm \sqrt{-25}}{10}$ $-\frac{1}{2} \pm \frac{1}{2}i$

In 35–40, perform the operations and write the answer in $a + bi$ form. 35) $1 + 12i$ 36) $-4 + 7i$

35. $(3 + 7i) + (-2 + 5i)$ **36.** $(8 + i) - (12 - 6i)$

37. $i(10 + 6i)$ $-6 + 10i$ **38.** $(4 + i)(9 - i)$ $37 + 5i$

39. $\frac{-6 + 3i}{2i}$ $\frac{3}{2} + 3i$ **40.** $\frac{12}{4 - i}$ $\frac{48}{17} + \frac{12}{17}i$

In 41–46, suppose $u = 3 - i$ and $v = 8i + 5$. Evaluate and simplify.

41. uv $23 + 19i$ **42.** u^2 $8 - 6i$

43. $3u - v$ $4 - 11i$ **44.** $iu + v$ $6 + 11i$

45. $\frac{u}{v}$ $\frac{7}{89} - \frac{29}{89}i$ **46.** $\frac{v}{u}$ $\frac{7}{10} + \frac{29}{10}i$

20) $a = \frac{-3}{8} \pm i\frac{\sqrt{23}}{8}$ 24) $x = \frac{-1}{2} \pm \frac{\sqrt{5}}{2}$

26) $n = \frac{1}{3} \pm \frac{i\sqrt{59}}{3}$

Chapter 6 Review

Resources
From the *Teacher's Resource File*
- Answer Master for Chapter 6 Review
- Assessment Sourcebook: Chapter 6 Test, Forms A–D Chapter 6 Test, Cumulative Form Comprehensive Test, Chapters 1–6

Additional Resources
- Quiz and Test Writer

The main objectives for the chapter are organized in the Chapter Review under the four types of understanding this book promotes–Skills, Properties, Uses, and Representations.

Whereas end-of-chapter material may be considered optional in some texts, in *UCSMP Advanced Algebra* we have selected these objectives and questions with the expectation that they will be covered. Students should be able to answer these questions with about 85% accuracy after studying the chapter.

You may assign these questions over a single night to help students prepare for a test the next day, or you may assign the questions over a two-day period. If you work the questions over two days, we recommend assigning the *evens* for homework the first night so that students get feedback in class the next day and then assigning the *odds* the night before the test because answers are provided to the odd-numbered questions.

Setting Up Lesson 7-1
Homework We recommend that you assign the Chapter 7 Opener and Lesson 7-1 both reading and some questions in Lesson 7-1 for homework the evening of the test.

413

It is effective to ask students which questions they still do not understand and use the day or days as a total class discussion of the material which the class finds most difficult.

Assessment

Evaluation The *Assessment Sourcebook* provides five forms of the Chapter 6 Test. Forms A and B present parallel versions in a short-answer format. Forms C and D offer performance assessment. The fifth test is Chapter 6 Test, Cumulative Form. About 50% of this test covers Chapter 6, 25% covers Chapter 5, and 25% covers earlier chapters. In addition to these tests, Comprehensive Test Chapters 1–6 gives roughly equal attention to all chapters covered thus far.

For information on grading, see *General Teaching Suggestions; Grading* in the *Professional Sourcebook*, which begins on page T20 in this Teacher's Edition.

Feedback After students have taken the test for Chapter 6 and you have scored the results, return the tests to students for discussion. Class discussion of the questions that caused trouble for the most students can be very effective in identifying and clarifying misunderstandings. You might want to have them write down the items they missed and work, either in groups or at home, to correct them. It is important for students to receive feedback on every chapter test, and we recommend that students see and correct their mistakes before proceeding too far into the next chapter.

PROPERTIES DEAL WITH THE PRINCIPLES BEHIND THE MATHEMATICS.

Objective E: *Apply the definition of absolute value and the Absolute Value-Square Root Theorem.* (Lesson 6-2) **47)** all nonpositive numbers

47. For what real numbers does $|x| = -x$?

48. For what real numbers does $|x| = -2$? none

In 49–52, simplify.

49. $\sqrt{(6+3)^2}$ 9

50. $-\sqrt{y^2}$ $-|y|$

51. $-\sqrt{(-4)^2}$ -4

52. $\sqrt{(-3x)^2}$ $3|x|$

53a) 0   b) 1   c) rational
54a) 10,400   b) 2   c) rational
55a) 45   b) 2   c) irrational
56a) -111   b) 0   c) nonreal

Objective F: *Use the discriminant of a quadratic equation to determine the nature of the solutions to the equation.* (Lesson 6-10)

In 53–56, an equation is given. **a.** Evaluate its discriminant. **b.** Give the number of real solutions. **c.** Tell whether the solutions are rational, irrational, or nonreal. See left.

53. $9 + 4y^2 - 12y = 0$

54. $z^2 = 100z + 100$

55. $6 + t = t^2 - 5$

56. $8x^2 + 9x + 6 = 0$

57. How many real solutions does $2x^2 = 3x$ have? How can you tell? Two; the discriminant is 9, which is greater than 0.

USES DEAL WITH APPLICATIONS OF MATHEMATICS IN REAL SITUATIONS.

Objective G: *Use quadratic equations to solve area problems or problems dealing with velocity and acceleration.* (Lessons 6-1, 6-2, 6-4, 6-7)

58. A 20''-by-36'' picture is to be surrounded by a frame w inches wide.

  a. What is the total area of the picture and frame? $4w^2 + 112w + 720 \text{ in}^2$

  b. If the total area is to be $\frac{4}{3}$ the area of the picture, how wide should the frame be? 2 in.

59. Daniel wants to construct a rectangular pen alongside his house for his dog. He plans to use 22 meters of chicken wire. What should be the dimensions of the pen if Daniel wants his dog to have as much area as possible? 5.5 m × 11 m

60. Suppose a ball is thrown upward from a height of 4.5 feet with an initial velocity of 21 feet per second.

  a. Write an equation relating the time t and height h of the ball. $h = -16t^2 + 21t + 4.5$

  b. When will the ball hit the ground? 1.5 sec

61. A package of supplies is dropped from a helicopter hovering 100 m above the ground. The attached parachute fails to open. After how many seconds will the package reach the ground? (Neglect air resistance.) 4.52 sec

62. A ball is hit by a bat when 3 feet off the ground. It is caught at the same height 300 feet from the batter. How far from the batter did it reach its maximum height? 150 ft

Objective H: *Fit a quadratic model to data.* (Lesson 6-6)

63. The following pictures show the first five pentagonal numbers. a, b) See margin.

1   5   12   22   35

  a. Find the next two pentagonal numbers.

  b. Fit a quadratic model to find a formula for $p(n)$, the nth pentagonal number.

  c. Find the 50th pentagonal number. 3725

64. Jeremy was in charge of scheduling for the local Little League. Each team played each other team twice. He needed to know the total number of games played so that he could provide umpires. The first year, with 4 teams, he scheduled 12 games. The second year, with 5 teams, he scheduled 20 games. The third year with 6 teams, he scheduled 30 games. Find the number of games needed for a league with

  a. 2 teams. 2   **b.** 3 teams. 6

  c. With the number of teams as the independent variable, make a scatterplot of these data. c, d) See margin.

  d. Fit an appropriate model to these data.

  e. How many games would be necessary for a 10-team league? 90

414

Additional Answers, pages 414–415

63a.   51, 70

  b. $p(n) = \frac{3}{2}n^2 - \frac{1}{2}n$

64c.

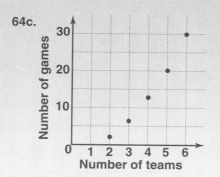

64d. $G(n) = n(n-1)$

66. $y = |x - 3|$ is the image of $y = |x|$ translated 3 units to the right.

68.   The solutions to $6 = (x - 2)^2$ are 2 more than the solutions to $6 = x^2$.

69.   The solutions to $(k - 1)^2 = 36$ are 1 more than the solutions to $k^2 = 36$.

Objective I: *Use the Graph-Translation Theorem to interpret equations and graphs.*
(Lessons 6-3)

65. $y = x^2$ is translated 7 units to the left and 5 units down. What is an equation for its image? $y + 5 = (x + 7)^2$

66. Describe how the graphs of $y = |x|$ and $y = |x - 3|$ are related. See margin.

67. *Multiple choice.* Which of the following is *not* true for the graph of the parabola with equation $y - 5 = -2(x + 1)^2$? **d**
  (a) The vertex is (-1, 5).
  (b) The maximum point is (-1, 5).
  (c) The equation of the axis of symmetry is $x = -1$.
  (d) The graph opens up.

68. Compare the solutions to $6 = (x - 2)^2$ with the solutions to $6 = x^2$. See margin.

69. Compare the solutions to $(k - 1)^2 = 36$ with the solutions to $k^2 = 36$. See margin.

70. Assume that parabola A is congruent to parabola B in the graph below.

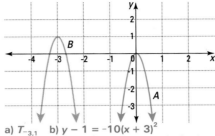

a) $T_{-3,1}$ b) $y - 1 = -10(x + 3)^2$
  a. What translation maps parabola A onto B?
  b. What is the equation of parabola B if parabola A has equation $y = -10x^2$?

71. If the graph of $y = (3x + 11)^2$ is congruent to the graph of $y = ax^2$, find a. $a = 9$

REPRESENTATIONS DEAL WITH PICTURES, GRAPHS, OR OBJECTS THAT ILLUSTRATE CONCEPTS.

Objective J: *Graph quadratic functions or absolute value functions and interpret them.*
(Lessons 6-2, 6-3, 6-4)

In 72–75, graph the parabola, identifying its vertex and x-intercepts. See margin.

72. $y = 5x^2 - 20x$ **73.** $y - 4 = -\frac{1}{3}(x + 2)^2$

74. $y + 4 = 3(x - 1)^2$ **75.** $y = -2x^2 + 4x - 1$

In 76 and 77, refer to the parabolas below.

76. Tell whether the graph could represent solutions to an equation of the form $y - k = a(x - h)^2$.

a. 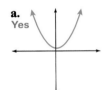 Yes

b. 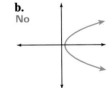 No

c. 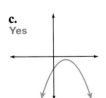 Yes

d. 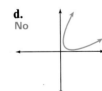 No

77. Given $y - k = a(x - h)^2$, for which of the graphs in Question 76 is a negative? **c**

78. The height of a baseball thrown upward at time t is shown on the graph at the right.

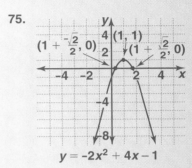

  a. When did the ball reach its maximum height? About how high did it get? ≈ 1.2 sec; ≈21 ft
  b. When was the ball 10 feet high? ≈ 0.4 sec and ≈ 2.1 sec

In 79 and 80, graph. See margin.
79. $y = |x + 3|$ **80.** $y - 2 = |x - 1|$

Objective K: *Use the discriminant of a quadratic equation to determine the number of x-intercepts of the graph.* *(Lesson 6-10)* **83)** See margin.

In 81 and 82, give the number of x-intercepts of the graph of the parabola.

81. $y = 3x^2 + 2x - 2$ **2** **82.** $y = \frac{1}{2}(x + 5)^2 - 3$ **2**

83. Does the parabola $y = 6x^2 - 12x$ ever intersect the line $y = -5$? Justify your answer.

84. If the graph of $y = -\frac{1}{4}x^2$ has one x-intercept, how many x-intercepts does the graph of $y = -\frac{1}{4}(x - a)^2$ have if $a \neq 0$? **one**

74.
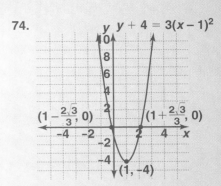

$y + 4 = 3(x - 1)^2$
$(1 - \frac{2\sqrt{3}}{3}, 0)$ $(1 + \frac{2\sqrt{3}}{3}, 0)$
$(1, -4)$

75.
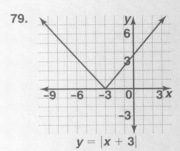

$(1 + \frac{-\sqrt{2}}{2}, 0)$ (1, 1) $(1 + \frac{\sqrt{2}}{2}, 0)$
$y = -2x^2 + 4x - 1$

79.
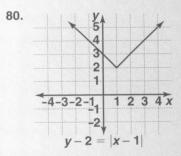

$y = |x + 3|$

80.
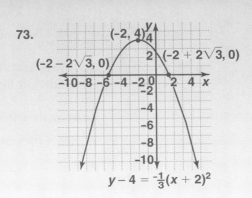

$y - 2 = |x - 1|$

83. Yes; the discriminant of the equation $6x^2 - 12x = -5$ is $(-12)^2 - 4 \cdot 6 \cdot 5 = 24 > 0$. Therefore, this equation has two real solutions, which means the parabola $y = 6x^2 - 12x$ intersects the line $y = -5$ at two points.

72.
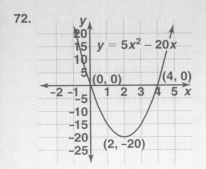

$y = 5x^2 - 20x$
(0, 0)   (4, 0)
(2, -20)

73.
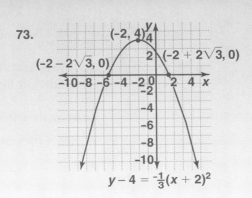

$(-2, 4)$
$(-2 - 2\sqrt{3}, 0)$ $(-2 + 2\sqrt{3}, 0)$
$y - 4 = -\frac{1}{3}(x + 2)^2$

415

Table of Contents

The Reasons for UCSMP

Recommendations for Change

As a result of an increasing number of students staying in school longer, the need for a greater number of technically competent workers and citizens, and major advances in mathematics itself, the mathematics curriculum has undergone changes in every country of the world throughout this century. In the last twenty years, these developments have accelerated due to the widespread appearance of computers with their unprecedented abilities to handle and display information.

In the last 100 years, national groups have examined the curriculum periodically in light of these changes in society. A study of reports before 1970 can be found in *A History of Mathematics Education in the United States and Canada,* the 30th Yearbook of the National Council of Teachers of Mathematics, 1970. A summary of reports from 1970 to 1984 can be found in Z. Usiskin, "We Need Another Revolution in Secondary School Mathematics," in *The Secondary School Mathematics Curriculum,* the 1985 Yearbook of NCTM.

The most recent era of reports can be said to have begun in the years 1975–1980, with the publication of reports by various national mathematics organizations calling attention to serious problems in the education of our youth. These reports from inside mathematics education were joined by governmental and private reports through the 1980s decrying the state of American education and providing broad recommendations for school practice. Two of the most notable of these reports for their specific remarks about mathematics education appeared in the year that UCSMP began.

1983: National Commission on Excellence in Education. *A Nation At Risk.*

> The teaching of mathematics in high school should equip graduates to: (a) understand geometric and algebraic concepts; (b) understand elementary probability and statistics; (c) apply mathematics in everyday situations; and (d) estimate, approximate, measure, and test the accuracy of their calculations.
>
> In addition to the traditional sequence of studies available for college-bound students, new, equally demanding mathematics curricula need to be developed for those who do not plan to continue their formal education immediately. (p. 25)

1983: College Board (Project EQuality). *Academic Preparation for College: What Students Need to Know and Be Able to Do.*

> All students (college-bound or not) should have:
>
> The ability to apply mathematical techniques in the solution of real-life problems and to recognize when to apply those techniques.
>
> Familiarity with the language, notation, and deductive nature of mathematics and the ability to express quantitative ideas with precision.
>
> The ability to use computers and calculators.
>
> Familiarity with the basic concepts of statistics and statistical reasoning.
>
> Knowledge in considerable depth and detail of algebra, geometry, and functions. (p. 20)

The specific remarks about school mathematics in these documents for the most part mirror what appeared in the earlier reports. Thus, given what seemed to be a broad consensus on the problems and desirable changes in pre-college mathematics instruction, it was decided, at the outset of UCSMP, that UCSMP would not attempt to form its own set of recommendations, but undertake the task of translating the existing recommendations into the reality of classrooms and schools. It was also decided that UCSMP would look at the best that other countries had to offer, and so in 1983 UCSMP began to translate materials from Japan and some countries of Eastern Europe known for excellence in mathematics education.

Universities for many years have recognized that mathematics encompasses far more than algebra, geometry, and analysis. The term *mathematical sciences* is an umbrella designation which includes traditional mathematics as well as a number of other disciplines. The largest of these other disciplines today are statistics, computer science, and applied mathematics, not coincidentally the areas in which recent reports have recommended greater emphasis. In 1983, the Conference Board of the Mathematical Sciences produced a report, *The Mathematical Sciences Curriculum: What Is Still Fundamental and What Is Not.* The UCSMP Grades 7–12 curriculum is the first mathematical sciences curriculum for average students in the United States.

In the middle 1980s, as the first edition of UCSMP secondary textbooks were being developed and tested, studies comparing the achievement of secondary school students in the U.S. with the achievement of students in other countries verified our conception that we were quite a bit behind those countries in performance.

The Second International Mathematics Study (SIMS) was conducted in 1981–1982 and involved 23 populations in 21 countries. At the eighth-grade level, virtually all students attend school in all those countries, and our students scored at or below the international average on all five subtests: arithmetic, measurement, algebra, geometry, and statistics. We were far below the top: Japan looked at the test and decided it was too easy for their 8th-graders, and so they gave it at 7th grade. Still, the median Japanese 7th-grader performed at the 95th percentile of the United States 8th-graders. SIMS recommended steps to renew school mathematics in the United States.

At the 12th-grade level in 1981–82, about 13% of our population was enrolled in precalculus or calculus; the mean among developed countries was about 16%. Thus, the U.S. no longer kept more students in mathematics than other developed countries, yet our advanced placement students did not perform well when compared to their peers in other countries. SIMS found:

1987: Second International Mathematics Study (SIMS). *The Underachieving Curriculum.*

In the U.S., the achievement of the Calculus classes, the nation's best mathematics students, was at or near the average achievement of the advanced secondary school mathematics students in other countries. (In most countries, all advanced mathematics students take calculus. In the U.S., only about one-fifth do.) The achievement of the U.S. Precalculus students (the majority of twelfth grade college-preparatory students) was substantially below the international average. In some cases the U.S. ranked with the lower one-fourth of all countries in the Study, and was the lowest of the advanced industrialized countries. (*The Underachieving Curriculum,* p. vii)

The situation has been even worse for those who do not take precalculus mathematics in high school. Such students either have performed poorly in their last mathematics course, a situation which has caused them not to go on in mathematics, or they were performing poorly in junior high school and had to take remedial mathematics as 9th-graders. If these students go to college, they invariably take remedial mathematics, which is taught at a faster pace than in high school, and the failure rates in such courses often exceed 40%. If they do not go to college but join the job market, they lack the mathematics needed to understand today's technology. It is no understatement to say that **UCSMP has received its funding from business and industry because those who leave schooling to join the work force are woefully weak in the mathematics they will need.**

The SIMS results have been confirmed in other studies comparing students at the eighth-grade levels. In a study conducted by the Educational Testing Service in 1988–89, U.S. eighth-grade students were last in average mathematics proficiency compared with students in Ireland, South Korea, Spain, the United Kingdom, and Canada (Center for the Assessment of Educational Progress, *A World of Differences,* 1989).

Why do we perform so poorly? National Assessment results have shown that emphasizing algebra and geometry in elementary and middle schools leads to higher test scores for eighth graders (U.S. Department of Education, National Center for Education Statistics, *The State of Mathematics Achievement: NAEP's 1990 Assessment of the Nation and the Trial Assessment of the States,* 1992). Historically, schools in the United States have delayed concentrated study of algebra and geometry longer than schools in other countries of the world.

SIMS recommended:

A fundamental revision of the U.S. school mathematics curriculum, in both form and substance, is needed. This activity should begin at the early grades of the elementary school.

With respect to form, the excessive repetition of topics from year to year should be eliminated. A more focused organization of the subject matter, with a more intense treatment of topics, should be considered.

Concerning substance, the continued dominating role of arithmetic in the junior high school curriculum results in students entering high school with very limited mathematical backgrounds. The curriculum for all students should be broadened and enriched by the inclusion of appropriate topics in geometry, probability and statistics, as well as algebra. (*The Underachieving Curriculum,* p. xii)

The UCSMP secondary curriculum implements the curriculum recommendations of the Second International Mathematics Study.

In 1986, the National Council of Teachers of Mathematics began an ambitious effort to detail the curriculum it would like to see in schools. The "NCTM Standards," as they have come to be called, involve both content and methodology. The long Curriculum and Evaluation Standards document is divided into four sections, K–4, 5–8, 9–12, and Evaluation. Space limits our discussion here to just a few quotes from the 9–12 standards.

1989: National Council of Teachers of Mathematics. *Curriculum and Evaluation of Standards for School Mathematics.*

The standards for grades 9–12 are based on the following assumptions:

Students entering grade 9 will have experienced mathematics in the context of the broad, rich curriculum outlined in the K–8 standards.

The level of computational proficiency suggested in the K–8 standards will be expected of all students; however, no student will be denied access to the study of mathematics in grades 9–12 because of a lack of computational facility.

Although arithmetic computation will not be a direct object of study in grades 9–12, conceptual and procedural understandings of number, numeration, and operations, and the ability to make estimations and approximations and to judge the reasonableness of results will be strengthened in the context of applications and problem solving, including those situations dealing with issues of scientific computation.

Scientific calculators with graphing capabilities will be available to all students at all times.

A computer will be available at all times in every classroom for demonstration purposes, and all students will have access to computers for individual and group work.

At least three years of mathematical study will be required of all secondary school students.

These three years of mathematical study will revolve around a core curriculum differentiated by the depth and breadth of the treatment of topics and by the nature of applications.

Four years of mathematical study will be required of all college-intending students.

These four years of mathematical study will revolve around a broadened curriculum that includes extensions of the core topics and for which calculus is no longer viewed as the capstone experience.

All students will study appropriate mathematics during their senior year. (pp. 124–125)

In 1991, NCTM came out with a second Standards document, concerned with the development of teachers and classroom teaching processes. Space limits our discussion to just a few quotes from the Standards for Teaching Mathematics section of this document.

1991: National Council of Teachers of Mathematics. *Professional Standards for Teaching Mathematics.*

> The standards for teaching are based on four assumptions about the practice of mathematics teaching:
>
> 1. The goal of teaching mathematics is to help all students develop mathematical power . . .
>
> 2. What students learn is fundamentally connected with *How* they learn.
>
> 3. All students can learn to think mathematically.
>
> 4. Teaching is a complex practice and hence not reducible to recipes or prescriptions. (pp. 21–22)
>
> The teacher of mathematics should pose tasks that are based on—
>
> > sound and significant mathematics;
> >
> > knowledge of students' understandings, interests, and experiences;
> >
> > knowledge of the range of ways that diverse students learn mathematics;
>
> and that
>
> > engage students' intellect;
> >
> > develop students' mathematical understandings and skills;
> >
> > stimulate students to make connections and develop a coherent framework for mathematical ideas;
> >
> > call for problem formulation, problem solving, and mathematical reasoning;
> >
> > promote communication about mathematics;
> >
> > represent mathematics as an ongoing human activity;
> >
> > display sensitivity to, and draw on, students' diverse background experiences and dispositions;
> >
> > promote the development of all students' dispositions to do mathematics. (p. 25)

The UCSMP secondary curriculum is the first full mathematics curriculum that is consistent with the recommendations of the NCTM standards.

In 1989, the Mathematical Sciences Education Board (MSEB), a committee of the National Research Council that coordinates efforts for improvement of mathematics education in the United States, came out with the report *Everybody Counts,* emphasizing the need for the mathematics curriculum to be appropriate for as many students as possible. This thrust reflects the UCSMP position that as many students as possible be accommodated with the curriculum taken by those who go to college. It represents a change in thinking from the two-tiered system recommended in *A Nation at Risk.*

Following up and elaborating on the NCTM Evaluation Standards, many national reports have dealt with issues related to assessment. Among these are three MSEB reports: *For Good Measure* (1991), *Measuring Up* (1993), and *Measuring What Counts* (1993). A Working draft of *Assessment Standards for School Mathematics* has also been distributed. The themes of these reports are that we need to change assessment instruments to be aligned with new curricula, to incorporate a variety of ways in which students can demonstrate their knowledge of mathematics, and to ensure that assessments are used in positive ways to enhance learning and teaching rather than in negative ways to keep students from having future opportunities to learn. (For further discussion of assessment, see pages T51–T54.)

Some changes have already occurred in assessment. The SAT, Mathematics Achievement, and Advanced Placement calculus exams of the Educational Testing Service now allow any calculator without a QWERTY keyboard. Some states have altered their testing to focus on applying mathematics and higher-order thinking rather than on skills out of context.

Many of the ideas of recent reports are summarized in a 1991 MSEB report, *Reshaping School Mathematics: A Philosophy and Framework for Curriculum.* Six changes are identified there as affecting the context of mathematics education:

- ■ Changes in the need for mathematics.
- ■ Changes in mathematics and how it is used.
- ■ Changes in the role of technology.
- ■ Changes in American society.
- ■ Changes in understanding of how students learn.
- ■ Changes in international competitiveness.

In the UCSMP secondary curriculum we have attempted to respond to each of these changes.

Accomplishing the Goals

Three general problems in mathematics education in the United States lead to three major goals of the UCSMP secondary mathematics curriculum.

General Problem 1: Students do not learn enough mathematics by the time they leave school.

Specifically:

(A) Many students lack the mathematics background necessary to succeed in college, on the job, or in daily affairs.

(B) Even those students who possess mathematical skills are not introduced to enough applications of the mathematics they know.

(C) Students do not get enough experience with problems and questions that require some thought before answering.

(D) Many students terminate their study of mathematics too soon, not realizing the importance mathematics has in later schooling and in the marketplace.

(E) Students do not read mathematics books and, as a result, do not learn to become independent learners capable of acquiring mathematics outside of school when the need arises.

Goal 1: Upgrade students' achievement.

General Problem 2: The school mathematics curriculum has not kept up with changes in mathematics and the ways in which mathematics is used.

Specifically:

(A) Many mathematics curricula have not taken into account today's calculator and computer technology.

(B) Students who do succeed in secondary school mathematics generally are prepared for calculus, but generally are not equipped for the other mathematics they will encounter in college.

(C) Statistical ideas are found everywhere, from newspapers to research studies, but are not found in most secondary school mathematics curricula.

(D) The emergence of computer science has increased the importance of a background in discrete mathematics.

(E) Mathematics is not applied to areas outside the realm of the physical sciences, as much as within the field itself, but these applications are rarely taught and even more rarely tested.

(F) Estimation and approximation techniques are important in all of mathematics, from arithmetic on.

Goal 2: Update the mathematics curriculum.

General Problem 3: Too many students have been sorted out of the mathematics needed for employment and further schooling.

Specifically:

(A) Tracks make it easy to go down levels but almost impossible to go up.

(B) Remedial programs tend to put students further behind instead of catching them up.

(C) Enrichment classes often cover many topics, such as probability, statistics, discrete mathematics, and applications, and with activities of broader scope that are appropriate and important for all students.

(D) Courses for better students are often taught following the belief that the difficulty of a course is more important than its content, and with the view that if all survive, then the course was not a good one.

(E) Relative standards and preset numbers of students who go into special classes are incorrectly used as absolute indicators of ability to perform.

Goal 3: Increase the number of students who take mathematics beyond algebra and geometry.

We at UCSMP believe that these goals can be accomplished, and they already have been realized in some school districts using UCSMP materials. But substantial

reworking of the curriculum has to be involved.

It is not enough simply to insert applications, a bit of statistics, and take students a few times a year to a computer. Currently the greatest amount of time in arithmetic is spent on calculation, in algebra on manipulating polynomials and rational expressions, in geometry on proof, in advanced algebra and later courses on functions. These topics are the most affected by technology.

It is also not enough to raise graduation requirements, although that is the simplest action to take. Increases in requirements often lead to one of two situations. If the courses are kept the same, the result is typically a greater number of failures and an even greater number of dropouts. If the courses are eased, the result is lower performance for many students as they are brought through a weakened curriculum.

The fundamental problem, as SIMS noted, is the curriculum, and the fundamental problem in the curriculum is *time*. There is not enough time in the current 4-year algebra-geometry-algebra-precalculus curriculum to prepare students for calculus. The data reported by Bert Waits and Frank Demana in the *Mathematics Teacher* (January, 1988) are typical. Of students entering Ohio State University with exactly four years of college preparatory high-school mathematics, only 8% placed into calculus on the Ohio State mathematics placement test. The majority placed into pre-calculus, with 31% requiring one semester and 42% requiring two semesters of work. The remaining 19% placed into remedial courses below precalculus. Thus, even with the current curriculum, four years are not enough to take a typical student from algebra to calculus.

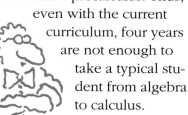

Today even most students who take four years of college preparatory mathematics successfully in

high schools do not begin college with calculus. Given that the latest recommendations ask for students to learn more mathematics, *we believe five years of college preparatory mathematics beginning with algebra are necessary to provide the time for students to learn the mathematics they need for college in the 1990s.* Thus we do not believe the current NCTM Curriculum Standards for grades 9–12 can be accomplished in four years.

The time can be found by starting reform in grades 6–8. Examining textbooks of the early 1980s, James Flanders found that over half the pages in grades 6–8 are totally review ("How Much of the Content in Mathematics Textbooks Is New?" *Arithmetic Teacher,* September, 1987). This amount of review, coupled with the magnitude of review in previous years, effectively decelerates students at least 1–2 years compared to students in other countries. It explains why almost all industrialized countries of the world, except the U.S. and Canada (and some French-speaking countries who do geometry before algebra), can begin concentrated study of algebra and geometry in the 7th or 8th grade.

In stark contrast to the review in grades 6–8, Flanders found that almost 90% of the pages of first-year algebra texts have content new to the student. This finding indicates why so many students in the U.S. have difficulty in first-year algebra. The student, having sat for years in mathematics classes where little was new, is overwhelmed. Some people interpret the overwhelming as the student "not being ready" for algebra, but we interpret it as the student being swamped by the pace. When you have been in a classroom in which at most only 1 of 3 days is devoted to anything new, you are not ready for a new idea every day. Thus we believe that algebra should be taught one year earlier to most students than is currently the case (Z. Usiskin, "Why Elementary Algebra Can, Should, and Must Be an Eighth-Grade Course for Average Students," *Mathematics Teacher,* September, 1987).

Some school districts are attempting to do away with tracking by placing all students in the same classes, with very similar expectations. We believe this is too simplistic a solution. Almost all of the many

schools that have implemented the UCSMP secondary curriculum with all their students at the same time have found that student differences in interests, cultural background, and learning style can be handled by their teachers who take advantage of the richness of the UCSMP textbooks and the wealth of teaching suggestions and ancillary materials that accompany them. Even so, they have almost all had to create slower-paced sections for students who enter with the least knowledge or who are unwilling to do homework. And they almost all realize that many students could have begun the curriculum a year earlier than the other students.

The most successful school districts realize that complex problems seldom have simple solutions. We believe strongly that the UCSMP curriculum is appropriate for virtually all students, but not at the same time. No student should be deprived of the opportunity to be successful in any of the courses, but no child who is ready should have to wait a year or two to begin the curriculum. Our evidence is strong that the national percentiles that we show on page T29 are good predictors of readiness for UCSMP courses. We recommend that school districts follow these percentiles by strongly recommending that students who fit them take our courses. Additionally, students who miss these percentiles by small amounts or who very much wish to take our courses should be allowed to take them. We strongly urge school districts to emphasize the importance of entering knowledge by strengthening their curricula in the preceding years, and stress that students must do homework every day when studying from UCSMP materials.

Finally, because UCSMP materials are not like traditional materials, we urge that school districts provide sufficient in-service training on the newer ideas incorporated in them. Teachers differ in ability, entering knowledge, preferred teaching style, and cultural background almost as much as students differ. Some love cooperative learning; others have never used it. Some are computer experts; others are neophytes. Some enjoy using manipulative materials; others avoid them. Some have had courses in statistics and discrete mathematics; others have not. Some are already trying writing and alternate assessment in their classrooms; others

have not heard of these things. No single in-service can handle such variety. We encourage school districts to send teachers to professional conferences where teachers have choices on what to attend. In particular, districts should take advantage of in-service opportunities offered by UCSMP and ScottForesman. It is also beneficial to hold periodic meetings on site to discuss local issues.

The UCSMP Secondary Curriculum

The Six UCSMP Courses

Each UCSMP course is designed for the equivalent of a school year of at least 170 days in which mathematics is taught for at least 45 minutes (preferably 50 minutes or more) each day. Our testing indicates that teachers whose mathematics classes meet every other day for twice the amount of time should expect to cover about 10–15% less material. We believe those teachers whose mathematics classes meet every day for twice the amount of time, but only for half the year, will cover even less material. All of the courses have the following general features: wider scope of content; continual emphasis on applications to the real world and to problem solving; up-to-date use of calculators and computers; a multi-dimensional (SPUR) approach to understanding; and review and mastery strategies for enhancing performance. These are described below and on pages *iv–v* of the Student Edition.

Transition Mathematics **(TM)** weaves three themes—applied arithmetic, pre-algebra, and pre-geometry—by focusing on arithmetic operations in mathematics and the real world. Variables are used as pattern generalizers, abbreviations in formulas, and unknowns in problems, and are represented on the number line and graphed in the coordinate plane. Basic arithmetic and algebraic skills are connected to corresponding geometry topics. A scientific calculator is assumed to be available.

Algebra has a scope far wider than most other algebra texts. Applications motivate all topics. Exponential growth and compound interest are covered. Statistics

and geometry are settings for work with linear expressions and sentences. Probability provides a context for algebraic fractions, functions, and set ideas. Technology for graphing is highly recommended.

Geometry integrates coordinates and transformations throughout, and gives strong attention to measurement formulas and three-dimensional figures in the first two-thirds of the book. Work with proof-writing follows a carefully sequenced development of the logical and conceptual precursors to proof. Geometry drawing technology is highly recommended.

Advanced Algebra emphasizes facility with algebraic expressions and forms (especially linear and quadratic forms), powers and roots, and functions based on these concepts. Students study logarithmic, trigonometric, polynomial, and other special functions both for their abstract properties and as tools for modeling real-world situations. A geometry course or its equivalent is a prerequisite, for geometric ideas are utilized throughout. A graphics calculator is assumed to be available.

Functions, Statistics, and Trigonometry (FST) integrates statistical and algebraic concepts, and previews calculus in work with functions and intuitive notions of limits. Technology is assumed to be available for student use in plotting functions, analyzing data, and simulating experiments. Enough trigonometry is available to constitute a standard precalculus course in trigonometry and circular functions.

Precalculus and Discrete Mathematics (PDM) integrates the background students must have to be successful in calculus (advanced work with functions and trigonometry, an introduction to limits and other calculus ideas) with the discrete mathematics (number systems, combinatorics, recursion, graphs) helpful in computer science. Mathematical thinking, including specific attention to formal logic and proof, is a theme throughout. Technology for graphing is assumed to be available for students.

Target Populations

We believe that all high-school graduates should take courses through *Advanced Algebra,* that all students planning to go to college should take courses through *Functions, Statistics, and Trigonometry,* and that students planning majors in technical areas should take all six UCSMP courses.

The fundamental principle in placing students into courses is that entry should not be based on age, but on mathematical knowledge. Our studies indicate that with a standard curriculum, about 10% of students nationally are ready for *Transition Mathematics* at 6th grade, about another 40% at 7th grade, another 20% at 8th grade, and another 10–15% at 9th grade. We caution that these percentages are national, not local percentages, and the variability in our nation is enormous. We have tested the materials in school districts where few students are at grade level, where *Transition Mathematics* is appropriate for no more than the upper half of 8th-graders. We have tested also in school districts where as many as 90% of the students have successfully used *Transition Mathematics* in 7th grade. School districts have increased the percentages at the 6th and 7th grade by strengthening the mathematics curriculum in grades K–5 or K–6.

We also caution that the percentages are not automatic. Students who do not reach 7th-grade competence until the 9th-grade level often do not possess the study habits necessary for successful completion of these courses. At the 9th-grade level, *Transition Mathematics* has been substituted successfully either for a traditional pre-algebra course or for the first year of an algebra course spread out over two years. It often does not work as a substitute for a general mathematics course in which there is no expectation that students will take algebra the following year.

On page T29 is a chart identifying the courses and the populations for which they are intended. The percentiles are national percentiles on a 7th-grade standardized mathematics test using 7th-grade norms, and apply to potential *Transition Mathematics* students. Pages T29–T30 also provide advice for starting in the middle of the series.

Left column: All qualified students should be afforded the possibility of taking *Transition Mathematics* in 6th grade so as to maximize the potential for them to complete *Algebra* in 7th grade and thus take calculus in high school. These students are often very interested in school, and they should be offered the Challenges suggested in the Teacher's Edition. Teachers may also wish to enrich courses

for these students further with problems from mathematics contests.

2nd column: These students should be expected to take mathematics at least through the 11th grade, by which time they will have the mathematics needed for all college majors except those in the hard sciences and engineering. For that they will have the opportunity to take PDM in the 12th grade.

3rd column: Students in the 30th–70th percentile can complete *Advanced Algebra* by taking three years of high school mathematics. Currently over half of these students go to college. By completing FST, they will have studied the kind of mathematics needed for all majors.

Right column: Students in the 15th–50th percentile should not be tracked into courses that put them further behind. Rather they should be put into this curriculum and counseled on study skills. The logic is simple: Students who are behind in mathematical knowledge need to work harder at it, not less, in order to catch up.

Starting in the Middle of the Series

Every UCSMP course has been designed so that it could be used independently of other UCSMP courses. Accordingly, about half of the testing of UCSMP courses after *Transition Mathematics* has been with students who have not had any previous UCSMP courses. We have verified that any of the UCSMP courses can be taken successfully following the typical prerequisite courses in the standard curriculum.

Starting with *UCSMP Algebra* No additional prerequisites other than those needed for success in any algebra course are needed for success in *UCSMP Algebra*.

Grade	**The top 10% of students nationally** are ready for *Transition Mathematics* in 6th grade. These students can proceed through the entire curriculum by the 11th grade and take calculus in the 12th grade.	**Students in the 50th–90th percentile** on a 7th-grade standardized mathematics test should be ready to take *Transition Mathematics* in 7th grade.	Students who do not reach the 7th-grade level in mathematics until the 8th grade **(in the 30th–70th percentile)** begin *Transition Mathematics* in 8th grade.	Students who do not reach the 7th-grade level in mathematics until the 9th grade **(in the 15th–50th percentile)** begin *Transition Mathematics* in 9th grade.
6	Transition Mathematics			
7	Algebra	Transition Mathematics		
8	Geometry	Algebra	Transition Mathematics	
9	Advanced Algebra	Geometry	Algebra	Transition Mathematics
10	Functions, Statistics, and Trigonometry	Advanced Algebra	Geometry	Algebra
11	Precalculus and Discrete Mathematics	Functions, Statistics, and Trigonometry	Advanced Algebra	Geometry
12	Calculus (not available through UCSMP)	Precalculus and Discrete Mathematics	Functions, Statistics, and Trigonometry	Advanced Algebra

Students who have studied *Transition Mathematics* tend to cover more of *UCSMP Algebra* than other students because they have been introduced to more of the applications of algebra.

UCSMP Algebra prepares students for any standard geometry course.

Starting with *UCSMP Geometry* No additional prerequisites other than those needed for success in any geometry course are needed for success in *UCSMP Geometry*.

UCSMP Geometry can be used with faster, average, and slower students who have these prerequisites. Prior study of *Transition Mathematics* and *UCSMP Algebra* ensures this background, but this content is also found in virtually all existing middle school or junior high school texts. Classes of students who have studied *UCSMP Algebra* tend to cover more *UCSMP Geometry* than other classes because they know more geometry and are better at the algebra used in geometry. Students who have studied *UCSMP Geometry* are ready for any second-year algebra text.

Starting with *UCSMP Advanced Algebra* *UCSMP Advanced Algebra* can be used following any standard geometry text.

Students who have had *UCSMP Geometry* before *UCSMP Advanced Algebra* tend to be better prepared in the transformations and coordinate geometry they will need in this course, and geometry courses using other books should be careful to cover this content. Students who have studied from *UCSMP Algebra* tend

to be better prepared for the graphing and applications found in this course.

Students who have studied *UCSMP Advanced Algebra* are prepared for courses commonly found at the senior level, including trigonometry or precalculus courses.

Starting with *Functions, Statistics, and Trigonometry (FST)* FST assumes that students have completed a second-year algebra course. Students who have studied some trigonometry, like that found in *UCSMP Advanced Algebra,* will be at an advantage. No additional prerequisites other than those found in any second-year algebra text are needed for success in FST.

FST provides sufficient background for success in a non-proof-oriented calculus, such as is often taken by business or social studies majors in college, and for many of the reform calculus courses that emphasize applications and technology.

Starting with *Precalculus and Discrete Mathematics (PDM)* PDM can be taken successfully by students who have had FST, by students who have had typical senior level courses that include study of trigonometry and functions, and by top students who have successfully completed full advanced algebra and trigonometry courses.

PDM provides the background necessary for any typical calculus course, either at the high school or college level, including those that place a heavy emphasis on proof, and including advanced placement calculus courses at either the AB or BC level.

Professional Sourcebook: SECTION **2** **ABOUT *UCSMP ADVANCED ALGEBRA***

Goals of *UCSMP ADVANCED ALGEBRA*

UCSMP Advanced Algebra introduces students to all the dimensions of the understanding of algebra: its

skills, its properties, its uses, and its representations. For each, we want to update the curriculum and upgrade students' achievement. Specifically, we want students to master linear, quadratic, and exponential expressions, sentences, and functions; and we want

them to begin to develop an understanding of logarithmic, trigonometric, and higher order trigonometric functions. We want students to be better able to apply algebra; we want them to be able to connect algebra to geometry, to statistics, and to probability; and we want them to be more successful in future years in their study of mathematics.

Additionally, we want students to learn how to study mathematics. To accomplish this goal we want students to learn to take advantage of many resources. They should try to learn from the reading of the lesson, as well as from their teacher and from their fellow classmates.

Finally, we have another, more lofty goal. We want students to view their study of mathematics as worthwhile, as full of interesting and entertaining information, as related to almost every endeavor. We want them to realize that mathematics is still growing and is changing fast. We want them to look for and recognize mathematics in places they haven't before, to use the library, to search through newspapers or almanacs, to get excited by knowledge.

In summary, we would like to help students develop what the NCTM Standards call *mathematical power,* that is, the ability to explore, conjecture, and reason logically; to solve non-routine problems; to communicate about and through mathematics; and to connect ideas within mathematics and between mathematics and other disciplines. We also want students to develop personal self-confidence, positive attitudes, and effective study skills in mathematics.

Who Should Take *UCSMP Advanced Algebra?*

Virtually every student who expects to graduate from high school should take advanced algebra. College-bound students should take advanced algebra for many reasons: two years of algebra are required for admission to most colleges; algebra is found on all college-entrance examinations; algebra is necessary to understand even the basics of science, statistics, computers, and economics; and algebra helps students understand the social sciences and business. Without algebra, doors are open to only a few colleges, and even at those colleges a student who has

only one year of algebra has the choice of only a few college majors.

There are just as many reasons for non-college-bound students to take two years of algebra. Technical schools, such as those for the trades, require that students be familiar with functions, graphs, and trigonometry. Computers abound in the workplace; algebra is the language of programs and algebraic thinking underlies the operation of spreadsheets and many other software packages. Algebra is the language of generalization; without it arithmetic is often seen merely as a collection of unrelated rules and procedures. It is no surprise that study of algebra helps competence in arithmetic.

Students who take *UCSMP Advanced Algebra* should have the following prerequisites:

(1) a geometry course that includes some transformations and coordinates, such as *UCSMP Geometry;*
(2) a year-long algebra course or its equivalent;
(3) a willingness and the maturity to do homework every night.

In addition, the teacher of *UCSMP Advanced Algebra* should believe that every student with the above prerequisites can learn the material of the course.

Problems *UCSMP Advanced Algebra* Addresses

The general problems addressed by the UCSMP secondary curriculum are discussed in Section 1, on pages T21–T30. More specifically, *UCSMP Advanced Algebra* responds to eight serious problems which cannot be treated by small changes in content or approach.

Problem 1: Large numbers of students do not know why they need algebra.

Some advanced algebra courses have been motivated almost exclusively by the needs of a minority of the population: those who will take calculus four or five years later. Other advanced algebra courses consist entirely of dozens of problems of one type followed by dozens of another, or of one skill after another, introduced without motivation, ostensibly designed for the poorer student but actually of ultimate use to few if any students.

Most word problems in those courses do not constitute applications; problems like them are not encountered outside of school. It is no surprise, then, that many adults—even many of the most educated of adults—wonder why they studied algebra. We believe that this is a result of the kind of algebra courses they studied, and the lack of applications in them. Algebra has many real-world applications even though school algebra has often ignored them. Most age, digit, work, and other so-called "word problems" or "story problems" do not constitute applications; problems like them are not encountered outside school.

The *UCSMP Advanced Algebra* response: Instead of holding off on applications until after skills have been developed, applications are used to motivate all concepts and skills. The ability to apply algebra is made a priority. Word problems that have little or no use are replaced by more meaningful types of problems. Algebra is continually connected with the arithmetic the student knows and the geometry the student has studied. We have evidence from the First Edition of *UCSMP Advanced Algebra* that we can greatly reduce and almost eliminate the "Why are we studying this?" kind of question.

Problem 2: Students are not skillful enough, regardless of what they are taught.

Our response to this problem covers more than just this course. The evidence is that students are rather skillful at routine problems but not with problems involving complicated numbers, different wordings, or new contexts. It is obvious that in order to obtain such skill, students must see problems with all sorts of numbers, in a variety of wordings, and in many different contexts.

We believe that courses that are preoccupied with skill have demonstrated that few students acquire considerable skill in only two years of algebra study. In UCSMP, we give specific attention to algebraic skills over six years. Simple linear equations, graphing, and simplifications are in *Transition Mathematics*. *Algebra* stresses linear and quadratic sentence-solving, polynomial manipulations, some work with exponents, and more graphing. *Geometry* reviews the work with lines, slopes, radicals, proportions, systems, and formulas. *Advanced Algebra* emphasizes further manipulations with linear and quadratic expressions, powers, roots, logarithms, trigonometric, and other functions.

Appendix A in the Student Edition of *UCSMP Advanced Algebra*, "Algebra Properties from Earlier Courses," highlights the algebra we expect students to have had prior to entering this course.

UCSMP courses employ a four-stage approach to develop skill.

Stage 1: involves a concentrated introduction to the ideas surrounding the skill: why it is done, how it is done, and the kinds of problems that can be solved with it. Most books are organized to have this stage, because teachers recognize that explanations of an idea require time. At the end of this stage, typically only the best students have the skill. But in *UCSMP Advanced Algebra* this is only the beginning.

Stage 2: occupies the following lessons in the chapter and consists of questions designed to establish some competence in the skill. These are found in the Review questions. By the end of the lessons of the chapter, most students should have some competence in the skills, but some may not have enough.

Stage 3: involves mastery learning. At the end of each chapter is a Progress Self-Test for students to take and judge how they are doing. Worked-out solutions are included to provide feedback and help to the student. This is followed by a Chapter Review, organized by objectives, to enable students to acquire those skills they didn't have when taking the Progress Self-Test. Teachers are expected to spend 1–3 days on these sections to give students time to reach mastery. By the end of this stage, most students should have gained mastery at least at the level of typical students covering the content.

Stage 4: continues the review through daily Review questions in subsequent chapters. Vital algebra skills, such as solving linear equations, receive consistent emphasis throughout the book. Included also are skill sequences consisting of 3 or 4 questions that provide practice on related problems. The evidence is that this four-stage process enables students to gain competence over a wider range of content than comparable students normally possess. (See pages T54–T58 on research.)

Problem 3: The mathematics curriculum has been lagging behind today's widely available and inexpensive technology.

Calculators and computers allow students to work with realistic numbers, to practice estimation skills, to avoid tedious and repetitious calculations, and to solve problems that would not be accessible otherwise. There is unanimous sentiment in recent national reports on mathematics education in favor of the use of calculators and computers in all mathematics courses. Yet until the development of materials by UCSMP, there was no curriculum for secondary schools that made systematic use of this technology.

The *UCSMP Advanced Algebra* response: We support the recommendations of the NCTM regarding access to calculators and computers. In particular, we assume that graphics calculators are available to students at all times in *UCSMP Advanced Algebra*—and that they are used starting in Chapter 1. Graphics calculators are used as tools for making and analyzing graphs, fitting models to data, operating with matrices, and generating tables of values.

Many connections with computers are given in this course. We introduce the notation of the BASIC computer language, give templates for programs, and introduce spreadsheets. But the influence of computers ranges further than this. Certain content has been included because of its importance in a computer age, including discrete and continuous domains, iteration, interpretation of algorithms, and a great deal of interpretation of graphs. However, we note that many of the functions performed only by computers as recently as a few years ago are now available on hand-held graphics calculators.

Appendix D in the Student Edition of *UCSMP Advanced Algebra,* "Programming Languages," contains a collection of useful BASIC programs and parallel programs for a graphics calculator.

At the time of publication of this book, there exist *symbol manipulators*—calculators and computer software that can rewrite algebraic expressions and solve equations symbolically. Although these are not yet inexpensive, they are valuable purchases for the serious student, and we have taken their existence into account in the selection of content and in the design of some activities.

Problem 4: Even students who succeed in advanced algebra often forget the geometry they have learned.

Most advanced algebra texts are written as if the student had never studied geometry. This creates two difficulties: the student forgets the geometry that was learned, and the student does not integrate the important ideas found in geometry with their corresponding applications in algebra.

In *UCSMP Advanced Algebra,* we assume the student has studied geometry, and we are thus able to use geometry in four ways. First, we utilize measurement relationships (formulas for area or volume, ratios in similar figures, and so on) as subject matter to be analyzed from an algebraic point of view. Second, we apply geometric concepts to the study of algebra (such as the use of transformations to study graphs). Third, we emphasize graphing to take advantage of the geometric intuitions students have (such as that the sine and cosine graphs are congruent). Fourth, we use the language developed from studying geometry as a mathematical system (such as postulate, theorem, counterexample, and proof) throughout the text.

We do our concentrated work with advanced algebra *after* geometry because we can so easily take advantage of that geometry. The reverse is not as productive; a student who has taken two years of algebra does not possess much more mathematics to apply in elementary geometry than a student who has taken one year of algebra. Furthermore, we believe as many students as possible should have concentrated work in geometry. Thus we view the algebra-algebra-geometry sequence used in some schools as not as effective as the algebra-geometry-algebra sequence found in UCSMP.

Appendix B in the Student Edition of *UCSMP Advanced Algebra*, "Geometry Properties from Earlier Courses," highlights the geometry we expect students to have had prior to entering this course.

Problem 5: *Students don't read mathematics and are not capable of learning mathematics on their own.*

Students using traditional texts tell us they don't read because (1) the text is uninteresting, and (2) they don't have to read because the teacher explains it for them. But students must learn to read for future success in mathematics.

The *UCSMP Advanced Algebra* response to (1) above: We have paid careful attention to the explanations, examples, and questions in each lesson. So every lesson of this book contains reading and questions covering the reading. *UCSMP Advanced Algebra* is more than a resource for questions; it is a resource for information, for examples of how to do problems, for the history of major ideas, for applications of the ideas, for connections between ideas in one place in the book and in another, and for motivation.

Our response to (2) above is to encourage teachers not to explain everything *in advance* to students. Because students can read and understand the *UCSMP Advanced Algebra* text, the teacher has the freedom to teach in a variety of ways, and it is not necessary to explain every day what the textbook says. The teacher can concentrate on helping students with difficult new symbols and vocabulary, or on developing further examples, explanations, and investigations tailored to his or her class. More detailed information about reading can be found on pages T47–T48.

In our studies, teachers new to UCSMP texts have always been skeptical at first about the amount of reading in the book. As the year progressed, they joined those who had taught our books in viewing the reading as one of the strongest features of this series. Some teachers felt that UCSMP was teaching reading comprehension; they all felt that the requirement to read helped develop thinkers who were more critical and aware. Now the UCSMP approach to reading is being adopted by many other textbooks.

Comments from students and teachers of the First Edition published by ScottForesman continue to support the positive features of the reading.

Problem 6: *Even educated adults sometimes have not been introduced to fundamentally important mathematical ideas.*

Mathematics was created rather recently in human history, and mathematics is a growing subject. These important ideas are often ignored in students' mathematical education, but without this knowledge a person must find it difficult to understand why the mathematics important in one age might not be as important in another. In *UCSMP Advanced Algebra,* we consider the development of mathematics as an important topic.

Trigonometry is often left to later courses taken by far fewer students. Matrices, counting problems, probability, and statistics are often never encountered. We believe that every educated adult should be exposed to these topics, at least to the extent covered in *UCSMP Advanced Algebra.*

Problem 7: *Students are not very good at communicating mathematics in writing.*

Students write mathematics every time they "show work," but they typically do not realize that they are engaged in a task to communicate an argument.

Rather, they see their writing as somehow proving that they did the work that was required, and writing becomes simply showing a more detailed answer. Geometry students have great difficulty writing even the simplest of proofs. In general, students at the level of *UCSMP Advanced Algebra* are quite poor at putting together any sort of logical argument. We think this is because they are seldom given writing tasks that require such arguments.

There are many reasons to put some emphasis on writing. Writing can organize and clarify thinking, thus making it a route for exploring a subject and gaining ownership of it. This makes it a valuable learning tool. Writing stimulates communication among individuals; students can express frustrations and other difficulties with a concept at hand. Some who might not otherwise ask questions may use writing as their means to communicate with a teacher. Thus writing can also be a valuable teaching tool.

There is also a strong link between problem solving and writing. Both require critical decision making and involve the development of strategies. Both provide the learner with many possible avenues to follow, demonstrating that there are many ways to approach a problem.

The *UCSMP Advanced Algebra* response: Writing is developed from the beginning of the year. Lesson questions ask students to explain their methods, describe representations and procedures, and compare algorithms. Writing questions are found on Progress Self-Tests and in the Chapter Review questions. The notes in the Teacher's Edition also provide suggestions for incorporating writing.

What's New in the Second Edition

The publication of the complete six-year UCSMP series has given another perspective on each text and its role in the long-term development of mathematical concepts and competence. National reports that have been issued since the publication of the first project version of *UCSMP Advanced Algebra* in 1985 have stressed the importance of many of the innovations present in UCSMP texts. Widespread availability of graphics calculators and computer spreadsheets indicates that algebra courses can incorporate technology beyond the scientific calculator. The Second Edition of *UCSMP Advanced Algebra* has also benefited from user reports, focus group discussions, and ScottForesman surveys of users from all regions throughout the United States.

A person familiar with the First Edition of *UCSMP Advanced Algebra* will note a large number of small changes in each lesson, and the following more major changes:

- The study of functions now begins in Chapter 1 due to the power of automatic graphers to obtain values and display graphs of functions.

- Lessons on finding linear, quadratic, and exponential models have been added.

- The treatment of powers and roots has been reorganized.

- The use of automatic graphers has been incorporated throughout the text.

- Full-page In-class Activities and shorter Activities (within lessons) are included to provide students with more hands-on experiences. Many of the In-class Activities are especially suitable for small-group work.

- Each chapter includes a set of Projects to provide students opportunities to explore concepts in a more in-depth way. Students may find it beneficial to work on the Projects in small groups. (See pages T42–T43.)

- Colored headers appear in the lessons to help outline the reading.

- Solutions to Examples are printed in a special font to help model what students should write when they do the Questions.

- A global, multicultural view of mathematics is enhanced with new photos from around the world. Informative captions are now included.

■ Graphic displays are drawn with a contemporary look to emphasize that the data in the text are like that found in newspapers, magazines, and other sources outside the classroom.

■ Chapter 14 on Dimensions and Space from the First Edition has been deleted.

■ An enhanced Teacher's Edition now provides daily suggestions for adapting to individual needs, optional activities, and assessment alternatives.

■ An augmented ancillary package offers two sets of Lesson Masters, performance tests and forms for authentic assessment, and an expanded Technology Sourcebook.

■ Interactive multimedia videotape, videodisc, and CD–ROM components in *Wide World of Mathematics,* emphasizing real-world applications, are designed to further enhance instruction and provide motivation.

Professional Sourcebook: SECTION 3

GENERAL TEACHING SUGGESTIONS FOR *UCSMP ADVANCED ALGEBRA*

UCSMP Advanced Algebra is the core of a mathematics course. It is not meant to stand alone without a teacher or without other materials. Nor does it attempt to prescribe a single way of teaching mathematics. We have seen the First Edition of this text used effectively with a variety of models of teaching—from direct instruction through cooperative learning, and we expect the Second Edition to be at least as flexible.

We feel a need to restate one of the assumptions of the Professional Standards for Teaching Mathematics (NCTM, 1991), that "teaching is a complex practice and hence not reducible to recipes or prescriptions." The suggestions which follow should not be construed as rigid, as students, teachers, classes, and schools vary greatly. But the suggestions should not be ignored. They come from extensive discussions with teachers of earlier versions of these materials, written comments from experienced users of the First Edition, and from test results. We encourage you to read them, and to try as many of them as you can in your classroom.

Planning

It hardly needs to be said that good teaching begins with careful planning. In this section we concentrate on features that may be different from other books from which you have taught.

First Steps

1. Find out more about these materials. If you have not already done so, skim Section 1 and read Section 2 of this Professional Sourcebook. These sections will inform you if your students are among the typical *UCSMP Advanced Algebra* students. They also give the motivation for many of the features you will find. Also read pages iv–v of the Student Edition for additional information on UCSMP and *UCSMP Advanced Algebra*.

2. Make certain that you have all the materials you need. A list of components that are available with the Second Edition of *UCSMP Advanced Algebra* is on page T19 of this book. If you do not have all the materials, contact your local ScottForesman representative or call ScottForesman at 1–800–554–4411.

Before the school year starts you should assemble some resources for your teaching. Some materials you will want to have in your classroom throughout the year are: a dictionary, an atlas, an almanac, and either a globe or a large world map for the wall. It is also important to know the technology that you can have available for display; an overhead projector with a

display panel connected to a calculator or computer is recommended at all times.

3. Check that your students will have all the materials they need. In addition to pencils and various types of paper, all students are expected to have a graphics calculator, a ruler, and a protractor. A list of specifications is given in the "To the Student" section on pages 1–3. Be certain to cover this section with your students.

4. Familiarize yourself with the general layout of the two-part Teacher's Edition (this part and one other). Part 1 of the Teacher's Edition contains Chapters 1–6. Part 2 contains Chapters 7–13. At the beginning of each chapter are four extra pages (tinted) that display pacing schedules, objectives, available materials, and overall notes for the chapter. Following Chapter 6 in Part 1 are all four Appendices, the Selected Answers (for Chapters 1–6), and the Glossary and Index to the entire Student Edition. In Part 2, Chapter 13 is followed by the four Appendices, the Selected Answers (for Chapters 7–13), and again the Glossary and Index.

5. Familiarize yourself with the features of the Student Edition. There are 13 chapters, with 8–11 lessons each. Each chapter begins with a 2-page chapter opener that serves as an introduction and is meant to be read. Then come the lessons, each with reading followed by four types of questions: Covering the Reading, Applying the Mathematics, Review, and Exploration. Following the lessons are Projects. (See pages T42–T43.) Each chapter ends with a Summary and list of new Vocabulary for the chapter, a Progress Self-Test, and a Chapter Review. The Progress Self-Test and Chapter Review are not optional; they are designed to focus students' attention on the important material and objectives of the chapter. (See pages T39–T40.) The Selected Answers section, beginning on page 897 in the Student Edition, provides answers to odd-numbered Applying the Mathematics and Review Questions.

6. Consider sending information about *UCSMP Advanced Algebra* home with your students. A letter or flyer to parents conveys your and your school district's concern for each child and at the same time can let parents know your expectations regarding materials and homework. Suggestions concerning what form a letter or flyer can take, and what to put in it are provided below. These suggestions come to us from UCSMP users.

Sample Letter to Parents

Because the adoption of books is generally done by a school or school district, it may be best if the letter comes from the mathematics department, the mathematics department chair or supervisor, or the principal. The letter should be on school or school district stationery. Here are the kinds of information schools have conveyed:

UCSMP beliefs/philosophy Mathematics is valuable to the average citizen. All students can learn a significant amount of mathematics. We can learn from other countries. A major cause of our problems lies in the curriculum. The mathematics curriculum can make better use of time by spending less time on review (from previous years) and outmoded content and skills. Calculators and computers render some content obsolete, make other content more important, and change the ways we should view still other content. The scope of mathematics should expand at all levels. The classroom should draw examples from the real world. To make significant changes in any school, teachers, administrators, and parents must work together.

Features of UCSMP texts that parents will notice Students are expected to read. They are expected to use calculators. There are a variety of problems in each question set rather than a single type of problem repeated a large number of times. It is best if each feature is followed by a sentence or two with a rationale for that feature. Such information may be found throughout this Sourcebook.

Materials students need This can be similar to the list found in the "To The Student" section of the student book (pages 1–3). This should include a list of the features of the calculators students should have,

and information on how students can obtain such calculators (whether from the school or from a local store). If possible, include prices.

How parents can help It is wise to include statements that describe the roles of parents in their child's education, particularly because at this level, parents are sometimes given the feeling that they no longer are integral. Here are some suggestions: Encourage your child to read the textbook. Check with your children to see that they have the supplies they need. See that your children are doing homework every night. Encourage determination and perseverance; if your child is having a problem, ask your child to tell you what he or she knows about the idea. Monitor your child's absences (perhaps include the school's absence policy). Contact the teacher as soon as a problem arises; do not wait. Encourage your child to seek help whenever necessary (give places to get help).

With this letter, some school districts include their mathematics course sequence. Some indicate their grading policies. Whatever you include, you should expect responses from parents who seek clarification. *Welcome* each response as a sign of an interested parent and because the responses will help you in drafting what you send next year.

Planning for Teaching

Planning for teaching with *UCSMP Advanced Algebra* is similar to the planning you might do for any mathematics class.

Global planning can be done by looking over the Table of Contents and setting goals for each grading period. The chapters in this book are meant to be covered in order, at a pace of about one lesson per day, and we suggest that first-time users adhere to this pattern. This means that most teachers should plan to cover

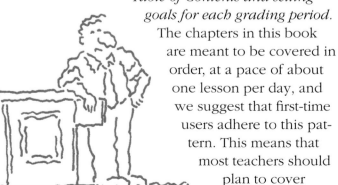

11–12 chapters. This amounts to approximately two chapters each marking period if you give grades every six weeks, or three chapters per marking period if you give grades every nine or ten weeks. Teachers of very well-prepared students in schools which do not lose much instructional time to other matters are likely to be able to cover more, and those who are teaching under-prepared students in classes with numerous interruptions may cover less.

To get an overview of the content in each chapter, read the Chapter Overview on the tinted pages in this Teacher's Edition; read the lesson titles; and scan the Summary and Vocabulary, Progress Self-Test, and Chapter Review at the end of the chapter. Collectively these will give you a good idea of what the chapter is about, and how much of the content will be new to you or your students. Make a tentative schedule for working through the chapter. Be sure to leave 2 or 3 days for review before the chapter test. (See Strategies for Mastery on page T40.)

Read each lesson in the Student Edition. Then read the Overview, the Notes on Reading, the Notes on the Questions, and other side and bottom notes in the Teacher's Edition. They indicate the Resources you may need for the lesson. They also provide ideas for various ways of approaching the lesson. They will help you decide what instructional modes (whole-class discussion, small-group work, demonstration, lecture, etc.) you might use, how you might go over the assignment from the previous day, how you could sequence the class activities from opening to closing, and what assignment you can make for the next class.

Do all of the Questions before assigning them. Note any questions with directions which might need clarification to your students, or any questions which you think are particularly important or exceptionally difficult.

Pace

There is a natural tendency, when using a new book, to go more slowly, to play it safe should you forget something. Teachers using these materials for the first time have almost invariably said that they would move more quickly the next year. Do not be

afraid to move quickly. As in all UCSMP texts, virtually all lessons in *UCSMP Advanced Algebra* are intended to be read and discussed in one day.

Students adjust to the pace set by the teacher. It is especially important that Chapter 1 be taught at a one-day-per-lesson pace. At the end of the chapter, spend a few days on the Progress Self-Test and Chapter Review to cinch the major skills. We know from our studies that this pace produces the highest performance levels. Students need to be exposed to content in order to learn it.

Some classes in our studies of this book went very slowly; their teachers seemed reluctant to move to any new content. Where this happens, the students get into a rut. Better students are bored because they know the material. Slower students are frustrated because they are being asked to spend more time on the stuff they don't know. They all get discouraged and perform far lower than any other comparable students at the end of the year. We can state this rather strongly: If you want to guarantee poor performance, go slowly through a book.

There are times when it will be difficult to maintain this pace. But be advised: a slow pace can make it too easy to lose perspective and difficult to relate ideas. You need to get to later content to realize why you were asked to learn earlier content. If you spend too much time in the lessons, you may find that your slowest students may have learned more by having gone through content slowly, but all the other students will have learned less. The wise teacher strikes a balance, goes quickly enough to keep things interesting but slowly enough to have time for explanations. David R. Johnson's booklets *Every Minute Counts* and *Making Minutes Count Even More* give excellent practical suggestions on making use of class time.

Average students should be able to complete 11 chapters of *UCSMP Advanced Algebra*. If you find in spring that you have been going through the chapters more slowly than recommended, rather than omitting entire chapters, we suggest omitting certain lessons. However, please be aware that these lessons are reviewed later. You will need to adjust your homework assignments accordingly.

Assignments

We recommend that a typical homework assignment be one of the following:

1. Read Lesson n; write answers to all Questions in Lesson n.

or

2. Read Lesson n; write answers to Questions Covering the Reading in Lesson n, and Applying the Mathematics, Review, and Exploration in Lesson $n - 1$.

Thus virtually every day students should be expected to do the equivalent of a complete set of questions from a lesson. At times you will want to preview the reading, but for typical classes this should not be a regular part of the plan. (See *Using the Reading,* pages T47–T48.)

The Questions in each lesson have been designed to cover the key skills, properties, uses, and representations in the lesson. The Questions were not written with an odd-even assignment plan in mind. Skipping questions may lead to gaps in student understanding. The Exploration questions may be assigned for all to do, or left as optional work for extra credit.

We also recommend that assignments be given on the days following chapter tests. If this is not done, then there will be up to 11 days without homework, the equivalent of a complete chapter's work.

Taking Review Into Account

Every lesson includes a set of Review questions. These questions serve a variety of purposes. First, they develop competence in a topic. Because we do not expect students to master a topic on the day they are introduced to it, these questions, coming on the days after introduction, help to solidify the ideas. Second, they maintain competence from preceding chapters. This review is particularly effective with topics that have not been studied for some time.

At times, we are able to give harder questions in reviews than we could expect students to be able to do on the day they were introduced to the topic. Thus the reviews sometimes serve as questions which integrate ideas from previous lessons.

Finally, we occasionally review an idea that has not been discussed for some time, just before it is to surface again in a lesson. The Notes on Questions (in the Teacher's Edition) usually alert you to this circumstance.

Teachers of classes that perform the best assign all the Review questions, give students the answers each day, and discuss them when needed. Those who do not assign all reviews tend to get poorer performance; their students never get enough practice to solidify and master the ideas and, even when mastered, the ideas are forgotten. *The Review questions must be assigned to ensure optimum performance.*

Strategies for Mastery

Some students master the content of one lesson in one day; but many do not. Why then do we suggest that you spend only one day per lesson? We do so because the combination of Review questions in each lesson and the end-of-chapter material has proved to be a powerful vehicle for achieving mastery, while allowing teachers and students to cover a substantial amount of material.

The mastery strategy used at the end of each chapter of *UCSMP Advanced Algebra* is one that has been validated by a great deal of research. Its components are a Progress Self-Test (the "formative test" in the parlance of some mastery learning literature), solutions to that test in the student's textbook (the "feedback"), review questions tied to the same objectives used to make up the self-test (the "correctives"), and finally a chapter test covering the same objectives.

Following the strategy means assigning the Progress Self-Test as a homework assignment to be done under simulated test conditions. The next day should be devoted to answering student questions about the problems and doing some problems from the Chapter Review.

For most classes, as a second night's assignment, we suggest the even-numbered questions from the Chapter Review. Neither solutions nor answers to the even-numbered questions are in the student text, so students will have to work on their own without these aids. The next day, discuss these questions in class.

Give the test on the third day. The odd-numbered Chapter Review questions, for which answers are given in the student text, can be useful for studying for that test. In some classes, a third day before the test may be needed. If so, either the odd-numbered Chapter Review questions, selected Lesson Masters, or questions generated by the Quiz and Test Writer software can be used as sources of problems.

We strongly recommend that, except for classes of exceptionally talented students (where less review may be needed), teachers follow this strategy. The evidence is substantial that it promotes higher levels of performance.

Using Technology

We use calculators and computers in UCSMP because they are tools important to most users of mathematics today, whether on the job or in one's personal life. They are popular because they make important mathematical ideas accessible to students at an early age and to people who might otherwise find mathematics difficult; they relieve the drudgery of calculation, particularly with numbers and equations encountered in realistic contexts; they enable quick picturing of mathematical ideas; and they facilitate exploration and open-ended problem solving by making multiple instances easy to examine. Furthermore, as indicated in Section 4 (Research and Development), our use of technology has resulted in no loss of paper-and-pencil skill in arithmetic, and has freed up time in the curriculum to spend on other topics that lead to overall better performance by UCSMP students.

Calculators Hand-held calculators first appeared in 1971. Not until 1976 did the price for a four-function calculator come below $50 (equivalent to well over $100 today). Still, in 1975, a national commission recommended that hand calculators be used on all mathematics tests starting in eighth grade, and in 1980 the National Council of Teachers of Mathematics recommended that calculators be used in all grades of school from kindergarten on. The

SATs, Achievement, and Advanced Placement tests of the College Board already allow all standard scientific and graphing calculators. Several standardized test batteries are being developed with calculators. And slowly but surely calculators are being expected on more and more licensing exams outside of school.

The business and mathematics education communities generally believe that paper-and-pencil algorithms are becoming obsolete. Do not be surprised. The long division algorithm we use was born only in the late 1400s; it can have a death as well. Increasingly, businesses do not want their employees to use paper-and-pencil algorithms to get answers to arithmetic problems. Banks require that their tellers do all arithmetic using a calculator.

It is wonderful to live in the age when calculators have been developed that quickly and efficiently do arithmetic. This frees us to use arithmetic more and allows students to spend more time on mental arithmetic, estimation, and problem solving. It is inevitable that calculators will be considered as natural as pencils for doing mathematics. A century from now people will be amazed when they learn that some students as recently as the 1990s went to schools where calculators were not used. Students of the future will no doubt consider it cruel and unusual punishment.

Students will overuse calculators. Part of learning to use any machine is to make mistakes: using it when you shouldn't, not using it when you should. Anyone who has a word processor has used it for short memos that could much more easily have been handwritten. Anyone who has a microwave has used it for food that could have been cooked either in a conventional oven or on top of the stove.

The overuse dies down, but it takes some months. In the meantime, stress this important idea. There are three ways to get answers to arithmetic problems: by paper and pencil, mentally, or by using some automatic means (a table, a calculator, a trusty friend, etc.). Some problems require more than one of these means, but the wise applier of arithmetic knows when to use each of these ways.

Generally this means that good arithmeticians do a lot of calculations mentally, either because they are basic facts (e.g., 3×5) or because they follow simple rules (e.g., $2/3 \times 4/5$ or 100×4.72). They may not use a calculator on these because the likelihood of making an error entering or reading is greater than the likelihood of making a mental error. As a rule, we seldom say, "Do not use calculators here." We want students to learn for themselves when calculator use is appropriate and when it is not. However, you may feel the need to prod some students to avoid the calculator. An answer of 2.9999999 to $\sqrt{9}$ should be strongly discouraged.

Many lessons include questions to be done "in your head." These are designed to develop skill in mental arithmetic and show students situations in which mental calculation is an appropriate approach to calculation. You may wish to give quizzes on these kinds of problems and have a "no calculator" rule for these problems.

Graphics calculators For this course, we assume that students have graphics calculators like the TI-81, TI-82, Casio fx-7700G, or Sharp EL 9300C. A good graphics calculator should display as many as four graphs simultaneously, allow the window to be changed with ease, and in general be easy to use. These calculators can perform all the operations we expect in a scientific calculator. Though their order of operations is often different from that found in scientific calculators, and key sequences for scientific calculators will often not work with them, their key sequences more closely parallel what is written on a page. Throughout *UCSMP Advanced Algebra,* we give key sequences for scientific calculators and graphic calculators when both can be used.

Some questions ask students to use an *automatic grapher*. By this we mean a graphics calculator or a computer with a function grapher. If students do not have access to a computer or graphics calculator and such questions are assigned, students may not be successful.

The reasons for a graphics calculator go beyond the fact that they can display the graph of any function students will encounter in this course. They have the advantage of displaying numbers in computations, allowing students to more easily see patterns and detect errors in their work. In this course we use graphics calculators to perform statistical operations such as finding a line of best fit and performing matrix operations. Recent models can generate tables, which enables them to simulate spreadsheet operations.

On the horizon are calculator-size devices that can do all algebraic manipulation. We encourage their use when they become available.

Computers The computer is a powerful tool for you to use in your classroom to demonstrate the relationships, patterns, properties, and algorithms of arithmetic. Do not ignore the computer questions even if you do not have computers available. The goal is not to teach computer programming, but to use the computer as a tool. Students are not surprised that the computer can do difficult tasks, but many students are surprised that a computer can do easy things, for instance, act as a calculator.

Some questions ask students to use a computer. If students do not have access to a computer, exercise caution in your assigning of such questions. As mathematical tools, a desirable computer has the ability to deal with a good amount of data and to display graphs with accuracy and precision. *GraphExplorer, StatExplorer,* and *GeoExplorer* software, published by Scott-Foresman for IBM (or IBM compatibles) and Macintosh computers, is designed for this course.

Programming Today many graphics calculators are programmable. Thus, at times in *UCSMP Advanced Algebra* we also give programs in a calculator programming language. We have chosen the TI-81 or TI-82 languages because these are the most commonly found calculators in UCSMP classes, and because the syntax of the programs closely parallels that of the BASIC language.

In the First Edition of *UCSMP Advanced Algebra,* the BASIC computer language was incorporated because it was available for the computers which were most popular in American schools and because it was

easy to understand and translate into other languages. As the Second Edition goes to press, BASIC is not as widely used. However, there is no other computer language that seems as easy for a novice to understand. Thus, we continue to use BASIC as a sample language. The programs have been kept short so that students can type them relatively quickly. It may not be necessary for every student to type and run a program. Some programs can be used as classroom demonstrations. Almost all the BASIC programs have counterparts that can be run on programmable calculators.

Computer educators have recommended that students be required to provide a block structure to programs; document their programs with abundant remarks; and declare variables. Since this is a mathematics course, not a programming course, you should emphasize the computational steps of a program. Can the student follow the steps of a program and tell what the output will be? Can the student modify a given program to solve an exercise with different values?

Whether you are a novice or expert in programming, we encourage you to try the programs we provide on your own system. Appendix D in the Student Edition, "Programming Languages," contains a collection of useful BASIC programs and parallel programs for a graphics calculator. Our programs may need to be modified slightly for your system.

Projects

Based on very positive responses from teachers and students of both *Functions, Statistics, and Trigonometry* and *Precalculus and Discrete Mathematics* to the projects in those books, and numerous requests from teachers for some similar activities for this course, we have developed projects for each chapter of the Sec-

ond Edition of *UCSMP Advanced Algebra*. Each project is an extended activity, often open-ended, meant to take the student several hours to complete. Some provide an opportunity to engage in library research; others require that students draw or build something; some require the student to collect data through surveys or measurements; others involve independent work with computers. The projects are designed for the wide range of interests and abilities one might find in a class of average students.

The projects serve many purposes.

(a) Students experience using real data in a mode comparable to that actually used by people in business, science, and many other careers.

(b) Students understand that a higher level of persistence than normal is expected. Too often in mathematics the greatest demand we make of students is to apply 5–10 minutes of effort on a single task. Longer-term projects demand more persistence and stretch a student's personal level of expectation.

(c) Projects, with some allowances for student choice, provide a sense of ownership of a task.

(d) Projects provide a chance for students to share their learning publicly in a visual or oral presentation.

(e) Projects provide an opportunity for students to apply graphic, writing, and oral talents in mathematical situations.

(f) Projects provide an alternative way to assess students' achievement.

The projects appear immediately after the last lesson in the chapter, but we do not recommend that they be done immediately after the last lesson has been completed. Typically this would interrupt the flow of the chapter. You can schedule work on them in a number of ways. Here are two suggestions: (1) Assign one project when you reach the middle of a chapter, due in the middle of the next chapter. (2) Assign one project per grading period from any of the chapters covered in that period. Some teachers are more

comfortable limiting the students' choice of projects at the beginning (e.g., do either of Projects 2 or 5); other teachers want to give students free choice at all times. Do whatever makes sense for you and your class.

All students need guidance on projects, even if they have done projects in previous UCSMP courses. Be very specific and clear on what you expect (e.g. length of paper, format of poster, number of minutes of oral presentation, etc.). If possible, show sample student work. Tell students how you will grade their work. You may want to use the first project as a trial run, with somewhat relaxed grading standards. Then you can show (without mentioning names) work you consider exemplary, and work which is good but not exemplary, in preparation for the second project. English, social studies or art teachers, or the school librarian can often assist with advice on how to structure assigning or grading projects.

Here are two suggested ways to grade projects: (1) Give a certain number of points for various parts of the project, e.g., 20 points for completing all required work, 20 points for the mathematical content, 5 points for neatness and organization, and 5 points for mechanics of the paper (spelling, grammar, etc.); then convert the total number of points (in the previous case as a percent of 50) to the grading scale you use on other assignments. Teachers using this type of grading scheme often give a small number of bonus points for creativity. (2) Use a holistic approach. Develop a set of general criteria (often called a rubric), and sort the papers into categories based on your criteria. This is the way many English and social studies teachers grade papers. See Stenmark (1989, 1991) for descriptions of rubrics with four and seven categories developed in California for use in a new state mathematics assessment program.

We recommend that however you use the projects, please do not avoid them. They often have impact far beyond the mathematics classroom. Teachers from one school remarked that by the end of the year graphs like those that had been made for projects were appearing in the school yearbook! In fact, you may find students to be encouraged if they are given time to put together a first-rate presentation to be displayed on a bulletin board or a school display case, or to be entered in a mathematics fair.

Teaching

Teaching Models and Strategies

Traditionally teachers have relied heavily on lecture, supervised practice, and recitation of answers as their dominant modes of instruction. When these dominate instruction, the mathematics studied is often limited to simple algorithms which can be easily mimicked, and students learn to depend almost exclusively on the teacher as the sole source of their information.

In recent years the importance of communication skills in all school subjects has been noted. To achieve these skills students must read, write, and speak to each other in class. These skills are in line with the broader curricular and process goals of *UCSMP Advanced Algebra* and are more easily developed in classrooms which are dominated less by the teacher, that is, in classrooms in which students are actively engaged throughout the period.

Thus, in effective UCSMP classrooms, one sees smaller amounts of lecture, recitation, and individual seatwork than in comparison classes; more discussions in small groups or with the whole class, individual or group work with calculators, computers, or other physical materials; and opportunities for students to do extended projects outside of class. Also, students read more of the book outside of class because they realize that this reading enables more to go on inside class.

The notes with each lesson in this Teacher's Edition provide a variety of teaching ideas, grouped under the following categories: Warm-up, Notes on Reading, Additional Examples, Optional Activities, Notes on Questions, Adapting to Individual Needs, Assessment, and Extension. All lessons contain more ideas than can be used in one period. None of the lists is exhaustive; there are, no doubt, many other ways to teach the lesson.

You should use your professional judgment to select and sequence the activities you think are appropriate for the length of your class period and your students' needs. This selection needs to be made before you enter class. We note that teachers who have never used group work, manipulatives, or technology often assume that they are very time-consuming. Our experience is that, when well-planned ahead of time, many such activities can be done in relatively short periods of time, and we encourage you to try them. Also, you should understand that when a particular type of activity is done for the first time, it always takes longer because students need more guidance. The second time to the computer lab, or using group work, or presenting projects, or bringing out some manipulatives should go more easily than the first.

A variety of teaching models and strategies have been effectively used in the classroom by UCSMP teachers. Some teachers have students read each lesson and do all the questions before class. Then the teacher and students (sometimes in small groups, sometimes as the entire class) discuss the lesson and engage in various activities related to it during the next period. Some teachers preview the next day's lesson with some guidance as to the key points they think their students will need in reading or doing the questions. Some teachers begin the reading of the next lesson in class.

With less-prepared students, teachers need to adjust strategies. Most teachers do more reading out loud in class, and engage in more manipulative activities and use more Lesson Masters. Group work is often more important in these classes.

To give you a better picture of the variety of instructional techniques employed in classes using UCSMP materials, we have included reprints of the articles, "A 'Typical Day' in a UCSMP Classroom" and "Using Cooperative Reading Strategies," both written by experienced UCSMP teachers.

A "TYPICAL DAY" IN A UCSMP CLASSROOM

by Sharon Mallo, Lake Park High School, Roselle, IL

No matter how much our textbooks may or may not change over the years, one fact remains: students have different learning styles, and teachers need to address each of them. Therefore, there's really no "typical day" in the classroom. In my classroom, means of presentation vary from lesson to lesson, with common threads woven in for continuity and class management. The threads that tie my teaching strategies together are those that reinforce good mathematics study skills and those that help students "learn how to learn."

The UCSMP program gives me an easy-to-use, flexible tool through which to accomplish these goals. I'd like to show you some of the ways I use the supplementary materials and options in the program for presenting lessons—particularly the UCSMP Lesson Masters, Technology Masters, Teaching Aids, and Activity Sourcebook. Each class begins with a warm-up activity, followed by coverage of the previous day's homework. These two activities take up no more than half of the class period. Next, there is an introduction to the new lesson, followed by a related activity.

Warm-up Activity

The warm-up activity usually consists of the Lesson Master from the previous day's lesson being handed out as students arrive. I ask students to work out some or all of the questions, depending on the length of the master. This allows me to identify students who are having difficulty. I give individual help, reteach, and/or ask students to help each other as I circulate. For example, on the day I will be teaching Lesson 4-2 of *Transition Mathematics,* I will use Lesson Master 4-1 as the warm-up. This Lesson Master on order of operations allows me to say "No calculators" and check for understanding.

The warm-up can also be cooperative, such as with Lesson 5-4 on turns. I'll have each student use a protractor to draw a circle with ten equally spaced spokes, and label each spoke with a different letter like on the Ferris wheel in questions 22–24 from the homework. Each student writes three problems about his/her diagram. Then students exchange papers and solve the problems.

The warm-up can also be a lead-in for today's lesson or a problem-solving activity that will later tie into today's lesson.

Going Over Homework

One of my most import requirements is that students correct each answer on their homework and write out the steps for answers they've gotten wrong. Using the answers found at the back of the book to correct their work is part of the assignment. Students have already marked problems they need help with before coming to class. After we've done the warm-up activity, I'll put answers on the overhead projector. Then we discuss problems I've chosen as the most important or students have identified as stumbling blocks. Three or four times during the chapter, I have students discuss their questions within their cooperative groups. (Groups have one high, two middle, and one low student, and they change after every two chapter tests.)

Students need a reason to be concerned about whether or not their homework answers are correct and, more importantly, how to get the correct answer. I give an unannounced Homework Quiz once or twice a week. Students use their own notebooks of homework assignments and a clean sheet of paper—no textbook. They divide their papers into four or six sections. I do the same on a transparency to show them which questions I want. Students are to copy the correct answer for each question from their notebooks. If they've made the corrections in their notebooks, each student should have a perfect paper. It takes five to ten minutes to correct a set of these quizzes. Scores are low at the beginning but they steadily get better.

Lesson 4-2	
#8	#12
#18	#22

Lesson 5-6	Lesson 5-7
#14	#18
Lesson 5-8	**Lesson 5-8**
#14	#30
Lesson 5-9	**Lesson 5-9**
#18	#24

Presenting a Lesson

The method I choose to present a lesson depends on the difficulty of the content and the applications. For instance, Lesson 4-2 is one that the class usually reads together. I stop students at each Example. Using Teaching Aid 42 and different-colored overhead pens, we choose a variable and fill in the blanks of the patterns. Then we reverse the problem where I write the pattern on the overhead and we identify the variable. Students take turns making up instances.

If the students are able to read a lesson on their own, either in school or at home, I focus their reading. Vocabulary words (not their definitions) are pointed out. Sometimes I write an Additional Example from the margin of the Teacher's Edition and tell students that they should have an idea of how to solve it once they've read the lesson. Now they have a purpose for reading.

When students have read a difficult lesson in class, I put one of the Additional Examples on the overhead. (Some are already on transparencies in the Teaching Aids.) Then I ask students to find the parallel Example in the reading. This is one of the hardest things for them to do when they get stuck on a problem at home, so we practice it in class.

I do lectures and give notes on a lesson about 10–15 percent of the time. This is usually after students have read the lesson and done the Covering the Reading questions. The most common assignment I give is to complete the Applying the Mathematics, Review, and Exploration questions of a given lesson and then to read or re-read the following lesson and do Covering the Reading. Occasionally, they read a lesson and do all the questions, and once in a while I develop an assignment from outside the book.

As you can see, there is no "typical day" in my classroom. With UCSMP, my students have much stronger number sense by the end of the year. They are working with all types of numbers: fractions, decimals, integers, and percents—*every day* in practice problems, literal examples, and applications. They're not afraid to tackle problems, and they're learning how to learn.

Sharon Mallo has been teaching UCSMP Courses in the Chicago area since 1984. She is an author on the Second Edition of Transition Mathematics.

USING COOPERATIVE READING STRATEGIES:

Students helping each other understand their textbook

by Tom Stone, Sheldon High School, Eugene, OR

There are many ways in which cooperative learning strategies can be used effectively in the mathematics classroom. Because of the important role reading plays in determining students' success in the UCSMP program, I would like to focus on this application of these strategies and to share some ways that the use of cooperative learning groups can help students learn good reading habits.

First, let me briefly explain my classroom organization. My students are familiar with two seating arrangements: 1) individual seating in six rows of desks, and 2) group seating with each set of four desks formed into a tight square. Each student in the group is assigned a number, 1 through 4. I do this for management purposes which should become clear later. The following scenarios illustrate how I use small-group instruction to help my students with their reading. (All section references are to *UCSMP Geometry*.)

Scenario 1 (Key Ideas)

Students are seated individually. After identifying a few vocabulary words they will encounter, I assign the reading of Section 1-3 in the textbook. Students read the material individually and take notes as they go along. When they have had time to finish, they move into their groups. Using his/her notes, Student 1 in each group selects a major idea from the reading and shares it with the group. After several minutes, Student 2 in each group discusses another idea found in the reading. This is continued until all four students in each group have had an opportunity to share. In this way, students receive important practice identifying the key ideas from a given section of their book.

Scenario 2 (Share the Pain)

Say the reading of Section 7-5 is to be done outside of class as part of the homework assignment. It includes two examples that I expect will be difficult for my students to read. Therefore, I have them encounter the challenging part of the reading in class in teams before they try to handle it on their own outside of class. I assign the reading of the first example to Students 1 and 2 in each group and the second example to Students 3 and 4. After students have completed the reading, they move into their groups. Students 1 and 2 discuss their understanding of the first example while Students 3 and 4 do the same with the second example. Now all students should be able to comprehend the reading of the section on their own.

Scenario 3 (Experts)

Section 9-7 breaks down into four main ideas. Student 1 is assigned to read the first idea, Student 2 the second, and so on. Upon finishing the reading, students move into their groups and each student takes a turn presenting to the rest of the group. Then students begin working on the problem set for the section. Each student acts as the "expert" for questions related to the idea for which he/she was responsible.

Scenario 4 (The Set-up)

Let's suppose my geometry class is going to learn about traversability of networks (as in the Königsberg Bridge problem) tomorrow. Today, I have students move into their groups and I give each team a worksheet with five figures. After determining which figures are traversable and which are not, teams list the number of even and odd vertices for each figure. Finally, each group writes out and tests a conjecture for the connection between traversability and the number of even and/or odd vertices in a figure. Tomorrow, the students will be well prepared to read about the applications of traversability in networks.

The above scenarios are only a few examples of how small-group instruction and cooperative-learning strategies can be used to help students develop the skill needed for reading mathematics. Equally important, they provide variety in lesson structure. I hope that the ideas presented here are helpful and can serve as catalysts for generating more ideas that can be put to effective use in the classroom.

Tom Stone taught UCSMP courses in the Oregon area for many years. He was chosen as the 1991 Oregon Secondary Mathematics Teacher of the Year by the American Electronic Association.

Using the Reading

In order to become an independent learner of mathematics, a student must learn to learn mathematics from reading. You should expect students to read all lessons. At the beginning of the course, this may require time in class. Do not expect overnight changes in behavior from students who have never read their math book before.

A student in *UCSMP Advanced Algebra* who has studied from previous UCSMP texts will generally be accustomed to reading mathematics. But students new to UCSMP texts may require some period of adjustment to a new style of text and to new types of questions. Such students may never have been asked to read mathematics. As a result, it is common for students to ask why they have to read.

We tell them: You must read because you must learn to read for success in all future courses that use mathematics, not just in mathematics; because you must learn to read for success in life outside of school and on any job; because the reading will help you understand the uses of mathematics; because the reading contains interesting information; because the reading tells you how the material from one lesson is related to other material in the book; because there is not enough time in class to spend doing something that you can do in a study period or at home.

Students often do not know how to read a mathematics text. They read too quickly and they gloss over little words ("if," "but," "not," and so on) that may be very important to the meaning of a statement. They may not realize that text and graphics are often related and they should move back and forth from one to the other. Students may not be able to read 2^5 (2 to the 5th power) or 8! (8 factorial) or $x + 5 < 9$ (x plus 5 is less than 9). Thus it is important to have students read out loud as well as to give them assignments that involve silent reading.

To teach students how to read mathematics, we suggest that at the beginning of the school year some class time be spent each day reading the lesson in class. Some days you can have students read out loud, and provide feedback on their ability to read technical words and symbols correctly. (In general, it is not a good idea to call on students in any particular obvious order. That just gets some students nervous that their turn is coming up, and encourages others not to pay attention, because they are likely not to be called on.) Be sure to point out how the colored headers in the lessons help outline the important concepts and provide an overview (advance organizer) of what they are about to read.

You might have students answer the Covering the Reading questions orally, and point out how these questions are meant to test comprehension of the material in the text. The answers for these questions can be found literally in the reading or by mimicking worked examples. The questions can be used as oral exercises during or after oral reading of the text, or as part of a written assignment. Once students are comfortable with the format of the lessons, we suggest you begin to expect that reading be done outside of class on a regular basis.

Some days you may want to ask some questions that set up the reading of the lesson. Other days you might give a brief summary of the key ideas in the reading, have students read silently in class, and then ask them to identify where in the exposition those main ideas are covered. Once students have become somewhat comfortable with reading on their own, you can rely more and more on them to summarize or probe key ideas without your assistance.

To help stress the importance of reading as a tool for learning mathematics, some teachers give brief (2–5 minute) "reading quizzes" at the beginning of class. These may consist of a request for a summary of the key ideas in the text, or the answers to several even-numbered questions from the homework. Doing so for 3 or 4 consecutive days early in the year lets students know you are serious about their attempts to do the reading and to answer the questions. Allowing students to use their notes, but not their book, encourages students to take good notes and to organize their solutions to homework problems.

Although we believe that reading their text is an important strategy by which students learn mathematics, we know that it is not the only way they learn. In particular, if you want to give a brief overview of the new lesson before students read it, please do. We do, however, wish to discourage the practice of always explaining how to do questions before the students have had the opportunity to learn on their own. Particularly counterproductive is to tell students that certain problems do not have to be tried "because we have not yet done them in class." This only teaches students that they cannot learn on their own and to be dependent on you.

Students learn enormous amounts from discussing alternate strategies to problems with you and their classmates, from engaging in well-constructed activities, and from doing open-ended explorations and projects. By teaching students to read outside of class, you are free to use class time more creatively and effectively than if you were compelled to develop all major ideas yourself in class.

Going Over Homework Questions

Feedback to student work is very important, and to reinforce the positive aspects of doing homework it is important to go over questions. We are frequently

asked how we want the teacher to go over the questions. Our response is that there are multiple ways to do so. We recommend that each teacher use a couple of methods regularly so students can get used to a routine, and use a couple of others occasionally for variety.

Below are some of the more commonly used techniques which we support:

1. Show answers (using the Answer Masters provided) on an overhead projector at beginning of period; have students correct their own papers (you can use time to take roll); have a whole-class discussion on questions that were particularly troublesome.

2. Same as (1) above; but after students have checked their own papers, have them form groups of 2 to 4 to discuss what they missed; after a few minutes have a whole-class discussion only on questions the groups could not resolve.

3. Have students form small groups; provide one copy of answers on paper to each group; have groups discuss what they missed; after a few minutes have a whole class discussion only on questions the groups could not resolve.

4. Read all answers out loud; have students correct their own papers; when done reading answers, have a whole-class discussion to explain questions that were particularly troublesome.

5. Have students write the numbers of the questions they could not answer on the board as they come into class; have them put tick marks after numbers to indicate how many students want to discuss that one; have student volunteers do those problems on the board, and explain their work; explain how to do the ones no student could solve.

6. Preselect questions which you feel are particularly important or may be particularly troublesome; have a whole class discussion about those.

It is important to remember that "going over the homework" should be more than providing correct answers. It is a wonderful opportunity to consider alternate solution strategies, to address any misconceptions that are uncovered, to relate ideas in one question to ideas in another, and to extend ideas in the questions via "what if" questions. In short, it is an opportunity to have the kind of rich classroom discourse described in the NCTM's *Professional Teaching Standards*. Many ideas are given in the Notes on Questions for each lesson. Do not ignore these notes; they indicate which questions are important to discuss so that students will be better prepared for the next lesson.

Writing in Mathematics

The NCTM *Curriculum and Evaluation Standards* stress the importance of students' ability to communicate mathematics. Through writing, communication opens up in the classroom on a variety of levels. As they write, students apply concepts to their own experience; construct meaning for mathematical symbols, procedures, and concepts; and internalize meaning as they explore and examine mathematical ideas in words.

At times, writing may consist simply of the steps in answering a question, but to be most effective it should be more than that. It can include comments about what was being done, why a particular strategy was chosen, and how the student felt about the question. The careful examination of thought that writing requires may lead students to see the process of thinking as more important than the ability to quote rules; consequently, mathematics becomes a richer pastime. Furthermore, students will be developing a skill that many of them will need throughout their lives, the ability to explain what they are thinking to others.

In *UCSMP Advanced Algebra* we often ask students to write explanations of what they are doing. Do not be surprised if at first students' explanations are vague, imprecise, or too brief. Writing good explanations takes time, experience, and guidance, and students may have never been asked to write in their previous mathematics classes. You can encourage greater thoroughness and effectiveness by discussing

good explanations in the text with your students. The solutions of the examples in each lesson are meant to serve as models. The portions of the solutions that you may expect students to write are printed in a special font.

To be considered important by students, writing must be discussed in class. Reading good student efforts aloud in class can encourage good writing. Having students read their own efforts in small groups or to the entire class can inform them about whether others understood what they wrote.

There are different forms which writing may take. *Chatter* refers to writing explanations of procedures a student used to solve a problem. It can communicate a student's thought process, and can therefore alert you (and the student!) to hidden misconceptions and incomplete understandings as well as to wonderful insights. Arthur Powell of Rutgers University suggests that chatter be written in a separate column of the page from the actual solution of the problem.

Journal writing is believed by some people to be one of the most effective methods of writing to learn mathematics; however, *informal explorative writing* in class and on homework (not necessarily in a bound or spiral notebook) achieves similar results. Journals and informal explorative writing allow students to put concepts in their own words, to speculate on extensions to problems, and to relate material they are learning to what they already know. This kind of writing allows students to write freely without worrying excessively over mechanics. It also can focus students' minds. Writing at the beginning of a period can interest and involve students in a topic; writing at the end of a period can help them to summarize and organize what happened that day.

Here is some general advice: If you use journals, you may wish to keep the journals in the classroom; asking students to bring yet another item to class may prove difficult for them and frustrating to you. For this reason, informal explorative writing on ideas and on homework may prove to be a better option.

In general, undirected journal writing does not provoke as much focus or response from students as carefully and thoughtfully worded questions, sometimes called *prompts*. The more concise the prompt, the better. Longer, more complex prompts that are intended to yield more writing often do not.

Collect and examine journals regularly to communicate to students that they are important. You do not have to examine all journals at the same time. (Reading students' writing is often not as time-consuming as you might think, and it can be very interesting.) Give credit for journals, but don't grade them. When giving credit, look for frequency and length of entries and for self-initiated topics. Give students feedback on their writing; comments indicate that you care. Comments also can help students focus on what is clear or not clear in their writing. Do not focus only on mechanics or grammar. Above all, be patient and flexible.

When students have difficulty writing, claiming they do not know what to say, you might try freewriting, an activity where the goal is simply to empty thoughts on the page without censoring. Write yourself and share what you wrote with your students.

If you use portfolios, keep examples of student writing along with other examples of their work.

Dealing with Individual Differences

Every student differs from all others in many ways. Differences in ability, entering knowledge, willingness to work, interest, learning style, and cultural background are the most commonly referred to by teachers and researchers.

In Section 1 of this Professional Sourcebook, we point out that not enough is known about individual differences in ability to make judgments based on them. Individual differences in entering knowledge are far better predictors. These differences are great enough to warrant differences in what is offered to students at a particular grade level, and based on them we suggest that students take UCSMP courses at different ages. However, a wide range of entering knowledge exists within every class and needs to be considered when teaching.

Thus, the pupil's edition includes an enormous variety of activities, questions, and contexts to bring out the brilliance, surprise, applicability, and structure of mathematics, and to appeal to students with the panoply of cultural backgrounds found in the United States. Note the many cultural activities in this Teacher's Edition as well. You should take these into account, because familiar contexts are critical to the understanding of mathematics, the contributions of various cultures are important in conveying the universality of mathematical ideas, and they help students to develop a sense of ownership of these ideas. Differences in interest can be handled by giving students choice of the end-of-chapter Projects, by asking students to elaborate on questions and/or ideas they particularly liked, and by other optional activities.

For better-prepared students, or students with more willingness to work, you may wish to offer, assign, and discuss:

- Challenge and Extension problems and activities contained in the Teacher's Edition;

- Some technology activities from the *Technology Sourcebook;*

- Contest problems from such sources as the American High School Mathematics Examination (AHSME).

For students needing more preparation or with limited language development, consider using:

- Suggestions for additional practice contained in the Teacher's Edition;

- Manipulative activities from the *Activity Sourcebook;*

- English Language Development and Extra Help activities provided in the Teacher's Edition.

We must stress that *many of these ideas should be used with all your students.* In particular, manipulative, technology, and other activities are appropriate for all students, and all students need some practice in order to develop high levels of competence.

Assessment

The NCTM Evaluation Standards provide some sensible guidelines for student assessment. The first is *Alignment.* Simply put, this standard suggests that you assess what you teach. In particular, because the *UCSMP Advanced Algebra* course has much broader goals than most other courses at this level, many tests, quizzes, final exams, and other forms of assessment you have used in the past will not be appropriate for this course.

The second Evaluation Standard is *Multiple Forms of Assessment.* This standard reminds us that no single instrument is perfect. Each test, quiz, or homework assignment provides a small picture of what each student knows. A teacher who wants to develop mathematical power must use instruments that reflect the broad range of goals of the curriculum. In particular, using the Projects to assess understanding will give you insights into student thinking that you cannot get from tests and quizzes.

The third Evaluation Standard is *Purposes of Assessment.* This standard reminds the reader that instruments developed for one purpose usually are not appropriate for another purpose. Specifically, traditional standardized tests are usually not appropriate for evaluating students at the end of any single mathematics course because they are usually not well-aligned with the objectives of the course. The best measure of success of a student is the extent to which the student has accomplished the goals and objectives of the individual course.

Assessment Options

To help you accomplish the above goals, the *Assessment Sourcebook* (in the Teacher's Resource File) provides a wide variety of assessment instruments. These include Quizzes, Chapter Tests, Cumulative Tests (by chapter), Comprehensive Tests, and several types of alternative assessment. The Chapter Tests include parallel traditional Forms A and B, in which most questions are short-answer, and Forms C and D, which provide more open-ended performance assessment. The *Quiz and Test Writer* software

enables you to produce a virtually unlimited number of versions for a quiz or chapter test. The notes in the Teacher's Edition provide additional assessment suggestions for every lesson.

Tests, quizzes, or homework assignments provide only a small picture of what each student knows. In order to help you develop your students' abilities to do open-ended questions or longer, more elaborate tasks, you should consider the Exploration questions at the end of each lesson and the Projects at the end of each chapter as part of your assessment tool kit. (The grading of Projects is discussed on page T43.)

Understanding—The SPUR Approach

"Understanding" is an easy goal to have, for who can be against it? Yet understanding means different things to different people. In UCSMP texts an approach to the development of mathematical power is taken that we call the SPUR approach. The SPUR approach involves four different aspects, or dimensions, of understanding.

Skills: For many people, understanding mathematics means simply knowing how to get an answer to a problem with no help from any outside source. But in classrooms, when we speak of understanding how to use a calculator or a computer, we mean using the technology to do something for us. In UCSMP texts, these are both aspects of the same kind of understanding, the understanding of algorithms (procedures) for getting answers. This is the S of SPUR, the Skills dimension, and it ranges from the rote memorization of basic facts to the development of new algorithms for solving problems. These include doing things "in your head," with paper and pencil, or with technology.

Properties: During the 1960s, understanding *why* became at least as important as understanding how. Mathematicians often view this kind of understanding as the ultimate goal. For instance, mathematics courses for prospective elementary school teachers assume these college students can do arithmetic, and instead teach the properties and principles behind that arithmetic. This is the P of SPUR, the Properties dimension,

and it ranges from the rote identification of properties to the discovery of new proofs.

Uses: To the person who applies mathematics, neither knowing how to get an answer nor knowing the mathematical reasons behind the process is as important as being able to *use* the answer. For example, a person does not possess full understanding of linear equations until that person can apply them appropriately in real situations. This dimension, the U of SPUR, ranges from the rote application of ideas (for instance, when you encounter a direct-variation situation, form a proportion) to the discovery of new applications or models for mathematical ideas. *UCSMP Advanced Algebra* is notable for its attention to this dimension of understanding.

Representations: To some people, even having all three dimensions of understanding given above does not comprise full understanding. They require that students *represent* a concept and deal with the concept in that representation in some way. Ability to use concrete materials and models or graphs and other pictorial representations demonstrates this dimension of understanding. This is the R of SPUR, the Representations dimension, and it ranges from the rote manipulation of objects to the invention of new representations of concepts.

There are continual arguments among educators as to which dimension should come first and which should be emphasized. For each there are people for whom that type of understanding is preeminent, and who believe that the other types do not convey the real understanding of mathematics.

Each dimension has aspects that can be memorized, and each has the potential for the highest level of creative thinking. Also, each dimension has its easy aspects and its difficult ones. Some skills (for example, long division) take at least as long to learn as geometry proofs; some uses are as easy as putting together beads. Furthermore, some students prefer applications, some would rather do manipulative skills, some want to know the theory, and still others like the models and representations best. Thus we believe that the most effective teaching allows students opportunities in all these dimensions.

For a specific example of what understanding means in these four dimensions, consider solving $1.06^x = 2$ and what would constitute evidence of that understanding.

Skills understanding means knowing a way to obtain a solution. (Obtain $x = 12$ by some means.)

Properties understanding means knowing properties which you can apply. (Identify or justify the steps in obtaining an answer—such as invoking the definition of logarithm.)

Uses understanding means knowing situations in which you could apply the solving of this equation. (Set up or interpret a solution: If money is invested at a 6% yield per year, in how many years will it double?)

Representations understanding means having a representation of the solving process or a graphical way of interpreting the solution. (Where does the graph of $y = 1.06^x$ intersect the line $y = 2$?)

The SPUR approach is not a perfect sorter of knowledge; many ideas and many problems involve more than one dimension. Some understandings do not fit any of these dimensions. In some UCSMP texts we add a fifth dimension, C—the Culture dimension—for it provides still another way of looking at knowledge. (Leonhard Euler, in his most influential book *Algebra,* was the first to use logarithms to solve exponential equations like $1.06^x = 2$, more than a century after logarithms were invented.)

In this book, you see the SPUR categorization of objectives at the end of each chapter with the Chapter Review questions. The Progress Self-Test for each chapter and the Lesson Masters (in the Teacher's Resource File) are also keyed to these objectives. We never ask students (or teachers) to categorize tasks into the various kinds of understanding; that is not a suitable goal. The categorization is meant to be a convenient and efficient way to ensure that the book provides the opportunity for teachers to teach and for

students to gain a broader and deeper understanding of mathematics than is normally the case.

Grading

No problem seems more difficult than the question of grading. If a teacher has students who perform so well that they all deserve *A*s and the teacher gives them *A*s as a result, the teacher will probably not be given plaudits for being successful but will be accused of being too easy. This suggests that the grading scale ought to be based on a fixed level of performance, which is what we recommend. Thus, the performance that gives an *A* in one school or with one teacher should rate an *A* in another.

Seldom in this book are there ten similar questions in a row. To teach students to be flexible, the wording of questions is varied, and principles are applied in many contexts. Furthermore, in *UCSMP Advanced Algebra* we emphasize the relations between algebra and geometry and between various parts of algebra. Learning to solve problems in a variety of contexts or to discern relationships between properties is more difficult than learning to perform a routine skill. Thus, a natural question that arises is, "How should I grade students in UCSMP courses?"

We believe a student should be able to do each set of objectives at about the 85% mastery level. An 85% score on a test deserves no less than a high *B*, and probably an *A*. In the past, our tests have often led us to the following curve: 85–100 = *A*, 72–84 = *B*, 60–71 = *C*, 50–59 = *D*, 0–49 = *F*. Such a low curve alarms some teachers, but students in UCSMP courses generally learn more mathematics overall than students in comparison classes. We believe that the above grading policy rewards students fairly for work well done.

We have found that a word to students about why your grading scale is "different" is helpful. They may be so accustomed to another grading scale that they feel they are doing poorly, while you think they are doing well. To encourage students, we often make a basketball analogy. In a traditional course, all the shots students ever have are lay-ups (exercises) and an occasional free throw (easy problems). They shoot these

over and over again, from the same spot ("Do the odds from 1–49."). In *UCSMP Advanced Algebra,* almost every question is a different shot (a problem)— some close in, some from middle distance, and a few from half-court. To expect percentages of correct shots to be the same is unrealistic.

Some teachers have found that because of the way that the Review questions maintain and improve performance, cumulative tests at the end of each marking period give students an opportunity to do well. The *Assessment Sourcebook* has Cumulative Tests for each chapter beginning with Chapter 2. When you want to practice one specific shot to make it automatic, we suggest focusing in on a few topics for quizzes.

Two final points: First, let students know what they need to know in order to get good grades. All research on the subject indicates that telling students what they are supposed to learn increases the amount of material covered and tends to increase performance. Second, have confidence in your students. Do not arbitrarily consign some of them to low grades. Let them know that it is possible for all of them to get *A*s if they learn the material. If students perform well on tests, it has a real effect on interest and motivation. As the newer evaluation documents stress, you should endeavor to use grading as a vehicle for breeding success as well as for evaluating students.

Professional Sourcebook: SECTION **4**

RESEARCH AND DEVELOPMENT OF
UCSMP ADVANCED ALGEBRA

Development of the First Edition

The development of the First Edition of each UCSMP text was in four stages. First, the overall goals for each course were created by UCSMP in consultation with a national advisory board of distinguished professors, and through discussion with classroom teachers, school administrators, and district and state mathematics supervisors. At the second stage, UCSMP selected authors who wrote first drafts of the courses. Half of all UCSMP authors currently teach mathematics in secondary schools, and all authors and editors for the first five courses have secondary school teaching experience. After teaching by the authors, selected teachers, and revision by the authors and UCSMP editors, materials entered the third stage in the text development. Classes of teachers not connected with the project used the books, and independent evaluators closely studied student achievement, attitudes, and issues related to implementation. The fourth stage consisted of a wider comparative evaluation.

Some of the specific ideas for *UCSMP Advanced Algebra* originated as a result of two previous undertakings directed by Zalman Usiskin at the University of Chicago. The first was the writing of the text *Advanced Algebra with Transformations and Applications,* tested in 1970–72 and published by Laidlaw Brothers in 1975. In developing that text, we found that the use of transformations enhanced the understanding of functions and provided an elegant way to develop trigonometry. We also began to incorporate the applications that are a feature of all UCSMP texts.

In 1973–76, with NSF sponsorship, we developed a first-year algebra text entitled *Algebra Through Applications with Probability and Statistics.* The text was distributed by the National Council of Teachers of Mathematics in a two-volume paperback version from 1979–85. In developing that text, we used the specific identification of models for algebraic expressions that are found in this text. We also developed the precursor to the end-of-chapter mastery strategy that is a feature of all UCSMP texts.

In the summer of 1985, a six-member team spent 8 weeks at the University of Chicago writing the first draft of *UCSMP Advanced Algebra*. This draft was edited in Chicago by UCSMP staff (all experienced mathematics teachers) and used in five schools in the year 1985–86. The teachers during that year received loose-leaf materials a chapter at a time, often only days before they had to teach from them. They gave opinions directly to the authors and to the project continually during the year. Twice they came to the University of Chicago for full-day meetings to discuss the materials.

In the summer of 1986, four of the authors returned to revise the materials. The revision was guided by the comments of the pilot teachers and by the algebra needed for *UCSMP Geometry,* which was then in its planning stages. A second pilot took place in 1986–87 in six schools. (The schools in this and in the previous year's evaluations are acknowledged on page *iii* of the student text.) Again the materials were loose-leaf. This time the teachers reported in writing to the project about how each lesson in each chapter fared. Again there were full-day meetings of all the teachers at which the materials were discussed.

The results of the 1986–87 evaluations showed that students generally performed very well, but there were many places where small improvements could be made. The materials were revised accordingly. Also, by this time drafts of the preceding and following UCSMP courses existed, and lessons were added, deleted, rewritten, or reordered to coordinate with those courses.

First Edition Formative Evaluation and Test Results

In 1987–88, a formative evaluation of *UCSMP Advanced Algebra* was conducted with a third version of what became the First Edition. The materials were spiral-bound in three volumes. The formative evaluation differed from the pilots in several ways: Teachers periodically came to the University and commented on how things were going, what they thought were strong and weak points, how long it took to cover various lessons, which questions were most interesting, which questions might be deleted, and so on. Comparison classes were chosen in an attempt to have a controlled study of performance of matched pairs of classes. Evaluators visited classes and interviewed teachers and administrators.

Five teachers in five schools taught nine classes of *UCSMP Advanced Algebra.* Two of the schools were public high schools in Chicago, one was in a suburban working-class community, and the other two were in more affluent suburbs. Typical (not honors) second-year algebra classes were used. In one of the city schools and one of the suburban schools, some students had studied from *UCSMP Geometry.* A similar number of Comparison classes were selected and tested, but only 4 of the 9 pairs matched based on scores at the beginning of the year.

At the end of the school year, fifty multiple-choice and 4 open-ended items were given to all classes over two days of testing. The questions were subdivided into the SPUR categories for analysis. The results, presented in Table 1 for all students who were present for fall and spring testing in the four well-matched pairs, are quite consistent over those categories.

Table 1: Mean Percents Correct for All Students in the Sample of Well-matched Pairs			
Category	UCSMP (n = 59)	Comparison (n = 57)	Difference (UCSMP minus Comparison)
Skills (15 items)	39.7	33.0	+6.7
Properties (9 items)	23.7	21.4	+2.3
Uses (11 items)	35.3	31.1	+4.2
Representations (15 items)	35.9	31.5	+4.5
Total (50 items)	34.7	30.1	+4.7

Overall, UCSMP students scored more than 15% higher than the matched comparison students. They outperformed comparison students by more than 20% on the following items:

- solving an exponential equation
- telling when matrices cannot be multiplied
- determining the output of a computer program in BASIC
- giving an equation for a circle with a given center and radius

Teachers felt that particularly strong features of the 1987–88 version of *UCSMP Advanced Algebra* were its clarity and organization, the examples of applications of mathematics, and its suggestions for teaching, particularly for the use of technology. Overall, both UCSMP and comparison students found the examples and questions in their texts difficult, but UCSMP students had more positive attitudes towards reading, applications, and technology.

Many changes were made in the text based on this testing for the first ScottForesman edition, which was first available for the 1989–90 school year.

Second Edition Studies

Over the years 1989–92, UCSMP had also kept notes on comments made by many users of *Advanced Algebra*. To help in preparation for the Second Edition, during the school year 1992–93, ScottForesman asked a small number of *Advanced Algebra* users to evaluate each chapter of the text as they completed it. ScottForesman also mailed a series of questionnaires during the year to a larger number of users. The results from these surveys were used to help in the planning and writing of the second edition materials. Writing of the first draft of the second edition began in the summer and continued through the fall of 1993.

During the 1993–94 school year, 27 classes in 13 schools participated in a formal study of the second edition materials. The schools were chosen to reflect the wide range of students who are currently using *UCSMP Advanced Algebra*. Teachers completed detailed forms evaluating the materials. Their students were tested along with students from 27 comparable classes at the same grade level in the same school. Because we felt that the First Edition studies had compared *UCSMP Advanced Algebra* with traditional textbooks, the majority of the comparable classes in the Second Edition studies used First Edition *UCSMP Advanced Algebra* materials. To our knowledge, these Second Edition UCSMP studies constitute the first time that a mathematics textbook has been compared with an earlier edition of itself.

From these 27 pairs, we were able to obtain 22 pairs of classes between which there were no significant differences on two pretests scores of those students who took all tests. Listed in Table 2 are the mean pretest and posttest scores of these 22 pairs of classes. In fourteen pairs, the comparison class used the First Edition of *UCSMP Advanced Algebra*. In the other eight pairs, the comparison classes did not use UCSMP materials. The only students included in this analysis are those who were present for all pretests and posttests.

All tests were designed by UCSMP staff because there do not exist standardized tests at this level appropriate to a curriculum like the UCSMP curriculum. The Entering Advanced Algebra Student Test is a test of algebra that students would be expected to know from

prior years. Part 1 consists of 32 items; Part 2 of 14 items. The Advanced Algebra Posttest covers a wide range of content usually found in second-year algebra courses like *UCSMP Advanced Algebra*. It contains 36 items. Another test, the Advanced Algebra Problem-Solving and Understanding Test (PS&U) was designed to test the problem-solving and understanding ability of the students. It consists of six free-response items requiring students to explain their reasoning. These are the kinds of long-answer items that have been encouraged in recent recommendations about assessment. All students were allowed to use calculators on all tests.

Table 2: Mean Scores of Students in Matched Pairs (Standard deviations are in parentheses.)

Group	N	Pretest Part 1	Pretest Part 2	Posttest *Advanced Algebra*	Posttest PS&U
UCSMP 2nd Edition	225	14.72 (4.51)	6.18 (2.26)	18.14 (5.36)	8.11 (4.70)
UCSMP 1st Edition	212	14.94 (4.15)	6.43 (2.12)	18.99 (5.17)	8.52 (4.72)
UCSMP 2nd Edition	177	14.90 (4.35)	6.33 (2.22)	**20.19** (5.55)	**10.38** (5.44)
non-UCSMP	180	14.44 (4.48)	6.44 (2.37)	15.49 (4.71)	6.39 (3.54)

In Table 2, mean scores in the boldface for "UCSMP Second Edition" are significantly higher than the corresponding scores for non-UCSMP students at the 0.0001 level. No other differences of means are statistically significant.

At the class level on the Advanced Algebra test, one UCSMP First Edition class outperformed its UCSMP Second Edition matched pair. Seven of the eight UCSMP Second Edition classes outperformed their non-UCSMP matched pairs on this test. At the class level on the PS&U test, two UCSMP Second Edition classes outperformed their matched pair-UCSMP First Edition counterparts, one UCSMP First Edition class outperformed its matched-pair, and seven UCSMP Second Edition classes outperformed their non-UCSMP counterparts.

The entries in Table 3 are the mean scores on the six individual items of the Problem-Solving and Understanding Test (PS&U) from the same students in each group as in Table 2. Descriptions of the six items are given below.

Item 1:   application using system of two linear equations
Item 2:   comparing two quadratic functions
Item 3:   solve $x^4 > 10$
Item 4:   application leading to quadratic equation
Item 5:   analyze whether $\log (x+3) = \log x \cdot \log 3$
Item 6:   find equation of line of fit

Table 3: Mean Scores for Each Item on the Problem-Solving and Understanding (PS&U) Test
(Standard deviations are in parentheses.) Maximum score per item = 4

Group	Item 1	Item 2	Item 3	Item 4	Item 5	Item 6
UCSMP 2nd Edition	2.14 (1.62)	2.28 (1.51)	1.06 (0.59)	1.04 (1.35)	1.17 (1.59)	0.42 (0.88)
UCSMP 1st Edition	2.29 (1.66)	2.47 (1.47)	1.02 (0.58)	1.18 (1.33)	1.23 (1.73)	0.33 (0.84)
UCSMP 2nd Edition	2.18 (1.71)	**2.97** (1.27)	**1.16** (0.80)	**1.88** (1.64)	**1.36** (1.67)	**0.84** (1.23)
non-UCSMP	2.46 (1.73)	2.49 (1.61)	0.80 (0.58)	0.22 (0.64)	0.39 (1.04)	0.03 (0.23)

In Table 3, mean scores in the boldface for "UCSMP Second Edition" are significantly higher than the corresponding scores for non-UCSMP students on five of the six items. In all these cases the differences are significant at the 0.001 level, except for item 2, in which the difference is significant at the 0.002 level.

These results confirm conclusions from the first edition studies, namely that *Advanced Algebra* students maintain their hold on traditional advanced algebra skills while enriching their advanced algebra background in the application of algebra and in problem-solving and understanding of mathematics. They also show that students using the second edition perform as well as those using the first edition in all areas. The differences between *UCSMP Advanced Algebra* students and students using other texts in the Advanced Algebra Posttest and Problem-Solving and Understanding Test, especially on items dealing with quadratic functions and logarithmic functions, and on fitting a line to a data set, are particularly consistent and very strong.

Results not given here also show the vast range that exists among users of *UCSMP Advanced Algebra*. There is also a vast range in the mean amount of growth that took place over the year, and that variable shows remarkable school effects. That is, comparison and Second Edition classes in the same school tended either both to show large increases or both to show small increases. This indicates how important school climate is if one wishes to improve achievement.

Continuing Research and Development

Since August of 1989, UCSMP has sponsored an inservice on its texts open to all those who will be using the materials the next school year. We encourage users to attend these conferences.

Since November of 1985, UCSMP has sponsored an annual conference at the University of Chicago at which users *and* prospective users of its materials can meet with each other and with authors. This conference also provides UCSMP authors and staff with a valuable opportunity for reports on UCSMP materials from those not involved in formal studies.

Both ScottForesman and UCSMP welcome comments on our books, and desire to know of any studies school districts conduct using these materials. Please address comments either to Mathematics Product Manager, ScottForesman, 1900 East Lake Avenue, Glenview, IL 60025, or to Zalman Usiskin, Director, UCSMP, 5835 S. Kimbark Avenue, Chicago, IL 60637.

Professional Sourcebook: SECTION **BIBLIOGRAPHY**

References for Sections 1–4 of Professional Sourcebook

Center for the Assessment of Educational Progress. *A World of Differences*. Princeton, NJ: Educational Testing Service, 1989.

College Board. *Academic Preparation for College: What Students Need To Know and Be Able To Do*. New York: College Board, 1983.

Flanders, James. "How Much of the Content in Mathematics Textbooks Is New?" *Arithmetic Teacher,* September 1987: 18–23.

Hirschhorn, Daniel B., and Senk, Sharon L. "Calculators in the UCSMP Curriculum for Grades 7 and 8." *Calculators in Mathematics Education,* edited by James T. Fey and Christian R. Hirsch, pp. 79–90. Reston, VA: National Council of Teachers of Mathematics, 1992.

Johnson, David R. *Every Minute Counts*. Palo Alto, CA: Dale Seymour Publications, 1982.

Johnson, David R. *Making Minutes Count Even More*. Palo Alto, CA: Dale Seymour Publications, 1986.

Jones, Philip, and Coxford, Arthur F. *A History of Mathematics Education in the United States and Canada.* 30th Yearbook of the National Council of Teachers of Mathematics. Reston, VA: National Council of Teachers of Mathematics, 1970.

McKnight, Curtis, et al. *The Underachieving Curriculum: Assessing U.S. School Mathematics from an International Perspective.* Champaign, IL: Stipes Publishing Company, 1987.

National Commission on Excellence in Education. *A Nation at Risk: The Imperative for Educational Reform.* Washington, DC: U.S. Department of Education, 1983.

National Council of Teachers of Mathematics. *Curriculum and Evaluation Standards for School Mathematics.* Reston, VA: National Council of Teachers of Mathematics, 1989.

National Council of Teachers of Mathematics. *Professional Standards for Teaching Mathematics.* Reston, VA: National Council of Teachers of Mathematics, 1991.

National Research Council. *Everybody Counts.* Washington, DC: National Academy Press, 1989.

National Research Council. *For Good Measure.* Washington, DC: National Academy Press, 1991.

National Research Council. *Measuring Up: Prototypes for Mathematics Assessment.* Washington, DC: National Academy Press, 1993.

National Research Council. *Measuring What Counts.* Washington, DC: National Academy Press, 1993.

National Research Council. *Reshaping School Mathematics: A Philosophy and Framework for Curriculum.* Washington, DC: National Academy Press, 1991.

Polya, George. *How To Solve It.* Princeton, NJ: Princeton University Press, 1952.

Senk, Sharon L. "How Well Do Students Write Geometry Proofs?" *Mathematics Teacher,* September 1985: 448–456.

Steen, Lynn, editor. *On the Shoulders of Giants.* Washington, DC: National Academy Press, 1991.

Stenmark, Jean Kerr. *Assessment Alternatives in Mathematics.* Berkeley, CA: EQUALS, 1989.

Stenmark, Jean Kerr, editor. *Mathematics Assessment: Myths, Models, Good Questions, and Practical Suggestions.* Reston, VA: National Council of Teachers of Mathematics, 1991.

Usiskin, Zalman. "Conceptions of School Algebra and Uses of Variables." *The Ideas of Algebra, K–12,* edited by Arthur F. Coxford and Albert P. Shulte, pp. 8–19. Reston, VA: National Council of Teachers of Mathematics, 1988.

Usiskin, Zalman. "Why Elementary Algebra Can, Should, and Must Be an Eighth-Grade Course for Average Students." *Mathematics Teacher,* September 1987: 428–438.

Waits, Bert, and Demana, Franklin. "Is Three Years Enough?" *Mathematics Teacher,* January 1988: 11–15.

Additional General References

Fey, James T., and Hirsch, Christian R., editors. *Calculators in Mathematics Education.* Reston, VA: National Council of Teachers of Mathematics, 1992.
This 1992 Yearbook of the NCTM contains dozens of articles about using calculators, including graphics calculators, in teaching and assessment from Grades K–12.

Hirsch, Christian R., and Laing, Robert, editors. *Activities for Active Learning and Teaching: Selections from the Mathematics Teacher.* Reston, VA: National Council of Teachers of Mathematics, 1993.

Hirsch, Christian R., and Zweng, Marilyn J., editors. *The Secondary School Mathematics Curriculum.* Reston, VA: National Council of Teachers of Mathematics, 1985.
This forward-looking NCTM yearbook gives background for many of the ideas found in UCSMP texts.

Joseph, Goerge Gheverghese. *The Crest of the Peacock: Non-European Roots of Mathematics.* New York, NY: Penguin Books USA, 1991.
This book contains a broad account of the history of algebra.

Katz, Victor J. *A History of Mathematics.* New York, NY: HarperCollins, 1993.
This very fine recently published history of mathematics is notable for its scope, its mention of the original sources for our knowledge, and its inclusion of contributions from China, India, and the Islamic world.

Kieran, Carolyn, and Wagner, Sigrid, editors. *Research Issues in Learning and Teaching Algebra.* Reston, VA: National Council of Teachers of Mathematics, 1989.
An overview of recent research and its implications for learning and teaching algebra. See particularly the chapters by Fey and Senk on the impact of computer technology.

Mathematics Teacher. National Council of Teachers of Mathematics. 1906 Association Drive, Reston, VA.
This journal is an excellent source of applications and other teaching suggestions. We believe that every secondary school mathematics teacher should join the NCTM and read this journal regularly.

Shulte, Albert, and Smart, James R. *Teaching Statistics and Probability.* Reston, VA: National Council of Teachers of Mathematics, 1981.
This NCTM yearbook contains many ideas for the teaching of these topics.

Silver, Edward A., Kilpatrick, Jeremy, and Schlesinger, Beth. *Thinking through Mathematics: Fostering Inquiry and Communication in Mathematics Classrooms.* New York: College Entrance Examination Board, 1990.
This booklet contains many practical suggestions for improving communication in the classroom, techniques for reaching all students, not just a select few, and some suggestions for how to modify traditional tests and quizzes to make them more open-ended.

Whitmer, John C. *Spreadsheets in Mathematics and Science Teaching.* Bowling Green, OH: School, Science and Mathematics Association, 1992.
Specific ideas on how to use spreadsheets from algebra through precalculus, chemistry and physics.

Sources for Additional Problems

Austin, Joe Dan, editor. *Applications of Secondary School Mathematics:* Readings from the Mathematics Teacher. Reston, VA: National Council of Teachers of Mathematics, 1991.

Burrill, Gail, et al. *Data Analysis and Statistics.* Reston, VA: National Council of Teachers of Mathematics, 1992.
As part of the NCTM's Addenda Series for Grades 5–8, this booklet gives teachers ideas and hands-on materials to support the Data Analysis and Statistics strand of the *Curriculum and Evaluation Standards.*

Coxford, Arthur F., and Shulte, Albert P., editors. *The Ideas of Algebra, K–12.* Reston, VA: National Council of Teachers of Mathematics, 1988.
This NCTM yearbook contains 34 articles on all aspects of the teaching of algebra, including articles by authors of *UCSMP Algebra.*

The Diagram Group. *Comparisons.* New York: St. Martin's Press, 1980.
This is an excellent source of visual and numerical data on such quantities as distance, area and volume, and time and speed.

Eves, Howard. *An Introduction to the History of Mathematics.* 5th ed. Philadelphia. Saunders College Publishing, 1983.
This comprehensive history includes references to recent 20th century mathematics, such as the proof of the four-color theorem. There is an outstanding collection of problems.

Hanson, Viggo P., and Zweng, Marilyn J., editors. *Computers in Mathematics Education.* Reston, VA: National Council of Teachers of Mathematics, 1984.
This NCTM yearbook provides practical suggestions about some computer activities that can be added to mathematics classes. Chapter 15 is a particularly good overview of our view of how programming-related exercises can help teach mathematics.

Hoffman, Mark, editor. *The World Almanac and Book of Facts,* 1995. New York: World Almanac, 1995.

Johnson, Otto, executive ed. *The 1995 Information Please Almanac.* Boston: Houghton Mifflin Company, 1995.

Joint Committee of the Mathematical Association of America and the National Council of Teachers of Mathematics. *A Sourcebook of Applications of School Mathematics.* Reston, VA: National Council of Teachers of Mathematics, 1980.
This comprehensive source of applied problems is organized in sections by mathematical content (advanced arithmetic through combinatorics and probability).

Kastner, Bernice. *Applications of Secondary School Mathematics.* Reston, VA.: National Council of Teachers of Mathematics, 1978.
This short paperback book provides interesting applications in physics, chemistry, biology, economics, and other fields. There is a chapter on mathematical modeling.

Sharron, Sidney, and Reys, Robert E., editors. *Applications in School Mathematics.* Reston, VA: National Council of Teachers of Mathematics, 1979.
This NCTM yearbook is a collection of essays on applications, ways of including applications in the classroom, mathematical modeling, and other issues related to applications. There is an extensive bibliography on sources of applications.

UMAP Journal, Consortium for Mathematics and Its Applications Project, Inc. 271 Lincoln Street, Suite Number 4, Lexington, MA.
This journal is a wonderful source of applications, although many of them are at the college level. COMAP also publishes a quarterly newsletter called *Consortium* that includes "The HiMAP Pull-Out Section." *Consortium* provides information on COMAP modules which are appropriate for high schools.

U.S. Bureau of the Census. *Statistical Abstract of the United States: 1994,* 115th ed. Washington, D.C., 1994.
This outstanding data source, published annually since 1878, summarizes statistics on the United States and provides reference to other statistical publications.

Software

Abrams, Joshua. *GraphExplorer.* Glenview, IL: ScottForesman.
For Macintosh or IBM/Tandy/Compatibles. A powerful user-friendly piece of software which can be used with all UCSMP courses beginning with *Algebra*. It has a feature for drawing families of functions easily.

GeoExplorer, Glenview, IL: ScottForesman.
For Macintosh, IBM/Tandy/Compatibles, or Apple II. With this sophisticated software, students can easily draw, measure, and transform geometric figures to illustrate and explore geometric postulates, definitions, and theorems. Teachers can use *GeoExplorer* to demonstrate complex figures, theorems, and properties.

StatExplorer, Glenview, IL: ScottForesman.
For Macintosh or IBM/Tandy/Compatibles. Students can enter data in a spreadsheet format, then build bar, circle, line, and scatter graphs, histograms, and box plots. They can perform general statistical analysis on any data set or group of data sets. Other features include mathematical modeling, simulations, and frequency tables.

Selected Properties of Real Numbers

For any real numbers a, b, and c:

Postulates of Addition and Multiplication (Field Properties)

Algebra Properties from Earlier Courses

	Addition	*Multiplication*
Closure properties	$a + b$ is a real number.	ab is a real number.
Commutative properties	$a + b = b + a$	$ab = ba$
Associative properties	$(a + b) + c = a + (b + c)$	$(ab)c = a(bc)$
Identity properties	There is a real number 0 with $0 + a = a + 0 = a$.	There is a real number a with $1 \cdot a = a \cdot 1 = a$.
Inverse properties	There is a real number $-a$ with $a + -a = -a + a = 0$.	If $a \neq 0$, there is a real number $\frac{1}{a}$ with $a \cdot \frac{1}{a} = \frac{1}{a} \cdot a = 1$.
Distributive property	$a(b + c) = ab + ac$	

Postulates of Equality

Reflexive property	$a = a$
Symmetric property	If $a = b$, then $b = a$.
Transitive property	If $a = b$ and $b = c$, then $a = c$.
Substitution property	If $a = b$, then a may be substituted for b in any arithmetic or algebraic expression.
Addition property	If $a = b$, then $a + c = b + c$.
Multiplication property	If $a = b$, then $ac = bc$.

Postulates of Inequality

Trichotomy property	Either $a < b$, $a = b$, or $a > b$.
Transitive property	If $a < b$ and $b < c$, then $a < c$.
Addition property	If $a < b$, then $a + c < b + c$.
Multiplication property	If $a < b$ and $c > 0$, then $ac < bc$. If $a < b$ and $c < 0$, then $ac > bc$.

Postulates of Powers

For any nonzero bases ($a \neq 0$, $b \neq 0$) and integer exponents m and n:

Product of Powers property	$b^m \cdot b^n = b^{m+n}$
Power of a Power property	$(b^m)^n = b^{mn}$
Power of a Product property	$(ab)^m = a^m b^m$

884

Quotient of Powers property $\quad \dfrac{b^m}{b^n} = b^{m-n}$, for $b \neq 0$

Power of a Quotient property $\quad \left(\dfrac{a}{b}\right)^m = \dfrac{a^m}{b^m}$, for $b \neq 0$

Selected Theorems Of Graphing

The set of points (x, y) satisfying $Ax + By = C$, where A and B are not both 0, is a line.

The line with equation $y = mx + b$ has slope m and y-intercept b.

Two non-vertical lines are parallel if and only if they have the same slope.

Two non-vertical lines are perpendicular if and only if the product of their slopes is -1.

The set of points (x, y) satisfying $y = ax^2 + bx + c$ is a parabola.

Selected Theorems of Algebra

For any real numbers a, b, c, and d (with denominators of fractions not equal to 0):

Multiplication Property of 0	$0 \cdot a = 0$
Multiplication Property of -1	$-1 \cdot a = -a$
Opposite of an Opposite Property	$-(-a) = a$
Opposite of a Sum	$-(b + c) = -b + -c$
Distributive Property of Multiplication over Subtraction	$a(b - c) = ab - ac$
Addition of Like Terms	$ac + bc = (a + b)c$
Addition of Fractions	$\dfrac{a}{c} + \dfrac{b}{c} = \dfrac{a+b}{c}$
Multiplication of Fractions	$\dfrac{a}{b} \cdot \dfrac{c}{d} = \dfrac{ac}{bd}$
Equal Fractions	$\dfrac{ac}{bc} = \dfrac{a}{b}$
Means-Extremes	If $\dfrac{a}{b} = \dfrac{c}{d}$, then $ad = bc$.
Binomial Square	$(a + b)^2 = a^2 + 2ab + b^2$
Extended Distributive Property	To multiply two polynomials, multiply each term in the first polynomial by each term in the second.
Zero Exponent	If $b \neq 0$, $b^0 = 1$.
Negative Exponent	If $b \neq 0$, then $b^{-n} = \dfrac{1}{b^n}$.
Zero Product Theorem	$ab = 0$ if and only if $a = 0$ or $b = 0$.
Absolute Value-Square Root	$\sqrt{a^2} = |a|$
Product of Square Roots	If $a \geq 0$ and $b \geq 0$, then $\sqrt{ab} = \sqrt{a} \cdot \sqrt{b}$.
Quadratic Formula	If $ax^2 + bx + c = 0$ and $a \neq 0$, then $x = \dfrac{-b \pm \sqrt{b^2 - 4ac}}{2a}$.

Geometry Properties from Earlier Courses

In this book, we use many measurement formulas. The following symbols are used.

A = area
a = length of apothem
a, b, and c are lengths of sides (when they appear together)
b_1 and b_2 are lengths of bases
B = area of base
C = circumference
d = diameter
d_1 and d_2 are lengths of diagonals
h = height
L = lateral area

ℓ = length or slant height
n = number of sides
p = perimeter
P = perimeter of base
r = radius
S = total surface area
s = side
θ = measure of angle
T = sum of measures of angles
V = volume
w = width

Two-Dimensional Figures	Perimeter, Length, and Angle Measure	Area
n-gon	$T = 180(n - 2)$	
regular n-gon	$p = ns$ $\theta = \dfrac{180(n - 2)}{n}$	$A = \frac{1}{2}ap$
triangle	$p = a + b + c$	$A = \frac{1}{2}bh$ $A = \sqrt{\frac{p}{2}\left(\frac{p}{2} - a\right)\left(\frac{p}{2} - b\right)\left(\frac{p}{2} - c\right)}$ (Hero's formula)
right triangle	$c^2 = a^2 + b^2$ (Pythagorean theorem)	$A = \frac{1}{2}ab$
equilateral triangle	$p = 3s$	$A = \dfrac{\sqrt{3}}{4}s^2$
trapezoid		$A = \frac{1}{2}h(b_1 + b_2)$
parallelogram		$A = bh$
rhombus	$p = 4s$	$A = \frac{1}{2}d_1 d_2$
rectangle	$p = 2\ell + 2w$	$A = \ell w$
square	$p = 4s$	$A = s^2$
circle	$C = \pi d = 2\pi r$	$A = \pi r^2$

T64

Three-Dimensional Figures	Lateral Area and Total Surface Area	Volume
prism		$V = Bh$
right prism	$L = Ph$ $S = Ph + 2B$	$V = Bh$
box	$S = 2(\ell w + \ell h + hw)$	$V = \ell wh$
cube	$S = 6s^2$	$V = s^3$
pyramid		$V = \frac{1}{3}Bh$
regular pyramid	$L = \frac{P\ell}{2}$ $S = \frac{P\ell}{2} + B$	$V = \frac{1}{3}Bh$
cylinder		$V = Bh$
right circular cylinder	$L = 2\pi rh$ $S = 2\pi rh + 2\pi r^2$	$V = \pi r^2 h$
cone		$V = \frac{1}{3}Bh$
right circular cone	$L = \pi r\ell$ $S = \pi r\ell + \pi r^2$	$V = \frac{1}{3}\pi r^2 h$
sphere	$S = 4\pi r^2$	$V = \frac{4}{3}\pi r^3$

Selected Theorems of Geometry

Parallel Lines

Two lines are parallel if and only if:

> corresponding angles are congruent.
> alternate interior angles are congruent.
> alternate exterior angles are congruent.
> they are perpendicular to the same line.

Triangle Congruence

Two triangles are congruent if:

SSS   three sides of one are congruent to three sides of the other.

SAS   two sides and the included angle of one are congruent to two sides and the included angle of the other.

ASA   two angles and the included side of one are congruent to two angles and the included side of the other.

AAS   two angles and a non-included side of one are congruent to two angles and the corresponding non-included side of the other.

SsA   two sides and the angle opposite the longer of the two sides of one are congruent to two sides and the angle opposite the corresponding side of the other.

Angles and Sides of Triangles

Triangle Inequality	The sum of the lengths of two sides of a triangle is greater than the length of the third side.
Isosceles Triangle	If two sides of a triangle are congruent, then the angles opposite those sides are congruent.
Unequal Sides	If two sides of a triangle are unequal in length, then the angle opposite the larger side is larger than the angle opposite the smaller side.
Unequal Angles	If two angles of a triangle are unequal in measure, then the side opposite the larger angle is larger than the side opposite the smaller angle.
Pythagorean Theorem	In a right triangle with legs a and b and hypotenuse c, $c^2 = a^2 + b^2$.
30-60-90 Triangle	In a 30-60-90 triangle, the sides are in the extended ratio $x:x\sqrt{3}:2x$.
45-45-90 Triangle	In a 45-45-90 triangle, the sides are in the extended ratio $x:x:x\sqrt{2}$.

Parallelograms

A quadrilateral is a parallelogram if and only if:

> one pair of opposite sides are congruent and parallel.
> both pairs of opposite sides are congruent.
> both pairs of opposite angles are congruent.
> its diagonals bisect each other.

888

Quadrilateral Hierarchy

If a figure is of any type in the hierarchy pictured here, it is also of all types above it to which it is connected.

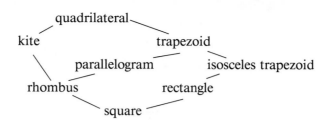

Properties of Transformations

A-B-C-D Every isometry (composite of reflections) preserves angle measure, betweenness, collinearity, and distance.

Two-Reflection The composite of two reflections over intersecting lines is a rotation whose center is the intersection of the lines and whose magnitude is twice the measure of the nonobtuse angle formed by the lines in the direction from the first line to the second. The composite of two reflections over parallel lines is a translation whose direction is perpendicular to the lines from the first line to the second and whose magnitude is twice the distance between the lines.

Isometry Every isometry is a reflection, rotation, translation, or glide reflection.

Size Change Every size change with magnitude k preserves angle measure, betweenness, and collinearity; a line is parallel to its image; distance is multiplied by k.

Fundamental Theorem of Similarity

If two figures G and G' are similar with ratio of similitude k, then:

angle measures in G' = corresponding angle measures in G;
lengths in G' = $k \cdot$ corresponding lengths in G;
perimeters in G' = $k \cdot$ corresponding perimeters in G;
areas in G' = $k^2 \cdot$ corresponding areas in G;
volumes in G' = $k^3 \cdot$ corresponding volumes in G.

Triangle Similarity

Two triangles are similar if:

three sides of one are proportional to three sides of the other (SSS).
two sides of one are proportional to two sides of the other and the included angles are congruent (SAS).
two angles of one are congruent to two angles of the other (AA).

Coordinate plane formulas

For all $A = (x_1, y_1)$ and $B = (x_2, y_2)$:

Distance formula $AB = \sqrt{(x_2 - x_1)^2 + (y_2 - y_1)^2}$

Midpoint formula   The midpoint of $\overline{AB}$ is $\left(\frac{x_1 + x_2}{2}, \frac{y_1 + y_2}{2}\right)$.

For all points (x, y):

reflection over the x-axis	$(x, y) \rightarrow (x, -y)$
reflection over the y-axis	$(x, y) \rightarrow (-x, y)$
reflection over $y = x$	$(x, y) \rightarrow (y, x)$
size change of magnitude k, center $(0,0)$	$(x, y) \rightarrow (kx, ky)$
translation h units horizontally, k units vertically	$(x, y) \rightarrow (x+h, y+k)$

An asterisk (*) preceding a theorem indicates that the theorem is also found in a previous UCSMP text.

Theorems of UCSMP Advanced Algebra

Chapter 1

Vertical-Line Test for Functions: No vertical line intersects the graph of a function in more than one point.

***Opposite of a Sum Theorem:** For all real numbers a and b, $-(a + b) = -a + -b$.

Chapter 2

The Fundamental Theorem of Variation:

a. If y varies directly as x^n (that is, $y = kx^n$), and x is multiplied by c, then y is multiplied by c^n.

b. If y varies inversely as x^n $\left(\text{that is, } y = \frac{k}{x^n}\right)$, and x is multiplied by a nonzero constant c, then y is divided by c^n.

Theorem: The graph of the direct-variation function $y = kx$ has constant slope k.

Converse of the Fundamental Theorem of Variation:

a. If multiplying every x-value of a function by c results in multiplying the corresponding y-value by c^n, then y varies directly as the nth power of x. That is, $y = kx^n$.

b. If multiplying every x-value of a function by c results in dividing the corresponding y-value by c^n, then y varies inversely as the nth power of x. That is, $y = \frac{k}{x^n}$.

Chapter 3

***Theorem:** If two lines have the same slope, then they are parallel.

***Theorem:** If two non-vertical lines are parallel, then they have the same slope.

***Theorem:** The graph of $Ax + By = C$, where A and B are not both 0, is a line.

Point-Slope Theorem: If a line contains (x_1, y_1) and has slope m, then it has equation $y - y_1 = m(x - x_1)$.

Theorem: The sequence defined by the recursive formula

$\begin{cases} a_1 \\ a_n = a_{n-1} + d, \end{cases}$ for integers $n \geq 2$, is the arithmetic sequence with first term a_1 and constant difference d.

Theorem (*n*th Term of an Arithmetic Sequence) The nth term a_n of an arithmetic sequence with first term a_1 and constant difference d is given by the explicit formula $a_n = a_1 + (n - 1)d$.

Chapter 4

Theorem: $\begin{bmatrix} k & 0 \\ 0 & k \end{bmatrix}$ is the matrix for S_k.

Theorem: $\begin{bmatrix} a & 0 \\ 0 & b \end{bmatrix}$ is the matrix for $S_{a,b}$.

Theorem: $\begin{bmatrix} -1 & 0 \\ 0 & 1 \end{bmatrix}$ is the matrix for r_y.

Theorem: $\begin{bmatrix} 1 & 0 \\ 0 & -1 \end{bmatrix}$ is the matrix for r_x.

Theorem: $\begin{bmatrix} 0 & 1 \\ 1 & 0 \end{bmatrix}$ is the matrix for $r_{y=x}$.

Matrix Basis Theorem: Suppose T is a transformation represented by a 2×2 matrix. If T: $(1, 0) \rightarrow (x_1, y_1)$ and

T: $(0, 1) \rightarrow (x_2, y_2)$ then T has the matrix $\begin{bmatrix} x_1 & x_2 \\ y_1 & y_2 \end{bmatrix}$.

Theorem: If M_1 is the matrix for transformation T_1 and M_2 is the matrix for transformation T_2, then $M_2 M_1$ is the matrix for $T_2 \circ T_1$.

Theorem: A rotation of $b°$ following a rotation of $a°$ with the same center results in a rotation of $(a + b)°$. In symbols: $R_b \circ R_a = R_{a+b}$.

Theorem: $\begin{bmatrix} 0 & -1 \\ 1 & 0 \end{bmatrix}$ is the matrix for R_{90}.

Theorem: $\begin{bmatrix} -1 & 0 \\ 0 & -1 \end{bmatrix}$ is the matrix for R_{180}.

Theorem: $\begin{bmatrix} 0 & 1 \\ -1 & 0 \end{bmatrix}$ is the matrix for R_{270}.

*__Theorem:__ If two lines with slopes m_1 and m_2 are perpendicular, then $m_1 m_2 = -1$.
*__Theorem:__ If two lines have slopes m_1 and m_2 and $m_1 m_2 = -1$, then the lines are perpendicular.
*__Theorem:__ Under a translation, a line is parallel to its image.

Chapter 5

Inverse Matrix Theorem: If $ad - bc \neq 0$, the inverse of

$\begin{bmatrix} a & b \\ c & d \end{bmatrix}$ is $\begin{bmatrix} \dfrac{d}{ad - bc} & \dfrac{-b}{ad-bc} \\ \dfrac{-c}{ad - bc} & \dfrac{a}{ad-bc} \end{bmatrix}$.

System-Determinant Theorem: A 2×2 system has exactly one solution if and only if the determinant of the coefficient matrix is *not* zero.

Linear-Programming Theorem: The feasible region of every linear-programming problem is convex, and the maximum or minimum quantity is determined at one of the vertices of this feasible region.

Chapter 6

Binomial Square Theorem: For all real numbers x and y:
$(x + y)^2 = x^2 + 2xy + y^2$; $(x - y)^2 = x^2 - 2xy + y^2$.

*__Absolute Value—Square Root Theorem:__ For all real numbers x, $\sqrt{x^2} = |x|$.

Graph-Translation Theorem: In a relation described by a sentence in x and y, the following two processes yield the same graph:
(1) replacing x by $x - h$ and y by $y - k$;
(2) applying the translation $T_{h,k}$ to the graph of the original relation.

Corollary: The image of the parabola $y = ax^2$ under the translation $T_{h,k}$ is the parabola with the equation $y - k = a(x - h)^2$.

Theorem: The graph of the equation $y = ax^2 + bx + c$ is a parabola congruent to the graph of $y = ax^2$.

Theorem: To complete the square on $x^2 + bx$, add $\left(\frac{1}{2}b\right)^2$. So $x^2 + bx + \left(\frac{1}{2}b\right)^2 = \left(x + \frac{1}{2}b\right)^2 = \left(x + \frac{b}{2}\right)^2$.

*__Quadratic Formula:__ If $ax^2 + bx + c = 0$ and $a \neq 0$, then $x = \dfrac{-b \pm \sqrt{b^2 - 4ac}}{2a}$.

Theorem: If $k > 0$, $\sqrt{-k} = i\sqrt{k}$.

Discriminant Theorem: Suppose a, b, and c are real numbers with $a \neq 0$. Then the equation $ax^2 + bx + c = 0$ has: (i) two real solutions if $b^2 - 4ac > 0$; (ii) one real solution if $b^2 - 4ac = 0$; (iii) two complex conjugate solutions if $b^2 - 4ac < 0$.

Chapter 7

*__Zero Exponent Theorem:__ If b is a nonzero real number, $b^0 = 1$.

*__Negative Exponent Theorem:__ For any positive base b and real exponent n, or any nonzero base b and integer exponent n, $b^{-n} = \frac{1}{b^n}$.

*__Annual Compound Interest Formula:__ Let P be the amount of money invested at an annual interest rate of r compounded annually. Let A be the total amount after t years. Then $A = P(1 + r)^t$.

General Compound Interest Formula: Let P be the amount invested at an annual interest rate r compounded n times per year. Let A be the amount after t years. Then $A = P\left(1 + \frac{r}{n}\right)^{nt}$.

Recursive Formula for a Geometric Sequence: The sequence defined by the recursive formula
$$\begin{cases} g_1 \\ g_n = rg_{n-1}, \text{ for integers } n \geq 2, \text{ where } r \text{ is a} \end{cases}$$
nonzero constant, is the geometric, or exponential, sequence with first term g_1 and constant multiplier r.

Explicit Formula for a Geometric Sequence: In the geometric sequence with first term g_1 and constant ratio r, $g_n = g_1(r)^{n-1}$, for integers $n \geq 1$.

$\frac{1}{n}$ Exponent Theorem: When $x \geq 0$ and n is an integer greater than 1, $x^{\frac{1}{n}}$ is an nth root of x.

Number of Real Roots Theorem: Every positive real number has 2 real nth roots when n is even, and 1 real nth root when n is odd. Every negative real number has 0 real nth roots when n is even, and 1 real nth root when n is odd.

Rational Exponent Theorem: For any nonnegative real number x and positive integers m and n, $x^{\frac{m}{n}} = \left(x^{\frac{1}{n}}\right)^m$, the mth power of the positive nth root of x, and $x^{\frac{m}{n}} = (x^m)^{\frac{1}{n}}$, the positive nth root of the mth power of x.

Chapter 8

Inverse Relation Theorem: Suppose f is a relation and g is the inverse of f. Then:
(1) A rule for g can be found by switching x and y.
(2) The graph of g is the reflection image of the graph of f over the line $y = x$.
(3) The domain of g is the range of f, and the range of g is the domain of f.

Horizontal-Line Test for Inverses Theorem: The inverse of a function f is itself a function if and only if no horizontal line intersects the graph of f in more than one point.

Inverse Functions Theorem: Two functions f and g are inverse functions if and only if: (1) For all x in the domain of f, $g \circ f(x) = x$, and (2) for all x in the domain of g, $f \circ g(x) = x$.

Power Function Inverse Theorem: If $f(x) = x^n$ and $g(x) = x^{\frac{1}{n}}$ and the domains of f and g are the set of nonnegative real numbers, then f and g are inverse functions.

Root of a Power Theorem: For all positive integers $m > 1$ and $n \geq 2$, and all nonnegative real numbers x, $\sqrt[n]{x^m} = \left(\sqrt[n]{x}\right)^m = x^{\frac{m}{n}}$.

Root of a Product Theorem: For any nonnegative real numbers x and y, and any integer $n \geq 2$: $(xy)^{\frac{1}{n}} = x^{\frac{1}{n}} \cdot y^{\frac{1}{n}}$ (power form); $\sqrt[n]{xy} = \sqrt[n]{x} \cdot \sqrt[n]{y}$ (radical form).

Theorem: When $\sqrt[n]{x}$ and $\sqrt[n]{y}$ are defined and are real numbers, then $\sqrt[n]{xy}$ is also defined and $\sqrt[n]{xy} = \sqrt[n]{x} \cdot \sqrt[n]{y}$.

Chapter 9

Exponential Growth Model: If a quantity a grows by a factor b ($b > 0$, $b \neq 1$) in each unit period, then after a period of length x, there will be ab^x of the quantity.

Continuously Compounded Interest Formula: If an amount P is invested in an account paying an annual interest rate r compounded continuously, the amount A in the account after t years will be $A = Pe^{rt}$.

Log of 1 Theorem: For every base b, $\log_b 1 = 0$.

Log_b of b^n Theorem: For every base b and any real number n, $\log_b b^n = n$.

Product Property of Logarithms: For any base b, and positive real numbers x and y, $\log_b (xy) = \log_b x + \log_b y$.

Quotient Property of Logarithms: For any base b, and for any positive real numbers x and y, $\log_b \left(\frac{x}{y}\right) = \log_b x - \log_b y$.

Power Property of Logarithms: For any base b, and for any positive real number x, $\log_b (x^n) = n \log_b x$.

Change of Base Property: For all positive real numbers a, b, and t, $b \neq 1$ and $t \neq 1$, $\log_b a = \dfrac{\log_t a}{\log_t b}$.

Chapter 10

Complements Property: For all θ between $0°$ and $90°$, $\sin \theta = \cos(90° - \theta)$ and $\cos \theta = \sin(90° - \theta)$.

Pythagorean Identity: For all θ between $0°$ and $90°$, $(\cos \theta)^2 + (\sin \theta)^2 = 1$.

Tangent Theorem: For all θ between $0°$ and $90°$, $\tan \theta = \frac{\sin \theta}{\cos \theta}$.

892

Exact-Value Theorem: $\sin 30° = \cos 60° = \frac{1}{2}$; $\sin 45° = \cos 45° = \frac{\sqrt{2}}{2}$; $\sin 60° = \cos 30° = \frac{\sqrt{3}}{2}$.

Law of Cosines: In any $\triangle ABC$, $c^2 = a^2 + b^2 - 2ab \cos C$.

Law of Sines: In any $\triangle ABC$, $\frac{\sin A}{a} = \frac{\sin B}{b} = \frac{\sin C}{c}$.

Supplements Theorem: For all θ in degrees, $\sin \theta = \sin(180° - \theta)$.

Conversion Factors for Degrees and Radians: To convert radians to degrees, multiply by $\frac{180 \text{ degrees}}{\pi \text{ radians}}$. To convert degrees to radians, multiply by $\frac{\pi \text{ radians}}{180 \text{ degrees}}$.

Chapter 11

*__Extended Distributive Property:__ To multiply two polynomials, multiply each term in the first polynomial by each term in the second.

*__Binomial-Square Factoring Theorem:__ For all a and b, $a^2 + 2ab + b^2 = (a + b)^2$; $a^2 - 2ab + b^2 = (a - b)^2$.

*__Difference-of-Squares Factoring Theorem:__ For all a and b, $a^2 - b^2 = (a + b)(a - b)$.

Discriminant Theorem for Factoring Quadratics: Suppose a, b, and c are integers with $a \neq 0$, and let $D = b^2 - 4ac$. Then the polynomial $ax^2 + bx + c$ can be factored into first degree polynomials with integer coefficients if and only if D is a perfect square.

*__Zero-Product Theorem:__ For all a and b, $ab = 0$ if and only if $a = 0$ or $b = 0$.

Factor Theorem: $x - r$ is a factor of a polynomial $P(x)$ if and only if $P(r) = 0$.

Rational-Zero Theorem: Suppose that all the coefficients of the polynomial function defined by $f(x) = a_n x^n + a_{n-1} x^{n-1} + \ldots + a_2 x^2 + a_1 x + a_0$ are integers with $a_n \neq 0$ and $a_0 \neq 0$. Let $\frac{p}{q}$ be a rational number in lowest terms. If $\frac{p}{q}$ is a zero of f, then p is a factor of a_0 and q is a factor of a_n.

Fundamental Theorem of Algebra: Every polynomial equation $P(x) = 0$ of any degree with complex number coefficients has at least one complex number solution.

Number of Roots of a Polynomial Equation Theorem: Every polynomial equation of degree n has exactly n roots, provided that multiplicities of multiple roots are counted.

Polynomial-Difference Theorem: $y = f(x)$ is a polynomial function of degree n if and only if, for any set of x-values that form an arithmetic sequence, the nth differences of corresponding y-values are equal and the $(n - 1)$st differences are not equal.

Chapter 12

Theorem: The graph of $y = ax^2$ is the parabola with focus $\left(0, \frac{1}{4a}\right)$ and directrix $y = -\frac{1}{4a}$.

Center-Radius Equation for a Circle Theorem: The circle with center (h, k) and radius r is the set of points (x, y) that satisfy $(x - h)^2 + (y - k)^2 = r^2$.

Corollary: The circle with center at the origin and radius r is the set of points (x, y) that satisfy the equation $x^2 + y^2 = r^2$.

Interior and Exterior of a Circle Theorem: Let C be the circle with center (h, k) and radius r. Then the interior of C is described by $(x - h)^2 + (y - k)^2 < r^2$. The exterior of C is described by $(x - h)^2 + (y - k)^2 > r^2$.

Equation for an Ellipse: The ellipse with foci $(c, 0)$ and $(-c, 0)$ and focal constant $2a$ has equation $\frac{x^2}{a^2} + \frac{y^2}{b^2} = 1$, where $b^2 = a^2 - c^2$.

Theorem: In the ellipse with equation $\frac{x^2}{a^2} + \frac{y^2}{b^2} = 1$, $2a$ is the length of the horizontal axis, and $2b$ is the length of the vertical axis.

Theorem: The image of the unit circle with equation $x^2 + y^2 = 1$ under $S_{a,b}$ is the ellipse with equation $\left(\frac{x}{a}\right)^2 + \left(\frac{y}{b}\right)^2 = 1$.

Graph Scale-Change Theorem: In a relation described by a sentence in x and y, the following two processes yield the same graph:
(1) replacing x by $\frac{x}{a}$ and y by $\frac{y}{b}$;
(2) applying the scale change $S_{a,b}$ to the graph of the original relation.

Theorem: An ellipse with axes of lengths $2a$ and $2b$ has area $A = \pi ab$.

Equation for a Hyperbola: The hyperbola with foci $(c, 0)$ and $(-c, 0)$ and focal constant $2a$ has equation $\frac{x^2}{a^2} - \frac{y^2}{b^2} = 1$, where $b^2 = c^2 - a^2$.

Theorem: The asymptotes of the hyperbola with equation $\frac{x^2}{a^2} - \frac{y^2}{b^2} = 1$ are $\frac{y}{b} = \pm \frac{x}{a}$ $\left(\text{or } y = \pm \frac{b}{a} x\right)$.

Theorem: The graph of $y = \frac{k}{x}$ or $xy = k$ is a hyperbola. When $k > 0$, this is the hyperbola with foci $(\sqrt{2k}, \sqrt{2k})$ and $(-\sqrt{2k}, -\sqrt{2k})$ and focal constant $2\sqrt{2k}$.

Chapter 13

Theorem: The sum of the integers for 1 to n is $\frac{1}{2}n(n + 1)$.

Theorem: Let $S_n = a_1 + a_2 + \ldots + a_n$ be an arithmetic series. Then $S_n = \frac{n}{2}(a_1 + a_n)$.

Corollary: Let $S_n = a_1 + a_2 + \ldots + a_n$ be an arithmetic series with constant difference d. Then $S_n = \frac{n}{2}\{2a_1 + (n - 1)d\}$.

Theorem: Let S_n be the sum of the first n terms of the geometric sequence with first term g_1 and constant ratio $r \neq 1$. Then
$$S_n = \frac{g_1(1 - r^n)}{1 - r} \text{ or } S_n = \frac{g_1(r^n - 1)}{r - 1}.$$

Theorem: There are $n!$ permutations of n distinct objects.

Pascal's Triangle Explicit-Formula Theorem: If n and r are integers with $0 \leq r \leq n$, then
$$\binom{n}{r} = \frac{n!}{r!(n - r)!}.$$

Binomial Theorem: For all complex numbers a and b, and for all integers n and r with $0 \leq r \leq n$,
$$(a + b)^n = \sum_{r=0}^{n} \binom{n}{r} a^{n-r}b^r.$$

Theorem: The number of subsets of r elements which can be formed from a set of n elements is $\frac{n!}{r!(n - r)!}$, the binomial coefficient $\binom{n}{r}$.

Theorem: A set with n elements has 2^n subsets.

Binomial Probability Theorem: Suppose a binomial experiment has n trials. If the probability of success is p, and the probability of failure is $q = 1 - p$, then the probability that there are r successes in n trials is $\binom{n}{r} p^r q^{n-r}$.

Corollary: Suppose a trial in a binomial experiment has probability $\frac{1}{2}$. Then the probability of r successes in n trials of the experiment is $\frac{\binom{n}{r}}{2^n}$.

Central Limit Theorem: Suppose samples of size n are chosen from a population in which the probability of an element of the sample having a certain characteristic is p. Let $P(x)$ equal the probability that x elements have the characteristic. Then P is approximated by a normal distribution with mean np and standard deviation $\sqrt{np(1 - p)}$.

894

Programming Languages

COMMANDS

The BASIC commands used in this course, their translation into one calculator language, and examples of their use are given below.

LET . . .

A value is assigned to a given variable. Some versions of BASIC allow you to omit the word LET in the assignment statement.

LET A = 5   5 → A

The number 5 is stored in a memory location called A.

LET N = N + 2   N + 2 → N

The value in the memory location called N is increased by 2 and then restored in the location called N. (N is replaced by N + 2.)

PRINT . . .

The computer/calculator displays on the screen what follows the PRINT command. If what follows is a constant or variable, the value of that constant or variable is displayed. If what follows is in quotes, the quote is displayed exactly.

PRINT A   Disp A

The computer prints the number stored in memory location A.

PRINT "X = " A/B   Disp "X = ", A/B

Displayed is X = (value of A/B). Notice that the space after the equal sign in the quotes is transferred into a space after the equal sign in the displayed sentence. On some calculators, the display will place X = and the value on separate lines.

INPUT . . .

The computer asks the user to give a value to the variable named, and stores that value.

INPUT X   Input X

When the program is run, the computer/calculator will prompt you to give it a value by displaying a question mark, and then store the value you type in memory location X.

INPUT "HOW OLD"; AGE   Input "How Old", Age

The computer/calculator displays HOW OLD? and stores your response in memory location AGE.

REM . . .

This command allows remarks to be inserted in a program. These may describe what the variables represent, what the program does, or how it works. REM statements are often used in long complex programs or in programs others will use.

REM PYTHAGOREAN THEOREM

The statement appears when the LIST command is given, but it has no effect when the program is run. Some calculators have no corresponding command.

FOR . . .
NEXT . . .
STEP . . .

The FOR command assigns a beginning and ending value to a variable. The first time through the loop, the variable has the beginning value in the FOR command. When the program hits the line reading NEXT, the value of the variable is increased by the amount indicated by STEP. The commands between FOR and NEXT are then repeated.

```
10  FOR N = 3 TO 10 STEP 2        For (N, 3, 10, 2)
20  PRINT N                       Disp N
30  NEXT N                        End
40  END
```

The program assigns 3 to N and then displays the value of N. On reaching NEXT, the program increases N by 2 (the STEP amount), and prints 5. The next N is 7, then 9, but

▶

▶ 11 is too large, so the program executes the command after NEXT, ending itself. The NEXT command is not needed in some calculator languages. The output from both programs is given here.

$$3$$
$$5$$
$$7$$
$$9$$

IF . . . THEN . . .   The program performs the consequent (the THEN part) only if the antecedent (the IF part) is true. When the antecedent is false, the program *ignores* the consequent and goes directly to the next line of the program.

IF X > 100 THEN END	If X ≤ 100
PRINT X	Then Disp X
END	End

If the X value is greater than 100, the program goes to the end statement. If the X value is less than or equal to 100, the computer/calculator displays the value stored in X.

GOTO . . .   The program goes to whatever line of the program is indicated. GOTO statements are generally avoided because they interrupt program flow and make programs hard to interpret.

5 (Command)	5 (Command)
10 GOTO 5	Goto 5

The program goes to line 5 and executes that command.

END . . .   The computer stops running the program. A program should have only one end statement.

END	End

FUNCTIONS

A large number of functions are built in to most versions of BASIC and to all calculators. They are the same functions used outside of programming. Each function name must be followed by a variable or constant enclosed in parentheses. Here are some examples of the uses of functions in programs.

ABS   The absolute value of the number that follows is calculated.

LET A = ABS(-10)	ABS(-10) → A

The computer calculates $|-10| = 10$ and assigns the value 10 to memory location A.

Like the absolute value function, the trigonometric functions SIN, COS, and TAN are identified in the same way in virtually all programming languages. Other functions are also similar.

INT   The greatest integer less than or equal to the number that follows is calculated.

B = INT(N + .5)	INT(N + .5) → B

The program adds .5 to the value of N, calculates $\lfloor N + .5 \rfloor$, and stores the result in B.

Some functions are identified differently in different languages. Here are two examples.

LOG or LN   The natural logarithm (logarithm to base e) of the number that follows, is calculated.

LET J = LOG(6)	LN(6) → J

The program calculates $ln\ 6$ and assigns the value 1.791759469228 to memory location J. It may display only some of these decimal places.

SQR   The square root of the number or expression that follows is calculated.

C = SQR(A*A + B*B)	$\sqrt{(A*A + B*B)}$ → C

The program calculates $\sqrt{A^2 + B^2}$ using the values stored in A and B and stores the result in C.

896

LESSON 1-1 (pp. 6–11)
19. (b) **21.** (e) **23.** (d) **25.** Sample: Mark is building a deck requiring x feet of lumber. He already has y feet of lumber. How much more lumber should he buy or how much lumber will he have left? **27.** Sample: A meteor falls x meters in y seconds. At what rate is it approaching the Earth? **29.** -0.12 **31.** 120 mg **33.** (a) **35. a.** $x = -9$ **b.** Does $3 \cdot (-9) = 5 \cdot (-9) + 18$? Does $-27 = -45 + 18$? $-27 = -27$. Yes, it checks.

LESSON 1-2 (pp. 12–17)
21. a. the set of positive real numbers **b.** 43.3 cm^2 **23. a.** Yes; each year corresponds to exactly one value. **b.** No; $M = 24.3$ corresponds to both $F = 21.3$ and $F = 21.5$. **25.** 9600 **27.** $a + b$ **29.** ab **31.** (b)

LESSON 1-3 (pp. 19–23)
13. $g(15)$; $g(15) = 32,768$; $h(15) = 225$; $32,768 > 225$ **15.** 50 **17. a.** 57.5 **b.** Sample: The increase in the average price of one gal of unleaded gasoline from 1978 to 1980 is about 58¢. **19.** $x = 1984$ **21.** Yes; each value of x corresponds to only one value of y. **23. a.** \$428 **b.** \$$(278 + 25n)$ **25. a.** $n = \frac{1}{2}$ **b.** $\frac{1}{2} + 10 = 3\left(\frac{1}{2}\right) + 9$? $10\frac{1}{2} = 1\frac{1}{2} + 9$? Yes, it checks.

LESSON 1-4 (pp. 24–29)
13. $B(5) \approx 42$ **15.** $t = 1, 8, 14$ **17. a.** Sample: $(0, 0)$; $(1, 1)$; $(2, 4)$ **b.** Sample: **See below. c.** Yes **19. See below. 21.** ≈ 460 acres **23.** $\approx 2,105,000$ **25. a.** 25 **b.** -23 **c.** $1 + \frac{3n^3}{8}$ **27. a.** $f(3) = 0$; $f(6) = 9$ **b.** $\{3, 4, 5, 6, \ldots\}$ **29.** $n = 244$; $\frac{1}{2}(244) - 72 = 50$? $122 - 72 = 50$? Yes.

17. b.

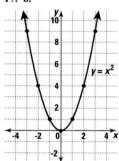

19.

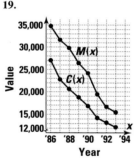

LESSON 1-5 (pp. 30–35)
13. 162.5 **15.** $y = 9$ **17.** $y = \frac{12}{5} = 2.4$ **19.** $x = 10$ **21. a.** $f(18) = \frac{1}{20}$ **b.** $n = 97$ **23.** $\approx$ \$100 billion **25.** approximately 1976 to 1992 **27.** ≈ 10.19 ft

LESSON 1-6 (pp. 36–40)
9. (a) **11. a.** $\pi = \frac{C}{D}$ **b.** Sample: π is the ratio of the circumference of a circle to its diameter. **13.** Sample: $P = \frac{.8 \text{ cm}}{.5 \cdot 4.2 \text{ cm}} \approx 0.38$ **15. a.** $S = \frac{2R}{P}$ **b.** 60 ft **17.** $n = \frac{t - a}{d} + 1$ **19.** $x = 12$ **21.** 1.42 sec **23.** (c)

LESSON 1-7 (pp. 42–47)
17. 18,000; 18,900; 19,845 **19. a.** n **b.** s **c.** Sample: the set of positive integers less than 40 **21.** (c) **23.** $n = \frac{S}{180} + 2$ or $\frac{S + 360}{180}$ **25. a.** $P(x) = 3x + 4$ **b.** $P(40) = 124$ **c.** $x = 12$ **27.** 70%

LESSON 1-8 (pp. 48–54)
13. a. $\begin{cases} s_1 = 15 \\ s_n = \text{previous term} + 2, \text{ for integers } n \geq 2 \end{cases}$ **b.** $s_{10} = 33$ **15. a.** 3, 12, 48, 192 **b.** 3, 12, 48, 192 **c.** True **17.** Sample: A recursive sequence is dependent on previous terms. Therefore, an initial value is needed in order to use the formula. **19. a.** $c_3 = 225,000$ **b.** \$3,844,335.94 **21. a.** 30,782,000 people **b.** 2006 **23. a.** 16 square units **b.** $8\sqrt{5} \approx 17.9$ units **c. See below.**

23. c. Sample:

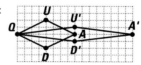

LESSON 1-9 (pp. 55–60)
13. a. The first term is 3. Each term after the first is found by adding 11 to the previous term.
b. $\begin{cases} t_1 = 3 \\ t_n = t_{n-1} + 11, \text{ for integers } n \geq 2 \end{cases}$
15. a. 100, 102, 105, 109, 114 **b.** Sample: If 99 is subtracted from each term, the result is the triangular number sequence.
17. a. 29, 47, 76, 123 **b.** $\begin{cases} L_1 = 1 \\ L_2 = 3 \\ L_n = L_{n-2} + L_{n-1}, \text{ for integers } n \geq 3 \end{cases}$
19. a. $a_4 = 40$; This means after 4 weeks Antonio has \$40.00 in his account. **b.** 50th term **21. a.** $V = \frac{nRT}{P}$ **b.** $T = \frac{PV}{nR}$ **23. a.** $\{x: 0 \leq x \leq 50\}$ **b.** $\{y: 10 \leq y \leq 80\}$ **25.** the set of all real numbers

---

CHAPTER 1 PROGRESS SELF-TEST (pp. 64–65)

1. $t_1 = 5 + 7(1) = 12$; $t_2 = 5 + 7(2) = 19$; $t_3 = 5 + 7(3) = 26$; $t_4 = 5 + 7(4) = 33$ **2. a.** $S_1 = 5$; $S_2 = 5 + 7 = 12$; $S_3 = 12 + 7 = 19$; $S_4 = 19 + 7 = 26$ **b.** The first term is 5. Each term after the first is found by adding 7 to the previous term. **3.** $t_8 = 5 + 7(8) = 61$ **4.** $S_5 = 26 + 7 = 33$; $S_6 = 33 + 7 = 40$; $S_7 = 40 + 7 = 47$; $S_8 = 47 + 7 = 54$ **5.** $f(3) = 9(3)^2 - 11(3) = 81 - 33 = 48$ **6.** $T(12) = \frac{(12)(12 + 1)}{2} = \frac{(12)(13)}{2} = 78$ **7.** (b) **8.** $s = \frac{12}{t}$ miles per hour **9.** $4(3x - 8) = 11$; $12x - 32 = 11$;

$12x = 43$; $x = \frac{43}{12}$ **10.** $1.2y = 0.9$; $y = .75$ **11.** Multiply both sides by 100; $12p + 8(15,000 - p) = 148,000$; $12p + 120,000 - 8p = 148,000$; $4p + 120,000 = 148,000$; $4p = 28,000$; $p = 7000$ **12.** $\left(\frac{1}{3}\right)(\pi)(4)^2(6) = 100.53 \approx 101$ cm^3 **13.** A reasonable domain is the set of positive real numbers since length can be any positive number. **14.** $h = \frac{3V}{\pi r^2}$ **15.** domain: $\{1, 3, 5\}$; range: $\{2, 4, 6\}$ **16.** (b), (c), (d) **17.** Yes, it is a function because each x value corresponds to only one y value. **18.** No, since $x = 1$ corresponds to $y = 1$ and $y = -1$, it is not a function.

19. $\begin{cases} m_1 = 20 \\ m_n = \text{previous amount} + 10 \text{ or } \boxed{\text{ANS}} + 10, \text{ for integers } n \ge 2 \end{cases}$
or $\begin{cases} m_1 = 20 \\ m_n = m_{n-1} + 10, \text{ for integers } n \ge 2. \end{cases}$ **20. a.** Multiply through by 10; $5z + 2z + 900 = 10z$; $900 = 3z$; $z = 300$ **b.** Sample: Mary had a certain amount of money. She spent half of it on clothes and $\frac{1}{5}$ of it on groceries. She has 90 dollars left. How much did she originally have? **21.** $P(1) = 2\pi \cdot \sqrt{\frac{1}{9.8}} \approx 2$ seconds **22.** $B = 45w$; $250 = 45w$; $w = 5.56$; after about 6 weeks, the class will have earned a pizza party. **23.** $C(1975) \approx 10.5$ million. The number of students enrolled in college in 1975 was about 10.5 million. **24.** $x = 1988$. In 1988, the number of students enrolled in college was equal to the number of students enrolled in high school. **25.** $\{x: 1970 \ge x \le 2000$, where x is an integer$\}$

The chart below keys the **Progress Self-Test** questions to the objectives in the **Chapter Review** on pages 66–69 or to the **Vocabulary** (Voc.) on page 63. This will enable you to locate those **Chapter Review** questions that correspond to questions students missed on the **Progress Self-Test**. The lesson where the material is covered is also indicated on the chart.

Question	1	2	3	4	5	6	7	8	9	10
Objective	E	F	E	E	B	B	D	I	C	C
Lesson	1-7	1-8, 1-9	1-7	1-8, 1-9	1-3	1-3	1-6	1-1	1-5	1-5

Question	11	12	13	14	15	16	17	18	19	20
Objective	C	A	H	D	H	M	G	G	J	C, K
Lesson	1-5	1-1	1-2	1-6	1-2	1-4	1-2	1-2	1-8, 1-9	1-5

Question	21	22	23	24	25
Objective	J	K	L	L	L
Lesson	1-2, 1-3	1-3	1-4	1-4	1-4

CHAPTER 1 REVIEW (pp. 66–69)

1. 119 **3.** 6973.57 **5.** 5 **7.** −243 **9.** $g(5) = 11$; $g(6) = 13$ **11.** 6; $\frac{3}{2}(6) = 9$? Yes, it checks. **13.** $\frac{3}{4}$; $\frac{6}{\frac{3}{4}} = 8$? $6 \cdot \frac{4}{3} = 8$? Yes, it checks.

15. $\frac{1}{5}$; $3 - \left(\frac{1}{5} + 2\right) = 4\left(\frac{1}{5}\right)$? $3 - \frac{11}{5} = \frac{4}{5}$? Yes, it checks. **17.** 60; $\frac{60}{2} + \frac{60}{2} + 10 = 60$? $30 + 20 + 10 = 60$? Yes, it checks.
19. $n = \frac{t - 4}{-5}$ **21.** $\frac{g}{2}$ **23.** (a), (d) **25.** 23, 26, 29, 32, 35 **27.** 10, 3, −4, −11, −18 **29. a.** 16, 11, 6, 1, −4
b. $\begin{cases} t_1 = 16 \\ t_n = t_{n-1} - 5, \text{ for integers } n \ge 2 \end{cases}$
31. a. The first term is 6. All other terms are obtained by adding 6 to the previous term.
b. $\begin{cases} t_1 = 6 \\ t_n = t_{n-1} + 6, \text{ for integers } n \ge 2 \end{cases}$
33. No; $x = -1$ corresponds to $y = 1$ and $y = -1$.

35. a. Sample:

x	0	1	1	4
y	0	1	−1	2

b. No

37. a. Sample:

x	−5	−5	−5	−5
y	0	1	3	3

b. No

39. a. $\{-9, -\frac{1}{2}, 2, 3\}$ **b.** $\{-3, -2, \frac{1}{2}, 9\}$ **41. a.** the set of real numbers **b.** No **c.** the set of nonnegative real numbers **43.** $100x$ cm **45.** $\frac{B}{M}$ blocks per minute **47.** $20 - c$ sticks **49. a.** $26,000, $27,560, $29,213.60, $30,966.42, $32,824.40 **b.** $78,665.59 **51.** 315 feet **53.** the population of Baltimore in 1950 **55. a.** −51,000 **b.** Sample: In Baltimore, the population dropped by 51,000 people from 1980 to 1990. **57. a.** $14,000 = 4000 + 200d$ **b.** $d = 50$ days **59.** 170 minutes or about 3 hours **61.** domain: $\{x: -6 \le x \le 6\}$; range: $\{y: -1 \le y \le 1\}$ **63.** 0 **65.** No; a vertical line intersects the graph twice. **67.** Yes; no vertical line intersects the graph in more than one point.

LESSON 2-1 (pp. 72–77)
13. a. $P = kw^3$; P, dependent; w, independent **b.** 32.4 watts
15. a.

r	1	2	3	4	5	6	7	8	9	10
A	π	4π	9π	16π	25π	36π	49π	64π	81π	100π

b. 4 times as large **c.** 4 times as large **d.** 4 times as large
e. quadruples **f.** is multiplied by 9 **17.** 3.9 **19.** 3^6 **21.** 3^{15}
23. $150,000 **25.** 1988-1989; 1990-1991; 1991-1992 **27. See right.**

27.

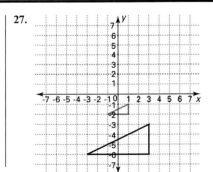

LESSON 2-2 (pp. 78–82)

9. $t = \frac{k}{w}$ **11. a.** $I = \frac{k}{D^2}$ **b.** $k = 1346.7$ lumens · m²
c. ≈ 3.37 lumens **13.** directly

15. a.

s	1	2	3	4	5	6	7	8	9	10	11	12
t	36	18	12	9	$7\frac{1}{5}$	6	$5\frac{1}{7}$	$4\frac{1}{2}$	4	$3\frac{3}{5}$	$3\frac{3}{11}$	3

b. is halved **c.** is multiplied by $\frac{1}{3}$ **17.** ≈ 117.63 pounds
19. $y = 80$ **21.** x^8 **23. a. See below. b.** $y = -5$ **c.** $x = 2$

23. a.

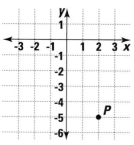

LESSON 2-3 (pp. 84–88)

7. y is multiplied by 81. By the Fundamental Theorem of
Variation, if x is multiplied by 3, then y is multiplied by 3^4 or 81.
9. y is multiplied by $\frac{1}{2}$. **11.** y is divided by $\frac{1}{2}$ or y is multiplied by 2.
13. 2 : 1 **15.** multiplied by 8; $V = \frac{4}{3}\pi r^3$ for a sphere, so if the
radius is doubled, the volume is multiplied by 2^3 or 8.
17. ≈ 45.4 lb **19.** (c) **21. a.** cp cents **b.** $\frac{rd}{2}$ cents

23. See right.

23.

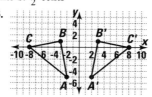

LESSON 2-4 (pp. 89–93)

9. $\frac{3}{50}$ **11.** 7 **13. a.** $c = 1.25\,g$ **b.** domain: nonnegative real
numbers; range: nonnegative real numbers **c.** Sample: (4, 5),
(7, 8.75), (14, 17.5) **d.** Sample: **See below. e.** 1.25 dollars/gal
f. For every gallon increase, the cost increases by $1.25.
15. $\triangle ABC \sim \triangle DEF$ by Angle Angle Similarity. Because they are
similar, their corresponding sides are proportional. So, the ratios
between the vertical and horizontal legs, or slopes, are equal.
17. 8 : 1 **19.** direct variation **21.** inverse variation **23. a.** $Z = \frac{V}{I}$
b. $V = ZI$

13. d.

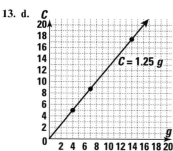

LESSON 2-5 (pp. 96–102)

9. When $x = 0$, $y^2 = k(0)^2 = 0$. Therefore, when $x = 0$, $y = 0$.
11. a.

d	0	10	20	30	40
N	0	50	200	450	800

b. Sample: 610 houses **c. See below. d.** ≈ 625 houses **e.** They are
close. **f.** 612 homes **13. a. See below. b.** 4; $\frac{1}{4}$; $-\frac{1}{4}$; -4 **c.** $y = 4x$
and $y = -\frac{1}{4}x$; or $y = -4x$ and $y = \frac{1}{4}x$ **15. a.** $I = \frac{k}{s^2}$ **b.** The intensity
of sound will be divided by 16. **17. a.** The set of natural numbers.
b. 5, 20, 43, 74, 113 **19. a.** $\triangle DEF$, $\triangle KLM$ **b.** $\triangle DEF \cong \triangle ABC$
by ASA Congruence Theorem; $\triangle KLM \cong \triangle ABC$ by SSS
Congruence Theorem

11. c.

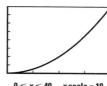

0 ≤ x ≤ 40,   x scale = 10
0 ≤ y ≤ 800,   y scale = 100

13. a.

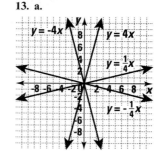

LESSON 2-6 (pp. 104–109)

11. a. $k = 200$ ft-lb; $d = \frac{200}{w}$

b.

w	10	20	30	40	50	60	70	80	90	100
d	20	10	$6\frac{2}{3}$	5	4	$3\frac{1}{3}$	$2\frac{6}{7}$	$2\frac{1}{2}$	$2\frac{2}{9}$	2

c. Sample: **See below. d.** Yes; w can be any positive real number.
13. No. If $f(x) = 0$, then $\frac{1}{x^2} = 0$ or $x^2 \cdot 0 = 1$ which is impossible.
Therefore, $f(x) \neq 0$ for all values of x. **15.** $P_2 = -6x^2$ **17.** No;
a direct variation graph must go through the origin. **19. a.** Mikki
cleared the fractions by multiplying both sides of the equation by 6,
the least common denominator. **b.** $x = 6$

11. c.

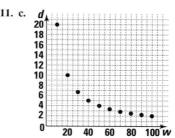

LESSON 2-7 (pp. 110–115)

9. a. (II) **b.** $k = \frac{1}{2}$ **c.** When $x = 4$, $y = \frac{1}{2}(4)^2 = \frac{1}{2}(16) = 8$; Yes, it
checks. **d.** 18 **11. a. See below. b.** $d = kt^2$; using the point (2, 19.6),
we find that $k = 4.9$. Check: for $t = 5$, $d = (4.9) \cdot 5^2 = 122.5$; it
checks. **c.** 99.225 meters **13.** (e) **15.** (d) **17.** y is multiplied by $\frac{1}{16}$.
19. about 1¢

11. a.

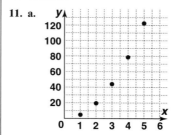

9. (c) 11. $P = \frac{kw}{h^2}$ 13. none 15. $x = 0$; $y = 0$ 17. **a.** the set of all real numbers **b.** $\{y: y \le 0\}$ 19. line; $\frac{3}{4}$ 21. **a.** The first term is $^-3$. Each term after the first is equal to the square of the previous term plus two. **b.** $^-3$; 11; 123; 15,131; 228,947,163

11. **a.** The volume of a rectangular solid varies jointly as its length, width, and height. **b.** 1 13. **a.** $H = kA(T_I - T_O)$
b. $k \approx 1.13 \frac{\text{Btu}}{(\text{ft}^2)(°F)}$ **c.** $H \approx 1.13\,A(T_I - T_O)$ **d.** ≈ 1446.4 Btu
15. $f(3)$ 17. False
19. **a.** Sample:

x	y
-3	90
-2	40
-1	10
0	0
1	10
2	40
3	90

b. See below. c. parabola **d.** 30 **e.** No; a parabola does not have a constant rate of change. 21. $f(\pi) = 4\pi^2 + 2 \approx 41.48$ 23. Adding Fractions Property

19. **b.**

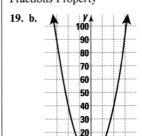

CHAPTER 2 PROGRESS SELF-TEST (pp. 132–133)

1. $n = \frac{k}{d^2}$ 2. $w = \frac{kd^4}{L^2}$ 3. y varies directly as the fifth power of x.
4. $S = kp^2$ is the variation equation. Find k. $10 = k(3)^2$; $k = \frac{10}{9}$.
Rewrite the variation equation using the constant. $S = \frac{10}{9}p^2$;
$S = \frac{10}{9}(8)^2$; $S = \frac{640}{9} \approx 71.1$ 5. The Fundamental Theorem of Variation says that if $y = kx^2$, and x is multiplied by 2, y is multiplied by $2^2 = 4$. So, the y-value is quadrupled. Sample: $(1, 3)$ and $(2, 12)$. 6. The Fundamental Theorem of Variation says that if $y = \frac{6}{x}$ and x is multiplied by c, then y is divided by $c^1 = c$.
7. At $x = 3$, $y = 9$, and at $x = 4$, $y = 16$. The rate of change is $\frac{16 - 9}{4 - 3} = \frac{7}{1} = 7$. 8. False 9. parabola, $k > 0$ 10. x can be any real number except zero, so the domain $= \{x: x \ne 0\}$. 11. **a.** neither inversely nor directly **b.** inversely **c.** S.A. $= 4\pi r^2$ which is the form S.A. $= kr^2$, with $k = 4\pi$. The surface area of a sphere varies directly with the square of its radius.
12. **a.** Sample:

x	y
-2	10
-1	5
0	0
1	-5
2	-10

b. See right. c. -5; slope is determined from the slope-intercept form or by finding the rate of change from two pairs in the table.
13. **a. See right. b.** the x-axis and y-axis 14. (c) 15. **a.** See right. **b.** If $F = \frac{k}{L}$, when $L = 3$ and $F = 120$, $k = 360$ in.-lb and $F = \frac{360}{L}$. This formula is valid for the rest of the data. So $F = (k, L)$ is a good model. **c.** Since $F = \frac{360}{L}$, when $L = 12$ in., $F = (360, 12) = 30$ lb of force to turn the bolt. 16. Sample: The number of CD's a student could buy with a week's paycheck varies directly as the number of hours worked. 17. The variation equation is $C = kd^3$. First, find k. $.79 = k(2)^3$; $k = .09875 \frac{\text{cents}}{\text{inches}^3}$

Now, rewrite the variation equation using k. $C = .09875(d)^3$; $C = .09875(3)^3$; $C = \$2.67$. 18. (d) 19. $V = khg^2$ 20. The variation equation is $S = kPr^4$. First, find k. $.09604 = k(100)(.065)^4$; $k = 53.8$. The unit of k is $\frac{1}{\text{cm-sec-mmHg}}$. Now, rewrite the variation equation using k. $.09604 = 53.8(P)(.05)^4$; $P = 285.6$ mmHg (millimeters of mercury).

12. **b.**

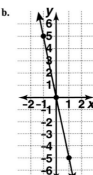

13. **a.**

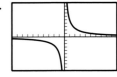

$-10 \le x \le 10$, **x-scale** $= 1$
$-10 \le y \le 10$, **y-scale** $= 1$

15. **a.**

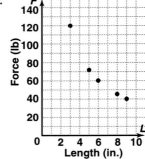

The chart below keys the **Progress Self-Test** questions to the objectives in the **Chapter Review** on pages 132–133 or to the **Vocabulary** (Voc.) on page 131. This will enable you to locate those **Chapter Review** questions that correspond to questions you missed on the **Progress Self-Test**. The lesson where the material is covered is also indicated on the chart.

Question	1	2	3	4	5	6	7	8	9	10
Objective	A	A	A	B	D	D	C	E	E	E
Lesson	2-2	2-9	2-1	2-1	2-3	2-3	2-5	2-6	2-5	2-6
Question	11	12	13	14	15	16	17	18	19	20
Objective	F	C, I	E, I	J	H	F	G	K	H	G
Lesson	2-1, 2-2	2-4	2-6	2-4, 2-6	2-7	2-1	2-1	2-5	2-8	2-9

CHAPTER 2 REVIEW (pp. 134–137)

1. $y = kx^2$ **3.** $z = kxt$ **5.** directly; the square of r **7.** y varies inversely as the square of x. **9.** 21 **11.** −32 **13.** $\frac{9}{5} = 1.8$ **15.** −15
17. $-\frac{3}{4} = -.75$ **19.** y is tripled. **21.** p is divided by $2^2 = 4$.
23. divided by c^n **25.** not affected **27.** (0, 0) **29.** (b) **31.** domain: the set of real numbers; range: the set of nonnegative real numbers
33. $x = 0$ **35.** $n = \frac{k}{r^3}$ **37.** $p = \frac{km}{d^2}$ **39.** inversely **41.** directly
43. \$13.50 **45.** 3 min **47.** ≈ 1020.2 lb of force **49. a. See below.**
b. $L = kS^2$ **c.** Sample: $k \approx .045 \frac{\text{ft}}{(\text{mph})^2}$; $L = .045S^2$ **d.** Sample: 220.5 ft **51. a. i. See below.** ii. P varies directly as R. Sample: The slope between any two points is constant. **b. i. See right.**
ii. P varies directly as I^2. **c.** $P = kRI^2$ **d.** $k = 1$; $P = RI^2$
e. $P = 1600$ watts
53. a. Sample: **b. See right. 55. a.** Sample: **b. See right.**

x	y
−2	−1
−1	−0.5
0	0
1	0.5
2	1

x	y
−2	−8
−1	−2
0	0
1	−2
2	−8

57. See right. 59. (c) **61.** (b) **63.** positive real **65. See right.**
67. a. Sample: $-10 \le x \le 10$; $-5 \le y \le 10$ **b.** Sample: $-20 \le x \le 0$; $-5 \le y \le 10$

49. a.

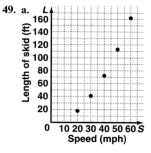

51. ai.

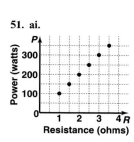

51. bi.

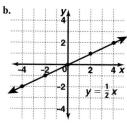

53. b.

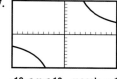

55. b.

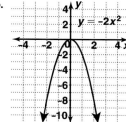

$y = -2x^2$

57.

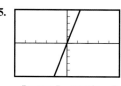

$-10 \le x \le 10$, x-scale = 1
$-10 \le y \le 10$, y-scale = 1

65.

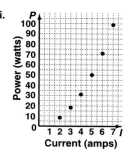

$-5 \le x \le 5$, x-scale = 1
$-5 \le y \le 5$, y-scale = 1

LESSON 3-1 (pp. 140–145)

19. a. Sample: (6, 92), (9, 88), (12, 84) **b.** $C = 100 - \frac{4}{3}h$
c. 30 hours **d.** No, it would take 75 hours to sell all the cars.
21. a. 1.2 miles **b.** 30 min or .5 hr **c.** −0.8 mi/hr **d.** Sample: How long does Carmen work after school? Answer: $1\frac{3}{4}$ hrs.
23. a. See right. b. $y = \frac{1}{4}x$ **25.** $x = 15$

23. a.

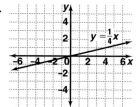

$y = \frac{1}{4}x$

901

LESSON 3-2 (pp. 146–151)

13. a. See below. **b.** $y = \frac{2}{5}x - 6$ **c.** $x = 22\frac{1}{2}$; Does $3 = \frac{2}{5}\left(22\frac{1}{2}\right) - 6$? Does $3 = 9 - 6$? Yes, it checks. **15. a.** See below. **b.** The rate of change (slope) for both lines is the constant 2, so the lines are parallel. **17. a.** See below. **b.** $y = -2.5x + 50$ **19.** negative **21.** zero **23.** $S_4 = 54$

13. a.

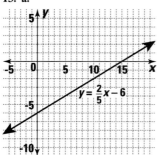

$y = \frac{2}{5}x - 6$

15. a.

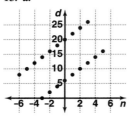

17. a.

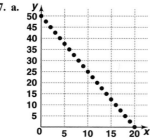

LESSON 3-3 (pp. 152–156)

7. a. $3.23 **b.** $.49Z + .59T$
c. $.49Z + .59T = 5$
9. $2.4S + 112B + 26.2R$ minutes
11. See right. **13.** $\frac{2}{3}$
15. a. $R = 100 - \frac{3}{4}d$ **b.** after
120 days **17.** False; you can't tell whether Terry went uphill or not.
19. $\sqrt{(a - c)^2 + (b - d)^2}$

11.

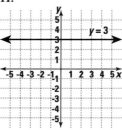

$y = 3$

LESSON 3-4 (pp. 157–161)

15. a. oblique; neither A nor B is 0. **b.** x-intercept = 9; y-intercept = -6 **c.** See below. **17.** $10x - 5y = 1$
19. a. $1.2 = 0.1N + 0.2Y$ **b.** See below. **c.** 2 oz **21. a.** domain: $\{2\}$
b. range: the set of real numbers **23.** $10.20x + 12.35y$
25. a. $2500P + 3000S = 310,000$ **b.** 112

15. c.

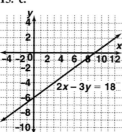

$2x - 3y = 18$

19. b

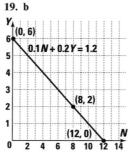

$(0, 6)$
$0.1N + 0.2Y = 1.2$
$(8, 2)$
$(12, 0)$

LESSON 3-5 (pp. 162–167)

13. a. Sample: $c - 1290 = 3(b - 30)$ **b.** $1200 **c.** $1500
15. a. $13.15; $13.15; $13.85 **b.** See below.
c. $\begin{cases} C = 13.15, & n \le 80 \\ C = 13.15 + 0.035(n - 80), & n > 80 \end{cases}$ **17. a.** See below.
b. $\overline{PQ}$: $x = 3$; $\overline{QR}$: $y = -5$; $\overline{RS}$: $x = -2$; $\overline{SP}$: $y = 4$ **c.** 45 units^2
19. ≈ 87 lb **21.** 80

15. b.

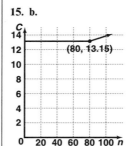

$(80, 13.15)$

17. a.

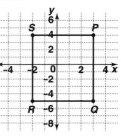

LESSON 3-6 (pp. 169–174)

15. a. ≈ 92 **b.** ≈ 86.7 **17.** (d)
19. (b) **21.** Sample:
$S - 180 = 180(n - 3)$
23. See right.
25. a. $.4x + .2y = 10$
b. 22.45 ounces **27.** $6.50

23.

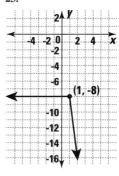

$(1, -8)$

LESSON 3-7 (pp. 175–179)

9. $\begin{cases} a_1 = 13 \\ a_n = a_{n-1} + 6, \text{ for integers } n \ge 2 \end{cases}$ **11.** 85 in.
13. Sample:
```
10 LET A = 1
20 FOR N = 1 TO 1000
30 PRINT A
40 A = A + 2
50 NEXT N
60 END
```
15. a., c. See right. **b.** about
$y = .14x - 10.25$ **d.** ≈ 2.35 million
e. ≈ 4.03 million **f.** Sample: better reporting of child-abuse cases; increased awareness of the problem of child abuse
17. They are identical; both lines have slope $-\frac{3}{4}$ and y-intercept 3. **19.** The number of tiles needed is divided by 4.
21. a. (iv) **b.** (ii) **c.** (iii) **d.** (i)

15. a, c.

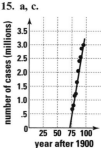

number of cases (millions)

year after 1900

LESSON 3-8 (pp. 180–185)

9. a. explicit; you can find any specific term without relying on previous terms. **b.** 626 **11. a.** 8.1, 9.8, 11.5 **b.** $a_n = 8.1 + (n - 1)1.7$ **13.** 2.5 mi/week **15.** 49 **17. a.** $7x - 5y = 4$
b. x-intercept = $\frac{4}{7}$; y-intercept = $-\frac{4}{5}$ **19.** $H = \frac{kz}{w}$ **21.** (c)
23. a. $-8, -7, -6$ **b.** See below.

23. b.

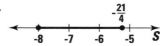

$-\frac{21}{4}$
$-8 \quad -7 \quad -6 \quad -5 \quad S$

902

T80

LESSON 3-9 (pp. 186–191)

13. (b) **15. a.** $500 **b.** $w = 275 + 75 \cdot \left\lfloor \dfrac{d}{300} \right\rfloor$ **17. a.** $2.79;
$9.27; $11.43 **b. See right.**

19. a. $\begin{cases} a_1 = 46 \\ a_n = a_{n-1} - 3.5 \text{ for integers } n \geq 2 \end{cases}$
b. $a_n = 46 - (n - 1) \cdot 3.5$ **21.** Sample: $y + 1 = 2(x - 3)$
23. See right.

17. b.

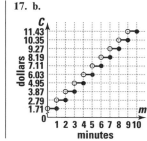

23.

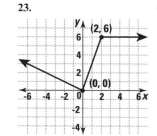

CHAPTER 3 PROGRESS SELF-TEST (pp. 195–196)

1. y-intercept $= -5$; $m = 3$ **See right. 2.** vertical
3. a. $4x - 5y = 12$; $-5y = -4x + 12$; $y = \frac{4}{5}x - \frac{12}{5}$; slope is $\frac{4}{5}$.
b. Let $y = 0$, then $4x = 12$; $x = 3$; 3 is the x-intercept.
Let $x = 0$, then $-5y = 12$; $y = -\frac{12}{5}$; $-\frac{12}{5}$ is the y-intercept.
4. $\{m: m < 0\}$ **5.** $m = \frac{3 - 2}{-5 - 4} = -\frac{1}{9}$; Sample: $y - 2 = -\frac{1}{9}(x - 4)$
6. Since the line is parallel to line $y = \frac{5}{3}x + 4$, $m = \frac{5}{3}$; $y + 1 = \frac{5}{3}(x - 5)$. **7. a.** vertical **b.** horizontal **8.** $36S + 48L$ in.
9. $d = -40 + .8t$; $-10 = -40 + .8t$; $30 = .8t$; $t = 37.5$ seconds
10. a. 1, 6, 11, 16, 21, 26, 31, 36, 41, 46, 51, 56 **b.** Yes. There is a constant difference of 5 between successive terms. **11. a. See right. b.** By reading the graph in part **a**, the cost for a call of more than 6 minutes but less than or equal to 7 minutes is $14.50.
12. No. An arithmetic sequence must have a constant difference between successive terms, but $8 - 5 \neq 2 - (-3)$.
13. $10 \cdot \left\lfloor \dfrac{(365 + 5)}{10} \right\rfloor = 10 \cdot \left\lfloor \dfrac{370}{10} \right\rfloor = 10 \cdot \lfloor 37 \rfloor = 10 \cdot 37 = 370$

14. $m = \dfrac{80 - 0}{100 - 0} = .8$; $R - 0 = .8(C - 0)$; $R = .8C$ **15.** $a_1 = -7$;
$d = -10 - (-7) = -3$; $a_n = -7 - 3(n - 1)$
16. $\begin{cases} a_1 = -7; \\ a_n = a_{n-1} - 3, \text{ for integers } n \geq 2 \end{cases}$ **17.** (a) **18. a.** Yes; the points all lie relatively close to a line. **b.** Sample: about
$y = -.83x + 73.07$ **c.** $y = -.83(42) + 73.07$; $y = -34.86 + 73.07$;
$y = 38.21$; a 42-year old has about 38 expected years of life left.
19. a. $m = \dfrac{800 - 400}{900 - 600} = \dfrac{400}{300} = \dfrac{4}{3}$ **b.** The left has the steepest slope for the first 200 feet of horizontal distance.

1.

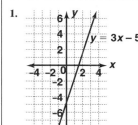

11. a.

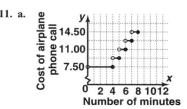

The chart below keys the **Progress Self-Test** questions to the objectives in the **Chapter Review** on pages 197–201 or to the **Vocabulary** (Voc.) on page 194. This will enable you to locate those **Chapter Review** questions that correspond to questions missed on the **Progress Self-Test.** The lesson where the material is covered is also indicated on the chart.

Question	1	2	3	4	5	6	7	8	9	10
Objective	L	E	A	E	B	B	E	H	G	D, F
Lesson	3-2	3-4	3-2, 3-4	3-1	3-5	3-5	3-4	3-3	3-1	3-7

Question	11	12	13	14	15	16	17	18	19
Objective	M	F	C	I	D	D	M	J	K
Lesson	3-9	3-7	3-9	3-5	3-8	3-7	3-1, 3-9	3-6	3-1

CHAPTER 3 REVIEW (pp. 197–201)

1. a. 7 **b.** -2 **3. a.** 0 **b.** 4 **5. a.** -4.7 **b.** none **7.** $y - 75 = 8(x - 40)$ **9.** Sample: $y - 4 = -\frac{2}{3}(x - 2)$ **11.** Sample: $y - 2 = -\frac{3}{2}(x + 1)$ **13. a.** 16 **b.** -17 **15.** -17 **17. a.** $a_n = 7 + 5(n - 1)$
b. $\begin{cases} a_1 = 7 \\ a_n = a_{n-1} + 5, \text{ for integers } n \geq 2 \end{cases}$ **c.** 377
19. $\begin{cases} a_1 = -9 \\ a_n = a_{n-1} + 2, \text{ for integers } n \geq 2 \end{cases}$ **21.** Sample: **a.** 1, 3, 5, 7, 9
b. $\begin{cases} a_1 = 1 \\ a_n = a_{n-1} + 2, \text{ for integers } n \geq 2 \end{cases}$ **c.** $a_n = 1 + 2(n - 1)$
23. a. 10 **b.** 5; 7; 9; 11; 13 **25.** (b) **27.** domain: the set of all real numbers; range: the set of all real numbers **29.** slopes are equal **31.** horizontal **33. a.** horizontal **b.** oblique **c.** vertical **35.** False **37.** The graph is a set of collinear points. **39.** Yes **41.** No **43.** No

45. a. $w = 3 + .2n$ **b.** 7.4 kg **47.** 240 ft **49. a.** $1.7F + 2.5S = 250$ **b.** 32 **51.** $124,000 **53. a. See page 904. b.** Sample: No; the data do not seem to lie on a line. **c.** about $y = .74x - 9.39$ **d.** The correlation coefficient is .203. This indicates a weak fit of the data to this line. **55. a. See page 904. b.** Sample: $y - 334 = 14.07(x - 1970)$ **c.** Sample: 530,980 physicians **d.** about $y = 14.45x - 28144.96$ **e.** Sample: Increase in number of physicians per year. **f.** about 523.84 thousands or 523,840 physicians **g.** Sample: The correlation coefficient is .998, which indicates a very strong linear relationship between the regression equation and the data. **57. a.** $19.62 **b.** $84.24 **59. a.** 30 mi **b.** 35 mph **c.** 210 mi **61.** (c) **63. See page 904. 65. See page 904. 67.** positive **69.** negative **71. a. See page 904. b.** domain: the set of all real numbers; range: $\{y: y \leq 3\}$ **73. See page 904. 75. a. See page 904. b.** False

53. a.

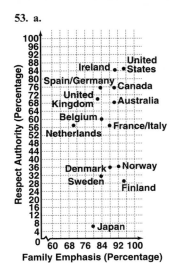

55. a.

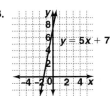

65.

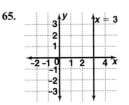

71. a.

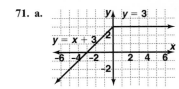

63.

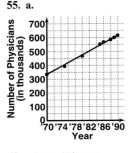

73.

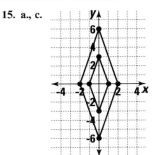

75. a.

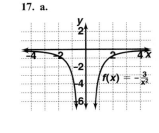

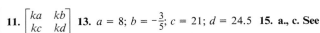

LESSON 4-1 (pp. 204–208)

15. 7; 8 **17. a.** Sample:

	from A	from B	from C
to A	0	2	5
to B	3	0	3
to C	1	4	0

b. Adam, 4; Barbara, 6; Clem, 8 **19.** Sample: When $k = -100$, the graph is a line slanting downward from left to right with a very steep slope. As k increases, but remains less than 0, the slant is still downward from left to right, but the slope is less steep. When $k = 0$, the slope is 0 and the line becomes horizontal. For positive values of k, the slant of the line is upward from left to right. The line gets steeper as the value of k increases. When $k = 100$, the graph is a line slanting upward from left to right with a very steep slope. **See below.** **21.** $(5 + x)(3 + y) = 15 + 3x + 5y + xy$ **23.** For all real numbers a, b, and c, $a + (b + c) = (a + b) + c$.

19.

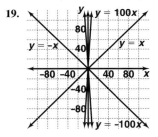

LESSON 4-2 (pp. 209–213)

9. a.
$$M = \begin{bmatrix} -9 & 3 & 6 & -12 \\ -13 & 15 & -2 & -28 \\ -7 & -1 & 8 & -6 \\ 5 & -4 & -1 & 9 \\ 1 & -4 & 3 & 5 \\ 4 & -9 & 5 & 13 \end{bmatrix}$$

b. how many more points each team had in 1993-94 than in 1992-93 **c.** how many more wins, losses, ties, and total points Boston had in 1993-94 than in 1992-93

11. $\begin{bmatrix} ka & kb \\ kc & kd \end{bmatrix}$ **13.** $a = 8$; $b = -\frac{3}{5}$; $c = 21$; $d = 24.5$ **15. a., c. See below. b.** rhombus **17. a. See below. b.** domain: set of all real numbers except 0; range: set of all negative real numbers **19.** reflection **21.** rotation **23.** $PQ = 17$

15. a., c.

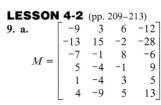

17. a.

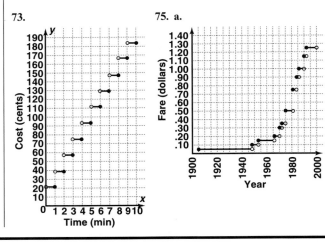

LESSON 4-3 (pp. 214–219)

13. Sample:

	band uniforms	basketball uniforms	track uniforms	swimsuits
a. east	10	20	15	10
central	20	0	10	0
west	15	20	0	10

b. $\begin{bmatrix} 10 & 20 & 15 & 10 \\ 20 & 0 & 10 & 0 \\ 15 & 20 & 0 & 10 \end{bmatrix} \begin{bmatrix} 90 \\ 40 \\ 50 \\ 25 \end{bmatrix} = \begin{bmatrix} 2700 \\ 2300 \\ 2400 \end{bmatrix}$; East $2700, Central $2300, West $2400 **15.** $x = \frac{1}{3}$ **17.** $2 \times n$ **19.** The distance between $(2, -1)$ and $(7, 6)$ is $\sqrt{74}$; the distance between $(2, -1)$ and $(-5, 4)$ is $\sqrt{74}$; the distance between $(7, 6)$ and $(-5, 4)$ is $\sqrt{148}$. The triangle is isosceles. **21.** $f(20) = \frac{1}{2}$ **23.** 3

904

LESSON 4-4 (pp. 221–226)

15. a. $P' = (7.5, 10)$; $OP' = \sqrt{(7.5 - 0)^2 + (10 - 0)^2} = \sqrt{156.25} = 12.5$, and $OP = \sqrt{3^2 + 4^2} = \sqrt{25} = 5$; $\frac{OP'}{OP} = \frac{12.5}{5} = 2.5$ **b.** $y = \frac{4}{3}x$ **17. a.** $\frac{7}{2}$ **b.** $\frac{7}{2}$ **c.** Yes, because the slopes are equal.
19. $a = -\frac{1}{2}$; $b = -\frac{7}{6}$ **21.** from the 35th to the 50th second
23. 56.25 cm^2

LESSON 4-5 (pp. 227–231)

9. The slope of $\overline{AB}$ is $\frac{7}{2}$ and the slope of $\overline{A'B'}$ is $\frac{35}{4}$. Since the slopes are different, the lines cannot be parallel. **11. a.** rectangle
b. $\begin{bmatrix} 0 & 12 & 12 & 0 \\ 0 & 0 & 12 & 12 \end{bmatrix}$ **c.** square

d. See right. 13. a. $S_3 = \begin{bmatrix} 3 & 0 \\ 0 & 3 \end{bmatrix}$

b. $\begin{bmatrix} 3 & 0 \\ 0 & 3 \end{bmatrix}\begin{bmatrix} 5 & 4 \\ 1 & 2 \end{bmatrix} = \begin{bmatrix} 15 & 12 \\ 3 & 6 \end{bmatrix}$

15. a. 5,263,904 **b.** Sample: Texas has the biggest problem because it has the greatest number of uninsured residents.
17. a. $x = 225$ **b.** $y = 25$

11. d.
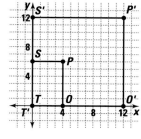

LESSON 4-6 (pp. 232–238)

13. $\begin{bmatrix} 0 & 1 \\ 1 & 0 \end{bmatrix}\begin{bmatrix} x \\ y \end{bmatrix} = \begin{bmatrix} 0 \cdot x & + & 1 \cdot y \\ 1 \cdot x & + & 0 \cdot y \end{bmatrix} = \begin{bmatrix} y \\ x \end{bmatrix}$ **15.** The area is multiplied by 9.
17. Factory X: $72 for a trick ski, $48 for a slalom ski, $55 for a cross-country ski; Factory Y: $64.50 for a trick ski, $43 for a slalom ski, $49.25 for a cross-country ski **19. See right.**

19.
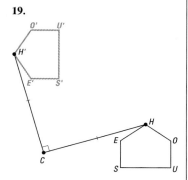

LESSON 4-7 (pp. 240–245)

13. a. $\begin{bmatrix} 0 & 1 \\ -1 & 0 \end{bmatrix}$ **b.** R_{270} **c.** not the same; $r_{y=x} \circ r_x = R_{90}$
15. a. (i) identity transformation (ii) identity transformation (iii) identity transformation **b.** If a point is reflected over a line and then its image is reflected over the same line, the final image is the original point. **17.** $M_k \cdot C = \begin{bmatrix} k & 0 \\ 0 & k \end{bmatrix}\begin{bmatrix} m & n \\ p & q \end{bmatrix} = \begin{bmatrix} km & kn \\ kp & kq \end{bmatrix}$

$C \cdot M_k = \begin{bmatrix} m & n \\ p & q \end{bmatrix}\begin{bmatrix} k & 0 \\ 0 & k \end{bmatrix} = \begin{bmatrix} km & kn \\ kp & kq \end{bmatrix}$

19. a., d. See right.
b. isosceles triangle
c. $\begin{bmatrix} -28 & 28 & 0 \\ 0 & 0 & 7 \end{bmatrix}$
e. isosceles **f.** No. Sample: the angles at the corresponding vertices do not have the same measure.
21. a. 1994. **b.** about 10,450,000 **23.** (a)

19. a., d.
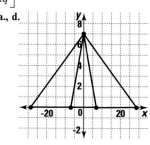

LESSON 4-8 (pp. 246–250)

11. $\begin{bmatrix} -1 & 0 \\ 0 & -1 \end{bmatrix}\begin{bmatrix} -1 & 0 \\ 0 & -1 \end{bmatrix} = \begin{bmatrix} 1 & 0 \\ 0 & 1 \end{bmatrix}$ $R_{180} \circ R_{180} = R_{360}$, which shows that the matrix for R_{360} is the identity matrix. **13. See below.**
15. a., b. See below. 17. $\begin{bmatrix} 1 & 0 \\ 0 & 1 \end{bmatrix}$ **19.** $\begin{bmatrix} 1 & 0 \\ 0 & 3 \end{bmatrix}$ **21. a., b. See below.**
c. reflection about x-axis and size change of magnitude 2
23. $a^2 + b^2 = c^2$ **25. a.** similar and congruent **b.** rotation **27.** $-\frac{1}{2}$

13.
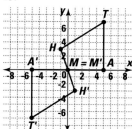

15. a., b.
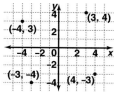

21. a., b.
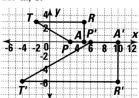

LESSON 4-9 (pp. 251–255)

7. a. 3 **b.** $y + 2 = 3(x - 7)$ **9.** The reciprocal of 0 is undefined.
11. $x = 6$ **13. a.** $A' = (3, -7)$; $B' = (1, 4)$ **b. See below. c.** $\overleftrightarrow{AB}$: $\frac{2}{11}$; $\overleftrightarrow{A'B'}$: $-\frac{11}{2}$ **d.** Their product is -1; the lines are perpendicular. **e.** 90°

15. a. $\perp$ **b. See below. 17. a.** $//$ **b. See below. 19.** $M = \begin{bmatrix} \frac{4}{3} & 0 \\ 0 & \frac{3}{4} \end{bmatrix}$

21. a. $\begin{bmatrix} 89.82 \\ 99.43 \end{bmatrix}$ **b.** $99.43 **23. a.** $x = \frac{w - u}{v - y}$ **b.** when $v = y$

13. b.
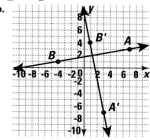

15. b.
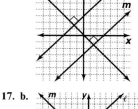

17. b.

LESSON 4-10 (pp. 256–260)

9. No. The contrapositive of the theorem must hold true; that is, if a line is not parallel to its image, then they are not translation images of each other. **11.** $T_{10, 14}$ **13.** $y = -2x + 12$ **15.** $-\frac{3}{2}$
17. a. $H' = (-5, 1)$; $I' = (3, -1)$ **b.** Both equal $\sqrt{68}$. **c.** No; the product of their slopes is not -1. **19. a.** $\begin{bmatrix} 1 & 0 \\ 0 & -1 \end{bmatrix}$ **b.** $(a, -b)$
21. a. $\begin{bmatrix} 1 & 0 \\ 0 & 6 \end{bmatrix}$ **b.** $(a, 6b)$ **23. a.** $\begin{bmatrix} 0 & 1 \\ 1 & 0 \end{bmatrix}$ **b.** (b, a) **25.** $\begin{bmatrix} 0 & -1 \\ -5 & 2 \end{bmatrix}$

1. See right. 2. 1st
$$\begin{matrix} & P & B & G \\ \text{1st} & \begin{bmatrix} 14 & 3 & 8 \\ 120 & 190 & 250 \end{bmatrix} \\ \text{Econ} & \end{matrix}$$
3. Two matrices with dimensions $m \times n$ and $n \times p$ can be multiplied—the number of columns in the left matrix matches the number of rows in the right matrix. AB would be a 3×2 times a 2×2 matrix; the product does exist. BA would be a 2×2 times a 3×2 matrix; the product does not exist. **4.** $BC = \begin{bmatrix} 2 & 0 \\ 1 & 5 \end{bmatrix}\begin{bmatrix} 8 & 6 \\ -2 & 2 \end{bmatrix} = \begin{bmatrix} 16 + 0 & 12 + 0 \\ 8 - 10 & 6 + 10 \end{bmatrix} =$

$\begin{bmatrix} 16 & 12 \\ -2 & 16 \end{bmatrix}$ **5.** $B - C = \begin{bmatrix} 2 & 0 \\ 1 & 5 \end{bmatrix} - \begin{bmatrix} 8 & 6 \\ -2 & 2 \end{bmatrix} = \begin{bmatrix} 2 - 8 & 0 - 6 \\ 1 - -2 & 5 - 2 \end{bmatrix} =$

$\begin{bmatrix} -6 & -6 \\ 3 & 3 \end{bmatrix}$ **6.** $7B = 7\begin{bmatrix} 2 & 0 \\ 1 & 5 \end{bmatrix} = \begin{bmatrix} 14 & 0 \\ 7 & 35 \end{bmatrix}$ **7.** $\begin{bmatrix} 1 & 0 \\ 0 & 1 \end{bmatrix}\begin{bmatrix} a & b \\ c & d \end{bmatrix} =$

$\begin{bmatrix} 1a + 0c & 1b + 0d \\ 0a + 1c & 0b + 1d \end{bmatrix} = \begin{bmatrix} a & b \\ c & d \end{bmatrix}$ and $\begin{bmatrix} a & b \\ c & d \end{bmatrix}\begin{bmatrix} 1 & 0 \\ 0 & 1 \end{bmatrix} =$

$\begin{bmatrix} a \cdot 1 + b \cdot 0 & a \cdot 0 + b \cdot 1 \\ c \cdot 1 + d \cdot 0 & c \cdot 0 + d \cdot 1 \end{bmatrix} = \begin{bmatrix} a & b \\ c & d \end{bmatrix}$. The result of multiplying

any 2×2 matrix by $\begin{bmatrix} 1 & 0 \\ 0 & 1 \end{bmatrix}$ is the original matrix. In other words, the image of any point under that transformation is the same as the preimage. **8.** The slope of the line $y = 5x - 3$ is 5, so the slope of the line perpendicular to this line is $-\frac{1}{5}$. Using the point $(3, -2.5)$ and this slope in $y - y_1 = m(x - x_1)$, the desired equation is $y - (-2.5) = -\frac{1}{5}(x - 3)$, or $y + 2.5 = \frac{1}{5}(x - 3)$. **9.** $r_x \circ R_{270} =$

$\begin{bmatrix} 1 & 0 \\ 0 & -1 \end{bmatrix} \cdot \begin{bmatrix} 0 & 1 \\ -1 & 0 \end{bmatrix} = \begin{bmatrix} 0 + 0 & 1 + 0 \\ 0 + 1 & 0 + 0 \end{bmatrix} = \begin{bmatrix} 0 & 1 \\ 1 & 0 \end{bmatrix}$ **10.** Each point is moved 8 units to the right and 8 units down, so the translation is $T_{8,-8}$. **11.** Under a translation, a line is parallel to its image, so $\overleftrightarrow{FI} // \overleftrightarrow{F'I'}$. This can be shown directly. $F = (-6, 6)$ and $I = (-4, 7)$. So the slope of $\overleftrightarrow{FI}$ is $\frac{6 - 7}{-6 - -4} = \frac{1}{2}$. $F' = (2, -2)$ and $I' = (4, -1)$. So the slope of $\overleftrightarrow{F'I'}$ is $\frac{-2 - -1}{2 - 4} = \frac{1}{2}$.

12. $\begin{bmatrix} -1 & 0 \\ 0 & 1 \end{bmatrix}\begin{bmatrix} -6 & -4 & -2 & -4 & -6 & -4 \\ 6 & 7 & 4 & 1 & 2 & 4 \end{bmatrix} = \begin{bmatrix} 6 & 4 & 2 & 4 & 6 & 4 \\ 6 & 7 & 4 & 1 & 2 & 4 \end{bmatrix}$

13. Prices

	Deckshoes	Pumps	Sandals	Boot	
Los Angeles	23	8	10	5	
Tucson	11	5	10	15	
Santa Fe	2	3	15	15	

$\cdot \begin{matrix} \text{Deckshoes} \\ \text{Pumps} \\ \text{Sandals} \\ \text{Boots} \end{matrix} \begin{bmatrix} 18 \\ 58 \\ 12 \\ 76 \end{bmatrix}$

3×4

The product is: $\begin{bmatrix} 23 \cdot 18 + 8 \cdot 58 + 10 \cdot 12 + 5 \cdot 76 \\ 11 \cdot 18 + 5 \cdot 58 + 10 \cdot 12 + 15 \cdot 76 \\ 2 \cdot 18 + 3 \cdot 58 + 15 \cdot 12 + 15 \cdot 76 \end{bmatrix} =$

4×1

$\begin{bmatrix} 1378 \\ 1748 \\ 1530 \end{bmatrix}$. The revenues are: $1,378,000 for Los Angeles; $1,748,000 for Tucson; and $1,530,000 for Santa Fe. **14.** The

sum of the two matrices is $\begin{bmatrix} 8 & 11 \\ 5 & 4 \\ 15 & 16 \\ 2 & 0 \end{bmatrix} + \begin{bmatrix} 10 & 14 \\ 11 & 13 \\ 7 & 9 \\ 0 & 3 \end{bmatrix} =$

$\begin{bmatrix} 8 + 10 & 11 + 14 \\ 5 + 11 & 4 + 13 \\ 15 + 7 & 16 + 9 \\ 2 + 0 & 0 + 3 \end{bmatrix} = \begin{bmatrix} 18 & 25 \\ 16 & 17 \\ 22 & 25 \\ 2 & 3 \end{bmatrix}$ **15.** This is a scale change

represented by $S_{a,b}$ with matrix $\begin{bmatrix} a & 0 \\ 0 & b \end{bmatrix}$. So the matrix for a

horizontal stretch of 2 and vertical shrink of $\frac{1}{4}$ is $\begin{bmatrix} 2 & 0 \\ 0 & \frac{1}{4} \end{bmatrix}$.

16. $(x, y) \to (y, x)$ is a reflection over $y = x$, so the matrix is $\begin{bmatrix} 0 & 1 \\ 1 & 0 \end{bmatrix}$. **17.** $\begin{bmatrix} 1 & 0 \\ 0 & -1 \end{bmatrix}\begin{bmatrix} 7 & -1 & 3 \\ 6 & 2 & -4 \end{bmatrix} = \begin{bmatrix} 7 & -1 & 3 \\ -6 & -2 & 4 \end{bmatrix}$ means that the reflection of $\triangle ABC$ over the x-axis is the image $\triangle A'B'C'$ with vertices $A' = (7, -6)$, $B' = (-1, -2)$, and $C' = (3, 4)$. **18.** $A' = (-6, 7)$, $B' = (-2, -1)$, and $C' = (4, 3)$. **See below. 19.** Sample: Two points on the line $x + 2y = 5$ are $(5, 0)$ and $(1, 2)$. The matrix describes the translation $T_{3,2}$. Apply the translation to the two points to get image points $(8, 2)$ and $(4, 4)$. So an equation of the image is $y - 2 = \frac{4 - 2}{4 - 8}(x - 8)$ or $y = -\frac{1}{2}x + 6$.

20. a. $\begin{bmatrix} 3 & 0 \\ 0 & 3 \end{bmatrix}\begin{bmatrix} 5 & 2 & -3 \\ -3 & 2 & -5 \end{bmatrix} = \begin{bmatrix} 15 & 6 & -9 \\ -9 & 6 & -15 \end{bmatrix}$

b. $\begin{bmatrix} 4 & 0 \\ 0 & 4 \end{bmatrix}\left(\begin{bmatrix} 3 & 0 \\ 0 & 3 \end{bmatrix}\begin{bmatrix} 5 & 2 & -3 \\ -3 & 2 & -5 \end{bmatrix}\right) = \begin{bmatrix} 60 & 24 & -36 \\ -36 & 24 & -60 \end{bmatrix}$

1.

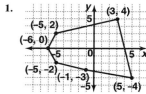

18.

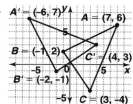

The chart below keys the **Progress Self-Test** questions to the objectives in the **Chapter Review** on pages 266-269 or to the **Vocabulary** (Voc.) on page 264. This will enable you to locate those **Chapter Review** questions that correspond to questions missed on the **Progress Self-Test**. The lesson where the material is covered is also indicated on the chart.

Question	1	2	3	4	5	6	7	8	9	10
Objective	I	G	D	B	A	A	D	C	F	F
Lesson	4-1	4-1	4-3	4-3	4-2	4-2	4-3	4-9	4-7, 4-8	4-10
Question	11	12	13	14	15	16	17	18	19	20
Objective	E	F	H	H	F	F	F	I	F	F
Lesson	4-10	4-6	4-3	4-2	4-5	4-6	4-6	4-8	4-10	4-4,4-7

CHAPTER 4 REVIEW (pp. 266–269)

1. $\begin{bmatrix} 11 & 6 \\ 4 & -8 \\ 8 & 2 \end{bmatrix}$ **3.** $\begin{bmatrix} 5 & 0 & 8 \\ 16 & 13 & -1 \\ 6 & 13 & 2 \end{bmatrix}$ **5.** $a = 1.6$; $b = -10.1$ **7.** [59]

9. $\begin{bmatrix} -18 & -24 & -30 \\ 11 & 13 & 15 \\ 40 & 50 & 60 \end{bmatrix}$ **11.** $a = 5$; $b = -3$ **13.** $y + 1 = 2(x - 3)$

15. $y - 2 = 4(x - 2)$ **17. a.** True **b.** Sample: $\begin{bmatrix} 2 & 3 \\ 1 & -4 \end{bmatrix} + \begin{bmatrix} 1 & 7 \\ 5 & 6 \end{bmatrix} =$

$\begin{bmatrix} 1 & 7 \\ 5 & 6 \end{bmatrix} + \begin{bmatrix} 2 & 3 \\ 1 & -4 \end{bmatrix} = \begin{bmatrix} 3 & 10 \\ 6 & 2 \end{bmatrix}$ **19. a.** No **b.** Yes **21.** $\begin{bmatrix} 1 & 0 \\ 0 & 1 \end{bmatrix}$

23. (a) **25.** (d) **27.** −0.2 **29.** $\begin{bmatrix} 1 & 0 \\ 0 & 1 \end{bmatrix}$; it is the identity

transformation. **31. a.** $\begin{bmatrix} -1 & 0 \\ 0 & 1 \end{bmatrix}$ **b.** r_y **33. a.** $T_{2,-1}$ **b.** Because the

matrix for *PEAR* is $\begin{bmatrix} 0 & 6 & 7 & 2 \\ 6 & 7 & -2 & 2 \end{bmatrix}$, the translation matrix has

four columns represented by $\begin{bmatrix} 2 & 2 & 2 & 2 \\ -1 & -1 & -1 & -1 \end{bmatrix}$. Then

$\begin{bmatrix} 2 & 2 & 2 & 2 \\ -1 & -1 & -1 & -1 \end{bmatrix} + \begin{bmatrix} 0 & 6 & 7 & 2 \\ 6 & 7 & -2 & 2 \end{bmatrix} = \begin{bmatrix} 2 & 8 & 9 & 4 \\ 5 & 6 & -3 & 1 \end{bmatrix}$ which is

the matrix for the vertices of the image $P'E'A'R'$. **35.** $\begin{bmatrix} 4 & 0 \\ 0 & 6 \end{bmatrix}$

37. $\begin{bmatrix} 1 & 0 & -4 & 0 \\ 3 & .5 & -1 & 5 \end{bmatrix}$ **39.** $\begin{bmatrix} 3 & 4 & 1 \\ 0 & 2 & 0 \end{bmatrix}$

41.

	Boys	Girls
freshmen	490	487
sophomores	402	416
juniors	358	344
seniors	293	300

43. the price for a dozen of eggs, a pound each of plums, peaches,

and bananas at Market II **45.** $[270 \quad 320 \quad 210] \begin{bmatrix} 15 & 6 \\ 10 & 8 \\ 2 & 1 \end{bmatrix} =$

$[7670 \quad 4390]$ Factory 1: \$7,670,000; Factory 2: \$4,390,000

47. a. 0.6 **b.** $\begin{bmatrix} 249.00 & 403.20 & 154.80 \\ 118.80 & 236.40 & 65.40 \end{bmatrix}$ **49.** $\begin{bmatrix} 1 & 3 & 9 & 6 \\ 1 & 7 & 1 & -6 \end{bmatrix}$

51. See below.

51.
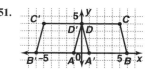

LESSON 5-1 (pp. 272–278)

17. a. See below. **b.** $\{x: 45 \le x \le 55\}$ **19.** He should use "or"
instead of "and," since "$x = 2$ and $x = -2$" has no solutions.
21. no more than 500 miles **23. a.** $y = x + 250$ **b.** $y = -50$
25. a. y is divided by 64. **b.** y is multiplied by 8.

17. a.

LESSON 5-2 (pp. 279–284)

11. a. two solutions **b.** $(2, 1), \left(-\frac{1}{2}, -4\right)$ **c.** Check $(2, 1)$: Is $2 \cdot 1 = 2$?

Yes. Is $2 \cdot 2 - 1 = 3$? Yes. Check $\left(-\frac{1}{2}, -4\right)$: Is $\left(-\frac{1}{2}\right) \cdot (-4) = 2$? Yes.

Is $2 \cdot \left(-\frac{1}{2}\right) - (-4) = 3$? Yes. **13. a.** See below. **b.** 2 solutions

c. $(-4.3, 9.3), (2.3, 2.7)$ **15. a.** $y = 9x$ **b.** father: 9m; daughter:
45 m **c.** 10 seconds after he started **d.** 90 m from the start
17. a. $(-1.28, 4.89)$ **b.** $(2.61, 20.44)$ **19. a.** See below. **b.** See
below. **21. a.** 45

b. $S_n = \frac{n(n + 1)}{2}$ or $\begin{cases} t_1 = 1 \\ t_n = t_{n-1} + n \end{cases}$ for integers $n \ge 2$

23. a. Yes; all squares are similar. Similar figures with equal areas
must be congruent. **b.** No; a counterexample is a right triangle
with length 3 in. and height 4 in. and a right triangle with length
2 in. and height 6 in. Both have area of 6 in.^{2}, but they are not
congruent.

13. a.
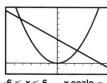

$-6 \le x \le 6$, x-scale = 1
$-2 \le y \le 10$, y-scale = 1

19. a.

19. b.

LESSON 5-3 (pp. 285–291)

11. a. See below. **b.** consistent **c.** $(0, 0), (1, 1)$

13. a. $\begin{cases} y = .3x \\ y = 2 + .25x \end{cases}$ **b.** 40 prints **c.** \$12.00 **15. a.** See

below. **b.** 100 **c.** Under the incentive plan, anyone selling
fewer than 100 gadgets receives a pay cut. **d.** \$500; \$550.
e. Sample: Salespeople have an incentive to sell more gadgets
because they make more money by selling more gadgets.

17. $\begin{bmatrix} 58 & 14 & -4 \\ -10 & 7 & -1 \end{bmatrix}$ **19. a.** $40a + 50p \le 500$ **b.** 0 apples and

10 pears, 5 apples and 6 pears, or 10 apples and 2 pears
21. $\angle ROC = 70°$; $\angle CKR = 60°$; $\angle OCK = 150°$; $\angle KRO = 80°$

11. a.
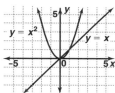

15. a.
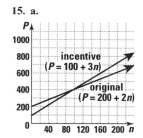

LESSON 5-4 (pp. 292–297)

13. 90¢ **15.** $(u, v) = (-2, -2)$ **17.** design: \$50; editing: \$80;
production: \$60 **19.** (c)

21. a. $\begin{cases} a_1 = 112 \\ a_n = a_{n-1} + 8, \text{ for integers } n \ge 2 \end{cases}$

b. $a_n = 112 + (n - 1) \cdot 8$ or $a_n = 104 + 8n$

23. $\begin{bmatrix} 7 & 8 & 9 \\ \sqrt{5} & \sqrt{6} & \sqrt{7} \\ -1 & 0 & 1 \end{bmatrix}$

LESSON 5-5 (pp. 299–304)

15. Sample: $\begin{bmatrix} 2 & 6 \\ 1 & 3 \end{bmatrix}$ **17. a.** $\begin{bmatrix} 0 & 1 \\ -1 & 0 \end{bmatrix}$ **b.** Sample: The matrix in part **a** represents R_{270} or R_{-90}. Geometrically, R_{-90} and R_{90} are opposite transformations. **19.** $\frac{1}{3}$ kg for bread, $\frac{1}{6}$ kg for pizza crust **21.** (2, 8) **23.** in 20 hours

LESSON 5-6 (pp. 305–311)

13. a. $\begin{cases} u + b + 3t = 561 \\ 7b + t = 906 \\ 5u + 2b + 7t = 1758 \end{cases}$ **b.** unicycle: \$183; bicycle: \$117; tricycle: \$87

15. $n = -3$ **17. a.** Sample: $\begin{bmatrix} 2 & 3 \\ 3 & 5 \end{bmatrix}$ **b.** Sample: $\begin{bmatrix} 5 & -3 \\ -3 & 2 \end{bmatrix}$

19. (17, −7) **21.** 1.6 oz **23.** See below.

23.

LESSON 5-7 (pp. 312–318)

15. $y < -3$ **17. a.** $10x + 15y < 75$ **b.** See below. **c.** 24 solutions
19. $y < -\frac{3}{4}x - 4$
21. a. $\begin{cases} 3x + 4y = 0 \\ x + 2y = -2 \end{cases}$

b. (4, −3) **23.** −100
25. (a) and (c)

17. b.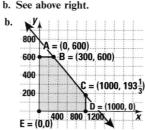

LESSON 5-8 (pp. 319–324)

13. a. $\begin{cases} x \geq 0 \\ y \leq x + 1 \\ y \leq \frac{1}{2}x + 3 \\ x \leq 6 \\ y \geq 0 \end{cases}$ **b.** True **c.** (4, 5)

15. a. $\begin{cases} 0 \leq x \leq 1000 \\ 0 \leq y \leq 600 \\ 20x + 30y \leq 24,000 \end{cases}$

b. See above right.

17. a. $R \leq \dfrac{D - 200}{9}$
b. \$144.44 **19.** (2, 4)
21. $5x + 8y$ dollars
23. a. $8n + 64$ **b.** $n^2 + 8n$
c. $n^2 + 16n + 64$
d. $n^2 + 16n + 64$

15. b.

A = (0, 600)
B = (300, 600)
C = (1000, 193⅓)
D = (1000, 0)
E = (0,0)

LESSON 5-9 (pp. 325–330)

11. *T.* Sample: The following table shows the values of P corresponding to each of the vertices of the feasible region. The profit value is the greatest at vertex T. By the Linear-Programming Theorem, this vertex maximizes profit over the feasible set. **13. a.** (ii) **b.** (iii) **c.** (iv) **d.** (i) **15. a.** (0, 0), (0, 50), (40, 10), (48, 0) **b.** $P = 75C + 85S$ **c.** (0, 50) **17.** (b)

Vertex	P
Q	250
R	460
S	580
T	680
U	660
V	610

19. $S_{-\frac{1}{3}} = \begin{bmatrix} -\frac{1}{3} & 0 \\ 0 & -\frac{1}{3} \end{bmatrix}$ **21.** $y \geq x^2$

LESSON 5-10 (pp. 331–335)

7. a. *h*: oz of hamburger; *p*: number of medium potatoes
b. $\begin{cases} .8h + 1.1p \geq 5 \\ 10h \geq 30 \\ 6.5h + 4p \geq 35 \\ h \geq 0 \\ p \geq 0 \end{cases}$ **c.** See below. **d.** $.15h + 10p$

e. (4.68, 1.14) **f.** 4.68 oz of hamburger and 1.14 oz of potatoes per person gives the proper nutrition for the lowest cost.

9. a. See below. **b.** $\left(-\frac{10}{3}, \frac{23}{3}\right)$ **11.** $x = -1$, $y = 4$ **13.** 32 kg of 25% aluminum; 128 kg of 75% aluminum **15. a.** 10; 9.5; 9

b. $\begin{cases} a_1 = 10 \\ a_n = a_{n-1} - .5, \text{ for integers } n \geq 2 \end{cases}$
c. $-2a_n + 21 = n$ **d.** 99th term

7. c.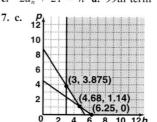

(3, 3.875)
(4.68, 1.14)
(6.25, 0)

9. a.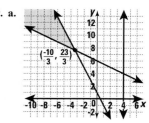

$\left(\frac{-10}{3}, \frac{23}{3}\right)$

CHAPTER 5 PROGRESS SELF-TEST (p. 339)

1. $n > -2$, **See page 909. 2.** See page 909. **3.** (−1.7, −2.8), (1.2, −1.4)
4. a. inconsistent **b.** The graphs of these equations are both vertical lines, but they have different *x*-intercepts. Since the lines do not intersect, the system is inconsistent. **5.** Sample: In the third equation, substitute *r* with *t* + 11 and *s* with 4*t*. This gives $3(t + 11) - 8(4t) = 4$. Solve this equation to get $t = 1$. Substitute $t = 1$ into the original system's first and second equation; $s = 4(1) = 4$, $r = 1 + 11 = 12$; $(r, s, t) = (12, 4, 1)$
6. Sample: $-3x + 3y = 2$ (multiply by 2) $\quad -6x + 6y = 4.$
$\qquad\quad -4x - 2y = 3$ (multiply by 3) $\quad \dfrac{-12x - 6y = 9}{}$
$\qquad\qquad\qquad\qquad\qquad$ (add) $\qquad\qquad -18x = 13$
$\qquad\qquad\qquad\qquad\qquad\qquad\qquad\qquad\qquad x = -\dfrac{13}{18}$

Substitute $x = -\dfrac{13}{18}$ into the first equation; $-3\left(-\dfrac{13}{18}\right) + 3y = 2$; $y = -\dfrac{1}{18}$; $\left(-\dfrac{13}{18}, -\dfrac{1}{18}\right)$. **7.** Let e = the price for 1 egg; let s = the price for one

sausage link. The system $\begin{cases} 2e + 2s = 2.78 \\ 3e + 4s = 4.99 \end{cases}$ describes our situation.

$2e + 2s = 2.78$ (multiply by −2)
$-4e - 4s = -5.56$
$\dfrac{3e + 4s = 4.99}{}$
$-e \qquad\quad = -.57 \qquad$ (add)
$e = .57$
They might charge 57¢ for one egg.

8. a. The coefficient matrix is $\begin{bmatrix} 8 & 3 \\ 6 & 5 \end{bmatrix}$.

b. The inverse of $\begin{bmatrix} 8 & 3 \\ 6 & 5 \end{bmatrix}$ is $\dfrac{1}{8 \cdot 5 - 6 \cdot 3} \begin{bmatrix} 5 & -3 \\ -6 & 8 \end{bmatrix}$

$= \dfrac{1}{22} \begin{bmatrix} 5 & -3 \\ -6 & 8 \end{bmatrix} = \begin{bmatrix} \frac{5}{22} & \frac{-3}{22} \\ \frac{-6}{22} & \frac{8}{22} \end{bmatrix}$.

c. $\begin{bmatrix} \frac{5}{22} & \frac{-3}{22} \\ \frac{-6}{22} & \frac{8}{22} \end{bmatrix} \begin{bmatrix} 8 & 3 \\ 6 & 5 \end{bmatrix} \begin{bmatrix} x \\ y \end{bmatrix} = \begin{bmatrix} \frac{5}{22} & \frac{-3}{22} \\ \frac{-3}{11} & \frac{4}{11} \end{bmatrix} \begin{bmatrix} 41 \\ 39 \end{bmatrix}$;

$\begin{bmatrix} 1 & 0 \\ 0 & 1 \end{bmatrix} \begin{bmatrix} x \\ y \end{bmatrix} = \begin{bmatrix} \frac{88}{22} \\ \frac{33}{11} \end{bmatrix}$; $\begin{bmatrix} x \\ y \end{bmatrix} = \begin{bmatrix} 4 \\ 3 \end{bmatrix}$; The solution to the system is

$x = 4$ and $y = 3$. **9. a.** Sample: $\begin{bmatrix} 2 & 4 \\ 1 & 2 \end{bmatrix}$

b. The determinant of the matrix is $2 \cdot 2 - 4 \cdot 1 = 0$.
10. See right. **11.** Pick a point in the shaded region; $(0, -1)$ satisfies only (c) and (d); since the boundary $y = x$ is included, the answer is (c). **12. a.** Let c = the number of chairs built per day, and s = the number of sofas built per day. The number of hours the carpenters can work per day satisfies $7c + 4s \leq 133$, and the upholsterers' hours satisfy $2c + 6s \leq 72$. Since the manufacturer cannot make a negative number of chairs or sofas, $c \geq 0$ and $s \geq 0$.

$\begin{cases} 7c + 4s \leq 133 \\ 2c + 6s \leq 72 \\ c \geq 0 \\ s \geq 0 \end{cases}$

b. See right. The vertices of the feasible region will be solutions to the systems:

$\begin{cases} s = 0 \\ 7c + 4s = 133 \end{cases}$ $\begin{cases} 7c + 4s = 133 \\ 2c + 6s = 72 \end{cases}$

$\begin{cases} 2c + 6s = 72 \\ c = 0 \end{cases}$ $\begin{cases} s = 0 \\ c = 0 \end{cases}$

The vertices of the feasible set are the points $(0, 12)$, $(0, 0)$, $(19, 0)$, and $(15, 7)$. **c.** The profit equation is $P = 80c + 70s$.

By the Linear-Programming Theorem, we know that P is maximized at one of the vertices of the feasible region. So check the vertices to find which one gives the maximum value.

$$80(0) + 70(12) = 840$$
$$80(0) + 70(0) = 0$$
$$80(19) + 70(0) = 1520$$
$$80(15) + 70(7) = 1690$$

The profit is maximized in the feasible region at the point $(15, 7)$. The manufacturer can maximize profits, earning \$1690, by producing 15 chairs and 7 sofas per day.

1.  **2.**

10. 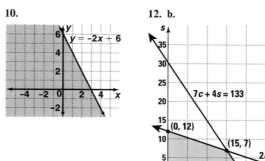 **12. b.**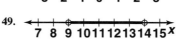

The chart below keys the **Progress Self-Test** questions to the objectives in the **Chapter Review** on pages 340–343 or to the **Vocabulary** (Voc.) on page 338. This will enable you to locate those **Chapter Review** questions that correspond to questions missed on the **Progress Self-Test**. The lesson where the material is covered is also indicated on the chart.

Question	1	2	3	4	5	6	7	8	9
Objective	H	H	I	D	A	A, C	F	B, C	B
Lesson	5-1	5-1	5-2	5-3	5-3	5-3, 5-4, 5-6	5-3, 5-4, 5-6	5-5, 5-6	5-5

Question	10	11	12
Objective	J	E, K	G
Lesson	5-7	5-8	5-9, 5-10

CHAPTER 5 REVIEW (pp. 340–343)

1. (a) **3.** inconsistent or no solutions **5.** $(-6.5, -10.5)$; $-10.5 = -6.5 - 4$ and $2(-6.5) + 10.5 = -2.5$ **7.** $\left(\frac{3}{2}, \frac{1}{2}, \frac{1}{5}\right)$; $2\left(\frac{3}{2}\right) + 15\left(\frac{1}{5}\right) = 6, \frac{3}{2} = 3\left(\frac{1}{2}\right)$, and $\frac{1}{5} = \frac{2}{5}\left(\frac{1}{2}\right)$

9. a. 2 **b.** $\begin{bmatrix} \frac{1}{2} & 0 \\ 0 & 1 \end{bmatrix}$ **11. a.** 0 **b.** The inverse does not exist.

13. $\begin{bmatrix} \frac{6}{69} & -\frac{9}{69} \\ \frac{7}{69} & \frac{1}{69} \end{bmatrix}$

15. Since the determinant, $3 \cdot 4 - 6 \cdot 2$, equals zero, the matrix has no inverse. **17.** $(7, 0)$ **19.** $m = 39, n = 28$ **21.** Yes; the solution $(7, 2)$ satisfies both systems. **23.** inconsistent **25. a.** consistent **b.** infinitely many solutions **27. a.** consistent **b.** two solutions **29.** $\frac{21}{4}$ **31.** False **33.** (a), (c) **35.** Yes; it is one

of the vertices of the feasible region. **37.** Sugar-O's: $8\frac{1}{3}$ g; Health-Nut: $16\frac{2}{3}$ g **39. a.** about 53 **b.** more than 53
41. \$790 first class, \$700 for business class, and \$550 for tourist class **43.** 88 Olde English shelves; 112 Cool Contemporary shelves
45. (c) **47.** $x < \frac{-5}{2}$, See below. **49.** See below. **51.** See below.
53. $x \leq -1$ or $x > 3$ **55.** See page 910. **57.** See page 910. **59.** See page 910. **61.** $y \geq -\frac{5}{8}x + 5$ **63.** See page 910. **65.** $y \leq -1$ and $x \leq -3$

47.

49.

51.

55.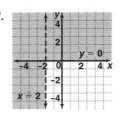

57.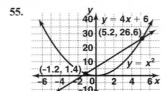

59.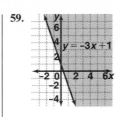

63.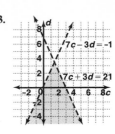

LESSON 6-1 (pp. 346–350)

17. $140w + 4w^2$ m^2 **19.** $\frac{1}{2}n^3 + n^2 + \frac{1}{2}n$ **21.** $-3x^2 + 12x - 12$
23. $h = -1$ **25. a.** 7.475 million visitors/year
b. 0.13 billion dollars/year **27. a.** See below. **b.** They have the
same vertex (0, 0) and they are both symmetric to the y-axis.

27. a.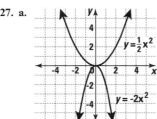

LESSON 6-2 (pp. 351–355)

23. a. See below. **b.** They coincide everywhere. **25.** $x - 3$ or $3 - x$
27. a. $\pm\sqrt{13}$ **b.** $\pm\sqrt{14}$ **29.** False; for instance, when $n = 1$,
$(1 + 11)^2 = 144$ and $1^2 + 11^2 = 122$; so $(n + 11)^2 = n^2 + 11^2$ is
not true. **31.** under r_x: $y = -3x^2$; under r_y: $y = 3x^2$

23. a.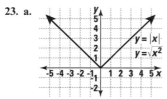

LESSON 6-3 (pp. 357–362)

15. a. $y - 3 = -1.4x^2$ **b.** $y = -1.4(x - 3)^2$ **17.** $x = 11$
19. $n = -0.25$ or -0.75 **21. a.** 4500 sq ft
b. $6000 - 320x + 4x^2$ sq ft **23. a.** $2x^2 + 16x + 32$
b. $2x^2 + 16x + 35$ **25.** $\left\lfloor\frac{s - 0.5}{40}\right\rfloor + 1$; or $\left\lfloor\frac{s}{40}\right\rfloor + 1$ when s is not a
multiple of 40, $\left\lfloor\frac{s}{40}\right\rfloor$ when s is a multiple of 40

LESSON 6-4 (pp. 363–369)

13. x-intercepts (1, 0), (3, 0), y-intercept (0, 3), vertex (2, -1)
See above right. **15. a.** See above right. **b.** $x = 2.5$
c. (2.5, -12.25) **17. a.** $h = -4.9t^2 + 6700$ **b.** See above right.
c. $\approx$ 37 seconds **19.** $y = -.5x^2 - 2x + 2$ **21. a.** See above right.
b. The graph of $y + 4 = |x - 5|$ is the image of $y = |x|$ under the
translation $T_{5,-4}$. **23. a.** $96 + 40w + 4w^2$ sq. in. **b.** $40 + 8w$ in.
25. $a = 12$ **27. a.** $y \approx -411x + 823{,}031$ **b.** $\approx$ \$2675
c. The truck does not continue to depreciate in value at the same
rate. In this case, one gets a negative value for the truck in the year
2006 if the line of best fit is used.

13.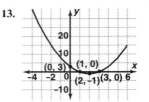

15. a.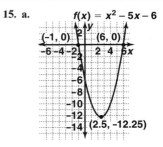

$f(x) = x^2 - 5x - 6$

17. b.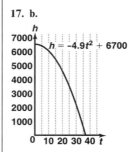

21.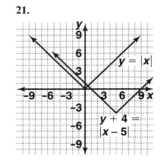

LESSON 6-5 (pp. 370–375)

13. a. the set of all real numbers
b. (-2, 4) **c.** $\{y: y \geq 4\}$
15. a. $h = -4.9t^2 + 629$
b. about 11.3 seconds
17. a. $y = 6x^2 + 6x + \frac{3}{2}$
b. See right. **c.** $\left(0, 1\frac{1}{2}\right)$
19. $y = \pm\sqrt{20} \approx \pm 4.47$
21. -1

17. b.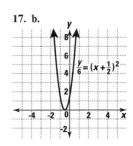

LESSON 6-6 (pp. 376–381)

9. a. Sample: $h = -16t^2 + 55t + 325$ **b.** 325 ft **c.** $\approx$ 5.8 sec
d. $\approx$ 6.5 sec **11. a.** $(x + 3)(x + 7)$ **b.** $x^2 + 10x + 21$
13. a. (0, -20) **b.** $y + 92 = 2(x + 6)^2$ **c.** (-6, -92)

15. $\begin{bmatrix} 100 & 10 & 1 \\ 400 & 20 & 1 \\ 900 & 30 & 1 \end{bmatrix}\begin{bmatrix} a \\ b \\ c \end{bmatrix} = \begin{bmatrix} 19 \\ 42 \\ 73 \end{bmatrix}$; $\begin{bmatrix} 1 & 0 & 0 \\ 0 & 1 & 0 \\ 0 & 0 & 1 \end{bmatrix}\begin{bmatrix} a \\ b \\ c \end{bmatrix} =$

$\begin{bmatrix} \frac{1}{200} & -\frac{1}{100} & \frac{1}{200} \\ -\frac{1}{4} & \frac{2}{5} & -\frac{3}{20} \\ 3 & -3 & 1 \end{bmatrix}\begin{bmatrix} 19 \\ 42 \\ 73 \end{bmatrix}$; $\begin{bmatrix} a \\ b \\ c \end{bmatrix} = \begin{bmatrix} \frac{1}{25} \\ \frac{11}{10} \\ 4 \end{bmatrix} = \begin{bmatrix} .04 \\ 1.1 \\ 4 \end{bmatrix}$

17. 6 **19.** 17 **21.** True; $\frac{4 \pm \sqrt{12}}{6} = \frac{4 \pm 2\sqrt{3}}{6} = \frac{2 \pm \sqrt{3}}{3}$.

910

LESSON 6-7 (pp. 382–387)

17. $n = 3$ **19. a.** $x = -3 + \sqrt{10} \approx .16$ or $x = -3 - \sqrt{10} \approx -6.16$; x-intercepts **b.** $(-3, -10)$ **c. See below. d.** $x = -3$ **21. a. See below. b.** Sample: $r = -.0025i^2 + .825i$ **c.** Sample: $r = .6i + 3.75$ **d.** Sample: The quadratic model is more appropriate because the points are closer to the quadratic model than the linear model.

23. a. See below. b. preimage: $y = x$, $y = -x$; image: $y = x - 2$, $y = -x - 2$ **25. a.** $2808 + 192w + 2w^2$ in^2 **b.** 3608 in^2

19. c.

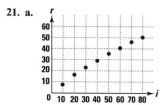

$y = x^2 + 6x - 1$

$(-6.2, 0)$ $(.16, 0)$ $(-3, -10)$

21. a.

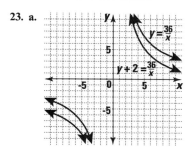

23. a.

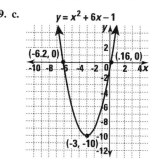

$y = \frac{36}{x}$

$y + 2 = \frac{36}{x}$

LESSON 6-8 (pp. 388–392)

23. $659i$ **25.** False; Sample: $2i + (-2i) = 0$.

27. $x = \frac{-0 \pm \sqrt{0^2 - 4 \cdot 1 \cdot 1}}{2 \cdot 1} = \frac{\pm \sqrt{-4}}{2} = \frac{2i}{2} = \pm i$

29. a. $x = \pm 3i$ **b.** $x = 3 \pm 3i$ **31.** $x = -6 \pm \sqrt{38}$

33. $2\pi rh + \pi h^2$

LESSON 6-9 (pp. 393–398)

21. $1 + 0i$ **23.** $2a$ **25. a.** $1 \pm 2i$ **b.** $(1 + 2i)^2 - 2(1 + 2i) + 5 = 0$?; $1 + 4i - 4 - 2 - 4i + 5 = 0$?; $0 = 0$? Yes. $(1 - 2i)^2 - 2(1 - 2i) + 5 = 0$?; $1 - 4i - 4 - 2 + 4i + 5 = 0$?; $0 = 0$? Yes. **27.** Ms^4p^2 **29.** $\frac{1 \pm \sqrt{3}}{2}$

LESSON 6-10 (pp. 400–407)

13. See below. 15. False; if the discriminant $= 0$, the graph has exactly one x-intercept. **17. a.** error message in line 300 **b.** add lines: 110   IF A $= 0$, THEN 610 **19.** 9 **21.** -48 **23.** $5 - 3i$
     610   PRINT "NOT A QUADRATIC **25.** $56 - 20i$
             EQUATION" **27. a.** $y = -\frac{7}{6}x^2 - \frac{3}{2}x + \frac{47}{3}$
     620   GOTO 999 **b. See below.**

13.

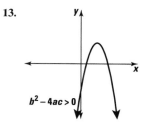

$b^2 - 4ac > 0$

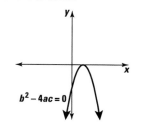

$b^2 - 4ac = 0$

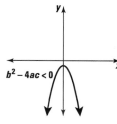

$b^2 - 4ac < 0$

27. b.

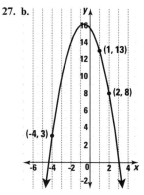

$(1, 13)$ $(2, 8)$ $(-4, 3)$

CHAPTER 6 PROGRESS SELF-TEST (p. 412)

1. $y - 12 = x^2 - 8x$; $y - 12 + 16 = x^2 - 8x + 16$; $y + 4 = (x - 4)^2$ **2.** $(4, -4)$ **3.** $0 + 4 = (x - 4)^2$; $\pm\sqrt{4} = x - 4$; $x = 4 \pm 2$; $x = 6$ or $x = 2$. Or let $y = 0$, that is, $x^2 - 8x + 12 = 0$; $x = \frac{8 \pm \sqrt{64 - 48}}{2} = \frac{8 \pm 4}{2}$; $x = 2$ or $x = 6$. **4.** $2i \cdot i = 2i^2 = -2$

5. $\sqrt{-8} \cdot \sqrt{-2} = 2i\sqrt{2} \cdot i\sqrt{2} = i^2 \cdot 2(\sqrt{2})^2 = -4$ **6.** $\frac{4 + \sqrt{-8}}{2} = \frac{4 + 2i\sqrt{2}}{2} = 2 + i\sqrt{2}$ **7.** $18i^2 + 12i - 12i - 8 = -18 - 8 = -26$

8. $2 - 4i - (1 + 5i) = 1 - 9i$ **9.** The vertex of $y - 2 = -(x + 1)^2$ is $(-1, 2)$. This is a translation $T_{-1,2}$ of the preimage $y = -x^2$. (c)

10. See page 912. 11. $a = 3$, $b = 14$, $c = -5$; $x = \frac{-14 \pm \sqrt{14^2 - 4 \cdot 3 \cdot (-5)}}{2 \cdot 3}$; $x = \frac{-14 \pm \sqrt{196 + 60}}{6}$; $x = \frac{-14 \pm \sqrt{256}}{6}$; $x = \frac{-14 \pm 16}{6}$; $x = \frac{1}{3}$ or $x = -5$ **12.** $m + 40 = \pm\sqrt{2}$; $m = -40 \pm \sqrt{2}$

13. $3x^2 - 18x + 75 = 0$; $x^2 - 6x + 25 = 0$; $x = \frac{6 \pm \sqrt{6^2 - 4 \cdot 1 \cdot 25}}{2} = \frac{6 \pm \sqrt{-64}}{2} = \frac{6 \pm 8i}{2} = 3 \pm 4i$; $x = 3 + 4i$ or $x = 3 - 4i$. **14.** True

15. a. one **b.** two **16. a.** There is one real root. **b.** There are two complex conjugate roots. **17.** $(a^2 - 6a + 9) + (a^2 + 6a + 9) = 2a^2 + 18$ **18.** $64v^2 + 16v + 1$ **19.** $h = -4.9t^2 + 10t + 20$ **20.** $h = -16(.5)^2 + 12(.5) + 4 = 6$; after .5 second, the ball is 6 feet high. **21.** $0 = -16t^2 + 12t + 4$; $t = \frac{-12 \pm \sqrt{144 - 4(4)(-16)}}{2(-16)} = \frac{-12 \pm 20}{-32}$; $t = -\frac{1}{4}$ or $t = 1$. The ball hits the ground after 1 second. **22.** $A = (30 - 2s)(40 - 2s) = 1200 - 140s + 4s^2 = 4s^2 - 140s + 1200$ **23.** (a) **24. a. See right. b.** The quadratic model is $H = an^2 + bn + c$; choose three points, (1, 0), (3, 3), and (5, 10), and substitute them into the model.

$$\begin{cases} 0 = a + b + c \\ 3 = 9a + 3b + c \\ 10 = 25a + 5b + c; \end{cases}$$

subtract each equation from the one below it;

$$\begin{cases} 3 = 8a + 2b \\ 7 = 16a + 2b; \end{cases}$$

subtract again to obtain $4 = 8a$, or $a = \frac{1}{2}$.

Substituting $a = \frac{1}{2}$ into $3 = 8a + 2b$ gives $b = -\frac{1}{2}$; substituting into $0 = a + b + c$ gives $c = 0$, $H = \frac{1}{2}n^2 - \frac{n}{2}$. **c.** 4950 **25.** $y - 4 = 2x^2 - 6x$; $\frac{y-4}{2} = x^2 - 3x$; $\frac{y-4}{2} + \frac{9}{4} = x^2 - 3x + \frac{9}{4}$; $y - 4 + \frac{9}{2} = 2\left(x - \frac{3}{2}\right)^2$; $y + \frac{1}{2} = 2\left(x - \frac{3}{2}\right)^2$; the parabola is the image of $y = 2x^2$ under the translation $T_{\frac{3}{2}, -\frac{1}{2}}$. So it opens upward, has the vertex $\left(\frac{3}{2}, -\frac{1}{2}\right)$, and has an axis of symmetry $x = \frac{3}{2}$.

10.
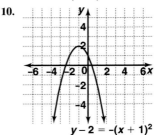
$y - 2 = -(x + 1)^2$

24. a.
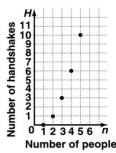
Number of handshakes / Number of people

The chart below keys the **Progress Self-Test** questions to the objectives in the **Chapter Review** on pages 413–415 or to the **Vocabulary** (Voc.) on page 411. This will enable you to locate those **Chapter Review** questions that correspond to questions missed on the **Progress Self-Test**. The lesson where the material is covered is also indicated on the chart.

Question	1	2	3	4	5	6	7	8	9	10
Objective	B	B	C	D	D	D	D	D	I	J
Lesson	6-5	6-5	6-7	6-8	6-8	6-8	6-9	6-9	6-3	6-3

Question	11	12	13	14	15	16	17	18	19	20
Objective	C	C	C	E	K	F	A	A	G	G
Lesson	6-7	6-7	6-7	6-2	6-10	6-10	6-1	6-1	6-7	6-7

Question	21	22	23	24	25
Objective	G	G	I	H	B
Lesson	6-7	6-1	6-3	6-6	6-5

CHAPTER 6 REVIEW (pp. 413–415)

1. $a^2 + 2ax + x^2$ **3.** $9x^2 + 24x + 16$ **5.** $9t^2 - 90t + 225$ **7.** $y = 3x^2 + 12x + 12$ **9.** $y + 31 = (x + 5)^2$ **11.** $y + 63 = 3(x - 5)^2$ **13.** $x = 3$ **15.** $z = \pm 2i\sqrt{2}$ **17.** $x = -\frac{1}{2} \pm \frac{\sqrt{5}}{2}$ **19.** $z = 4$ **21.** $k = 2 \pm \sqrt{6}$ **23.** $x = \pm 5i$ **25.** $p = \frac{1}{2}$ or -3 **27.** 1 **29.** -28 **31.** $50i\sqrt{2}$ **33.** $2 \pm 2i\sqrt{5}$ **35.** $1 + 12i$ **37.** $-6 + 10i$ **39.** $\frac{3}{2} + 3i$ **41.** $23 + 19i$ **43.** $4 - 11i$ **45.** $\frac{7}{89} - \frac{29}{89}i$ **47.** all nonpositive numbers **49.** 9 **51.** -4 **53. a.** 0 **b.** 1 **c.** rational **55. a.** 45 **b.** 2 **c.** irrational **57.** Two; the discriminant is 9 which is greater than 0. **59.** 5.5 m × 11 m **61.** 4.52 sec **63. a.** 51, 70 **b.** $p(n) = \frac{3}{2}n^2 - \frac{1}{2}n$ **c.** 3725 **65.** $y + 5 = (x + 7)^2$ **67.** (d) **69.** The solutions to $(k - 1)^2 = 36$ are 1 more than the solutions to $k^2 = 36$. **71.** $a = 9$ **73. See right.** vertex $(-2, 4)$, x-intercepts $(-2 \pm 2\sqrt{3}, 0)$ **75. See right.** vertex $(1, 1)$, x-intercepts $(1 \pm \frac{\sqrt{2}}{2}, 0)$ **77.** (c) **79. See right.** **81.** 2 **83.** Yes; the discriminant of the equation $6x^2 - 12x = -5$ is $(-12)^2 - 4 \cdot 6 \cdot 5 = 24 > 0$. Therefore, this equation has two real solutions which means the parabola $y = 6x^2 - 12x$ intersects the line $y = -5$ at two points.

73.
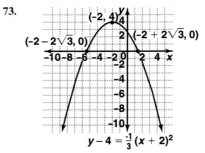
$(-2, 4)$, $(-2 - 2\sqrt{3}, 0)$, $(-2 + 2\sqrt{3}, 0)$
$y - 4 = -\frac{1}{3}(x + 2)^2$

75.
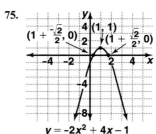
$(1, 1)$, $(1 + \frac{-\sqrt{2}}{2}, 0)$, $(1 + \frac{\sqrt{2}}{2}, 0)$
$y = -2x^2 + 4x - 1$

79.
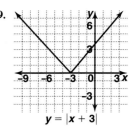
$y = |x + 3|$

absolute value The operation or function defined by $|x| = \begin{cases} x \text{ when } x \geq 0 \\ -x \text{ when } x < 0 \end{cases}$. The distance of x from 0 on a number line. (351)

absolute value function The function with equation $f(x) = |x|$. (352)

acceleration The rate of change of the velocity of an object. (366)

acidic A substance whose pH is between 0 and 7. (565)

algebraic expression A combining of numbers, variables and operations in a way that stands for a number. Sometimes called simply an *expression*. (6)

algebraic sentence A sentence in which expressions are related by equality or inequality. (6)

alkaline A substance whose pH is between 7 and 14. (565)

angle of depression The angle between the line of sight and the horizontal when the line of sight points down. (612)

angle of elevation The angle between the line of sight and the horizontal when the line of sight points up. (612)

annual yield The rate of interest earned after all the compoundings have taken place in one year. Also called *effective annual yield*. (440)

annual growth factor For a given decade, it is the positive number b such that b^{10} gives the decade growth factor. Also called *yearly growth factor*. (554)

argument of a function A value of the domain variable in a function. (20)

arithmetic mean The result of adding the n numbers in a data set and dividing the sum by n. Also called the *average* or *mean*. (502)

arithmetic sequence A sequence with a constant difference between consecutive terms. Also called *linear sequence*. (175)

arithmetic series An indicated sum of successive terms of an arithmetic sequence. (813)

arrow notation The notation $f: x \rightarrow y$ used to describe y as a function of x. Also called *mapping notation*. (21)

asymptote A line approached by the graph of a function. (778)

asymptotes of a hyperbola Two lines which are approached by the points on the branches of a hyperbola as the points get farther from the foci. The asymptotes of the hyperbola with equation $\frac{x^2}{a^2} - \frac{y^2}{b^2} = 1$ are $\frac{y}{b} = \pm \frac{x}{a}$. (777)

automatic grapher A calculator or computer program that can automatically display graphs when an equation is entered. (94)

average The result of adding the n numbers in a data set and dividing the sum by n. Also called *arithmetic mean* or *mean*. (502)

axis of symmetry of a parabola The line with equation $x = h$ of the parabola with equation $y - k = a(x - h)^2$; the line containing the focus of the parabola perpendicular to the directrix. (359, 748)

base b in the expression b^n. (418)

bearing The direction of an object, as measured clockwise from due north. (607)

bel A unit of sound intensity; 10 bels is a decibel. (563)

binomial A polynomial with two terms. (680)

binomial coefficients The coefficients of terms in the expansion of $(a + b)^n$. (843)

binomial distribution A probability function in which the values of the function are proportional to binomial coefficients. Also called *binomial probability distribution*. (862)

binomial expansion The result of writing the power of a binomial as a sum. (841)

binomial experiment A situation in which n independent trials occur, and each trial has exactly two mutually exclusive outcomes. (852)

binomial probability distribution A probability function in which the values of the function are proportional to binomial coefficients. Also called *binomial distribution*. (862)

boundary A line or curve separating a plane or part of a plane into two regions. (312, 760)

branches of a hyperbola The two separate parts of the graph of a hyperbola. (105)

calculator key sequence A list of keystrokes to be performed on a calculator. (14)

center of a circle The fixed point from which the set of points of the circle are at a given distance. (754)

center of an ellipse The intersection of the axes of the ellipse. (767)

circle The set of all points in a plane at a given distance from a fixed point. (754)

clearing fractions. The process of multiplying both sides of an equation by a common multiple of the denominators to eliminate the fractions. (32)

closure One of the field properties; if you multiply two 2×2 matrices, the result is a 2×2 matrix. (240)

coefficient matrix A matrix which represents the coefficients of the variables of a system. (305)

coefficients of a polynomial The numbers $a_n, a_{n-1}, a_{n-2}, \ldots, a_0$ in the polynomial $a_n x^n + a_{n-1} x^{n-1} + a_{n-2} x^{n-2} + \ldots + a_0$. (674)

column A vertical list in a table, rectangular array, or spreadsheet. (204)

combination Any choice of r objects from n objects. (847)

combined variation A situation in which direct and inverse variations occur together. (122)

common logarithm A logarithm to the base 10. (558)

common logarithm function The function with equation $y = \log_{10} x$ or $y = \log x$. Also called *logarithm function with base 10*. (560)

completing the square A technique used to transform a quadratic from $ax^2 + bx + c$ form to $a(x - h)^2 + k$ form. (371)

complex conjugate The complex conjugate of $a + bi$ is $a - bi$. (395)

complex number A number that can be written in the form $a + bi$, where a and b are real numbers and $i = \sqrt{-1}$; a is called the real part and b the imaginary part. (393)

composite of f and g The composite $g \circ f$ of two functions f and g is the function that maps x onto $g(f(x))$, and whose domain is the set of all values in the domain of f for which $f(x)$ is in the domain of g. (479)

composition of functions The function that results from first applying one function, then another; denoted by the symbol $\circ$. (480)

composite of transformations The transformation $T_2 \circ T_1$ that maps a figure F onto F'' if transformation T_1 maps figure F onto figure F', and transformation T_2 maps figure F' onto figure F''. (242)

compound sentence A sentence in which two clauses are connected by the word "and" or by the word "or." (273)

compounding The process of earning interest on the interest of an investment. (438)

concentric circles Two or more circles with the same center. (754)

congruent figures Two figures such that one is the image of the other under a composite of isometries (reflections, rotations, translations, glide reflections). (213)

conic graph paper Graph paper consisting of two intersecting sets of concentric circles. (764)

conic section A cross-section of a double cone; the intersection of a double cone with a plane. Also called *conic*. (747)

conjecture An educated guess. (62)

conjugate For any expression of the form $a + \sqrt{b}$, the conjugate is the expression $a - \sqrt{b}$. (507)

consistent system A system that has one or more solutions. (287)

constant difference In an arithmetic sequence, the difference of two consecutive terms. (175)

constant matrix A matrix which represents the constants in a system of equations. (305)

constant multiplier In a geometric sequence, the ratio of two consecutive terms. Also called *constant ratio*. (444)

constant of variation The non-zero real constant k in the equation $y = kx^n$ or $y = \frac{k}{x^n}$ for a variation function. (72)

constant ratio In a geometric sequence, the ratio of two consecutive terms. Also called *constant multiplier*. (444)

constant-decrease situation A situation in which a quantity y decreases by a constant amount for every fixed increase in x. (141)

constant-increase situation A situation in which a quantity y increases by a constant amount for every fixed increase in x. (140)

constraint A restriction on a variable or variables in a situation. (271)

Continuous Change Model The equation $N(t) = N_0 e^{rt}$, where N_0 is the initial amount and r is the growth factor over a time t. (548)

continuous compounding The limit of the process of earning interest with periods of compounding approaching zero. Also called *instantaneous compounding*. (547)

convex region A region of the plane in which any two points of the region can be connected by a line segment which lies entirely in the region. (324)

coordinate plane A plane in which there is a one-to-one correspondence between the points in the plane and the set of ordered pairs of real numbers. (24)

corollary A theorem that follows immediately from another theorem. (358)

correlation coefficient A number between –1 and 1 that indicates how well a linear or other equation fits data. (171)

$\cos^{-1} x$ The number between 0 and 180°, or between 0 and π, whose cosine is x. (611, 653)

cosine function The correspondence $\theta \rightarrow \cos \theta$ that associates θ with the x-coordinate of the image of (1, 0) under R_θ. (647)

cosine of θ (cos θ) In a right triangle with acute angle θ, $\cos \theta = \frac{\text{length of leg adjacent to } \theta}{\text{length of hypotenuse}}$. The first coordinate of R_θ (1, 0). (605, 624)

counting number A member of the set $\{1, 2, 3, 4, 5, \ldots\}$. Also called the *natural numbers*. (14)

cube of x The third power of x, denoted by x^3. (418)

cube root A cube root t of x, denoted by $\sqrt[3]{x}$, is a solution to the equation $t^3 = x$. (450)

cubic polynomial A polynomial of a single variable with degree 3, such as $ax^3 + bx^2 + cx + d$. (675)

cubing function The powering function f defined by $f(x) = x^3$. (420)

data set A collection of elements in which an element may appear more than once. (830)

decade growth factor The ratio of an amount in a specific year to the amount ten years earlier. (554)

decibel (dB) A unit of sound intensity. $\frac{1}{10}$ of a bel. (563)

default window The window that is set on an automatic grapher by the manufacturer. (94)

degree of a polynomial in several variables The largest sum of the exponents of the variables in any term in a polynomial expression. (680)

degree of a polynomial in a single variable The largest exponent of the variable in the polynomial. (674)

dependent variable A variable whose values always depend on the value(s) of other variable(s). (12)

depreciation The decrease in value over time of manufactured goods. (539)

determinant of a 2×2 matrix For the matrix $M = \begin{bmatrix} a & b \\ c & d \end{bmatrix}$, the number $ad - bc$. (301)

difference of matrices The result of subtracting two matrices. (210)

dimensions $m \times n$ A descriptor of a matrix with m rows and n columns has dimensions $m \times n$; a rectangle with adjacent sides of lengths m and n. (204)

direct variation A function mapping x onto y with an equation of the form $y = kx^n$, $k \neq 0$, and $n > 0$. (72)

directly proportional Two variables x and y so related that when one of the variables is multiplied by k, so is the other. (72)

directrix A line associated with a parabola such that the distance from it to any point on the parabola is equal to the distance from that point to the focus. (748)

discrete graph A graph that is made up of unconnected points. (105)

discriminant of a quadratic equation For the equation $ax^2 + bx + c = 0$, the value of $b^2 - 4ac$. (403)

domain of a function The set of values which are allowable substitutions for the independent variable. (13)

double cone The surface generated by a line rotating about an axis that contains a point on the line. (747)

double root The root of a quadratic equation when the discriminant is 0; a root with multiplicity of 2. (718)

e The constant 2.718281828459... that the sequence of numbers of the form $\left(1 + \frac{1}{n}\right)^n$ approaches as n increases without bound. The base of natural logarithms. (547, 583)

eccentricity The ratio of the distance between the foci to the focal constant in an ellipse or hyperbola. (774)

element of a matrix The object in a particular row and column of a matrix. (203)

ellipse The set of points P in a plane which satisfy $PF_1 + PF_2 = d$, where F_1 and F_2 (its *foci*) are any two points and d (its *focal constant*) is a constant with $d > F_1F_2$. (765)

equal complex numbers Two complex numbers with equal real parts and equal imaginary parts. $a + bi = c + di$ if and only if $a = c$ and $b = d$. (393)

equal matrices Two matrices which have the same dimensions and in which corresponding elements are equal. (205)

equation A sentence stating that two expressions are equal. (8)

Euler's $f(x)$ notation Notation that represents the value of a function f with argument x as $f(x)$. (20)

evaluating an expression Substituting for the variables in an expression and calculating a result. (8)

expanding a polynomial Writing a power of a polynomial or the product of polynomials as a polynomial. (674)

explicit formula for nth term A formula which describes any term in a sequence in terms of its position in the sequence. (43)

exponent n in the expression b^n. (418)

exponential curve A graph of an exponential equation. (535)

exponential decay A situation described by an exponential function where the growth factor is between 0 and 1. (539)

exponential function A function with the independent variable in the exponent. A function with an equation of the form $y = ab^x$. (535)

exponential growth A situation described by an exponential function where the growth factor is greater than one. (535)

Exponential Growth Model If a quantity a has growth factor b for each unit period, then after a period of length x, there will be ab^x of the quantity. (541)

exponential sequence A sequence with a constant ratio between consecutive terms. Also called *geometric sequence*. (444)

exponentiation An operation by which a variable is raised to a power. Also called *powering*. (418)

expression A combining of numbers, variables and operations in a way that stands for a number. (6)

exterior of a circle The region outside a circle. (760)

extraneous solution A solution that is gained but does not check in the original equation. (518)

f^{-1} The symbol for the inverse of function f. (491)

$f(x)$ notation The notation used to describe functions, read "f of x." (20)

factor: A number or expression which evenly divides a given expression. (686)

factored form The product of two or more factors which equals the given expression. (686)

factorial function The function defined by the equation $f(n) = n!$ where $n!$ is the product of the integers from n to 1. (826)

factoring The rewriting of a polynomial as a product of factors. (686)

fair coin A coin that has an equal probability of landing on either side. (853)

feasible region The set of solutions to a system of linear inequalities. Also called *feasible set*. (319)

Fibonacci sequence The sequence 1, 1, 2, 3, 5, 8, 13, ... A recursive definition is
$$\begin{cases} F_1 = 1, \\ F_2 = 1, \\ F_n = t_{n-1} + t_{n-2} \end{cases} \text{for } n \geq 3. \text{ (57)}$$

field properties The assumed properties of addition and multiplication for real numbers. (Appendix A)

floor function The function that maps x onto $\lfloor x \rfloor$, the greatest integer less than or equal to x. Also called *greatest integer function* or *rounding down function*. (187)

focal constant The constant sum of the distances from a point on an ellipse to the two foci of the ellipse. The absolute value of the difference of the distances from a point on a hyperbola to the two foci of the hyperbola. (765, 777)

931

focus (plural *foci*) In a parabola, the point along with the directrix from which a point is equidistant. The two points from which the sum (ellipse) or difference (hyperbola) of distances to a point on the conic section is constant. (748, 761, 777)

formula A sentence stating that a single variable is equal to an expression with one or more different variables. (8)

function A relation in which for each ordered pair the first coordinate has exactly one second coordinate. (12)

function composition The function that results from first applying one function, then another; denoted by the symbol $\circ$. (480)

general form of a quadratic relation An equation of the form $Ax^2 + Bxy + Cy^2 + Dx + Ey + F = 0$, where A, B, C, D, E and F are real numbers and at least one of A, B, or C is not zero. (786)

geometric mean The nth root of the product of n numbers. (502)

geometric sequence A sequence with a constant ratio between successive terms. Also called *exponential sequence*. (444)

geometric series An indicated sum of successive terms of a geometric sequence. (817)

gravitational constant The acceleration of a moving object due to gravity, often denoted by g. Near the Earth's surface, $g \approx 32$ ft/sec$^2 \approx$ 9.8 m/sec^2. (366)

greatest integer function The function that maps x onto $\lfloor x \rfloor$, the greatest integer less than or equal to x. Also called *floor function* or *rounding down function*. (187)

growth factor In the exponential function $y = ab^x$, the amount b by which y is multipled for every unit increase in x. (535)

half-life The amount of time required for a quantity in an exponential decay situation to decay to half its original value. (540)

half-plane Either of the two sides of a line in a plane. (312)

hierarchy A diagram that shows how various ideas are related, with a direction that moves from more specific to more general. (889)

horizontal asymptote A horizontal line that is approached by the graph as the values of x get very large (or very small). (107)

horizontal line A line with an equation of the form $y = b$. (148)

horizontal magnitude The number a in the scale change that maps (x, y) onto (ax, by). (227)

horizontal scale change The stretching or shrinking of a figure in only the horizontal direction. A transformation which maps (x, y) onto (kx, y). (227)

hyperbola The graph of every function with an equation of the form $y = \frac{k}{x}$, where $k \neq 0$; the set of points P in a plane which satisfy $|PF_1 - PF_2| = d$, where F_1 and F_2 are any two points and d is a constant with $0 < d < F_1F_2$. (104, 777)

i One of the two square roots of -1, denoted by $\sqrt{-1}$. (389)

identity function The function defined by $f(x) = x$. (420)

2 × 2 identity matrix The matrix $\begin{bmatrix} 1 & 0 \\ 0 & 1 \end{bmatrix}$. (219)

3 x 3 identity matrix: The matrix $\begin{bmatrix} 1 & 0 & 0 \\ 0 & 1 & 0 \\ 0 & 0 & 1 \end{bmatrix}$. (219, 309)

identity transformation The transformation in which each point coincides with its image. (223)

image The result of applying a transformation to a preimage. (221)

imaginary number A number which is the square root of a negative real number. (388)

imaginary part In the complex number $a + bi$, the real number b. (393)

imaginary unit The number i. (389)

in terms of A sentence which is written with one variable in terms of another has the form of the first variable set equal to an expression with one or more terms involving the second variable. (36)

inconsistent system A system with no solutions. (287)

independent events Two or more events whose outcomes do not affect each other. (851)

independent variable In a formula, a variable upon whose value other variables depend. (12)

index The subscript used for a term in a sequence indicating the position of the term in the sequence. The variable under the Σ sign in summation notation. (44, 824)

index variable The variable under the Σ sign in summation notation; also called *index*. (824)

inequality An open sentence containing one of the symbols $<$, $>$, $\leq$, $\geq$, $\neq$ or $\approx$. (272)

initial condition The starting point in a situation. (141)

input A value of an independent variable. (13)

integer An element of the set $\{0, 1, -1, 2, -2, 3, -3, \ldots\}$. (14)

interior of a circle The region inside a circle. (760)

intersection of two sets The set consisting of those values common to both sets. (273)

interval A solution to an inequality of the form $x \leq a$ or $a \leq x \leq b$, where the $\leq$ can be replaced by $<$, $>$, or $\geq$. (272)

inverse of a matrix Matrices M and N are inverse matrices if and only if their product is the identity matrix. (299)

inverse of a relation The relation obtained by reversing the order of the coordinates of each ordered pair in the relation. (485)

inverse trigonometric functions One of the functions $\cos^{-1}$, $\sin^{-1}$, or $\tan^{-1}$. (611)

inverse-square curve The graph of $y = \frac{k}{x^2}$. (106)

inverse-square variation A variation that can be described by the equation $y = \frac{k}{x^2}$, with $k \neq 0$. (80)

inverse-variation function A function with a formula of the form $y = \frac{k}{x^n}$, with $k \neq 0$, *and* $n > 0$. (78)

932

inversely proportional to   A relationship between two variables whose product is a constant. Also called *varies inversely as*. (78)

irrational number   A real number which cannot be written as a ratio of integers. (354)

irreducible polynomial   A polynomial that cannot be factored into polynomials of lower degree with coefficients in the same domain as the coefficients of the given polynomial. Also called *prime polynomial*. (689)

joint variation   A situation in which one quantity varies directly as the product of two or more independent variables, but not inversely as any variable. (124)

lattice point   A point with integer coordinates. (758)

leading coefficient   The coefficient of the variable of highest power in a polynomial in a single variable. (674)

least squares line   A line that best fits the data. Also called *regression line* or *line of best fit*. (170)

limit   A number or figure which the terms of a sequence approach as n gets larger. (54)

line of best fit   A line that best fits the data. Also called *regression line* or *least squares line*. (170)

line of reflection   The line over which a figure is reflected. (232)

line of sight   An imaginary line from one position to another, or in a particular direction. (612)

line of symmetry   For a figure F, a line m such that the reflection image of F over m equals F itself. (99)

linear combination   An expression of the form $Ax + By$ is called a linear combination of x and y. (152)

linear function   A function f with the equation $f(x) = mx + b$, where m and b are real numbers. (141)

linear inequality   An inequality in which both sides are linear expressions. (272)

linear polynomial   A polynomial of the first degree, such as $y = mx + b$. (675)

linear scale   A scale with units spaced so that the difference between successive units is the same. (565)

linear sequence   A sequence with a constant difference. Also called *arithmetic sequence*. (176)

linear-combination method   A method of solving systems which involves adding multiples of the given equations. (294)

linear-combination situation   A situation in which all variables are to the first power and are not multiplied or divided by each other. (154)

linear-programming problem   A problem which leads to a system of linear inequalities in which the goal is to maximize or minimize a linear combination of the solutions to the system. (326)

log x   The logarithm of x to the base 10. The exponent to which 10 must be raised to equal x. (558)

logarithm function to the base 10   The function with equation $y = \log_{10} x$ or $y = \log x$. See also *common logarithm function*. (560)

logarithm function to the base b   The function with equation $y = \log_b x$. (570)

logarithm of m to the base b   Let $b > 0$ and $b \neq 1$. Then n is the logarithm of m to the base b, written $n = \log_b m$, if and only if $b^n = m$. (570)

logarithm of x to the base 10 y is the logarithm of x to the base 10, written $y = \log x$, if and only if $10^y = x$. (558)

logarithmic curve   The graph of a function of the form $y = \log_b x$. (558, 571)

logarithmic equation   An equation of the form $y = \log_b x$. (560)

logarithmic scale   A scale in which the units are spaced so that the ratio between successive units is the same. (565)

lottery   A game or procedure in which prizes are distributed among people by pure chance. (857)

magnitude of a size change   In the size change that maps (x, y) onto (kx, ky), the number k. Also called *size change factor*. (221)

major axis of an ellipse   The segment which contains the foci and has two vertices of an ellipse as its endpoints. (767)

mapping notation   The notation $f: x \rightarrow y$ for a function f. Also called *arrow notation*. (21)

mathematical model   A graph, sentence, or other mathematical idea that describes an aspect of a real-world situation. (111)

matrix   A rectangular arrangement of objects, its *elements*. (203)

matrix addition   If two matrices A and B have the same dimensions, their sum $A + B$ is the matrix in whose element in each position is the sum of the corresponding elements in A and B. (209)

matrix form of a system   A representation of a system using matrices. The matrix form for $\begin{cases} ax + by = e \\ cx + dy = f \end{cases}$ is $\begin{bmatrix} a & b \\ c & d \end{bmatrix} \begin{bmatrix} x \\ y \end{bmatrix} = \begin{bmatrix} e \\ f \end{bmatrix}$. (305)

matrix multiplication   Suppose A is an $m \times n$ matrix and B is an $n \times p$ matrix. The product $A \cdot B$ or AB is the $m \times p$ matrix whose element in row i and column j is the product of row i of A and column j of B. (215)

matrix subtraction   If two matrices A and B have the same dimensions, their difference $A - B$ is the matrix whose element in each position is the difference of the corresponding elements in A and B. (210)

maximum   The largest value in a set. (99)

mean   The result of adding the n numbers in a data set and dividing the sum by n. Also called *arithmetic mean* or *average*. (830)

measure of center   A number which in some sense is at the "center" of a data set; the mean or median of a data set. Also called *measure of central tendency*. (831)

measure of spread   A number, like standard deviation, which describes the extent to which elements of a data set are dispersed or spread out. (831)

933

median When the terms of a data set are placed in increasing order, if the set has an odd number of terms, the middle term; if the set has an even number of terms, the average of the two terms in the middle. (830)

method of finite differences A technique used to determine whether a data set can be modeled by a polynomial function. If taking differences of consecutive y-values eventually produces differences which are constant, then the data set can be modeled by a polynomial function. (726)

midpoint formula the midpoint of the segment with endpoints (x_1, y_1) and (x_2, y_2) is $\left(\frac{x_1 + x_2}{2}, \frac{y_1 + y_2}{2}\right)$. (60)

minimum The smallest value in a set. (99)

minor axis of an ellipse The segment which has two vertices of an ellipse as its endpoints and does not contain the foci. (767)

mode The number or numbers which occur most often in a data set. (830)

model for an operation A pattern that describes many uses of that operation. (7)

monomial A polynomial with one term. (680)

multiplicity of a root For a root r of a polynomial equation $P(x) = 0$, the highest power of $x - r$ that appears as a factor of $P(x)$. (718)

mutually exclusive events Two or more events which cannot happen at the same time. (851)

Napierian logarithm Another name for natural logarithm. (583)

natural logarithm A logarithm to the base e, written ln. Also called *Napierian logarithm*. (583)

natural number An element of the set $\{1, 2, 3, 4, 5, \ldots\}$. Also called *counting number*. (14)

neutral A substance whose pH is 7; a substance which is neither acidic or alkaline. (565)

normal curve The curve of a normal distribution. (864)

normal distribution A function whose graph is the image of the graph of $y = \frac{1}{\sqrt{2}} e^{\frac{-x^2}{2}}$ under a composite of translations or scale transformations. (864)

normalized scores Scores whose distribution is a normal curve. Also called *standardized scores*. (865)

nth power function The function defined by $f(x) = x^n$, where n is a positive integer. (420)

nth root Let n be an integer greater than one. Then b is an nth root of x if and only if $b^n = x$. (450)

nth term The term occupying the nth position in the listing of a sequence. The general term of a sequence. (43)

oblique line A line that is neither horizontal or vertical. (159)

one-to-one correspondence A mapping in which each member of one set is mapped to a distinct member of another set, and vice versa. (221)

open sentence A sentence that may be true or false depending on what values are substituted for the variables in it. (272)

opens down A description of the shape of a parabola whose vertex is a maximum; a parabola whose equation is of the form $y = ax^2 + bx + c$, where $a < 0$. (99)

opens up A description of the shape of a parabola whose vertex is a minimum; a parabola whose equation is of the form $y = ax^2 + bx + c$, where $a > 0$. (99)

order of operations Rules used to evaluate expressions worldwide. 1. Perform operations within grouping symbols from inner to outer. 2. Take powers. 3. Do multiplications or divisions from left to right. 4. Do additions or subtractions from left to right. (8)

output A value of the dependent variable in a function. (13)

parabola The set consisting of every point in the plane of a line ℓ (its *directrix*) and a point F not on ℓ (its *focus*) whose distance from F equals its distance from ℓ. (99, 748)

paraboloid A three-dimensional figure created by rotating a parabola in space around its axis of symmetry. The set of points equidistant from a point F (its focus) and a plane P. (751)

Pascal's triangle The sequence satisfying $\binom{n}{0} = \binom{n}{n} = 1$ for all integers $n \geq 0$, and $\binom{n+1}{r+1} = \binom{n}{r} + \binom{n}{r+1}$, where n and r are any integers with $0 \leq r \leq n$. The triangular array

where if x and y are located next to each other on a row, the element just below and directly between them is $x + y$. (47, 837)

perfect-square trinomial A trinomial of the form $a^2 + 2ab + b^2$ or $a^2 - 2ab + b^2$. (370)

period The horizontal translation of smallest positive magnitude that maps the graph of a function onto itself. (649)

periodic function A function whose graph can be mapped to itself under a horizontal translation. (649)

permutation An arrangement of n different objects in a specific order. (826)

pH scale A logarithmic scale used to measure the acidity of a substance. (565)

piecewise-linear graph A graph made of parts, each of which is a piece of a line. (142)

pitch The measure of the steepness of the slant of a roof. (39)

point matrix A 2×1 matrix. (205)

point-slope form of a linear equation An equation of the form $y - y_1 = m(x - x_1)$, where (x_1, y_1) is a point on the line with slope m. (163)

934

polynomial equation An equation of the form $y = a_nx^n + a_{n-1}x^{n-1} + \ldots + a_1x^1 + a_0$, where n is a positive integer and $a_n \neq 0$. (673)

polynomial function A function f of the form $f(x) = a_nx^n + a_{n-1}x^{n-1} + \ldots + a_1x^1 + a_0$, where n is a positive integer and $a_n \neq 0$. (675)

polynomial in x An expression of the form $a_nx^n + a_{n-1}x^{n-1} + a_{n-2}x^{n-2} + \ldots + a_1x^1 + a_0$, where n is a positive integer and $a_n \neq 0$. (674)

polynomial model A polynomial equation which fits a data set. (730)

population In a sampling situation, the set of all people, events, or items that could be sampled. (868)

Power of a Power Postulate For any nonnegative bases and nonzero real exponents or any nonzero base and integer exponents, $(b^m)^n = b^{mn}$. (427)

Power of a Product Postulate For any positive bases and real exponents or any nonzero bases and integer exponents, $(ab)^m = a^m b^m$. (428)

Power of a Quotient Postulate For any positive bases and real exponents, or any nonzero bases and integer exponents, $\left(\frac{a}{b}\right)^m = \frac{a^m}{b^m}$. (429)

power The expression x^n; the result of the operation of exponentiation or powering. (418)

powering An operation by which a variable is raised to a power. Also called *exponentiation*. (418)

preimage An object to which a transformation is applied. (221)

prime polynomial A polynomial that cannot be factored into polynomials of lower degree with coefficients in the same domain as the coefficients of the given polynomial. Also called *irreducible polynomial*. (689)

principal The amount of money invested in an investment. (438)

probability of an event If a situation has a total of t equally likely possibilities and e of these possibilities satisfy conditions for a particular event, then the probability of the event is $\frac{e}{t}$. (851)

probability distribution A function which maps a set of events onto their probabilities. Also called *probability function*. (862)

Product of Powers Postulate For any nonnegative bases and nonzero real exponents, or any nonzero bases and integer exponents, $b^m \cdot b^n = b^{m+n}$. (426)

quadratic An expression, equation, or function that involves sums of constants and first and second powers of variables, but no higher power. (346)

quadratic equation An equation which involves quadratic expressions. (346)

quadratic equation in two variables An equation of the form $Ax^2 + Bxy + Cy^2 + Dx + Ey + F = 0$, where $A, B, C, D, E,$ and F are real numbers and at least one of $A, B,$ or C is not zero. (747)

quadratic expression An expression which contains one or more terms in x^2, y^2, or xy, but no higher powers of x or y. (346)

quadratic form An expression of the form $Ax^2 + Bxy + Cy^2 + Dx + Ey + F$. (346)

quadratic function The function with equation $f(x) = ax^2 + bx + c$. (346)

quadratic model A quadratic equation which fits a set of data. (376)

quadratic polynomial A polynomial of a single variable with degree 2, such as $ax^2 + bx + c$. (675)

quadratic relation in two variables The sentence $Ax^2 + Bxy + Cy^2 + Dx + Ey + F = 0$ (or the inequality using one of the symbols $>, <, \geq, \leq$) where $A, B, C, D, E,$ and F are real numbers and at least one of $A, B,$ or C is not zero. (747)

quadratic system A system that involves at least one quadratic sentence. (789)

quadratic-linear system A system that involves linear and quadratic sentences. (789)

quadratic-quadratic system A system that involves two quadratic sentences. (794)

quartic equation A fourth degree polynomial equation. (717)

quartic polynomial A polynomial of a single variable with degree 4, such as $ax^4 + bx^3 + cx^2 + dx + e$. (675)

quintic equation A fifth degree polynomial equation. (717)

Quotient of Powers Property For any positive bases and real exponents, or any nonzero bases and integer exponents: $\frac{b^m}{b^n} = b^{m-n}$. (429)

r_m The reflection over line m. (232)

r_x The reflection over the x-axis. (234)

r_y The reflection over the y-axis. (233)

$r_{y=x}$ The reflection over line $y = x$. (234)

R_{90} The rotation of magnitude 90° counterclockwise with center at the origin. (247)

R_{180} The rotation of magnitude 180° counterclockwise with center at the origin. (243)

R_{270} A rotation of magnitude 270° counterclockwise with center at the origin. (248)

R_x A rotation of magnitude x counterclockwise with center at the origin. (246)

radian (rad) A measure of an angle, arc, or rotation such that π radians = 180 degrees. (658)

radical notation $\sqrt[n]{x}$ The notation for the nth root of an expression. (495)

radical sign $\sqrt{x}$ The symbol for the square root of x. (495)

radius The distance between any point on a circle and the center of the circle. (754)

random numbers Numbers which have the same probability of being selected. (869)

random sample A sample in which each element has the same probability as every other element in the population of being selected for the sample. (869)

935

range of a function The set of values of the function. (13)

rate of change Between two points, the quantity $\frac{y_2 - y_1}{x_2 - x_1}$. For a line, its slope. (89)

ratio of similitude In two similar figures, the ratio between a length in one figure and the corresponding length in the other. (222)

rational number A number which can be written as a simple fraction. A finite or infinitely repeating decimal. (14)

rationalizing the denominator When a fraction has irrational or complex numbers in its denominator, the process of rewriting a fraction without irrational or complex numbers in its denominator. (507)

real numbers Those numbers that can be represented by finite or infinite decimals. (14)

real part In a complex number of the form $a + bi$, the real number a. (393)

rectangular hyperbola A hyperbola with perpendicular asymptotes. (786)

recursive formula A set of statements that indicates the first term of a sequence and gives a rule for how the nth term is related to one or more of the previous terms. Also called *recursive definition*. (49)

reflecting line In a reflection, the perpendicular bisector of the line segment connecting a preimage point and its image. (232)

reflection A transformation under which the image of a point P over a reflecting line m is (1) P itself, if P is on m; (2) the point P' such that m is the perpendicular bisector of the segment connecting P with P', if P is not on m. (232)

reflection-symmetric figure A figure which coincides with a reflection image of itself. (99)

refraction When a beam of light in air strikes the surface of water it is refracted or bent. (643)

regression line A line that best fits a set of data. Also called *line of best fit* or *line of least squares*. (170)

relation A set of ordered pairs. (26)

repeated multiplication model for powering If b is a real number and n is a positive integer, then $b^n = \underbrace{b \cdot b \cdot b \cdot b \cdot \ldots \cdot b}_{n \text{ factors}}$. (418)

Richter scale A logarithmic scale used to measure the magnitude of intensity of an earthquake. (568)

root of an equation A solution to an equation. (403)

rotation A transformation with a center O under which the image of O is O itself and the image of any other point P is the point P' such that $m\angle POP'$ is a fixed number (its *magnitude*). (246)

rounding down function The function, denoted by $\lfloor x \rfloor$, whose values are the greatest integer less than or equal to x. Also called *greatest integer function* or *floor function*. (187)

row A horizontal list in a table, rectangular array, or spreadsheet. (204)

sample In a sampling situation, the subset of the population actually studied. (868)

sampling Using a subset of a population to estimate a result for an enitre population. (868)

scalar A real number by which a matrix is multiplied. (210)

scalar multiplication An operation leading to the product of a scalar k and a matrix A, namely the matrix kA in which each element is k times the corresponding element in A. (210)

scale change The stretching or shrinking of a figure in either a horizontal direction only, in a vertical direction only, or in both directions. The horizontal scale change of magnitude a and a vertical scale change of magnitude b maps (x, y) onto (ax, by), and is denoted by $S_{a,b}$. (227)

scatterplot A plot with discrete points used to display a data set. (169)

scientific calculator A calculator which performs arithmetic using algebraic order of operations, and with keys such as those for exponents, powering, logarithms, inverses, and trigonometric functions. (15)

sequence An ordered list. (41)

series An indicated sum of terms in a sequence. (813)

shrink A scale change in which a magnitude in some direction has absolute value less than one. (227)

sigma notation (Σ-notation) A shorthand notation used to restate a series. Also called *summation notation*. (824)

similar figures Two figures such that one is the image of the other under a composite of isometries (reflections, rotations, translations, glide reflections) and size changes. (222)

simple fraction A fraction of the form $\frac{a}{b}$, where a and b are integers and $b \neq 0$. (354)

simple interest The amount of interest I earned when calculated using the formula $I = Prt$, where P is the principal, r is the annual rate, and t is the time in years. (442)

simplified form An expression rewritten so that like terms are combined, fractions are reduced, and only rational numbers are in the denominator. (501)

simplify an nth root The process of factoring the expression under the radical sign into perfect nth powers and then applying the Root of a Product Theorem. (501)

simulation A procedure used to answer questions about real-world situations by performing experiments that closely model them. (869)

$\sin^{-1} x$ The number between $-90°$ and $90°$, or between $-\frac{\pi}{2}$ and $\frac{\pi}{2}$, whose sine is x. If $\sin u = v$, then on a restricted domain, $\sin^{-1} v = u$. (611, 653)

sine function The correspondence $\theta \rightarrow \sin \theta$ that associates θ with the y-coordinate of the image of $(1, 0)$ under R_θ. (647)

936

sine of θ (sin θ) In general, the second coordinate of $R_\theta(1, 0)$. In a right triangle with acute angle θ, $\sin \theta = \frac{\text{length of leg opposite } \theta}{\text{length of hypotenuse}}$. (605, 624)

sine wave A graph which can be mapped onto the graph of $g(\theta) = \sin \theta$ by any composite of reflections, translations, and scale changes. (649)

sinusoidal situations Situations that lead to sine waves. (649)

size change For any $k \neq 0$, the transformation that maps the point (x, y) onto (kx, ky); a transformation with center O such that the image of O is O itself and the image of any other point P is the point P' such that $OP' = k \cdot OP$ and P' is on ray OP if k is positive, and on the ray opposite ray OP if k is negative. (221)

size change factor In the size change $(x, y) \rightarrow (kx, ky)$, the number k. (221)

slope The slope determined by two points (x_1, y_1) and (x_2, y_2) is $\frac{y_2 - y_1}{x_2 - x_1}$. Also called *rate of change*. (90)

slope-intercept form of a linear equation A linear equation of the form $y = mx + b$, where m is the slope and b is the y-intercept. (141)

solution set for a system The intersection of the solution sets of the individual sentences of a system. (279)

solving a sentence Finding all solutions to a sentence. (30)

solving a triangle The use of trigonometry to find all the missing measures of sides and angles of a triangle. (655)

square matrix A matrix with the same number of rows and columns. (299)

square of x The second power of x, denoted by x^2. (418)

square root A square root of t is a solution to $y^2 = t$. The positive square root of a positive number x is denoted $\sqrt{x}$. (352, 450)

square root function The function f with equation $f(x) = \sqrt{x}$, where x is a nonnegative real number. (14)

squaring function The powering function f defined by $f(x) = x^2$. (420)

standard deviation Let S be a data set of n numbers $\{x_1, x_2, \ldots, x_n\}$. Let m be the mean of S. Then the standard deviation (s.d.) of S is $\sqrt{\frac{\sum_{i=1}^{n}(x_i - m)^2}{n}}$. (832)

standard form of a linear equation An equation for a line in the form $Ax + By = C$, where A and B are not both zero. (157)

standard form of a polynomial: A polynomial written in the form $a_n x^n + a_{n-1} x^{n-1} + \ldots + a_1 x^1 + a_0$, where n is a positive integer and $a_n \neq 0$. (674)

standard form of a quadratic equation An equation of the form $ax^2 + bx + c = 0$, with $a \neq 0$. (385)

standard form of a quadratic relation An equation in the form $Ax^2 + Bxy + Cy^2 + Dx + Ey + F = 0$ where $A, B, C, D, E,$ and F are real numbers and at least one of $A, B,$ or C is nonzero. (786)

standard form of an equation for a hyperbola An equation for a hyperbola in the form $\frac{x^2}{a^2} - \frac{y^2}{b^2} = 1$, where $b^2 = c^2 - a^2$, the foci are $(c, 0)$ and $(-c, 0)$ and the focal constant is $2a$. (779)

standard form of an equation for a parabola An equation for a parabola in the form $y = ax^2 + bx + c$, where $a \neq 0$. (363)

standard form of an equation for an ellipse An equation for an ellipse in the form $\frac{x^2}{a^2} + \frac{y^2}{b^2} = 1$, where $b^2 = a^2 - c^2$, with foci $(c, 0)$ and $(-c, 0)$ and focal constant $2a$. (767)

standard position for an ellipse (or hyperbola) A location in which the origin of a coordinate system is midway between the foci with the foci on an axis. (765, 779)

standardized scores Scores whose distribution is a normal curve. Also called *normalized scores*. (865)

statistical measure A single number which is used to describe an entire set of numbers. (830)

step function A graph that looks like a series of steps, such as the graph of the function with equation $y = \lfloor x \rfloor$. (186)

stratified ramdom sample A sample that is the union of samples chosen randomly from subpopulations of the entire population. (869)

stratified sample A sample in which the population has first been split into subpopulations and then, from each subpopulation, a sample is selected. (869)

stretch A scale change $(x, y) \rightarrow (ax, by)$ in which a or b is greater than one. (227)

subscript A number or variable written below and to the right of a variable. (44)

subscripted variable A variable with a subscript. (44)

subset A set whose elements are all chosen from a given set. (845)

subtraction of matrices Given two matrices A and B having the same dimensions, their difference $A - B$ is the matrix whose element in each position is the difference of the corresponding elements in A and B. (210)

sum of cubes pattern For all a and b, $a^3 + b^3 = (a + b)(a^2 - ab + b^2)$. (691)

summation notation A shorthand notation used to restate a series. Also called Σ-*notation or sigma notation*. (824)

symbol manipulator Computer software of a calculator preprogrammed to perform operations on variables. (675)

system A set of conditions joined by the word "and"; a special kind of compound sentence. (279)

tan^{-1} The number between 0° and 180°, or between 0 and π whose tangent is x. If $\tan u = v$, then on a restricted domain, $\tan^{-1} v = u$. (611)

tangent of θ (tan θ) In general, $\tan \theta = \frac{\sin \theta}{\cos \theta}$, provided $\cos \theta \neq 0$. In a right triangle with acute angle θ, $\tan \theta = \frac{\text{length of leg opposite } \theta}{\text{length of leg adjacent to } \theta}$. (605, 618)

tangent line A line that intersects a circle or ellipse in exactly one point. (791)

term of a sequence An element of a sequence. (42)

937

theorem In a mathematical system, a statement that has been proved. (27)

transformation A one-to-one correspondence between sets of points. (221)

translation A transformation that maps (x, y) onto $(x + h, y + k)$, denoted by $T_{h,k}$. (256)

trial One occurrence of an experiment. (852)

triangular number An element of the sequence 1, 3, 6, 10, . . ., whose nth term is $\frac{n(n+1)}{2}$. (42)

triangulation The process of determining the location of points using triangles and trigonometry. (641)

trigonometric ratios The ratios of the lengths of the sides in a right triangle. (605)

trinomial A polynomial with three terms. (680)

union of two sets The set consisting of those elements in either one or both sets. (274)

unit circle The circle with center at the origin and radius 1. (623)

value of a function If $y = f(x)$, the value of y. (20)

variable A symbol that can be replaced by any one of a set of numbers or other objects. (6)

varies directly as The situation that occurs when two variables x and y are so related that when one of the variables is multiplied by k, so is the other. Also called *directly proportional to*. (72)

varies inversely as The situation that occurs when two variables x and y are so related that when one of the variables is multiplied by k, the other is divided by k. Also called *inversely proportional to*. (78)

velocity The rate of change of distance with respect to time. (366)

vertex form of an equation of a parabola An equation of the form $y - k = a(x - h)^2$ where (h, k) is the vertex of the parabola. (359)

vertex of a parabola The intersection of a parabola and its axis of symmetry. (359, 748)

vertical asymptote A vertical line that is approached by the graph of a relation. (107)

vertical line A line with an equation of the form $x = h$. (158)

vertical magnitude In the scale change $(x, y) \rightarrow (ax, by)$, the number b. (227)

vertical scale change A transformation that maps (x, y) onto (x, by). (227)

vertices of a hyperbola The points of intersection of the hyperbola and the line containing its foci. (777)

vertices of an ellipse The endpoints of the major and minor axes of the ellipse. (767).

whole number An element of the set {0, 1, 2, 3, 4, 5, . . . }. (14)

window The part of the coordinate grid shown on the screen of an automatic grapher. (94)

x-axis The line in the coordinate plane in which the second coordinates of points are 0. (24)

x-intercept The value of x at a point where a graph crosses the x-axis. (159)

y-axis The line in the coordinate plane in which the first coordinates of points are 0. (24)

y-intercept The value of y at a point where a graph crosses the y-axis. (141)

yield The rate of interest earned after all the compoundings have taken place in one year. Also called *effective annual yield or annual yield*. (440)

zero of a function For a function f, a value of x for which $f(x) = 0$. (700)

zoom A feature on an automatic grapher which enables the window of a graph to be changed without keying in interval endpoints for x and y. Also called *rescaling*. (282)

$A \cap B$	intersection of sets A and B	f^{-1}	inverse of a function f
$A \cup B$	union of sets A and B	$\log_b m$	logarithm of m to the base b
$f(x)$	function notation read "f of x"	e	2.71828 . . .
$f{:}x \rightarrow y$	function notation read "f maps x onto y"	$x!$	x factorial
A'	image of A	$\ln x$	natural logarithm of x
S_k	size change of magnitude k	$\sin \theta$	sine of θ
$S_{a,b}$	scale change with horizontal magnitude a and vertical magnitude b	$\cos \theta$	cosine of θ
		$\tan \theta$	tangent of θ
r_x	reflection over the x-axis	rad	radian
r_y	reflection over the y-axis	a_n	"a sub n"; the nth term of a sequence
$r_{y=x}$	reflection over the line $y = x$	$\sum\limits_{i=1}^{n} i$	the sum of the integers from 1 to n
$T_2 \circ T_1$	composite of transformations T_1 and T_2	S_n	the partial sum of the first n terms of a sequence
R_θ	rotation of magnitude θ counterclockwise	$\binom{n}{r}, \ _nC_r$	the number of ways of choosing r objects from n objects
$T_{h,k}$	translation of h units horizontally and k units vertically	INT (X)	the BASIC equivalent for $\lfloor x \rfloor$
$\begin{bmatrix} a & b \\ c & d \end{bmatrix}$	2×2 matrix	$\boxed{\sqrt[x]{\ }}, \boxed{\sqrt[x]{y}}$	calculator nth root key
M^{-1}	inverse of matrix M	$\boxed{x!}$	calculator factorial key
det M	determinant of matrix M	$\boxed{y^x}$	calculator powering key
$\sqrt{}$	radical sign; square root	$\boxed{x^{-1}}$	calculator reciprocal key
$\sqrt[n]{x}$	the real nth root of x	$\boxed{\log}$	calculator common logarithm key
i	$\sqrt{-1}$	$\boxed{e^x}$	calculator e^x key
$\sqrt{-k}$	a solution of $x^2 = -k$, $k > 0$	$\boxed{\ln}$	calculator natural logarithm key
$a + bi$	a complex number, where a and b are real numbers	$\boxed{\sin}$	calculator sine key
$g \circ f$	composite of functions f and g	$\boxed{\cos}$	calculator cosine key
$|x|$	absolute value of x	$\boxed{\tan}$	calculator tangent key
$\lfloor x \rfloor$	greatest integer less than or equal to x		

Acknowledgments

Unless otherwise acknowledged, all photographs are the property of Scott, Foresman & Company. Page abbreviations are as follows: (T)top, (C)center, (B)bottom, (L)left, (R)right, (INS)inset.

COVER & TITLE PAGE: Steven Hunt (c) 1994 **vi(l)** William J. Warren/West Light **vi(r)** Tim Laman/Adventure Photo **vii(l)** Peticdas/Megna/Fundamental Photographs **vii(r)** Jack Krawczyk/Panoramic Images, Chicago **viii** Index Stock International **ix** Telegraph Colour Library/FPG **x** Steve Chenn/West Light **3** Brooks Kraft/Sygma **4C** Steve Vance/Stockworks **4BL** David Phillips/Photo Researchers **5C** William J. Warren/West Light **5BR** Pfetschinger/Peter Arnold, Inc. **6** Sidney Harris **8** David Joel/Tony Stone Images **10** Courtesy Tsakurshori, Second Mesa, AZ/Jerry Jacka Photography **12** Tony Freeman/Photo Edit **19** Milt & Joan Mann/Cameramann International, Ltd. **22** Myrleen Cate/Photo Edit **23** David Ahrenberg/Tony Stone Images **30** Milt & Joan Mann/Cameramann International, Ltd. **32** Christopher Brown/Stock Boston **34** Michael Newman/Photo Edit **36** Eric Neurath/Stock Boston **39** Mark Segal/Tony Stone Images **40** Tony Freeman/Photo Edit **42** David Carriere/Tony Stone Images **45** CNRI/SPL/Photo Researchers **48** John D. Cunningham/Visuals Unlimited **54** Ed Simpson/Tony Stone Images **57** Oxford Scientific Films/ANIMALS ANIMALS **58** Sidney Harris **61ALL** Ron Kimball **62** Claude Nuridsany & Marie Perennou/Photo Researchers **70TL** NASA **70-71T** R.Kord/H. Armstrong Roberts **70-71C** H.D.Thoreau/West Light **70B** Tim Laman/Adventure Photo **71B** Tom Tracy/The Stock Shop **72** David Joel/Tony Stone Images **73** Guido A. Rossi/The Image Bank **75** Milt & Joan Mann/Cameramann International, Ltd. **77** Phyllis Picardi/Stock Boston **78** James Shaffer/Photo Edit **80** NASA **82** Al Tielemans/Duomo Photography Inc. **84** John Chellman/ANIMALS ANIMALS **86** Tom McHugh/Natural History Museum of Los Angeles County/Photo Researchers **89** Tom Ives **92** Courtesy General Dynamics, Electric Boat Division **101** VU/Carlyn Galati/Visuals Unlimited **102** Milt & Joan Mann/Cameramann International, Ltd. **104** National Optical Astronomy Observatories & Lowell Observatory **110** Darryl Torckler/Tony Stone Images **113** Bob Newman/Visuals Unlimited **116** Edward Lee/Tony Stone Images **122** David Young-Wolff/Photo Edit **124** Milt & Joan Mann/Cameramann International, Ltd. **125** Brent Jones **126** Courtesy Andersen Windows **138TL** The Stock Market **138-139T** Tim Brown/Profiles West **138C** Peticolas/Megna/Fundamental Photographs **138-139B** Art Wolfe/Tony Stone Images **139C** Lance Nelson/The Stock Market **140** Jean Francois Causse/Tony Stone Images **141** John Cancalosi/Stock Boston **143** Linc Correll/Stock Boston **145** David Ball/The Stock Market **151** Patti Murray/ANIMALS ANIMALS **152** Focus On Sports **155** John Curtis/The Stock Market **157** Stephen Frisch/Stock Boston **159** V.Jane Windsor/St.Petersburg Times **161** Bob Strong/The Image Works **164** Francis Lepine/Valan Photos **166** Andrew Sacks/Tony Stone Images **167** Don Mason/Susan Havel/The Stock Market **169** James Marshall/The Stock Market **170** Milt & Joan Mann/Cameramann International, Ltd. **171** Milt & Joan Mann/Cameramann International, Ltd. **175** Laima Druskis/Stock Boston **176** Milt & Joan Mann/Cameramann International, Ltd. **178** Michael Keller/The Stock Market **182** Don Dubroff/Tony Stone Images **184** Charles Gupton/Stock Boston **185** Ariel Skelley/The Stock Market **186** Fujifotos/The Image Works **191T** DOLLEY MADISON by Bass, Otis (c)1817, The New-York Historical Society, New York City **191B** ANNA ELEANOR ROOSEVELT, detail, Copyright by the White House Historical Association **192** The Stock Shop **193T** David Madison **202-203T** Jack Krawczyk/Panoramic Images, Chicago **202CL** P.George/H. Armstrong Roberts **202CR** Index Stock International **202-203B** C.Ursillo/H. Armstrong Roberts **203C** Douglas Pulsipher/The Stock Solution **204** Courtesy of United Musical Instruments U.S.A.Inc. **207** U. S. Army Photo Center of Military History **210** John Colwell/Grant Heilman Photography **212** Alan Carey/The Image Works **213** Courtesy The Kohler Company **214** Michael Newman/Photo Edit **216** M.Granitsas/The Image Works **218T** Jerry Jacka Photography **218B** Chip & Rosa Maria de la Cueva Peterson **223ALL** Courtesy of Jim Jennings, Jennings Chevrolet & Geo Inc., Glenview, IL **225ALL** Everett Collection 226 Nubar Alexanian/Stock Boston **229** Tony Freeman/Photo Edit **230** Terry Donnelly/Tony Stone Images **232** Leo Keeler/Earth Scenes **238** Dirk Gallian/Focus on Sports **240** Milt & Joan Mann/Cameramann International, Ltd. **246** Brent Jones **249** Jeffrey Muir Hamilton/Stock Boston **254** Alex MacLean/Landslides **255** Rosemary Finn **261T** Wiley/Wales/Profiles West **261BL** Library of Congress **261BR** Library of Congress **268B** Courtesy R.R.Donnelley & Sons Co. **269** David R. Frazier Photolibrary **270-271T** Gary Mirando/New England Stock Photo **270C** Color Box/FPG **270B** Index Stock International **271C** SuperStock, Inc. **271B** Color Box/FPG **272** David Madison **274** Michael Newman/Photo Edit **278** Corbis-Bettmann **283** Suzanne Murphy/Tony Stone Images **284** Wendy Stone/Odyssey Productions, Chicago **286** Giuliano Colliva/The Image Bank **296** Mark Antman/The Image Works **302** Corbis-Bettmann Archive **304** Doug Miner/Sygma **305** Ralph Mercer/Tony Stone Images **311** John Eastcott/YVA Momatiuk/The Image Works **312** Randy G. Taylor/Leo de Wys **313** D. & J. Heaton/Stock Boston **315** David Falconer/David R. Frazier Photolibrary **318** Brooks Kraft/Sygma **320** Henkel-Harris Furnit/Stock Boston **326** John Eastcott/YVA Momatiuk/Stock Boston **329** Thomas Hovland/Grant Heilman Photography **331** Eastcott/Momatiuk/The Image Works **333(all)** UPI-Corbis-Bettmann **335** Courtesy McDonnell-Douglas **336-337** John Kelly/Tony Stone Images **336INS** Stockworks **337INS** Headhunters **344T** Travelpix/FPG **344C** Backgrounds/West Light **344BL** Gary A. Bartholomew/West Light **344-345BR&B** Ron Watts/West Light **345T** Sipa/Fritz/Leo de Wys **346** Greig Cranna/Stock Boston **350** Jeff Gnass **355** Vandystadt/Photo Researchers **357** Bob Amft **362** Nancy Pierce/Photo Researchers **363** Jeff Gnass **364** Corbis-Bettmann Archive **365** Corbis-Bettmann Archive **368** Zalman Usiskin **372** Focus On Sports **376** Bob Daemmrich/Stock Boston **378** Jeff Gnass **381** Corbis-Bettmann Archive **386** Focus On Sports **389** Sidney Harris **392** Neg.A91033/Field Museum of Natural History, Chicago **393** From CHAOS by J.Glieck, (c)1987 Viking Press **395** Philippe Plailly/SPL/Photo Researchers **405** Hulton Deutsch Collection Ltd. **408T** Jay Silverman/The Image Bank **408B** David Madison **409T** Arthur Tilley/FPG **409C** H.M.Gousha, a division of Simon & Schuster, Inc. All rights reserved. Used by permission. **409B** West Light **416T** R.Price/West Light **416-417B** Michael Schimpf/Mon Tresor/Panoramic Images, Chicago **417T** Ralph A.Clevenge/West Light **417C** Roberto Villa/Leo de Wys **418** Everett Collection **423** Breck P. Kent/ANIMALS ANIMALS **424** Porterfield/Chickering/Photo Researchers **426** NASA **429** National Optical Astronomy Observatories **433** Biophoto Associates/Photo Researchers **437** Copyright by the White House Historical Association, Photo: National Geographic Society **441** Jose L.Pelaez/The Stock Market **443** Focus On Sports **444** Joel Gordon Photography **448** Lee Boltin **450** Teri Bloom **452** David Spangler **455** Miro Vintoniv/Stock Boston **461** Instituto E. Museo di Storia Della Scienza **462** John Gerlach/Earth Scenes **464** Grant Heilman/Grant Heilman Photography **467** Catherine Koehler **468** James W.Kay **469T** Bill Losh/FPG **469C** Sussane Kaspar/Leo de Wys 469B Jon Feingersh/The Stock Market **470L** Rob Bolster/Stockworks **470R** Charles Waller/Stockworks **476–477** Pete Turner, Inc./The Image Bank **476C** Bill Ross/West Light **476B** (c)1991 Cindy Lewis **477C** Mark Harwood/Tony Stone Images **477B** Steven M. Rollman/Natural Selection **478** Mugshots/The Stock Market **482** Zig Leszczynski/ANIMALS ANIMALS **483** Tony Freeman/Photo Edit **489** Campbell **494** Photo Courtesy Ringling Brothers and Barnum & Bailey Combined Shows, Inc. **495** Sidney Harris **499** Mike Mazzaschi/Stock Boston **500** PhotoFest **502, 503** **NASA** **506** Lawrence Migdale **509** David Wells/The Image Works **511** Bob Amft **516, 517** Milt & Joan Mann/Cameramann International, Ltd. **521T** Drake Well Museum **521B** Milt & Joan Mann/Cameramann International, Ltd. **523B** Mary Evans Picture Library **530TL** Telegraph Colour Library/FPG **530TR** Medichrome/The Stock Shop **530C** Ed Honowitz/Tony Stone Images **530B** Chuck Davis/Tony Stone Images **531B** Derek Trask/Leo de Wys **532** Dr.Kari Lounatmaa/SPL/Photo Researchers **536** David R. Frazier Photolibrary **538** Luis Villotai/The Stock Market **539** Bernard Boutrit/Woodfin Camp & Associates **540** Jean Clottes/Sygma **545** Robert Frerck/Woodfin Camp & Associates **548** R.Bossu/Sygma **550** D.Gontier/The Image Works **551** Courtesy Maxine Waters **552** Doug Wechsler/Earth Scenes **555** St.Joseph Museum, St.Joseph, Missouri **556T** E.J.Camp/Outline Press Syndicate Inc. **556C** Everett Collection **556B** Everett Collection **562** USDA/SS/Photo Researchers **563** Brooks Kraft/Sygma **568** AP/Wide World **575** Dion Ogust/The Image Works **576** Stuart Franklin/Magnum Photos **580** Dennis Cox/ChinaStock **583, 585** NASA **587** Viviane Holbrooke/The Stock Market **589** Larry House/Tony Stone Images **593** (c) 1991 Cindy Lewis **594** M.Barrett/H. Armstrong Roberts **602-603T** Randy Faris/West Light **602C** Dennis O'Clair/Tony Stone Images **602BL** Per Eriksson/Leo de Wys **602-603B** Telegraph Colour Library/FPG **603CL** Henryk Kaiser/Leo de Wys **603R** Tom Van Sant/The Stock Market **604** Jan Kanter **607** U.S.Defense Department **609** Daniel Forster/Stock Newport **611** David Pollack/The Stock Market **615** Alex Quesada/Woodfin Camp & Associates **620** Joe Sohm/The Image Works **623** Villota/The Stock Market **625** Everett Collection **627** Joe Bator/The Stock Market **631** David Spangler **632** Courtesy Todd-Page Construction **637** Everett Collection **639** Chuck Nacke/Woodfin Camp & Associates **643, 647** Milt & Joan Mann/Cameramann International, Ltd. **651** Julie Houck/Stock Boston **653** Bob Daemmrich/Stock Boston **657** Cary Wolinsky/Stock Boston **658** Peter Beck/The Stock Market **664T** Steve Kahn/FPG **664B** Ron Watts/West Light **665** Kevin Alexander/Profiles West **672-673T** Marvy!/The Stock Market **672C** V.Cody/West Light **672B** Charles Bowman/Leo de Wys **673C** Will & Deni McIntyre/Tony Stone Images **673B** David Bishop/Phototake **674** PhotoFest **676** Tony Freeman/Photo Edit **679** Terry Murphy/ANIMALS ANIMALS **680** Rhoda Sidney/Photo Edit **683** Richard Lord **684** Ken Krueger/Tony Stone Images **692** David R. Frazier Photolibrary **706** Biophoto Associates/SS/Photo Researchers **717** Corbis-Bettmann Archive **722** Alan Oddie/Photo Edit **734** Library of Congress **737–738** Mark Segal/Panoramic Images, Chicago **738INS** Gary A. Bartholomew/West Light **746-747T** Tecmap/West Light **746C** Bill Ross/West Light **746B** Dennis Welsh/Adventure Photo **747C** Craig Aurness/West Light **747B** Craig Aurness/West Light **751L** Runk/Schoenberger/Grant Heilman Photography **751R** Milt & Joan Mann/Cameramann International, Ltd. **753** Corbis-Bettmann Archive **754T** A.T.Willett/The Image Bank **754B** January 31, 1994/Newsweek Magazine **757** (c)Woodfield Associates. Reprinted with permission. **759** David Delossy/The Image Bank **765** Robert Llewellyn **768** Matthew Neal McVay/Stock Boston **771** Benn Mitchell/The Image Bank **775** Dave Bartruff/Stock Boston **787** Cynthia Clampitt **789** Courtesy British Airways **793** David Young-Wolff/Photo Edit **795** John Conger **797** Library of Congress **798** M.Harker/G&J Images/The Image Bank **799T** J.Blank/H. Armstrong Roberts **799B** R.Kord/H. Armstrong Roberts **800T** ChromoSohm/Sohm **800B** Richard J.Wainscoat/Peter Arnold, Inc. **808T** Peter Steiner/The Stock Market **808C** SuperStock, Inc. **808B** Steve Chenn/West Light **809T** Al Francekevich/The Stock Market **809B** Rick Gayle/The Stock Market **814T** David Ball/Tony Stone Images **814B** David Spangler **816** Ron Spomer/Visuals Unlimited **818** Larry Lefever/Grant Heilman Photography **821** William J. Weber/Visuals Unlimited **822** Tom McCarthy/Photo Edit **826** Bob Daemmrich **829** Everett Collection **833** Chris Arend/AlaskaStock Images **847** Tony Freeman/Photo Edit **849** Rosemary Finn **850** Martin Rogers/Tony Stone Images **857** AP/Wide World **862** Anup & Manuj Shah/ANIMALS ANIMALS **864** Independence National Historical Park, Philadelphia, PA. **868** Michael Newman/Photo Edit **869** Everett Collection **875T** Japack/Leo de Wys **875B** Corbis-Bettmann Archive **876** Weinberg/Clark/The Image Bank